Science Fundamentals
Third Edition

A Pearson Custom Publication

Science Fundamentals
Third Edition

Compiled from:

Statistical and Data Handling Skills in Biology
by Roland Ennos

College Physics
Sixth Edition
by Jerry D. Wilson, Anthony J. Buffa and Bo Lou

Chemistry: The Central Science
Eleventh Edition
Theodore L. Brown, H. Eugene LeMay, Jr.,
Catherine J. Murphy,
with contributions from Patrick Woodward

Chemistry
Fifth Edition
John E. McMurry and Robert C. Fay

PEARSON
Custom
Publishing

Pearson Education Limited
Edinburgh Gate
Harlow
Essex CM20 2JE

And associated companies throughout the world

Visit us on the World Wide Web at:
www.pearsoned.co.uk

First published 2006
This Custom Book Edition © 2009 Published by Pearson Education Limited

Compiled from:

Statistical and Data Handling Skills in Biology
by Roland Ennos
ISBN 978 0 13 195584 4
Copyright © Pearson Education Limited 2000

College Physics
Sixth Edition
by Jerry D. Wilson, Anthony J. Buffa and Bo Lou
ISBN 978 0 13 149579 1
Copyright © 2007, 2003, 2000, 1997, 1994, 1990 by Pearson Education, Inc
Pearson Prentice Hall
Pearson Education, Inc.
Upper Saddle River, New Jersey 07458

Chemistry: The Central Science
Eleventh Edition
by Theodore L. Brown, H. Eugene LeMay, Jr., Catherine J. Murphy,
with contributions from Patrick Woodward
ISBN 978 0 13 600617 6
Copyright © 2009, 2006, 2003, 2000, 1997, 1994, 1991, 1988, 1985, 1981, 1977
by Pearson Education, Inc., Upper Saddle River, New Jersey 07458

Chemistry
Fifth Edition
by John McMurry and Robert C. Fay
ISBN 978 0 13 199323 5
Copyright © 2008, 2004, 2001, 1998, 1995 by Pearson Education, Inc.,
Upper Saddle River, New Jersey 07458

ISBN 978 1 84776 436 2

Printed and bound in Great Britain by Henry Ling Limited at the Dorset Press,
Dorchester, DT1 1HD

Contents

Chemistry   413

Chapters taken from:
Chemistry: The Central Science Eleventh Edition
by Theodore L. Brown, H. Eugene LeMay, Jr.,
Catherine J. Murphy,
with contributions from Patrick Woodward

Chapters taken from:
Chemistry Fifth Edition
by John E. McMurry and Robert C. Fay

Preface

Science Fundamental-1X and 1Y are level-1 courses at Glasgow University that have been developed to assist students wishing to take biological degrees. The courses are also suitable for students wishing to take degree subjects other than biology but have, for whatever reason, limited knowledge in the areas of mathematics, physics and chemistry.

Science Fundamentals covers basic mathematical and statistical skills to a level which should be a suitable introduction for a biology degree. The concepts of physics and chemistry often seem daunting to those who have not covered these subjects at school. These courses aim to introduce concepts that are essential to understanding aspects of biological science whether studied at the molecular or whole organism level.

By necessity this text has been put together by extracting sections from various books on chemistry, physics and statistics which are considered relevant by the course lecturers. This should enable students to have support material for the Science Fundamentals courses at a reasonable cost, without the need to purchase several books that contain large amounts of nonessential material. Any comments on the omission or inclusion of material should be passed onto the course coordinator (or any of the lecturers) so that the text can be refined in future years.

Dr A.J. Lapthorn

Statistics

2 Dealing with variation

2.1 Introduction

We saw in the last chapter that it is because of the problem of **variability** that we need to do so much work in biology carrying out **replicated** surveys and experiments. This chapter outlines how and why most biological measurements vary, describes how variation is quantified and finally shows how, by combining results from replicated measurements, you can obtain useful quantitative information about a population, despite the variation.

2.2 Variability: causes and effects

There are three main reasons why the measurements we take of biological phenomena vary. The first is that organisms differ because their genetic make-up varies. Most of the continuous characteristics, like height, weight, metabolic rate

'So men aren't all the same!'

7

distribution
The pattern by which a measurement or frequency varies.

or blood [Na⁺], are influenced by a large number of genes, each of which has a small effect; they act either to increase or decrease the value of the character by a small amount. Second, organisms also vary because they are influenced by a large number of environmental factors, each of which has similarly small effects. Third, we may make a number of small errors in our actual measurements.

So how will these factors influence the **distribution** of the measurements we take? Let's look first at the simplest possible system; imagine a population of rats whose length is influenced by a single factor that is found in two forms. Half the time it is found in the form which increases length by 20% and half the time in the form which decreases it by 20%. The distribution of heights will be that shown in Figure 2.1a. Half the rats will be 80% of the average length and half 120% of the average length.

What about the slightly more complex case in which length is influenced by two factors, each of which is found half the time in a form which increases length by 10% and half the time in a form which decreases it by 10%. Of the four possible combinations of factors, there is one in which both factors

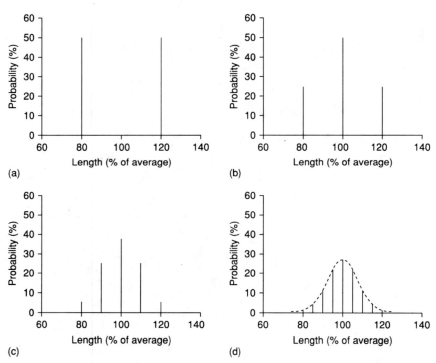

Figure 2.1 Length distributions for a randomly breeding population of rats.
Length is controlled by a number of factors, each of which is found 50% of the time in the form which reduces length and 50% in the form which increases length. The graphs show length control by **(a)** 1 factor, **(b)** 2 factors, **(c)** 4 factors and **(d)** 8 factors. The greater the number of influencing factors, the greater the number of peaks and the more nearly they approximate a smooth curve (dashed outline).

8

increase length (and hence length will be 120% of average), and one in which they both reduce length (making length 80% of average). The chances of being either long or short are $\frac{1}{2} \times \frac{1}{2} = \frac{1}{4}$. However, there are two possible cases in which overall length is average: if the first factor increases length and the second decreases it; and if the first factor decreases length and the second increases it. Therefore one-half of the rats will have average length (Figure 2.1b).

Figure 2.1c gives the results for the even more complex case when length is influenced by four factors, each of which is found half the time in the form which increases length by 5% and half the time in the form which decreases it by 5%. In this case, of 16 possible combinations of factors, there is only one combination in which all four factors are in the long form and one combination in which all are in the short form. The chances of each are therefore $\frac{1}{2} \times \frac{1}{2} \times \frac{1}{2} \times \frac{1}{2} = \frac{1}{16}$. The rats are much more likely to be intermediate in size, because there are four possible combinations in which three long and one short factor (or three short and one long) can be arranged, and six possible combinations in which two long and two short factors can be arranged. It can be seen that the central peak is higher than those further out. The process is even more apparent, and the shape of the distribution becomes more obviously humped, if there are eight factors, each of which increases or decreases length by 2.5% (Figure 2.1d). The resulting distributions are known as **binomial distributions**.

binomial distribution
The pattern by which the sample frequencies in two groups tends to vary.

If length were affected by more and more factors, this process would continue; the curve would become smoother and smoother until, if length were affected by an infinite number of factors, we would get a bowler-hat-shaped distribution curve (Figure 2.2). This is the so-called **normal distribution** (also known as the Z distribution). If we measured an infinite number of rats, most would have length somewhere near the average, and the numbers would tail off on each side. Because so many biological characteristics are influenced by large numbers of genes and environmental factors, many follow the normal distribution more or less closely. Many statistics can be calculated, and many statistical tests have been developed which assume that the characters *do* follow the normal distribution.

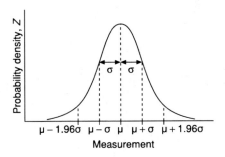

Figure 2.2 A normal distribution. Here 68% of measurements are found within one standard deviation σ from the mean μ; 95% are found within 1.96 times the standard deviation from the mean.

9

2.3   Describing the normal distribution

parameter
A measure, such as
the mean and standard
deviation, which describes
or characterizes a
population. These are
usually represented by
Greek letters.

Once we know (or assume) that a measurement follows the normal distribution, we can describe the distribution of the measurements using just two numbers or **parameters**. The position of the centre of the distribution is described by the **population mean** μ, which on the graph is located at the central peak of the distribution. The mean is the average value of the measurement and is found mathematically by dividing the sum of the lengths of all the rats by the number of rats:

$$\mu = \frac{\sum x_i}{N} \tag{2.1}$$

where x_i is the values of length and N is the number of rats.

The width of the distribution is described by the **population standard deviation** σ, which is the distance from the central peak to the point of inflexion of the curve (where it changes from being convex to concave). This standard deviation is a measure of about how much, on average, points differ from the mean. It is actually calculated by a two-stage process. The first stage is to calculate the **population variance** V, which is the average amount of the square of the distance of each point from the mean. The variance is, therefore, equal to the 'sum of squares' divided by the number of points:

$$V = \frac{\sum (x_i - \mu)^2}{N} \tag{2.2}$$

standard deviation (σ)
A measure of spread of a
group of measurements:
the amount by which on
average they differ from the
mean. The estimate of σ is
called *s*.

To calculate the **standard deviation** it is necessary to take the square root of this value, which gets us back to the same units as the mean. Mathematically, standard deviation σ is given by

$$\sigma = \sqrt{\frac{\sum (x_i - \mu)^2}{N}} \tag{2.3}$$

It turns out that 68.2% of measurements will be within one standard deviation of the mean, 95% of all measurements will be within 1.96 times the standard deviation from the mean, 99% within 2.58 times the standard deviation from the mean and 99.9% within 3.29 times the standard deviation from the mean.

Example 2.1

Suppose adult cats have a mean mass of 3.52 kg with a standard deviation of 0.65 kg. What are the upper and lower limits of mass between which 95% of the cats are found?

Solution

We know that 95% of cats will be within $(1.96 \times 0.65) = 1.27$ kg of 3.52 kg. Therefore, 95% will have mass between 2.25 kg and 4.79 kg.

10

2.4   Estimating the mean and standard deviation

statistic
An estimate of a population parameter, found by random sampling. Statistics are represented by Latin letters.

It is all very well being able to say things about populations whose means and standard deviations we know with certainty. However, in real life it is virtually impossible to find the exact mean and standard deviation of any population since to calculate them we would have to measure every single member of the population!

The only practical thing to do is to take a **sample** of a manageable size and use the results from the measurements we have taken to **estimate** the population mean and standard deviation. These estimates are known as **statistics**. It is very easy to calculate an **estimate of the population mean**. It is simply the average of the sample, or the sample mean $\bar{x}$. This is calculated just like the population mean; it is simply the sum of all the lengths divided by the number of rats measured. In mathematical terms this is given by the expression

$$\bar{x} = \frac{\sum x_i}{N} \tag{2.4}$$

where x_i is the values of length and N is the number of rats.

The **estimate of the population standard deviation**, written s or σ_{n-1}, is given by a different expression from equation (2.3). Rather than dividing the sum of squares by N, we divide by $(N-1)$ to give the formula

$$s = \sigma_{n-1} = \sqrt{\frac{\sum (x_i - \bar{x})^2}{N - 1}} \tag{2.5}$$

We use $(N-1)$ because this expression will give an unbiased estimate of the population standard deviation, whereas using N would tend to underestimate it. To see why this is so, it is perhaps best to consider the case when we have only taken one measurement. Since the estimated mean $\bar{x}$ necessarily equals the single measurement, the standard deviation we calculate when we use N will be zero. Similarly, if there are two points, the estimated mean will be constrained to be exactly halfway between them, whereas the real mean is probably not. Thus the variance (calculated from the square of the distance of each point to the mean) and hence standard deviation will probably be underestimated.

degrees of freedom (DF)
A concept used in parametric statistics, based on the amount of information you have when you examine samples. The number of degrees of freedom is generally the total number of observations you make minus the number of parameters you estimate from the samples.

The quantity $(N-1)$ is known as the number of **degrees of freedom** of the sample. Since the concept of degrees of freedom is repeated throughout the rest of this book, it is important to describe what it means. In a sample of N observations each is free to have any value. However, if we have used the measurements to calculate the sample mean, this restricts the value the last point can have. Take a sample of two measurements, for instance. If the mean is 17 and the first measurement is $17 + 3 = 20$, the other measurement *must* have the value $17 - 3 = 14$. Thus, knowing the first measurement fixes the second, and there will only be one degree of freedom. In the same way, if you calculate the mean of any sample of size N, you restrict the value of the last measurement, so there will be only $(N-1)$ degrees of freedom.

11

It can take time calculating the standard deviation by hand, but fortunately few people have to bother nowadays; estimates for the mean and standard deviation of the population can readily be found using computer statistics packages or even scientific calculators. All you need do is type in the data values and press the $\bar{x}$ button for the mean and the s, σ_{n-1} or $x_{\sigma n-1}$ button for the population standard deviation. Do not use the σ_n or $x_{\sigma n}$ button, since this is for equation (2.3) not equation (2.5).

| **Example 2.2** | The masses (in tonnes) of a sample of 16 bull elephants from a single reserve in Africa were as follows. |

> 4.6, 5.0, 4.7, 4.3, 4.6, 4.9, 4.5, 4.6,
> 4.8, 4.5, 5.2, 4.5, 4.9, 4.6, 4.7, 4.8

Using a calculator, estimate the population mean and standard deviation.

Solution

The estimate for the population mean is 4.70 tonnes and the population standard deviation is 0.2251 tonne, rounded to 0.23 tonne to two decimal places. Note that both figures are given to one more degree of precision than the original data points because so many figures have been combined.

2.5 The variability of samples and the central limit theorem

It is relatively easy to calculate estimates of a population mean and standard deviation from a sample. Unfortunately, though, the estimate we calculated of the population mean $\bar{x}$ is unlikely to exactly equal the real mean of the population μ. In our elephant survey we might by chance have included more light elephants in our sample than one might expect, or more heavy ones. The estimate itself will be variable, just like the population. However, as the sample size increases, the small values and large values will tend to cancel themselves out more and more. The estimated mean will tend to get closer and closer to the real population mean (and the estimated standard deviation will get closer and closer to the population standard deviation). Take the results for the bull elephants given in Example 2.3. Figure 2.3a shows the cumulative mean of the weights. Note how the fluctuations of the cumulative mean start to get less and less and how the line starts to level off. Figure 2.3b shows the cumulative standard deviation. This also tends to level off. If we increased the sample size more and more, we would expect the fluctuations to get less and less until the sample mean converged on the population mean and the sample standard deviation converged on the population standard deviation. We can actually work out how quickly this should happen and, knowing the sample size, we can work out just how much the mean of any sample is likely to vary. We can also work out limits between which the real mean is likely to be found.

12

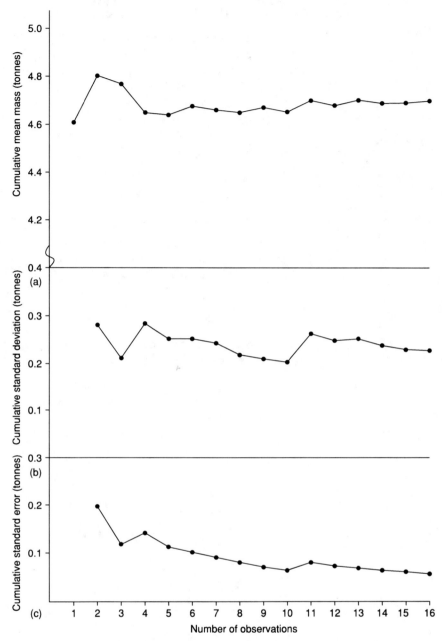

Figure 2.3 The effect of sample size. Changes in the cumulative **(a)** mean, **(b)** standard deviation and **(c)** standard error of the mass of bull elephants from Example 2.2 after different numbers of observations. Notice how the values for men and standard deviation start to level off as the sample size increases, as you get better and better estimates of the population parameters. Consequently the standard error (c), a measure of the variability of the mean falls.

2.5.1 **The variability of samples from a known population**

If we took an infinite number of samples from a population whose mean μ and standard deviation σ we knew, their means $\bar{x}$ would themselves be normally distributed (a result known as the **central limit theorem**) with a mean equal to the population mean μ (Figure 2.4). However, the spread of the means would be much narrower because high and low measurements would tend to cancel each other out in each sample, particularly in large samples. The **standard error** (SE) of the mean is a measure of how much the sample means would on average differ from the population mean. Just like standard deviation, standard error is the distance from the centre of the distribution to the inflexion point of the curve (Figure 2.4). It is given by the formula

$$SE = \sigma/\sqrt{N} \tag{2.6}$$

where σ is the standard deviation and N is the number of observations in the sample. Note that the bigger the sample size, the smaller the standard error. Just as we saw for standard deviation, 95% of the samples would have a mean within 1.96 times the standard error of the population, 99% within 2.58 times the standard error and 99.9% within 3.29 times the standard error. These limits are called 95%, 99% and 99.9% **confidence intervals**.

standard error (SE)
A measure of the spread of sample means: the amount by which they differ from the true mean. Standard error equals standard deviation divided by the square root of the number in the sample. The estimate of SE is called $\overline{SE}$.

2.5.2 **The variability of estimates of population means – the standard error**

If we just take just one sample and calculate its mean $\bar{x}$, as we did for the elephants in Example 2.2, there will be a problem with calculating the variability

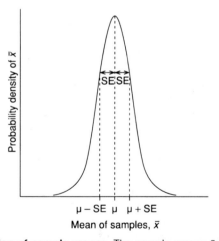

Figure 2.4 Distribution of sample means. The sample means $\bar{x}$ have a normal distribution with mean μ and standard error SE. The distribution is narrower than for single points (Figure 2.2) because, in a sample, high and low values tend to cancel each other out.

14

of that mean. We cannot use equation (2.6) because we do not know σ precisely, we only have an **estimate** of it, s. All we can do is make an **estimate of the standard error**:

$$\overline{SE} = s/\sqrt{N} \qquad (2.7)$$

Note that the larger the sample size, the smaller the value of $\overline{SE}$.

The standard error is an extremely important statistic because it is a measure of just how variable your estimate of the mean is.

2.6   Confidence limits for the population mean

t distribution
The pattern by which sample means of a normally distributed population tend to vary.

confidence limits
Limits between which estimated parameters have a defined likelihood of occurring. It is common to calculate 95% confidence limits, but 99% and 99.9% confidence limits are also used. The range of values between the upper and lower limits is called the confidence interval.

critical values
Tabulated values of test statistics; if the absolute value of a calculated test statistic is usually greater than or equal to the appropriate critical value, the null hypothesis must be rejected.

Because standard error is only estimated, $\overline{SE}$ will have a wider distribution relative to it than the normal distribution shown in Figure 2.4. In fact it will follow what is known as the **t distribution** (Figure 2.5). The exact shape of the t distribution depends on the number of degrees of freedom; it becomes progressively more similar to the normal distribution as the number of degrees of freedom increases (and hence as the estimate of standard deviation becomes more exact).

Knowing all this, it is fairly straightforward to calculate **confidence limits** for the population mean μ using the tabulated **critical values** of the t statistic given in Table S1 in the Appendix. The critical t value $t_{(N-1)}(5\%)$ is the number of standard errors $\overline{SE}$ away from the estimate of population mean $\bar{x}$ within which the real population mean μ will be found 95 times out of 100. The 95% confidence limits define the 95% confidence interval, or 95% CI; this is expressed as follows:

$$95\% \text{ CI(mean)} = \text{mean } \bar{x} \pm (t_{(N-1)}(5\%) \times \overline{SE}) \qquad (2.8)$$

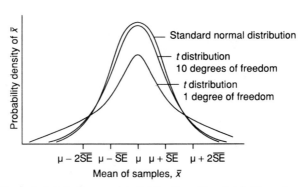

Figure 2.5 Normal distribution and t distribution. The distribution of sample means $\bar{x}$ relative to the estimate of the standard error $\overline{SE}$ calculated from samples with 1, 10 and infinite degrees of freedom. With infinite degrees of freedom the distribution equals the normal distribution. However, it becomes more spread out as the sample size decreases (fewer degrees of freedom) because the estimate of standard error becomes less reliable.

15

where $(N - 1)$ is the number of degrees of freedom. It is most common to use a 95% confidence interval, but it is also possible to calculate 99% and 99.9% confidence intervals for the mean by substituting the critical t values for 1% and 0.1%, respectively, into equation (2.8).

Note that the larger the sample size N, the narrower the confidence interval. This is because as N increases, not only will the standard error $\overline{SE}$ be lower but so will the critical t values. Quadrupling the sample size reduces the distance between the upper and lower limits of the confidence interval by more than one-half.

Take the results for the bull elephants given in Example 2.2. Figure 2.3c shows the standard error of the weights. Note how the standard error falls as the sample size increases. Figure 2.6 shows the cumulative 95% confidence intervals for weight. Note that the distance between the upper and lower intervals falls off extremely rapidly, especially at first; the bigger the sample size the more confident we can be of the population mean.

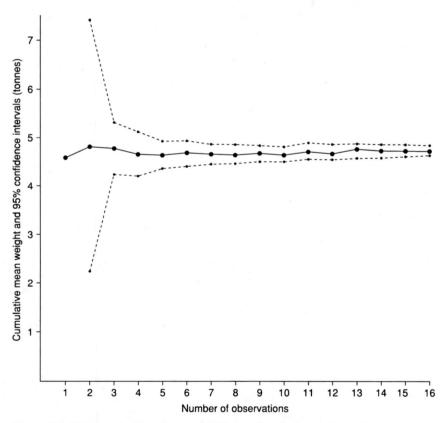

Figure 2.6 Changes in the mean and 95% confidence intervals for the mass of the bull elephants from Example 2.2 after different numbers of observations. Notice how the 95% confidence intervals converge rapidly as sample size increases.

16

Example 2.3

Our survey of the 16 bull elephants gave an estimate of mean mass of 4.70 tonnes and an estimate of standard deviation of 0.2251 tonne. We want to calculate 95% and 99% confidence limits for the mean mass.

Solution

The estimate of standard error is $\overline{SE} = 0.2251/\sqrt{16} = 0.0563$ tonne, which is rounded to 0.056 tonne to three decimal places. Notice that standard errors are usually given to one more decimal place than the mean or standard deviation.

To calculate the 95% confidence limits we must look in Table S1 in the Appendix for the critical value of t for $16 - 1 = 15$ degrees of freedom. In fact $t_{15}(5\%) = 2.131$. Therefore 95% confidence limits of the population mean are $4.70 \pm (2.131 \times 0.0563) = 4.70 \pm 0.12 = 4.58$ and 4.82 tonnes. So 95 times out of 100 the real population mean would be between 4.58 and 4.82 tonnes.

Similarly, $t_{15}(1\%) = 2.947$. Therefore 99% confidence limits of the population mean are $4.70 \pm (2.947 \times 0.0563) = 4.70 \pm 0.16 = 4.54$ and 4.86 tonnes. So 99 times out of 100 the real population mean would be between 4.54 and 4.86 tonnes.

2.7 Calculating the descriptive statistics

descriptive statistics
Statistics which summarise the distribution of a single set of measurements.

We have seen that it is straightforward to calculate the mean, standard deviation, standard error of the mean and 95% confidence limits of a sample. Together these summarise what you know about your sample and they are called **descriptive statistics**. Calculating them is the first and most important step in looking at the results of your surveys or experiments. You should work them out as soon as possible and try to see what they tell you.

2.8 Using a computer package: SPSS

Nowadays you don't usually have to perform statistical calculations yourself. You can use one of the many computer-based statistical packages that are available, such as SPSS, MINITAB, SAS, SYSTAT or Excel. You simply enter all your results straight into a spreadsheet in the computer package and let the computer take the strain. Using a package has two advantages: (1) the computer carries out the calculations more quickly; and (2) you can save the results for future analysis.

In this book we will examine how to carry out the statistical tests on one of the most commonly used packages, SPSS (Statistics Package for the Social Sciences). It works in much the same way as most other packages. You enter the results from different samples into their own separate columns. You can then

17

run tests on the different columns from the command screen of the package. However, it is worth here giving a brief introduction to the quirks of SPSS.

2.9   How SPSS works

Because SPSS was designed for social scientists it has a slightly awkward way of working; it assumes you are putting in lots of data about a certain number of **cases** (usually people). It can then look at how a wide range of factors affect the characteristics of these people (e.g. how does gender affect people's income) and how those characteristics are related to each other (e.g. do richer people tend to be more healthy). Data are entered into a spreadsheet, rather like that of Excel. However, in SPSS, each row represents a particular person (or in biology a particular replicate such as a plant or cell), so you can't put data about two different groups of people or organisms into different columns and use SPSS to analyse them. They have to be identified as members of different groups using another column, and since only numbers are allowed in the spreadsheet, different groups have to be identified by the use of **subscripts**. An example is shown below, giving the heights, weights and genders of eight different people. Here the genders are given as the subscripts 1 and 2 in a separate column, representing female and male.

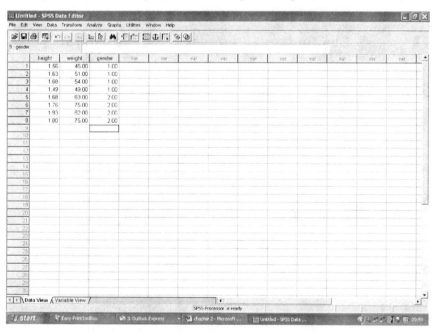

Having entered data into the **Data Editor Screen** which is shown above, you can order statistical tests to be carried out or plot graphs by pulling down menus with your mouse. The results will be printed out in the **Output Screen**. As each of the statistical procedures is introduced, this book will give you instructions about carrying it out in SPSS.

18

2.10   Entering and editing data in SPSS

Your screen will be split into two main zones: the **Output Screen** where SPSS prints the results of tests and the **Data Editor** where you enter data. This in turn is split into two: the **Variable View** screen which gives you information about the data, and the **Data View** screen where the data actually are and where you enter them. When you switch on the program this is where you will be. The screen is a data grid (not unlike that of Excel) with columns along the top and rows 1–1000 down the sides. You can move around the grid using the arrow keys of your computer or your mouse. Once in position data can be entered by simply keying in the numbers.

Example 2.4

Keying in the data on the bull elephants

Data are entered into column 1 (var00001), by positioning the cursor into the top space on the left hand side and typing 4.6. Moving down with the arrows, 5.0 is entered below it and so on. Any mistakes can be corrected simply by typing the correct figures over them. Blocks of numbers can be deleted or moved by selecting them and either pressing delete or cutting and pasting, as in Excel. You will get the following.

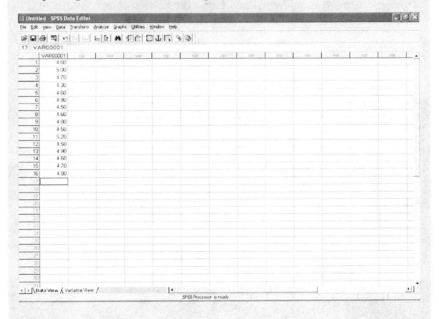

Naming the column

This is done by clicking onto the **Variable View** tab at the bottom left of the screen. This tells you about the data you have entered. The following screen will be displayed.

19

To name the column simply type in the name in the **Name** box. You can also change the width of the column (in the **Width** box) to allow you to get longer numbers on and change the number of decimal places SPSS shows your data to by altering the **Decimals** box. To return to the data simply click onto the **Data View** tab at the bottom left.

2.11 Calculating descriptive statistics using SPSS

mean (μ)
The average of a population. The estimate of μ is called $\bar{x}$.

variance
A measure of the variability of data: the square of their standard deviation.

SPSS allows you quickly and easily to find the **mean**, **standard deviation**, **standard error**, **variance** and **95% confidence limits** of your variable, plus other, less useful information!

First click on the **Analyze** menu; from there move onto the **Descriptive Statistics** bar, then click on **Explore**. This brings up the **Explore** dialogue window (below).

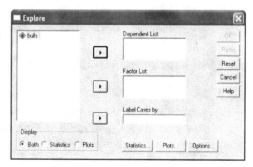

20

You must enter the column you want to examine into the **Dependent** box, in this case by clicking on **bulls** in the box on the left and on the arrow pointing to the dependent box. Click on **Statistics** in the **Display** box. The completed box is shown below.

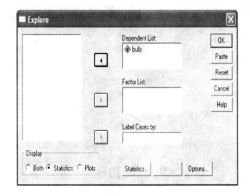

Finally, click on **OK** to perform the calculation. SPSS will produce the following results.

Explore

Case Processing Summary

	Cases					
	Valid		Missing		Total	
	N	Percent	N	Percent	N	Percent
BULLS	16	100.0%	0	.0%	16	100.0%

Descriptives

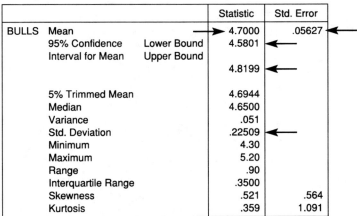

			Statistic	Std. Error
BULLS	Mean		4.7000	.05627
	95% Confidence Interval for Mean	Lower Bound	4.5801	
		Upper Bound	4.8199	
	5% Trimmed Mean		4.6944	
	Median		4.6500	
	Variance		.051	
	Std. Deviation		.22509	
	Minimum		4.30	
	Maximum		5.20	
	Range		.90	
	Interquartile Range		.3500	
	Skewness		.521	.564
	Kurtosis		.359	1.091

The top box is not very useful. It is the second one that gives you the useful information. Take note especially of the **Mean, Standard Deviation, Standard Error**, and the **95% Confidence Interval for Mean**. Note that the package

21

gives some of the items with *too much precision*. Don't copy things from computer screens without thinking!

2.12 Entering and examining data from more than one group

We saw in Section 2.9 that SPSS expects you to put all your data about two or more groups of people or sets of organisms into a single column, because each row represents observations about a certain individual. The different groups have to be identified by a second **subscript** column. For instance, we might measure the weights of 16 cow elephants as well as the 16 bull elephants and want to compare the mean weights of the two groups. In this case, you should put the weights of all 32 animals into the first column. Call it something sensible, like **weight**. You should then produce a second, **sex**, column, identifying each animal by its gender. Unfortunately you can't just put **male** or **female** into this column because SPSS will only accept numbers. You have to put in subscripts, which are usually whole numbers. Here, you can put in 1 for male and 2 for female to give the following data sheet.

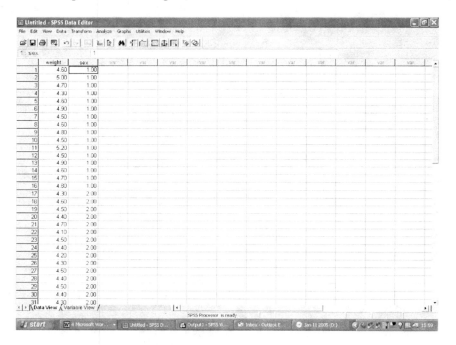

Fortunately SPSS allows you to identify what the subscripts 1 and 2 mean. Just click on the **Variable View** tab at the bottom of the screen and click on the **Values** box for the **sex** column. Click on the three dots at the right hand side of the box, which will bring up the **Value Labels** dialogue box. Put 1 into the **Value:** box and label it in the **Value Label:** box, calling it, say, bull. The box is shown below.

22

Click on **Add** to enter this. Then do the same for the females, entering 2 and cow and then **Add**. The completed dialogue box is shown below.

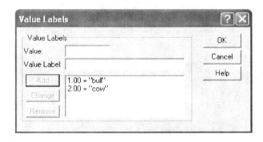

Finally, click on **OK** and the information will be put into the **Variable View** table as below.

Having entered the data you can now use the **Explore** command to look at the weights of the two sexes. Put **weight** into the **Dependent** box as before but put the **sex** column into the **Factor List:** box to give the dialogue box below.

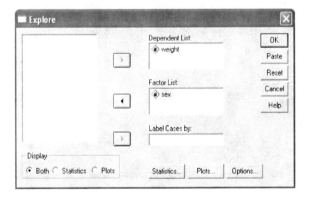

Finally, click on **OK** to perform the task. SPSS will produce separate sets of results for the two different genders.

23

2.13 Presenting descriptive statistics

2.13.1 In text or tables

Once you have obtained your descriptive statistics, you need to express them in the correct way in your write-ups. There are two main ways of doing this. The simplest is just to write them in your text or in tables as the mean followed by the standard deviation or the standard error in parentheses, e.g. $\bar{x}$ (s) or $\bar{x}$ ($\overline{SE}$). You must say whether you are giving the standard deviation or standard error and you must give the number of observations in your sample; this is so that the reader can calculate the other statistic. A 95% confidence interval can be given as $\bar{x} \pm (t_{(N-1)}(5\%) \times \overline{SE})$. For example, in our elephants example:

$$\text{Mean and standard deviation} = 4.70 \ (0.22) \ t \ (n = 16)$$
$$\text{Mean and standard error} = 4.70 \ (0.056) \ t \ (n = 16)$$
$$95\% \ \text{confidence interval} = 4.70 \pm 0.12 \ t \ (n = 16)$$

2.13.2 Graphically

The other way to present data is on a point graph or a bar chart (Figure 2.7). The mean is the central point of the graph or the top of the bar. **Error bars**

error bars
Bars drawn upwards and downwards from the mean values on graphs; error bars can represent the standard deviation or the standard error.

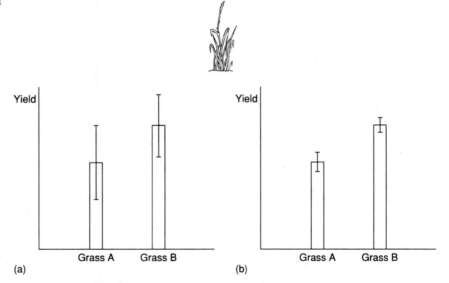

Figure 2.7 Graphing data with error bars. (a) The mean yield of two species of grass with error bars showing their standard deviation; this emphasises the high degree of variability in each grass, and the fact that the distributions overlap a good deal. **(b)** Standard error bars emphasise whether or not the two means are different; here the error bars do not overlap, suggesting that the means *might* be significantly different.

24

are then added. From the mean, bars are drawn both up and down a length equal to either the standard deviation or standard error. Finally, lines are drawn across the ends of the bars. Again you must say in the captions or legends which measure of error you are using.

The choice of standard deviation or standard error bars depends on what you want to emphasise about your results. If you want to show how much **variation** there is, you should choose standard deviation (Figure 2.7a). On the other hand, if you want to show how confident you can be of the mean, you should choose standard error (Figure 2.7b). In general, if two samples have overlapping standard error bars, they are unlikely to be statistically different (Chapter 3). Since people in general want to show mean results and tend to want to compare means (see Chapters 3 and 4), **standard error bars** are by far more the commonly used ones, though some people prefer standard deviation, as it does not hide the variability.

2.14   Self-assessment problems

Problem 2.1

In a population of women, heart rate is normally distributed with a mean of 75 and a standard deviation of 11. Between which limits will 95% of the women have their heart rates?

Problem 2.2

The masses (in grams) for a sample of 10 adult mice from a large laboratory population were measured. The following results were obtained:

5.6,   5.2,   6.1,   5.4,   6.3,   5.7,   5.6,   6.0,   5.5,   5.7

Calculate estimates of the mean and standard deviation of the mass of the mice.

Problem 2.3

Nine measurements were taken of the pH of nine leaf cells. The results were as follows:

6.5,   5.9,   5.4,   6.0,   6.1,   5.8,   5.8,   5.6,   5.9

(a) Use the data to calculate estimates of the mean, standard deviation and standard error of the mean. Use these estimates to calculate the 95% confidence interval for cell pH.
(b) Repeat the calculation assuming that you had only taken the first four measurements. How much wider is the 95% confidence interval?

25

Problem 2.4

The masses (in kilograms) of 25 newborn babies were as follows.

3.5,	2.9,	3.4,	1.8,	4.2,	2.6,	2.2,	2.8,	2.9,	3.2,	2.7,	3.4,	3.0,
3.2,	2.8,	3.2,	3.0,	3.5,	2.9,	2.8,	2.5,	2.9,	3.1,	3.3,	3.1	

Calculate the mean, standard deviation and standard error of the mean and present your results (a) in figures and (b) in the form of a bar chart with error bars showing standard deviation.

26

3 Testing for differences 1: *t* tests

3.1 Introduction

We saw in the last chapter that we can get over the variability of biological things. By taking measurements on just a sample of the population, we can estimate the average value of the measurement, estimate its variability and estimate the limits between which the average is likely to lie. This is very useful but, if we are going to carry out biological research, we often want to answer specific *questions* about the things we are measuring. In particular there are several *comparisons* that we might want to make.

- We might want to *compare* the average value of a measurement taken on a single population with an expected value. Is the birthweight of babies from a small town *different* from the national average?
- We might want to *compare* two sets of related measurements or paired measurements made on a single population. Are male gibbons heavier than their mates? Do patients have a *different* heart rate before and after taking beta blockers? Or is the pH of ponds *different* at dawn and dusk?
- We might want to *compare* experimentally treated organisms or cells with controls. Do shaken sunflowers have *different* mean height from unshaken controls?

'But 2-1 isn't a significant difference.'

- We might want to *compare* two groups of organisms or cells. Do different strains of bacteria have *different* growth rates?

This chapter describes how you can use statistical tests to help determine whether there are differences and how to work out how big those differences are.

3.2   Why we need statistical tests for differences

3.2.1 The problem

You might imagine it would be easy to find out whether there are differences. You would just need to take measurements on your samples and compare the average values to see if they were different. However, there is a problem. Because of variation we can never be certain that the differences between our **sample means** reflect real differences in the **population means**. We might have got different means just by chance.

3.2.2 The solution

Suppose μ is the mean length of a population of rats. If we take measurements on a sample of rats, it is quite likely we could get a mean value $\bar{x}$ that is one standard error $\overline{SE}$ greater or smaller than μ. In fact, the chances of getting a mean that different *or more* from μ is equal to the shaded area in Figure 3.1a. In contrast, it is much less likely that we could get a value that is different by more than three standard errors from μ (Figure 3.1b). The probability is given by the tiny (though still real) area in the two tails of the distribution.

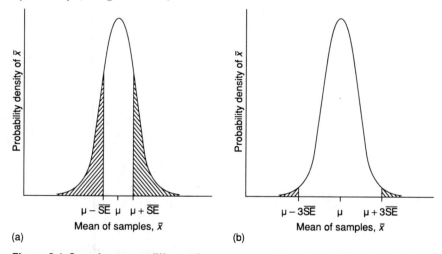

(a)   (b)

Figure 3.1 Sample means different from an expected value. (a) There is a high probability (shaded areas) of obtaining a mean at least one standard error $\overline{SE}$ away from the expected mean μ. **(b)** There is a very low probability (shaded areas) of getting a mean at least three standard errors 3 $\overline{SE}$ away from the expected mean μ.

28

There is a point, usually around or just above two standard errors, where the probability of getting a mean that different or more by chance will fall below 5%. Therefore, if a sample mean is more than this different from the expected mean, we can say that it is **significantly different**. However, because of variability, we cannot be *sure* that these differences are real.

3.3   How we test for differences

As we saw in Chapter 1, carrying out statistical tests involves a somewhat inverted form of logic that has four main stages. The stages involved in carrying out *t* tests for differences are shown below.

Step 1: Formulating a null hypothesis

The first stage is to assume the opposite of what you are testing. Here, as you are testing whether there is a difference, the **null hypothesis** is that there is **no** difference.

Step 2: Calculating the test statistic

The next stage is to examine the data values and calculate a test statistic from them. When testing for differences, the test statistic is usually a measure of how different the means are relative to the variability. The greater the difference in the means and the smaller the scatter in the data, the bigger the absolute value of the test statistic t, (i.e. the further away from zero it will be). The smaller the difference in the means and the greater the scatter, the smaller the absolute value of the test statistic.

Step 3: Calculating the significance probability

Next you must examine the test statistic t and assess the probability of getting an absolute value that high or greater if the null hypothesis were true. The larger the absolute value of the test statistic (i.e. the further away from zero it is), hence the greater the distance between the means, the smaller the probability will be. The smaller the absolute value of the test statistic, the larger the probability will be.

Step 4: Deciding whether to reject the null hypothesis

significant difference
A difference which has less than a 5% probability of having happened by chance.

- If the significance probability is below a cut off point, you must reject the null hypothesis and conclude that there is a **significant difference**. As we have seen, usually in biology one rejects the null hypothesis if the significance probability is less than or equal to 1 in 20. This probability is often written as the decimal 0.05, or as 5%. This criterion for rejecting the null hypothesis is therefore known as the 5% significance level.
- If the significance probability is greater than 5%, you have no evidence to reject the null hypothesis. But this does not mean you have evidence to support it.

29

Statisticians have taken a lot of the hard work out of deciding whether to reject the null hypothesis by preparing tables of **critical values** for test statistics. Several of these tables, including the one for the *t* statistic, are given in the Appendix. If the absolute value of your test statistic is (usually) greater than or equal to the critical value for the 5% significance level, then there is a less than 5% probability of getting these results by chance. Therefore, you can reject the null hypothesis. It is even easier if you are carrying out a statistical test in SPSS or another computer package. It will work out the significance probability for you, and all you have to do is compare that probability with 0.05.

Sometimes you may find the probability *P* falls below critical levels of 1 in 100 or 1 in 1000. If this is true, you can reject the null hypothesis at the 1% or 0.1% levels respectively.

Step 5: Calculating confidence limits

Whether or not there is a **significant difference**, you can calculate **confidence limits** to give a set of plausible values for the differences of the means. Calculating 95% confidence limits for the difference of means is just as straightforward as calculating 95% confidence limits for the means themselves (Section 2.6).

3.4   One- and two-tailed tests

two-tailed tests
Tests which ask merely whether observed values are different from an expected value or each other, not whether they are larger or smaller.

Statistical tables often come in two different versions: one-tailed and two-tailed. Most biologists use **two-tailed tests**. These test whether there are differences from expected values but do not make any presuppositions about which way the differences might be. With our rats, therefore, we would be testing whether they had a different length but not whether they were longer or shorter than expected. The criterion for rejecting the null hypothesis in the two-tailed test is when the total area in the two tails of the distribution (Figure 3.1) is less than 5%, so each tail must have an area of less than 2.5%. All the statistical tables in this text (Appendix) are two-tailed. The tests carried out by SPSS are also by default two-tailed.

3.5   The types of *t* test

There are three main types of *t* test, which are used in different situations. The simplest one, the **one-sample *t* test**, is used to determine whether the mean of a single sample is different from an expected value. If you want to see if there are differences between two sets of paired observations, you need to use the **paired *t* test**. Finally, to test whether the means of two independent sets of measurements are different you need to carry out a **two-sample *t* test**, also known as an **independent sample *t* test**. These tests all have fairly easy to grasp logic and are straightforward to carry out mathematically. Therefore, instructions will be given to carry out these tests both using a calculator and using SPSS.

30

3.6 The one-sample *t* test

3.6.1 Purpose

To test whether the sample mean of one set of measurements taken on a single population is different from an expected value *E*.

3.6.2 Rationale

The one-sample *t* test calculates how many standard errors the sample mean is away from the expected value. It is therefore found using the formula

$$t = \frac{\text{Sample mean} - \text{Expected value}}{\text{Standard error of mean}} = \frac{\bar{x} - E}{\overline{SE}} \qquad (3.1)$$

The further away the mean is from the expected value, the larger the value of *t*, and the less probable it is that the real population mean *could* be the expected value. Note, however, that it does not matter whether *t* is positive or negative. It is the *difference* from zero that matters, so you must consider the absolute value of *t* |*t*|. If |*t*| is greater than or equal to a critical value, then the difference is significant.

3.6.3 Carrying out the test

To see how to carry out a test in practice it is perhaps best to run through a straightforward example.

Example 3.1

Do the bull elephants we first met in Example 2.2 have a different mean mass from the mean value for the entire population of African elephants of 4.50 tonnes?

Solution

Step 1: Formulating the null hypothesis

The null hypothesis is that the mean of the population *is not* different from the expected value. Here, therefore, the null hypothesis is that the mean weight of bull elephants *is* 4.50 tonnes.

Step 2: Calculating the test statistic

Using a calculator

Here, the mean weight $\bar{x}$ of the sample of bull elephants is 4.70 tonnes with an estimate of the standard error $\overline{SE}$ of 0.0563 tonnes. Therefore, using equation (3.1)

$$t = (4.70 - 4.50)/0.0563 = 3.55$$

The mean is 3.55 standard errors away from the expected value.

31

Using SPSS

To carry out a one-sample *t* test, you first need to enter all the data into a single column, and give the column a name (here **bulls**). To run the test, click on the **Analyze** menu, then move onto the **Compare Means** bar and click on **One-Sample T Test**. SPSS will present you with the following dialogue box.

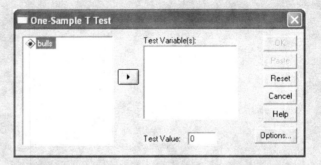

Put the column you want to compare (here **bulls**) into the **Test Variable(s):** box, and the value you want to compare it with (here **4.50**) in the **Test Value:** box. This will give:

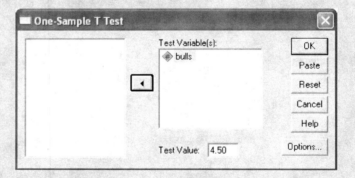

Finally, click on **OK** to run the test. SPSS will produce the following output.

T-Test

One-Sample Statistics

	N	Mean	Std. Deviation	Std. Error Mean
BULLS	16	4.7000	.22509	.05627

32

One-Sample Test

	Test Value = 4.50				95% Confidence Interval of the Difference	
	t	df	Sig. (2-tailed)	Mean Difference	Lower	Upper
BULLS	3.554	15	.003	.2000	.0801	.3199

SPSS gives you all the descriptive statistics you need in the top table, and the value of *t* (3.554) in the lower table.

Step 3: Calculating the significance probability

You must calculate the probability *P* that the absolute value of *t*, written $|t|$, would be this high or greater if the null hypothesis were true.

Using a calculator

You must compare your value of $|t|$ with the critical value of the *t* statistic for ($N − 1$) degrees of freedom and at the 5% level ($t_{(N−1)}(5\%)$). This is given in Table S1 in the Appendix.

Here, there are $16 − 1 = 15$ degrees of freedom, so the critical value that $|t|$ must exceed for the probability to drop below the 5% level is 2.131.

Using SPSS

SPSS will directly work out the probability *P* and calls it **Sig. (2-tailed)**. (Note that the bigger the value of $|t|$, the smaller the value of Sig. (2 tailed).)
Here Sig. (2 tailed) = 0.003.

Step 4: Deciding whether to reject the null hypothesis

Using a calculator

- If $|t|$ is greater than or equal to the critical value, you must reject the null hypothesis. Therefore, you can say that the mean is significantly different from the expected value.
- If $|t|$ is less than the critical value, you have no evidence to reject the null hypothesis. Therefore, you can say that the mean is not significantly different from the expected value.

Here $|t| = 3.55 > 2.131$.

Using SPSS

- If Sig. (2 tailed) ≤ 0.05, you must reject the null hypothesis. Therefore, you can say that the mean is significantly different from the expected value.

33

- If Sig. (2 tailed) > 0.05, you have no evidence to reject the null hypothesis. Therefore, you can say that the mean is not significantly different from the expected value.

Here Sig. (2 tailed) = 0.003 < 0.05.

Therefore we can reject the null hypothesis. We can say that bull elephants have a weight significantly different from 4.50 tonnes; in fact, with a mean of 4.70 tonnes, they are heavier.

Step 5: Calculating confidence limits

Just as you can find confidence intervals for the means of a measurement like weight, so you can also find confidence intervals for the difference between the mean and the expected mean.

Using a calculator

The 95% confidence limits for the difference are given by the equation

$$95\% \text{ CI(difference)} = \bar{x} - E \pm (t_{(N-1)}(5\%) \times \overline{SE}) \tag{3.2}$$

Here, the mean is 4.70, with a standard error of 0.0563, and the critical t value for 15 degrees of freedom is 2.131. Therefore

$$95\% \text{ CI(difference)} = (4.70 - 4.50) \pm (2.131 \times 0.0563)$$
$$= 0.08 \text{ to } 0.32$$

Bull elephants are 95% likely to be between 0.08 and 0.32 tonnes heavier than 4.5 tonnes.

Using SPSS

95% confidence intervals for the difference are given in the second table as between 0.0801 to 0.3199. As ever you should not just write this down but round it up to a sensible number of significant figures. Here this rounds to 0.08 to 0.32.

3.7 The paired t test

3.7.1 Purpose

To test whether the means of two sets of **paired measurements** are different from each other. Examples might be a single group of people measured twice, e.g. before vs after a treatment; or related people measured once, e.g. older vs younger identical twins.

34

3.7.2 Rationale

The idea behind the paired *t* test is that you look at the difference between each pair of points and then see whether the mean of these values is different from 0. The test, therefore, has two stages. You first calculate the difference *d* between each of the paired measurements you have made. You can then use these figures to calculate the mean difference between the two sets of measurements and the standard error of the difference. You then use a one-sample *t* test to determine whether the mean difference $\bar{d}$ is different from zero. The test statistic *t* is the number of standard errors the difference is away from zero. It can be calculated using a calculator or using SPSS using the following equation:

$$t = \frac{\text{Mean difference}}{\text{Standard error of difference}} = \frac{\bar{d}}{\overline{SE}_d} \tag{3.3}$$

This procedure has the advantage that it removes the variability within each sample, concentrating only on the *differences* between each pair, so it improves your chances of detecting an effect.

3.7.3 Carrying out the test

To see how to carry out a test in practice it is perhaps best to run through a straightforward example.

Example 3.2

Two series of measurements were made of the pH of nine ponds: at dawn and at dusk. The results are shown in Table 3.1.

Carrying out descriptive statistics shows that the mean difference $\bar{d} = 0.19$ and the standard error of the difference $\overline{SE}_d = 0.043$.

Do the ponds have a different pH at these times?

Table 3.1 pH levels of nine ponds, taken at dawn and dusk, and the differences between these values.

Pond	Dawn pH	Dusk pH	Difference
1	4.84	4.91	0.07
2	5.26	5.62	0.36
3	5.03	5.19	0.16
4	5.67	5.89	0.22
5	5.15	5.44	0.29
6	5.54	5.49	−0.05
7	6.01	6.12	0.11
8	5.32	5.61	0.29
9	5.44	5.70	0.26
$\bar{x}$	5.362	5.552	0.190
s	0.352	0.358	0.129
$\overline{SE}$	0.1174	0.1194	0.0431

35

Solution

Step 1: Formulating the null hypothesis

The null hypothesis is that the mean difference $\bar{d}$ is *not* different from zero. Here, the null hypothesis is that the mean of the differences in the pH *is* 0, i.e. the ponds have the same pH at dawn and dusk.

Step 2: Calculating the test statistic

Using a calculator

Using equation (3.3), we can calculate that $t = 0.190/0.0431 = 4.40$. The difference is 4.40 standard errors away from zero.

Using SPSS

SPSS can readily work out *t* as well as other important elements in the test. Simply put the data side by side into two columns so that each pair of observations has a single row and give each column a name (here **dawnph** and **duskph**). Next, click on the **Analyze** menu, move onto the **Compare Means** bar, and click on the **Paired-Samples T Test** bar. SPSS will produce the **Paired-Samples T Test** dialogue box. Put the columns to be compared into the **Variables:** box as shown below by clicking on both of them and then on the arrow. The completed data and dialogue box are shown below.

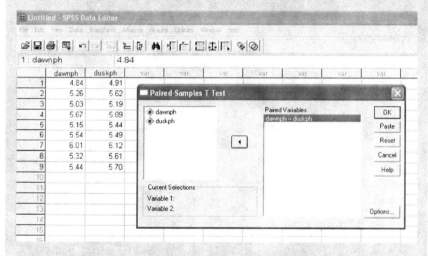

Finally, click on **OK** to run the test. SPSS will produce the following output.

T-Test

Paired Samples Statistics

		Mean	N	Std. Deviation	Std. Error Mean
Pair 1	dawnph	5.3622	9	.35220	.11740
	duskph	5.5522	9	.35818	.11939

Paired Samples Correlations

		N	Correlation	Sig.
Pair 1	dawnph & duskph	9	.934	.000

Paired Samples Test

	Paired Differences					t	df	Sig. (2-tailed)
				95% Confidence Interval of the Difference				
	Mean	Std. Deviation	Std. Error Mean	Lower	Upper			
Pair 1 dawnph − duskph	−.19000	.12942	.04314	−.28948	−.09052	−4.404	8	.002

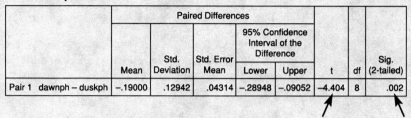

SPSS gives the descriptive statistics in the first table and in the last table calculates *t*, which here is −4.404. (Note that version 13 of SPSS always takes the column which is second in the alphabet from that which is first.)

Step 3: Calculating the significance probability

You must calculate the probability *P* that the absolute value of the test statistic would be equal to or greater than *t* if the null hypothesis were true.

Using a calculator

You must compare your value of $|t|$ with the critical value of the *t* statistic for $(N − 1)$ degrees of freedom where *N* is the number of pairs of observations, and at the 5% level ($t_{(N-1)}(5\%)$). This is given in Table S1 in the Appendix.

Here there are 9 − 1 = 8 degrees of freedom, so the critical value of *t* for the 5% level is 2.306.

Using SPSS

SPSS will directly work out the probability *P* and calls it Sig. (2-tailed).
Here Sig. (2-tailed) = 0.002.

Step 4: Deciding whether to reject the null hypothesis

Using a calculator

- If $|t|$ is greater than or equal to the critical value, you must reject the null hypothesis. Therefore, you can say that the mean difference is significantly different from zero.
- If $|t|$ is less than the critical value, you have no evidence to reject the null hypothesis. Therefore, you can say that the mean difference is not significantly different from zero.

Here $|t| = 4.40 > 2.306$.

37

Using SPSS

- If Sig. (2-tailed) ≤ 0.05, you must reject the null hypothesis. Therefore, you can say that the mean difference is significantly different from zero.
- If Sig. (2-tailed) > 0.05, you have no evidence to reject the null hypothesis. Therefore, you can say that the mean difference is not significantly different from zero.

Here Sig. (2-tailed) = 0.002 < 0.05

Therefore, we must reject the null hypothesis. We can say that the mean difference between dawn and dusk is significantly different from 0. In other words, the pH of ponds is significantly different at dusk from at dawn; in fact it's higher at dusk.

Step 5: Calculating confidence limits

The 95% confidence limits for the mean difference are given by the equation

$$95\% \text{ CI(difference)} = \bar{d} \pm (t_{(N-1)}(5\%) \times \overline{SE}_d) \tag{3.4}$$

Using a calculator

The 95% confidence intervals can be calculated from equation 3.4.

$$95\% \text{ CI(difference)} = 0.19 \pm (2.306 \times 0.043)$$
$$= 0.09 \text{ to } 0.29.$$

It is 95% likely that the pH at dusk will be between 0.09 and 0.29 higher than the pH at dawn.

Using SPSS

SPSS gives the 95% confidence interval for the difference as –0.0905 to –0.2895. Note that the difference is negative because it has calculated dawnph – duskph, not the reverse.

3.8   The two-sample *t* test

3.8.1 Purpose

To test whether the means of two sets of **unpaired** measurements are different from each other. For instance it is used to test whether experimentally treated organisms are different from controls, or one species is different from another.

3.8.2 Rationale

This test is rather more complex than the previous two because you have to decide the probability of overlap between the distributions of *two* sample

38

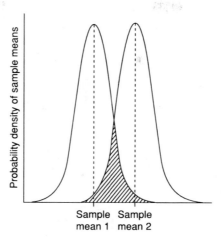

Figure 3.2 Overlapping populations. The estimated probability distributions of two overlapping populations worked out from the results of samples.

standard error of the difference ($\overline{SE}_d$)
A measure of the spread of the difference between two estimated means.

means (Figure 3.2). To do this you have to calculate *t* by comparing the difference in the means of the two populations with an estimate of the **standard error of the difference** between the two populations, using the equation

$$t = \frac{\text{Mean difference}}{\text{Standard error of difference}} = \frac{\bar{x}_A - \bar{x}_B}{\overline{SE}_d} \qquad (3.5)$$

In this case, however, it is much more complex to calculate the standard error of the difference $\overline{SE}_d$ because this would involve comparing each member of the first population with each member of the second. Using a calculator $\overline{SE}_d$ can be estimated if we assume that the variance of the two populations is the same. It is given by the equation

$$\overline{SE}_d = \sqrt{(\overline{SE}_A)^2 + (\overline{SE}_B)^2} \qquad (3.6)$$

where $\overline{SE}_A$ and $\overline{SE}_B$ are the standard errors of the two populations. If the populations are of similar size, $\overline{SE}_d$ will be about $1\frac{1}{2}$ times as big as either population standard error. SPSS can also perform a more complex calculation of $\overline{SE}_d$ that makes no such simplifying assumption.

The two-sample *t* test also makes an important assumption about the measurements: it assumes the two sets of measurements are **independent** of each other. This would not be true of the data on the ponds we examined in Example 3.2, because each measurement has a pair, a measurement from the same pond at a different time of day. Therefore, it is not valid to carry out a two-sample *t* test on this data.

3.8.3 Carrying out the test

To see how to carry out a test in practice it is perhaps best to run through a straightforward example.

39

| **Example 3.3** | The following data were obtained by weighing 16 cow elephants as well as the 16 bull elephants we have already weighed. We will test whether bull elephants have a different mean mass from cow elephants. |

Masses of bull elephants (tonnes)

4.6,	5.0,	4.7,	4.3,	4.6,	4.9,	4.5,	4.6,
4.8,	4.5,	5.2,	4.5,	4.9,	4.6,	4.7,	4.8

Masses of cow elephants (tonnes)

4.3,	4.6,	4.5,	4.4,	4.7,	4.1,	4.5,	4.4,
4.2,	4.3,	4.5,	4.4,	4.5,	4.4,	4.3,	4.3

Solution

Carrying out descriptive statistics yields the following results:

Bull elephants: mean = 4.70, $s = 0.23$, $\overline{SE} = 0.056$
Cow elephants: mean = 4.40, $s = 0.15$, $\overline{SE} = 0.038$

It looks like bulls are heavier, but are they significantly heavier?

Step 1: Formulating the null hypothesis

The null hypothesis is that the mean of the differences *is not* different from zero. In other words, the two groups have the same mean. Here the null hypothesis is that the bull and cow elephants have the same mean weight.

Step 2: Calculating the test statistic

Using a calculator

Using equations (3.5) and (3.6) we can calculate that

$$t = 4.70 - 4.40 / \sqrt{(0.056^2 + 0.038^2)}$$
$$= 0.30/0.068 = 4.43.$$

The means are 4.43 pooled standard errors apart.

Using SPSS

To perform a two-sample *t* test in SPSS, you must first *put all the data into the same column* because each measurement is on a different organism. Call it something like **weight**. To distinguish between the two groups, you must create a second, subscript, column with one of two values, here 1 and 2. We will call it **sex**. You can also identify the subscripts using the **Values** box as described in Section 2.12 page 22. Once you have entered your data, simply click on the **Analyze** menu, move onto the **Compare Means** bar and click on **Independent-Samples T Test**. SPSS will come up with the **Independent-Samples T Test** dialogue box, shown below with some of the data.

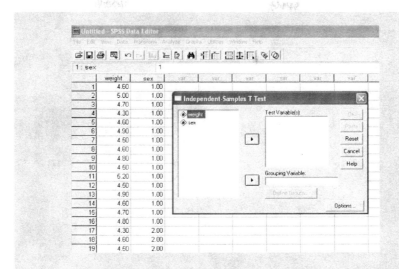

Put the variable you want to test (here **weight**) into the **Test Variable(s):** box and the subscript column (here **sex**) into the **Grouping Variable:** box. Define the groups by clicking on the **Define Groups** tab to bring up the **Define Groups** dialogue box. Put in the values of the subscript column (here 1 and 2) into that box to give the completed boxes shown below.

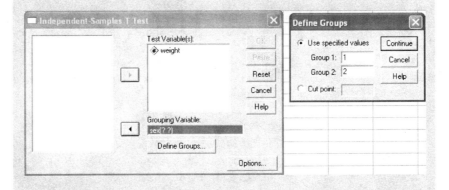

Click on **Continue** to get back to the main dialogue box and finally click on **OK** to run the tests. SPSS comes up with the following results.

T-Test

Group Statistics

	sex	N	Mean	Std. Deviation	Std. Error Mean
weight	bull	16	4.7000	.22509	.05627
	cow	16	4.4000	.15055	.03764

41

Independent Samples Test

		Levene's Test for Equality of Variances		t-test for Equality of Means						
									95% Confidence Interval of the Difference	
		F	Sig.	t	df	Sig. (2-tailed)	Mean Difference	Std. Error Difference	Lower	Upper
weight	Equal variances assumed	2.301	.140	4.431	30	.000	.30000	.06770	.16174	.43826
	Equal variances not assumed			4.431	26.183	.000	.30000	.06770	.16089	.43911

In the first box it gives the descriptive statistics for the two sexes (note that I have given names for the values of the subscripts 1 and 2) and then performs the *t* test, both with and without making the assumption of equal variances. In both cases here, $t = 4.431$. They are usually similar. The first test is only valid if the variances are not significantly different and this is, in fact, tested by Levene's test for equality of variances, the results of which are given at the left of the second table. If Sig. < 0.05 then the test is not valid. Here Sig. = 0.140, so you could use either test. If in doubt though, use the second, more accurate statistic.

Step 3: Calculating the significance probability

Using a calculator

You must compare your value of $|t|$ with the critical value of the *t* statistic for $N_A + N_B - 2$ degrees of freedom, where N_A and N_B are the sample sizes of groups A and B.

Here there are $16 + 16 - 2 = 30$ degrees of freedom; the critical value of *t* for the 5% level is 2.042.

Using SPSS

SPSS will directly work out the probability, Sig. (2-tailed). (Note that the bigger the value of $|t|$, the smaller the value of Sig. (2-tailed).)

Here Sig. (2-tailed) = 0.000.

Step 4: Deciding whether to reject the null hypothesis

Using a calculator

- If $|t|$ is greater than or equal to the critical value, you must reject the null hypothesis. Therefore, you can say that the mean difference is significantly different from zero.
- If $|t|$ is less than the critical value, you have no evidence to reject the null hypothesis. Therefore, you can say that the mean difference is not significantly different from zero.

Here $t = 4.43 > 2.042$.

42

Using SPSS

- If Sig. (2 tailed) ≤ 0.05, you must reject the null hypothesis. Therefore, you can say that the mean difference is significantly different from zero.
- If Sig. (2 tailed) > 0.05, you have no evidence to reject the null hypothesis. Therefore, you can say that the mean is not significantly different from zero.

Here Sig. (2 tailed) = 0.000 < 0.05.

Therefore, we must reject the null hypothesis. We can say that the mean weights of the bull and cow elephants were different. In fact the bulls were significantly heavier than the cows.

Step 5: Calculating confidence limits

The 95% confidence intervals for the mean difference are given by the equation

$$95\% \text{ CI(difference)} = \bar{x}_A - \bar{x}_B \pm (t_{N_A+N_B-2}(5\%) \times \overline{SE}_d) \qquad (3.7)$$

Using a calculator

$$95\% \text{ CI(difference)} = 4.70 - 4.40 \pm (2.042 \times 0.0680)$$
$$= 0.16 \text{ to } 0.44$$

Using SPSS

SPSS calculates these limits directly as 0.016089 to 0.43911, but you should round up to two significant figures to give 0.16 to 0.44.

3.9   Self-assessment problems

Problem 3.1

The scores (in percent) of 25 students in a statistics test were as follows.

58,	65,	62,	73,	70,	42,	56,	53,	59,	56,	60,	64,	63,
78,	90,	31,	65,	58,	59,	21,	49,	51,	58,	62,	56	

Calculate the mean, standard deviation and standard error of the mean for these scores. The mean mark of students in finals exams is supposed to be 58%. Perform a one-sample t test to determine whether these students did significantly differently from expected.

Problem 3.2

The masses (in grams) of 16 randomly chosen tomatoes grown in a commercial glasshouse were as follows.

43

| 32, | 56, | 43, | 48, | 39, | 61, | 29, | 45, |
| 53, | 38, | 42, | 47, | 52, | 44, | 36, | 41 |

Other growers have found that the mean mass of this sort of tomato is 50 g. Perform a one-sample *t* test to determine whether the mean mass of tomatoes from this glasshouse is different from the expected mass. Give the 95% confidence intervals for the mean mass.

Problem 3.3

Students were tested on their ability to predict how moving bodies behave, both before and after attending a course on Newtonian physics. Their marks are given in Table 3.2. Did attending the course have a significant effect on their test scores, and if so by how much?

Table 3.2 Student marks before and after taking a course on Newtonian mechanics.

	Before	After
Martha	45	42
Denise	56	50
Betty	32	19
Amanda	76	78
Eunice	65	63
Ivy	52	43
Pamela	60	62
Ethel	87	90
Letitia	49	38
Patricia	59	53

Problem 3.4

The pH of cactus cells was measured at dawn and at dusk using microprobes. The following results were obtained.

| Dawn: | 5.3, | 5.6, | 5.2, | 7.1, | 4.2, | 4.9, | 5.4, | 5.7, | 6.3, | 5.5, | 5.7, | 5.6 |
| Dusk: | 6.7, | 6.4, | 7.3, | 6.2, | 5.2, | 5.9, | 6.2, | 6.5, | 7.6, | 6.4, | 6.5 | |

(a) Using a statistical package such as SPSS, carry out a two-sample *t* test to determine if there is any significant difference in pH between the cells at these times.
(b) The cactus was identifiable and two sets of measurements were carried out on it. So why can't you analyse this experiment using the paired *t* test?

Problem 3.5

An experiment was carried out to investigate the effect of mechanical support on the yield of wheat plants. The masses of seed (in grams) produced by 20 control plants and 20 plants whose stems had been supported throughout their life were as follows.

44

Control:	9.6,	10.8,	7.6,	12.0,	14.1,	9.5,	10.1,	11.4,	9.1,	8.8,
	9.2,	10.3,	10.8,	8.3,	12.6,	11.1,	10.4,	9.4,	11.9,	8.6
Supported:	10.3,	13.2,	9.9,	10.3,	8.1,	12.1,	7.9,	12.4,	10.8,	9.7,
	9.1,	8.8,	10.7,	8.5,	7.2,	9.7,	10.1,	11.6,	9.9,	11.0

Using a statistical package such as SPSS, carry out a two-sample t test to determine whether support has a significant effect on yield.

4 Testing for differences between more than two groups: ANOVA

Introduction

We saw in the last chapter how you can use *t* tests to compare one set of measurements with an expected value, or two sets of measurements with each other. However, there are many occasions in biology when we might want to save time and effort by comparing three or more groups.

- We might want to *compare* two or more groups of experimentally treated organisms or cells with controls. Do two sets of rats with mutations on separate chromosomes have *different* life expectancies from control 'wild type' rats?

It can prove tricky to tell the difference between groups. . . .

46

- We might want to *compare* three or more groups of organisms or cells. Do people on four drug regimes have different blood pressures? Do five strains of bacteria have different growth rates?
- We might want to *compare* three or more sets of related measurements or measurements repeated three or more times made on a single population. Are levels of aluminium in the same set of fish *different* at three or more times? Is the number of four species of birds recorded every hour at a feeding station *different* from each other?
- We might want to *compare* organisms or cells that have been influenced by two separate types of treatment. Do wheat plants given different levels of both nitrogen and phosphorous have *different* yields?

4.1.1 Why *t* tests are unsuitable

To answer these sorts of questions, you might think that you could simply compare each group with all the others using *t* tests. However, there are two good reasons why you should not do this. First, there is the problem of convenience. As the number of groups you are comparing goes up, the number of tests you must carry out rises rapidly, from three tests when comparing three groups to 45 tests for 10 groups. It would take a lot of time to do all these tests and it would be near impossible to present the results of them all!

Number of groups	3,	4,	5,	6,	7,	8,	9,	10
Number of *t* tests	3,	6,	10,	15,	21,	28,	36,	45

However, there is a second, more important, problem. We reject a null hypothesis with 95% confidence, not 100% confidence. This means that in 1 in 20 tests we will falsely assume there is a significant difference between groups when none really exists (a type I error). If we carry out a lot of tests, the chances of making such an error go up rapidly, so if we carry out 45 tests there is about a 90% chance we will find significant effects even if none exist.

ANOVA
Abbreviation for analysis of variance: a widely used series of tests which can determine whether there are significant differences between groups.

Consequently you must use a rather different set of statistical tests to determine whether there is a difference between many groups; these are called **analysis of variance**, usually shortened to **ANOVA**. They all use similar logic, and it is perhaps easiest to see how they work by starting with the simplest form of the test, **one-way ANOVA**.

4.2 One-way ANOVA

4.2.1 Purpose

To test whether the means of two or more sets of **unrelated** measurements are different from each other. For instance, it is used to test whether one or more groups of experimentally treated organisms are different from controls, or two or more species are different from one another.

47

4.2.2 **The rationale of one-way ANOVA**

One-way ANOVA works in a very different manner from t tests. Rather than examine the difference between the means directly, ANOVA looks at the **variability** of the data. Let's examine a simple example in which the means of the weights of just two small samples of fish are compared (Figure 4.1a). The overall

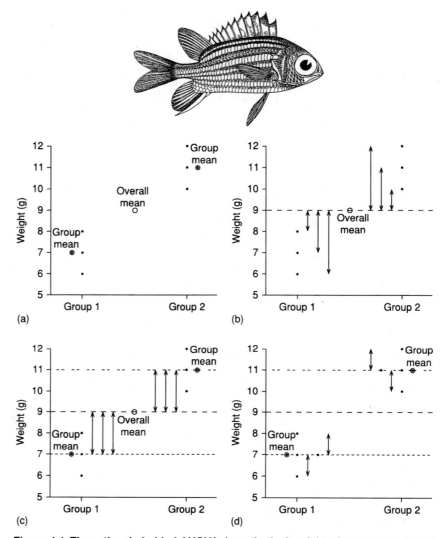

Figure 4.1 The rationale behind ANOVA: hypothetical weights for two samples of fish. (a) Calculate the overall mean and the group means. **(b)** The total variability is the sum of the squares of the distances of each point from the overall mean; this can be broken down into between-group variability and within-group variability. **(c)** The between-group variability is the sum of the squares of the distances from each point's group mean to the overall mean. **(d)** The within-group variability is the sum of the squares of the distances from each point to its group mean.

48

variability is the sum of the squares of the distances from each point to the overall mean (Figure 4.1b); here it is $3^2 + 2^2 + 1^2 + 3^2 + 2^2 + 1^2 = 28$. However, this can be split into two parts. First, there is the between-group variability, which is due to the differences between the group means. This is the sum of the squares of the distances of each point's group mean from the overall mean (Figure 4.1c); here it is $(6 \times 2^2) = 24$. Second, there is the within-group variability, which is due to the scatter within each group. This is the sum of the squares of the distance from each point to its group mean (Figure 4.1d); here it is $(4 \times 1^2) + (2 \times 0^2) = 4$.

ANOVA compares the between-group variability and the within-group variability. To show how this helps, let's look at two contrasting situations. In Figure 4.2a the two means are far apart and there is little scatter within each group; the between-group variability will clearly be much larger than the within-group variability. In Figure 4.2b the means are close together and there is much scatter within each group; the between-group variability will be lower than the within-group variability.

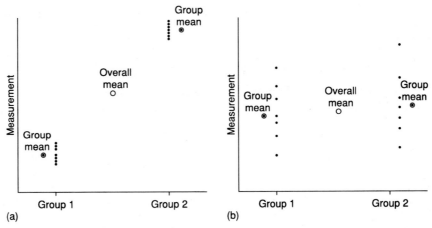

Figure 4.2 Two contrasting situations. (a) Most of the variability is caused by the group means being far apart. **(b)** Most of the variability is caused by differences within the groups.

The test statistic in ANOVA tests is the *F* statistic, a measure of the ratio of between-group to within-group variability. Calculating *F* is quite a long-winded process, however, and involves producing a table like the one shown below and in Example 4.1.

ANOVA

FISHWEIG

	Sum of Squares	df	Mean Square	F	Sig.
Between Groups	24.000	1	24.000	24.000	.008
Within Groups	4.000	4	1.000		
Total	28.000	5			

49

(1) The first stage is to calculate the variabilities due to each factor to produce the so-called **sums of squares** (SS).

(2) You cannot directly compare sums of squares, however, because they are the result of adding up different numbers of points. The next stage is therefore to calculate the actual **variance** or **mean squares** (MS) due to each factor. This is calculated by dividing each sum of squares by the correct number of **degrees of freedom** (DF).

mean square
The variance due to a particular factor in analysis of variance (ANOVA).

(a) If there are n groups, the between-group degrees of freedom $DF_B = n - 1$.

(b) If there are N items in total and r items in each group, there will be $r - 1$ degrees of freedom in each group, hence $n(r - 1)$ in total. The within-group degrees of freedom, $DF_W = N - n$.

(c) If there are N items in total, the total number of degrees of freedom $DF_T = N - 1$.

(3) The last stage is to calculate the test statistic F. This is the ratio of the between-group mean square MS_B to the within-group mean square MS_W:

$$F = MS_B/MS_W \qquad (4.1)$$

The larger the value of F, the more likely it is that the means are significantly different.

4.2.3 Problems with names

Unfortunately, because ANOVA was developed separately by different branches of science, there are problems with its nomenclature; there are two synonyms for *between* and *within*:

between = treatment = factor
within = error   = residual

You must be able to recognise all of them because different names may be used in scientific papers or different computer packages. Then you can cope with any statistics book or any lecturer!

4.2.4 Carrying out a one-way ANOVA test using SPSS

The actual workings of ANOVA tests are quite complex, so you are best advised to use a computer package such as SPSS to perform them, but they involve the same four basic steps as the t tests we have already carried out. Once again the test is best described by running through a simple example, in this case of the fish shown in Figure 4.1.

Example 4.1

> Mass of group 1:   6,   7,   8
> Mass of group 2: 10, 11, 12

Are the masses of the two groups of fish significantly different from each other?

50

Solution

Step 1: Formulating the null hypothesis

The null hypothesis is that the groups have the same mean. In this case the hypothesis is that the two groups of fish have the same mean weight.

Step 2: Calculate the test statistic

Using SPSS

Just as for the two-sample *t* test, when performing one-way ANOVA *all the data points should be entered into a single column*. Call it something like **fishweight**. To distinguish between the separate groups, you must then create a second, subscript, column with different integer values for each group (here 1 and 2) and give it a name (here **sample**). To carry out the test, click on the **Analyze** menu, then move to the **Compare Means** bar and click on **One-Way ANOVA**. SPSS will come up with the **One-Way ANOVA** dialogue box.

Put the variable you are testing (here **fishweight**) into the **Dependent Variable** box and the factor (here **sample**) into the **Factor:** box. You should also click on the **Options** box and tick the **Descriptive** box to get SPSS to calculate the means, standard deviations and standard errors for each group. The completed data sheet and dialogue boxes are shown below.

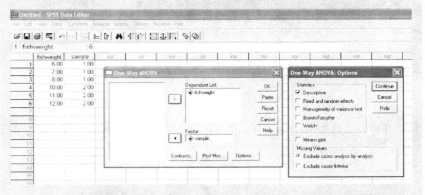

Click on **Continue** to get back to the original dialogue box and finally click on **OK** to start the test. SPSS will print the following results.

One-way

Descriptives

fishweight

	N	Mean	Std. Deviation	Std. Error	95% Confidence Interval for Mean Lower Bound	95% Confidence Interval for Mean Upper Bound	Minimum	Maximum
1.00	3	7.0000	1.00000	.57735	4.5159	9.4841	6.00	8.00
2.00	3	11.0000	1.00000	.57735	8.5159	13.4841	10.00	12.00
Total	6	9.0000	2.36643	.96609	6.5166	11.4834	6.00	12.00

ANOVA

fishweight

	Sum of Squares	df	Mean Square	F	Sig.
Between Groups	24.000	1	24.000	24.000	.008
Within Groups	4.000	4	1.000		
Total	28.000	5			

The first table gives the descriptive statistics for the two groups. The second gives the completed ANOVA table which shows that $F = 24.00$.

Step 3: Calculating the significance probability

SPSS automatically calculates not only the test statistic F, but also the significance probability Sig. Here Sig. = 0.008.

Step 4: Deciding whether to reject the null hypothesis

- If Sig. ≤ 0.05, you must reject the null hypothesis.
- If Sig. > 0.05, you have no evidence to reject the null hypothesis.

Here Sig. = $0.008 < 0.05$ so we can reject the null hypothesis and say that the fish samples have different mean weights. In fact sample 2 is significantly heavier.

4.3   Deciding which groups are different – *post hoc* tests

post hoc tests
Statistical tests carried out if an analysis of variance is significant; they are used to determine which groups are different from each other.

The problem with the basic ANOVA test is that, although it tells us whether there are differences between groups, it doesn't tell us how big the differences are or even which groups are different. This does not matter with the fish because there were only two groups, but it will be a problem if you have three or more groups. Fortunately, statisticians have worked out several different **post hoc tests** that you can use to see which groups are different from each other, *but only if the ANOVA is itself significant.*

SPSS allows you to perform several of these *post hoc* tests, and different ones can be used depending on what you want to test.

- If you want to compare each group with all the others, the tests most used by biologists are the **Tukey** test and the **Scheffe** test.
- If you want to compare experimental groups with a control, then the test to use is the **Dunnett** test.

Let's have a look at a typical example, to see how to perform one-way ANOVA and a relevant *post hoc* test.

52

| Example 4.2 | **The effect of antibiotics on bacterial growth** |

The effect of three different antibiotics on the growth of a bacterium was examined by adding them to Petri dishes, which were then inoculated with the bacteria. The diameter of the colonies (in millimetres) was measured after three days. A control where no antibiotics were added was also included. The following results were obtained.

Control:	4.7,	5.3,	5.9,	4.6,	4.9,	5.0,	5.3,	4.2,
	5.7,	5.3,	4.6,	5.8,	4.7,	4.9		
Antibiotic A:	3.5,	4.6,	4.4,	3.9,	3.8,	3.6,	4.1,	4.3,
	4.3,	4.8,	4.1,	5.0,	3.4,	4.3		
Antibiotic B:	4.7,	5.2,	5.4,	4.4,	6.1,	4.8,	5.3,	5.5,
	4.7,	5.2						
Antibiotic C:	4.3,	5.7,	5.3,	5.6,	4.5,	4.9,	5.1,	5.3,
	4.7,	6.3,	4.8,	4.9,	5.2,	5.4,	4.8,	5.0

Carry out a one-way ANOVA test to determine whether any of the antibiotic treatments affected the growth of the bacteria and, if so, which ones.

Solution

Step 1: Formulating the null hypothesis

The null hypothesis is that there was no difference in the mean diameters of the four groups of bacteria.

Step 2: Calculating the test statistic

In SPSS enter all the measurements of diameter into a single column and call it, say, **diameter**. Next create a second column (called, say, **treatment**) with subscripts for the control given 1, and 2, 3 and 4 for antibiotics A, B and C, respectively.

To carry out the test click on the **Analyze** menu, then move to the **Compare Means** bar and click on **One-Way ANOVA**. SPSS will come up with the **One-Way ANOVA** dialogue box. Put the variable you are testing (here **diameter**) into the **Dependent Variable** box and the factor (here **treatment**) into the **Factor:** box. You should also click on the **Options** box and tick the **Descriptive** box to get SPSS to calculate the means, standard deviations and standard errors for each group. The completed dialogue boxes are shown below.

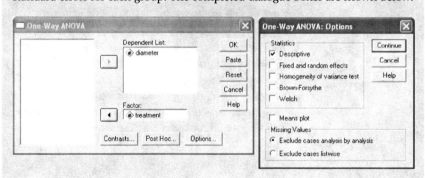

Finally, click on **Continue** then on **OK** to start the test. SPSS will print the following results.

One-way

Descriptives

diameter

	N	Mean	Std. Deviation	Std. Error	95% Confidence Interval for Mean		Minimum	Maximum
					Lower Bound	Upper Bound		
1.00	14	5.0643	.50476	.13490	4.7728	5.3557	4.20	5.90
2.00	14	4.1500	.47677	.12742	3.8747	4.4253	3.40	5.00
3.00	10	5.1300	.49453	.15638	4.7762	5.4838	4.40	6.10
4.00	16	5.1125	.49379	.12345	4.8494	5.3756	4.30	6.30
Total	54	4.8537	.63713	.08670	4.6798	5.0276	3.40	6.30

ANOVA

diameter

	Sum of Squares	df	Mean Square	F	Sig.
Between Groups	9.389	3	3.130	12.905	.000
Within Groups	12.126	50	.243		
Total	21.514	53			

SPSS calculates a value for $F = 12.905$.

Step 3: Calculating the significance probability

SPSS calculates that the significance probability Sig. = 0.000.

Step 4: Deciding whether to reject the null hypothesis

Here Sig. = 0.000 < 0.05 so we can reject the null hypothesis and say that there are significant differences between the mean diameters of the bacteria.

Step 5: Deciding which groups are different

The aim of the experiment was to test which, if any, of the treatments altered the diameter of the bacterial colonies, so you need to compare *each of the treatments against the control*. The test to use is the Dunnett test. Repeat the ANOVA test but click on **Post Hoc** to reveal the **Post Hoc Multiple Comparisons** dialogue box. Tick the **Dunnett** box. The control is given by the subscript 1, so you need to change the **Control Category:** from **Last** to **First**. The completed dialogue box is shown below.

54

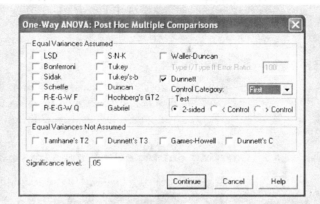

Finally, click on **Continue** and **OK** in the main dialogue box. As well as the results for the ANOVA, SPSS will produce the following table.

Post Hoc Tests

Multiple Comparisons

Dependent Variable: diameter
Dunnett t (2-sided)[a]

(I) treatment	(J) treatment	Mean Difference (I–J)	Std. Error	Sig.	95% Confidence Interval Lower Bound	95% Confidence Interval Upper Bound
2.00	1.00	–.91429*	.18613	.000	–1.3658	–.4628
3.00	1.00	.06571	.20390	.978	–.4289	.5603
4.00	1.00	.04821	.18022	.987	–.3890	.4854

*. The mean difference if significant at the .05 level.
[a]. Dunnett t-tests treat one group as a control, and compare all other groups against it.

The important column is the **Sig.** column. This tells you that of the three treatment groups, 2, 3 and 4, only 2 has a significantly different mean (Sig. = 0.000 which is less than 0.05) from the control. At 4.15 mm its mean diameter is almost 1 mm less than that of the control (5.06 mm). In groups 3 and 4 the significance probabilities (0.978 and 0.987) are well over 0.05, so they are not different from the control.

4.4   Repeated measures ANOVA

4.4.1 Purpose

To test whether the means of two or more sets of **related** measurements are different from each other. For instance, it is used to test whether one group of experimentally treated organisms are different at several times before and after

55

a treatment or if two or more sets of measurements taken at known time points are different from each other.

4.4.2 Rationale

Repeated measures ANOVA acts in the same way as one-way ANOVA, but it improves the chances of detecting differences between groups by removing the within-group variability, just as a paired t test does.

4.4.3 Carrying out repeated measures ANOVA test using SPSS

Carrying out repeated measures ANOVA tests in SPSS is an even more long-winded process than doing one-way ANOVA, so it is best demonstrated by an example.

Example 4.3

In an experiment to investigate the time course of the effect of exercise on the rate of sweating in soldiers in the desert, the following results were obtained

Soldier	1	2	3	4	5	6	7	8	9	10
Rate before (litres/hour)	3.6	3.9	4.2	4.0	3.8	3.5	4.2	4.0	3.9	3.8
During	4.5	4.4	4.8	4.3	4.6	4.5	5.0	4.6	4.1	4.6
1 hour after	3.9	4.4	3.7	3.9	3.5	4.2	4.0	4.1	3.6	4.6

Carry out a repeated measures ANOVA to find out whether the rate of sweating altered during exercise and afterwards compared with before.

Solution

Step 1: Formulating the null hypothesis

The null hypothesis is that there was no difference in the rate of sweating between the times the measurements were taken.

Step 2: Calculating the test statistic

In SPSS enter the measurements of sweating rate into **three separate columns**, making sure the results from each soldier are put into the same row each time. Call the columns, say, **before**, **during** and **after**.

To carry out the test, click on the **Analyze** menu, then move to the **General Linear Model** bar and click on **Repeated Measures**. SPSS will come up with the **Repeated Measures Define Factor(s)** dialogue box. You first need to tell the computer the name of the factor that might affect the results. Here it's time before during and after exercise, so type **time** into the **Within Subject Factor Name:** box. Next, you need to tell the computer how many experimental conditions or *levels* there were. Here there were three (before, during and after), so type 3 into the **Number of Levels:** box.

56

Next, click on the **Add** tab to input this data. The computer will print time(3) in the large box. The completed table is shown below.

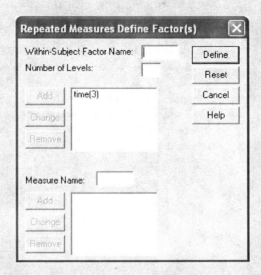

Now click on the **Define** tab to get into the main **Repeated Measures** dialogue box. Next, you must tell the computer which are the three Within-Subject Variables (time). To do this, click on each of the three columns – before, during and after – in turn and click on the top arrow. The data are now entered. The completed box and the data on the data screen are shown below.

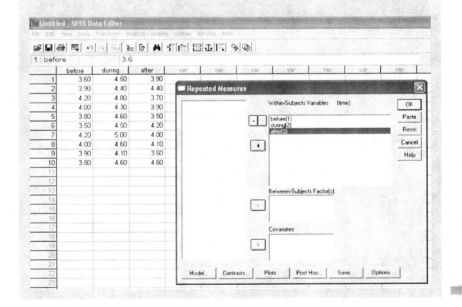

57

To obtain other useful statistics you should now also click on the **Options** tab. This brings up the **Repeated Measures: Options** dialogue box. Click on **Descriptives** to get the means and standard deviations. Unfortunately there is no Dunnett test to compare groups with a control, but you can carry out tests that compare each group with all the others. Other authors who know much more about this (see Field, 2000) than myself suggest that the **Bonferroni** is the most reliable *post hoc* test to use for repeated measures ANOVA. To perform it, click on **Time** within the **Estimated Marginal Means** box and move it with the arrow into the **Display Means for:** box. Now you can tick the **Compare main effects** and change the **Confidence interval adjustment:** box from LSD (none) to **Bonferroni**. The completed box is shown below.

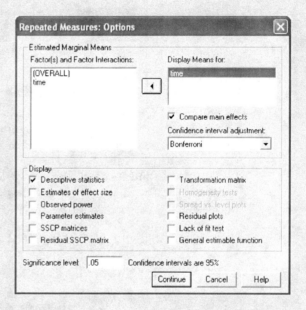

Finally, click on the **Continue** tab and, when the main dialogue box appears again, click on **OK** to run the test. SPSS comes up with a huge mass of results. However, only the ones that are important for us are shown below.

General Linear Model

Descriptive Statistics

	Mean	Std. Deviation	N
before	3.8900	.22828	10
during	4.5400	.25033	10
after	3.9900	.34785	10

58

Mauchly's Test of Sphericity[b]

Measure: MEASURE_1

Within Subjects Effect	Mauchly's W	Approx. Chi-Square	df	Sig.	Epsilon[a]		
					Greenhouse-Geisser	Huynh-Feldt	Lower-bound
time	.681	3.069	2	.216	.758	.880	.500

Tests the null hypthesis that the error covariance matrix of the orthonormalized transformed dependent variables is proportional to an identity matrix.

[a.] May be used to adjust the degrees of freedom for the averaged tests of significance. Corrected tests are displayed in the Tests of Within-Subjects Effects table.

[b.] Design: Intercept
Within Subjects Design: time

Tests of Within-Subjects Effects

Measure: MEASURE_1

Source		Type III Sum of Squares	df	Mean Square	F	Sig.
time	Sphericity Assumed	2.450	2	1.225	16.662	.000
	Greenhouse-Geisser	2.450	1.517	1.615	16.662	.000
	Huynh-Feldt	2.450	1.760	1.392	16.662	.000
	Lower-bound	2.450	1.000	2.450	16.662	.003
Error(time)	Sphericity Assumed	1.323	18	.074		
	Greenhouse-Geisser	1.323	13.650	.097		
	Huynh-Feldt	1.323	15.836	.084		
	Lower-bound	1.323	9.000	.147		

Pairwise Comparisons

Measure: MEASURE_1

(I) time	(J) time	Mean Difference (I–J)	Std. Error	Sig.[a]	95% Confidence Interval for Difference[a]	
					Lower Bound	Upper Bound
1	2	−.650*	.082	.000	−.891	−.409
	3	−.100	.144	1.000	−.522	.322
2	1	.650*	.082	.000	.409	.891
	3	.550*	.129	.006	.171	.929
3	1	.100	.144	1.000	−.322	.522
	2	−.550*	.129	.006	−.929	−.171

Based on estimated marginal means

*. The mean difference if significant at the .05 level.

[a.] Adjustment for multiple comparisons: Bonferroni.

The first thing you must check is whether the data passes Mauchley's sphericity test in the second table. If the data shows significant non-sphericity Sig. < 0.05. Here, fortunately, Sig. = 0.216, so we can go along to examine the F ratio for **Sphericity Assumed** which is shown in the **Tests of Within-Subjects Effects** box. Here $F = 16.662$.

Step 3: Calculating the significance probability

SPSS calculates that the significance probability Sig. = 0.000.

Step 4: Deciding whether to reject the null hypothesis

- If Sig. ≤ 0.05, you must reject the null hypothesis.
- If Sig. > 0.05, you have no evidence to reject the null hypothesis.

Here Sig. = 0.000 < 0.05 so we can reject the null hypothesis and say that there are significant differences between the mean rates of sweating at the three times.

Step 5: Deciding which groups are different

The aim of the experiment was to test when the rate of sweating was different from before exercise. Here during (group 2) vs before (group 1) has Sig. = 0.000, so clearly the soldiers sweated more during exercise. However, after (group 3) vs before (group 1) has Sig. = 1.000, so clearly soldiers didn't have significantly different rates of sweating after exercise from before.

Note: I have just covered the very basics of this test. To find out about the theory behind repeated measures ANOVA, and the meaning and importance of sphericity, you are advised to go to more comprehensive books such as Field (2000).

4.5   Two-way ANOVA

4.5.1 Purpose

To analyse experiments or trials in which you can look at the effect of two factors at once. For instance:

- you might want to examine the effect on corn yield of adding different amounts of nitrate and phosphate;
- you might want to examine the effect on yield of adding different amounts of nitrate to more than one wheat variety.

4.5.2 Rationale

Two-way ANOVA acts in the same way as one-way ANOVA, but with two factors it tests three questions.

(1) Are there differences caused by factor 1?
(2) Are there differences caused by factor 2?
(3) Do the two factors interact with each other? In other words, does one factor alter the response of the subjects to the other? Does adding nitrate affect the response of the corn to phosphate? Or does one variety show a greater response to nitrate than the other?

60

4.5.3 Carrying out a test in SPSS

Carrying out two-way ANOVA tests in SPSS is also a fairly long process, so once again it is best demonstrated by an example.

| **Example 4.4** | In a field trial to look at the effects of fertilizers, wheat was grown at two different levels of nitrogen and at two different levels of phosphorus. To allow analysis, all possible combinations of nitrogen and phosphorus levels were grown (so there were $2 \times 2 = 4$ combinations in total). The yields (t ha^{-1}) from the experiment are tabulated below. |

> No nitrate or phosphate: 1.4, 1.8, 2.1, 2.7, 1.7, 1.9, 1.5, 2.0, 2.1
> Mean = 1.91, s = 0.39, $\overline{SE}$ = 0.128
>
> Added nitrate only: 2.4, 2.7, 3.1, 2.9, 2.8, 3.0, 2.6, 3.1, 2.6
> Mean = 2.80, s = 0.24, $\overline{SE}$ = 0.082
>
> Added phosphate only: 3.5, 3.2, 3.7, 2.8, 4.0, 3.2, 3.9, 3.6, 3.1
> Mean = 3.44, s = 0.40, $\overline{SE}$ = 0.132
>
> Added nitrate and phosphate: 7.5, 6.4, 8.1, 6.3, 7.2, 6.8, 6.4, 6.7, 6.5
> Mean = 6.88, s = 0.61, $\overline{SE}$ = 0.203

Analyse this experiment using **two-way ANOVA** to determine the effects of nitrate and phosphate on yield.

Solution

Step 1: Formulating the null hypotheses

There are three null hypotheses:

(1) that nitrate addition had no effect on yield;
(2) that phosphate addition had no effect on yield;
(3) that there was no interaction between the actions of nitrate and phosphate.

Step 2: Calculating the test statistics

In SPSS enter all the measurements of yield into a single column and call it, say, **yield**. Next create two more columns: a second column (called, say, **nitrate**) with subscripts 0 and 1 for no nitrate and added nitrate respectively; and a third column (called, say, **phosphate**) with subscripts 0 and 1 for no phosphate and added phosphate respectively.

To carry out the test, click on the **Analyze** menu, then move to the **General Linear Model** bar and click on **Univariate**. SPSS will come up with the **Univariate** dialogue box. Put **yield** into the **Dependent Variable:** box, and **nitrate** and **phosphate** into the **Fixed Factor(s):** box. Next, click on the **Options** tab and click on the **Descriptive Statistics** box to give you the mean yields, etc. for each experimental treatment. The data and completed main dialogue box are shown below.

61

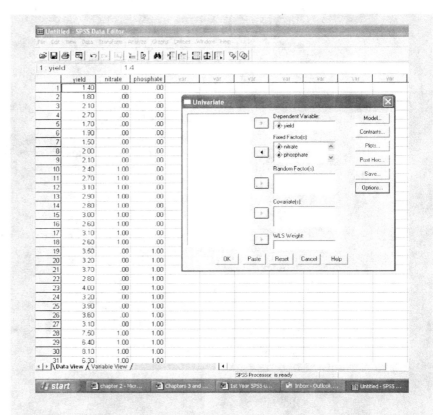

Finally, click on the **Continue** tab to get back to the main dialogue box and click on **OK**. SPSS will produce lots of results, the most important of which are shown below.

Descriptive Statistics

Dependent Variable: yield

nitrate	phosphate	Mean	Std. Deviation	N
.00	.00	1.9111	.38550	9
	1.00	3.4444	.39721	9
	Total	2.6778	.87552	18
1.00	.00	2.8000	.24495	9
	1.00	6.8778	.60782	9
	Total	4.8389	2.14562	18
Total	.00	2.3556	.55436	18
	1.00	5.1611	1.83532	18
	Total	3.7583	1.95176	36

Science Fundamentals

Tests of Between-Subjects Effects

Dependent Variable: yield

Source	Type III Sum of Squares	df	Mean Square	F	Sig.	
Corrected Model	127.441[a]	3	42.480	230.923	.000	
Intercept	508.503	1	508.503	2764.227	.000	
nitrate	42.034	1	42.034	228.495	.000	←
phosphate	70.840	1	70.840	385.089	.000	←
nitrate * phosphate	14.567	1	14.567	79.186	.000	←
Error	5.887	32	.184			
Total	641.830	36				
Corrected Total	133.328	35				

[a] R Squared = .956 (Adjusted R Squared = .952)

Just like the one-way ANOVA we have already looked at, two-way ANOVA partitions the variability and variance. However, there will not be two possible causes of variability but four: the effect of nitrate; the effect of phosphate; the **interaction** between the effects of nitrate and phosphate (shown here as nitrate * phosphate); and, finally, variation within the groups (here called Error).

These possibilities are here used to produce three F ratios, which test the null hypotheses:

(1) the effect of nitrate: $F = 228.5$;
(2) the effect of phosphate: $F = 385.1$;
(3) the interaction between nitrate and phosphate: $F = 79.2$.

Step 3: Calculating the significance probability

(1) For the effect of nitrate: Sig. = 0.000.
(2) For the effect of phosphate: Sig. = 0.000.
(3) For the interaction: Sig. = 0.000.

Step 4: Deciding whether to reject the null hypothesis

(1) Here Sig. = 0.000 < 0.05, so we can reject the null hypothesis and say that nitrate has a significant effect on yield. In fact, looking at the descriptive statistics we can see that adding nitrate increases yield by 0.89 t ha^{-1}.
(2) Here Sig. = 0.000 < 0.05, so we can reject the null hypothesis and say that phosphate has a significant effect on yield. In fact, looking at the descriptive statistics we can see that adding phosphate also increases yield by 1.53 t ha^{-1}.
(3) Here Sig. = 0.000 < 0.05, so we can reject the null hypothesis and say that nitrate and phosphate have a significant interaction. What does this mean? Well, looking at the descriptive statistics we can see that the yield with both nitrate and phosphate is very large. If the separate effects of nitrate and phosphate acting alone were added together, their combined

63

effect would be to increase the yield by 0.89 + 1.53 = 2.42 t ha^{-1}. However, when they are actually added together the increase in yield is much larger at 4.97 t ha^{-1}. In this case, therefore, the two nutrients potentiate each other's effects (although you would also get a significant interaction if they had **inhibited** each other's effects).

Step 5: Deciding which groups are different

It is also possible to carry out *post hoc* tests for each of the main effects in two-way ANOVA, just as in one-way ANOVA. In this example, though, since there are only two levels of nitrate and two of phosphate this is not possible. If you have three or more levels, you can just click on the **Post Hoc** tab, put the factors you want to examine into the box and tick the *post hoc* test you want to perform.

4.6 Self-assessment problems

Problem 4.1

The levels of calcium binding protein activity were followed in isolated plant protoplasts following delivery of a heat shock stimulus. Measurements were taken on six samples of protoplasts just before and one, two, four and eight hours after the stimulus was applied. The following results were obtained.

Before:	3.2,	2.2,	3.8,	2.8,	2.7,	3.0
1 Hour:	3.4,	2.7,	3.2,	4.0,	2.8,	2.9
2 Hours:	3.5,	3.7,	4.1,	3.6,	4.7,	3.8
4 Hours:	4.5,	4.3,	4.9,	5.1,	3.9,	4.4
8 Hours:	3.4,	3.1,	3.6,	2.7,	3.5,	3.2

Using SPSS, investigate the way in which protein activity changes during the time course of the experiment. Carry out a one-way ANOVA and appropriate *post hoc* tests to determine if any of the apparent changes are significant.

Problem 4.2

Interpret the following ANOVA table. How many groups were being compared? What was the total number of observations? And was there a significant difference between the groups?

	Sum of Squares	df	Mean Square	F	Sig.
Between Groups	654	4	164	1.71	0.35
Within Groups	2386	25	95		
Total	3040	29			

64

Problem 4.3

In an experiment to investigate the uptake of aluminium by snails, 20 snails were placed in each of eight tanks of water, each of which had an initial aluminium concentration of 20 mM. The water in each tank was sampled at weekly intervals for five weeks after the start of the experiment and the concentration of aluminium measured. The following results were obtained.

Tank	1	2	3	4	5	6	7	8
Week 1	16.5	14.3	14.6	15.5	13.1	15.2	14.5	13.9
Week 2	12.1	11.2	12.5	10.9	10.5	11.6	13.2	10.5
Week 3	10.9	8.6	10.2	8.7	8.9	9.3	11.0	9.5
Week 4	10.5	7.8	9.6	7.6	6.8	8.0	9.1	8.5
Week 5	10.2	7.4	8.6	7.9	5.7	7.6	8.4	8.2

Carry out a repeated measures ANOVA to test whether aluminium level changes significantly through time. Carry out a *post hoc* test to determine whether levels *continue* to fall throughout the period.

Problem 4.4

In a field trial, two different varieties of wheat, Widgeon and Hereward, were grown at three different levels of nitrogen. The results given in Tables 4.2 and 4.3 were obtained.

Table 4.1 The effect of addition of nitrates on the yield of wheat variety Widgeon.

Widgeon	Nitrates added (kg m^{-2})		
	0	1	2
Yield (t ha^{-1})	4.7	6.4	7.8
	5.3	7.5	7.4
	5.1	6.9	8.3
	6.0	8.1	6.9
	6.5	5.9	6.5
	4.8	7.6	7.2
	5.6	7.1	6.3
	5.8	6.4	7.9
	5.4	8.6	7.7

65

Table 4.3 The effect of addition of nitrates on the yield of wheat variety Hereward.

Hereward	Nitrates added (kg m^{-2})		
	0	1	2
Yield (t ha^{-1})	1.3	6.1	10.8
	2.2	7.2	9.8
	2.1	7.4	11.4
	3.3	8.6	10.6
	1.8	5.7	12.2
	2.4	7.2	9.6
	2.6	6.7	11.1
	2.7	6.9	10.4
	3.1	8.4	10.9

Carry out a two-way ANOVA in SPSS to answer the following questions.

(a) Which of the three possible effects, variety, nitrogen and interaction, are significant?
(b) Examine the descriptive statistics to work out what these results mean in real terms.

5 Finding associations

Introduction

association
A numerical link between two sets of measurements.

We saw in Chapter 3 that we can use a paired *t* test to determine whether two sets of paired measurements are different. For instance, we can test whether students have a different heart rate after drinking coffee compared with before. However, we may instead want to know if and how the two sets of measurements are **associated**. Do the students who have a higher heart rate before drinking coffee also have a higher heart rate afterwards? Or we might ask other questions. How are the lengths of snakes related to their age? How are the wing areas of birds related to their weight? Or how are the blood pressures of stroke patients related to their heart rate?

This chapter has three sections. First, it shows how to examine data to see whether variables are associated. Second, it shows how you can use statistical tests to work out whether, despite the inevitable variability, there is a real **linear** association between the variables and, if so, how to determine what it is. Finally, it describes some of the non-linear ways in which biological variables can be related and shows how data can be transformed to make a linear relationship, the equation of which can be determined statistically.

An experiment to test whether the more really is the merrier.

5.2   Examining data for associations

scatter plot
A point graph between two variables which allows one to visually determine whether they are associated.

independent variable
A variable in a regression which affects another variable but is not itself affected.

dependent variable
A variable in a regression which is affected by another variable.

The first thing you should do if you feel that two variables might be associated is to draw a **scatter plot** of one against the other. This will allow you to see at a glance what is going on. For instance, it is clear from Figure 5.1 that as the age of eggs increases, their mass decreases. However, it is important to make sure you plot the graph the correct way round. This depends on how the variables affect each other. One of the variables is called the independent variable; the other is called the dependent variable. The independent variable affects, or may affect, the dependent variable but is not itself affected. Plot the **independent variable** along the horizontal axis, often called the *x*-axis. Plot the **dependent variable** along the vertical axis, often called the *y*-axis. You would then say you were plotting the dependent variable *against* the independent variable. In Figure 5.1, age is the independent variable and mass is the dependent variable. This is because age can affect an egg's mass, but mass can't affect an egg's age.

Things are not always so clear-cut. It is virtually impossible to tell whether blood pressure would affect heart rate or vice versa. They are probably both affected by a third variable – artery stiffness. In this case, it does not matter so much; however, the one you wish to predict from the relationship should go on the *y*-axis.

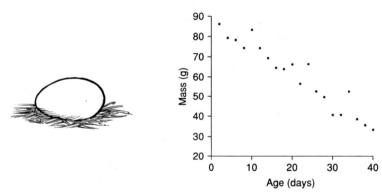

Figure 5.1 The relationship between the age of eggs and their mass. Note that the dependent variable, mass, is plotted along the vertical axis.

5.3   Examining graphs

Once you have plotted your graph, you should examine it for associations. There are several main ways in which variables can be related:

● there may be no relationship: points are scattered all over the graph paper (Figure 5.2a);

68

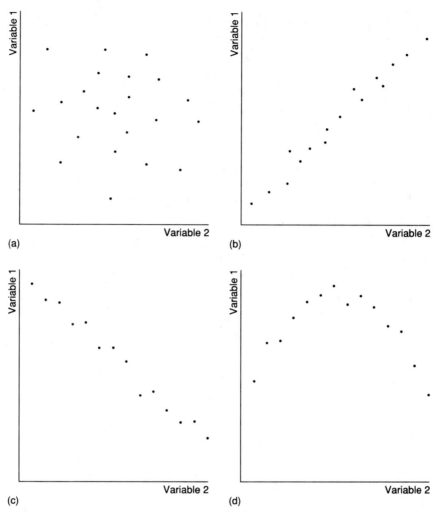

Figure 5.2 Ways in which variables can be related. (a) No association. **(b)** Positive association. **(c)** Negative association. **(d)** A complex curvilinear association.

- there may be a positive association (Figure 5.2b): the dependent variable increases as the independent variable increases;
- there may be a negative association (Figure 5.2c): the dependent variable decreases as the independent variable increases;
- there may be a more complex relationship: Figure 5.2d shows a relationship in which the dependent variable rises and falls as the independent variable increases.

69

5.4   Linear relationships

There are an infinite number of ways in which two variables can be related, most of which are rather complex. Perhaps the simplest relationships to describe are linear relationships such as the one shown in Figure 5.3. In these cases, the dependent variable y is related to the independent variable x by the general equation

$$y = a + bx \qquad (5.1)$$

slope
The gradient of a straight line.

where b is the **slope** of the line and a is the constant or **intercept**. The intercept is the value of y where the line crosses the y-axis. Note that this equation is *exactly the same* as the equation

intercept
The point where a straight line crosses the y-axis.

$$y = mx + c \qquad (5.2)$$

which is the form in which many students encounter it at school.

transformation
A mathematical function used to make the distribution of data more symmetrical and so make parametric tests valid.

Linear relationships are important because they are by far the easiest to analyse statistically. When biologists test whether two variables are related, they are usually testing whether they are linearly related. Fortunately, linear relationships between variables are surprisingly common in biology. Many other common relationships between variables can also be converted into linear relationships by **transforming** the data using logarithms as we shall see in Section 5.8.

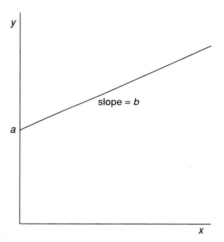

Figure 5.3 A straight line relationship. The straight line $y = a + bx$ has y-intercept a and slope b.

5.5   Statistical tests for linear associations

The points on your plots will never exactly follow a straight line, or indeed any exact mathematical function, because of the variability that is inherent in biology. There will always be some scatter away from a line. The difficulty in determining whether two measurements are really associated is that when you were taking a sample you might have chosen points which followed a straight line even if there was no association in the population. If there appears only to be a slight association and if there are only a few points, this is quite likely (Figure 5.4a). In contrast, it is very unlikely that you would choose large numbers of points all along a straight line just by chance if there was no real relationship (Figure 5.4b). Therefore, you have to carry out statistical tests to work out the probability that you could get your apparent association by chance. If there is an association, you may also be able to work out what the linear relationship is. There are two main tests for association: correlation and regression.

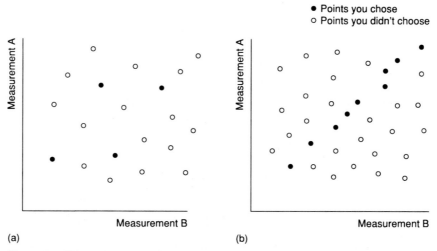

(a)   (b)

Figure 5.4 Effect of sample size on the likelihood of getting an apparent association. Even if there is no real relationship, you might be quite likely to choose a few points which seem to show an association **(a)**. However, if you have a large sample it is very unlikely you would choose points that all fitted onto a straight line **(b)**.

5.6   Correlation

correlation
A statistical test which determines whether there is linear association between two sets of measurements.

5.6.1 Purpose

To test whether two sets of paired measurements, neither of which is clearly independent of the other, are linearly associated.

5.6.2 The rationale behind correlation

Correlation analysis examines the strength with which two sets of measurements show positive or negative linear association. The basic idea is that if there is positive association, all points will either be above and to the right or below

71

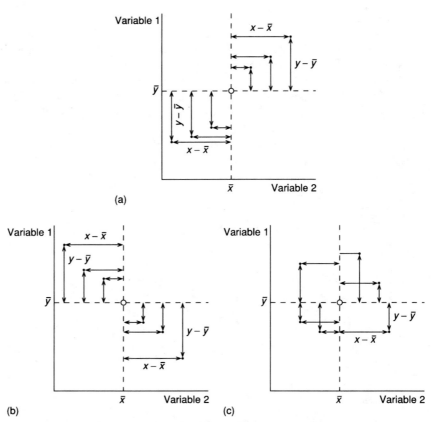

Figure 5.5 Correlation. (a) Positive correlation: $\Sigma(x - \bar{x})(y - \bar{y})$ is large and positive. **(b)** Negative correlation: $\Sigma(x - \bar{x})(y - \bar{y})$ is large and negative. **(c)** No correlation: $\Sigma(x - \bar{x})(y - \bar{y})$ is small.

and to the left of the distribution's centre ($\bar{x}$, $\bar{y}$) (Figure 5.5a). If there is negative association, all points will be above and to the left or below and to the right of the distribution's centre (Figure 5.5b). If there is no association, the points will be scattered on all sides (Figure 5.5c).

Correlation analysis measures the extent of the association by calculating a single statistic, the **Pearson correlation coefficient r**. It is calculated in three stages.

Stage 1

The first step is to calculate the means of the two sets of measurements, $\bar{x}$ and $\bar{y}$.

Stage 2

The next step is to calculate, for each point, the product of its x and y distances from the mean $(x - \bar{x})(y - \bar{y})$. Note that if both x and y are greater than the

72

mean, this figure will be positive because both $(x - \bar{x})$ and $(y - \bar{y})$ will be positive. It will also be positive if both x and y are smaller than the mean, because both $(x - \bar{x})$ and $(y - \bar{y})$ will be negative and their product will be positive. However, if one is larger than the mean and the other smaller, the product will be negative.

These points are added together to give

$$\text{Sum} = \Sigma(x - \bar{x})(y - \bar{y})$$

- If there is positive association (Figure 5.5a), with points all either above and to the right or below and to the left of the overall mean, the sum will be large and positive.
- If there is negative association (Figure 5.5b), with points all either above and to the left or below and to the right of the overall mean, the sum will be large and negative.
- If there is no association (Figure 5.5c), points will be on all sides of the overall mean, and the positive and negative numbers will cancel each other out. The sum will therefore be small.

Stage 3

The final stage is to scale the sum obtained in stage 2 by dividing it by the product of the variation within each of the measurements. The correlation coefficient r is therefore given by the formula

$$r = \frac{\Sigma(x - \bar{x})(y - \bar{y})}{[\Sigma(x - \bar{x})^2 \, \Sigma(y - \bar{y})^2]^{1/2}} \tag{5.3}$$

However, this equation is rather clumsy, and can be simplified to allow it to be calculated somewhat more quickly to give

$$\frac{n\Sigma xy - \Sigma x \, \Sigma y}{\sqrt{[(n\Sigma x^2 - (\Sigma x)^2)(n\Sigma y^2 - (\Sigma y)^2)]}} \tag{5.4}$$

The correlation coefficient can vary from -1 (perfect negative correlation) through 0 (no correlation) up to a value of 1 (perfect positive correlation). The further r is away from zero and the larger the sample size, the less likely it is such a correlation could have occurred by chance if there was no real association between the measurements.

5.6.3 Carrying out the test

The best way to see how correlation analysis can be performed is to examine an example.

73

Example 5.1

In an investigation of the cardiovascular health of elderly patients, the heart rate and blood pressure of 30 patients were taken. The results shown in Table 5.1 were obtained. Is there a linear association between the variables?

Table 5.1 Heart rate and blood pressure of 30 elderly patients.

Patient	Heart rate (min^{-1})	Blood pressure (mm Hg)
1	67	179
2	75	197
3	63	175
4	89	209
5	53	164
6	76	180
7	98	212
8	75	187
9	71	189
10	65	176
11	69	167
12	74	186
13	80	198
14	58	170
15	76	187
16	68	175
17	64	169
18	76	190
19	79	176
20	72	168
21	60	158
22	67	160
23	63	167
24	90	221
25	50	149
26	73	180
27	64	168
28	68	162
29	65	168
30	70	157

Solution

Plotting association data in SPSS

As well as carrying out statistical tests, SPSS can first be used to graphically examine the data. Simply put the data into two columns and name them, here **heart** and **pressure**. Now go into the **Graphs** menu and click on **Scatter/Dot**. In the little dialogue box that pops up, click on **Simple Scatter** and then **Define**. SPSS will produce the **Simple Scatterplot** dialogue box. Move **heart** into the Y Axis: box and **pressure** into the X Axis: box (actually it doesn't matter which way round in this case). The completed box with the data screen is shown below.

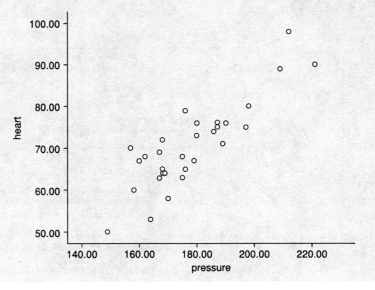

Finally, click on **OK** to get SPSS to draw the graph. It will produce a graph like the one shown below.

It looks like there is a clear positive correlation, but is it significant? To find out we must carry out a correlation analysis.

Step 1: Formulating the null hypothesis

In correlation, the null hypothesis is that there is no association between the two measurements, i.e. they show random scatter. Here the null hypothesis is that blood pressure and heart rate are not associated.

Step 2: Calculating the test statistic

Using a calculator

Putting the data into equation (5.4), or using the correlation facility of a scientific calculator, gives a correlation coefficient of 0.86.

Using SPSS

The test statistic can be calculated using equation (5.4), but it is probably most easily found using SPSS. Click on the **Analyze** menu, move onto the **Correlation** bar and click on **Bivariate**. SPSS will produce the **Bivariate Correlations** dialogue box. Move **heart** and **pressure** into the **Variables:** box and make sure that **Pearson** is ticked. The completed box is shown below.

Finally, click on **OK**. SPSS will come up with the following results.

Correlations

Correlations

		heart	pressure
heart	Pearson Correlation	1	.860 **
	Sig. (2-tailed)	.	.000
	N	30	30
pressure	Pearson Correlation	.860**	1
	Sig. (2-tailed)	.000	.
	N	30	30

**. Correlation is significant at the 0.01 level (2-tailed).

Reading from the table the Pearson correlation coefficient $r = 0.860$.

Step 3: Calculating the significance probability

Using a calculator

Critical values of $|r|$ required for P to fall below 0.05, and hence for the association to be significant, are given for a range of degrees of freedom in Table S2 in the Appendix. You must look up in Table S2 the critical value of r for $(N - 2)$ degrees of freedom, where N is the number of pairs of observations. Here $N = 30$ so there are 28 degrees of freedom, so $r_{crit} = 0.36$.

Using SPSS

SPSS calculates the significance probability **Sig. (2-tailed)** directly. Here it is 0.000.

Step 4: Deciding whether to reject the null hypothesis

Using a calculator

- If $|r|$ is greater than or equal to the critical value, you must reject the null hypothesis. You can say that the two variables show significant correlation.
- If $|r|$ is less than the critical value, you cannot reject the null hypothesis. There is no evidence of a linear association between the two variables.

Here $r = 0.86 > 0.36$.

Using SPSS

- If Sig. (2 tailed) ≤ 0.05, you must reject the null hypothesis. Therefore, you can say that there is a significant association between the variables.
- If Sig. (2 tailed) > 0.05, you have no evidence to reject the null hypothesis. Therefore, you can say that there is no significant association between the variables.

Here Sig. (2-tailed) $= 0.000 < 0.05$.

Therefore, we must reject the null hypothesis. We can say that heart rate and blood pressure are significantly correlated. In fact as $r > 0$ they show a significant positive association.

5.6.4 Uses of the correlation coefficient

Correlation is a useful technique since it tells you whether two measurements are associated, and it can be used even if neither of the variables is independent of the other. However, the results of correlation analysis need to be treated with caution for three reasons.

- Correlation only finds linear associations between measurements, so a non-significant correlation does not prove that there is no association between the variables.

77

causal relationship
Relationship between two variables whereby one affects the other but is not itself affected.

- A significant correlation does not imply a **causal relationship** between the two measurements.
- The size of the correlation coefficient does not reflect the slope of the relationship between the two measurements, it just reflects how close or strong the association is. If you want to determine the nature of the linear relationship between two sets of measurements, you need to carry out regression analysis. However, this is only valid if one of the variables is obviously independent of the other and so is plotted along the *x*-axis of your graph.

5.7   Regression

regression
A statistical test which analyses how one set of measurements is (usually linearly) affected by another.

5.7.1 Purpose

To quantify the linear relationship between two sets of paired measurements, one of which is clearly independent of the other. Good examples of independent variables are:

- age or time;
- an experimentally manipulated variable, such as temperature or humidity.

5.7.2 Rationale

Regression analysis finds an estimate of the line of best fit $y = \bar{a} + \bar{b}x$ through the scattered points on your graph. If you measure the vertical distance of each point from the regression line (Figure 5.6a), the line of best fit is the one which minimises the sum of the squares of the distances.

The estimate of the slope $\bar{b}$ is actually worked out in a similar way to the correlation coefficient, using the formula

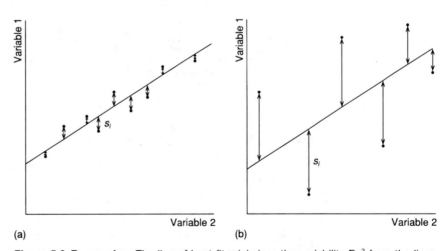

(a)   (b)

Figure 5.6 Regression. The line of best fit minimises the variability Σs_i^2 from the line. **(a)** Significant regression: Σs_i^2 is low. **(b)** Non-significant regression: Σs_i^2 is high.

78

$$\bar{b} = \frac{\Sigma(x - \bar{x})(y - \bar{y})}{\Sigma(x - \bar{x})^2} \qquad (5.5)$$

which can be simplified to the following

$$\bar{b} = \frac{n\Sigma xy - \Sigma x \Sigma y}{n\Sigma x^2 - (\Sigma x)^2} \qquad (5.6)$$

Since the line of best fit always passes through the means of x and y, $\bar{x}$ and $\bar{y}$, the estimate of the constant $\bar{a}$ can then be found by substituting them into the equation to give

$$\bar{a} = \bar{y} - \bar{b}\bar{x} \qquad (5.7)$$

This is all very well, but data with very different degrees of scatter, such as those shown in Figure 5.6, can have identical regression lines. In Figure 5.6a there is clearly a linear relationship. However, in Figure 5.6b there may actually be no relationship between the variables; you might have chosen a sample that suggests there is a relationship just by chance.

In order to test whether there is really a relationship, therefore, you would have to carry out one or more statistical tests. You could do this yourself, but the calculations needed are somewhat long and complex, so it is much better now to use a computer package. SPSS not only calculates the regression equation but also performs two statistical tests and gives you the information you need to carry out a whole range of other tests.

t tests
Statistical tests which analyse whether there are differences between measurements on a single population and an expected value, between paired measurements, or between two unpaired sets of measurements.

- It works out the **standard deviation** of $\bar{a}$ and $\bar{b}$ and uses them to carry out two separate **t tests** to determine whether they are significantly different from zero. The data can also be used to calculate 95% confidence intervals for a and b.
- It carries out an **ANOVA** test, which essentially compares the amount of variation explained by the regression line with that due to the scatter of the points away from the regression line. This tells you whether there is a significant slope, e.g. if b is significantly different from zero.
- It also tells you the percentage of the total variation that the regression line explains. This r^2 value is equal to the square of the correlation coefficient.

5.7.3 Carrying out the test

Once again it is best to demonstrate how to carry out a regression analysis by using an example.

Example 5.2

In a survey to investigate the way in which chicken eggs lose weight after they are laid, one egg was collected newly laid every two days. Each egg was put into an incubator, and after 40 days all 20 eggs were weighed. The results are tabulated here and plotted in Figure 5.1. Carry out a regression analysis to determine whether age significantly affects egg weight. If there is a relationship, determine what it is.

79

Age (days)	2	4	6	8	10	12	14	16	18	20	22
Mass (g)	87	80	79	75	84	75	70	65	64	67	57
Age (days)	24	26	28	30	32	34	36	38	40		
Mass (g)	67	53	50	41	41	53	39	36	34		

Solution

Step 1: Formulating the null hypothesis

The null hypothesis is that age has no effect on egg weight. In other words, that the slope of the regression line is zero.

Step 2: Calculating the test statistic

To carry out the test in SPSS you must first put the data into two columns called, say, **mass** and **day**. Next, click on the **Analyze** menu, move onto the **Regression** bar and click on **Linear**. SPSS will produce the **Linear Regression** dialogue box. Put the dependent variable (here **mass**) into the **Dependent:** box and the independent variable (here **day**) into the **Independent(s):** box. The completed box, and the data screen are shown below.

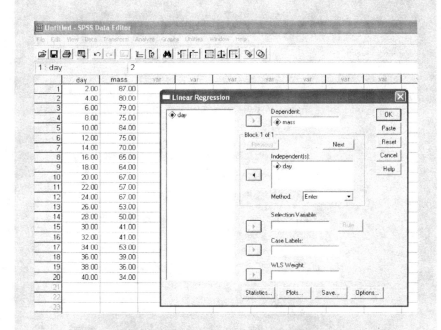

Finally, click on **OK**. SPSS will produce the following output.

80

Regression

Variables Entered/Removed[b]

Model	Variables Entered	Variables Removed	Method
1	day[a]	.	Enter

a. All requested variables entered.
b. Dependent Variable: mass

Model Summary

Model	R	R Square	Adjusted R Square	Std. Error of the Estimate
1	.959[a]	.919	.915	4.90669

a. Predictors: (Constant), day

ANOVA[b]

Model		Sum of Squares	df	Mean Square	F	Sig.
1	Regression	4929.188	1	4929.188	204.738	.000[a]
	Residual	433.362	18	24.076		
	Total	5362.550	19			

a. Predictors: (Constant), day
b. Dependent Variable: mass

Coefficients[a]

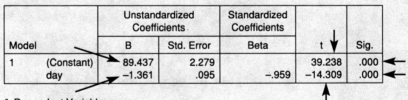

Model		Unstandardized Coefficients		Standardized Coefficients	t	Sig.
		B	Std. Error	Beta		
1	(Constant)	89.437	2.279		39.238	.000
	day	−1.361	.095	−.959	−14.309	.000

a. Dependent Variable: mass

The most important table is the last one, which gives you an estimate (B) of the Constant and slope(day) from equation (5.1). Here, the line of best fit is the equation

$$\text{Mass} = 89.437 - (1.361 \times \text{Day})$$

The slope of the regression equation is −1.36, which appears to be well below zero. But is this difference significant? SPSS has also calculated the standard error of the slope (0.095) and has performed a t test to determine whether the slope is significantly different from zero. Here $t = -14.309$.

Step 3: Calculating the significance probability

SPSS has also directly worked out the probability Sig. that the slope would be different from 0. Here Sig. = 0.000.

81

Step 4: Deciding whether to reject the null hypothesis

- If Sig. ≤ 0.05, you should reject the null hypothesis. Therefore, you can say that the slope is significantly different from zero.
- If Sig. > 0.05, you have no evidence to reject the null hypothesis. Therefore, you can say that the slope is not significantly different from zero.

Here Sig. = 0.000 < 0.05. Therefore, we must reject the null hypothesis. We can say that age has a significant effect on egg weight; in fact older eggs are lighter.

Step 5: Calculating confidence limits

SPSS also calculates confidence intervals for the slope. Simply go into the **Statistics** tab and tick the **Confidence Intervals** box when you are carrying out the test. SPSS will produce the slightly larger final table shown below.

Coefficients[a]

Model		Unstandardized Coefficients B	Unstandardized Coefficients Std. Error	Standardized Coefficients Beta	t	Sig.	95% Confidence Interval for B Lower Bound	95% Confidence Interval for B Upper Bound
1	(Constant)	89.437	2.279		39.238	.000	84.648	94.226
	day	−1.361	.095	−.959	−14.309	.000	−1.561	−1.161

a. Dependent Variable: mass

This shows that the confidence intervals for the slope of the line are between −1.561 and −1.161.

5.7.4 Other tests on regression data

The difference from an expected value

The t tests worked out by the computer investigate whether the slope and constant are different from zero. The value of t is simply given by the expression

$$t = \frac{\text{Observed value} - 0}{\text{Standard deviation}} \tag{5.8}$$

However, it is also possible from SPSS output to carry out a whole range of **one-sample t tests** to determine whether the slope or constant are different from any expected value. Then t is simply given by the expression

$$t = \frac{\text{Observed value} - \text{Expected value}}{\text{Standard deviation}} \tag{5.9}$$

Just like equation (3.1), and you can carry out the t test for $N - 2$ degrees of freedom just as the computer did to determine whether the slope or constant were different from zero.

82

Example 5.3 From the egg weight data in Example 5.2, we want to determine whether the initial egg weight was significantly different from 90 g, which is the mean figure for the general population. In other words, we must test whether the intercept (or Constant as SPSS calls it) is different from 90.

Solution

Step 1: Formulating the null hypothesis

The null hypothesis is that the constant is equal to 90.

Step 2: Calculating the test statistic

The necessary data can be extracted from the SPSS output in Example 5.2 (see p.81). This shows that the estimate of the intercept = 89.437 and its standard deviation = 2.279. Therefore, if the expected value = 90, the test statistic is

$$t = \frac{89.437 - 90}{2.279}$$

$$= -0.247$$

Step 3: Calculating the significance probability

Here $|t|$ must be compared with the critical value for $20 - 2 = 18$ degrees of freedom. This is 2.101.

Step 4: Deciding whether to reject the null hypothesis

We have $|t| = 0.247 < 2.101$. Hence there is no evidence to reject the null hypothesis. We can say that initial egg mass is not significantly different from 90 g.

The difference between two regression lines

If you have calculated two regression lines and want to test whether their slopes or intercepts are *different from each other* you can also carry out **two-sample t tests**, using equations (3.5) and (3.6) to give, for instance

$$t = \frac{\text{Slope 1} - \text{Slope 2}}{\sqrt{[(\text{SE}_{slope1})^2 + (\text{SE}_{slope2})^2]}} \qquad (5.10)$$

where there are $N + M - 4$ degrees of freedom, where N and M are the two sample sizes.

5.7.5 Validity

You must be careful to use regression appropriately; there are many cases where it is not valid.

● Simple regression is not valid for data in which there is no independent variable. For example, you should not regress heart rate against blood pressure,

83

because each factor could affect the other. In that case you could, in fact, use **Reduced Major Axis Regression**, although debate continues to rage about whether even this approach is really valid. Details of how to carry out this (not too difficult!) analysis can be found in Zar (2005).

- All of your measurements must be independent. Therefore, you should not use regression to analyse repeated measures, such as the height of a single plant at different times. If that is the case you will need to use growth analysis, which is a subject in itself.

5.8 Studying common non-linear relationships

As we have seen, not all relationships between variables are linear. There are, in fact, two particularly common non-linear ways in which measurements in biology may be related. Fortunately, as we shall see, these relationships can be changed into linear relationships by transforming one or both of the variables, allowing them to be quantified using regression analysis.

5.8.1 Scaling and power relationships

power relationship
A relationship which follows the general equation $y = ax^b$.

If you examine organisms of different size, many of their characteristics scale according to **power relationships**. If an organism changes in size by a given ratio, some characteristic will increase or decrease by the square, cube or some other power of that ratio. For instance, the mass of unicellular algae would be expected to rise with the cube of their diameter; and the metabolic rate of mammals rises with mass to the power of around 0.75. Other physical processes are also related in this way. The lift produced by a bird's wings should rise with the square of the flight speed. In these sorts of relationships, the dependent variable y is related to the independent variable x by the general equation

$$y = ax^b \tag{5.11}$$

Looking at the curves produced by this sort of relationship (Figure 5.7a), it is very difficult to determine the values of a and b. However, it is possible, by using some clever mathematical tricks, to produce a straight line graph from which a and b can be easily calculated. The first thing to do is to take logarithms of both sides of the equation. We have $y = ax^b$, so

$$\log_{10} y = \log_{10}(ax^b) \tag{5.12}$$

Now logarithms have two important properties:

$$\log_{10}(c \times d) = \log_{10} c + \log_{10} d \tag{5.13}$$

and

$$\log_{10}(c^d) = d \times \log_{10} c \tag{5.14}$$

Using these properties we can rearrange the equation to show that

$$\log_{10} y = \log_{10} a + b \log_{10} x \tag{5.15}$$

84

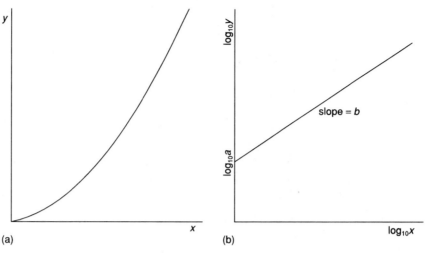

Figure 5.7 How to describe a power relationship. The curvilinear relationship $y = ax^b$ **(a)** can be converted to a straight line **(b)** by taking logarithms ($\log_{10}$) of both x and y. The graph has y-intercept $\log_{10} a$ and slope b.

Therefore, plotting $\log_{10} y$ against $\log_{10} x$ (Figure 5.7b) will produce a straight line with slope b and intercept $\log_{10} a$.

5.8.2 Exponential growth and decay

exponential relationship
A relationship which follows the general equation $y = ae^{bx}$. If $b > 0$ this is exponential growth; if $b < 0$ this is exponential decay.

Other biological phenomena have an **exponential relationship** with time. In these cases, when a given period of time elapses, some characteristic increases or decreases by a certain ratio. For instance, bacterial colonies demonstrate exponential growth, doubling in number every few hours. In contrast, radioactivity shows exponential decay, halving over a given period. Other physical processes are also related in this way. Rates of reaction, indeed the metabolic rates of many whole organisms, increase exponentially with temperature.

In these sorts of relationship, the dependent variable y can be related to the independent variable x by the general equation

$$y = ae^{bx} \tag{5.16}$$

where e is the base of natural logarithms ($e = 2.718$). Looking at the curve produced by this sort of relationship (Figure 5.8a), it is very difficult to determine the values of a and b, just as it was with power relationships. However, we can again use some clever mathematical tricks to produce a straight line graph. As before, the first thing to do is to take logarithms of both sides of the equation. Therefore

$$\log_e y = \log_e(ae^{bx}) \tag{5.17}$$

and rearranging

$$\log_e y = \log_e a + bx \tag{5.18}$$

Therefore plotting $\log_e y$ against x (Figure 5.8b) will produce a straight line with slope b and y-intercept $\log_e a$.

85

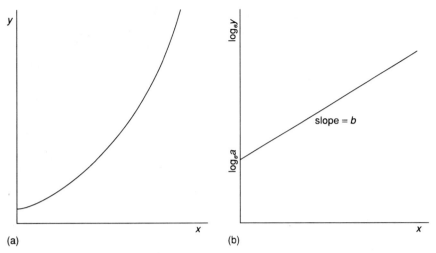

Figure 5.8 How to describe an exponential relationship. The curvilinear relationship $y = ae^{bx}$ **(a)** can be converted to a straight line **(b)** by taking natural logarithms ($\log_e$) of y. The graph has y-intercept $\log_e a$ and slope b.

Example 5.4

An investigation was carried out into the scaling of heads in worker army ants. Body length and jaw width were measured in 20 workers of contrasting size. The following results were obtained.

Length (mm)	3.2	3.6	4.2	4.3	4.6	5.0	5.2	5.3	5.5	5.5
Jaw width (mm)	0.23	0.29	0.32	0.38	0.45	0.44	0.55	0.43	0.60	0.58
Length (mm)	5.7	6.2	6.6	6.9	7.4	7.6	8.5	9.2	9.7	9.9
Jaw width (mm)	0.62	0.73	0.74	0.88	0.83	0.93	1.03	1.15	1.09	1.25

It was suggested that these ants showed allometry, the jaws of larger ants being relatively wider than those of smaller ants. It certainly looks that way as the largest ants are around three times as long as the smallest ones but have heads that are around 4–5 times wider. To investigate whether there is a significant change in proportions, the body length and jaw width must first both be log transformed using SPSS (to see how to transform data see Section 7.3.5). This gives data, which, when plotted in SPSS, gives the following graph.

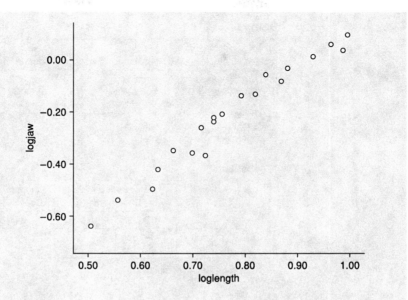

If ants scaled isometrically, head width would be directly proportional to length, so the slope of the log/log graph would equal 1. Therefore, we need to determine whether the slope of this graph is significantly different from 1.

Solution

Step 1: Formulating the null hypothesis

The null hypothesis is that the slope of the line is equal to 1.

Step 2: Calculating the test statistic

Performing a regression analysis in SPSS of logjaw vs loglength gives the following results.

Regression

Variables Entered/Removed[b]

Model	Variables Entered	Variables Removed	Method
1	loglength[a]	.	Enter

a. All requested variables entered.
b. Dependent Variable: logjaw

Model Summary

Model	R	R Square	Adjusted R Square	Std. Error of the Estimate
1	.983[a]	.966	.964	.04022

a. Predictors: (Constant), loglength

ANOVA[b]

Model		Sum of Squares	df	Mean Square	F	Sig.
1	Regression	.817	1	.817	504.939	.000[a]
	Residual	.029	18	.002		
	Total	.846	19			

[a] Predictors: (Constant), loglength
[b] Dependent Variable: logjaw

Coefficients[a]

Model		Unstandardized Coefficients		Standardized Coefficients	t	Sig.
		B	Std. Error	Beta		
1	(Constant)	−1.362	.052		−26.294	.000
	loglength	1.485	.066	.983	22.471	.000

[a] Dependent Variable: logjaw

The regression line of best fit is given, therefore, as

$$\text{Logjaw} = 1.485 \, \text{loglength} - 1.362.$$

This means that the equation relating jaw width to length is

$$\text{Jaw Width} = 10^{-1.362} \times \text{length}^{1.485}$$
$$= 0.0435 \times \text{length}^{1.485}$$

It looks *as if* the exponent (1.485) *is* greater than 1 but, to work it whether there is a significant difference, we must carry out a t test using the statistics SPSS has calculated:

$$t = \frac{\text{Slope} - \text{Expected slope}}{\text{Standard error of slope}}$$
$$= (1.485 - 1)/0.066$$
$$= 7.35$$

Step 3: Calculating the significance probability

Here $|t|$ must be compared with the critical value for $20 - 2 = 18$ degrees of freedom. This is 2.101.

Step 4: Deciding whether to reject the null hypothesis

We have $|t| = 7.35 > 2.101$. Hence there is good evidence to reject the null hypothesis. In fact we can say that the slope is significantly greater than 1. This means that the ants do show positive allometry, larger ants having relatively wider jaws than smaller ones.

5.9   Self-assessment problems

Problem 5.1

Which way round would you plot the following data?

(a) Cell number of an embryo and time since fertilisation.
(b) Pecking order of hens and of their chicks.
(c) Height and body weight of women.
(d) Length and breadth of limpets.

Problem 5.2

A study of the density of stomata in vine leaves of different areas came up with the following results. Calculate the correlation coefficient r between these two variables and determine whether this is a significant correlation. What can you say about the relationship between leaf area and stomatal density?

Leaf area (mm^2)	45	56	69	32	18	38	48	26	60	51
Stomatal density (mm^{-2})	36	28	27	39	56	37	32	45	24	31

Problem 5.3

In a survey to investigate why bones become more brittle in older women, the density of bone material was measured in 24 post-menopausal women of contrasting ages. Bone density is given as a percentage of the average density in young women.

Age (years)	43	49	56	58	61	63	64	66	68	70	72	73
Relative bone density	108	85	92	90	84	83	73	79	80	76	69	71

Age (years)	74	74	76	78	80	83	85	87	89	92	95	98
Relative bone density	65	64	67	58	50	61	59	53	43	52	49	42

(a) Plot the data.
(b) Using SPSS, carry out a regression analysis to determine the relationship between age and bone density. Does bone density change significantly with age?
(c) Calculate the expected bone density of women of age 70.

Problem 5.4

In an experiment to examine the ability of the polychaete worm *Nereis diversicolor* to withstand zinc pollution, worms were grown in solutions containing different concentrations of zinc and their internal zinc concentration was measured. The following results were obtained.

$\log_{10}$ [Zn]$_{water}$	1.96	2.27	2.46	2.65	2.86	2.92	3.01	3.24	3.37	3.49
$\log_{10}$ [Zn]$_{worm}$	2.18	2.23	2.22	2.27	2.25	2.30	2.31	2.34	2.36	2.35

89

(a) Plot the data.
(b) Using SPSS, carry out a regression analysis to determine how zinc in the solution affects the concentration within the worm. If *Nereis* did not actively control its level of zinc, the concentrations inside and outside would be equal and the slope of the regression line would be 1. Work out the t value which compares a slope of 1 with the slope of the line you obtained and hence determine whether *Nereis* does actively control its zinc level.

Problem 5.5

A study of the effect of seeding rate on the yield of wheat gave the following results.

Seeding rate (m^{-2})	50	80	100	150	200	300	400	500	600	800
Yield (tonnes)	2.5	3.9	4.7	5.3	5.6	5.9	5.4	5.2	4.6	3.2

(a) Plot a graph of yield against seeding rate.
(b) Using SPSS, carry out regression analysis to determine whether there is a significant linear relationship between seeding rate and yield.
(c) What can you say about the relationship between seeding rate and yield?

Problem 5.6

(a) The logarithms of the wing area A of birds and their body length L are found to be related by the straight line relationship $\log_{10} A = 0.3 + 2.36 \log_{10} L$. What is the relationship between A and L?
(b) The natural logarithm of the numbers of cells N in a bacterial colony is related to time T by the equation $\log_e N = 2.3 + 0.1T$. What is the relationship between N and T?

Problem 5.7

An investigation was carried out into the temperature dependence of the metabolism of a species of coecilian (a worm-like amphibian). A captive animal was kept at temperatures ranging from 0 to 30 °C at intervals 2 °C and its metabolic rate determined by measuring the rate of output of carbon dioxide. The following results were obtained.

Temperature	0	2	4	6	8	10	12	14
CO_2 production (ml/min)	0.35	0.43	0.45	0.55	0.60	0.78	0.82	0.99
Temperature	16	18	20	22	24	26	28	30
CO_2 production (ml/min)	1.32	1.43	1.64	1.71	2.02	2.35	2.99	3.22

(a) Transform the data by taking natural logarithms of CO_2 production.
(b) Use regression analysis to examine the relationship between temperature and metabolic rate.

90

6 Dealing with categorical data

Introduction

Often in biology you do not take **measurements** on organisms or other items, but classify them into different **categories**. For instance, birds belong to different species and have different colours; habitats (and Petri dishes) can have particular species present or absent; and people can be healthy or diseased. You cannot sensibly assign numbers to such arbitrarily defined classes; green is not larger in any real sense than yellow! For this reason you cannot use any of the statistical tests we examined in Chapters 3, 4 or 5 that look for differences or associations between measurements.

Instead, this categorical data is best quantified by counting the numbers of observations in the different categories. This will allow you to estimate the

Among professors there are significantly more goats than expected.

91

frequency with which each character state turns up. This data can then be used to answer one of two questions.

- We might want to know whether the character frequencies in a single group are different from expected values. Do rats in a maze turn to the right rather than left at a different frequency from the expected 1 : 1? Or is the frequency of rickets different in a small mining town from that in the general population?
- We might want to know whether the character frequencies in two or more groups are different from each other. In other words, are certain characteristics associated with each other? For example, is smoking more common in men than women? Or do different insect species preferentially visit different species of flower?

6.2 The problem of variation

At first glance, it might seem easy to tell whether character frequencies are different. When looking at a sample of sheep, if we found that eight were black and six white, we might conclude that black ones were commoner than white. Unfortunately, there might easily have been the same number of black and white sheep in the population and we might just have picked more black ones by chance.

A character state is, in fact, unlikely to appear at exactly the same frequency in a small sample as in the whole population. Let's examine what happens when we take samples of a population of animals, 50% of which are white and 50% black. In a sample of two there is only a 50% chance of getting a 1 : 1 ratio; the other times both animals would be either black or white. With four animals there will be a 1 : 1 ratio only six times out of 16; there will be a 3 : 1 or 1 : 3 ratio four times out of 16 and a 4 : 0 or 0 : 4 ratio once every 16 times.

As the number of animals in the sample increases, the most likely frequencies are those closer and closer to 1 : 1, but the frequency will hardly ever equal 1 : 1 exactly. In fact, the probability distribution will follow an increasingly tight **binomial distribution** (Figure 6.1) with **mean** $\bar{x}$ equal to $n/2$, where n is the sample size and **standard deviation** s approaching $\sqrt{(n/2)}$. The probability that the ratio is near 1 : 1 increases, and the chance of it being further away decreases. However, there is always a finite, if increasingly tiny, chance of getting all white animals.

Things get more complex if the expected frequencies are different from 1 : 1 and if there are a larger number of categories, but essentially the same pattern will occur: as the sample size increases, the frequencies will tend to approach, but seldom equal, the frequencies in the population. The probability of obtaining frequencies similar to that of the population rises, but there is still a finite probability of the frequencies being very different. As expected, in a population where a character occurs at a frequency p, the mean frequency at which it will turn up in a sample is also p. However, the standard deviation

92

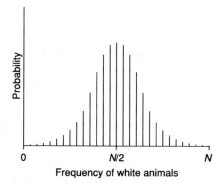

Figure 6.1 Binomial distribution. Probabilities of choosing different numbers of white animals in a sample of size N from a population with 50% white animals.

s (also confusingly called the standard error) is given by the rather complex formula

$$s = \sqrt{p(1-p)/(n-1)} \qquad (6.1)$$

So, if the results from a sample are different from the expected frequency, you cannot be sure this is because the population you are sampling is really different. Even if you sampled 100 animals and all were white, the population still might have contained a ratio of 1 : 1; you might just have been very unlucky. However, the greater the difference and the larger the sample, the less likely this becomes. To determine whether differences from an expected frequency are likely to be real, there are several types of test you can use: the **chi-squared (χ^2) test**; the **G test**; the **Kolgomorov-Smirnov one-sample test** and **Fisher's exact test**. However, by far the most commonly used is the **chi-squared (χ^2) test**, which we will examine here. There are two main types of χ^2 test:

chi-squared (χ^2)
A statistical test which determines whether there are differences between real and expected frequencies in one set of categories, or associations between two sets of categories.

- the χ^2 test for differences;
- the χ^2 test for association.

6.3 The χ² test for differences

6.3.1 Purpose

To test whether character frequencies are different from expected values. It is best used when you expect numbers in different categories to be in particular ratios. Here are some examples:

- experiments in Mendelian genetics;
- maze or choice chamber experiments;
- examining sex ratios;
- comparing your results with figures from the literature;
- comparing figures from a small sample with national averages.

93

6.3.2 **Rationale**

The test calculates the chi-squared (χ^2) statistic; this is a measure of the difference between the observed frequencies and the expected frequencies. Basically, the larger χ^2, the less likely it is that the results could have been obtained by chance if the population frequency was the expected one.

The χ^2 statistic is given by the simple expression

$$\chi^2 = \sum \frac{(O - E)^2}{E} \tag{6.2}$$

where O is the observed frequency and E is the expected frequency for each character state. The larger the difference between the frequencies, the larger the value of χ^2 and the less likely it is that observed and expected frequencies are different just by chance. Similarly, the bigger the sample, the larger O and E, hence the larger the value of χ^2; this is because of the squared term in the top half of the fraction. So the bigger the sample you take, the more likely you will be to detect any differences.

The greater the number of possible categories there are, the greater the number of degrees of freedom; this also tends to increase χ^2. The distribution of χ^2 has been worked out for a range of degrees of freedom, and Table S3 (in the Appendix) gives the critical values of χ^2 above which there is less than a 5%, 1% or 0.1% probability of getting the observed values by chance.

6.3.3 **Carrying out the test**

To see how to carry out a χ^2 test for differences it is best to run through a straightforward example.

Example 6.1

In a Mendelian genetics experiment, F1 hybrids of smooth and wrinkled peas were crossed together. The following results were obtained:

Number of smooth peas = 69
Number of wrinkled peas = 31

Test whether the ratio of smooth to wrinkled peas in the 100 progeny is different from the 3 : 1 ratio predicted by Mendelian genetics. Carrying out the test involves the usual four stages.

Solution

Step 1: Formulating the null hypothesis

The null hypothesis is that the ratio obtained was equal to that expected. Here the null hypothesis is that the ratio of smooth : wrinkled peas equals 3 : 1.

Step 2: Calculating the test statistic

Using a calculator

The first thing to do is to calculate the expected values. Here 3/4 should be smooth and 1/4 wrinkled. Since there are 100 progeny,

94

Expected number of smooth $= (3 \times 100)/4 = 75$
Expected number of wrinkled $= (1 \times 100)/4 = 25$

So we have

	Observed	Expected	Observed – Expected
Smooth	69	75	–6
Wrinkled	31	25	6

Now we can caclulate χ^2:

$$\chi^2 = \sum \frac{(O - E)^2}{E}$$

$$= \frac{(69 - 75)^2}{75} + \frac{(31 - 25)^2}{25}$$

$$= 36/75 + 36/25 = 0.48 + 1.44 = 1.92$$

Using SPSS

Conventionally, carrying out χ^2 tests for differences in SPSS involves putting in data about each organism or item and then carrying out the test. Since sample sizes are invariably large, this approach could be extremely time-consuming. Fortunately, there is a quicker approach which involves weighting the data you enter.

As usual, the first thing is to enter your data correctly. In this case you will have to enter data into two columns. In the first you should enter subscripts for each of the **categories** (here 1 and 2). You can label these categories **smooth** and **wrinkled**. In the second column you should put the numbers in each of the categories. You should call this **weighting**. The completed data is shown below.

To weight the cases, go into **Data** and click on **Weight Cases**. This will bring up the **Weight Cases** dialogue box. Click on **Weight cases by** and enter **Weighting** into the **Frequency Variable:** box. The completed dialogue box and data are shown below.

95

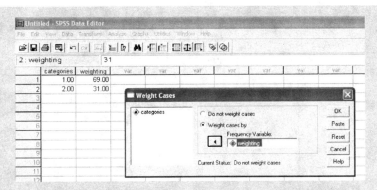

Click on **OK** to weight the data. Now you can carry out the test (which you could also do if you had a column with 69 1's and 31 2's!). Click on **Analyze**, go into **Non-parametric Tests** and click on **Chi-Square**. This will bring up the **Chi-Square Test** dialogue box. Put the **Categories** column into the **Test Variable List:** box. Finally, you need to enter the expected ratios of your two categories (here 3 : 1). To do this click on **Values** in the **Expected Values** box and type in 3 (the expected value for category 1) and click on **Add** to enter it. Then enter 1 and **Add** to do the same for category 2. The completed data and dialogue box are shown below.

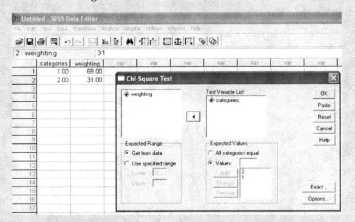

Finally, click on **OK** to run the test. SPSS will print the following.

NPar Tests

Chi-Square Test

Frequencies

categories

	Observed N	Expected N	Residual
1.00	69	75.0	−6.0
2.00	31	25.0	6.0
Total	100		

Science Fundamentals
94

Test Statistics

	categories
Chi-Square[a]	1.920 ←
df	1
Asymp. Sig.	.166 ←

[a.] 0 cells (.0%) have expected frequencies less than 5. The minimum expected cell frequency is 25.0.

Observed and expected values are given in the first table, the value of Chi-Square (here 1.920) in the second.

Step 3: Calculating the significance probability

Using a calculator

You must compare your value of χ^2 with the critical value of the χ^2 statistic for $(N - 1)$ degrees of freedom, where N is the number of character states, and at the 5% level. Here for $2 - 1 = 1$ degree of freedom, the critical value of $\chi^2 = 3.84$.

Using SPSS

SPSS directly gives the significance probability, here called **Asymp. Sig.** Here Asymp. Sig. = 0.166.

Step 4: Deciding whether to reject the null hypothesis

Using a calculator

- If χ^2 is greater than or equal to the critical value, you must reject the null hypothesis. You can say that the distribution is significantly different from expected.
- If χ^2 is less than the critical value, you cannot reject the null hypothesis. You have found no significant difference from the expected distribution.

Here, $\chi^2 = 1.92 < 3.84$.

Using SPSS

- If Asymp. Sig. ≤ 0.05, you must reject the null hypothesis. You can say that the distribution is significantly different from expected.
- If Asymp. Sig. > 0.05, you have no evidence to reject the null hypothesis. You have found no significant difference from the expected distribution.

Here Asymp. Sig. = 0.166 > 0.05.

Therefore, we have no evidence to reject the null hypothesis. The relative frequencies of smooth and wrinkled peas are not significantly different from the expected 3 : 1 ratio.

6.4 The χ^2 test for associations

6.4.1 Purpose

To test whether the character frequencies of two or more groups are different from each other. In other words, to test whether character states are associated in some way. It is used when there is no expected frequency. Here are some examples.

- Ecological surveys: are different species found in different habitats?
- Medical surveys: are infection rates different for people in different blood groups?
- Sociological surveys: do men and women have a different probability of smoking?

6.4.2 Rationale

The test investigates whether the distribution is different from what it would be if the character states were distributed randomly among the population. The tricky part is determining the expected frequencies. Once these have been determined, however, the value of χ^2 is found in just the same way as for the χ^2 test for differences, using equation (6.2).

6.4.3 Carrying out the test

To see how to carry out a test, it is best as usual to run through an example.

Example 6.2

A sociological study has found that out of 30 men, 18 were smokers and 12 non-smokers, while of the 60 women surveyed, 12 were smokers and 48 were non-smokers. Test whether the rates of smoking are significantly different between the sexes.

Solution

Step 1: Formulating the null hypothesis

The null hypothesis is that there is no association between the character states. Here, the null hypothesis is that there is no association between gender and the likelihood that a person will smoke, so men and women are equally likely to smoke.

contingency table
A table showing the frequencies of two sets of character states, which allows you to calculate expected values in a chi-squared test for association.

Step 2: Calculating the test statistic

Using a calculator

This is a long-winded process because, before we can calculate χ^2, we must first calculate the expected values for each character state if there had been no association. The first stage is to arrange the data in a **contingency table**.

98

	Smoking	Non-smoking	Total
Men	18	12	30
Women	12	48	60
Total	30	60	90

It is now possible to calculate the frequencies we would expect *if there had been no association between smoking and gender.* Of the total number of people examined, one-third (30) were men, and one-third (30) of all people smoked. Therefore, if the same proportion of men smoked as in the general population, you would expect one-third of all men (10) to be smokers. Hence 20 men should be non-smokers. Similarly, of the 60 women only one-third (20) should be smokers and 40 should be non-smokers.

A general expression for the expected number E in each cell of the contingency table is given by

$$E = \frac{\text{Column total} \times \text{Row total}}{\text{Grand total}} \tag{6.3}$$

where the grand total is the total number of observations (here 90). Therefore, the expected value for male smokers is found by multiplying its row total (30) by the column total (30) and dividing by 90, to give 10. These expected values are then put into the contingency table, written in parentheses. It is now straightforward to calculate χ^2 using equation (6.1).

	Smoking	Non-smoking	Total
Men	18 (10)	12 (20)	30
Women	12 (20)	48 (40)	60
Total	30	60	90

$$\chi^2 = \sum \frac{(O - E)^2}{E}$$

$$= \frac{(18 - 10)^2}{10} + \frac{(12 - 20)^2}{20} + \frac{(12 - 20)^2}{20} + \frac{(48 - 40)^2}{40}$$

$$= 6.4 + 3.2 + 3.2 + 1.6 = 14.4$$

Using SPSS

Once again, SPSS can calculate χ^2 if you enter each person separately in a large data sheet, with separate columns for each characteristic. Since there are 90 people here, this involves entering 180 numbers. However, you can also do it much quicker by weighting the data as in Example 6.1.

First, you will need to put the data into **two columns**, one for **gender** (give men the subscript 1 and women 2), the other for **smoking** (give non-smokers the subscript 0 and smokers 1). Doing it longhand, for the **gender** column give the first 30 people the subscript 1 (meaning men), and for 31–90 give them subscript 2 (meaning women). In the **smoking** column give the first 18 men the subscript 1 (meaning smoking) and the final 12 the subscript 0 (meaning non-smoking). Finally give the first 12 women the subscript 1 and the final 48 women the subscript 0.

To do it quicker produce three columns: a **gender** column, a **smoking** column and a **weighting** column. You need just four rows, one for each combination of categories, and the weighting column should give the numbers in each of the categories. The completed columns are shown below.

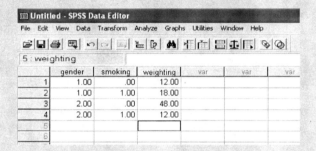

To weight the data click on **Data** and then on **Weight Cases**. You then weight the data by clicking on **Weight cases by** and moving **Weighting** into the **Frequency Variable:** box. The completed dialogue box is shown below.

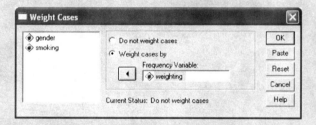

Finally, click on **OK** to weight the cases.

To carry out the test, click on **Analyze**, move onto **Descriptive Statistics** and click on **Crosstabs**. This will bring up the **Crosstabs** dialogue box. Put **gender** into the **Row(s):** box and **smoking** into the **Column(s):** box. Next, click on the **Statistics:** box to bring up the **Crosstab: Statistics** dialogue box and tick **Chi-square**. Your dialogue boxes and data screen will look like the following.

100

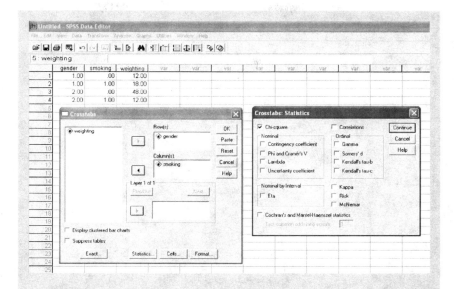

Click on **Continue** then click on **Cells** to bring up the **Crosstabs: Cell Display** dialogue box. Make sure both **Observed** and **Expected** are ticked as below.

Finally, click on **Continue** and **OK** to run the test. SPSS will come up with the following output.

Crosstabs

Case Processing Summary

	Cases					
	Valid		Missing		Total	
	N	Percent	N	Percent	N	Percent
gender * smoking	90	100.0%	0	.0%	90	100.0%

101

gender * smoking Crosstabulation

			smoking		
			.00	1.00	Total
gender	1.00	Count	12	18	30
		Expected Count	20.0	10.0	30.0
	2.00	Count	48	12	60
		Expected Count	40.0	20.0	60.0
Total		Count	60	30	90
		Expected Count	60.0	30.0	90.0

Chi-Square Tests

	Value	df	Asymp. Sig. (2-sided)	Exact Sig. (2-sided)	Exact Sig. (1-sided)
Pearson Chi-Square	14.400[b]	1	.000		
Continuity Correction[a]	12.656	1	.000		
Likelihood Ration	14.144	1	.000		
Fisher's Exact Test				.000	.000
Linear-by-Linear Association	14.240	1	.000		
N of Valid Cases	90				

[a.] Computed only for a 2 × 2 table
[b.] 0 cells (.0%) have expected count less than 5. The minimum expected count is 10.00.

The second table is the contingency table, and the statistic you require is the **Pearson Chi-Square**. Here Pearson Chi-Square = 14.400.

Step 3: Calculating the significance probability

Using a calculator

To calculate the significance probability you must look up the value that χ^2 must exceed at $(R - 1) \times (C - 1)$ degrees of freedom, where R is the number of rows in the table and C is the number of columns, for the probability to be less than 5%. Here there are two rows and two columns, so the number of degrees of freedom = $(2 - 1) \times (2 - 1) = 1$. The critical value of χ^2 for one degree of freedom = 3.84.

Using SPSS

SPSS gives you the significance probability (here called **Asymp. Sig. (2-Sided)**) directly. Here Asymp. Sig. (2-Sided) = 0.000.

Step 4: Deciding whether to reject the null hypothesis

Using a calculator

- If χ^2 is greater than or equal to the critical value, you must reject the null hypothesis. You can say that the distribution is significantly different from expected, hence there is a significant association between the characters.

- If χ^2 is less than the critical value, you cannot reject the null hypothesis. You have found no significant difference from the expected distribution, hence no evidence of an association between the characters.

Here $\chi^2 = 14.4 > 3.84$.

Using SPSS

- If Asymp. Sig. (2-Sided) ≤ 0.05, you should reject the null hypothesis. You can say that the distribution is significantly different from expected, hence there is a significant association between the characters.
- If Asymp. Sig. (2-Sided) > 0.05, you have no evidence to reject the null hypothesis. You have found no significant difference from the expected distribution, hence no evidence of an association between the characters.

Here Sig. $= 0.000 < 0.05$.

Therefore, you can reject the null hypothesis. You can say there is a significant association between sex and smoking. In other words, the two sexes are different in the frequency with which they smoke. In fact men smoke more than women.

You can tell even more about your results by looking at the χ^2 values for each of the cells. The larger the value, the more the results for the cell differ from the expected results. In this example χ^2 for male smokers is by far the largest at 6.4. Therefore, we can say that, in particular, more men smoke than one would expect.

6.4.4 The Yates continuity correction

Note that for 2×2 contingency tables like this, some people believe that you should make a correction for the fact that you can only get integer values in each category. This would tend to result in an overestimation of χ^2. To correct for this, one can add or subtract 0.5 from each observed value to make them closer to the expected values. This **Continuity Correction** results in a lower value for χ^2, and can be read off the SPSS output. In our example $\chi^2 = 12.656$ rather than 14.400. Opinions are divided about whether this is a valid procedure. In any case, this correction can only be made in 2×2 tables.

6.5 Validity of χ^2 tests

(1) You must only carry out χ^2 tests on the raw numbers of observations that you have made. *Never* use percentages. This is because the larger the number of observations, the more likely you are to be able to detect differences or associations with the χ^2 test.

103

(2) Another point about sample size is that χ^2 tests are only valid if all expected values are larger than 5. If any expected values are lower than 5, there are two possibilities:

- You could combine data from two or more groups, but only if this makes biological sense. For instance, different species of fly could be combined in Problem 6.4 because flies have more in common with each other than with the other insects studied.
- If there is no sensible reason for combining data, small groups should be left out of the analysis.

Example 6.3

In a survey of the prevalence of a heart condition in 300 people of different races, the following results were obtained.

	White	Asian	Afro Caribbean	Mixed race
Have the condition	35	9	13	3
Healthy	162	43	29	6

Do people from different races differ in their likelihood of having the condition? In other words, is there an association between race and the condition?

Solution

The first thing to notice is that there are too few mixed race people in the survey. The expected value for mixed race people with the condition, for instance, is $(9 \times 60)/300 = 1.8$, which is well below 5. There is no justification for putting mixed race people into any other category so they must be ignored. Now we can carry out a χ^2 test for association for the other three races.

Step 1: Formulating the null hypothesis

The null hypothesis is that there is no association between race and the condition.

Step 2: Calculating the test statistic

The contingency table must be reduced and the expected values calculated.

	White	Asian	Afro Caribbean	Total
Have the condition	35 (38.6)	9 (10.2)	13 (8.2)	57
Healthy	162 (158.4)	43 (41.8)	29 (33.8)	234
Total	197	52	42	291

104

Now χ^2 can be found using equation (6.2):

$$\chi^2 = \frac{(35 - 38.6)^2}{38.6} + \frac{(9 - 10.2)^2}{10.2} + \frac{(13 - 8.2)^2}{8.2} + \frac{(162 - 158.4)^2}{158.4}$$

$$+ \frac{(43 - 41.8)^2}{41.8} + \frac{(29 - 33.8)^2}{33.8}$$

$$= 0.34 + 0.14 + 2.81 + 0.08 + 0.03 + 0.68$$

$$= 4.08$$

Step 3: Calculating the significance probability

You must look up the value that χ^2 must exceed at $(3 - 1) \times (2 - 1) = 2$ degrees of freedom. The critical value of χ^2 for two degrees of freedom = 5.99.

Step 4: Deciding whether to reject the null hypothesis

Here $\chi^2 = 4.08 < 5.99$ so you have no evidence to reject the null hypothesis. You can say there is no significant difference in the incidence of the condition between people of the different races.

6.6 Self-assessment problems

Problem 6.1

In an experiment to test the reactions of mice to a potential pheromone, they were run down a T-junction maze; the pheromone was released in one of the arms of the T. After the first 10 trials, three mice had turned towards the scent and seven had turned away. After 100 trials, 34 had turned towards the scent and 66 had turned away. Is there any evidence of a reaction to the scent:

(a) after 10 trials?
(b) after 100 trials?

Problem 6.2

A cross was carried out between peas which were heterozygous in the two characters: height (tall H or short h) and pea colour (green G or yellow g). The following offspring were obtained.

Tall plants, green peas	87
Tall plants, yellow peas	34
Short plants, green peas	28
Short plants, yellow peas	11

105

For unlinked genes the expected ratios of each sort of plant are 9 : 3 : 3 : 1. Carry out a χ^2-squared test to determine whether there is any evidence of gene linkage between these characters.

Problem 6.3

A study of the incidence of a childhood illness in a small mining town showed that out of a population of 165 children, nine had developed the disease. This compares with a rate of 3.5% in the country as a whole. Is there any evidence of a different rate in the town?

Problem 6.4

In a study of insect pollination, the numbers of insect visitors belonging to different taxonomic groups were investigated at flowers of different colours. The results given in Table 6.1 were obtained.

Table 6.1 Numbers of insects of different taxonomic groups visiting flowers of different colours.

Insect visitors	Flower colour			Total
	White	Yellow	Blue	
Beetles	56	34	12	102
Flies	31	74	22	127
Bees and wasps	57	103	175	335
Total	144	211	209	564

(a) Carry out a χ^2 test to determine whether there is any association between the types of insects and the colour of the flowers they visit.
(b) Which cells have the three highest χ^2 values? What do these results tell you about the preferences of different insects?

Problem 6.5

A study was carried out to determine whether there is a link between the incidence of skin cancer and the possession of freckles. Of the 6045 people examined, 978 had freckles, of whom 33 had developed skin cancer. Of the remaining people without freckles, 95 had developed skin cancer. Is there any evidence that people with freckles have an increased risk of developing skin cancer?

Problem 6.6

A field study on the distribution of two species of newt found that of 745 ponds studied, 180 contained just smooth newts, 56 just palmate newts, 236 had both species present and the remainder had neither. Is there any association between the two species and, if so, what is it?

10 Dealing with measurements and units

10.1 Introduction

It is surprising, considering that most students of biology have studied mathematics for many years, how often they make errors in the ways they deal with and present numerical information. In fact, there are many ways of getting things wrong. Primary data can be measured wrongly, or given too high or low a degree of precision. The data can be taken and presented in non-SI units, or mistakes can be made while attempting to convert to SI units. Calculations based on primary data can be carried out incorrectly. Finally, the answers can be given to the wrong degree of precision, in the wrong units or with no units at all!

Many of the errors are made not only through ignorance but also because of haste, lack of care or even panic. This chapter shows how you can avoid such mistakes by carrying out the following logical sequence of steps carefully and in the right order: measuring, converting data into SI units, combining data together and expressing the answer in SI units to the correct degree of precision. It also gives some useful tables which can be consulted at any time for reference.

'6.3452×10^4, 6.3453×10^4 . . .'

170

10.2   Measuring

Measurements should always be taken to the highest possible degree of precision. This is straightforward with modern digital devices, but it is more difficult in the more old-fashioned devices, which have a graduated analogue scale. The highest degree of precision of analogue instruments is usually to the smallest graduation of the scale. Using a 30 cm ruler, lengths can only be measured to the nearest millimetre. However, if the graduations are far enough apart, as they are on some thermometers, it is usually possible to judge the measurements to the next decimal place. This is made even easier by devices, like calipers or microscope stages, which have a vernier scale.

10.3   Converting to SI units

SI
Système International: the common standard of units used in modern science based on the metre, second and kilogram.

10.3.1 SI units

Before carrying out any further manipulation of data or expressing it, it should be converted into the correct SI units. The *Système International d'Unités* (SI) is the accepted scientific convention for measuring physical quantities, under which the most basic units of length, mass and time are kilograms, metres and seconds respectively. The complete list of the basic SI units is given in Table 10.1.

All other units are derived from these basic units. For instance, volume should be expressed in cubic metres or m^3. Similarly, density, mass per unit volume, should be expressed in kilograms per cubic metre or $kg\,m^{-3}$. Some important derived units have their own names; the unit of force ($kg\,m\,s^{-2}$) is called a newton (N), and the unit of pressure ($N\,m^{-2}$) is called a pascal (Pa). A list of important derived SI units is given in Table 10.2.

Table 10.1 The base and supplementary SI units.

Measured quantity	SI unit	Symbol
Base		
Length	metre	m
Mass	kilogram	kg
Time	second	s
Amount of substance	mole	mol
Temperature	kelvin	K
Electric current	ampere	A
Luminous intensity	candela	cd
Supplementary		
Plane angle	radian	rad
Solid angle	steradian	sr

171

Table 10.2 Important derived SI units.

Measured quantity	Name of unit	Symbol	Definitions
Mechanics			
Force	newton	N	$kg\ m\ s^{-2}$
Energy	joule	J	$N\ m$
Power	watt	W	$J\ s^{-1}$
Pressure	pascal	Pa	$N\ m^{-2}$
Electricity			
Charge	coulomb	C	$A\ s$
Potential difference	volt	V	$J\ C^{-1}$
Resistance	ohm	Ω	$V\ A^{-1}$
Conductance	siemens	S	Ω^{-1}
Capacitance	farad	F	$C\ V^{-1}$
Light			
Luminous flux	lumen	lm	$cd\ sr^{-1}$
Illumination	lux	lx	$lm\ m^{-2}$
Others			
Frequency	hertz	Hz	s^{-1}
Radioactivity	becquerel	Bq	s^{-1}
Enzyme activity	katal	kat	$mol\ substrate\ s^{-1}$

10.3.2 Dealing with large and small numbers

The problem with using a standard system, like the SI system, is that the units may not always be convenient. The mass of organisms ranges from 0.000 000 000 1 kg for algae to 100 000 kg for whales. For convenience, therefore, two different systems can be used to present large and small measurements. Both these systems also have the added advantage that large numbers can be written without using a large number of zeros, which would imply an unrealistic degree of precision. It would be difficult to weigh a whale to the nearest kilogram (and pointless, since the weight will fluctuate wildly at this degree of precision), which is what the weight of 100 000 kg implies.

prefix
A multiple or divisor of 1000 which allows large or small numbers to be readily expressed.

Use of prefixes

Using prefixes, each of which stands for a multiplication factor of 1000 (Table 10.3), is the simplest way to present large or small measurements. Any quantity can be simply presented as a number between 0.1 and 1000 multiplied by a suitable prefix. For instance, 123 000 J is better presented as 123 kJ or 0.123 MJ. Similarly, 0.000 012 m is better presented as 12 μm (not 0.012 mm).

Use of scientific notation

The problem with using prefixes is that they are rather tricky to combine mathematically when carrying out calculations. For this reason, when performing a

Table 10.3 Prefixes used in SI.

Small numbers						
Multiple	10^{-3}	10^{-6}	10^{-9}	10^{-12}	10^{-15}	10^{-18}
Prefix	milli	micro	nano	pico	femto	atto
Symbol	m	μ	n	p	f	a
Large numbers						
Multiple	10^{3}	10^{6}	10^{9}	10^{12}	10^{15}	10^{18}
Prefix	kilo	mega	giga	tera	peta	exa
Symbol	k	M	G	T	P	E

scientific notation
A method of representing large or small numbers, giving them as a number between 1 and 10 multiplied by a power of 10.

calculation it is usually better to express your data using **scientific notation**. As we shall see, this makes calculations much easier.

Any quantity can be expressed as a number between 1 and 10 multiplied by a power of 10 (also called an exponent). For instance, 123 is equal to 1.23 multiplied by 10 squared or 10^2. Here the exponent is 2, so it can be written as 1.23×10^2. Similarly, 0.001 23 is equal to 1.23 multiplied by the inverse of 10 cubed, or 10^{-3}. Therefore, it is best written as 1.23×10^{-3}. And 1.23 itself is equal to 1.23 multiplied by 10 to the power 0, so it does not need an exponent.

A simple way of determining the value of the exponent is to count the number of digits from the decimal point to the right of the first significant figure. For instance, in 18 000 there are four figures to the right of the 1, which is the first significant figure, so $18\ 000 = 1.8 \times 10^4$. Similarly, in 0.000 000 18 there are seven figures between the point and the right of the 1, so $0.000\ 000\ 18 = 1.8 \times 10^{-7}$.

Prefixes can readily be converted to exponents, since each prefix differs by a factor of 1000 or 10^3 (Table 10.3). The pressure 4.6 MPa equals 4.6×10^6 Pa and 46 MPa equals $4.6 \times 10^1 \times 10^6 = 4.63 \times 10^7$ Pa.

10.3.3 Converting from non-SI units

Very often textbooks and papers, especially old ones, present quantities in non-SI units, and old apparatus may also be calibrated in non-SI units. Before carrying out calculations, you will need to convert them to SI units. Fortunately, this is very straightforward.

metric
Units based on the metre, second and kilogram but not necessarily SI.

Non-SI metric units

The most common non-SI units are those which are metric but based on obsolete systems. The most useful biological examples are given in Table 10.4, along with a conversion factor. These units are very easy to convert into the SI system. Simply multiply your measurement by the conversion factor.

173

Table 10.4 Conversion factors from obsolete units to SI.[a]

Quantity	Old unit/Symbol	SI unit/Symbol	Conversion factor
Length	*angstrom/Å*	metre/m	1×10^{-10}
	yard	metre/m	0.9144
	foot	metre/m	0.3048
	inch	metre/m	2.54×10^{-2}
Area	*hectare/ha*	square metre/m^2	1×10^{4}
	acre	square metre/m^2	4.047×10^{3}
	square foot/ft^2	square metre/m^2	9.290×10^{-2}
	square inch/in^2	square metre/m^2	6.452×10^{-4}
Volume	*litre/l*	cubic metre/m^3	1×10^{-3}
	cubic foot/ft^3	cubic metre/m^3	2.832×10^{-2}
	cubic inch/in^3	cubic metre/m^3	1.639×10^{-5}
	UK pint/pt	cubic metre/m^3	5.683×10^{-4}
	US pint/liq pt	cubic metre/m^3	4.732×10^{-4}
	UK gallon/gal	cubic metre/m^3	4.546×10^{-3}
	US gallon/gal	cubic metre/m^3	3.785×10^{-3}
Angle	degree/°	radian/rad	1.745×10^{-2}
Mass	*tonne*	kilogram/kg	1×10^{3}
	ton (UK)	kilogram/kg	1.016×10^{3}
	hundredweight/cwt	kilogram/kg	5.080×10^{1}
	stone	kilogram/kg	6.350
	pound/lb	kilogram/kg	0.454
	ounce/oz	kilogram/kg	2.835×10^{-2}
Energy	*erg*	joule/J	1×10^{-7}
	kilowatt hour/kWh	joule/J	3.6×10^{6}
Pressure	*bar/b*	pascal/Pa	1×10^{5}
	mm Hg	pascal/Pa	1.332×10^{2}
Radioactivity	curie/Ci	becquerel/Bq	3.7×10^{10}
Temperature	*centigrade/°C*	kelvin/K	$C + 273.15$
	Fahrenheit/°F	kelvin/K	$^5/_9 (F + 459.7)$

[a] Metric units are given in italics. To get from a measurement in the old unit to a measurement in the SI unit, multiply by the conversion factor.

Example 10.1

Give the following in SI units:

(a) 24 ha
(b) 25 cm

Solution

(a) 24 ha equals $24 \times 10^{4}\,\text{m}^2 = 2.4 \times 10^{5}\,\text{m}^2$
(b) 25 cm equals $25 \times 10^{-2}\,\text{m} = 2.5 \times 10^{-1}\,\text{m}$

Litres and concentrations

The most important example of a unit which is still widely used even though it does not fit into the SI system is the litre (1 dm^3 or 10^{-3} m^3), which is used in the derivation of the concentration of solutions. For instance, if 1 litre contains 2 moles of a substance then its concentration is given as 2 *M* or molar.

174

The mole is now a bona fide SI unit, but it too was derived before the SI system was developed, since it was originally the amount of a substance which contains the same number of particles as 1 g (rather than the SI kilogram) of hydrogen atoms. In other words, the mass of 1 mole of a substance is its molecular mass in grams. When working out concentrations of solutions it is probably best to stick to these units, since most glassware is still calibrated in litres and small balances in grams.

The molarity M of a solution is obtained as follows:

$$M = \frac{\text{Number of moles}}{\text{Solution volume (l)}}$$

$$= \frac{\text{Mass (g)}}{\text{Molecular mass} \times \text{Solution volume (l)}}$$

Example 10.2	A solution contains 23 g of copper sulphate ($CuSO_4$) in 2.5 litres of water. What is its concentration?

Solution

$$\text{Concentration} = 23/((63.5 + 32 + 64) \times 2.5)$$
$$= 5.768 \times 10^{-2} M$$
$$= 5.8 \times 10^{-2} M \quad \text{(2 significant figures)}$$

Non-metric units

Imperial
Obsolete system of units from the United Kingdom.

Non-metric units, such as those based on the old **Imperial** scale, are also given in Table 10.4. Again you must simply multiply your measurement by the conversion factor. However, they are more difficult to convert to SI, since they must be multiplied by factors which are not just powers of 10. For instance

$$6 \text{ ft} = 6 \times 3.048 \times 10^{-1} \text{ m} = 1.83 \text{ m}$$

Note that the answer was given as 1.83 m, not the calculated figure of 1.8288 m. This is because a measure of 6 ft implies that the length was measured to the nearest inch. The answer we produced is accurate to the nearest centimetre, which is the closest SI unit.

If you have to convert square or cubic measures into metric, simply multiply by the conversion factor to the power of 2 or 3. So 12 cubic feet = $12 \times (3.038 \times 10^{-1})^3 \text{ m}^3 = 3.4 \times 10^{-1} \text{ m}^3$ to two significant figures.

10.4 Combining values

Once measurements have been converted into SI units with exponents, they are extremely straightforward to combine using either pencil and paper or calculator (most calculators use exponents nowadays). When multiplying two

175

measurements, for instance, you simply multiply the initial numbers, add the exponents and multiply the units together. If the multiple of the two initial numbers is greater than 10 or less than 1, you simply add or subtract 1 from the exponent. For instance

$$2.3 \times 10^2 \text{ m} \times 1.6 \times 10^3 \text{ m} = (2.3 \times 1.6) \times 10^{(2+3)} \text{ m}^2$$
$$= 3.7 \times 10^5 \text{ m}^2$$

Notice that the area is given to two significant figures because that was the degree of precision with which the lengths were measured. Similarly

$$2.3 \times 10^2 \text{ m} \times 6.3 \times 10^{-4} \text{ m} = (2.3 \times 6.3) \times 10^{(2-4)} \text{ m}^2$$
$$= 1.4 \times 10^1 \times 10^{-2} \text{ m}^2$$
$$= 1.4 \times 10^{-1} \text{ m}^2$$

In the same way, when dividing one measurement by another you divide the first initial number by the second, subtract the second exponent from the first and divide the first unit by the second. Therefore

$$(4.8 \times 10^3 \text{ m})/(1.5 \times 10^2 \text{ s}) = (4.8/1.5) \times 10^{(3-2)} \text{ m s}^{-1}$$
$$= 3.2 \times 10^1 \text{ m s}^{-1}$$

10.5   Expressing the answer

When you have completed all calculations, you must be careful how you express your answer. First, it should be given to the same level of precision as the *least* accurate of the measurements from which it was calculated. This book and many statistical packages use the following convention: the digits 1 to 4 go down, 6 to 9 go up and 5 goes to the nearest even digit. Here are some examples:

0.343	becomes	0.34	to	2	significant figures
0.2251	becomes	0.22	to	2	significant figures
0.6354	becomes	0.64	to	2	significant figures

Second, it is sometimes a good idea to express it using a prefix. So if we work out from figures given to two significant figures that a pressure is 2.678×10^6 Pa, it should be expressed as 2.7 MPa. Always adjust the degree of precision *at the end* of the calculation.

10.6   Doing all three steps

The various steps can now be carried out to manipulate data to reliably derive further information. It is important to carry out each step in its turn, producing an answer before going on to the next step in the calculation. Doing all the calculations at once can cause confusion and lead to silly mistakes.

176

Example 10.3

A sample of heartwood taken from an oak tree was 12.1 mm long by 8.2 mm wide by 9.5 mm deep and had a wet mass of 0.653 g. What was its density?

Solution

Density has units of mass (in kg) per unit volume (in m^3). Therefore, the first thing to do is to convert the units into kg and m. The next thing to do is to calculate the volume in m^3. Only then can the final calculation be performed. This slow building up of the calculation is ponderous but is the best way to avoid making mistakes.

$$\text{Mass} = 6.53 \times 10^{-4} \text{ kg}$$

$$\text{Volume} = 1.21 \times 10^{-2} \times 8.2 \times 10^{-3} \times 9.5 \times 10^{-3}$$
$$= 9.4259 \times 10^{-7} \text{ m}^3$$

$$\text{Density} = \frac{\text{mass}}{\text{volume}} = \frac{6.53 \times 10^{-4}}{9.4259 \times 10^{-7}}$$
$$= 0.6928 \times 10^3 \text{ kg m}^{-3}$$
$$= 6.9 \times 10^2 \text{ kg m}^{-3}$$

Notice that the answer is given to two significant figures, like the dimensions of the sample.

10.7 Constants and formulae

Frequently, raw data on their own are not enough to work out other important quantities. You may need to include physical or chemical constants in your calculations, or insert your data into basic mathematical formulae. Table 10.5 is a list of some useful constants and formulae. Many of them are worth memorising.

Example 10.4

A total of 25 micropropagated plants were grown in a 10 cm diameter Petri dish. At what density were they growing?

Solution

The first thing to calculate is the area of the Petri dish. Since its diameter is 10 cm, its radius R will be 5 cm (or 5×10^{-2} m). A circle's area A is given by the formula $A = \pi R^2$. Therefore

$$\text{Area} = 3.1416 \times (5 \times 10^{-2})^2$$
$$= 7.854 \times 10^{-3} \text{ m}^2$$

The density is the number per unit area, so

$$\text{Density} = 25/(7.854 \times 10^{-3})$$
$$= 3.183 \times 10^3 \text{ m}^{-2}$$
$$= 3.2 \times 10^3 \text{ m}^{-2} \quad \text{(2 significant figures)}$$

177

Table 10.5 Some useful constants and formulae.

Physical constants	
Density of water	$= 1000$ kg m^{-3}
Density of air	$= 1.2$ kg m^{-3}
Specific heat of water	$= 4.2 \times 10^3$ J K^{-1} kg^{-1}
Chemical constants	
1 mol	$= 6 \times 10^{23}$ particles
Mass of 1 mol	$=$ molecular mass (g) $= 10^{-3} \times$ molecular mass (kg)
Volume of 1 mol of gas	$= 24$ l $= 2.4 \times 10^{-2}$ m^3 (at room temperature and pressure)
1 molar solution (1 *M*)	$= 1$ mol l^{-1} $= 1000$ mol m^{-3}
1 normal solution (1 *N*)	$= 1$ mol l^{-1} $= 1000$ mol m^{-3} of ions
	pH $= -\log_{10}[\text{H}^+]$
Composition of air	$= 78.1\%$ nitrogen, 20.9% oxygen, 0.93% argon and 0.03% carbon dioxide, plus traces of others, by volume
Mathematical formulae	
Area of a circle of radius *R*	$= \pi R^2$
Volume of a sphere of radius *R*	$= \frac{4}{3}\pi R^3$
Area of a sphere of radius *R*	$= 4\pi R^2$
Volume of a cylinder of radius *R* and height *H*	$= \pi R^2 H$
Volume of a cone of radius *R* and height *H*	$= \frac{1}{3}\pi R^2 H$
Mathematical constants	
$\pi = 3.1416$	
$\log_e x = 2.30 \log_{10} x$	

10.8   Using calculations

Once you can reliably perform calculations, you can use them for far more than just working out the results of your experiments from your raw data. You can use them to put your results into perspective or extrapolate from your results into a wider context. You can also use calculations to help design your experiments: to work out how much of each ingredient you need, or how much the experiment will cost. However, even more usefully, they can help you to work out whether a particular experiment is worth attempting in the first place. Calculations are thus an invaluable tool for the research biologist to help save time, money and effort. They don't even have to be very exact calculations. Often, all that is required is to work out a rough or ballpark figure.

Example 10.5

Elephants are the most practical form of transport through the Indian rainforest because of the rough terrain; the only disadvantage is their great weight. A scientific expedition needs to cross a bridge with a weight limit of 10 tonnes, in order to enter a nature reserve. Will their elephants be able to cross this bridge safely?

Solution

You are unlikely, in the rainforest, to be able to look up or measure the weight of an elephant, but most people have some idea of just how big they are. Since the mass of an object is equal to volume × density, the first thing to calculate is the volume. What is the volume of an elephant? Well, elephants are around 2–3 m long and have a (very roughly) cylindrical body of diameter, say, 1.5 m (so the radius = 0.75 m). The volume of a cylinder is given by $V = \pi R^2 L$, so with these figures the volume of the elephant is approximately

$$V = \pi \times 0.75^2 \times 2 \quad \text{up to} \quad \pi \times 0.75^2 \times 3$$
$$= 3.53\text{–}5.30 \text{ m}^3$$

The volume of the legs, trunk, etc., is very much less and can be ignored in this rough calculation. So what is the density of an elephant? Well, elephants (like us) can just about float in water and certainly swim, so they must have about the same density as water, 1000 kg m^{-3}. The approximate mass of the elephant is, therefore

$$\text{Mass} = 1000 \times (3.5 \text{ to } 5.3)$$
$$= 3530\text{–}5300 \text{ kg}$$

Note, however, that the length of the beast was estimated to only one significant figure, so the weight should also be estimated to this low degree of accuracy. The weight of the elephant will be $(4\text{–}5) \times 10^3$ kg or 4–5 tonnes. (Textbook figures for weights of elephants range from 3 to 7 tonnes.) The bridge should easily be able to withstand the weight of an elephant.

This calculation would not have been accurate enough to determine whether our elephant could cross a bridge with weight limit 4.5 tonnes. It would have been necessary to devise a method of weighing it.

10.9 Logarithms, graphs and pH

10.9.1 Logarithms to base 10

logarithm to base 10 ($\log_{10}$)
A function of a variable y such that if $y = 10^x$ then $x = \log_{10} y$.

Though scientific notation (such as 2.3×10^4) is a good way of expressing large and small numbers (such as 23 000), it is a bit clumsy since the numbers consist of two parts, the initial number and the exponent. Nor does it help very

179

large and very small numbers to be conveniently represented on the same graph. For instance, if you plot the relationship between the numbers of bird species in woods of areas 100, 1000, 10 000, 100 000 and 1 000 000 m² (Figure 10.1a), most of the points will be congested at the left.

These problems can be overcome by the use of **logarithms**. Any number can be expressed as a single **exponent**, as 10 to the power of a second number, e.g. $23\,000 = 10^{4.362}$. The 'second number' (here 4.362) is called the logarithm to base 10 ($\log_{10}$) of the first, so that

$$4.362 = \log_{10} 23\,000$$

Numbers above 1 have a positive logarithm, whereas numbers below 1 have a negative logarithm, e.g.

$$0.0045 = 10^{-2.347} \quad \text{so} \quad -2.347 = \log_{10} 0.0045$$

exponent
A power of 10 which allows large or small numbers to be readily expressed and manipulated.

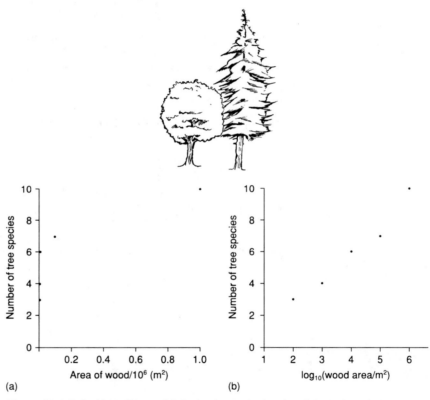

(a)

(b)

Figure 10.1 Using logarithms. (a) A simple graph showing the relationship between the size of woods and the number of tree species they contain; the points are hopelessly congested at the left of the plot. **(b)** Plotting number of species against $\log_{10}$ (area) spreads the data out more evenly.

180

Logarithms to the base 10 of any number can be found simply by pressing the log button on your calculator, and can be converted back to real numbers by pressing the 10^x button on your calculator.

Properties and uses of logarithms

The most important property of logarithms is that, if numbers have a constant ratio between them, their logarithms will differ by a constant amount. Hence the numbers 1, 10 and 100, which differ by ratios of 10, have logarithms of 0, 1 and 2, which differ by 1 each time. This gives them some useful mathematical properties, which can help us work out relationships between variables, as we saw in Chapter 5. However, it also gives them two immediate uses.

Use of logarithms for graphs

Logarithms allow very different quantities to be compared and plotted on the same graph. For instance, you can show the relationship between wood area and number of tree species (Figure 10.1a) more clearly by plotting species number against $\log_{10}$ (area) (Figure 10.1b).

pH

The single most important use of logarithms in biology is in the units for acidity. The unit pH is given by the formula

$$pH = -\log_{10}[H^+] \tag{10.1}$$

where [H$^+$] is the hydrogen ion concentration in moles per litre (M). Therefore, a solution containing 2×10^{-5} mole (mol) of hydrogen ions per litre will have a pH of $-\log_{10}(2 \times 10^{-5}) = 4.7$.

Example 10.6

A solution has a pH of 3.2. What is the hydrogen ion concentration?

Solution

The hydrogen ion concentration is $10^{-3.2} = 6.3 \times 10^{-4} \, M$.

10.9.2 Natural logarithms

natural logarithm (log$_e$ or ln)
A function of a variable y such that if $y = e^x$ then $x = \log_e y$ or ln y.

Logarithms can be calculated for other bases as well as 10. Other important types of logarithms are **natural logarithms** (log$_e$ or ln) in which numbers that differ by the ratio 2.718 (which is given the letter e) have logs that differ by 1. Thus ln 2.718 = 1. As we have seen in Chapter 5, natural logarithms are particularly useful when describing and investigating exponential increases in populations or exponential decay in radioactivity.

To convert from a number to its natural logarithm, you should press the ln button on your calculator. To convert back, you should press the e^x button.

181

10.10   Self-assessment problems

Problem 10.1

What are the SI units for the following measurements?

(a) Area.
(b) The rate of height growth for a plant.
(c) The concentration of red cells in blood.
(d) The ratio of the concentrations of white and red cells in blood.

Problem 10.2

How would you express the following quantities using appropriate prefixes?

(a) 192 000 000 N
(b) 0.000 000 102 kg
(c) 0.000 12 s
(d) 21.3 cm

Problem 10.3

How would you express the following quantities in scientific notation using appropriate exponents?

(a) 0.000 046 1 J
(b) 461 000 000 s

Problem 10.4

How would you express the following quantities in scientific notation using the appropriate exponents?

(a) 3.81 GPa
(b) 4.53 mW
(c) 364 mJ
(d) 4.8 mg
(e) 0.21 pg

Problem 10.5

Convert the following to SI units expressed in scientific notation.

(a) 250 tonnes
(b) 0.3 bar
(c) 24 angstroms

Problem 10.6

Convert the following into SI units.

(a) 35 yards
(b) 3 feet 3 inches
(c) 9.5 square yards

182

Physics

MEASUREMENT AND PROBLEM SOLVING

PHYSICS FACTS

- Tradition holds that in the twelfth century King Henry I of England decreed that the yard should be the distance from the tip of his royal nose to the thumb of his out-stretched arm. (Had King Henry's arm been 3.37 inches longer, the yard and the meter would be equal in length.)

- The abbreviation for the pound, *lb*, comes from the Latin word *libra*, which was a Roman unit of weight approximately equal to a pound. The word *pound* comes from the Latin *pondero*, "to weigh". Libra is also a sign of the zodiac and is symbolized by a set of scales (used for weight measurement).

- Thomas Jefferson suggested that the length of a pendulum with a period of one second be used as a length standard.

- Is the old saying, "A pint's a pound the world around," true? It depends on what you are talking about. The saying is a good approximation for water and other similar liquids. Water weighs 8.3 pounds per gallon, so one-eighth of that, or a pint, weighs 1.04 lb.

- Pi 1p2, the ratio of the circumference of a circle to its diameter is always the same number, no matter which circle. Pi is an irrational number; that is, it cannot be written as the ratio of two whole numbers and is an infinite, nonrepeating decimal. Computers have calculated p to billions of digits. According to the *Guinness Book of Records* (2004), p has been calculated to 1 241 100 000 000 decimal places.

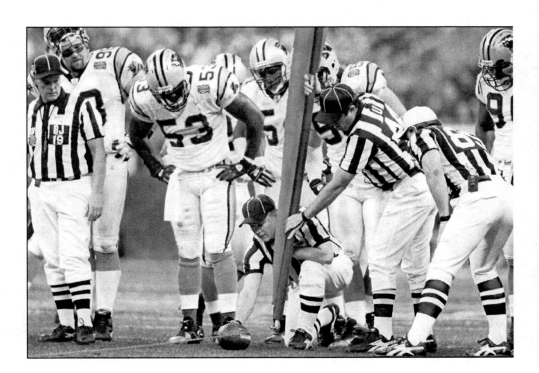

I s it first and ten? A measurement is needed, as with many other things in our lives. Length measurements tell us how far it is between cities, how tall you are, and as in the photo, if it's first and ten (yards to go). Time measurements tell you how long it is until the class ends, when the semester or quarter begins, and how old you are. Drugs taken because of illnesses are given in measured doses. Lives depend on various measurements made by doctors, medical technologists, and pharmacists in the diagnosis and treatment of disease.

Measurements enable us to compute quantities and solve problems. Units of measurement are also important in measurements and problem solving. For example, in finding the volume of a rectangular box, if you measure its dimensions in inches, the volume would have units of in^3 (cubic inches); if measured in centimeters, then it would be cm^3 (cubic centimeters). Measurement and problem solving are part of our lives. They play a particularly central role in our attempts to describe and understand the physical world, as we shall see in this chapter. But first, let's look at why one should study physics (Insight 1.1).

1

INSIGHT 1.1 WHY STUDY PHYSICS?

The question, "Why study physics?" occurs to many students sometime during their college careers. The truth is that there are probably as many answers as there are students, much as with any other subject. However, the answers can usually be arranged into several general groups as follows.

You are probably not a *physics major*, but for them, the answer is obvious. Introductory physics provides the foundation of their career. The fundamental goal of physics is to understand where the universe came from, how it has evolved and is still evolving, and the rules ("laws") that govern the phenomena we observe. These students will use their knowledge of physics continually during their careers. As an example of physics research, consider the discovery of the transistor in a special area of research known as solid-state physics in the late 1940s.

You are also probably not an *engineering "applied physics" major*. For them physics provides the basis of the engineering principles used to solve technological (applied and practical) problems. Some of these students may not use physics directly in their careers, but a good understanding of physics is crucial to the problem-solving needed in technological advances. For example, after the discovery of the transistor by physicists, engineers then developed uses for it. Decades later it evolved into the modern computer chip, which is an electrical computing network containing millions of tiny transistor elements.

More than likely you are a *life science* or *technology major* (premedicine, pre-physical therapy, preveterinary, industrial

technology, and so on). In this case, physics can provide a background understanding of the principles involved in your work. Although the applications of the laws of physics may not be immediately obvious, understanding them can be a valuable tool in your career. If you are a medical professional, for example, it may be necessary to evaluate MRI (magnetic resonance imaging) results, a procedure that is now commonplace. Would you be surprised to know that MRI scans are based on a physical phenomenon called *nuclear magnetic resonance*, first discovered by physicists and still used for measuring nuclear and solid-state properties?

If you are a student in a *nontechnical major*, the physics requirement is intended to provide a well-rounded education; that is, the ability to evaluate technology in the context of societal needs. For example, you may be called on to vote on tax benefits for an energy production source, and you might want to evaluate the pros and cons of the process. Or you might be tempted to vote for an official who has strong views on nuclear waste disposal. Are these views scientifically correct? To evaluate them, a knowledge of physics is necessary.

So as you can see, there is no one answer to the question, "Why study physics?" There is however, one overriding theme: Knowledge of the laws of physics can provide an excellent background for your career or an understanding of the world around you, or it can simply help make you a better and more well-rounded citizen.

1.1 Why and How We Measure

OBJECTIVES: To distinguish standard units and systems of units.

Imagine that someone is giving you directions to her house. Would you find it helpful to be told, "Drive along Elm Street for a little while, and turn right at one of the lights. Then keep going for quite a long way"? Or would you want to deal with a bank that sent you a statement at the end of the month saying, "You still have some money left in your account. Not a great deal, though."

Measurement is important to all of us. It is one of the concrete ways in which we deal with our world. This concept is particularly true in physics. *Physics is concerned with the description and understanding of nature* and measurement is one of its most important tools.

There are ways of describing the physical world that do not involve measurement. For instance, we might talk about the color of a flower or a dress. But the perception of color is subjective; it may vary from one person to another. Indeed, many people are color-blind and cannot tell certain colors apart. Light received by our eyes can be described in terms of wavelengths and frequencies. Different wavelengths are associated with different colors because of the physiological response of our eyes to light. But unlike the sensations or perceptions of color, the wavelengths can be measured. They are the same for everyone. In other words, measurements are objective. *Physics attempts to describe nature in an objective way through measurement.*

Standard Units

Measurements are expressed in terms of unit values, or units. As you are probably aware, a large variety of units are used to express measured values. Some of the earliest units of measurement, such as the foot, were originally referenced to parts of the human body. (Even today, the hand is still used as a unit to measure the height of horses. One hand is equal to 4 in.) If a unit becomes officially accepted, it is called a **standard unit**. Traditionally, a government or international body establishes standard units.

A group of standard units and their combinations is called a **system of units**. Two major systems of units are in use today—the metric system and the British system. The latter is still widely used in the United States, but has virtually disappeared in the rest of the world, having been replaced by the metric system.

Different units in the same system or units of different systems can be used to describe the same thing. For example, your height can be expressed in inches, feet, centimeters, meters—or even miles, for that matter (although this unit would not be very convenient). It is always possible to convert from one unit to another, and such conversions are sometimes necessary. However, it is best, and certainly most practical, to work consistently within the same system of units, as you will see.

1.2 SI Units of Length, Mass, and Time

OBJECTIVES: To (a) describe the SI, and (b) specify the references for the three main base quantities of this system.

Length, mass, and time are fundamental physical quantities that describe a great many quantities and phenomena. In fact, the topics of mechanics (the study of motion and force) covered in the first part of this book require *only* these physical quantities. The system of units used by scientists to represent these and other quantities is based on the metric system.

Historically, the metric system was the outgrowth of proposals for a more uniform system of weights and measures in France during the seventeenth and eighteenth centuries. The modern version of the metric system is called the **International System of Units**, officially abbreviated as **SI** (from the French *Système International des Unités*).

The SI includes *base quantities* and *derived quantities*, which are described by base units and derived units, respectively. **Base units**, such as the meter and the kilogram, are defined by standards. Other quantities that are expressed in terms of combinations of base units are called **derived units**. (Think of how we commonly measure the length of a trip in miles and the amount of time the trip takes in hours. To express how fast, or the rate we travel, the derived unit of miles per hour is used, which represents distance traveled per unit of time, or length per time.)

One of the refinements of the SI was the adoption of new standard references for some base units, including those of length and of time.

Length

Length is the base quantity used to measure distances or dimensions in space. We commonly say that length is the distance between two points. But the distance between any two points depends on how the space between them is traversed, which may be in a straight or a curved path.

The SI unit of length is the **meter** (**m**). The meter was originally defined as 1>10 000 000 of the distance from the North Pole to the equator along a meridian

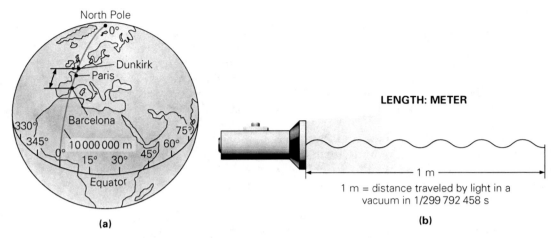

running through Paris (▲Fig. 1.1a).* A portion of this meridian between Dunkirk, France, and Barcelona, Spain, was surveyed to establish the standard length, which was assigned the name *metre*, from the Greek word *metron*, meaning "a measure." (The American spelling is *meter*.) A meter is 39.37 in.—slightly longer than a yard.

The length of the meter was initially preserved in the form of a material standard: the distance between two marks on a metal bar (made of a platinum–iridium alloy) that was stored under controlled conditions and called the Meter of the Archives. However, it is not desirable to have a reference standard that changes with external conditions, such as temperature. In 1983, the meter was redefined in terms of a more accurate standard, an unvarying property of light: the length of the path traveled by light in a vacuum during an interval of 1>299 792 458 of a second (Fig. 1.1b). In other words, light travels 299 792 458 m in a second, and the speed of light in a vacuum is defined to be c = 299 792 458 m>s. (c is the common symbol for the speed of light.) Note that the length standard is referenced to time, which can be measured with great accuracy.

Mass

Mass is the base quantity used to describe amounts of matter. The more massive an object, the more matter it contains. (We will encounter more discussions of mass in Chapters 4 and 7.)

The SI unit of mass is the **kilogram (kg)**. The kilogram was originally defined in terms of a specific volume of water, but is now referenced to a specific material standard: the mass of a prototype platinum–iridium cylinder kept at the International Bureau of Weights and Measures in Sèvres, France (▶Fig. 1.2). The United States has a duplicate of the prototype cylinder. The duplicate serves as a reference for secondary standards that are used in everyday life and commerce. It is hoped that the kilogram may eventually be referenced to something other than a material standard.

---

*Note that this book and most physicists have adopted the practice of writing large numbers with a thin space for three-digit groups—for example, 10 000 000 (not 10,000,000). This is done to avoid confusion with the European practice of using a comma as a decimal point. For instance, 3.141 in the United States would be written as 3,141 in Europe. Large decimal numbers, such as 0.537 84, may also be separated, for consistency. Spaces are generally used for numbers with more than four digits on either side of the decimal point.

You may have noticed that the phrase *weights and measures* is generally used instead of *masses and measures*. In the SI, mass is a base quantity, but in the British system, weight is used instead to describe amounts of mass—for example, weight in pounds instead of mass in kilograms. The weight of an object is the gravitational attraction that the Earth exerts on the object. For example, when you weigh yourself on a scale, your weight is a measure of the downward gravitational force exerted on you by the Earth. We can use weight as a measure of mass in this way because near the Earth's surface, because weight and mass are directly proportional to each other.

But treating weight as a base quantity creates some problems. A base quantity should have the same value everywhere. This is the case with mass—an object has the same mass, or amount of matter, regardless of its location. *But this is not true of weight.* For example, the weight of an object on the Moon is less than its weight on the Earth. This is because the Moon is less massive than the Earth, and the gravitational attraction exerted on an object by the Moon (the object's weight) is less than that exerted by the Earth. That is, an object with a given amount of mass has a particular weight on the Earth, but on the Moon, the same amount of mass will weigh only about one sixth as much. Similarly, the weight of an object would vary for different planets.

For now, keep in mind that in a given location, such as on the Earth's surface, *weight is related to mass, but they are not the same.* Since the weight of an object of a certain mass can vary with location, it is much more useful to take mass as the base quantity, as the SI does. Base quantities should remain the same regardless of where they are measured, under normal or standard conditions. The distinction between mass and weight will be more fully explained in a later chapter. Our discussion until then will be chiefly concerned with mass.

Time

Time is a difficult concept to define. A common definition is that time is the continuous, forward flow of events. This statement is not so much a definition but an observation that time has never been known to run backward, as it might appear to do when you view a film run backward in a projector. Time is sometimes said to be a fourth dimension, accompanying the three dimensions of space 1x, y, z, t2. That is, if something exists in space, it also exists in time. In any case, events can be used to mark time measurements. The events are analogous to the marks on a meterstick used for measurements of length. (See Insight 1.2 on What Is Time?)

The SI unit of time is the **second (s)**. The solar "clock" was originally used to define the second. A solar day is the interval of time that elapses between two successive crossings of the same longitude line (meridian) by the Sun. A second was fixed as 1>86400 of this apparent solar day (1 day = 24 h = 1440 min = 86400 s). However, the elliptical path of the Earth's motion around the Sun causes apparent solar days to vary in length.

As a more precise standard, an average, or mean, solar day was computed from the lengths of the apparent solar days during a solar year. In 1956, the second was referenced to this mean solar day. But the mean solar day is not exactly the same for each yearly period, because of minor variations in the Earth's motions and a steady slowing of its rate of rotation due to tidal friction. So scientists kept looking for something better.

In 1967, an atomic standard was adopted as a better reference. The second was defined by the radiation frequency of the cesium-133 atom. This "atomic clock" used a beam of cesium atoms to maintain our time standard, with a variation of about one second in 300 years. In 1999, another cesium-133 atomic clock was adopted, the atomic fountain clock, which, as the name implies, is based on the radiation frequency of a fountain of cesium atoms rather than a beam (▼Fig. 1.3). The variation of this timepiece is less than one second per 20 million years!*

---

*An even more precise clock, the all-optical atomic clock, is under development. It is so named because it uses laser technology and measures the shortest time interval ever recorded—0.00001 s. This new clock does not use cesium atoms, but rather a single cooled ion of liquid mercury linked to a laser oscillator. The frequency of the mercury ion is 100000 times the frequency of cesium atoms, hence the shorter, more precise time interval.

MASS: KILOGRAM

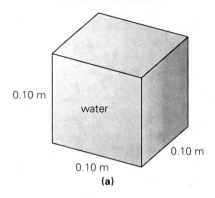

0.10 m

water

0.10 m

0.10 m

(a)

(b)

▲ **FIGURE 1.2 The SI mass standard: the kilogram (a)** The kilogram was originally defined in terms of a specific volume of water, that of a cube 0.10 m on a side, thereby associating the mass standard with the length standard. **(b)** The standard kilogram is now defined by a metal cylinder. The international prototype of the kilogram is kept at the French Bureau of Weights and Measures. It was manufactured in the 1880s of an alloy of 90% platinum and 10% iridium. Copies have been made for use as 1-kg national prototypes, one of which is the mass standard for the United States. It is kept at the National Institute of Standards and Technology (NIST) in Gaithersburg, MD.

INSIGHT 1.2 WHAT IS TIME?

For centuries the question, "What is time?" has been debated and attempted answers made, often philosophical in nature. But the definition of time still remains elusive to some degree. If you were asked to define or explain time, what would you say? General definitions may seem a bit vague. We commonly say:

Time is the continuous, forward flow of events.

Other thoughts on time include the following.
Plato, the great Greek philosopher observed:

The sun, moon, and .... the planets were made for defining and preserving the numbers of time.

St. Augustine pondered time too:

What then is time? If no one asks, I know; if I want to explain it to a questioner, I do not know.

Marcus Aurelius, the Roman emperor and philosopher, wrote:

Time is sort of a river of passing events, and strong is its current.

The Mad Hatter of Lewis Carroll's *Alice's Adventures in Wonderland* thought he knew time:

If you know Time as well as I do, you wouldn't talk about wasting it. It's him.... Now, if you only kept on good terms with him, he'd do almost anything you liked with the clock. For instance, suppose it were nine o'clock in the morning, just time to begin lessons; you'd only have to whisper a hint to Time, and around goes the clock in a twinkling; Half-past one, time for dinner.

The "forward" flow of time implies a direction, and this is sometimes described as *the arrow of time*. Events do not happen as they appear when a movie projector is run backward. You put cold milk into hot, black coffee and get a drinkable brown mixture—but you cannot get cold milk and hot, black coffee back out of the same brown mixture. Such is the irreversible arrow of a physical process (and time)—never the reverse of the coffee unmixing into cold and hot parts. This arrow of time will be described in Chapter 12 in terms of entropy, which tells how a thermodynamic process will "flow."

The question "What is time?" gives some insight as to what is meant by a *fundamental* physical quantity, such as mass, length, or time. Basically, these are the simplest properties of which we can think to describe nature. So, the safe answer is:

Time is a fundamental physical quantity.

This sort of masks our ignorance, and physics goes on from there, using time to describe and explain what we observe.

SI Base Units

The SI has seven *base units* for seven base quantities, which are assumed to be mutually independent. In addition to the meter, kilogram, and second for (1) length, (2) mass, and (3) time, SI units include (4) electric current (charge/second) in amperes (A), (5) temperature in kelvins (K), (6) amount of substance in moles (mol), and (7) luminous intensity in candelas (cd). See Table 1.1.

The foregoing quantities are thought to compose the smallest number of base quantities needed for a full description of everything observed or measured in nature.

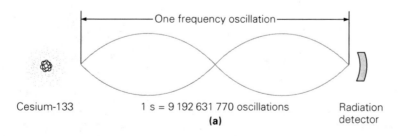

Cesium-133   1 s = 9 192 631 770 oscillations   Radiation detector
(a)

(b)

▲ **FIGURE 1.3 The SI time standard: the second** The second was once defined in terms of the average solar day. **(a)** It is now defined by the frequency of the radiation associated with an atomic transition. **(b)** The atomic fountain "clock" shown here, at NIST, is the time standard for the United States. The variation of this "timepiece" is less than one second per 20 million years.

TABLE 1.1	The Seven Base Units of the SI

Name of Unit (abbreviation)	Property Measured
meter (m)	length
kilogram (kg)	mass
second (s)	time
ampere (A)	electric current
kelvin (K)	temperature
mole (mol)	amount of substance
candela (cd)	luminous intensity

1.3 More about the Metric System

OBJECTIVES: To learn to use (a) metric prefixes, and (b) nonstandard metric units.

The metric system involving the standard units of length, mass, and time, now incorporated into the SI, was once called the **mks system** (for *meter–kilogram–second*). Another metric system that has been used in dealing with relatively small quantities is the **cgs system** (for *centimeter–gram–second*). In the United States, the system still generally in use is the British (or English) engineering system, in which the standard units of length, mass, and time are foot, slug, and second, respectively. You may not have heard of the slug, because, as we mentioned earlier, gravitational force (weight) is commonly used instead of mass—pounds instead of slugs—to describe quantities of matter. As a result, the British system is sometimes called the **fps system** (for *foot–pound–second*).

The metric system is predominant throughout the world and is coming into increasing use in the United States. Because it is simpler mathematically, the SI is the preferred system of units for science and technology. SI units are used throughout most of this book. All quantities can be expressed in SI units. However, some units from other systems are accepted for limited use as a matter of practicality—for example, the time unit of hour and the temperature unit of degree Celsius. British units will sometimes be used in the early chapters for comparison purposes, since these units are still employed in everyday activities and for many practical applications.

The increasing worldwide use of the metric system means that you should be familiar with it. One of the greatest advantages of the metric system is that it is a decimal, or base-10, system. This means that larger or smaller units are obtained by multiplying or dividing, respectively, a base unit by powers of 10. A list of some multiples and corresponding prefixes for metric units is given in Table 1.2.

TABLE 1.2	Some Multiples and Prefixes for Metric Units*

Multiple[†]	Prefix (and Abbreviation)	Pronunciation	Multiple[†]	Prefix (and Abbreviation)	Pronunciation
10^{12}	tera- (T)	ter′a (as in *terra*ce)	10^{-2}	centi- (c)	sen′ti (as in *senti*mental)
10^{9}	giga- (G)	jig′a (*jig* as in *jig*gle, *a* as in *a*bout)	10^{-3}	milli- (m)	mil′li (as in *mili*tary)
10^{6}	mega- (M)	meg′a (as in *mega*phone)	10^{-6}	micro-1m2	mi′kro (as in *micro*phone)
10^{3}	kilo- (k)	kil′o (as in *kilo*watt)	10^{-9}	nano- (n)	nan′o (*an* as in *an*nual)
10^{2}	hecto- (h)	hek′to (*heck-toe*)	10^{-12}	pico- (p)	pe′ko (*peek-oh*)
10	deka- (da)	dek′a (*deck* plus *a* as in *a*bout)	10^{-15}	femto- (f)	fem′to (*fem* as in *femi*nine)
10^{-1}	deci- (d)	des′i (as in *deci*mal)	10^{-18}	atto- (a)	at′toe (as in *a*natomy)

*For example, 1 gram (g) multiplied by 1000, or 10^3, is 1 kilogram (kg); 1 gram multiplied by 1>1000, or 10^{-3}, is 1 milligram (mg).

[†]The most commonly used prefixes are printed in blue. Note that the abbreviations for the multiples 10^6 and greater are capitalized, whereas the abbreviations for the smaller multiples are lowercased.

Illustration 1.2 Animations, Units, and Measurement

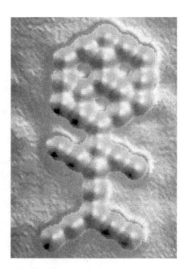

▲ **FIGURE 1.4 Molecular Man** This figure was crafted by moving 28 molecules, one at a time. Each of the gold-colored peaks is the image of a carbon monoxide molecule. The molecules rest on a single crystal platinum surface. "Molecular Man" measures 5 nm tall and 2.5 nm wide (hand to hand). More than 20 000 such figures, linked hand to hand, would be needed to span a single human hair. The molecules in the figure were positioned using a special microscope at very low temperatures.

Note: *Liter* is sometimes abbreviated as a lowercase "ell" (l), but a capital "ell" (L) is preferred in the United States so that the abbreviation is less likely to be confused with the numeral one. (Isn't 1 L clearer than 1 l ?)

In decimal measurements, the prefixes *micro-*, *milli-*, *centi-*, *kilo-*, and *mega-* are the ones most commonly used—for example, microsecond 1ms2, millimeter (mm), centimeter (cm), kilogram (kg), and megabyte (MB), as for computer disk or CD storage sizes). The decimal characteristics of the metric system make it convenient to change measurements from one size of metric unit to another. In the British system, different conversion factors must be used, such as 16 for converting pounds to ounces and 12 for converting feet to inches. The British system developed historically and not very scientifically.

You are already familiar with one base-10 system—U.S. currency. Just as a meter can be divided into 10 decimeters, 100 centimeters, or 1000 millimeters, the "base unit" of the dollar can be broken down into 10 "decidollars" (dimes), 100 "centidollars" (cents), or 1000 "millidollars" (tenths of a cent, or mills, used in figuring property taxes and bond levies). Since all the metric prefixes are powers of 10, there are no metric analogues for quarters or nickels.

The official metric prefixes help eliminate confusion. For example, in the United States, a billion is a thousand million 110^{9}2; in Great Britain, a billion is a million million 110^{12}2. The use of metric prefixes eliminates any confusion, since *giga-* indicates 10^9 and *tera-* stands for 10^{12}. You will probably be hearing more about *nano-*, the prefix that indicates 10^{-9}, with respect to nanotechnology (*nanotech* for short).

In general, nanotechnology is any technology done on the nanometer scale. A nanometer is one billionth 110^{-9}2 of a meter, about the width of three to four atoms. Basically, nanotechnology involves the manufacture or building of things one atom or molecule at a time, so the nanometer is the appropriate scale. One atom or molecule at a time? That may sound a bit farfetched, but it's not (see ◄Fig. 1.4).

The chemical properties of atoms and molecules are well understood. For example, rearranging the atoms in coal can produce a diamond. (We can already do this task without nanotechnology, using heat and pressure.) Nanotechnology presents the possibility of constructing novel molecular devices or "machines" with extraordinary properties and abilities; for example, in medicine. Nanostructures might be injected into the body to go to a particular site, such as a cancerous growth, and deliver a drug directly. Other organs of the body would then be spared any effects of the drug. (This process might be considered nanochemotherapy.)

It is difficult for us to grasp or visualize the new concept of nanotechnology. Even so, keep in mind that a nanometer is one billionth of a meter. The diameter of a human hair is about 200 000 nanometers—huge compared with the new nanoapplications. The future should be an exciting nanotime.

Volume

In the SI, the standard unit of volume is the cubic meter 1m^{3}2—the three-dimensional derived unit of the meter base unit. Because this unit is rather large, it is often more convenient to use the nonstandard unit of volume (or capacity) of a cube 10 cm (centimeters) on a side. This volume was given the name *litre*, which is spelled **liter (L)** in the United States. The volume of a liter is 1000 cm^3 110 cm × 10 cm × 10 cm2. Since 1 L = 1000 mL (milliliters), it follows that 1 mL = 1 cm^3. See ►Fig. 1.5a. (The cubic centimeter is sometimes abbreviated as cc, particularly in chemistry and biology. Also, the milliliter is sometimes abbreviated as ml, but the capital L is preferred (mL) so as not to be confused with the numeral one, 1.)

Recall from Fig. 1.2 that the standard unit of mass, the kilogram, was originally defined to be the mass of a cubic volume of water 10 cm, or 0.10 m, on a side, or the mass of one liter of water*. That is, *1 L of water has a mass of 1 kg* (Fig. 1.5b).

*This is specified at 4°C. A volume of water changes slightly with temperature (thermal expansion, Chapter 10). For our purposes here, we will consider a volume of water to remain constant under normal temperature conditions.

Also, since 1 kg = 1000 g and 1 L = 1000 cm³, then *1 cm³ (or 1 mL) of water has a mass of 1 g.*

Example 1.1 ■ The Metric Ton (or Tonne): Another Unit of Mass

As we have seen, the metric unit of mass was originally related to the length standard, with a liter $(1000\ cm^3)$ of water having a mass of 1 kg. The standard metric unit of volume is the cubic meter $(1\ m^3)$ and this volume of water was used to define a larger unit of mass called the *metric ton* (or *tonne*, as it is sometimes spelled). A metric ton is equivalent to how many kilograms?

Thinking It Through. A cubic meter is a relatively large volume and holds a large amount of water (more than a cubic yard; why?). The key is to find how many cubic volumes measuring 10 cm on a side (liters) are in a cubic meter. We expect, therefore, a large number.

Solution. Each liter of water has a mass of 1 kg, so we must find out how many liters are in 1 m³. Since there are 100 cm in a meter, a cubic meter is simply a cube with sides 100 cm in length. Therefore, a cubic meter $(1\ m^3)$ has a volume of $10^2\ cm \times 10^2\ cm \times 10^2\ cm = 10^6\ cm^3$. Since $1\ L = 10^3\ cm^3$, there must be $10^6\ cm^3 > 10^3\ cm^3 > L = 1000\ L$ in 1 m³. Thus, 1 metric ton is equivalent to 1000 kg.

Note that this line of reasoning can be expressed very concisely in a single ratio:

$$\frac{1\ m^3}{1\ L} = \frac{100\ cm \times 100\ cm \times 100\ cm}{10\ cm \times 10\ cm \times 10\ cm} = 1000 \quad \text{or} \quad 1\ m^3 = 1000\ L$$

Follow-Up Exercise. What would be the length of the sides of a cube that contained a metric kiloton of water *(Answers to all Follow-Up Exercises are at the back of the text.)**

You are probably more familiar with the liter than you think. The use of the liter is becoming quite common in the United States, as ▼Fig. 1.6 indicates.

Because the metric system is coming into increasing use in the United States, you may find it helpful to have an idea of how metric and British units compare. The relative sizes of some units are illustrated in ▶Fig. 1.7. The mathematical conversion from one unit to another will be discussed shortly.

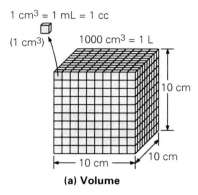

1 cm³ = 1 mL = 1 cc

(1 cm³)

1000 cm³ = 1 L

10 cm

10 cm

10 cm

(a) Volume

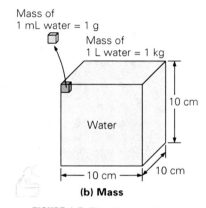

Mass of 1 mL water = 1 g

Mass of 1 L water = 1 kg

Water

10 cm

10 cm

10 cm

(b) Mass

▲ **FIGURE 1.5 The liter and the kilogram** Other metric units are derived from the meter. **(a)** A unit of volume (capacity) was taken to be the volume of a cube 10 cm, or 0.10 m, on a side and was given the name *liter* (L). **(b)** The mass of a liter of water was defined to be 1 kg. Note that the decimeter cube contains 1000 cm³, or 1000 mL. Thus, 1 cm³, or 1 mL, of water has a mass of 1 g.

◀ **FIGURE 1.6 Two, three, one, and one-half liters** The liter is now a common volume unit for soft drinks.

*The Answers to Follow-Up Exercises section after the appendices contains the answers—and, for Conceptual Exercises, the reasoning—for all Follow-Up Exercises in this book.

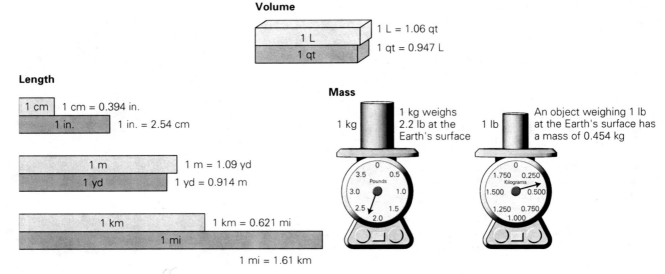

Volume

1 L

1 qt

1 L = 1.06 qt

1 qt = 0.947 L

Length

1 cm

1 in.

1 cm = 0.394 in.

1 in. = 2.54 cm

1 m

1 yd

1 m = 1.09 yd

1 yd = 0.914 m

1 km

1 mi

1 km = 0.621 mi

1 mi = 1.61 km

Mass

1 kg

1 kg weighs 2.2 lb at the Earth's surface

1 lb

An object weighing 1 lb at the Earth's surface has a mass of 0.454 kg

▲ **FIGURE 1.7 Comparison of some SI and British units** The bars illustrate the relative magnitudes of each pair of units. (*Note*: The comparison scales are different in each case.)

1.4 Unit Analysis

OBJECTIVES: To explain the advantages of, and apply, unit analysis.

The fundamental, or base, quantities used in physical descriptions are called *dimensions*. For example, length, mass, and time are dimensions. You could measure the distance between two points and express it in units of meters, centimeters, or feet, but the quantity would still have the dimension of length.

Dimensions provide a procedure by which the consistency of equations may be checked. In practice, it is convenient to use specific units, such as m, s, and kg. (See Table 1.3.) Such units can be treated as algebraic quantities and can be canceled. Using units to check equations is called **unit analysis**, which shows the consistency of units and whether an equation is dimensionally correct.

You have used equations and know that an equation is a mathematical equality. Since physical quantities used in equations have units, *the two sides of an equation must be equal not only in numerical value, but also in units (dimensions)*. For example, suppose you had the length quantities a = 3.0 m and b = 4.0 m. Inserting these values into the equation a × b = c gives 3.0 m × 4.0 m = 12 m².

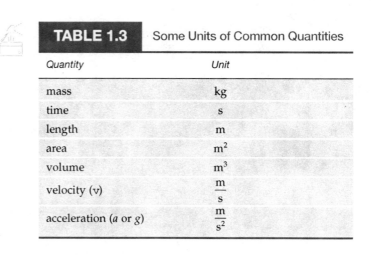

TABLE 1.3	Some Units of Common Quantities
Quantity	*Unit*
mass	kg
time	s
length	m
area	m²
volume	m³
velocity (*v*)	$\frac{m}{s}$
acceleration (*a* or *g*)	$\frac{m}{s^2}$

Both sides of the equation are numerically equal $13 \times 4 = 122$, and both sides have the same units, $m \times m = m^2 = (\text{length})^2$. If an equation is correct by unit analysis, it must be dimensionally correct. Example 1.2 demonstrates the further use of unit analysis.

Example 1.2 ■ Checking Dimensions: Unit Analysis

A professor puts two equations on the board: (a) $v = v_0 + at$ and (b) $x = v/2a$, where x is a distance in meters (m); v and v_0 are velocities in meters/second (m/s); a is acceleration in (meters/second)/second, or meters/second^2 (m/s^2); and t is time in seconds (s). Are the equations dimensionally correct? Use unit analysis to find out.

Thinking It Through. Simply insert the units for the quantities in each equation, cancel, and check the units on both sides.

Solution.

(a) The equation is

$$v = v_0 + at$$

Inserting units for the physical quantities gives (Table 1.3)

$$\frac{m}{s} = \frac{m}{s} + a\frac{m}{s^2} \times s \quad \text{or} \quad \frac{m}{s} = \frac{m}{s} + a\frac{m}{s \times s} \times s$$

Notice that units cancel like numbers in a fraction. Then, we have

$$\frac{m}{s} = \frac{m}{s} + \frac{m}{s} \quad \text{(dimensionally correct)}$$

The equation is dimensionally correct, since the units on each side are meters per second. (The equation is also a correct relationship, as we shall see in Chapter 2.)

(b) Using unit analysis, the equation

$$x = \frac{v}{2a}$$

is

$$m = \frac{a\dfrac{m}{s}}{\dfrac{m}{s^2}} = \frac{m}{s} \times \frac{s^2}{m} \quad \text{or} \quad m = s \quad \text{(not dimensionally correct)}$$

The meter (m) is not the same unit as the second (s), so in this case, the equation is not dimensionally correct (length ≠ time), and therefore is also not physically correct.

Follow-Up Exercise. Is the equation $ax = v^2$ dimensionally correct? (*Answers to all Follow-Up Exercises are at the back of the text.*)

Unit analysis will tell you if an equation is dimensionally correct, but a dimensionally consistent equation may not correctly express the real relationship of quantities. For example, in terms of units,

$$x = at^2$$

is

$$m = (m/s^2)(s^2) = m$$

This equation is dimensionally correct (length = length). But, as you will see in Chapter 2, it is not physically correct. The correct form of the equation—both dimensionally and physically—is $x = \frac{1}{2}at^2$. (The fraction $\frac{1}{2}$ has no dimensions; it is a dimensionless number.) Unit analysis cannot tell you if an equation is correct, only whether or not it is dimensionally consistent.

Mixed Units

Unit analysis also allows you to check for mixed units. In general, when working problems, you should always use the same system of units and the same unit for a given dimension throughout an exercise.

Suppose you wanted to buy a rug to fit a rectangular area, and you measure the sides to be 4.0 yd × 3.0 m. The area of the rug would then be $A = l \times w = 4.0$ yd × 3.0 m = 12 yd · m, which might cause a problem at the carpet store. Note that this equation is dimensionally correct, (length)^2 = (length)^2, but the units are inconsistent or mixed. So, unit analysis will point out *mixed units*. Note that it is possible for an equation to be dimensionally correct, even if the units are mixed.

Let's look at mixed units in an equation. Suppose that you used centimeters as the unit for x in the equation

$$v^2 = v_0^2 + 2ax$$

and the units for the other quantities as in Example 1.2. In terms of units, this equation would give

$$a\frac{m}{s}^2 b = a\frac{m}{s}^2 b + ¢\frac{m \times cm}{s^2}†$$

or

$$\frac{m^2}{s^2} = \frac{m^2}{s^2} + \frac{m \times cm}{s^2}$$

which is dimensionally correct, (length)^2×(time)^2—on both sides of the equation. But the units are mixed (m and cm). The terms on the right-hand side should not be added together without centimeters first being converted to meters.

Determining the Units of Quantities

Another aspect of unit analysis that is very important in physics is the determination of the units of quantities from defining equations. For example, the **density** (R) of an object (represented by the Greek letter rho, r) is defined by the equation

$$r = \frac{m}{V} \quad \text{(density)} \tag{1.1}$$

where m is its mass and V its volume. (Density is the mass per unit volume and is a measure of the compactness of the mass of an object or substance.) What are the units of density? In SI units, mass is measured in kilograms and volume in cubic meters. Hence, the defining equation

$$r = m > V \quad (kg > m^3)$$

gives the derived SI unit for density as kilograms per cubic meter.

What are the units of p? The relationship between the circumference (c) and the diameter (d) of a circle is given by the equation $c = pd$, so $p = c \times d$. If lengths are measured in meters, then unitwise we have

$$p = \frac{c}{d} \quad a\frac{m}{m}b$$

Thus, p has no units. It is unitless, or a dimensionless, constant—but one with a lot of digits, as pointed out in the Physics Facts at the beginning of the chapter.

1.5 Unit Conversions

OBJECTIVES: To (a) explain conversion-factor relationships, and (b) apply them in converting units within a system or from one system of units to another.

Because units in different systems, or even different units in the same system, can be used to express the same quantity, it is sometimes necessary to convert the units of a quantity from one unit to another. For example, we may need to convert feet to yards or convert inches to centimeters. You already know how to do many unit conversions. If a room is 12 ft long, what is its length in yards? Your immediate answer is 4 yd.

How did you do this conversion? Well, you must have known a relationship between the units of foot and yard. That is, you know that 3 ft = 1 yd. This is what we call an *equivalence statement*. As was seen in Section 1.4, the numerical values and units on both sides of an equation must be the same. In equivalence statements, we commonly use an equal sign to indicate that 1 yd and 3 ft stand for the *same*, or *equivalent*, *length*. The numbers are different because they stand for different *units* of length.

Mathematically, to change units we use **conversion factors**, which are simply equivalence statements expressed in the form of ratios—for example, 1 yd>3 ft or 3 ft>1 yd. (The "1" is often omitted in the denominators of such ratios for convenience—for example, 3 ft>yd.) To understand why such ratios are useful, note the expression 1 yd = 3 ft in ratio form:

$$\frac{1\ yd}{3\ ft} = \frac{3\ ft}{3\ ft} = 1 \qquad \text{or} \qquad \frac{3\ ft}{1\ yd} = \frac{1\ yd}{1\ yd} = 1$$

As you can see from this example, a conversion factor has an actual value of unity or one—and you can multiply any quantity by one without changing its value or size. Thus, *a conversion factor simply lets you express a quantity in terms of other units without changing its physical value or size.*

The manner in which 12 ft is converted to yards may be expressed mathematically as follows:

$$12\ ft \times \frac{1\ yd}{3\ ft} = 4\ yd \quad \textit{(units cancel)}$$

Using the appropriate conversion-factor form, the units cancel, as shown by the slash marks, giving the correct unit analysis, yd = yd.

Suppose you are asked to convert 12.0 in. to centimeters. You may not know the conversion factor in this case, but you can get it from a table (such as the one that appears inside the front cover of this book) that gives the needed relationships: 1 in. = 2.54 cm or 1 cm = 0.394 in. It makes no difference which of these equivalence statements you use. The question, once you have expressed the equivalence statement as a conversion factor, is whether to multiply or divide by that factor to make the conversion. *In doing unit conversions, take advantage of unit analysis*—that is, let the units determine the appropriate form of conversion factor.

Note that the equivalence statement 1 in. = 2.54 cm can give rise to two forms of the conversion factor: 1 in.>2.54 cm or 2.54 cm>in. When changing inches to centimeters, the appropriate form for multiplying is 2.54 cm>in. When changing centimeters to inches, use the form 1 in.>2.54 cm. (The inverse forms could be used in each case, but the quantities would have to be *divided* by the conversion factors for proper unit cancellation.) In general, the multiplication form of conversion factors will be used throughout this book.

A few commonly used equivalence statements are not dimensionally or physically correct; for example, consider 1 kg = 2.2 lb, which is used for quickly determining the weight of an object near the Earth's surface, given its mass. The kilogram is a unit of mass, and the pound is a unit of weight. This means that 1 kg is *equivalent* to 2.2 lb; that is, a 1-kg *mass* has a *weight* of 2.2 lb. Since mass and weight are directly proportional, we can use the dimensionally incorrect conversion factor 1 kg>2.2 lb (but *only* near the Earth's surface).

Note: 1 kg of mass has an equivalent weight of 2.2 lb near the surface of the Earth.

(a)

(b)

▲ **FIGURE 1.8** Unit conversion
Signs sometimes list both the
British and metric units, as shown
here for elevation and speed.

Example 1.3 ■ Converting Units: Use of Conversion Factors

(a) A basketball player is 6.5 ft tall. What is the player's height in meters? (b) How many seconds are in a 30-day month? (c) What is 50 mi/h in meters per second? (See the table of conversion factors inside the front cover of this book.)

Thinking It Through. If we use the correct conversion factors, the rest is arithmetic.

Solution.

(a) From the conversion table, we have 1 ft = 0.305 m, so

$$6.5 \text{ ft} \times \frac{0.305 \text{ m}}{1 \text{ ft}} = 2.0 \text{ m}$$

Another foot–meter conversion is shown in ◄Fig. 1.8. Is it correct?

(b) The conversion factor for days and seconds is available from the table 1 day = 86400 s2, but you may not always have a table handy. You can always use several better-known conversion factors to get the result:

$$30 \frac{\text{days}}{\text{month}} \times \frac{24 \text{ h}}{\text{day}} \times \frac{60 \text{ min}}{\text{h}} \times \frac{60 \text{ s}}{\text{min}} = \frac{2.6 \times 10^6 \text{ s}}{\text{month}}$$

Note how unit analysis checks the conversion factors for you. The rest is simple arithmetic.

(c) In this case, from the conversion table, 1 mi = 1609 m and 1 h = 3600 s. (The latter is easily computed.) These ratios are used to cancel the units that are to be changed, leaving behind the ones that are wanted:

$$\frac{50 \text{ mi}}{1 \text{ h}} \times \frac{1609 \text{ m}}{1 \text{ mi}} \times \frac{1 \text{ h}}{3600 \text{ s}} = 22 \text{ m/s}$$

Follow-Up Exercise. (a) Convert 50 mi/h directly to meters per second by using a single conversion factor, and (b) show that this single conversion factor can be derived from those in part (c) of this Example. (*Answers to all Follow-Up Exercises are at the back of the text.*)

Example 1.4 ■ More Conversions: A Really Long Capillary System

Capillaries, the smallest blood vessels of the body, connect the arterial system with the venous system and supply our tissues with oxygen and nutrients (▼Fig. 1.9). It is estimated that if all of the capillaries of an average adult were unwound and spread out end to end, they would extend to a length of about 64000 km. (a) How many miles is this length? (b) Compare this length with the circumference of the Earth.

Thinking It Through. (a) This conversion is straightforward—just use the appropriate conversion factor. (b) How do we calculate the circumference of a circle or sphere?

▶ **FIGURE 1.9** Capillary system
Capillaries connect the arterial
and venous systems in our
bodies. They are the smallest
blood vessels, but their total
length is impressive.

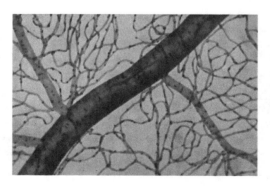

There is an equation to do so, but you must know the radius or diameter of the Earth. (If you do not remember one of these values, see the solar system data table inside the back cover of this book.)

Solution.

(a) We see in the conversion table that 1 km = 0.621 mi, so

$$64\,000 \; \cancel{\text{km}} \times \frac{0.621 \; \text{mi}}{1 \; \cancel{\text{km}}} = 40\,000 \; \text{mi} \quad \textit{(rounded off)}$$

(b) A length of 40 000 mi is substantial. To see how this length compares with the circumference (c) of the Earth, recall that the radius of the Earth is approximately 4000 mi, so the diameter (d) is 8000 mi. The circumference of a circle is given by $c = \pi d$, and

$$c = \pi d \approx 3 \times 8000 \; \text{mi} \approx 24\,000 \; \text{mi} \quad \textit{(rounded off)}$$

[To make a general comparison, $\pi = 3.14 \ldots$ is rounded off to 3. The $\approx$ symbol means "approximately equal to."]
So,

$$\frac{\text{capillary length}}{\text{Earth's circumference}} = \frac{40\,000 \; \text{mi}}{24\,000 \; \text{mi}} = 1.7$$

The capillaries of your body have a total length that would extend 1.7 times around the world. Wow!

Follow-Up Exercise. Taking the average distance between the East Coast and West Coast of the continental United States to be 4800 km, how many times would the total length of your body's capillaries cross the country? *(Answers to all Follow-Up Exercises are at the back of the text.)*

Example 1.5 ■ Converting Units of Area: Choosing the Correct Conversion Factor

A hall bulletin board has an area of 2.5 m². What is this area in square centimeters (cm^2)?

Thinking It Through. This problem is a conversion of area units, and we know that 1 m = 100 cm. So, some squaring must be done to get square meters related to square centimeters.

Solution. A common error in such conversions is the use of incorrect conversion factors. Because 1 m = 100 cm, it is sometimes assumed that 1 m² = 100 cm², which is *wrong*. The correct area conversion factor may be obtained directly from the correct linear conversion factor, 100 cm>1 m, or 10^2 cm>1 m, by *squaring* the linear conversion factor:

$$\left(\frac{10^2 \; \text{cm}}{1 \; \text{m}} \right)^2 = \frac{10^4 \; \text{cm}^2}{1 \; \text{m}^2}$$

Hence, 1 m² = 10^4 cm² 1= 10 000 cm²2. We can therefore write the following:

$$2.5 \; \text{m}^2 \times \left(\frac{10^2 \; \text{cm}}{1 \; \text{m}} \right)^2 = 2.5 \; \cancel{\text{m}^2} \times \frac{10^4 \; \text{cm}^2}{1 \; \cancel{\text{m}^2}} = 2.5 \times 10^4 \; \text{cm}^2$$

Follow-Up Exercise. How many cubic centimeters are in one cubic meter? *(Answers to all Follow-Up Exercises are at the back of the text.)*

Throughout this textbook, you will be presented with various Conceptual Examples. These examples show the reasoning used in applying particular concepts, often with little or no mathematics.

Conceptual Example 1.6 ▪ Comparing Speeds Using Unit Conversions

Two students disagree on which speed is faster, (a) 1 km⁄h or (b) 1 m⁄s. Which would you choose? *Clearly establish the reasoning used in determining your answer before checking it next. That is, **why** did you select your answer?*

Reasoning and Answer. To answer this, the quantities should be compared in the same units, so unit conversion is involved, and one looks for the easiest conversions. Observing the prefix *kilo-*, we know that 1 km is 1000 m. Also, 1 h is quickly expressed as 3600 s. Then the numerical ratio of km⁄h is less than 1, and 1 km⁄h < 1 m⁄s, so the answer is (b). [1 km⁄h = 1000 m⁄3600 s = 0.3 m⁄s]

Follow-Up Exercise. An American and a European are comparing the gas mileage they get with their RVs. The American calculates that he gets 10 mi⁄gal, and the European gives his as 10 km⁄L. Who is getting the better gas mileage? *(Answers to all Follow-Up Exercises are at the back of the text.)*

Some examples of the importance of unit conversion are given in the accompanying Insight 1.3.

INSIGHT 1.3 IS UNIT CONVERSION IMPORTANT?

The answer to this question is, you bet! Here are a couple of cases in point. In 1999, the $125 million Mars Climate Orbiter was making a trip to the Red Planet to investigate its atmosphere (Fig. 1). The spacecraft approached the planet in September, but suddenly contact between the Orbiter and personnel on Earth was lost, and the Orbiter was never heard from again. Investigations showed that the orbiter had approached Mars at a far lower altitude than planned. Instead of passing 147 km (87 mi) above the Martian surface, tracking data showed that the Orbiter was on a trajectory that would have taken it as close as 57 km (35 mi) from the surface. As a result, the spacecraft either burned up in the Martian atmosphere or crashed into the surface.

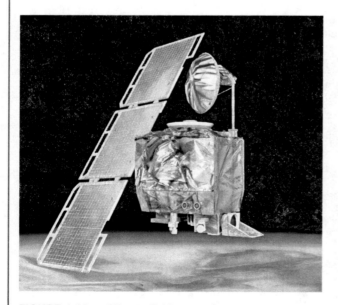

FIGURE 1 Mars Climate Orbiter An artist's conception of the orbiter near the surface of Mars. The actual orbiter either burned up in the Martian atmosphere or crashed into the surface. The cause was attributed to a mix-up in units, and a $125 million spacecraft was lost.

How could this have happened? Investigations showed that the failure of the Orbiter was primarily a problem of unit conversions. At Lockheed Martin Astronautics, which built the spacecraft, the engineers calculated the navigational information in British units. When scientists at NASA's Jet Propulsion Laboratory received the data, they assumed that the information was in metric units, as called for in the mission specifications. The unit conversions weren't made, and a $125 million spacecraft was lost on the Red Planet—causing more than a few red faces.

Closer to Earth, in 1983 Air Canada Flight 143 was on course from Montréal to Edmonton, Canada, with sixty-one passengers in a new Boeing 767, at the time the most advanced jetliner in the world. Almost halfway into the flight, a warning light came on for a fuel pump, then for another, and finally for all four pumps. The engines quit, and this advanced plane was now a glider, about 100 mi from the nearest major airport, at Winnipeg. Without engines, Flight 143's descent would bring it down 10 mi short of the airport, so it was diverted to an old Royal Canadian Air Force landing field at Gimli. The pilot maneuvered the powerless plane to a landing, stopping just short of a barrier. Did the plane, which was dubbed "The Gimli Glider," have bad fuel pumps? No, it had run out of fuel!

This near-disaster was caused by another conversion problem. The fuel computers weren't working properly so the mechanics had used the old procedure of measuring the fuel in the tanks with a dipstick. The length of the stick that is wet is used to determine the volume of fuel by means of conversion values in tables. Air Canada had for years computed the amount of fuel in pounds, whereas the new 767's fuel consumption was expressed in kilograms. Even worse, the dipstick procedure gave the amount of fuel onboard in liters instead of pounds or kilograms. The result was that the aircraft was loaded with 22 300 lb of fuel instead of the required 22 300 kg. Since 1 lb has a mass of 0.45 kg, the plane had less than half the required fuel.

These incidents underscore the importance of using appropriate units, making correct unit conversions, and working consistently in the same system of units. Several exercises at the end of the chapter will challenge you to develop your skills in accurate unit conversions.

1.6 Significant Figures

OBJECTIVES: To (a) determine the number of significant figures in a numerical value, and (b) report the proper number of significant figures after performing simple calculations.

Most of the time, you will be given numerical data when asked to solve a problem. In general, such data are either exact numbers or measured numbers (quantities). **Exact numbers** are numbers without any uncertainty or error. This category includes numbers such as the 100 used to calculate a percentage and the 2 in the equation $r = d/2$ relating the radius and diameter of a circle. **Measured numbers** are numbers obtained from measurement processes and thus generally have some degree of uncertainty or error.

When calculations are done with measured numbers, the error of measurement is *propagated*, or carried along, by the mathematical operations. The question of how to report the error for a result arises. For example, suppose that you are asked to find time (t) from the equation $x = vt$ and are given that $x = 5.3$ m and $v = 1.67$ m/s. Then

$$t = \frac{x}{v} = \frac{5.3 \text{ m}}{1.67 \text{ m/s}} = \,?$$

Doing the division operation on a calculator yields a result such as 3.173 652 695 seconds (▶Fig. 1.10). How many figures, or digits, should you report in the answer?

The error or uncertainty of the result of a mathematical operation may be computed by statistical methods. A simpler and more widely used procedure for estimating this uncertainty involves the use of **significant figures** (sf), sometimes called *significant digits*. The degree of accuracy of a measured quantity depends on how finely divided the measuring scale of the instrument is. For example, you might measure the length of an object as 2.5 cm with one instrument and 2.54 cm with another. The second instrument provides more significant figures and thus a greater degree of accuracy.

Basically, *the significant figures in any measurement are the digits that are known with certainty, plus one digit that is uncertain.* This set of digits is usually defined as all of the digits that can be read directly from the instrument used to make the measurement, plus one uncertain digit that is obtained by estimating the fraction of the smallest division of the instrument's scale.

The quantities 2.5 cm and 2.54 cm have two and three significant figures, respectively. This is rather evident. However, some confusion may arise when a quantity contains one or more zeros. For example, how many significant figures does the quantity 0.0254 m have? What about 104.6 m? 2705.0 m? In such cases, we will use the following rules:

1. Zeros at the beginning of a number are not significant. They merely locate the decimal point. For example,

   0.0254 m has three significant figures (2, 5, 4)

2. Zeros within a number are significant. For example,

   104.6 m has four significant figures (1, 0, 4, 6)

3. Zeros at the end of a number after the decimal point are significant. For example,

   2705.0 m has five significant figures (2, 7, 0, 5, 0).

4. In whole numbers without a decimal point that end in one or more zeros (trailing zeros)—for example, 500 kg—the zeros may or may not be significant. In such cases, it is not clear which zeros serve only to locate the decimal point and which are actually part of the measurement. That is, if the first zero from the left (5_0_0 kg) is the estimated digit in the measurement, then only two digits are reliably known, and there are only two significant figures. Similarly, if the last zero is the estimated digit (50_0_ kg), then there are

▲ **FIGURE 1.10 Significant figures and insignificant figures** For the division operation 5.3/1.67, a calculator with a floating decimal point gives many digits. A calculated quantity can be no more accurate than the least accurate quantity involved in the calculation, so this result should be rounded off to two significant figures—that is, 3.2.

three significant figures. This ambiguity may be removed by using scientific (powers-of-ten) notation:

5.0×10^2 kg has two significant figures

5.00×10^2 kg has three significant figures

This notation is helpful in expressing the results of calculations with the proper numbers of significant figures, as we shall see shortly. (Appendix I includes a review of scientific notation.)

(*Note*: To avoid confusion regarding numbers having trailing zeros used as given quantities in text examples and exercises, we will consider the trailing zeros to be significant. For example, assume that a time of 20 s has two significant figures, even if it is not written out as 2.0×10^1 s.)

It is important to report the results of mathematical operations with the proper number of significant figures. This is accomplished by using rules for (1) multiplication and division and (2) addition and subtraction. To obtain the proper number of significant figures, the results are rounded off. Here are some general rules that will be used for mathematical operations and rounding.

Significant Figures in Calculations

1. When multiplying and dividing quantities, leave as many significant figures in the answer as there are in the quantity with the least number of significant figures.
2. When adding or subtracting quantities, leave the same number of decimal places (rounded) in the answer as there are in the quantity with the least number of decimal places.

Rules for Rounding*

1. If the first digit to be dropped is less than 5, leave the preceding digit as is.
2. If the first digit to be dropped is 5 or greater, increase the preceding digit by one.

The rules for significant figures mean that the result of a calculation can be no more accurate than the least accurate quantity used. That is, you cannot gain accuracy performing mathematical operations. Thus, the result that should be reported for the division operation discussed at the beginning of this section is

$$\frac{\overset{(2\ sf)}{5.3 \text{ m}}}{\underset{(3\ sf)}{1.67 \text{ m/s}}} = 3.2 \text{ s} \quad (2\ sf)$$

The result is rounded off to two significant figures. (See Fig. 1.10.)

Applications of these rules are shown in the following Examples.

Example 1.7 ■ Using Significant Figures in Multiplication and Division: Rounding Applications

The following operations are performed and the results rounded off to the proper number of significant figures:

Multiplication

$$\underset{(2\ sf)}{2.4 \text{ m}} \times \underset{(3\ sf)}{3.65 \text{ m}} = 8.76 \text{ m}^2 = 8.8 \text{ m}^2 \quad (\textit{rounded to two sf})$$

Division

$$\frac{\overset{(4\ sf)}{725.0 \text{ m}}}{\underset{(3\ sf)}{0.125 \text{ s}}} = 5800 \text{ m/s} = 5.80 \times 10^3 \text{ m/s} \quad (\textit{represented with three sf; why?})$$

*It should be noted that these rounding rules give an approximation of accuracy, as opposed to the results provided by more advanced statistical methods.

Follow-Up Exercise. Perform the following operations, and express the answers in the standard powers-of-ten notation (one digit to the left of the decimal point) with the proper number of significant figures: (a) 12.0×10^5 kg$2$$10.035 \times 10^2$ kg2 and (b) 1148×10^{-6} m$2>$$10.4906 \times 10^{-6}$ m2. *(Answers to all Follow-Up Exercises are at the back of the text.)*

Example 1.8 ■ Using Significant Figures in Addition and Subtraction: Application of Rules

The following operations are performed by finding the number that has the least number of decimal places. (Units have been omitted for convenience.)

Addition
In the numbers to be added, note that 23.1 has the least number of decimal places (one):

$$
\begin{array}{r}
23.1 \\
0.546 \\
\underline{1.45} \\
25.096
\end{array}
\quad \xrightarrow[\text{(rounding off)}]{} \quad 25.1
$$

Subtraction
The same rounding procedure is used. Here, 157 has the least number of decimal places (none).

$$
\begin{array}{r}
157 \\
\underline{-5.5} \\
151.5
\end{array}
\quad \xrightarrow[\text{(rounding off)}]{} \quad 152
$$

Follow-Up Exercise. Given the numbers 23.15, 0.546, and 1.058, (a) add the first two numbers and (b) subtract the last number from the first. *(Answers to all Follow-Up Exercises are at the back of the text.)*

Suppose that you must deal with mixed operations—multiplication and/or division *and* addition and/or subtraction. What do you do in this case? Just follow the regular rules for order of algebraic operations, and observe significant figures as you go.

The number of digits reported in a result depends on the number of digits in the given data. The rules for rounding will generally be observed in this book. However, there will be exceptions that may make a difference, as explained in the following Problem-Solving Hint.

Problem-Solving Hint: The "Correct" Answer

When working problems, you naturally strive to get the correct answer and will probably want to check your answers against those listed in the Answers to Odd-Numbered Exercises section in the back of the book. However, on occasion, you may find that your answer differs slightly from that given, even though you have solved the problem correctly. There are several reasons why this could happen.

As stated previously, it is best to round off only the final result of a multipart calculation, but this practice is not always convenient in elaborate calculations. Sometimes, the results of intermediate steps are important in themselves and need to be rounded off to the appropriate number of digits as if each were a final answer. Similarly, Examples in this book are often worked in steps to show the stages in the *reasoning* of the solution. The results obtained when the results of intermediate steps are rounded off may differ slightly from those obtained when only the final answer is rounded.

Rounding differences may also occur when using conversion factors. For example, in changing 5.0 mi to kilometers using the conversion factor listed in the front of this book in different forms,

$$
5.0 \text{ mi } a\frac{1.609 \text{ km}}{1 \text{ mi}}b = 18.045 \text{ km}2 = 8.0 \text{ km} \quad \textit{(two significant figures)}
$$

and

$$
5.0 \text{ mi } a\frac{1 \text{ km}}{0.621 \text{ mi}}b = 18.051 \text{ km}2 = 8.1 \text{ km} \quad \textit{(two significant figures)}
$$

(continues on next page)

PHYSLET®

Exploration 1.1 Click-Drag to Get Position

The difference arises because of rounding of the conversion factors. Actually, 1 km = 0.6214 mi, so 1 mi = 11>0.62142 km = 1.609 269 km ≈ 1.609 km. (Try repeating these conversions with the unrounded factors, and see what you get.) To avoid rounding differences in conversions, we will generally use the multiplication form of a conversion factor, as in the first of the foregoing equations, unless there is a convenient exact factor, such as 1 min>60 s.

Slight differences in answers may occur when different methods are used to solve a problem, because of rounding differences. Keep in mind that when solving a problem (a general procedure for which is given in Section 1.7), *if your answer differs from that in the text in only the last digit, the disparity is most likely the result of a rounding difference for an alternative method of solution being used.*

1.7 Problem Solving

OBJECTIVES: To (a) establish a general problem-solving procedure, and (b) apply it to typical problems.

An important aspect of physics is problem solving. In general, this involves the application of physical principles and equations to data from a particular situation in order to find some unknown or wanted quantity. There is no universal method for approaching problem solving that will automatically produce a solution. However, although there is no magic formula for problem solving, there are some sound practices that can be very useful. The steps in the following procedure are intended to provide you with a framework that can be applied to solving most of the problems you will encounter during your course of study. (You may wish to make modifications to suit your own style.)

We will generally use these steps in dealing with the Example problems throughout the text. Additional Problem-Solving Hints will be given where appropriate.

General Problem-Solving Steps

1. *Read the problem carefully, and analyze it.* What is wanted, and what is given?
2. *Where appropriate, draw a diagram as an aid in visualizing and analyzing the physical situation of the problem.* This step may not be necessary in every case, but it is often useful.
3. *Write down the given data and what is to be found. Make sure the data is expressed in the same system of units (usually SI).* If necessary, use the unit conversion procedure learned earlier in the chapter. Some data may not be given explicitly. For example, if a car "starts from rest," its initial speed is zero 1v_0 = 02; in some instances, you may be expected to know certain quantities, such as the acceleration due to gravity, g, or to look them up in tables.
4. *Determine which principle(s) and equation(s) are applicable to the situation, and how they can be used to get from the information given to what is to be found.* You may have to devise a strategy that involves several steps. Also, try to simplify equations as much as possible through algebraic manipulation. The fewer calculations you do, the less likely you are to make a mistake—so *don't put in numbers until you have to.*
5. *Substitute the given quantities (data) into the equation(s) and perform calculations.* Report the result with the proper units and proper number of significant figures.
6. *Consider whether the results are reasonable.* Does the answer have an appropriate magnitude? (This means, is it in the right ballpark?) For example, if a person's calculated mass turns out to be 4.60×10^2 kg, the result should be questioned, since a mass of 460 kg has a weight of 1010 lb. ◄Fig. 1.11 summarizes the main steps in the form of a flowchart.

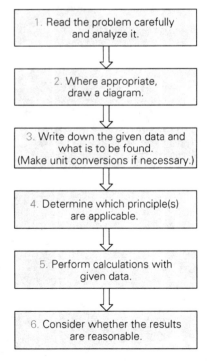

▲ FIGURE 1.11 A flowchart for the suggested problem-solving procedure

In general, there are three types of examples in this text as listed in Table 1.4. The preceding steps would be applicable to the first two types, because they include calculations. Conceptual Examples, in general, do not follow these steps, being primarily conceptual in nature.

In reading the worked Examples and Integrated Examples, you should be able to recognize the general application or flow of the preceding steps. This format will be used throughout the text. Let's take an Example and an Integrated Example as illustrations. Comments will be made in these examples to point out the problem-solving approach and steps that will not be made in the text Examples, but should be understood. Since no physical principles have really been covered, we will use math and trig problems, which should serve as a good review.

Example 1.9 ■ Finding the Outside Surface Area of a Cylindrical Container

A closed cylindrical container used to store material from a manufacturing process has an outside radius of 50.0 cm and a height of 1.30 m. What is the total outside surface area of the container?

Thinking It Through. (In this type of Example, the Thinking It Through section generally combines problem-solving steps 1 and 2 given previously.)

It should be noted immediately that the length units are given in mixed units, so a unit conversion will be in order. To visualize and analyze the cylinder, drawing a diagram is helpful (▶Fig. 1.12). With this information in mind, proceed to finding the solution, using the expression for the area of a cylinder (the combined areas of the circular ends and the cylinder's side).

Solution. Writing what is given and what is to be found (step 3 in our procedure):

Given: r = 50.0 cm   *Find:* A (the outside surface area of the cylinder)
         h = 1.30 m

First, let's tend to the mixed units. You should be able in this case to immediately write r = 50.0 cm = 0.500 m. But often conversions are not obvious, so going through the unit conversion for illustration:

$$r = 50.0 \text{ cm } \left(\frac{1 \text{ m}}{100 \text{ cm}}\right) = 0.500 \text{ m}$$

There are general equations for areas (and volumes) of commonly shaped objects. The area of a cylinder can be easily looked up (given in Appendix I), but suppose you didn't have such a source. In this case, you can figure it out for yourself. Looking at Fig. 1.12, note that the outside surface area of a cylinder consists of that of two circular ends and that of a rectangle (the body of the cylinder laid out flat). Equations for the areas of these common shapes are generally remembered. So the area of the two ends would be

$$2A_e = 2 \times p r^2 \quad \text{(2 times the area of the circular end; area of a circle = } pr^2)$$

and the area of the body of the cylinder is

$$A_b = 2pr \times h \quad \text{(circumference of circular end times height)}$$

Then the total area is

$$A = 2A_e + A_b = 2pr^2 + 2prh$$

The data could be put into the equation, but sometimes an equation may be simplified to save some calculation steps.

$$A = 2pr(r + h) = 2p(0.500 \text{ m})(0.500 \text{ m} + 1.30 \text{ m})$$
$$= p(1.80 \text{ m}^2)2 = 5.65 \text{ m}^2$$

and the result appears reasonable considering the cylinder's dimensions.

Follow-Up Exercise. If the wall thickness of the cylinder's side and ends is 1.00 cm, what is the inside volume of the cylinder? (*Answers to all Follow-Up Exercises are at the back of the text.*)

TABLE 1.4	Types of Examples

Example—primarily mathematical in nature

Sections: **Thinking It Through**
Solution

Integrated Example—(a) conceptual multiple choice, (b) mathematical follow-up

Sections: **(a) Conceptual Reasoning**
(b) Quantitative Reasoning and Solution

Conceptual Example—in general, needs only reasoning to obtain the answer, although some simple math may be required at times to justify the reasoning

Sections: **Reasoning and Answer**

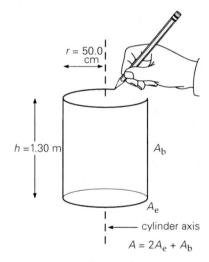

▲ **FIGURE 1.12 A helpful step in problem solving** Drawing a diagram helps you visualize and better understand the situation. See Example 1.9.

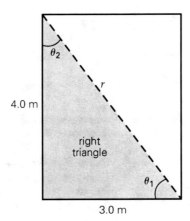

4.0 m

right triangle

3.0 m

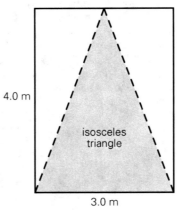

4.0 m

isosceles triangle

3.0 m

▲ **FIGURE 1.13 A flower bed project** Two types of triangles for a new flower bed. See Example 1.10.

Integrated Example 1.10 ■ Sides and Angles

(a) A gardener has a rectangular plot measuring 3.0 m × 4.0 m. She wishes to use half of this area to make a triangular flower bed. Of the two types of triangles shown in ◄Fig. 1.13, which should she use to do this? (1) The one right triangle, (2) the isosceles triangle—two sides equal, or (3) either one? (b) In laying out the flower bed, the gardener decides to use a right triangle. Wishing to line the sides with rows of stone, she wants to know the total length (L) of the triangle sides. She would also like to know the values of the acute angles of the triangle. Can you help her so she doesn't have to do physical measurements?

(a) Conceptual Reasoning. The rectangular plot has a total area of 3.0 m × 4.0 m = 12 m². It is obvious that the right triangle divides the plot in half (Fig. 1.13). This is not as obvious for the isosceles triangle. But with a little study you should see that the white areas could be arranged such that their combined area would be the same as that of the shaded isosceles triangle. So the isosceles triangle also divides the plot in half and the answer is (3). [This could be proven mathematically by computing the areas of the triangles. Area = $\frac{1}{2}$(altitude × base).]

(b) Quantitative Reasoning and Solution. To find the total length of the sides, we need to find the length of the hypotenuse of the triangle. This can be done using the Pythagorean theorem, $x^2 + y^2 = r^2$, and

$$r = \sqrt[3]{x^2 + y^2} = \sqrt[4]{13.0 \text{ m}^2 + 14.0 \text{ m}^2} = \sqrt[3]{25 \text{ m}^2} = 5.0 \text{ m}$$

(Or directly, you may have noticed that this is a 3-4-5 right triangle.) Then,

$$L = 3.0 \text{ m} + 4.0 \text{ m} + 5.0 \text{ m} = 12 \text{ m}$$

The acute angles of the triangle can be found by using trigonometry. Referring to the angles in Fig. 1.13,

$$\tan u_1 = \frac{\text{side opposite}}{\text{side adjacent}} = \frac{4.0 \text{ m}}{3.0 \text{ m}}$$

and

$$u_1 = \tan^{-1}\left(\frac{4.0 \text{ m}}{3.0 \text{ m}}\right) = 53°$$

Similarly,

$$u_2 = \tan^{-1}\left(\frac{3.0 \text{ m}}{4.0 \text{ m}}\right) = 37°$$

which add to 90° as would be expected with the right angle 190° + 90° = 180°2.

Follow-Up Exercise. What are the total length of the sides and the interior angles for the isosceles triangle in Fig. 1.13? (*Answers to all Follow-Up Exercises are at the back of the text.*)

Basic trigonometric functions:

$$\cos u = \frac{x}{r}\left(\frac{\text{side adjacent}}{\text{hypotenuse}}\right)$$

$$\sin u = \frac{y}{r}\left(\frac{\text{side opposite}}{\text{hypotenuse}}\right)$$

$$\tan u = \frac{\sin u}{\cos u} = \frac{y}{x}\left(\frac{\text{side opposite}}{\text{side adjacent}}\right)$$

These examples illustrate how the problem-solving steps are woven into finding the solution of a problem. You will see this pattern throughout the solved examples in the text, although not as explicitly explained. Try to develop your problem-solving skills in a similar manner.

Finally, let's take a Conceptual Example that has conceptual reasoning and some simple calculations.

Conceptual Example 1.11 ■ Climbing at an Angle

A jet pilot puts his plane through two straight, sharp inclined climbs at different angles. On the first climb, the plane travels 40.0 km at an angle of 15 degrees relative to the horizontal. On the second inclined climb, the plane travels 20.0 km at an angle of 30 degrees relative to the horizontal. How do the vertical distances of the two climbes compare? (a) That of the first incline is larger, (b) that of the second incline is larger, or (c) they both are the same.

Reasoning and Answer. At first glance it may appear that the vertical distances are the same. After all, the first incline's angle is half that of the second incline. And, the hypotenuse (distance) of the first climb is twice that of the second, so won't the two effects cancel out making the correct answer (c)? No. The flaw here is that the vertical distance is based on the sine of the angle (make a sketch) and the sine of an angle is *not* proportional to the angle. Check it out your calculator. 2 × sin 15° = 0.518 and sin 30° = 0.500. So they don't offset. Half the distance at double the angle produces a smaller vertical distance, and the correct answer is (a).

Follow-Up Exercise. In this Example, would the second climb have to be steeper than 30 degrees or less steep to make the climb distances the same? What should the angle be in this case?

Approximation and Order-of-Magnitude Calculations

At times when solving a problem, you may not be interested in an exact answer, but want only an estimate or a "ballpark" figure. Approximations can be made by rounding off quantities so as to make the calculations easier and, perhaps, obtainable without the use of a calculator. For example, suppose you want to get an idea of the area of a circle with radius $r = 9.5$ cm. Then, rounding 9.5 cm $\approx$ 10 cm, and $p \approx 3$ instead of 3.14,

$$A = pr^2 \approx 3110 \text{ cm}^2 = 300 \text{ cm}^2$$

(Note that significant figures are not a concern in calculations involving approximations.) The answer is not exact, but it is a good approximation. Compute the exact answer and see.

Powers-of-ten, or scientific, notation is particularly convenient in making estimates or approximations in what are called **order-of-magnitude calculations.** *Order of magnitude* means that we express a quantity to the power of 10 closest to the actual value. For example, in the foregoing calculation, approximating 9.5 cm $\approx$ 10 cm is expressing 9.5 as 10^1, and we say that the radius is *on the order of* 10 cm. Expressing a distance of 75 km $\approx 10^2$ km indicates that the distance is on the order of 10^2 km. The radius of the Earth is 6.4×10^3 km $\approx 10^4$ km, or on the order of 10^4 km. A nanostructure with a width of 8.2×10^{-9} m is on the order of 10^{-8} m, or 10 nm. (Why an exponent of -8?)

An order-of-magnitude calculation gives only an estimate, of course. But this estimate may be enough to provide you with a better grasp or understanding of a physical situation. Usually, the result of an order-of-magnitude calculation is precise within a power of 10, or *within an order of magnitude*. That is, the prefix to the power of 10 is somewhere between 1 and 10. For example, if we got a time result of 10^5 s, we would expect the exact answer to be somewhere between 1×10^5 s and 10×10^5 s.

Example 1.12 ■ Order-of-Magnitude Calculation: Drawing Blood

A medical technologist draws 15 cc of blood from a patient's vein. Back in the lab, it is determined that this volume of blood has a mass of 16 g. Estimate the density of the blood, in standard SI units.

Thinking It Through. The data are given in cgs (centimeter–gram–second) units, which are often used for practicality when dealing with small, whole-number quantities in some situations. The cc abbreviation is commonly used in the medical and chemistry fields for cm^3. Density $1r2$ is mass per unit volume, where $r = m > V$ (Section 1.4).

Solution.

Given: $m = 16 \text{ g} \left(\dfrac{1 \text{ kg}}{1000 \text{ g}}\right) = 1.6 \times 10^{-2} \text{ kg} \approx 10^{-2} \text{ kg}$ *Find:* estimate of r (density)

$$V = 15 \text{ cm}^3 \left(\frac{1 \text{ m}}{10^2 \text{ cm}}\right)^3 = 1.5 \times 10^{-5} \text{ m}^3 \approx 10^{-5} \text{ m}^3$$

So, we have

$$r = \frac{m}{V} \approx \frac{10^{-2} \text{ kg}}{10^{-5} \text{ m}^3} \approx 10^3 \text{ kg} > \text{m}^3$$

This result is quite close to the average density of whole blood, 1.05×10^3 kg>m^3.

Follow-Up Exercise. A patient receives 750 cc of whole blood. Estimate the mass of the blood, in standard units. (*Answers to all Follow-Up Exercises are at the back of the text.*)

Science Fundamentals

Example 1.13 ■ How Many Red Cells in Your Blood?

The blood volume in the human body varies with a person's age, body size, and sex. On average, this volume is about 5 L. A typical value of red blood cells (erythrocytes) per volume is 5 000 000 (5×10^6) cells per cubic millimeter. Estimate how many red blood cells you have in your body.

Thinking It Through. The red blood cell count in cells per cubic millimeter is sort of a red blood cell "number density." Multiplying this figure by the total volume of blood $(\text{cells/volume}) \times \text{total volume}$ will give the total number of cells. But note that we must have the volumes in the same units.

Solution.

Given: $V = 5\,L$

Find: the approximate number of red cells in the body

$$= 5\,L \left(10^{-3}\,\frac{m^3}{L}\right)$$

$$= 5 \times 10^{-3}\,m^3 \approx 10^{-2}\,m^3$$

$$\text{cells/volume} = 5 \times 10^6\,\frac{cells}{mm^3} \approx 10^7\,\frac{cells}{mm^3}$$

Then, changing to cubic meters,

$$\frac{cells}{volume} \approx 10^7\,\frac{cells}{mm^3}\left(\frac{10^3\,mm}{1\,m}\right)^3 \approx 10^{16}\,\frac{cells}{m^3}$$

(*Note:* The conversion factor for liters to cubic meters was obtained directly from the conversion tables, but there is no conversion factor given for converting cubic millimeters to cubic meters, so we just use a known conversion and cube it.) Then,

$$\left(\frac{cells}{volume}\right)(\text{total volume}) \approx \left(10^{16}\,\frac{cells}{m^3}\right)(10^{-2}\,m^3) = 10^{14}\ \text{red blood cells}$$

Red blood cells (erythrocytes) are one of the most abundant cells in the human body.

Follow-Up Exercise. The average number of white blood cells (leukocytes) in human blood is normally 5000 to 10000 cells per cubic millimeter. Estimate the number of white blood cells you have in your body. (*Answers to all Follow-Up Exercises are at the back of the text.*)

FORCE AND MOTION

PHYSICS FACTS

- Isaac Newton was born on Christmas Day, 1642, the same day that Galileo died. (By our current Gregorian calendar, Newton's birthdate is January 4, 1643. England did not begin using the Gregorian calendar until 1752.)

- Newton
  - found white light to be a mixture of colors, theorized that light was made up of particles, which he called corpuscles, rather than waves. We now have the dual nature of light, with light both behaving as a wave and made up of particles called photons.
  - developed the fundamentals of calculus. Gottfried Leibniz, a German mathematician, independently developed a similar version of calculus. There was a lifelong, bitter dispute between Newton and Leibniz over who should receive the credit for doing so first.
  - built the first reflecting telescope with a power of 40X.

- The astronomer Edmond Halley used Newton's work on gravitation and orbits to predict that a comet he had observed in 1682 would return in 1758. The comet returned as predicted and was named Halley's Comet in his honor. Contrary to popular belief, Halley did not discover the comet. Its periodic appearance had been recorded since 263 BCE, when it was first seen been by Chinese astronomers. Halley died in 1742 and did not get to see the return of his comet.

Y ou don't have to understand any physics to know that what's needed to get the car in the picture (or anything else) moving is a push or a pull. If the frustrated men (or the tow truck that may soon be called) can apply enough *force*, the car will move.

But what's keeping the car stuck in the snow? A car's engine can generate plenty of force—so why doesn't the driver just put the car into reverse and back out? For a car to move, another force is needed besides that exerted by the engine: *friction*. Here, the problem is most likely that there is not enough friction between the tires and the snow.

In Chapters 2 and 3, we learned how to analyze motion in terms of kinematics. Now our attention turns to the study of *dynamics*—that is, what *causes* motion and changes in motion. This will lead us to the concept of force and inertia.

The study of force and motion occupied many early scientists. The English scientist Isaac Newton (1642–1727 ►Fig. 4.1) summarized the various relationships and principles of those early scientists into three statements, or laws, which not surprisingly are known as *Newton's laws of motion*. These laws sum up the concepts of dynamics. In this chapter, you'll learn what Newton had to say about force and motion.

103

▲ **FIGURE 4.1** Isaac Newton
Newton (1642–1727), one of the greatest scientific minds of all time, made fundamental contributions to mathematics, astronomy, and several branches of physics, including optics and mechanics. He formulated the laws of motion and universal gravitation (Chapter 7) and was one of the inventors of calculus. He did some of his most profound work when he was in his mid-twenties.

Note: In the notation $\sum \vec{F}_i$, the Greek letter sigma means the "sum of" the individual forces, as indicated by the i subscript: $\sum \vec{F}_i = \vec{F}_1 + \vec{F}_2 + \vec{F}_3 + \cdots$, that is, a vector sum. The i subscripts are sometimes omitted as being understood, and we write $\sum \vec{F}$.

4.1 The Concepts of Force and Net Force

OBJECTIVES: To (a) relate force and motion, and (b) explain what is meant by a net or unbalanced force.

Let's first take a closer look at the meaning of force. It is easy to give examples of forces, but how would you generally define this concept? An operational definition of force is based on observed effects. That is, a force is described in terms of what it does. From your own experience, you know that *forces can produce changes in motion.* A force can set a stationary object into motion. It can also speed up or slow down a moving object or change the direction of its motion. In other words, a force can produce a change in velocity (speed and/or direction)—that is, an acceleration. Therefore, an observed *change* in motion, including motion starting from rest, is evidence of a force. This concept leads to a common definition of **force:**

A force is something that is capable of changing an object's state of motion, that is, changing its velocity.

The word *capable* is very significant here. It takes into account the fact that a force may be acting on an object, but its capability to produce a change in motion may be balanced, or canceled, by one or more other forces. The net effect is then zero. Thus, a single force *may not necessarily* produce a change in motion. However, it follows that if a force acts *alone*, the object on which it acts *will* accelerate.

Since a force can produce an acceleration—a vector quantity—force must itself be a vector quantity, with both magnitude and direction. When several forces act on an object, you will often be interested in their combined effect—the net force. The **net force**, $\vec{F}_{net}$, is the vector sum $\sum \vec{F}_i$, or resultant, of all the forces acting on an object or system. (See the note in the margin.) Consider the opposite forces illustrated in ▾Fig. 4.2a. The net force is zero when forces of equal magnitude act in opposite directions (Fig. 4.2b, where signs are used for directions). Such forces are said to be balanced forces. A nonzero net force is referred to as an unbalanced force (Fig. 4.2c). In this case, the situation can be analyzed as though only one force equal to the net force were acting. An unbalanced, or nonzero, net force always produces an acceleration. In some instances, an applied unbalanced force may also deform

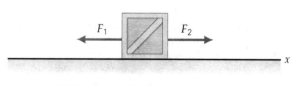

(a)

▶ **FIGURE 4.2** Net force
(a) Opposite forces are applied to a crate. **(b)** If the forces are of equal magnitude, the vector resultant, or the net force acting on the crate is zero. The forces acting on the crate are said to be balanced. **(c)** If the forces are unequal in magnitude, the resultant is not zero. A nonzero net force (F_{net}), or unbalanced force, then acts on the crate, producing an acceleration (for example, setting the crate in motion if it was initially at rest).

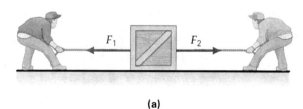

(b) Zero net force (balanced forces)

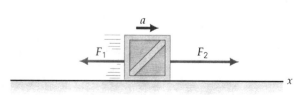

(c) Nonzero net force (unbalanced forces)

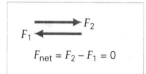

Science Fundamentals

an object, that is, change its size and/or shape (as we shall see in Chapter 9). A deformation involves a change in motion for some part of an object; hence, there is an acceleration.

Forces are sometimes divided into two types or classes. The more familiar of these classes is *contact forces*. Such forces arise because of physical contact between objects. For example, when you push on a door to open it or throw or kick a ball, you exert a contact force on the door or ball.

The other class of forces is called *action-at-a-distance forces*. Examples of these forces include gravity, the electrical force between two charges, and the magnetic force between two magnets. The Moon is attracted to the Earth and maintained in orbit by a gravitational force, but there seems to be nothing physically transmitting that force. In Chapter 30, you will learn the modern view of how such action-at-a-distance forces are thought to be transmitted.

Now, with a better understanding of the concept of force, let's see how force and motion are related through Newton's laws.

4.2 Inertia and Newton's First Law of Motion

OBJECTIVES: To (a) state and explain Newton's first law of motion, and (b) describe inertia and its relationship to mass.

The groundwork for Newton's first law of motion was laid by Galileo. In his experimental investigations, Galileo dropped objects to observe motion under the influence of gravity. (See the related Insight in Chapter 2.) However, the relatively large acceleration due to gravity causes dropped objects to move quite fast and quite far in a short time. From the kinematic equations in Chapter 2, you can see that 3.0 s after being dropped, an object in free fall has a speed of about 29 m/s (64 mi/h) and has fallen a distance of 44 m (about 48 yd, or almost half the length of a football field). Thus, experimental measurements of free-fall distance versus time were particularly difficult to make with the instrumentation available in Galileo's time.

To slow things down so that he could study motion, Galileo used balls rolling on inclined planes. He allowed a ball to roll down one inclined plane and then up another with a different degree of incline (▼Fig. 4.3). Galileo noted that the ball rolled to approximately the same height in every case, but it rolled farther in the horizontal direction when the angle of incline was smaller. When allowed to roll onto a horizontal surface, the ball traveled a considerable distance and went even farther when the surface was made smoother. Galileo wondered how far the ball would travel if the horizontal surface could be made perfectly smooth (frictionless). Although this situation is impossible to attain experimentally, Galileo reasoned that in this ideal case with an infinitely long surface, the ball would continue to travel indefinitely with straight-line, uniform motion, since there would be nothing (no net force) to cause its motion to change.

According to Aristotle's theory of motion, which had been accepted for about 1500 years prior to Galileo's time, the normal state of a body was to be at rest (with the exception of celestial bodies, which were thought to be naturally in motion). Aristotle probably observed that objects moving on a surface tend to slow down and come to rest, so this conclusion would have seemed logical to him. However, from his experiments, Galileo concluded that bodies in motion exhibit the behavior of maintaining that motion and that if an object is initially at rest, it will remain so, unless something causes it to move.

PHYSLET®

Exploration 4.2 Change the Two Forces Applied

PHYSLET®

Exploration 4.3 Change the Force Applied to Get to the Goal

PHYSLET®

Illsutration 3.2 Motion on an Incline

◀ **FIGURE 4.3** Galileo's experiment A ball rolls farther along the upward incline as the angle of incline is decreased. On a smooth, horizontal surface, the ball rolls a greater distance before coming to rest. How far would the ball travel on an ideal, perfectly smooth surface? (The ball would slide in this case because of the absence of friction.)

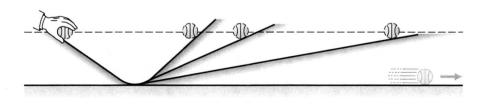

Galileo called this tendency of an object to maintain its initial state of motion **inertia.** That is,

> Inertia is the natural tendency of an object to maintain a state of rest or to remain in uniform motion in a straight line (constant velocity).

For example, if you've ever tried to stop a slowly rolling automobile by pushing on it, you felt its resistance to a change in motion, to slowing down. Physicists describe the property of inertia in terms of observed behavior. A comparative example of inertia is illustrated in ◄Fig. 4.4. If the two punching bags have the same density (mass per unit volume; see Chapter 1), the larger one has more mass and therefore more inertia, as you would quickly notice when you try to punch both bags.

Note: Inertia is *not* a force.

Newton related the concept of inertia to mass. Originally, he called mass a quantity of matter, but he later redefined it as follows:

> Mass is a quantitative measure of inertia.

That is, a massive object has more inertia, or more resistance to a change in motion, than does a less massive object. For example, a car has more inertia than a bicycle.

Newton's first law — the law of inertia

Newton's first law of motion, sometimes called the *law of inertia*, summarizes these observations:

> In the absence of an unbalanced applied force ($\vec{F}_{net} = 0$), a body at rest remains at rest, and a body already in motion remains in motion with a constant velocity (constant speed and direction).

That is, if the net force acting on an object is zero, then its acceleration is zero. It may be moving with a constant velocity, or be at rest—in both cases, $\Delta\vec{v} = 0$ or $\vec{v} =$ constant.

4.3 Newton's Second Law of Motion

OBJECTIVES: To (a) state and explain Newton's second law of motion, (b) apply it to physical situations, and (c) distinguish between weight and mass.

A change in motion, or an acceleration (that is, a change in velocity—speed and/or direction), is evidence of a net force. All experiments indicate that the acceleration of an object is directly proportional to, and in the direction of, the applied net force; that is,

$$\vec{a} \propto \vec{F}_{net}$$

where the boldface symbols with arrows indicate vector quantities. For example, suppose you hit two identical balls. If you hit the second ball twice as hard as the first one (that is, you applied twice as much force), you would expect the acceleration of the second ball to be twice as great as that of the first ball (and still in the direction of the force).

However, as Newton recognized, the inertia or mass of the object also plays a role. For a given net force, the more massive the object, the less its acceleration will be. For example, if you hit two balls of different masses with the same force, the less massive ball would experience a greater acceleration. That is, the acceleration is inversely proportional to mass.

Then we have

$$\vec{a} \propto \frac{\vec{F}_{net}}{m}$$

or, in words,

> The acceleration of an object is directly proportional to the net force acting on it and inversely proportional to its mass. The direction of the acceleration is in the direction of the applied net force.

▲ FIGURE 4.4 A difference in inertia The larger punching bag has more mass and hence more inertia, or resistance to a change in motion.

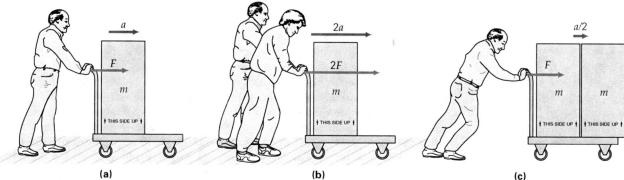

(a)
A nonzero net force accelerates the crate: $a \propto F/m$

(b)
If the net force is doubled, the acceleration is doubled.

(c)
If the mass is doubled, the acceleration is halved.

▲ **FIGURE 4.5 Newton's second law** The relationships among force, acceleration, and mass shown here are expressed by Newton's second law of motion (assuming no friction).

▲ Figure 4.5 presents some illustrations of this principle.

Rewritten as $\vec{F}_{net} \propto m\vec{a}$, **Newton's second law of motion** is commonly expressed in equation form as

$$\vec{F}_{net} = m\vec{a} \quad \text{Newton's second law} \tag{4.1}$$

SI unit of force: newton (N) or kilogram-meter
per second squared ($kg \cdot m/s^2$)

where $\vec{F}_{net} = \Sigma \vec{F}_i$. Equation 4.1 defines the SI unit of force, which is appropriately called the **newton (N)**.

By unit analysis, Eq. 4.1 shows that a newton in base units is defined as $1\,N = 1\,kg \cdot m/s^2$. That is, a net force of 1 N gives a mass of 1 kg an acceleration of $1\,m/s^2$ (▶Fig. 4.6). The British-system unit of force is the pound (lb). One pound is equivalent to about 4.5 N (actually, 4.448 N). An average apple weighs about 1 N.

Newton's second law, $\vec{F}_{net} = m\vec{a}$, allows the quantitative analysis of force and motion. We might think of it as a cause-and-effect relationship, with the force being the cause and acceleration being the motional effect.

Notice that if the net force acting on an object is zero, the object's acceleration is zero, and it remains at rest or in uniform motion, which is consistent with the first law. For a nonzero net force (an unbalanced force), the resulting acceleration is in the same direction as the net force.*

Weight

Equation 4.1 can be used to relate mass and weight. Recall from Chapter 1 that weight is the gravitational force of attraction that a celestial body exerts on an object. For us, this force is the gravitational attraction of the Earth. Its effects are easily demonstrated: When you drop an object, it falls (accelerates) toward the Earth. Since only one force is acting on the object, its **weight** ($\vec{w}$) is the net force $\vec{F}_{net}$, and the acceleration due to gravity ($\vec{g}$) can be substituted for $\vec{a}$ in Eq. 4.1. We can therefore write, in terms of magnitude,

$$w = mg \tag{4.2}$$
$$(F_{net} = ma)$$

Thus the weight of an object with 1.0 kg of mass is $w = mg = (1.0\,kg)(9.8\,m/s^2) = 9.8\,N$.

That is, 1.0 kg of mass has a weight of approximately 9.8 N, or 2.2 lb near the Earth's surface. Although weight and mass are simply related through Eq. 4.2, keep

*It may appear that Newton's first law is a special case of Newton's second law, but this is not so. The first law *defines* what is called an *inertial reference system* (as we shall see in Chapter 26): a system in which there is no net force, that is, not accelerating, or in which an isolated object is stationary or moves with a constant velocity. If Newton's first law holds, then the second law in the form $\vec{F}_{net} = m\vec{a}$ applies to the system.

PHYSLET®

Illustration 4.3 Newton's Second Law and Force

Newton's second law—force and acceleration

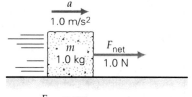

$F_{net} = ma$
$1.0\,N = (1.0\,kg)(1.0\,m/s^2)$

▲ **FIGURE 4.6 The newton (N)** A net force of 1.0 N acting on a mass of 1.0 kg produces an acceleration of 1.0 m/s² (on a frictionless surface).

PHYSLET®

Illustration 4.1 Newton's First Law and Reference Frames

in mind that *mass is the fundamental property*. Mass doesn't depend on the value of g, but weight does. As pointed out previously, the acceleration due to gravity on the Moon is about one sixth that on the Earth. The weight of an object on the Moon would thus be one sixth of its weight on the Earth, but its mass, which reflects the quantity of matter it contains and its inertia, would be the same in both places.

Newton's second law, along with the fact that $w \propto m$, explains why all objects in free fall have the same acceleration. Consider, for example, two falling objects, one with twice the mass of the other. The object with twice as much mass would have twice as much weight, or two times as much gravitational force acting on it. But the more massive object also has twice the inertia, so twice as much force is needed to give it the same acceleration. Expressing this relationship mathematically, for the smaller mass (m), we can write $a = F_{net}/m = mg/m = g$, and for the larger mass ($2m$), we have the same acceleration: $a = F_{net}/m = 2mg/(2m) = g$ (▸Fig. 4.7). Some other effects of g, which you may have experienced, are discussed in Insight 4.1.

INSIGHT 4.1 $g's$ OF FORCE AND EFFECTS ON THE HUMAN BODY

The value of g at the Earth's surface is referred to as the *standard acceleration* and is used as a nonstandard unit. For example, when a spacecraft lifts off, astronauts are said to experience an acceleration of "several g's." This expression means that the astronauts' acceleration is several times the standard acceleration g. Since $g = w/m$, we can also think of g as the (weight) *force per unit mass*. Thus, the term g**'s of force** is used to express force in terms of multiples of the standard acceleration.

To help understand this nonstandard unit of force, let's look at some examples. During the takeoff of a jet airliner, passengers experience an average horizontal force of about $0.20g$. This means that as the plane accelerates down the runway, the seat back exerts a horizontal force on you of about one fifth of your weight (to accelerate you along with the plane), but you experience a feeling of being pushed back into the seat. On takeoff at an angle of 30°, the force increases to about $0.70g$.

When a person is subjected to several g's vertically, blood can begin to pool in the lower extremities, which may cause blood vessels to distend or capillaries to rupture. Under such conditions, the heart has a difficult time pumping blood throughout the body. At a force of about $4g$, the pooling of blood in the lower body deprives the head of sufficient oxygen. Lack of blood circulation to the eyes can cause temporary blindness, and if the brain is deprived of oxygen, a person becomes disoriented and quickly "blacks out" or loses consciousness. The average person can withstand several g's of force for only a short period of time.

The maximum force on astronauts in a space shuttle on blastoff is about $3g$. But jet fighter pilots are subjected to as much as $9g$ when pulling out of a downward dive. These pilots wear "g-suits," which are designed to prevent blood pooling. The common g-suit is inflated by compressed air and applies pressure to the pilot's lower body to prevent blood from accumulating there. Work is being done on the development of a hydrostatic g-suit that contains liquid, which is less restrictive than air. When the number of g's increases, the liquid, like the blood in the body, flows into the lower part of the suit and applies pressure to the legs.

On the Earth, where only $1g$ is experienced, a partial "g-suit" of sorts is being used to prevent blood clots in patients who

have undergone hip replacement surgery. Each year 400 to 800 people die in the first three months after such surgery, primarily because blood clots form in a leg, break off into the bloodstream, and lodge in the lungs—giving rise to a condition called *pulmonary embolism*. In other cases, a blood clot in the leg may slow the flow of blood to the heart. These complications arise more often after hip replacement surgery than after almost any other surgery and occur after the patient has left the hospital.

Studies have shown that pneumatic (operated by air) compression of the legs during the hospital stay reduces these risks. A plastic leg cuff inflates every few minutes, forcing blood from the lower leg (Fig. 1). This mechanical massaging prevents blood from pooling in the veins and clotting. By using both this technique and anticlotting drug therapy, it is hoped that many of the postoperative deaths can be prevented.

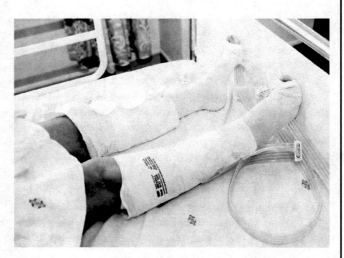

FIGURE 1 Pneumatic massage The leg cuffs inflate periodically, forcing the blood from the lower legs and preventing it from pooling in the veins.

Newton's second law allows us to analyze dynamic situations. In using this law, you should keep in mind that F_{net} is the *magnitude of the net force* and m is the *total mass of the system*. The boundaries defining a system may be real or imaginary. For example, a system might consist of all the gas molecules in a particular sealed vessel. But you might also define a system to be all the gas molecules in an arbitrary cubic meter of air. In studying dynamics, we often have occasion to work with systems made up of one or more discrete masses—the Earth and Moon, for instance, or a series of blocks on a tabletop, or a tractor and wagon, as in Example 4.1.

Note: The m in $F_{net} = ma$, is the total mass of the system.

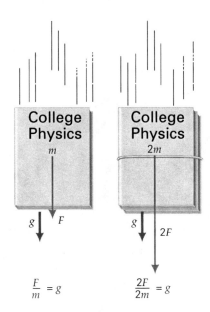

$$\frac{F}{m} = g \qquad\qquad \frac{2F}{2m} = g$$

▲ **FIGURE 4.7** Newton's second law and free fall In free fall, all objects fall with the same constant acceleration g. An object with twice the mass of another has twice as much gravitational force acting on it. But with twice the mass, the object also has twice as much inertia, so twice as much force is needed to give it the same acceleration.

Example 4.1 ■ Newton's Second Law: Finding Acceleration

A tractor pulls a loaded wagon on a level road with a constant horizontal force of 440 N (▼ Fig. 4.8). If the total mass of the wagon and its contents is 275 kg, what is the magnitude of the wagon's acceleration? (Ignore any frictional forces.)

Thinking It Through. This problem is a direct application of Newton's second law. Note that the total mass is given; we treat the two separate masses (wagon and contents) as one and look at the whole system.

Solution. Listing the data, we have

Given: $F = 440$ N   *Find:* a (acceleration)
               $m = 275$ kg

In this case, F is the net force, and the acceleration is given by Eq. 4.2, $F_{net} = ma$. Solving for the magnitude of a,

$$a = \frac{F_{net}}{m} = \frac{440 \text{ N}}{275 \text{ kg}} = 1.60 \text{ m/s}^2$$

and the direction of a is that in which the tractor is pulling.

Note that m is the *total* mass of the wagon and its contents. If the masses of the wagon and its contents had been given separately—say, $m_1 = 75$ kg and $m_2 = 200$ kg, respectively—they would have been added together in Newton's law: $F_{net} = (m_1 + m_2)a$. Also, in reality, there would be an opposing force of friction f. Suppose there were an effective frictional force of $f = 140$ N. In this case, the net force would be the vector sum of the force exerted by the tractor and the frictional force. Then the acceleration would be (using directional signs)

$$a = \frac{F_{net}}{m} = \frac{F - f}{m_1 + m_2} = \frac{440 \text{ N} - 140 \text{ N}}{275 \text{ kg}} = 1.09 \text{ m/s}^2$$

Again, the direction of a would be the direction in which the tractor is pulling.

With a constant net force, the acceleration is also constant, so the kinematic equations of Chapter 2 can be applied. Suppose the wagon started from rest ($v_o = 0$). Could you find how far it traveled in 4.00 s? Using the appropriate kinematic equation (Eq. 2.11, with $x_o = 0$) for the case with friction, we have

$$x = v_0 t + \tfrac{1}{2}at^2 = 0 + \tfrac{1}{2}(1.09 \text{ m/s}^2)(4.00 \text{ s})^2 = 8.72 \text{ m}$$

Follow-Up Exercise. Suppose the applied force on the wagon is 550 N. With the same frictional force, what would be the wagon's velocity 4.00 s after starting from rest? *(Answers to all Follow-Up Exercises are at the back of the text.)*

◀ **FIGURE 4.8** Force and acceleration See Example 4.1.

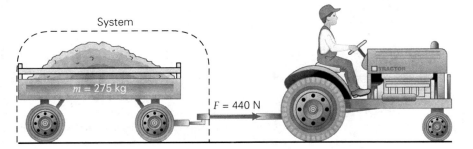

System

$m = 275$ kg

$F = 440$ N

Example 4.2 ■ Newton's Second Law: Finding Mass

A student weighs 588 N. What is her mass?

Thinking It Through. Newton's second law allows us to determine an object's mass if we know the object's weight (force), since g is known.

Solution.

Given: $w = 588$ N   *Find:* m (mass)

Recall that weight is a (gravitational) force and it is related to the mass of an object by $w = mg$ (Eq. 4.2), where g is the acceleration due to gravity (9.80 m/s^2). Rearranging the equation, we have

$$m = \frac{w}{g} = \frac{588 \text{ N}}{9.80 \text{ m/s}^2} = 60.0 \text{ kg}$$

In countries that use the metric system, the kilogram unit of mass is used to express "weight" rather than a force unit. It would be said that this student weighs 60.0 "kilos."

Recall that 1 kg of mass has a weight of 2.2 lb on the Earth's surface. Then in British units, she would weigh 60.0 kg (2.2 lb/kg) = 132 lb.

Follow-Up Exercise. (a) A person in Europe is a bit overweight and would like to lose 5.0 "kilos." What would be the equivalent loss in pounds? (b) What is your "weight" in kilos?

As we have seen, a dynamic system may consist of more than one object. In applications of Newton's second law, it is often advantageous, and sometimes necessary, to isolate a given object within a system. This isolation is possible because *the motion of any part of a system is also described by Newton's second law*, as Example 4.3 shows.

PHYSLET®

Illustration 4.5 Pull Your Wagons

Example 4.3 ■ Newton's Second Law: All or Part of the System?

Two blocks with masses $m_1 = 2.5$ kg and $m_2 = 3.5$ kg rest on a frictionless surface and are connected by a light string (▼ Fig. 4.9).* A horizontal force (F) of 12.0 N is applied to m_1, as shown in the figure. (a) What is the magnitude of the acceleration of the masses (that is, of the total system)? (b) What is the magnitude of the force (T) in the string? [When a rope or string is stretched taut, it is said to be under tension. For a very light string, the force at the right end of the string has the same magnitude (T) as the force at the left end.]

Thinking It Through. It is important to remember that Newton's second law may be applied to a total system or any part of it (a subsystem, so to speak). This capability allows for the analysis of a particular component of a system, if desired. Identification of all of

▼ **FIGURE 4.9 An accelerated system** See Example 4.3.

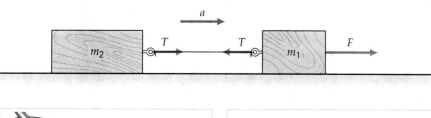

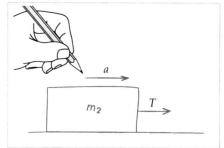 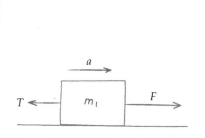

Isolating the masses

*When an object is described as being "light," its mass can be ignored in analyzing the situation given in the problem. That is, its mass is negligible relative to the other masses.

the acting forces is critical, as this Example shows. We then apply $F_{net} = ma$ to each subsystem or component.

Solution. Carefully listing the data and what is to be found:

Given: $m_1 = 2.5\,\text{kg}$ **Find:**   (a) a (acceleration)
                $m_2 = 3.5\,\text{kg}$ (b) T (tension, a force)
                $F = 12.0\,\text{N}$

Given an applied force, the acceleration of the masses can be found from Newton's second law. It is important to keep in mind that Newton's second law applies to the total system *or to any part of it*—that is, to the total mass $(m_1 + m_2)$, to m_1 individually, or to m_2 individually. However, *you must be sure to identify correctly the appropriate force or forces in each case.* The net force acting on the combined masses, for example, is not the same as the magnitude of the net force acting on m_2 considered separately, as will be seen.

(a) First, taking the system as a whole (that is, considering both m_1 and m_2), the net force acting on this system is F. Note that in considering the total system, we are concerned only about the net external force acting on it. The *internal* equal and opposite T forces are not a consideration in this case, since they cancel. Representing the total mass as M, in Newton's second law equation:

$$a = \frac{F_{net}}{M} = \frac{F}{m_1 + m_2} = \frac{12.0\,\text{N}}{2.5\,\text{kg} + 3.5\,\text{kg}} = 2.0\,\text{m/s}^2$$

The acceleration is in the direction of the applied force, as indicated in the figure.

(b) Under tension, a force is exerted on an object by strings (or ropes or wires) and is directed along the string. Note in the figure that we are assuming the tension to be transmitted *undiminished* through the string. That is, the tension is the same everywhere in the string. Thus, the magnitude of T acting on m_2 is the same as that acting on m_1. This is actually true only if the string has zero mass. Only such idealized *light* (that is, of negligible mass) strings or ropes will be considered in this book.

So there is a force of magnitude T on each of the masses, because of tension in the connecting string. To find the value of T, we must consider a *part* of the system that is affected by this force.

Each block may be considered as a separate system to which Newton's second law applies. In these subsystems, the tension comes into play explicitly. Looking at the sketch of the isolated m_2 in Fig. 4.9, we see that the only force acting to accelerate this mass is T. From the values of m_2 and a, the magnitude of this force is given directly by

$$F_{net} = T = m_2 a = (3.5\,\text{kg})(2.0\,\text{m/s}^2) = 7.0\,\text{N}$$

An isolated sketch of m_1 is also shown in Fig. 4.9, and Newton's second law can equally well be applied to this block to find T. The forces must be added vectorially to get the net force on m_1 that produces its acceleration. Recalling that vectors in one dimension can be written with directional signs and magnitudes, we have

$$F_{net} = F - T = m_1 a \quad (\text{direction of } F \text{ taken to be positive})$$

Then, solving for T,

$$T = F - m_1 a$$
$$= 12.0\,\text{N} - (2.5\,\text{kg})(2.0\,\text{m/s}^2) = 12.0\,\text{N} - 5.0\,\text{N} = 7.0\,\text{N}$$

Follow-Up Exercise. Suppose that an additional horizontal force to the left of 3.0 N is applied to m_2 in Fig. 4.9. What would be the tension in the connecting string in this case?

The Second Law in Component Form

Not only does Newton's second law hold for any part of a system, but it also applies to each component of the acceleration. For example, a force may be expressed in component notation in two dimensions as follows:

$$\sum \vec{F}_i = m\vec{a}$$

and

$$\sum (F_x \hat{\mathbf{x}} + F_y \hat{\mathbf{y}}) = m(a_x \hat{\mathbf{x}} + a_y \hat{\mathbf{y}}) = ma_x \hat{\mathbf{x}} + ma_y \hat{\mathbf{y}} \qquad (4.3a)$$

Hence, to satisfy both x and y directions independently, we have

$$\Sigma F_x = ma_x \quad \text{and} \quad \Sigma F_y = ma_y \qquad (4.3b)$$

and Newton's second law applies separately to each component of motion. Note that *both* equations must be true. (Also, $\Sigma F_z = ma_z$ in three dimensions.) Example 4.4 demonstrates how the second law is applied using components.

Example 4.4 ■ Newton's Second Law: Components of Force

A block of mass 0.50 kg travels with a speed of 2.0 m/s in the positive x-direction on a flat, frictionless surface. On passing through the origin, the block experiences a constant force of 3.0 N at an angle of 60° relative to the x-axis for 1.5 s (◄Fig. 4.10). What is the velocity of the block at the end of this time?

Thinking It Through. With the force at an angle to the initial motion, it would appear that the solution is complicated. But note in the insert in Fig. 4.10 that the force can be resolved into components. The motion can then be analyzed in each component direction.

Solution. First, listing the given data and what is to be found:

Given: $m = 0.50$ kg   *Find:* $\vec{v}$ (velocity at the end of 1.5 s)
$\quad v_{x_0} = 2.0$ m/s
$\quad v_{y_0} = 0$
$\quad F = 3.0$ N, $\theta = 60°$
$\quad t = 1.5$ s

Let's find the magnitudes of the force components:

$$F_x = F \cos 60° = (3.0 \text{ N})(0.500) = 1.5 \text{ N}$$
$$F_y = F \sin 60° = (3.0 \text{ N})(0.866) = 2.6 \text{ N}$$

Then, applying Newton's second law to each direction to find the components of acceleration, we get

$$a_x = \frac{F_x}{m} = \frac{1.5 \text{ N}}{0.50 \text{ kg}} = 3.0 \text{ m/s}^2$$

$$a_y = \frac{F_y}{m} = \frac{2.6 \text{ N}}{0.50 \text{ kg}} = 5.2 \text{ m/s}^2$$

Next, from the kinematic equation relating velocity and acceleration (Eq. 2.8), the velocity components of the block are given by

$$v_x = v_{x_0} + a_x t = 2.0 \text{ m/s} + (3.0 \text{ m/s}^2)(1.5 \text{ s}) = 6.5 \text{ m/s}$$
$$v_y = v_{y_0} + a_y t = 0 + (5.2 \text{ m/s}^2)(1.5 \text{ s}) = 7.8 \text{ m/s}$$

Then, at the end of the 1.5 s, the velocity of the block is

$$\vec{v} = v_x \hat{x} + v_y \hat{y} = (6.5 \text{ m/s})\hat{x} + (7.8 \text{ m/s})\hat{y}$$

Follow-Up Exercise. (a) What is the direction of the velocity at the end of the 1.5 s? (b) If the force were applied at an angle of 30° (rather than 60°) relative to the x-axis, how would the results of this Example be different?

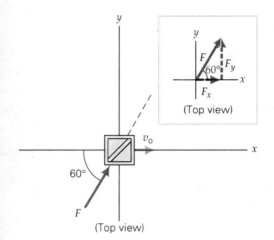

▲ **FIGURE 4.10 Off the straight and narrow** A force is applied to a moving block when it reaches the origin, and the block then begins to deviate from its straight-line path. See Example 4.4.

PHYSLET®

Exploration 4.4 Set the Force on a Hockey Puck

PHYSLET®

Exploration 4.5 Space Probe with Multiple Engines

PHYSLET®

Exploration 4.6 Pulled Golf Ball Breaks Toward the Hole

4.6 Friction

OBJECTIVES: To explain (a) the causes of friction, and (b) how friction is described by using coefficients of friction.

Friction refers to the ever-present resistance to motion that occurs whenever two materials, or media, are in contact with each other. This resistance occurs for all types of media—solids, liquids, and gases—and is characterized as the **force of friction (f)**. For simplicity, up to now we have generally ignored all kinds of friction (including air resistance) in examples and problems. Now that you know how to describe motion, you are ready to consider situations that are more realistic, in that the effects of friction are included.

In some real situations, we want to increase friction—for example, by putting sand on an icy road or sidewalk to improve traction. This might seem contradictory, since an increase in friction presumably would increase the resistance to motion. We commonly say that friction opposes motion, and think that the force of friction is in the opposite direction of motion. However, consider the forces involved in walking, as illustrated in ▸Fig. 4.17. The force of friction does resist motion (that of the foot), but is in the direction of the (walking) motion. Without friction, the foot would slip backward. (Think about walking on a slippery surface.) As another example, consider a worker standing in the center of the bed of a flatbed truck that is accelerating in the forward direction. If there were no friction between the worker's shoes and the truck bed, he would slide backwards. Obviously, there is friction between the shoes and the bed, which keeps him from sliding backward, and it is in the forward direction.

So there are situations where friction is desired (◂Fig. 4.18a), and situations where reduced friction is needed (Fig. 4.18b). Another situation where we try to reduce friction, we lubricate moving machine parts to allow them to move more freely, thereby lessening wear and reducing the expenditure of energy. Automobiles would not run without friction-reducing oils and greases.

This section is concerned chiefly with friction between solid surfaces. All surfaces are microscopically rough, no matter how smooth they appear or feel. It was originally thought that friction was due primarily to the mechanical interlocking of surface irregularities, or *asperities* (high spots). However, research has shown that friction between the contacting surfaces of ordinary solids (metals in particular) is due mostly to local adhesion. When surfaces are pressed together, local welding or bonding occurs in a few small patches where the largest asperities make contact. To overcome this local adhesion, a force great enough to pull apart the bonded regions must be applied.

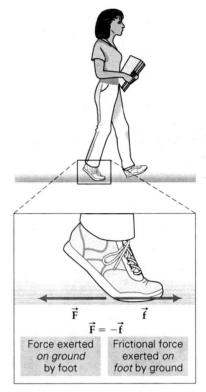

▲ **FIGURE 4.17 Friction and walking** The force of friction, $\vec{f}$, is shown in the direction of the walking motion. The force of friction prevents the foot from slipping backward while the other foot is brought forward. If you walk on a deep-pile rug, $\vec{F}$ is evident in that the pile will be bent backward.

(a)

(b)

▲ **FIGURE 4.18 Increasing and decreasing friction (a)** To get a fast start, drag racers need to make sure that their wheels don't slip when the starting light goes on. Just before the start of the race, they floor the accelerator to maximize the friction between their tires and the track by "burning in" the tires. This "burn in" is done by spinning the wheels with the brakes on until the tires are extremely hot. The rubber becomes so sticky that it almost welds itself to the surface of the road. **(b)** Water serves as a good lubricant to reduce friction in rides such as this one.

Friction between solids is generally classified into three types: static, sliding (kinetic), and rolling. **Static friction** includes all cases in which the frictional force is sufficient to prevent relative motion between surfaces. Suppose you want to move a large desk. You push it, but the desk doesn't move. The force of static friction between the desk's legs and the floor opposes and equals the horizontal force you are applying, so there is no motion—a static condition.

Sliding friction, or **kinetic friction**, occurs when there is relative (sliding) motion at the interface of the surfaces in contact. When pushing the desk, you can eventually get it sliding, but there is still a great deal of resistance between the desk's legs and the floor—kinetic friction.

Rolling friction occurs when one surface rotates as it moves over another surface, but does not slip or slide at the point or area of contact. Rolling friction, such as occurs between a train wheel and a rail, is attributed to small local deformations in the contact region. This type of friction is difficult to analyze and will not be discussed.

Frictional Forces and Coefficients of Friction

In this subsection, we will consider the forces of friction on stationary and sliding objects. These forces are called the *force of static friction* and the *force of kinetic* (or *sliding*) *friction*, respectively. Experimentally, it has been found that the force of friction depends on both the nature of the two surfaces and the *load*, or the normal force that presses the surfaces together. Thus we can write $f \propto N$. For an object on a horizontal surface, this force is equal in magnitude to the object's weight. (Why?) However, as was shown in the LBD figure on p. 116, on an inclined plane, only a component of the weight force contributes to the load.

The force of static friction (f_s) between surfaces in contact acts in the direction that opposes the initiation of relative motion between the surfaces. The magnitude takes on a range of values given by

$$f_s \leq \mu_s N \quad \text{(static conditions)} \tag{4.6}$$

where μ_s is a constant of proportionality called the **coefficient of static friction**. ("μ" is the Greek letter mu. Note that it is dimensionless. How do you know this from the equation?)

The less-than-or-equal-to sign ($\leq$) indicates that the force of static friction may have different values from zero up to some maximum value. To understand this concept, look at ▸Fig. 4.19. In Fig. 4.19a, one person pushes on a file cabinet, but it doesn't move. With no acceleration, the net force on the cabinet is zero, and $F - f_s = 0$, or $F = f_s$. Suppose that a second person also pushes, and the file cabinet still doesn't budge. Then f_s must now be larger, since the applied force has been increased. Finally, if the applied force is made large enough to overcome the static friction, motion occurs (Fig. 4.19c). The greatest, or maximum, force of static friction is exerted just before the cabinet starts to slide (Fig. 4.19b), and for this case, Eq. 4.6 gives the maximum value of static friction:

$$f_{s_{max}} = \mu_s N \tag{4.7}$$

Once an object is sliding, the force of friction changes to kinetic friction (f_k). This force acts in the direction opposite to the direction of the object's motion and has a magnitude of

$$f_k = \mu_k N \quad \text{(sliding conditions)} \tag{4.8}$$

where μ_k is the **coefficient of kinetic friction** (sometimes called the *coefficient of sliding friction*). Note that Eqs. 4.7 and 4.8 are *not* vector equations, since f and N are in different directions. Generally, the coefficient of kinetic friction is less than

▼ **FIGURE 4.19** **Force of friction versus applied force** (a) In the static region of the graph, as the applied force F increases, so does f_s; that is, $f_s = F$ and $f_s < \mu_s N$. (b) When the applied force F exceeds $f_{s_{max}} = \mu_s N$, the heavy file cabinet is set into motion. (c) Once the cabinet is moving, the frictional force decreases, since kinetic friction is less than static friction ($f_k < f_{s_{max}}$). Thus, if the applied force is maintained, there is a net force, and the cabinet is accelerated. For the cabinet to move with constant velocity, the applied force must be reduced to equal the kinetic friction force: $f_k = \mu_k N$.

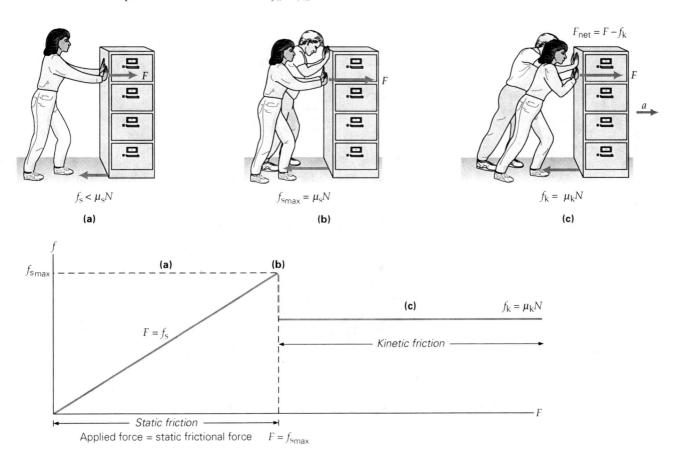

TABLE 4.1 Approximate Values for Coefficients of Static and Kinetic Friction between Certain Surfaces		
Friction between Materials	μ_s	μ_k
Aluminum on aluminum	1.90	1.40
Glass on glass	0.94	0.35
Rubber on concrete		
dry	1.20	0.85
wet	0.80	0.60
Steel on aluminum	0.61	0.47
Steel on steel		
dry	0.75	0.48
lubricated	0.12	0.07
Teflon on steel	0.04	0.04
Teflon on Teflon	0.04	0.04
Waxed wood on snow	0.05	0.03
Wood on wood	0.58	0.40
Lubricated ball bearings	<0.01	<0.01
Synovial joints (at the ends of most long bones—for example, elbows and hips)	0.01	0.01

Illustration 5.1 Static and Kinetic Friction

the coefficient of static friction ($\mu_k < \mu_s$), which means that the force of kinetic friction is less than $f_{s_{max}}$. The coefficients of friction between some common materials are listed in Table 4.1.

Note that the force of static friction (f_s) exists in response to an applied force. The magnitude of f_s and its direction depend on the magnitude and direction of the applied force. Up to its maximum value, the force of static friction is equal in magnitude and opposite in direction to the applied force (F), since there is no acceleration ($F - f_s = ma = 0$). Thus, if the person in Fig. 4.19a were to push on the cabinet in the opposite direction, f_s would also change direction to oppose the new push. If there were no applied force F, then f_s would be zero. When the magnitude of F exceeds that of $f_{s_{max}}$, the cabinet begins moving (accelerates), and kinetic friction comes into effect, with $f_k = \mu_k N$. If the magnitude of F is reduced to that of f_k, the cabinet will slide with a constant velocity; if the magnitude of F is maintained greater than that of f_k, the cabinet will continue to accelerate.

It has been experimentally determined that the coefficients of friction (and therefore the forces of friction) are nearly independent of the contact area between metal surfaces. This means that the force of friction between a brick-shaped metal block and a metal surface is the same regardless of whether the block is lying on a larger side or a smaller side.

Finally, keep in mind that although the equation $f = \mu N$ holds in general for frictional forces, it may not remain linear. That is, μ is not always constant. For example, the coefficient of kinetic friction varies somewhat with the relative speed of the surfaces. However, for speeds up to several meters per second, the coefficients are relatively constant. For simplicity, our discussion will neglect any variations due to speed (or area), and the forces of static and kinetic friction will be assumed to depend only on the load (N) and the nature of the two surfaces as expressed by the given coefficients of friction.

Science Fundamentals

Example 4.10 ■ Pulling a Crate: Static and Kinetic Forces of Friction

(a) In ▼ Fig. 4.20, if the coefficient of static friction between the 40.0-kg crate and the floor is 0.650. What is the magnitude of the minimum horizontal force the worker must pull to get the crate moving? (b) If the worker maintains that force once the crate starts to move and the coefficient of kinetic friction between the surfaces is 0.500, what is the magnitude of the acceleration of the crate?

Thinking It Through. This scenario involves applications of the forces of friction. In (a), the maximum force of static friction must be calculated. In (b), if the worker maintains an applied force of this magnitude after the crate is in motion, there will be an acceleration, since $f_k < f_{s_{max}}$.

Solution. Listing the given data and what is to be found,

Given: $m = 40.0 \text{ kg}$ *Find:* (a) F (minimum force necessary to move crate)
$\quad\quad \mu_s = 0.650$ (b) a (acceleration)
$\quad\quad \mu_k = 0.500$

(a) The crate will not move until the magnitude of the applied force F slightly exceeds that of the maximum static frictional force $f_{s_{max}}$. So $f_{s_{max}}$ must be found to see what force the worker needs to apply. The weight of the crate and the normal force are equal in magnitude in this case (see the free-body diagram in Fig. 4.20), so the magnitude of the maximum force of static friction is

$$f_{s_{max}} = \mu_s N = \mu_s (mg)$$
$$= (0.650)(40.0 \text{ kg})(9.80 \text{ m/s}^2) = 255 \text{ N}$$

So the crate will begin to move when the applied force F exceeds 255 N.

(b) Now the crate is in motion, and the worker maintains a constant applied force of $F = f_{s_{max}} = 255 \text{ N}$. The force of kinetic friction f_k acts on the crate. However, this force is smaller than the applied force F, because $\mu_k < \mu_s$. Hence, there is a net force on the crate, and the acceleration of the crate may be found by using Newton's second law in the x-direction:

$$\Sigma F_x = +F - f_k = F - \mu_k N = ma_x$$

Solving for a_x, we obtain

$$a_x = \frac{F - \mu_k N}{m} = \frac{F - \mu_k (mg)}{m}$$

$$= \frac{255 \text{ N} - (0.500)(40.0 \text{ kg})(9.80 \text{ m/s}^2)}{40.0 \text{ kg}} = 1.48 \text{ m/s}^2$$

Follow-Up Exercise. On the average, by what factor does μ_s exceed μ_k for nonlubricated, metal-on-metal surfaces? (See Table 4.1.)

▼ **FIGURE 4.20** Forces of static and kinetic friction See Example 4.10.

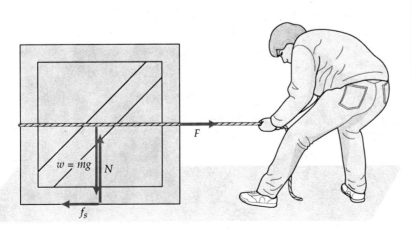

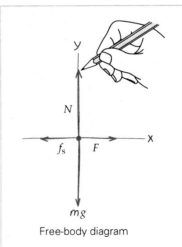

Free-body diagram

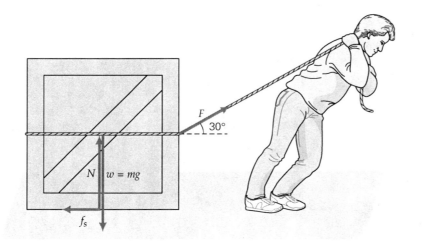

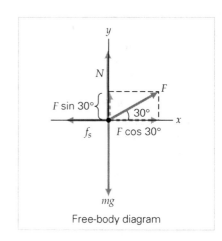

Free-body diagram

▲ **FIGURE 4.21** Pulling at an angle: a closer look at the normal force See Example 4.11.

Let's look at another worker with the same crate, but this time assume that the worker applies the force at an angle (▲Fig. 4.21).

Example 4.11 ■ Pulling at an Angle: A Closer Look at the Normal Force

A worker pulling a crate applies a force at an angle of 30° to the horizontal, as shown in Fig. 4.21. What is the magnitude of the minimum force he must apply to move the crate? (Before looking at the solution, would you expect that the force needed in this case would be greater or less than that in Example 4.10?)

Thinking It Through. Since the applied force is at an angle to the horizontal surface, the vertical component will affect the normal force. (See Fig. 4.11.) This change in the normal force will, in turn, affect the maximum force of static friction.

Solution. The data are the same as in Example 4.10, except that the force is applied at an angle.

Given: $\theta = 30°$ *Find:* F (minimum force necessary to move the crate)

In this case, the crate will begin to move when the *horizontal component* of the applied force, $F \cos 30°$, slightly exceeds the maximum static friction force. So we may write the following for the maximum friction:

$$F \cos 30° = f_{s_{max}} = \mu_s N$$

However, the magnitude of the normal force is not equal to the weight of the crate here, because of the upward component of the applied force. (See the free-body diagram in Fig. 4.21.) Then by Newton's second law, since $a_y = 0$, we have

$$\Sigma F_y = +N + F \sin 30° - mg = 0$$

or

$$N = mg - F \sin 30°$$

In effect, the applied force partially supports the weight of the crate. Substituting this expression for N into the first equation gives

$$F \cos 30° = \mu_s (mg - F \sin 30°)$$

Solving for F gives

$$F = \frac{mg}{(\cos 30°/\mu_s) + \sin 30°}$$

$$= \frac{(40.0 \text{ kg})(9.80 \text{ m/s}^2)}{(0.866/0.650) + 0.500} = 214 \text{ N}$$

Thus, less applied force is needed in this case, reflecting the fact that the frictional force is less, because of the reduced normal force.

Follow-Up Exercise. Note that in this Example, applying the force at an angle produces two effects. As the angle between the applied force and the horizontal increases, the horizontal component of the applied force is reduced. However, the normal force also gets smaller, resulting in a lower $f_{s_{max}}$. Does one effect always outweigh the other? That is, does the applied force F necessary to move the crate always decrease with increasing angle? (*Hint*: Investigate F for different angles. For example, compute F for 20° and 50°. You already have a value for 30°. What do the results tell you?)

Example 4.12 ■ No Slip, No Slide: Static Friction

A crate sits in the middle of the bed on a flatbed truck that is traveling at 80 km/h on a straight, level road. The coefficient of static friction between the crate and the truck bed is 0.40. When the truck comes uniformly to a stop, the crate does not slide, but remains stationary on the truck. What is the minimum stopping distance for the truck so the crate does not slide on the truck bed?

Thinking It Through. There are three forces on the crate, as shown in the free-body diagram in ▶Fig. 4.22 (assuming that the truck is initially traveling in the $+x$-direction). But wait. There is a net force in the $-x$-direction, and hence there should be an acceleration in that direction ($a_x < 0$). What does this mean? It means that relative to the ground, the crate is decelerating at the same rate as the truck, which is necessary for the crate not to slide—the crate and the truck slow down uniformly together.

The force creating this acceleration for the crate is the static force of friction. The acceleration is found using Newton's second law, and then used in one of the kinematic equations to find the distance.

Solution.

Given: $v_{x_0} = 80$ km/h $= 22$ m/s   *Find:* minimum stopping distance
      $\mu_s = 0.40$

Applying Newton's second law to the crate using the maximum f_s to find the minimum stopping distance,

$$\Sigma F_x = -f_{s_{max}} = -\mu_s N = -\mu_s mg = ma_x$$

Solving for a_x,

$$a_x = -\mu_s g = -(0.40)(9.8 \text{ m/s}^2) = -3.9 \text{ m/s}^2$$

which is the maximum deceleration of the truck so the crate does not slide.

Hence, the minimum stopping distance (x) for the truck is based on this acceleration and given by Eq. 2.12, where $v_x = 0$ and x_0 is taken to be zero. So,

$$v_x^2 = 0 = v_{x_0}^2 + 2(a_x)x$$

Solving for x, we obtain

$$x = \frac{v_{x_0}^2}{-2a_x} = \frac{(22 \text{ m/s})^2}{-2(-3.9 \text{ m/s}^2)} = 62 \text{ m}$$

Is the answer reasonable? This distance is about two thirds of a football field.

Follow-Up Exercise. Draw a free-body diagram and describe what happens in terms of accelerations and coefficients of friction if the crate starts to slide forward on the truck bed when the truck is braking to a stop (in other words, if a_x exceeds -3.9 m/s^2).

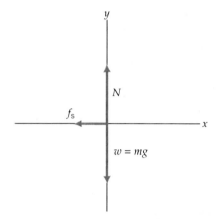

▲ **FIGURE 4.22** Free-body diagram
See Example 4.12.

Air Resistance

Air resistance refers to the resistance force acting on an object as it moves through air. In other words, air resistance is a type of frictional force. In analyses of falling objects, you can usually ignore the effect of air resistance and still get good approximations for falling relatively short distances. However, for longer distances, air resistance cannot be ignored.

▲ **FIGURE 4.23 Airfoil** The airfoil at the top of the truck's cab makes the truck more streamlined and therefore reduces air resistance.

Air resistance occurs when a moving object collides with air molecules. Therefore, air resistance depends on the object's shape and size (which determine the area of the object that is exposed to collisions) as well as its speed. The larger the object and the faster it moves, the more collisions there will be with air molecules. (Air density is also a factor, but this quantity can be assumed to be constant near the Earth's surface.) To reduce air resistance (and fuel consumption), automobiles are made more "streamlined," and airfoils are used on trucks and campers (◄Fig. 4.23).

Consider a falling object. Since air resistance depends on speed, as a falling object accelerates under the influence of gravity, the retarding force of air resistance increases (▼Fig. 4.24a). Air resistance for human-sized objects is proportional to the square of the speed, v^2, so the resistance builds up rather rapidly. Thus when the speed doubles, the air resistance increases by a factor of 4. Eventually, the magnitude of the retarding force equals that of the object's weight force (Fig. 4.24b), so the net force on it is zero. The object then falls with a maximum constant velocity, which is called the **terminal velocity**, with magnitude v_t.

This can be easily seen from Newton's second law. For the falling object, we have

$$F_{net} = ma$$

or

$$mg - f = ma$$

where downward has been taken as positive for convenience. Solving for a, we obtain

$$a = g - \frac{f}{m}$$

where a is the magnitude of the instantaneous downward acceleration.

Notice that the acceleration for a falling object when air resistance is included is less than g; that is, $a < g$. As the object continues to fall, its speed increases, and the force of air resistance, f, increases (since it is speed dependent) until $a = 0$, when $f = mg$ and $f - mg = 0$. The object then falls at its constant terminal velocity.

For a skydiver with an unopened parachute, terminal velocity is about 200 km/h (about 125 mi/h). To reduce the terminal velocity so that it can be reached sooner and the time of fall extended, a skydiver will try to increase exposed body area to a maximum by assuming a spread-eagle position (▶Fig. 4.25). This position takes advantage of the dependence of air resistance on the size and shape of the falling object. Once the parachute is open (giving a larger exposed area and a shape that catches the air), the additional air resistance slows the diver down to about 40 km/h (25 mi/h), which is preferable for landing.

Illustration 5.5 Air Friction

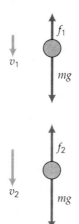

▼ **FIGURE 4.24 Air resistance and terminal velocity** (a) As the speed of a falling object increases, so does the frictional force of air resistance. (b) When this force of friction equals the weight of the object, the net force is zero, and the object falls with a constant (terminal) velocity. (c) A plot of speed versus time, showing these relationships.

(a) As v increases, so does f

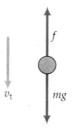

(b) When $f = mg$, the object falls with a constant (terminal) velocity.

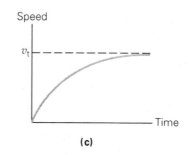

(c)

◄ **FIGURE 4.25** Terminal velocity Skydivers assume a spread-eagle position to maximize air resistance. This causes them to reach terminal velocity more quickly and prolongs the time of fall. Shown here is a formation of sky divers viewed from below.

Conceptual Example 4.13 ■ Race You Down: Air Resistance and Terminal Velocity

From a high altitude, a balloonist simultaneously drops two balls of identical size, but appreciably different in weight. Assuming that both balls reach terminal velocity during the fall, which of the following is true: (a) The heavier ball reaches terminal velocity first; (b) the balls reach terminal velocity at the same time; (c) the heavier ball hits the ground first; (d) the balls hit the ground at the same time? *Clearly establish the reasoning and physical principle(s) used in determining your answer before checking it next. That is, **why** did you select your answer?*

Reasoning and Answer. Terminal velocity is reached when the weight of a ball is balanced by the frictional air resistance. Both balls initially experience the same acceleration, g, and their speeds and the retarding forces of air resistance increase at the same rate. The weight of the lighter ball will be balanced first, so (a) and (b) are incorrect. The lighter ball reaches terminal velocity ($a = 0$) first, but the heavier ball continues to accelerate, speeding up, and pulls ahead of the lighter ball. Hence, the heavier ball hits the ground first, and the answer is (c), and (d) is incorrect.

Follow-Up Exercise. Suppose the heavier ball were much larger in size than the lighter ball. How might this difference affect the outcome?

You see an example of terminal velocity quite often. Why do clouds stay seemingly suspended in the sky? Certainly the water droplets or ice crystals (high clouds) should fall—and they do. However, they are so small that their terminal velocity is reached quickly, and the very slow rate of their descent goes unnoticed. Buoyancy in the air is also a factor (see Chapter 9). In addition, there may be some helpful updrafts that keep the water and ice from reaching the ground.

An extraterrestrial use of "air" resistance is called *aerobraking*. This spaceflight technique uses a planetary atmosphere to slow down an orbiting spacecraft. As the craft passes through the top layer of the planetary atmosphere, the atmospheric "drag" slows and lowers the craft's speed so as to put it in the desired orbit. Many passes may be needed, with the spacecraft passing in and out of the atmosphere to achieve the proper final orbit.

Aerobraking is a worthwhile technique because it eliminates the need for a heavy load of chemical propellants that would otherwise be needed to place the spacecraft in orbit. This allows a greater payload of scientific instruments for investigations. Aerobraking was used to adjust the spacecraft *Odyssey*'s orbit around Mars in 2001.

WORK AND ENERGY

PHYSICS FACTS

- *Kinetic* comes from the Greek *kinein*, meaning "to move."
- *Energy* comes from the Greek *energeia*, meaning "activity."
- The United States has 5% of the world's population, yet consumes 26% of its energy supply.
- Recycling aluminum takes 95% less energy than making aluminum from raw materials.
- The human body operates within the limits imposed by the law of conservation of total energy, needing dietary energy equal to the energy expended in the external work of daily activities, internal activities, and system heat losses.
- The basal metabolic rate (BMR) is a measurement of the rate at which the human body expends energy. An average 70-kg man requires about 7.5×10^6 J of basal energy per day for simply living or maintaining basic functions—for example, breathing, blood circulation, and digestion. Any type of exercise requires more energy—for example, an additional 4.6×10^6 J per hour to climb stairs.
- The human body uses muscles to propel itself, turning stored energy into motion. There are 630 active muscles in your body and they act in groups.

Source: Harold E. Edgerton/©Harold & Esther Edgerton Foundation, 2002, courtesy of Palm Press, Inc.

A description of pole vaulting, as shown in the photo, might be as follows: The athlete runs with a pole, plants it into the ground, and tries to vault his body over a bar set at a certain height. However, a physicist might give a different description: The athlete has chemical potential energy stored in his body. He uses this potential energy to do work in running down the path to gain speed, or kinetic energy. When he plants the pole, most of his kinetic energy goes into elastic potential energy of the bent pole. This potential energy is used to lift the vaulter or to do work against gravity, and is partially converted into gravitational potential energy. At the top, there is just enough kinetic energy left to carry the vaulter over the bar. On the way down, the gravitational potential energy is converted back to kinetic energy, which is absorbed by the mat in doing work to stop the fall. The pole vaulter participates in a game of work–energy, a game of give and take.

This chapter centers on these two concepts that are important in both science and everyday life—*work* and *energy*. We commonly think of work as being associated with doing or accomplishing something. Because work makes us physically (and sometimes mentally) tired, machines have been invented to decrease the amount of effort we expend personally. Thinking about energy tends to bring to mind the cost of fuel for transportation and heating, or perhaps the food that supplies the energy our bodies need to carry out life processes and to do work.

Although these notions do not really define work and energy, they point us in the right direction. As you might have guessed, work and energy are closely related. In physics, as in everyday life, when something possesses energy, it has the ability to do work. For example, water rushing through the sluices of a dam has energy of motion, and this energy allows the water to do the work of driving a turbine or dynamo to generate electricity. Conversely, no work can be performed without energy.

Energy exists in various forms: mechanical energy, chemical energy, electrical energy, heat energy, nuclear energy, and so on. A transformation from one form to another may take place, but the total amount of energy is *conserved*, meaning it always remains the same. This point makes the concept of energy very useful. When a physically measurable quantity is conserved, it not only gives us an insight that leads to a better understanding of nature, but also usually provides another approach to practical problems. (You will be introduced to other conserved quantities during the course of our study of physics.)

5.1 Work Done by a Constant Force

OBJECTIVES: To (a) define mechanical work, and (b) compute the work done in various situations.

The word *work* is commonly used in a variety of ways: We go to work; we work on projects; we work at our desks or on computers; we work problems. In physics, however, *work* has a very specific meaning. Mechanically, work involves force and displacement, and the word *work* is used to describe quantitatively what is accomplished when a force acts on an object as it moves through a distance. In the simplest case of a *constant* force acting on an object, work that the force does is defined as follows:

> The **work** done by a constant force acting on an object is equal to the product of the magnitudes of the displacement and the component of the force parallel to that displacement.

Work involves force and displacement

Work then involves a force acting on an object moving through a distance. A force may be applied, as in ▼Fig. 5.1a, but *if there is no motion (no displacement), then no work is done.* For a constant force F acting *in the same direction* as the displacement d (Fig. 5.1b), the work (W) done is defined as the product of their magnitudes:

$$W = Fd \qquad (5.1)$$

and work is a scalar. (As you might expect, when work is done as in Fig. 5.1b, energy is expended. We shall discuss the relationship between work and energy in Section 5.3.)

In general, work is done on an object only by a force, or force *component*, parallel to the line of motion or displacement of the object (Fig. 5.1c). That is, if the force acts at an angle θ to the object's displacement, then $F_\parallel = F \cos \theta$ is the

Note: The product of two vectors (force and displacement) in this case is a special type of vector multiplication and yields a scalar quantity equal to $(F \cos \theta)d$. Thus, work is a scalar—it does not have direction. It can, however, be positive, zero, or negative, depending on the angle.

▼ **FIGURE 5.1** **Work done by a constant force—the product of the magnitudes of the parallel component of force and the displacement** **(a)** If there is no displacement, no work is done: $W = 0$. **(b)** For a constant force in the same direction as the displacement, $W = Fd$. **(c)** For a constant force at an angle to the displacement, $W = (F \cos \theta)d$.

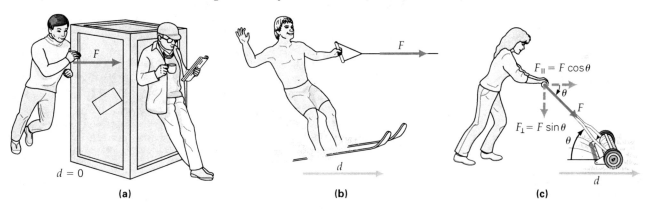

component of the force parallel to the displacement. Thus, a more general equation for work done by a constant force is

$$W = F_\parallel d = (F \cos \theta)d \quad \text{(work done by a constant force)} \quad (5.2)$$

The joule (J), pronounced "jool," was named in honor of James Prescott Joule (1818–1889), a British scientist who investigated work and energy.

Notice that θ is the angle *between* the force and the displacement vectors. To remind yourself of this factor, you can write $\cos \theta$ between the magnitudes of the force and displacement, $W = F(\cos \theta)d$. If $\theta = 0°$ (that is, force and displacement are in the same direction as in Fig. 5.1b), then $W = F(\cos 0°)d = Fd$, so Eq. 5.2 reduces to Eq. 5.1. The perpendicular component of the force, $F_\perp = F \sin \theta$, does no work, since there is no displacement in this direction.

The units of work can be determined from the equation $W = Fd$. With force in newtons and displacement in meters, work has the SI unit of newton-meter (N · m). This unit is called a **joule** (J):

$$Fd = W$$
$$1 \, N \cdot m = 1 \, J$$

For example, the work done by a force of 25 N on an object as the object moves through a parallel displacement of 2.0 m is $W = Fd = (25 \, N)(2.0 \, m) = 50 \, N \cdot m$, or 50 J.

From the previous displayed equation, we also see that in the British system, work would have the unit pound-foot. However, this name is commonly written in reverse: The British standard unit of work is the **foot-pound (ft · lb)**. One ft · lb is equal to 1.36 J.

We can analyze work graphically. Suppose a constant force F in the x direction acts on an object as it moves a distance x. Then $W = Fx$, and if F versus x is plotted, a straight-line graph is obtained such as shown in the accompanying Learn by Drawing. The area under the line is Fx, so this area is equal to the work done by the force over the given distance. We will consider a nonconstant, or variable, force later.*

Remember that *work is a scalar quantity* and, as such, may have a positive or negative value. In Fig. 5.1b, the work is positive, because the force acts in the same direction as the displacement (and $\cos 0°$ is positive). The work is also positive in Fig. 5.1c, because a force component acts in the direction of the displacement (and $\cos \theta$ is positive).

However, if the force, or a force component, acts in the opposite direction of the displacement, the work is negative, since the cosine term is negative. For example, for $\theta = 180°$ (force opposite to the displacement), $\cos 180° = -1$, so the work is negative: $W = F_\parallel d = F(\cos 180°)d = -Fd$. An example is a braking force that slows down or decelerates an object. See Learn by Drawing on p. 143.

LEARN BY DRAWING

Work: Area under the F-versus-x Curve

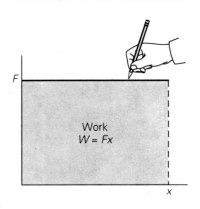

Work
$W = Fx$

Example 5.1 ■ Applied Psychology: Mechanical Work

A student holds her psychology textbook, which has a mass of 1.5 kg, out a second-story dormitory window until her arm is tired; then she releases it (◄Fig. 5.2). (a) How much work is done on the book by the student in simply holding it out the window? (b) How much work is done by the force of gravity during the time in which the book falls 3.0 m?

Thinking It Through. Analyze the situations in terms of the definition of work, keeping in mind that force and displacement are the key factors.

Solution. Listing the data, we have

Given: $v_o = 0$ (initially at rest)   *Find:* (a) W (work done by student in holding)
       $m = 1.5 \, kg$ (b) W (work done by gravity in falling)
       $d = 3.0 \, m$

(a) Even though the student gets tired (because work is performed within the body to maintain muscles in a state of tension), she does *no work on the book* in merely holding it stationary. She exerts an upward force on the book (equal in magnitude to its weight), but the displacement is zero in this case ($d = 0$). Thus, $W = Fd = F \times 0 = 0 \, J$.

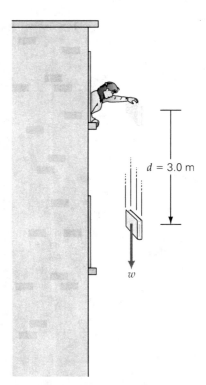

$d = 3.0 \, m$

w

▲ **FIGURE 5.2** Mechanical work requires motion See Example 5.1.

*Work is the area under the F-versus-x curve even if the curve is not a straight line. Finding the work in such cases generally requires advanced mathematics.

(b) While the book is falling, the only force acting on it is the force of gravity (neglecting air resistance), which is equal in magnitude to the weight of the book: $F = w = mg$. The displacement is in the same direction as the force ($\theta = 0°$) and has a magnitude of $d = 3.0$ m, so the work done by gravity is

$$W = F(\cos 0°)d = (mg)d = (1.5 \text{ kg})(9.8 \text{ m/s}^2)(3.0 \text{ m}) = +44 \text{ J}$$

(+ because the force and displacement are in the same direction.)

Follow-Up Exercise. A 0.20-kg ball is thrown upward. How much work is done on the ball by gravity as the ball rises between heights of 2.0 m and 3.0 m? (*Answers to all Follow-Up Exercises are at the back of the text.*)

Example 5.2 ■ Hard Work

A worker pulls a 40.0-kg crate with a rope, as illustrated in ▼Fig. 5.3. The coefficient of kinetic (sliding) friction between the crate and the floor is 0.550. If he moves the crate with a constant velocity a distance of 7.00 m, how much work is done?

Thinking It Through. A good first thing to do in problems such as this is to draw a free-body diagram. This is shown in the figure. To find the work, the force F must be known. As usual in such cases, this is done by summing the forces.

Solution.

Given: $m = 40.0$ kg   *Find:* W (the work done in moving the
      $\mu_k = 0.550$ crate 7.00 m)
      $d = 7.00$ m
      $\theta = 30°$ (from figure)

Then, summing the forces in the x and y directions:

$$\Sigma F_x = F \cos 30° - f_k = F \cos 30° - \mu_k N = ma_x = 0$$
$$\Sigma F_y = N + F \sin 30° - mg = ma_y = 0$$

To find F, the second equation may be solved for N, which is then substituted in the first equation.

$$N = mg - F \sin 30°$$

(Notice that N is not equal to the weight of the crate. Why?) And, substituting into the first equation,

$$F \cos 30° - \mu_k(mg - F \sin 30°) = 0 \qquad \textit{(continues on next page)}$$

(continues on next page)

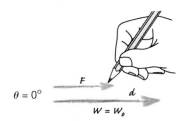

LEARN BY DRAWING

**Determining the Sign
of Work**

$\theta = 0°$ F d

$W = W_o$

$\theta < 90°$ F θ d

$W > 0$ but $< W_o$

$\theta = 90°$ F θ d

$W = 0$ (why?)

$\theta > 90°$ F θ d

$W < 0$

$\theta = 180°$ F d

$W = -W_o$

▼ **FIGURE 5.3** Doing some work. See Example 5.2.

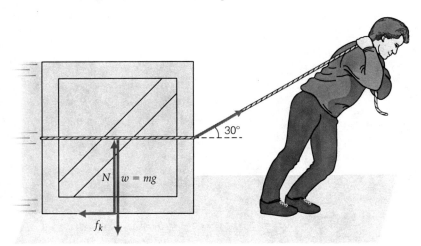

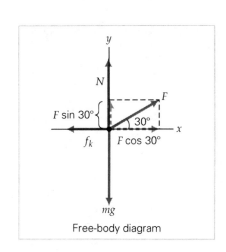

N $w = mg$

f_k

y

N

$F \sin 30°$

$30°$

x

f_k $F \cos 30°$

mg

Free-body diagram

Solving for F and putting in values:

$$F = \frac{\mu_k mg}{(\cos 30° + \mu_k \sin 30°)} = \frac{(0.550)(40.0 \text{ kg})(9.80 \text{ m/s}^2)}{(0.866) + (0.550)(0.500)]} = 189 \text{ N}$$

Then, $W = F(\cos 30°)d = (189 \text{ N})(0.866)(7.00 \text{ m}) = 1.15 \times 10^3 \text{ J}$

Follow-Up Exercise. It takes about 3.80×10^4 of work to lose 1.00 g of body fat. What distance would the worker have to pull the crate to lose 1 g of fat? (Assume all the work goes into fat reduction.) Make an estimate before solving and see how close you come.

We commonly specify which force is doing work *on* which object. For example, the force of gravity does work on a falling object, such as the book in Example 5.1. Also, when you lift an object, *you* do work *on* the object. We sometimes describe this as doing work *against* gravity, because the force of gravity acts in the direction opposite that of the applied lift force and opposes it. For example, an average-sized apple has a weight of about 1 N. So if you lifted such an apple a distance of 1 m with a force equal to its weight, you would have done 1 J of work against gravity [$W = Fd = (1 \text{ N})(1 \text{ m}) = 1 \text{ J}$]. This example gives you an idea of how much work 1 J represents.

In both Examples 5.1 and 5.2, work was done by a single constant force. If more than one force acts on an object, the work done by each can be calculated separately:

The *total*, or *net*, *work* is defined as the work done by all the forces acting on the object, or the scalar sum of all those quantities of work.

This concept is illustrated in Example 5.3.

Example 5.3 ■ Total or Net Work

A 0.75-kg block slides with a uniform velocity down a 20° inclined plane (▼Fig. 5.4). (a) How much work is done by the force of friction on the block as it slides the total length of the plane? (b) What is the net work done on the block? (c) Discuss the net work done if the angle of incline is adjusted so that the block accelerates down the plane.

Thinking It Through. (a) The length of the plane can be found using trigonometry, so this part boils down to finding the force of friction. (b) The net work is the sum of all the work done by the individual forces. (*Note*: Since the block has a uniform, or constant, velocity, the net force on it is zero. This observation should tell you the answer, but it will be shown explicitly in the solution.) (c) If there is acceleration, Newton's second law applies, which involves a net force, so there will be net work.

Solution. We list the information that is given. In addition, it is equally important to list specifically what is to be found.

▶ **FIGURE 5.4** Total or net work See Example 5.3.

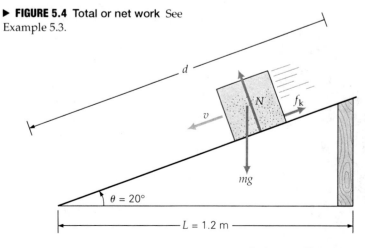

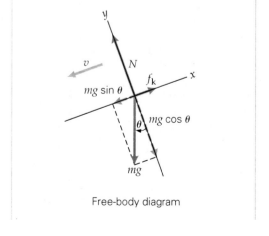

Free-body diagram

Given: $m = 0.75$ kg   **Find:**   (a) W_f (work done on the block by friction)
             $\theta = 20°$ (b) W_{net} (net work on the block)
             $L = 1.2$ m (from Fig. 5.4)   (c) W (discuss net work with block accelerating)

(a) Note from Fig. 5.4 that only two forces do work, because there are only two forces parallel to the motion: f_k, the force of kinetic friction, and $mg \sin \theta$, the component of the block's weight acting down the plane. The normal force N and $mg \cos \theta$, the components of the block's weight acting perpendicular to the plane, do no work on the block. (Why?)
    We first find the work done by the frictional force:

$$W_f = f_k(\cos 180°)d = -f_k d = -\mu_k N d$$

The angle 180° indicates that the force and displacement are in opposite directions. (It is common in such cases to write $W_f = -f_k d$ directly, since kinetic friction typically opposes motion.) The distance d the block slides down the plane can be found by using trigonometry. Note that $\cos \theta = L/d$, so

$$d = \frac{L}{\cos \theta}$$

We know that $N = mg \cos \theta$, but what is μ_k? It would appear that some information is lacking. When this situation occurs, look for another approach to solve the problem. As noted earlier, there are only two forces parallel to the motion, and they are opposite, so with a constant velocity their magnitudes are equal, $f_k = mg \sin \theta$. Thus,

$$W_f = -f_k d = -(mg \sin \theta)\left(\frac{L}{\cos \theta}\right) = -mgL \tan 20°$$
$$= -(0.75 \text{ kg})(9.8 \text{ m/s}^2)(1.2 \text{ m})(0.364) = -3.2 \text{ J}$$

(b) To find the net work, we need to calculate the work done by gravity and then add it to our result in part (a). Since $F_\parallel$ for gravity is just $mg \sin \theta$,

$$W_g = F_\parallel d = (mg \sin \theta)\left(\frac{L}{\cos \theta}\right) = mgL \tan 20° = +3.2 \text{ J}$$

where the calculation is the same as in part (a) except for the sign. Then

$$W_{net} = W_g + W_f = +3.2 \text{ J} + (-3.2 \text{ J}) = 0$$

Remember that work is a scalar quantity, so scalar addition is used to find net work.

(c) If the block accelerates down the plane, then from Newton's second law, we have $F_{net} = mg \sin \theta - f_k = ma$. The component of the gravitational force ($mg \sin \theta$) is greater than the opposing frictional force (f_k), so net work is done on the block, because now $|W_g| > |W_f|$. You may be wondering what the effect of nonzero net work is. As you will learn shortly, nonzero net work causes a change in the amount of energy an object has.

Follow-Up Exercise. In part (c) of this Example, is it possible for the frictional work to be greater in magnitude than the gravitational work? What would this condition mean in terms of the block's speed?

Note: Recall the discussion of friction in Section 4.6.

Problem-Solving Hint

Note that in part (a) of Example 5.3, the equation for W_f was simplified by using the algebraic expressions for N and d instead of by computing these quantities initially. It is a good rule of thumb not to plug numbers into an equation until you have to. Simplifying an equation through cancellation is easier with symbols and saves computation time.

5.2 Work Done by a Variable Force

OBJECTIVES: To (a) differentiate between work done by constant and variable forces, and (b) compute the work done by a spring force.

The discussion in the preceding section was limited to work done by constant forces. In general, however, forces are variable; that is, they change in magnitude and/or angle with time and/or position. For example, someone might push harder

▶ **FIGURE 5.5** Spring force **(a)** An applied force F_a stretches the spring, and the spring exerts an equal and opposite force F_s on the hand. **(b)** The magnitude of the force depends on the change Δx in the spring's length. This change is measured from to the end of the unstretched spring at x_o.

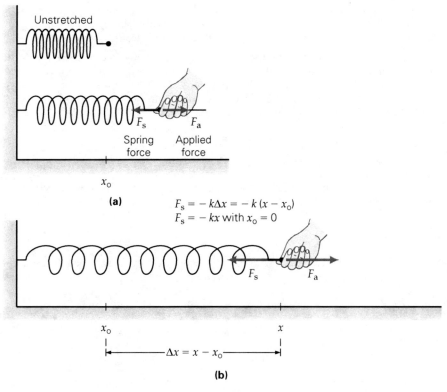

$$F_s = -k\Delta x = -k(x - x_o)$$
$$F_s = -kx \text{ with } x_o = 0$$

Note: In Fig. 5.5, the hand applies a variable force F_a in stretching the spring. At the same time, the spring exerts an equal and opposite force F_s on the hand.

and harder on an object to overcome the force of static friction, until the applied force exceeds $f_{s_{max}}$. However, the force of static friction does no work, because there is no motion or displacement.

An example of a variable force that does work is illustrated in ▲Fig. 5.5, which depicts a spring being stretched by an applied force F_a. As the spring is stretched (or compressed) farther and farther, its restoring force (the force that opposes the stretching or compression) becomes greater, and an increased applied force is required. For most springs, the spring force is directly proportional to the change in length of the spring from its unstretched length. In equation form, this relationship is expressed as

$$F_s = -k\Delta x = -k(x - x_o)$$

or, if $x_o = 0$,

$$F_s = -kx \quad (ideal\ spring\ force) \tag{5.3}$$

where x now represents the distance the spring is stretched (or compressed) from its unstretched length. As can be seen, the force varies with x. We describe this relationship by saying that the *force is a function of position*.

The k in this equation is a constant of proportionality and is commonly called the **spring constant**, or **force constant**. The greater the value of k, the stiffer or stronger is the spring. As you should be able to prove to yourself, the SI unit of k is newton per meter (N/m). The minus sign indicates that the spring force acts in the direction opposite to the displacement when the spring is either stretched or compressed. Equation 5.3 is a form of what is known as *Hooke's law*, named after Robert Hooke, a contemporary of Newton.

The relationship expressed by the spring force equation holds only for ideal springs. Real springs approximate this linear relationship between force and displacement within certain limits. If a spring is stretched beyond a certain point, called its *elastic limit*, the spring will be permanently deformed, and the linear relationship no longer applies.

To compute the work done by variable forces generally requires calculus. But we are fortunate in that the spring force is a special case that can be computed by using a graph. A plot of F (the applied force) versus x is shown in ▶Fig. 5.6. The graph has a straight-line slope of k, with $F = kx$, where F is the applied force doing work in stretching the spring.

PHYSLET

Illustration 6.3 Force and Displacement

Science Fundamentals

As described earlier, work is the area under an F-versus-x curve, and here it is in the form of a triangle as indicated by the shaded area in the figure. Then, computing this area,

$$\text{area} = W = \tfrac{1}{2}(\text{altitude} \times \text{base})$$

or

$$W = \tfrac{1}{2}Fx = \tfrac{1}{2}(kx)x = \tfrac{1}{2}kx^2$$

where $F = kx$. Thus we have

$$W = \tfrac{1}{2}kx^2 \quad \begin{array}{l} \textit{work done in stretching (or compressing)} \\ \textit{a spring from } x_o = 0 \end{array} \qquad (5.4)$$

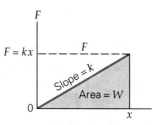

▲ **FIGURE 5.6 Work done by a uniformly variable spring force** A graph of F versus x, where F is the applied force doing work in stretching a spring, is a straight line with a slope of k. The work is equal to the area under the line, which is that of a triangle with area $= \tfrac{1}{2}(\text{altitude} \times \text{base})$. Then $W = \tfrac{1}{2}Fx = \tfrac{1}{2}(kx)x = \tfrac{1}{2}kx^2$.

Example 5.4 ■ Determining the Spring Constant

A 0.15-kg mass is attached to a vertical spring and hangs at rest a distance of 4.6 cm below its original position (▶Fig. 5.7). An additional 0.50-kg mass is then suspended from the first mass and allowed to descend to a new equilibrium position. What is the total extension of the spring? (Neglect the mass of the spring.)

Thinking It Through. The spring constant k appears in Eq. 5.3. Therefore, to find the value of k for a particular instance, the spring force and distance the spring is stretched (or compressed) must be known.

Solution. The data given are as follows:

Given: $m_1 = 0.15$ kg   *Find:* x (total stretch distance)
$\quad\quad\quad x_1 = 4.6$ cm $= 0.046$ m
$\quad\quad\quad m_2 = 0.50$ kg

The total stretch distance is given by $x = F/k$, where F is the applied force, which in this case is the weight of the mass suspended on the spring. However, the spring constant k is not given. This quantity may be found from the data pertaining to the suspension of m_1 and resulting displacement x_1. (This method is commonly used to determine spring constants.) As seen in Fig. 5.7a, the magnitudes of the weight force and the restoring spring force are equal, since $a = 0$, so we may equate their magnitudes:

$$F_s = kx_1 = m_1 g$$

Solving for k, we obtain

$$k = \frac{m_1 g}{x_1} = \frac{(0.15 \text{ kg})(9.8 \text{ m/s}^2)}{0.046 \text{ m}} = 32 \text{ N/m}$$

Then, knowing k, we find the total extension of the spring from the balanced-force situation shown in Fig. 5.7b:

$$F_s = (m_1 + m_2)g = kx$$

Thus,

$$x = \frac{(m_1 + m_2)g}{k} = \frac{(0.15 \text{ kg} + 0.50 \text{ kg})(9.8 \text{ m/s}^2)}{32 \text{ N/m}} = 0.20 \text{ m (or 20 cm)}$$

Follow-Up Exercise. How much work is done by gravity in stretching the spring through both displacements in Example 5.4?

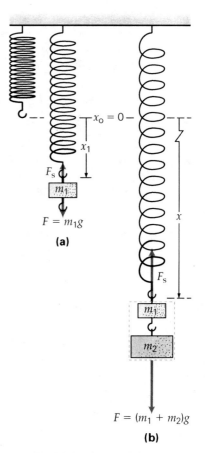

▲ **FIGURE 5.7 Determining the spring constant and the work done in stretching a spring** See Example 5.4.

Problem-Solving Hint

The reference position x_o used to determine the change in length of a spring is arbitrary and is usually chosen as zero for convenience. *The important quantity in computing work is the difference in position, Δx, or the net change in the length of the spring from its unstretched length.* As shown in ▼Fig. 5.8 for a mass suspended on a spring, x_o can be referenced to the unloaded length of the spring or to the loaded position, which may be taken as the zero position for convenience. In Example 5.4, x_o was referenced to the end of the unloaded spring.

When the net force on the suspended mass is zero, the mass is said to be at its *equilibrium position* (as in Fig. 5.7a with m_1 suspended). This position, rather than the unloaded length, may be taken as a zero reference ($x_o = 0$; see Fig. 5.8b). The equilibrium position is a convenient reference point for cases in which the mass oscillates up and down on the spring. Also, since the displacement is in the vertical direction, the x's are often replaced by y's.

▶ **FIGURE 5.8 Displacement reference** The reference position x_o is arbitrary and is usually chosen for convenience. It may be **(a)** at the end of the spring at its unloaded position or **(b)** at the equilibrium position when a mass is suspended on the spring. The latter is particularly convenient in cases in which the mass oscillates up and down on the spring.

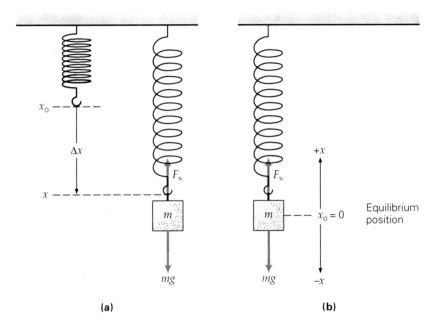

(a)   (b)

Illustration 6.4 Springs

Exploration 6.1 An Operational Definition of Work

5.3 The Work–Energy Theorem: Kinetic Energy

OBJECTIVES: To (a) study the work–energy theorem, and (b) apply it in solving problems.

Now that we have an operational definition of work, let's take a look at how work is related to energy. Energy is one of the most important concepts in science. We describe it as a quantity that objects or systems possess. Basically, work is something that is *done on* objects, whereas energy is something that objects *have*—the ability to do work.

One form of energy that is closely associated with work is *kinetic energy*. (Another form of energy, *potential energy*, will be described in Section 5.4.) Consider an object at rest on a frictionless surface. Let a horizontal force act on the object and set it in motion. Work is done *on* the object, but where does the work "go," so to speak? It goes into setting the object into motion, or changing its *kinetic* conditions. Because of its motion, we say the object has gained energy—kinetic energy, which gives it the capability to do work.

For a constant force doing work on a moving object, as illustrated in ▼Fig. 5.9, the force does an amount of work $W = Fx$. But what are the kinematic effects? The force gives the object a constant acceleration, and from Eq. 2.12, $v^2 = v_o^2 + 2ax$ (with $x_o = 0$),

$$a = \frac{v^2 - v_o^2}{2x}$$

▶ **FIGURE 5.9 The relationship of work and kinetic energy** The work done on a block by a constant force in moving it along a horizontal frictionless surface is equal to the change in the block's kinetic energy: $W = \Delta K$.

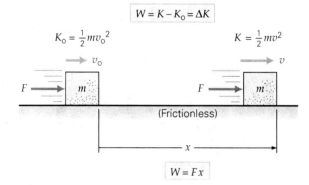

$$W = K - K_o = \Delta K$$

$K_o = \frac{1}{2}mv_o^2$

$K = \frac{1}{2}mv^2$

(Frictionless)

$W = Fx$

where v_0 may or may not be zero. Writing the magnitude of the force in the form of Newton's second law and substituting in the expression for a from the previous equation gives

$$F = ma = m\left(\frac{v^2 - v_0^2}{2x}\right)$$

Using this expression in the equation for work, we have

$$W = Fx = m\left(\frac{v^2 - v_0^2}{2x}\right)x$$

$$= \tfrac{1}{2}mv^2 - \tfrac{1}{2}mv_0^2$$

It is convenient to define $\tfrac{1}{2}mv^2$ as the **kinetic energy (K)** of the moving object:

$$K = \tfrac{1}{2}mv^2 \quad \text{(kinetic energy)} \tag{5.5}$$

SI unit of energy: joule (J)

Kinetic energy is often called the *energy of motion*. Note that it is directly proportional to the square of the (instantaneous) speed of a moving object, and therefore cannot be negative.

Then, in terms of kinetic energy, the previous expression for work can be written as

$$W = \tfrac{1}{2}mv^2 - \tfrac{1}{2}mv_0^2 = K - K_0 = \Delta K$$

Work–energy theorem

or

$$W = \Delta K \tag{5.6}$$

where it is understood that *W is the net work if more than one force acts on the object*, as shown in Example 5.3. This equation is called the **work–energy theorem**, and it relates the work done on an object to the change in the object's kinetic energy. That is, *the net work done on a body by all the forces acting on it is equal to the change in kinetic energy of the body*. Both work and energy have units of joules, and both are *scalar* quantities. Keep in mind that the work–energy theorem is true in general for variable forces and not just for the special case considered in deriving Eq. 5.6.

To illustrate that net work is equal to the change in kinetic energy, recall that in Example 5.1 the force of gravity did +44 J of work on a book that fell from rest through a distance of $y = 3.0$ m. At that position and instant, the falling book had 44 J of kinetic energy. Since $v_0 = 0$ in this case, $\tfrac{1}{2}mv^2 = mgy$. Substituting this expression into the equation for the work done on the falling book by gravity, we get

$$W = Fd = mgy = \frac{mv^2}{2} = K = \Delta K$$

where $K_0 = 0$. Thus the kinetic energy gained by the book is equal to the net work done on it: 44 J in this case. (As an exercise, confirm this fact by calculating the speed of the book and evaluating its kinetic energy.)

The work–energy theorem tells us that when work is done on an object, there is a change in or a transfer of energy. In general, then, we might say that *work is a measure of the transfer of kinetic energy* to the object. For example, a force doing work on an object that causes the object to speed up gives rise to an increase in the object's kinetic energy. Conversely, (negative) work done by the force of kinetic friction may cause a moving object to slow down and decrease its kinetic energy. So for an object to have a change in its kinetic energy, net work must be done on the object, as Eq. 5.6 tells us.

When an object is in motion, it possesses kinetic energy and has the capability to do work. For example, a moving automobile has kinetic energy and can do work in crumpling a fender in a fenderbender—not *useful* work in that case, but still work. Another example of work done by kinetic energy is shown in ▸Fig. 5.10.

▲ **FIGURE 5.10 Kinetic energy and work** A moving object, such as a wrecking ball, processes kinetic energy and can do work. A massive ball is used in demolishing buildings.

Exploration 6.4 Change the Direction of the Force Applied

Example 5.5 ■ A Game of Shuffleboard: The Work–Energy Theorem

A shuffleboard player (▼ Fig. 5.11) pushes a 0.25-kg puck that is initially at rest such that a constant horizontal force of 6.0 N acts on it through a distance of 0.50 m. (Neglect friction.) (a) What are the kinetic energy and the speed of the puck when the force is removed? (b) How much work would be required to bring the puck to rest?

Thinking It Through. Apply the work–energy theorem. If you can find the amount of work done, you know the change in kinetic energy, and vice versa.

Solution. Listing the given data as usual, we have

Given: $m = 0.25$ kg
$F = 6.0$ N
$d = 0.50$ m
$v_o = 0$

Find: (a) K (kinetic energy)
v (speed)
(b) W (work done in stopping puck)

(a) Since the speed is not known, we cannot compute the kinetic energy $\left(K = \frac{1}{2}mv^2\right)$ directly. However, kinetic energy is related to work by the work–energy theorem. The work done on the puck by the player's applied force F is

$$W = Fd = (6.0\text{ N})(0.50\text{ m}) = +3.0\text{ J}$$

Then, by the work–energy theorem, we obtain

$$W = \Delta K = K - K_o = +3.0\text{ J}$$

But $K_o = \frac{1}{2}mv_o^2 = 0$, because $v_o = 0$, so

$$K = 3.0\text{ J}$$

The speed can be found from the kinetic energy. Since $K = \frac{1}{2}mv^2$,

$$v = \sqrt{\frac{2K}{m}} = \sqrt{\frac{2(3.0\text{ J})}{0.25\text{ kg}}} = 4.9\text{ m/s}$$

(b) As you might guess, the work required to bring the puck to rest is equal to the puck's kinetic energy (that is, the amount of energy that the puck must lose to stop its motion). To confirm this equality, we essentially perform the reverse of the previous calculation, with $v_o = 4.9$ m/s and $v = 0$:

$$W = K - K_o = 0 - K_o = -\frac{1}{2}mv_o^2 = -\frac{1}{2}(0.25\text{ kg})(4.9\text{ m/s})^2 = -3.0\text{ J}$$

The minus sign indicates that the puck loses energy as it slows down. The work is done *against* the motion of the puck; that is, the opposing force is in a direction opposite that of the motion. (In a real-life situation, the opposing force would be friction.)

Follow-Up Exercise. Suppose the puck in this Example had twice the final speed when released. Would it then take twice as much work to stop the puck? Justify your answer numerically.

▶ **FIGURE 5.11 Work and kinetic energy** See Example 5.5.

Problem-Solving Hint

Notice how work–energy considerations were used to find speed in Example 5.5. This operation can be done in another way as well. First, the acceleration could be found from $a = F/m$, and then the kinematic equation $v^2 = v_o^2 + 2ax$ could be used to find v (where $x = d = 0.50$ m). The point is that many problems can be solved in different ways, and finding the fastest and most efficient way is often the key to success. As our discussion of energy progresses, you will see how useful and powerful the notions of work and energy are, both as theoretical concepts and as practical tools for solving many kinds of problems.

Conceptual Example 5.6 ■ Kinetic Energy: Mass versus Speed

In a football game, a 140-kg guard runs at a speed of 4.0 m/s, and a 70-kg free safety moves at 8.0 m/s. Which of the following is a correct statement? (a) Both players have the same kinetic energy. (b) The safety has twice as much kinetic energy as the guard. (c) The guard has twice as much kinetic energy as the safety. (d) The safety has four times as much kinetic energy as the guard?

Exploration 6.2 The Two-Block Push

Reasoning and Answer. The kinetic energy of a body depends on both its mass and its speed. You might think that, with half the mass but twice the speed, the safety would have the same kinetic energy as the guard, but this is not the case. As observed from the relationship $K = \frac{1}{2}mv^2$, kinetic energy is directly proportional to the mass, but it is also proportional to the *square* of the speed. Thus, having half the mass decreases the kinetic energy by a factor of two; so if the two athletes had equal speeds, the safety would have half as much kinetic energy as the guard.

However, doubling the speed increases the kinetic energy, not by a factor of 2 but by a factor of 2^2, or 4. Thus, the safety, with half the mass but twice the speed, would have $\frac{1}{2} \times 4 = 2$ times as much kinetic energy as the guard, and so the answer is (b).

Note that to answer this question, it was not necessary to calculate the kinetic energy of each player. But this can be done to verify our conclusions:

$$K_{safety} = \tfrac{1}{2}m_s v_s^2 = \tfrac{1}{2}(70 \text{ kg})(8.0 \text{ m/s})^2 = 2.2 \times 10^3 \text{ J}$$

$$K_{guard} = \tfrac{1}{2}m_g v_g^2 = \tfrac{1}{2}(140 \text{ kg})(4.0 \text{ m/s})^2 = 1.1 \times 10^3 \text{ J}$$

Thus, we see explicitly that our answer was correct.

Follow-Up Exercise. Suppose that the safety's speed were only 50 percent greater than the guard's, or 6.0 m/s. Which athlete would then have the greater kinetic energy, and how much greater?

Problem-Solving Hint

Note that the work–energy theorem relates the work done to the *change* in the kinetic energy. Often, we have $v_o = 0$ and $K_o = 0$, so $W = \Delta K = K$. But take care! You *cannot* simply use the square of the change in speed, $(\Delta v)^2$, to calculate ΔK, as you might at first think. In terms of speed, we have

$$W = \Delta K = K - K_o = \tfrac{1}{2}mv^2 - \tfrac{1}{2}mv_o^2 = \tfrac{1}{2}m(v^2 - v_o^2)$$

But $v^2 - v_o^2$ is not the same as $(v - v_o)^2 = (\Delta v)^2$, because $(v - v_o)^2 = v^2 - 2vv_o + v_o^2$. Hence, the change in kinetic energy, is *not* equal to $\tfrac{1}{2}m(v - v_o)^2 = \tfrac{1}{2}m(\Delta v)^2 \neq \Delta K$.

This observation means that to calculate work, or the change in kinetic energy, you must compute the kinetic energy of an object at one point or time (using the instantaneous speed to get the instantaneous kinetic energy) and also at another location or time. Then subtract the quantities to find the change in kinetic energy, or the work. Alternatively, you can find the difference of the *squares* of the speeds $(v^2 - v_o^2)$ first in computing the change, but remember never to use the square of the difference of the speeds. To see this hint in action, look at Conceptual Example 5.7.

Conceptual Example 5.7 ■ An Accelerating Car: Speed and Kinetic Energy

A car traveling at 5.0 m/s speeds up to 10 m/s, with an increase in kinetic energy that requires work W_1. Then the car's speed increases from 10 m/s to 15 m/s, requiring additional work W_2. Which of the following relationships accurately compares the two amounts of work: (a) $W_1 > W_2$, (b) $W_1 = W_2$, or (c) $W_2 > W_1$?

Reasoning and Answer. As noted previously, the work–energy theorem relates the work done on the car to the *change* in its kinetic energy. Since the speeds have the same increment in each case ($\Delta v = 5.0$ m/s), it might appear that (b) would be the answer. However, keep in mind that the work is equal to the *change* in kinetic energy and involves $v_2^2 - v_1^2$, *not* $(\Delta v)^2 = (v_2 - v_1)^2$.

So the greater the speed of an object, the greater its kinetic energy, and we would expect the *difference* in kinetic energy in changing speeds (or the work required to change speed) to be greater for higher speeds for the same Δv. So, (c) is the answer.

The main point is that the Δv values are the same, but more work is required to increase the kinetic energy of an object at higher speeds.

Follow-Up Exercise. Suppose the car speeds up a third time, from 15 m/s to 20 m/s, a change requiring work W_3. How does the work done in this increment compare with W_2? Justify your answer numerically. [*Hint*: Use a ratio.]

5.4 Potential Energy

OBJECTIVES: To (a) define and understand potential energy, and (b) learn about gravitational potential energy.

An object in motion has kinetic energy. However, whether an object is in motion or not, it may have another form of energy—potential energy. As the name implies, an object having potential energy has the *potential* to do work. You can probably think of many examples: a compressed spring, a drawn bow, water held back by a dam, a wrecking ball poised to drop. In all such cases, the potential to do work derives from the *position* or *configuration* of bodies. The spring has energy because it is compressed, the bow because it is drawn, the water and the ball because they have been lifted above the surface of the Earth (◀Fig. 5.12). Consequently, **potential energy, (U)**, is often called *the energy of position* (and/or configuration).

In a sense, potential energy can be thought of as stored work, just as kinetic energy can. You have already seen an example of potential energy in Section 5.2 when work was done in compressing a spring from its equilibrium position. Recall that the work done in such a case is $W = \frac{1}{2}kx^2$ (with $x_0 = 0$). Note that the amount of work done depends on the amount of compression (x). Because work is done, there is a *change* in the spring's potential energy (ΔU), which is equal to the work done *by the applied force* in compressing (or stretching) the spring:

$$W = \Delta U = U - U_0 = \tfrac{1}{2}kx^2 - \tfrac{1}{2}kx_0^2$$

Thus, with $x_0 = 0$ and $U_0 = 0$, as they are commonly taken for convenience, the *potential energy of a spring* is

$$U = \tfrac{1}{2}kx^2 \quad \text{(potential energy of a spring)} \qquad (5.7)$$

SI unit of energy: joule (J)

[*Note*: Since the potential energy varies as x^2, the previous Problem-Solving Hint also applies. That is, when $x_0 \neq 0$, then $x^2 - x_0^2 \neq (x - x_0)^2$.]

(a)

(b)

▲ **FIGURE 5.12 Potential energy**
Potential energy has many forms.
(a) Work must be done to bend the bow, giving it potential energy. That energy is converted into kinetic energy when the arrow is released.
(b) Gravitational potential energy is converted into kinetic energy when an object falls. (Where did the gravitational potential energy of the water and the diver come from?)

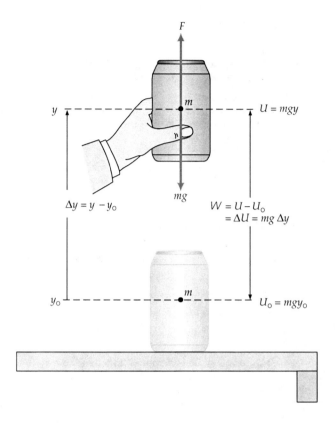

▲ **FIGURE 5.13 Gravitational potential energy** The work done in lifting an object is equal to the change in gravitational potential energy: $W = F\Delta y = mg(y - y_\text{o})$.

Perhaps the most common type of potential energy is gravitational potential energy. In this case, position refers to the height of an object above some reference point, such as the floor or the ground. Suppose that an object of mass m is lifted a distance Δy (▲Fig. 5.13). Work is done against the force of gravity, and an applied force at least equal to the object's weight is necessary to lift the object: $F = w = mg$. The work done in lifting is then equal to the change in potential energy. Expressing this relationship in equation form, since there is no overall change in kinetic energy, we have

work done by external force = change in gravitational potential energy

or

$$W = F\Delta y = mg(y - y_\text{o}) = mgy - mgy_\text{o} = \Delta U = U - U_\text{o}$$

where y is used as the vertical coordinate. With the common choice of $y_\text{o} = 0$, such that $U_\text{o} = 0$, the **gravitational potential energy** is

$$U = mgy \tag{5.8}$$

SI unit of energy: joule (J)

(Eq. 5.8 represents the gravitational potential energy on or near the Earth's surface, where g is considered to be constant. A more general form of gravitational potential energy will be given in Section 7.5.)

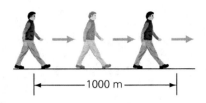

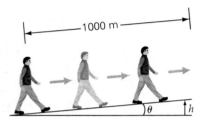

▲ **FIGURE 5.14** Adding potential energy See Example 5.8.

Example 5.8 ■ More Energy Needed

To walk 1000 m on level ground, a 60-kg person requires an expenditure of about 1.0×10^5 J of energy. What is the total energy required if the walk is extended another 1000 m along a 5.0° incline as shown in ◄Fig. 5.14?

Thinking It Through. To walk an additional 1000 m would require the 1.0×10^5 J *plus* the additional energy for doing work against gravity in walking up the incline. From the figure, the increase in height can be seen to be $h = d \sin \theta$.

Solution. Listing the given data:

Given: $m = 60$ kg   *Find:* Total expended energy
        $E_o = 1.0 \times 10^5$ J (for 1000 m)
        $\theta = 5.0°$
        $d = 1000$ m (for each part of the work)

The additional expended energy in going up the incline is equal to gravitational potential energy gained. So,

$$\Delta U = mgh = (60 \text{ kg})(9.8 \text{ m/s}^2)(1000 \text{ m}) \sin 5.0° = 5.1 \times 10^4 \text{ J}$$

Then, the total energy expended for the 2000 m walk is

$$\text{Total } E = 2E_o + \Delta U = 2(1.0 \times 10^5 \text{ J}) + 0.51 \times 10^5 \text{ J} = 2.5 \times 10^5 \text{ J}$$

Notice that the value of ΔU was expressed as a multiple of 10^5 in the last equation so it could be added to the E_o term, and the result was rounded to two significant figures per our rules from Chapter 1.

Follow-Up Exercise. If the angle of incline were doubled and the walk *just* up the incline is repeated, will the additional energy expended by the person in doing work against gravity be doubled? Justify your answer.

Example 5.9 ■ A Thrown Ball: Kinetic Energy and Gravitational Potential Energy

A 0.50-kg ball is thrown vertically upward with an initial velocity of 10 m/s (◄Fig. 5.15). (a) What is the change in the ball's kinetic energy between the starting point and the ball's maximum height? (b) What is the change in the ball's potential energy between the starting point and the ball's maximum height? (Neglect air resistance.)

Thinking It Through. Kinetic energy is lost and gravitational potential energy is gained as the ball travels upward.

Solution. Studying Fig. 5.15 and listing the data,

Given: $m = 0.50$ kg   *Find:* (a) ΔK (the change in kinetic energy)
      $v_o = 10$ m/s   (b) ΔU (the change in potential energy between y_o
      $a = g$ and y_{max})

(a) To find the *change* in kinetic energy, the kinetic energy is computed at each point. We know the initial velocity v_o, and at the maximum height $v = 0$, so $K = 0$. Thus,

$$\Delta K = K - K_o = 0 - K_o = -\tfrac{1}{2}mv_o^2 = -\tfrac{1}{2}(0.50 \text{ kg})(10 \text{ m/s})^2 = -25 \text{ J}$$

That is, the ball loses 25 J of kinetic energy as negative work is done on it by the force of gravity. (The gravitational force and the ball's displacement are in opposite directions.)

(b) To find the change in potential energy, we need to know the ball's height above its starting point when $v = 0$. Using Eq. 2.11', $v^2 = v_o^2 - 2gy$ (with $y_o = 0$ and $v = 0$) to find y_{max},

$$y_{max} = \frac{v_o^2}{2g} = \frac{(10 \text{ m/s})^2}{2(9.8 \text{ m/s}^2)} = 5.1 \text{ m}$$

Then, with $y_o = 0$ and $U_o = 0$,

$$\Delta U = U = mgy_{max} = (0.50 \text{ kg})(9.8 \text{ m/s}^2)(5.1 \text{ m}) = +25 \text{ J}$$

The potential energy increases by 25 J, as might be expected.

Follow-Up Exercise. In this Example, what are the overall changes in the ball's kinetic and potential energies when the ball returns to the starting point?

▲ **FIGURE 5.15** Kinetic and potential energies See Example 5.9. (The ball is displaced sideways for clarity.)

Exploration 7.2 *Choice of Zero for Potential Energy*

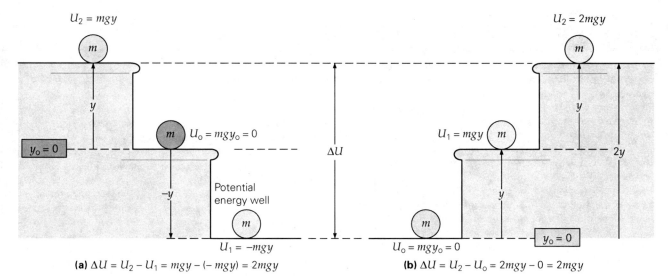

(a) $\Delta U = U_2 - U_1 = mgy - (-mgy) = 2mgy$ (b) $\Delta U = U_2 - U_o = 2mgy - 0 = 2mgy$

▲ **FIGURE 5.16 Reference point and change in potential energy**
(a) The choice of a reference point (zero height) is arbitrary and may give rise to a negative potential energy. An object is said to be in a potential-energy well in this case.
(b) The well may be avoided by selecting a new zero reference. Note that the difference, or *change*, in potential energy (ΔU) associated with the two positions is the same, regardless of the reference point. There is no physical difference, even though there are two coordinate systems and two different zero reference points.

Zero Reference Point

An important point is illustrated in Example 5.9, namely, the choice of a zero reference point. Potential energy is the energy of *position*, and the potential energy at a particular position (U) is meaningful only when referenced to the potential energy at some other position (U_o). The reference position or point is arbitrary, as is the origin of a set of coordinate axes for analyzing a system. Reference points are usually chosen with convenience in mind—for example, $y_o = 0$. The value of the potential energy at a particular position depends on the reference point used. However, *the difference, or change, in potential energy associated with two positions is the same regardless of the reference position.*

If, in Example 5.9, ground level had been taken as the zero reference point, then U_o at the release point would not have been zero. However, U at the maximum height would have been greater, and $\Delta U = U - U_o$ would have been the same. This concept is illustrated in ▲Fig. 5.16. Note in Fig. 5.16a that the potential energy can be negative. When an object has a negative potential energy, it is said to be in a potential-energy *well*, which is analogous to being in an actual well: work is needed to raise the object to a higher position in the well or to get it out of the well.

It is also said that gravitational potential energy is *independent of path*. This means that only the change in height Δh (or Δy) is the consideration, not the path that leads to the change in height. An object could travel many paths leading to the same Δh.

5.5 Conservation of Energy

OBJECTIVES: To (a) distinguish between conservative and nonconservative forces, and (b) explain their effects on the conservation of energy.

Conservation laws are the cornerstones of physics, both theoretically and practically. Most scientists would probably name conservation of energy as the most profound and far-reaching of these important laws. When we say that a physical quantity is *conserved*, we mean that it is constant, or has a constant value. Because so many things continually change in physical processes, conserved quantities are extremely helpful in our attempts to understand and describe the universe. Keep in mind, though, that many quantities are conserved only under special conditions.

One of the most important conservation laws is that concerning conservation of energy. (You may have seen this topic coming in Example 5.9.) A familiar statement is that the total energy of the universe is conserved. This statement is true, because

INSIGHT 5.1 PEOPLE POWER: USING BODY ENERGY

The human body is energy inefficient. That is, a lot of energy doesn't go into doing useful work and is wasted. It would be advantageous to convert some of this energy into useful work. Attempts are being made to do this through "energy harvesting" from the human body. Normal body activities produce motion, flexing and stretching, compression, and body heat—this is energy there for the taking. Harvesting the energy is a difficult job, but using advances in nanotechnology (Chapter 1) and materials science, the effort is being made.

One older example of using body energy is the self-winding wristwatch, which is wound mechanically from the wearer's arm movements. (Today, batteries have all but taken over.) An ultimate goal in "energy harvesting" is to convert some of the body's energy into electricity—even if only a small amount. How might this be done? Here are a couple of ways:

- Piezoelectric devices. When mechanically stressed, piezo-electric substances, which like some ceramics, can generate electrical energy.

- Thermoelectric materials, which convert heat resulting from some temperature difference into electrical energy.

These methods have severe limitations and produce only small amounts of electricity. But with miniaturization and nanotechnology, the results could be enough. Researchers have already developed boots that use the compression of walking on a compound to produce enough energy to power a radio.

A more recent application is the "backpack generator." The mounted backpack's load is suspended by springs. The up and down hip motion of a person wearing the backpack makes the suspended load bounce up and down. This motion turns a gear connected to a simple magnetic coil generator, similar to those used in flashlights that are energized by a rhythmic shaking (see Insight 20.1, page 664). The body's mechanical energy with this device can generate up to 7 watts of electrical energy. A typical cell phone operates on about 1 watt. (The watt is a unit of power, J/s, energy/second, see Section 5.6).

Who knows what the future of technology may hold? Reflect on how many advances have occurred in your own lifetime.

Note: A system is a physical arrangement with real or imaginary boundaries. A classroom might be considered a system, and so might an arbitrary cubic meter of air.

the whole universe is taken to be a system. A *system* is defined as a definite quantity of matter enclosed by boundaries, either real or imaginary. In effect, the universe is the largest possible closed, or isolated, system we can imagine. Within a *closed system*, particles can interact with each other, but have absolutely no interaction with anything outside. In general, then, the amount of energy in a system remains constant when no mechanical work is done on or by the system, and no energy is transferred to or from the system (including thermal energy and radiation).

Thus, the **law of conservation of total energy** may be stated as follows:

Conservation of total energy

| The total energy of an isolated system is always conserved. |

Illustration 7.1 *Choice of System*

Within such a system, energy may be converted from one form to another, but the total amount of all forms of energy is constant, or unchanged. Total energy can never be created or destroyed. The use of body energy is discussed in the accompanying Insight 5.1.

Conceptual Example 5.10 ■ Violation of the Conservation of Energy?

A static, uniform liquid is in one side of a double container as shown in ▶Fig. 5.17a. If the valve is open, the level will fall, because the liquid has (gravitational) potential energy. This may be computed by assuming all the mass of the liquid to be concentrated at its center of mass, which is at a height $h/2$. (More on the center of mass in Chapter 6.) When the valve is open, the liquid flows into the container on the right, and when static equilibrium is reached, each container has liquid to a height of $h/2$, with centers of mass at $h/4$. This being the case, the potential energy of the liquid before opening the valve was $U_0 = (mg)h/2$, and afterward, with half the total mass in each container (Fig. 5.16b), $U = (m/2)g(h/4) + (m/2)g(h/4) = 2(m/2)g(h/4) = (mg)h/4$. Whoa. Was half of the energy lost?

Reasoning and Answer. No; by the conservation of total energy, it must be around somewhere. Where might it have gone? When the liquid flows from one container to the other, because of internal friction and friction against the walls, half of the potential energy is converted to heat (thermal energy), which is transferred to the surroundings as the liquid comes to equilibrium. (This means the same temperature and no internal fluctuations.)

Follow-Up Exercise. What would happen in this Example in the absence of friction?

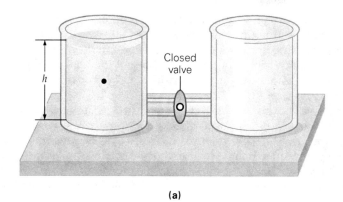

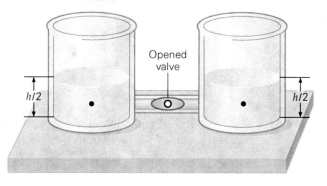

(a)   (b)

▲ **FIGURE 5.17** Is energy lost? See
Conceptual Example 5.10.

Note: Friction is discussed in
Section 4.6.

Conservative and Nonconservative Forces

We can make a general distinction among systems by considering two categories
of forces that may act within or on them: conservative and nonconservative forces.
You have already been introduced to a couple of conservative forces: the force due
to gravity and the spring force. We considered a classic nonconservative force,
friction, in Chapter 4. A conservative force is defined as follows:

> A force is said to be conservative if the work done by it in moving an object
> is independent of the object's path.

Conservative force — work
independent of path

This definition means that the work done by a **conservative force** depends only
on the initial and final positions of an object.

The concept of conservative and nonconservative forces is sometimes difficult
to comprehend at first. Because this concept is so important in the conservation of
energy, let's consider some illustrative examples to increase understanding.

First, what does *independent of path* mean? As an example of path indepen-
dence, consider picking an object up from the floor and placing it on a table. This
is doing work against the *conservative force of gravity*. The work done is equal to the
potential energy gained, $mg\Delta h$, where Δh is the *vertical* distance between the object's position on the floor and its position on the table. This is the important point.
You may have carried the object over to the sink before putting it on the table, or
walked around to the other side of the table. But only the vertical displacement
makes a difference in the work done because that is in the direction of the vertical
force. For any horizontal displacement no work is done, since the displacement
and force are at right angles. The magnitude of the work done is equal to the change
in potential energy (under frictionless conditions only), and in fact, *the concept of
potential energy is associated only with conservative forces*. A change in potential energy can be defined in terms of the work done by a conservative force.

Conversely, a **nonconservative force** *does* depend on path.

> A force is said to be nonconservative if the work done by it in moving an ob-
> ject does depend on the object's path.

Nonconservative force — work
dependent on path

Friction is a nonconservative force. A longer path would produce more work done by
friction than a shorter one, and more energy would be lost to heat on the longer
path. So the work done against friction certainly depends on the path. Hence, in a
sense, a conservative force allows you to conserve or store energy as potential energy, whereas a nonconservative force does not.

Another approach to explain the distinction between conservative and nonconservative forces is through an equivalent statement of the previous definition
of conservative force:

> A force is conservative if the work done by it in moving an object through a
> round trip is zero.

Another way of describing a
conservative force

Notice that for the *conservative* gravitational force, the force and displacement are sometimes in the same direction (in which case positive work is done by the force) and sometimes in opposite directions (in which case negative work is done by the force) during a round trip. Think of the simple case of the book falling to the floor and being placed back on the table. With positive and negative work, the total work done by gravity is zero.

However, for only a *nonconservative* force like that of kinetic friction, which always opposes the motion or is in the opposite direction to the displacement, the total work done in a round trip can *never* be zero and is always negative (that is, energy is lost). But don't get the idea that nonconservative forces only take energy away from a system. On the contrary, we often supply nonconservative pushes and pulls (forces) that add to the energy of a system, such as when you push a stalled car.

Conservation of Total Mechanical Energy

The idea of a conservative force allows us to extend the conservation of energy to the special case of mechanical energy, which greatly helps us better analyze many physical situations. The sum of the kinetic and potential energies is called the **total mechanical energy**:

Total mechanical energy—kinetic plus potential

$$E = K + U \qquad (5.9)$$

$$\underset{\substack{total \\ mechanical \\ energy}}{} = \underset{\substack{kinetic \\ energy}}{} + \underset{\substack{potential \\ energy}}{}$$

For a **conservative system** (that is, a system in which only conservative forces do work) the total mechanical energy is constant, or conserved:

$$E = E_o$$

Substituting for E and E_o from Eq. 5.9,

$$K + U = K_o + U_o \qquad (5.10a)$$

or

$$\tfrac{1}{2}mv^2 + U = \tfrac{1}{2}mv_o^2 + U_o \qquad (5.10b)$$

Equation 5.10b is a mathematical statement of the **law of the conservation of mechanical energy**:

Conservation of mechanical energy

| In a conservative system, the sum of all types of kinetic energy and potential energy is constant and equals the total mechanical energy of the system. |

Illustration 7.2 *Representations of Energy*

Note: while the kinetic and potential energies in a conservative system may change, their sum is always constant. For a conservative system when work is done and energy is transferred within a system, we can write Eq. 5.10a as

$$(K - K_o) + (U - U_o) = 0 \qquad (5.11a)$$

or as

$$\Delta K + \Delta U = 0 \quad \textit{(for a conservative system)} \qquad (5.11b)$$

This expression tells us that these quantities are related in a seesaw fashion: If there is a decrease in potential energy, then the kinetic energy must increase by an equal amount to keep the sum of the changes equal to zero. However, in a nonconservative system, mechanical energy is usually lost (for example, to the heat of friction), and thus $\Delta K + \Delta U < 0$. But keep in mind, as pointed out previously, that a nonconservative force may instead add energy to a system (or have no effect at all).

Example 5.11 ■ Look Out Below! Conservation of Mechanical Energy

PHYSLET®

Exploration 7.3 Elastic Collision

A painter on a scaffold drops a 1.50-kg can of paint from a height of 6.00 m. (a) What is the kinetic energy of the can when the can is at a height of 4.00? (b) With what speed will the can hit the ground? (Neglect air resistance.)

Thinking It Through. Total mechanical energy is conserved, since only the conservative force of gravity acts on the system (the can). The initial total mechanical energy can be found, and the potential energy decreases as the kinetic energy (as well as speed) increases.

Solution. Listing what is given and what we are to find, we have:

Given: $m = 1.50$ kg
$y_o = 6.00$ m
$y = 4.00$ m
$v_o = 0$

Find: (a) K (kinetic energy at $y = 4.00$ m)
(b) v (speed just before hitting the ground)

(a) First, it is convenient to find the can's total mechanical energy, since this quantity is conserved while the can is falling. Initially, with $v_o = 0$, the can's total mechanical energy is all potential energy. Taking the ground as the zero reference point,

$$E = K_o + U_o = 0 + mgy_o = (1.50 \text{ kg})(9.80 \text{ m/s}^2)(6.00 \text{ m}) = 88.2 \text{ J}$$

The relation $E = K + U$ continues to hold while the can is falling, but now we know what E is. Rearranging the equation, $K = E - U$ and U can be found at $y = 4.00$ m:

$$K = E - U = E - mgy = 88.2 \text{ J} - (1.50 \text{ kg})(9.80 \text{ m/s}^2)(4.00 \text{ m}) = 29.4 \text{ J}$$

Alternatively, we could have computed the change in (in this case, the loss of) potential energy, ΔU. Whatever potential energy was lost must have been gained as kinetic energy (Eq. 5.11). Then,

$$\Delta K + \Delta U = 0$$
$$(K - K_o) + (U - U_o) = (K - K_o) + (mgy - mgy_o) = 0$$

With $K_o = 0$ (because $v_o = 0$), we obtain

$$K = mg(y_o - y) = (1.50 \text{ kg})(9.8 \text{ m/s}^2)(6.00 \text{ m} - 4.00 \text{ m}) = 29.4 \text{ J}$$

(b) Just before the can strikes the ground ($y = 0, U = 0$), the total mechanical energy is all kinetic energy, or

$$E = K = \tfrac{1}{2}mv^2$$

Thus,

$$v = \sqrt{\frac{2E}{m}} = \sqrt{\frac{2(88.2 \text{ J})}{1.50 \text{ kg}}} = 10.8 \text{ m/s}$$

Basically, all of the potential energy of a free-falling object released from some height y is converted into kinetic energy just before the object hits the ground, so

$$|\Delta K| = |\Delta U|$$

Thus,

$$\tfrac{1}{2}mv^2 = mgy$$

or

$$v = \sqrt{2gy}$$

Note that the mass cancels and is not a consideration. This result is also obtained from the kinematic equation $v^2 = 2gy$ (Eq. 2.11′), with $v_o = 0$ and $y_o = 0$.

Follow-Up Exercise. A painter on the ground wishes to toss a paintbrush vertically upward a distance of 5.0 m to his partner on the scaffold. Use methods of conservation of mechanical energy to determine the minimum speed that he must give to the brush.

▶ **FIGURE 5.18** Speed and energy
See Conceptual Example 5.12.

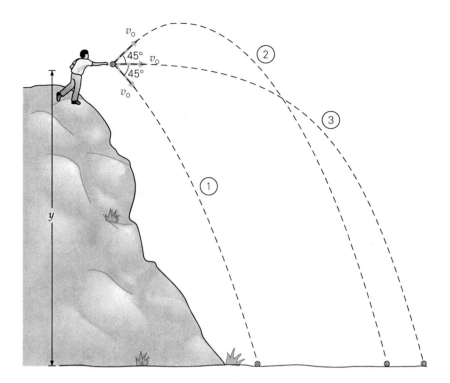

Conceptual Example 5.12 ■ A Matter of Direction? Speed and Conservation of Energy

Three balls of equal mass m are projected with the same speed in different directions, as shown in ▲Fig. 5.18. If air resistance is neglected, which ball would you expect to strike the ground with the greatest speed: (a) ball 1; (b) ball 2; (c) ball 3; or (d) all balls strike with the same speed?

Reasoning and Answer. All of the balls have the same initial kinetic energy, $K_o = \frac{1}{2}mv_o^2$. (Recall that energy is a scalar quantity, and the different directions of projection do not produce any difference in the kinetic energies.) Regardless of their trajectories, all of the balls ultimately descend a distance y relative to their common starting point, so they all lose the same amount of potential energy. (Recall that U is energy of *position* and is *independent* of path.)

By the law of conservation of mechanical energy, the amount of potential energy each ball loses is equal to the amount of kinetic energy it gains. Since all of the balls start with the same amount of kinetic energy and gain the same amount of kinetic energy, all three will have equal kinetic energies just before striking the ground. This means that their speeds must be equal, so the answer is (d).

Note that although balls 1 and 2 are projected at 45° angles, this factor is not relevant. Since the change in potential energy is independent of path, it is independent of the projection angle. The vertical distance between the starting point and the ground is the same (y) for projectiles at any angle. (*Note*: Although the strike speeds are equal, the *times* the balls take to reach the ground are different. Refer to Conceptual Example 3.11 for another approach.)

Follow-Up Exercise. Would the balls strike the ground with different speeds if their masses were different? (Neglect air resistance.)

Example 5.13 ■ Conservative Forces: Mechanical Energy of a Spring

A 0.30-kg block sliding on a horizontal frictionless surface with a speed of 2.5 m/s, as depicted in ▶Fig. 5.19, strikes a light spring that has a spring constant of 3.0×10^3 N/m. (a) What is the total mechanical energy of the system? (b) What is the kinetic energy K_1 of the block when the spring is compressed a distance $x_1 = 1.0$ cm? (Assume that no energy is lost in the collision.)

Thinking It Through. (a) Initially, the total mechanical energy is all kinetic energy. (b) The total energy is the same as in part (a), but it is now divided between kinetic energy and spring potential energy (assuming the spring is not fully compressed).

Solution.

Given: $m = 0.30$ kg   *Find:* (a) E (total mechanical energy)
$v_o = 2.5$ m/s   (b) K_1 (kinetic energy)
$k = 3.0 \times 10^3$ N/m
$x_1 = 1.0$ cm $= 0.010$ m

(a) Before the block makes contact with the spring, the total mechanical energy of the system is all in the form of kinetic energy; therefore,

$$E = K_o = \tfrac{1}{2}mv_o^2 = \tfrac{1}{2}(0.30 \text{ kg})(2.5 \text{ m/s})^2 = 0.94 \text{ J}$$

Since the system is conservative (that is, no mechanical energy is lost), this quantity is the total mechanical energy at any time.

(b) When the spring is compressed a distance x_1, it has gained potential energy $U_1 = \tfrac{1}{2}kx_1^2$, and

$$E = K_1 + U_1 = K_1 + \tfrac{1}{2}kx_1^2$$

Solving for K_1, we have

$$K_1 = E - \tfrac{1}{2}kx_1^2$$
$$= 0.94 \text{ J} - \tfrac{1}{2}(3.0 \times 10^3 \text{ N/m})(0.010 \text{ m})^2 = 0.94 \text{ J} - 0.15 \text{ J} = 0.79 \text{ J}$$

Follow-Up Exercise. How far will the spring in this Example be compressed when the block comes to a stop? (Solve using energy principles.)

See the accompanying Learn by Drawing for another example of energy exchange.

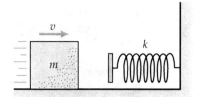

▲ **FIGURE 5.19 Conservative force and the mechanical energy of a spring** See Example 5.13.

Illustration 7.5 A Block on an Incline

Exploration 7.4 A Ball Hits a Mass Attached to a Spring

LEARN BY DRAWING   **ENERGY EXCHANGES: A FALLING BALL**

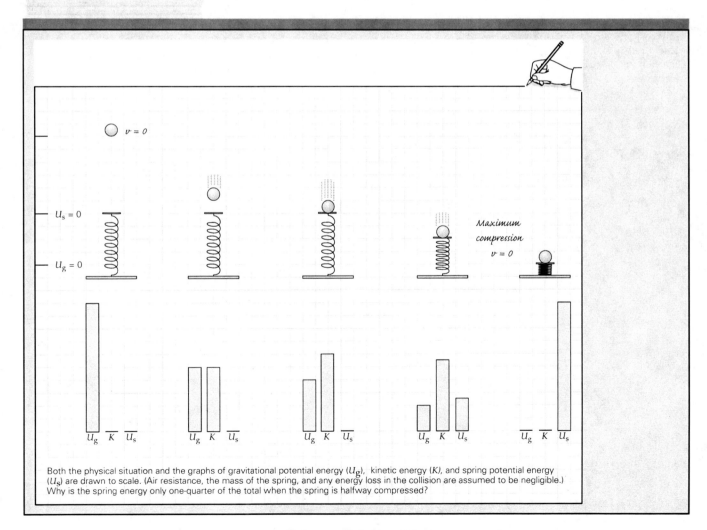

Both the physical situation and the graphs of gravitational potential energy (U_g), kinetic energy (K), and spring potential energy (U_s) are drawn to scale. (Air resistance, the mass of the spring, and any energy loss in the collision are assumed to be negligible.) Why is the spring energy only one-quarter of the total when the spring is halfway compressed?

Total Energy and Nonconservative Forces

In the preceding examples, we ignored the force of friction, which is probably the most common nonconservative force. In general, both conservative and nonconservative forces can do work on objects. However, when some nonconservative forces do work, the total mechanical energy is not conserved. Mechanical energy is "lost" through the work done by nonconservative forces, such as friction.

You might think that we can no longer use an energy approach to analyze problems involving such nonconservative forces, since mechanical energy can be lost or dissipated (◄Fig. 5.20). However, in some instances, we can use the total energy to find out how much energy was lost to the work done by a nonconservative force. Suppose an object initially has mechanical energy and that nonconservative forces do an amount of work W_{nc} on it. Starting with the work–energy theorem, we have

$$W = \Delta K = K - K_o$$

In general, the net work (W) may be done by both conservative forces (W_c) and nonconservative forces (W_{nc}), so

$$W_c + W_{nc} = K - K_o \tag{5.12}$$

But recall that the work done by conservative forces is equal to $-\Delta U$, or $W_{nc} = U_o - U$, and Eq. 5.12 then becomes

$$W_{nc} = K - K_o - (U_o - U)$$
$$= (K + U) - (K_o + U_o)$$

Therefore,

$$W_{nc} = E - E_o = \Delta E \tag{5.13}$$

Hence, the work done by the nonconservative forces acting on a system is equal to the change in mechanical energy. Notice that for dissipative forces, $E_o > E$. Thus, the change is negative, indicating a decrease in mechanical energy. This condition agrees in sign with W_{nc}, which, for friction, would also be negative. Example 5.14 illustrates this concept.

▲ FIGURE 5.20 Nonconservative force and energy loss Friction is a nonconservative force—when friction is present and does work, mechanical energy is not conserved. Can you tell from the photo what is happening to the work being done by the motor on the grinding wheel after the work is converted into rotational kinetic energy? (Note that the worker is wisely wearing a face shield rather than just goggles as the sign in the background suggests.)

PHYSLET®

Illustration 7.4 External Forces

Example 5.14 ■ Nonconservative Force: Downhill Racer

A skier with a mass of 80 kg starts from rest at the top of a slope and skis down from an elevation of 110 m (▼ Fig. 5.21). The speed of the skier at the bottom of the slope is 20 m/s. (a) Show that the system is nonconservative. (b) How much work is done by the nonconservative force of friction?

Thinking It Through. (a) If the system is nonconservative, then $E_o \neq E$, and these quantities can be computed. (b) We cannot determine the work from force–distance considerations, but W_{nc} is equal to the difference in total energies (Eq. 5.13).

Solution.

Given: $m = 80$ kg   *Find:*   (a) Show that E is not conserved.
          $v_o = 0$ (b) W_{nc} (work done by friction)
          $v = 20$ m/s
          $y_o = 110$ m

$v = 20$ m/s

110 m

► FIGURE 5.21 Work done by a nonconservative force See Example 5.14.

(a) If the system is conservative, the total mechanical energy is constant. Taking $U_o = 0$ at the bottom of the hill, the initial energy at the top of the hill is

$$E_o = U = mgy_o = (80 \text{ kg})(9.8 \text{ m/s}^2)(110 \text{ m}) = 8.6 \times 10^4 \text{ J}$$

And the energy at the bottom of the slope is

$$E = K = \tfrac{1}{2}mv^2 = \tfrac{1}{2}(80 \text{ kg})(20 \text{ m/s})^2 = 1.6 \times 10^4 \text{ J}$$

Therefore, $E_o \neq E$, so this system is not conservative.

(b) The amount of work done by the nonconservative force of friction is equal to the change in the mechanical energy, or to the amount of mechanical energy lost (Eq. 5.13):

$$W_{nc} = E - E_o = (1.6 \times 10^4 \text{ J}) - (8.6 \times 10^4 \text{ J}) = -7.0 \times 10^4 \text{ J}$$

This quantity is more than 80% of the initial energy. (Where did this energy actually go?)

Follow-Up Exercise. In free fall, air resistance is sometimes negligible, but for skydivers, air resistance has a very practical effect. Typically, a skydiver descends about 450 m before reaching a terminal velocity (Section 4.6) of 60 m/s. (a) What is the percentage of energy loss to nonconservative forces during this descent? (b) Show that after terminal velocity is reached, the rate of energy loss in J/s is given by $(60 \ mg)$, where m is the mass of the skydiver.

Example 5.15 ■ Nonconservative Force: One More Time

A 0.75-kg block slides on a frictionless surface with a speed of 20 m/s. It then slides over a rough area 1.0 m in length and onto another frictionless surface. The coefficient of kinetic friction between the block and the rough surface is 0.17. What is the speed of the block after it passes across the rough surface?

Thinking It Through. The task of finding the final speed implies that we use equations involving kinetic energy, where the final kinetic energy can be found by using the conservation of *total* energy. Note that the initial and final energies are kinetic energies, since there is no change in gravitational potential energy. It is always good to make a sketch of the situation for clarity and understanding. See ▼ Fig. 5.22.

Solution. Listing the data as usual,

Given: $m = 0.75$ kg   *Find:* v (final speed of block)
          $x = 1.0$ m
          $\mu_k = 0.17$
          $v_o = 2.0$ m/s

For this nonconservative system, we have from Eq. 5.13

$$W_{nc} = E - E_o = K - K_o$$

In the rough area, the block loses energy, because of the work done against friction (W_{nc}), and thus

$$W_{nc} = -f_k x = -\mu_k N x = -\mu_k mgx$$

[negative because f_k and the displacement x are in opposite directions; that is, $(f_k \cos 180°)x = -f_k x$].

Then, rearranging the energy equation and writing the terms out in detail,

$$K = K_o + W_{nc}$$

or

$$\tfrac{1}{2}mv^2 = \tfrac{1}{2}mv_o^2 - \mu_k mgx$$

(continues on next page)

◀ **FIGURE 5.22** A nonconservative rough spot See Example 5.15.

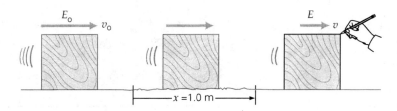

Simplifying yields

$$v = \sqrt{v_0^2 - 2\mu_k g x} = \sqrt{(2.0 \text{ m/s})^2 - 2(0.17)(9.8 \text{ m/s}^2)(1.0 \text{ m})} = 0.82 \text{ m/s}$$

Note that the mass of the block was not needed. And, it can be easily shown that the block lost more than 80% of its energy to friction.

Follow-Up Exercise. Suppose the coefficient of kinetic friction between the block and the rough surface were 0.25. What would happen to the block in this case?

Note that in a nonconservative system, the *total energy* (*not* the total mechanical energy) is conserved (including nonmechanical forms of energy, such as heat), but not all of it is available for mechanical work. For a conservative system, you get back what you put in, so to speak. That is, if you do work on the system, the transferred energy is available to do work. But keep in mind that conservative systems are idealizations, because all real systems are nonconservative to some degree. However, working with ideal conservative systems gives us an insight into the conservation of energy.

Total energy is always conserved. During this course of study, you will learn about other forms of energy, such as thermal, electrical, nuclear, and chemical energies. In general, on the microscopic and submicroscopic levels, these forms of energy can be described in terms of kinetic energy and potential energy. Also, you will learn that mass is a form of energy and that the law of conservation of energy must take this form into account in order to be applied to the analysis of nuclear reactions.

An example of energy conversion is given in Insight 5.2.

5.6 Power

OBJECTIVES: To (a) define power, and (b) describe mechanical efficiency.

A particular task may require a certain amount of work, but that work might be done over different lengths of time or at different rates. For example, suppose that you have to mow a lawn. This task takes a certain amount of work, but you might do the job in a half hour, or you might take an hour or two. There's a practical distinction to be made here. That is, there is usually not only an interest in the amount of work done, but also an interest in how fast it is done—that is, the rate at which it is done. *The time rate of doing work* is called **power**.

The average power is the work done divided by the time it takes to do the work, or work per unit of time:

$$\overline{P} = \frac{W}{t} \tag{5.14}$$

INSIGHT 5.2 HYBRID ENERGY CONVERSION

As you have learned, energy may be transformed from one form to another. An interesting example is the conversion that takes place in the new hybrid automobiles. A hybrid car has both a gasoline (internal combustion) engine and a battery-driven electric motor, both of which may be used to power the vehicle.

A moving car has kinetic energy, and when you step on the brake pedal to slow the car down, kinetic energy is lost. Normally, the brakes of a car accomplish this slowing by friction, and energy is dissipated as heat (conservation of energy). However, with the braking of a hybrid car, some of the energy is converted to electrical energy and stored in the battery of the electric motor. This is called *regenerative braking*. That is, instead of using regular friction brakes to slow the car, the electric motor is used. In this mode, the motor runs in reverse and acts as a generator, converting the lost kinetic energy into electrical energy. (See Section 20.2 for generator operation.) The energy is stored in the battery for later use (Fig. 1).

Hybrid cars must also have regular friction brakes to be used when rapid braking is needed. (See Insight 20.2, page 666 for a more detailed discussion on hybrids.)

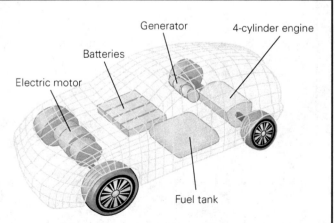

FIGURE 1 Hybrid car A diagram showing the major components. See text for description.

If we are interested in the work (and power) done by a constant force of magnitude F acting while an object moves through a parallel displacement of magnitude d, then

$$\overline{P} = \frac{W}{t} = \frac{Fd}{t} = F\left(\frac{d}{t}\right) = F\overline{v} \qquad (5.15)$$

SI unit of power: J/s or watt (W)

where it is assumed that the force is in the direction of the displacement. Here, $\overline{v}$ is the magnitude of the average velocity. If the velocity is constant, then $\overline{P} = P = Fv$. If the force and displacement are not in the same direction, then we can write

$$\overline{P} = \frac{F(\cos\theta)d}{t} = F\overline{v}\cos\theta \qquad (5.16)$$

where θ is the angle between the force and the displacement.

As you can see from Eq. 5.15, the SI unit of power is joules per second (J/s), but this unit is given another name, the **watt** (**W**):

$$1\,\text{J/s} = 1\,\text{watt (W)}$$

The SI unit of power is named in honor of James Watt (1736–1819), a Scottish engineer who developed one of the first practical steam engines. A common unit of electrical power is the *kilowatt* (kW).

The British unit of power is foot-pound per second (ft·lb/s). However, a larger unit, the **horsepower** (**hp**), is more commonly used:

$$1\,\text{hp} = 550\,\text{ft·lb/s} = 746\,\text{W}$$

Power tells you how fast work is being done *or* how fast energy is transferred. For example, motors have power ratings commonly given in horsepower. A 2-hp motor can do a given amount of work in half the time that a 1-hp motor would take, or twice the work in the same amount of time. That is, a 2-hp motor is twice as "powerful" as a 1-hp motor.

Note: In Watt's time, steam engines were replacing horses for work in mines and mills. To characterize the performance of his new engine, which was more efficient than existing ones, Watt used the average rate at which a horse could do work as a unit—a horsepower.

Example 5.16 ■ A Crane Hoist: Work and Power

A crane hoist like the one shown in ►Fig. 5.23 lifts a load of 1.0 metric ton a vertical distance of 25 m in 9.0 s at a constant velocity. How much useful work is done by the hoist each second?

Thinking It Through. The useful work done each second (that is, per second) is the power output, so this quantity is what is to be found.

Solution.

Given: $m = 1.0$ metric ton **Find:** Work per second ($=$ power, P)
     $= 1.0 \times 10^3\,\text{kg}$
   $y = 25\,\text{m}$
   $t = 9.0\,\text{s}$

Keep in mind that the work per unit time (work per second) is power, so this quantity is what we need to compute. Since the load moves with a constant velocity, $\overline{P} = P$. (Why?) The work is done against gravity, so $F = mg$, and

$$P = \frac{W}{t} = \frac{Fd}{t} = \frac{mgy}{t}$$

$$= \frac{(1.0 \times 10^3\,\text{kg})(9.8\,\text{m/s}^2)(25\,\text{m})}{9.0\,\text{s}} = 2.7 \times 10^4\,\text{W (or 27 kW)}$$

Thus, since a watt (W) is a joule per second (J/s), the hoist did 2.7×10^4 J of work each second. Note that the velocity has a magnitude of $v = d/t = 25\,\text{m}/9.0\,\text{s} = 2.8\,\text{m/s}$, and the power could be found using $P = Fv$.

Follow-Up Exercise. If the hoist motor of the crane in this Example is rated at 70 hp, what percentage of this power output goes into useful work?

▲ **FIGURE 5.23** Power delivery See Example 5.16.

Example 5.17 ■ Cleaning Up: Work and Time

The motors of two vacuum cleaners have net power outputs of 1.00 hp and 0.500 hp, respectively. (a) How much work in joules can each motor do in 3.00 min? (b) How long does each motor take to do 97.0 kJ of work?

Thinking It Through. (a) Since power is work/time ($P = W/t$), the work can be computed. Note that power is given in horsepower units which is converted to watts. (b) This part of the problem is another application of Eq. 5.15.

Solution.

Given: $P_1 = 1.00 \text{ hp} = 746 \text{ W}$ *Find:* (a) W (work for each)
$P_2 = 0.500 \text{ hp} = 373 \text{ W}$ (b) t (time for each)
$t = 3.00 \text{ min} = 180 \text{ s}$
$W = 97.0 \text{ kJ} = 97.0 \times 10^3 \text{ J}$

(a) Since $P = W/t$,

$$W_1 = P_1 t = (746 \text{ W})(180 \text{ s}) = 1.34 \times 10^5 \text{ J}$$

and

$$W_2 = P_2 t = (373 \text{ W})(180 \text{ s}) = 0.67 \times 10^5 \text{ J}$$

Note that in the same amount of time, the smaller motor does half as much work as the larger one, as you would expect.

(b) The times are given by $t = W/P$, and for the same amount of work,

$$t_1 = \frac{W}{P_1} = \frac{97.0 \times 10^3 \text{ J}}{746 \text{ W}} = 130 \text{ s}$$

and

$$t_2 = \frac{W}{P_2} = \frac{97.0 \times 10^3 \text{ J}}{373 \text{ W}} = 260 \text{ s}$$

Note that the smaller motor takes twice as long as the larger one to do the same amount of work.

Follow-Up Exercise. (a) A 10-hp motor breaks down and is temporarily replaced with a 5-hp motor. What can you say about the rate of work output? (b) Suppose the situation were reversed—a 5-hp motor is replaced with a 10-hp motor. What can you say about the rate of work output for this case?

Efficiency

Machines and motors are commonly used items in our daily lives, and we often talk about their efficiency. Efficiency involves work, energy, and/or power. Both simple and complex machines that do work have mechanical parts that move, so some input energy is always lost because of friction or some other cause (perhaps in the form of sound). Thus, not all of the input energy goes into doing useful work.

Mechanical efficiency is essentially a measure of what you get out for what you put in—that is, the *useful* work output compared with the energy input. **Efficiency**, ε, is given as a fraction (or percentage):

$$\varepsilon = \frac{\text{work output}}{\text{energy input}} (\times 100\%) = \frac{W_{\text{out}}}{E_{\text{in}}} (\times 100\%) \qquad (5.17)$$

Efficiency is a unitless quantity

For example, if a machine has a 100-J (energy) input and a 40-J (work) output, then its efficiency is

$$\varepsilon = \frac{W_{\text{out}}}{E_{\text{in}}} = \frac{40 \text{ J}}{100 \text{ J}} = 0.40 (\times 100\%) = 40\%$$

An efficiency of 0.40, or 40%, means that 60% of the energy input is lost because of friction or some other cause and doesn't serve its intended purpose. Note that if both terms of the ratio in Eq. 5.17 are divided by time t, we obtain $W_{out}/t = P_{out}$ and $E_{in}/t = P_{in}$. So, we can also write efficiency in terms of power, P:

$$\varepsilon = \frac{P_{out}}{P_{in}} \ (\times 100\%) \qquad (5.18)$$

Example 5.18 ■ Home Improvement: Mechanical Efficiency and Work Output

The motor of an electric drill with an efficiency of 80% has a power input of 600 W. How much useful work is done by the drill in 30 s?

Thinking It Through. This example is an application of Eq. 5.18 and the definition of power.

Solution.

Given: $\varepsilon = 80\% = 0.80$ *Find:* W_{out} (work output)
$P_{in} = 600$ W
$t = 30$ s

Given the efficiency and power input, we can readily find the power output P_{out} from Eq. 5.18, and this quantity is related to the work output ($P_{out} = W_{out}/t$). First, we rearrange Eq. 5.18:

$$P_{out} = \varepsilon P_{in} = (0.80)(600 \text{ W}) = 4.8 \times 10^2 \text{ W}$$

Then, substituting this value into the equation relating power output and work output, we obtain

$$W_{out} = P_{out}t = (4.8 \times 10^2 \text{ W})(30 \text{ s}) = 1.4 \times 10^4 \text{ J}$$

Follow-Up Exercise. (a) Is it possible to have a mechanical efficiency of 100%? (b) What would an efficiency of greater than 100% imply?

Table 5.1 lists the typical efficiencies of some machines. You may be surprised by the relatively low efficiency of the automobile. Much of the energy input (from gasoline combustion) is lost as exhaust heat and through the cooling system (more than 60%), and friction accounts for a great deal more. About 20% of the input energy is converted to useful work that goes into propelling the vehicle. Air conditioning, power steering, radio, and tape and CD players are nice, but they also use energy and contribute to the car's decrease in efficiency.

TABLE 5.1   Typical Efficiencies of Some Machines

Machine	Efficiency (approximate %)
Compressor	85
Electric motor	70–95
Automobile (hybrid cars increase fuel efficiency by 25%)	20
Human muscle*	20–25
Steam locomotive	5–10

*Technically not a machine, but used to perform work.

SOLIDS AND FLUIDS

PHYSICS FACTS

- The Mariana Trench in the Pacific Ocean is the deepest known point on Earth. It is about 11 km (6.8 mi) below sea level. At this depth, the ocean water exerts a pressure of about 108 MPa (15 900 lb/in^2), or more than 1000 atmospheres of pressure.

- The German zeppelin, *Hindenburg*, had a hydrogen gas volume of 20 000 m^3 (7 062 000 ft^3). It went down in a fiery crash in 1937 in Lakehurst, NJ. (Hydrogen is very flammable.) The ship was originally designed for nonflammable helium. But, the majority of helium was produced by the United States and a law was enacted that forbade the sale of helium to Nazi Germany.

- Although Archimedes is credited with the principle of buoyancy, it is questionable whether this occurred to him in his bathtub while pondering a way to see if the king's crown was pure gold and contained no silver, as the story goes. According to a Roman account, the solution came to him when he got into a bathtub and it overflowed. Supposedly, quantities of pure gold and silver equal in weight to the king's crown were each put into bowls filled with water, and the silver caused more water to overflow. Testing the crown, more water overflowed than for the pure gold, which implied some silver content. A crown of pure gold? Pure gold is soft and malleable (can be beaten into thin sheets) and ductile (can be drawn into thin wire).

Shown in the photo are solid mountains and the unseen fluid air that makes gliding possible. We walk on the solid surface of the Earth and in our daily lives use solid objects of all sorts, from scissors to computers. But we are surrounded by fluids—liquids and gases—on which we depend. Without the water that we drink, we could survive only for a few days at most; without the oxygen in the air we breathe, we could not live for more than a few minutes. Indeed, we ourselves are not nearly as solid as we think. By far the most abundant substance in our bodies is water, and it is in the watery environment of our cells that all chemical processes on which life depends take place.

On the basis of general physical distinctions, matter is commonly divided into three phases: solid, liquid, and gas. A *solid* has a definite shape and volume. A *liquid* has a fairly definite volume, but assumes the shape of its container. A *gas* takes on the shape and volume of its container. Solids and liquids are sometimes called *condensed matter*. We will use a different classification scheme and consider matter in terms of solids and fluids. Liquids and gases are referred to collectively as fluids. A **fluid** is a substance that can flow; liquids and gases qualify, but solids do not.

A simplistic description of solids is that they are made up of particles called atoms that are held rigidly together by interatomic forces. In Chapter 8, the concept of an ideal rigid body was used to describe rotational motion. Real solid bodies are not absolutely rigid and can be elastically deformed by external forces. Elasticity usually brings to mind a rubber band or spring that will resume its original dimensions even after being greatly deformed. In fact, all materials—even very hard steel—are elastic to some degree. But, as you will learn, such deformation has an *elastic limit*.

Fluids, however, have little or no elastic response to a force. Instead, the force merely causes an unconfined fluid to flow. This chapter pays particular

297

attention to the behavior of fluids, shedding light on such questions as how hydraulic lifts work, why icebergs and ocean liners float, and what "10W-30" on a can of motor oil means. You'll also discover why the person in the photo can neither float like a helium balloon nor fly like a hummingbird, yet, with the aid of a suitably shaped piece of plastic, can soar like an eagle.

Because of their fluidity, liquids and gases have many properties in common, and it is convenient to study them together. There are important differences as well. For example, liquids are not very compressible, whereas gases are easily compressed.

9.1 Solids and Elastic Moduli

OBJECTIVES: To (a) distinguish between stress and strain, and (b) use elastic moduli to compute dimensional changes.

As stated previously, all solid materials are elastic to some degree. That is, a body that is slightly deformed by an applied force will return to its original dimensions or shape when the force is removed. The deformation may not be noticeable for many materials, but it's there.

You may be able to visualize why materials are elastic if you think in terms of the simplistic model of a solid in ◄Fig. 9.1. The atoms of the solid substance are imagined to be held together by springs. The elasticity of the springs represents the resilient nature of the interatomic forces. The springs resist permanent deformation, as do the forces between atoms. The elastic properties of solids are commonly discussed in terms of stress and strain. **Stress** is a measure of the force causing a deformation. **Strain** is a relative measure of the deformation a stress causes. Quantitatively, *stress is the applied force per unit cross-sectional area*:

$$\text{stress} = \frac{F}{A} \qquad (9.1)$$

SI unit of stress: newton per square meter (N/m^2)

Here, F is the magnitude of the applied force normal (perpendicular) to the cross-sectional area. Equation 9.1 shows that the SI units for stress are newtons per square meter (N/m^2).

As illustrated in ▼Fig. 9.2, a force applied to the ends of a rod gives rise to either a *tensile stress* (an elongating tension, $\Delta L > 0$) or a *compressional stress* (a shortening tension, $\Delta L < 0$), depending on the direction of the force. In both these cases, the *tensile strain* is the ratio of the change in length ($\Delta L = L - L_o$) to the original length (L_o), without regard to the sign, so we use the absolute value, $|\Delta L|$:

$$\text{strain} = \frac{|\text{change in length}|}{\text{original length}} = \frac{|\Delta L|}{L_o} = \frac{|L - L_o|}{L_o} \qquad (9.2)$$

Strain is a positive unitless quantity

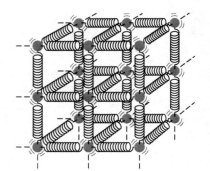

▲ **FIGURE 9.1 A springy solid** The elastic nature of interatomic forces is indicated by simplistically representing them as springs, which, like the forces, resist deformation.

▶ **FIGURE 9.2 Tensile and compressional stresses** Tensile and compressional stresses are due to forces applied normally to the surface area of the ends of bodies. **(a)** A tension, or tensile stress, tends to increase the length of an object. **(b)** A compressional stress tends to shorten the length. $\Delta L = L - L_o$ can be positive, as in (a), or negative, as in (b). The sign is not needed in Eq. 9.2, so the absolute value, $|\Delta L|$, is used.

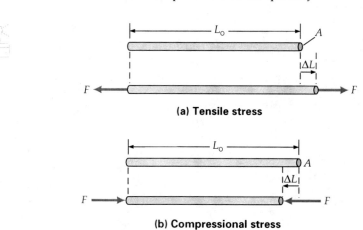

(a) Tensile stress

(b) Compressional stress

Thus the strain is the *fractional change* in length. For example, if the strain is 0.05, the length of the material has changed by 5% of the original length.

As might be expected, the resulting strain depends on the applied stress. For relatively small stresses, this is a direct (or linear) proportion, that is, stress ∝ strain. For relatively small stresses, this is a direct (or linear) proportion. The constant of proportionality, which depends on the nature of the material, is called the **elastic modulus**, that is,

$$\text{stress} = \text{elastic modulus} \times \text{strain}$$

or

$$\text{elastic modulus} = \frac{\text{stress}}{\text{strain}} \tag{9.3}$$

SI unit of elastic modulus: newton per square meter (N/m^2)

The elastic modulus is the stress divided by the strain, and the elastic modulus has the same units as stress. (Why?)

Three general types of elastic moduli (plural of *modulus*) are associated with stresses that produce changes in length, shape, or volume. These are called *Young's modulus*, the *shear modulus*, and the *bulk modulus*, respectively.

Change in Length: Young's Modulus

▾Figure 9.3 is a typical graph of the tensile stress versus the strain for a metal rod. The curve is a straight line up to a point called the *proportional limit*. Beyond this point, the strain begins to increase more rapidly to another critical point called the **elastic limit**. If the tension is removed at this point, the material will return to its original length. If the tension is applied beyond the elastic limit and then removed, the material will recover somewhat, but will retain some permanent deformation.

The straight-line part of the graph shows a direct proportionality between stress and strain. This relationship, first formalized by the English physicist Robert Hooke in 1678, is now known as *Hooke's law*. (It is the same general relationship as that given for a spring in Section 5.2—see Fig. 5.5.) The elastic modulus for a tension or a compression is called **Young's modulus (Y):***

$$\frac{F}{A} = Y\left(\frac{\Delta L}{L_o}\right) \quad \text{or} \quad Y = \frac{F/A}{\Delta L/L_o} \tag{9.4}$$

$$\underset{stress}{\qquad\qquad} \underset{strain}{\qquad\qquad}$$

SI unit of Young's modulus: newton per square meter (N/m^2)

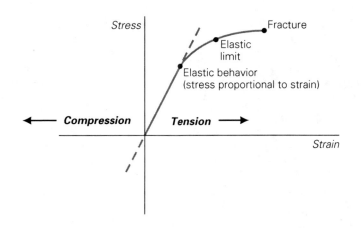

▶ **FIGURE 9.3 Stress versus strain** A plot of stress versus strain for a typical metal rod is a straight line up to the proportional limit. Then elastic deformation continues until the elastic limit is reached. Beyond that, the rod will be permanently deformed and will eventually fracture or break.

*Thomas Young (1773–1829) was an English physician and physicist who also demonstrated the wave nature of light. See Young's double-slit experiment, Section 24.1.

TABLE 9.1	Elastic Moduli for Various Materials (in N/m²)		
Substance	Young's modulus (Y)	Shear modulus (S)	Bulk modulus (B)
Solids			
Aluminum	7.0×10^{10}	2.5×10^{10}	7.0×10^{10}
Bone (limb)	Tension: 1.5×10^{10}	1.2×10^{10}	
	Compression: 9.3×10^{9}		
Brass	9.0×10^{10}	3.5×10^{10}	7.5×10^{10}
Copper	11×10^{10}	3.8×10^{10}	12×10^{10}
Glass	5.7×10^{10}	2.4×10^{10}	4.0×10^{10}
Iron	15×10^{10}	6.0×10^{10}	12×10^{10}
Nylon	5.0×10^{8}	8.0×10^{8}	
Steel	20×10^{10}	8.2×10^{10}	15×10^{10}
Liquids			
Alcohol, ethyl			1.0×10^{9}
Glycerin			4.5×10^{9}
Mercury			26×10^{9}
Water			2.2×10^{9}

The units of Young's modulus are the same as those of stress, newtons per square meter (N/m^2), since the strain is unitless. Some typical values of Young's modulus are given in Table 9.1.

To obtain a conceptual or physical understanding of Young's modulus, let's solve Eq. 9.4 for ΔL:

$$\Delta L = \left(\frac{FL_o}{A}\right)\frac{1}{Y} \quad \text{or} \quad \Delta L \propto \frac{1}{Y}$$

Hence, the larger Young's the modulus of a material, the smaller its change in length (other parameters being equal).

Example 9.1 ■ Pulling My Leg: Under a Lot of Stress

The femur (upper leg bone) is the longest and strongest bone in the body. Taking a typical femur to be approximately circular in cross-section with a radius of 2.0 cm, how much force would be required to extend a patient's femur by 0.010% while in horizontal traction?

Thinking It Through. Equation 9.4 should apply, but where does the percentage increase fit in? This question can be answered as soon as it is recognized that the $\Delta L/L_o$ term is the *fractional* increase in length. For example, if you had a spring with a length of 10 cm (L_o), and you stretched it 1.0 cm (ΔL), then $\Delta L/L_o$ = 1.0 cm/10 cm = 0.10. This ratio can readily be changed to a percentage, and we would say the spring's length was increased by 10%. So the percentage increase is really just the value of the $\Delta L/L_o$ term (multiplied by 100%).

Solution. Listing the data,

Given: r = 2.0 cm = 0.020 m   *Find:* F (tensile force)
       $\Delta L/L_o$ = 0.010% = 1.0×10^{-4}
           Y = 1.5×10^{10} N/m² (for bone from Table 9.1)

Using Eq. 9.4, we have

$$F = Y(\Delta L/L_o)A = Y(\Delta L/L_o)\pi r^2$$
$$= (1.5 \times 10^{10}\ \text{N/m}^2)(1.0 \times 10^{-4})\pi(0.020\ \text{m})^2 = 1.9 \times 10^{3}\ \text{N}$$

How much force is this? Quite a bit—in fact, more than 400 lb. The femur is a pretty strong bone.

Science Fundamentals

Follow-Up Exercise. A total mass of 16 kg is suspended from a 0.10-cm-diameter steel wire. (a) By what percentage does the length of the wire increase? (b) The tensile or ultimate strength of a material is the maximum stress the material can support before breaking or fracturing. If the tensile strength of the steel wire in (a) is 4.9×10^8 N/m², how much mass could be suspended before the wire would break? (*Answers to all Follow-Up Exercises are at the back of the text.*)

Most types of bone are composed of protein collagen fibers that are tightly bound together and overlapping. Collagen has great tensile strength, and the calcium salts within the collagen give bone great compressional strength. Collagen also makes up cartilage, tendons, and skin, which have good tensile strength.

Change in Shape: Shear Modulus

Another way an elastic body can be deformed is by a *shear stress*. In this case, the deformation is due to an applied force that is *tangential* to the surface area (▸Fig. 9.4a). A change in shape results without a change in volume. The *shear strain* is given by x/h, where x is the relative displacement of the faces and h is the distance between them.

The shear strain is sometimes defined in terms of the *shear angle ϕ*. As Fig. 9.4b shows, $\tan \phi = x/h$. But the shear angle is usually quite small, so a good approximation is $\tan \phi \approx \phi \approx x/h$, where ϕ is in radians.* (If $\phi = 10°$, for example, there is only 1.0% difference between ϕ and $\tan \phi$.) The **shear modulus (S)**, sometimes called the *modulus of rigidity*, is then

$$S = \frac{F/A}{x/h} \approx \frac{F/A}{\phi} \qquad (9.5)$$

SI unit of shear modulus: newton per square meter (N/m²)

Note in Table 9.1 that the shear modulus is generally less than Young's modulus. In fact, S is approximately $Y/3$ for many materials, which indicates a greater response to a shear stress than to a tensile stress. Note also the inverse relationship $\phi \approx 1/S$, similar to that pointed out previously for Young's modulus.

A shear stress may be of the torsional type, resulting from the twisting action of a torque. For example, a torsional shear stress may shear off the head of a bolt that is being tightened.

Liquids do not have shear moduli (or Young's moduli)—hence the gaps in Table 9.1. A shear stress cannot be effectively applied to a liquid or a gas because fluids deform continuously in response. It is often said that *fluids cannot support a shear*.

Change in Volume: Bulk Modulus

Suppose that a force directed inward acts over the entire surface of a body (▾Fig. 9.5). Such a *volume stress* is often applied by pressure transmitted by a fluid. An elastic material will be compressed by a volume stress; that is, the material will show a change in volume, but not in general shape, in response to a pressure change Δp. (Pressure is force per unit area, as we shall see in Section 9.2.) The change in pressure is equal to

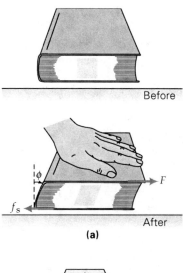
Before / After

(a)

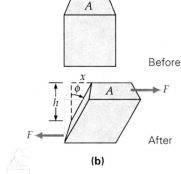
Before / After

(b)

▲ **FIGURE 9.4 Shear stress and strain (a)** A shear stress is produced when a force is applied tangentially to a surface area. **(b)** The strain is measured in terms of the relative displacement of the object's faces, or the shear angle ϕ.

◂ **FIGURE 9.5 Volume stress and strain (a)** A volume stress is applied when a normal force acts over an entire surface area, as shown here for a cube. This type of stress most commonly occurs in gases. **(b)** The resulting strain is a change in volume.

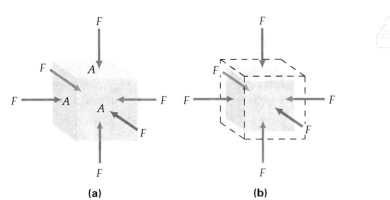

(a)   (b)

*See Learn by Drawing on page 219.

the volume stress, or $\Delta p = F/A$. The *volume strain* is the ratio of the volume change (ΔV) to the original volume (V_o). The **bulk modulus (B)** is then

$$B = \frac{F/A}{-\Delta V/V_o} = -\frac{\Delta p}{\Delta V/V_o} \tag{9.6}$$

SI unit of bulk modulus: newton per square meter (N/m^2)

The minus sign is introduced to make B a positive quantity, since $\Delta V = V - V_o$ is negative for an increase in external pressure (when Δp is positive). Similarly to the previous moduli relationships, $\Delta V \propto 1/B$.

Bulk moduli of some selected solids and liquids are listed in Table 9.1. Gases also have bulk moduli, since they can be compressed. For a gas, it is common to talk about the reciprocal of the bulk modulus, which is called the **compressibility (k)**:

$$k = \frac{1}{B} \quad \text{(compressibility for gases)} \tag{9.7}$$

The change in volume ΔV is thus directly proportional to the compressibility k.

Solids and liquids are relatively incompressible and thus have small values of compressibility. Conversely, gases are easily compressed and have large compressibilities, which vary with pressure and temperature.

Example 9.2 ■ Compressing a Liquid: Volume Stress and Bulk Modulus

By how much should the pressure on a liter of water be changed to compress it by 0.10%?

Thinking It Through. Similarly to the fractional change in length, $\Delta L/L_o$, the fractional change in volume is given by $-\Delta V/V_o$, which may be expressed as a percentage. The pressure change can then be found from Eq. 9.6. Compression implies a negative ΔV.

Solution.

Given: $-\Delta V/V_o = 0.0010$ (or 0.10%)   *Find:* Δp
  $V_o = 1.0\ L = 1000\ cm^3$
  $B_{H_2O} = 2.2 \times 10^9\ N/m^2$ (from Table 9.1)

Note that $-\Delta V/V_o$ is the *fractional* change in the volume. With $V_o = 1000\ cm^3$, the change (reduction) in volume is

$$-\Delta V = 0.0010\ V_o = 0.0010(1000\ cm^3) = 1.0\ cm^3$$

However, the change in volume is not needed. The fractional change, as listed in the given data, can be used directly in Eq. 9.6 to find the increase in pressure:

$$\Delta p = B\left(\frac{-\Delta V}{V_o}\right) = (2.2 \times 10^9\ N/m^2)(0.0010) = 2.2 \times 10^6\ N/m^2$$

(This increase is about twenty-two times normal atmospheric pressure. Not too compressible.)

Follow-Up Exercise. If an extra $1.0 \times 10^6\ N/m^2$ of pressure above normal atmospheric pressure is applied to a half liter of water, what is the change in the water's volume?

9.2 Fluids: Pressure and Pascal's Principle

OBJECTIVES: To (a) explain the pressure–depth relationship, and (b) state Pascal's principle and describe how it is used in practical applications.

A force can be applied to a solid at a point of contact, but this won't work with a fluid, since a fluid cannot support a shear. With fluids, a force must be applied over an area. Such an application of force is expressed in terms of **pressure**, or the *force per unit area*:

$$p = \frac{F}{A} \tag{9.8a}$$

SI unit of pressure: newton per square meter (N/m^2), or pascal (Pa)

Science Fundamentals

The force in this equation is understood to be acting normally (perpendicularly) to the surface area. F may be the perpendicular component of a force that acts at an angle to a surface (▸Fig. 9.6).

As Figure 9.6 shows, in the more general case we should write

$$p = \frac{F_\perp}{A} = \frac{F \cos \theta}{A} \qquad (9.8b)$$

Pressure is a scalar quantity (with magnitude only), even though the force producing it is a vector.

Pressure has SI units of newton per square meter (N/m^2), or **pascal (Pa)**, in honor of the French scientist and philosopher Blaise Pascal (1623–1662), who studied fluids and pressure. By definition,*

$$1 \text{ Pa} = 1 \text{ N/m}^2$$

In the British system, a common unit of pressure is pound per square inch (lb/in^2, or psi). Other units, some of which will be introduced later, are used in special applications. Before going on, here's a "solid" example of the relationship between force and pressure.

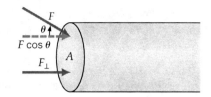

$$p = \frac{F_\perp}{A} = \frac{F \cos \theta}{A}$$

▲ **FIGURE 9.6 Pressure** Pressure is usually written $p = F/A$, where it is understood that F is the force or component of force normal to the surface. In general, then, $p = (F \cos \theta)/A$.

Conceptual Example 9.3 ■ Force and Pressure: Taking a Nap on a Bed of Nails

Suppose you are getting ready to take a nap, and you have a choice of lying stretched out on your back on (a) a bed of nails, (b) a hardwood floor, or (c) a couch. Which one would you choose for the most comfort, and *why*?

Reasoning and Answer. The comfortable choice is quite apparent—the couch. But here, the conceptual question is *why*.

First let's look at the prospect of lying on a bed of nails, an old trick that originated in India and used to be demonstrated in carnival sideshows (See Fig. 9.27). There is really no trick here, just physics—namely, force and pressure. It is the force per unit area, or pressure ($p = F/A$), that determines whether a nail will pierce the skin. The force is determined by the weight of the person lying on the nails. The area is determined by the *effective* area of the nails in contact with the skin (neglecting one's clothes).

If there were only one nail, the person's weight would not be supported by the nail, and with such a small area, the pressure would be very great—a situation in which the lone nail would pierce the skin. However, when a bed of nails is used, the same force (weight) is distributed over hundreds of nails, which gives a relatively large effective area of contact. The pressure is then reduced to a level at which the nails do not pierce the skin.

When you are lying on a hardwood floor, the area in contact with your body is appreciable and the pressure is reduced, but it still may be a bit uncomfortable. Parts of your body, such as your neck and the small of your back, are *not* in contact with a surface, but they would be on a soft couch, making for a comfortable pressure—the lower the pressure, the more comfort (same force over a larger area). So (c) is the answer.

Follow-Up Exercise. What are a couple of important considerations in constructing a bed of nails to lie on?

Now, let's take a quick review of density, which is an important consideration in the study of fluids. Recall from Chapter 1 that the density (ρ) of a substance is defined as mass per *unit* volume (Eq. 1.1):

$$\text{density} = \frac{\text{mass}}{\text{volume}}$$
$$\rho = \frac{m}{V}$$

SI unit of density: kilogram per cubic meter (kg/m^3)
(common cgs unit: gram per cubic centimeter, or g/cm^3)

The densities of some common substances are given in Table 9.2.

*Notice that the unit of pressure is equivalent to energy per volume, $N/m^2 = N \cdot m/m^3 = J/m^3$, an energy density.

INSIGHT 9.1 OSTEOPOROSIS AND BONE MINERAL DENSITY (BMD)

Bone is a living, growing tissue. Your body is continuously taking up old bone (resorption) and making new bone tissue. In the early years of life, bone growth is greater than bone loss. This continues until a peak bone mass is reached as a young adult. After this, bone growth is slowly outpaced by bone loss. Bones naturally become less dense and weaker with age. Osteoporosis ("porous bone") occurs when bones deteriorate to the point where they are easily fractured (Fig. 1).

Osteoporosis and low bone mass affect an estimated 24 million Americans, most of whom are women. Osteoporosis results in an increased risk of bone fractures, particularly of the hip and the spine. Many women take calcium supplements to help prevent this.

To understand how bone density is measured, let's first distinguish between *bone* and *bone tissue*. Bone is the solid material composed of a protein matrix, most of which has calcified. Bone tissue includes the marrow spaces within the matrix.

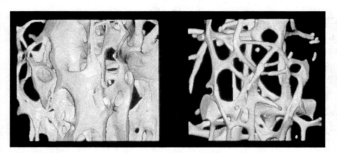

FIGURE 1 Bone mass loss An X-ray micrograph of the bone structure of the vertebrae of a 50-year old (left) and a 70-year old (right). Osteoporosis, a condition characterized by bone weakening caused by loss of bone mass, is evident for the vertebrae on the right.

(Marrow is the soft, fatty, vascular tissue in the interior cavities of bones and is a major site of blood cell production.) The marrow volume varies with the bone type.

If the volume of an intact bone is measured (for example, by water displacement), then, the *bone tissue density* can be computed, commonly in grams per cubic centimeter after the bone is weighed to determine mass. If you burn the bone, weigh the remaining ash, and divide by the volume of the overall bone (bone tissue), you get the *bone tissue mineral density*, which is commonly called the **bone mineral density (BMD)**.

To measure the BMD of bones *in vivo*, types of radiation transmission through the bone is measured, and this is related to the amount of bone mineral present. Also, a "projected" area of the bone is measured. Using these measurements, an areal or projected BMD is computed in units of mg/cm^2. Figure 2 illustrates the magnitude of the effect of bone density loss with aging.

The diagnosis of osteoporosis relies primarily on the measurement of BMD. The mass of a bone, measured by a BMD test (also called a *bone densitometry test*), generally correlates to the bone strength. It is possible to predict fracture risk, much as blood pressure measurements can help predict stroke risk. Bone density testing is recommended for all women age 65 and older, and for younger women at an increased risk of osteoporosis. This also applies to men. Osteoporosis is often thought to be a woman's disease, but 20% of osteoporosis cases occur in men. A BMD test cannot predict the certainty of developing a fracture, but only predicts the degree of risk.

So how is BMD measured? This is where the physics comes in. Various instruments, divided into *central devices* and *peripheral devices*, are used. Central devices are used primarily to measure the bone density of the hip and spine. Peripheral devices are smaller, portable machines that are used to measure the bone density in such places as the heel or finger.

TABLE 9.2	Densities of Some Common Substances (in kg/m^3)				
Solids	Density (ρ)	Liquids	Density (ρ)	Gases*	Density (ρ)
Aluminum	2.7×10^3	Alcohol, ethyl	0.79×10^3	Air	1.29
Brass	8.7×10^3	Alcohol, methyl	0.82×10^3	Helium	0.18
Copper	8.9×10^3	Blood, whole	1.05×10^3	Hydrogen	0.090
Glass	2.6×10^3	Blood plasma	1.03×10^3	Oxygen	1.43
Gold	19.3×10^3	Gasoline	0.68×10^3	Water vapor (100°C)	0.63
Ice	0.92×10^3	Kerosene	0.82×10^3		
Iron (and steel)	7.8×10^3 (general value)	Mercury	13.6×10^3		
Lead	11.4×10^3	Seawater (4°C)	1.03×10^3		
Silver	10.5×10^3	Water, fresh (4°C)	1.00×10^3		
Wood, oak	0.81×10^3				

*At 0°C and 1 atm, unless otherwise specified.

A common peripheral device uses *quantative ultrasound* (QUS). Instead of X-rays, a bone density screening is made using high-frequency sound waves (ultrasound). (See Section 14.1 for a discussion of ultrasound.) QUS measurements are usually done on the heel. The test takes only a minute or two; and the devices are now found in some pharmacies or drugstores. Its purpose is to tell you if you are "at risk," and may need a more thorough DXA test.

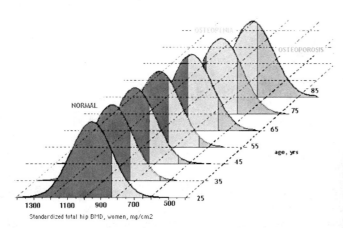

FIGURE 2 Bone density loss with aging An illustration of how normal bone density loss for a female hip bone increases with age (scale on right). Osteopenia refers to decreased calcification or bone density. A person with osteopenia is at risk for developing osteoporosis, a condition that causes bones to become brittle and prone to fracture.

The most widely used central device relies on *dual energy X-ray absorptiometry* (DXA), which uses X-ray imaging to measure bone density. (See Section 20.4 for a discussion of X-rays.) The DXA scanner produces two X-ray beams of different energy levels. The amount of X-rays that pass through a bone is measured for each beam and the amounts vary with the density of bone. The calculated bone density is based on the difference between the two beams. The procedure is nonintrusive and takes 10–20 min, and the X-ray exposure is usually about one tenth of that of a chest X-ray (Fig. 3).

FIGURE 3 Osteoporosis bone scanning A technician runs an X-ray bone scan on an elderly patient for osteoporosis. X-ray images are displayed on the monitor. Such images can confirm the presence of osteoporosis. Also, such bone densitometry tests can be used to diagnosis rickets, a children's disease characterized by softening of the bones.

Water has a density of 1.00×10^3 kg/m^3 (or 1.00 g/cm^3), from the original definition of the kilogram (Chapter 1). Mercury has a density of 13.6×10^3 kg/m^3 (or 13.6 g/cm^3). Hence, mercury is 13.6 times as dense as water. Gasoline, however, is less dense than water. See Table 9.2. (*Note:* Be careful not to confuse the symbol for density, ρ (Greek rho) with that for pressure, p.)

Note: $p \neq \rho$

We say that density is a measure of the compactness of the matter of a substance: The greater the density, the more matter or mass in a given volume. Notice that density quantifies the amount or mass per unit volume. For an important density consideration, see Insight 9.1 on Osteoporosis and Bone Mineral Density (BMD).

Pressure and Depth

If you have gone scuba diving, you well know that pressure increases with depth, having felt the increased pressure on your eardrums. An opposite effect is commonly felt when you fly in a plane or ride in a car going up a mountain: with increasing altitude, your ears may "pop" because of *reduced* external air pressure.

How the pressure in a fluid varies with depth can be demonstrated by considering a container of liquid at rest. Imagine that you can isolate a rectangular column of water,

Science Fundamentals

▶ **FIGURE 9.7 Pressure and depth**
The extra pressure at a depth h in a liquid is due to the weight of the liquid above: $p = \rho g h$, where ρ is the density of the liquid (assumed to be constant). This is shown for an imaginary rectangular column of liquid.

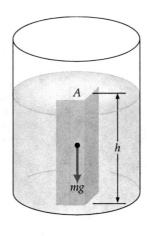

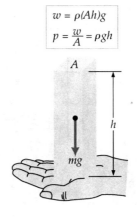

$$w = \rho(Ah)g$$
$$p = \frac{w}{A} = \rho g h$$

as shown in ▲Fig. 9.7. Then the force on the bottom of the container below the column (or the hand) is equal to the weight of the liquid making up the column: $F = w = mg$. Since density is $\rho = m/V$, the mass in the column is equal to the density times the volume; that is, $m = \rho V$. (The liquid is assumed incompressible, so ρ is constant.)

The volume of the isolated liquid column is equal to the height of the column times the area of its base, or $V = hA$. Thus, we can write

$$F = w = mg = \rho V g = \rho g h A$$

With $p = F/A$, the pressure at a depth h due to the weight of the column is

$$p = \rho g h \qquad (9.9)$$

This is a general result for incompressible liquids. The pressure is the same everywhere on a horizontal plane at a depth h (with ρ and g constant). Note that Eq. 9.9 is independent of the base area of the rectangular column: We could have taken the whole cylindrical column of the liquid in the container in Fig. 9.7 and gotten the same result.

The derivation of Eq. 9.9 did not take into account pressure being applied to the open surface of the liquid. This factor adds to the pressure at a depth h to give a *total* pressure of

$$p = p_0 + \rho g h \qquad \begin{array}{l}\textit{(incompressible liquid}\\ \textit{at constant density)}\end{array} \qquad (9.10)$$

where p_0 is the pressure applied to the liquid surface (that is, the pressure at $h = 0$). For an open container, $p_0 = p_a$, atmospheric pressure, or the weight (force) per unit area due to the gases in the atmosphere above the liquid's surface. The average atmospheric pressure at sea level is sometimes used as a unit, called an **atmosphere (atm)**:

$$1\ \text{atm} = 101.325\ \text{kPa} = 1.01325 \times 10^5\ \text{N/m}^2 \approx 14.7\ \text{lb/in}^2$$

The measurement of atmospheric pressure will be described shortly.

Example 9.4 ■ A Scuba Diver: Pressure and Force

(a) What is the total pressure on the back of a scuba diver in a lake at a depth of 8.00 m? (b) What is the force on the diver's back due to the water alone, taking the surface of the back to be a rectangle 60.0 cm by 50.0 cm?

Thinking It Through. (a) This is a direct application of Eq. 9.10 in which p_0 is taken as the atmospheric pressure p_a. (b) Knowing the area and the pressure due to the water, the force can be found from the definition of pressure, $p = F/A$.

Solution.

Given: $h = 8.00$ m   *Find:* (a) p (total pressure)
$\quad A = 60.0\ \text{cm} \times 50.0\ \text{cm}$ (b) F (force due to water)
$\qquad = 0.600\ \text{m} \times 0.500\ \text{m} = 0.300\ \text{m}^2$
$\quad \rho_{H_2O} = 1.00 \times 10^3\ \text{kg/m}^3$ (from Table 9.2)
$\quad p_a = 1.01 \times 10^5\ \text{N/m}^2$

PHYSLET®

Illustration 14.1 Pressure in a Liquid

Pressure–depth relationship

(a) The total pressure is the sum of the pressure due to the water and the atmospheric pressure (p_a). By Eq. 9.10, this is

$$p = p_a + \rho gh$$
$$= (1.01 \times 10^5 \text{ N/m}^2) + (1.00 \times 10^3 \text{ kg/m}^3)(9.80 \text{ m/s}^2)(8.00 \text{ m})$$
$$= (1.01 \times 10^5 \text{ N/m}^2) + (0.784 \times 10^5 \text{ N/m}^2) = 1.79 \times 10^5 \text{ N/m}^2 \text{ (or Pa)}$$
$$\text{(expressed in atmospheres)} \approx 1.8 \text{ atm}$$

This is also the pressure on the diver's cardrums.

(b) The pressure p_{H_2O} due to the water alone is the ρgh portion of the preceding equation, so $p_{H_2O} = 0.784 \times 10^5 \text{ N/m}^2$.
    Then, $p_{H_2O} = F/A$, and

$$F = p_{H_2O}A = (0.784 \times 10^5 \text{ N/m}^2)(0.300 \text{ m}^2)$$
$$= 2.35 \times 10^4 \text{ N (or } 5.29 \times 10^3 \text{ lb—about 2.6 tons!)}$$

Follow-Up Exercise. You might question the answer to part (b) of this Example—how could the diver support such a force? To get a better idea of the forces our bodies can support, what would be the force on the diver's back at the water surface from atmospheric pressure alone? How do you suppose our bodies can support such forces or pressures?

Pascal's Principle

When the pressure (for example, air pressure) is increased on the entire open surface of an incompressible liquid at rest, the pressure at any point in the liquid or on the boundary surfaces increases by the same amount. The effect is the same if pressure is applied to any surface of an enclosed fluid by means of a piston (▸Fig. 9.8). The transmission of pressure in fluids was studied by Pascal, and the observed effect is called **Pascal's principle**:

Pressure applied to an enclosed fluid is transmitted undiminished to every point in the fluid and to the walls of the container.

For an incompressible liquid, the change in pressure is transmitted essentially instantaneously. For a gas, a change in pressure will generally be accompanied by a change in volume or temperature (or both), but after equilibrium has been reestablished, Pascal's principle remains valid.

Common practical applications of Pascal's principle include the hydraulic braking systems used on automobiles. Through tubes filled with brake fluid, a force on the brake pedal transmits a force to the wheel brake cylinder. Similarly, hydraulic lifts and jacks are used to raise automobiles and other heavy objects (▾Fig. 9.9).

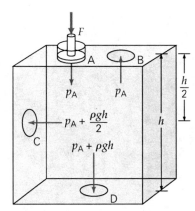

▲ **FIGURE 9.8 Pascal's principle** The pressure applied at point A is fully transmitted to all parts of the fluid and to the walls of the container. There is also pressure due to the weight of the fluid above at different depths (for instance, $\rho gh/2$ at C and ρgh at D).

▾ **FIGURE 9.9 The hydraulic lift and shock absorbers (a)** Because the input and output pressures are equal (Pascal's principle), a small input force gives a large output force proportional to the ratio of the piston areas. **(b)** A simplified exposed view of one type of shock absorber. (See Follow-Up Exercise 9.5 for description.)

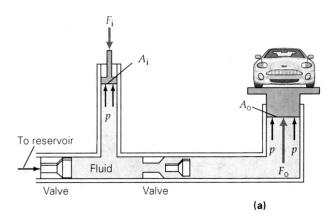

$$F_o = \left(\frac{A_o}{A_i}\right)F_i$$

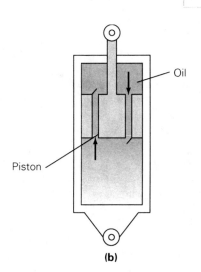

(a)

(b)

<blockquote>PHYSLET®

Illustration 14.2 Pascal's Principle</blockquote>

Using Pascal's principle, we can show how such systems allow us not only to transmit force from one place to another, but also to multiply that force. The input pressure p_i supplied by compressed air for a garage lift, for example, gives an input force F_i on a small piston area A_i (Fig. 9.9). The full magnitude of the pressure is transmitted to the output piston, which has an area A_o. Since $p_i = p_o$, it follows that

$$\frac{F_i}{A_i} = \frac{F_o}{A_o}$$

and

$$F_o = \left(\frac{A_o}{A_i}\right)F_i \quad \text{hydraulic force multiplication} \tag{9.11}$$

With A_o larger than A_i, F_o will be larger than F_i. The input force is greatly multiplied if the input piston has a relatively small area.

Example 9.5 ■ The Hydraulic Lift: Pascal's Principle

A garage lift has input and lift (output) pistons with diameters of 10 cm and 30 cm, respectively. The lift is used to hold up a car with a weight of 1.4×10^4 N. (a) What is the magnitude of the force on the input piston? (b) What pressure is applied to the input piston?

Thinking It Through. (a) Pascal's principle, as expressed in the hydraulic Eq. 9.11, has four variables, and three are given (areas via diameters). (b) The pressure is simply $p = F/A$.

Solution.

Given: $d_i = 10$ cm $= 0.10$ m   **Find:** (a) F_i (input force)
         $d_o = 30$ cm $= 0.30$ m   (b) p_i (input pressure)
         $F_o = 1.4 \times 10^4$ N

(a) Rearranging Eq. 9.11 and using $A = \pi r^2 = \pi d^2/4$ for the circular piston ($r = d/2$) gives

$$F_i = \left(\frac{A_i}{A_o}\right)F_o = \left(\frac{\pi d_i^2/4}{\pi d_o^2/4}\right)F_o = \left(\frac{d_i}{d_o}\right)^2 F_o$$

or

$$F_i = \left(\frac{0.10 \text{ m}}{0.30 \text{ m}}\right)^2 F_o = \frac{F_o}{9} = \frac{1.4 \times 10^4 \text{ N}}{9} = 1.6 \times 10^3 \text{ N}$$

The input force is one ninth of the output force; in other words, the force was multiplied by 9 (that is, $F_o = 9F_i$).

(Note that we didn't really need to write the complete expressions for the areas. We know that the area of a circle is proportional to the square of the diameter of the circle. If the ratio of the piston diameters is 3 to 1, the ratio of their areas must therefore be 9 to 1, and we could have used this ratio directly in Eq. 9.11.)

(b) Then we apply Eq. 9.8a:

$$p_i = \frac{F_i}{A_i} = \frac{F_i}{\pi r_i^2} = \frac{F_i}{\pi (d_i/2)^2} = \frac{1.6 \times 10^3 \text{ N}}{\pi (0.10 \text{ m})^2/4}$$

$$= 2.0 \times 10^5 \text{ N/m}^2 \, (= 200 \text{ kPa})$$

This pressure is about 30 lb/in², a common pressure used in automobile tires and about twice atmospheric pressure (which is approximately 100 kPa, or 15 lb/in².)

Follow-Up Exercise. Pascal's principle is used in shock absorbers on automobiles and on the landing gear of airplanes. (The polished steel piston rods can be seen above the wheels on aircraft.) In these devices, a large force (the shock produced on hitting a bump in the road or an airport runway at high speed) must be reduced to a safe level by removing energy. Basically, fluid is forced by the motion of a large-diameter piston through small channels in the piston on each stroke cycle (Fig. 9.9b).

Note that the valves allow for fluid through the channel, which creates resistance to the motion of the piston (effectively the reverse of the situation in Fig. 9.9a). The piston goes up and down, dissipating the energy of the shock. This is called *damping* (Section 13.2). Suppose that the input piston of a shock absorber on a jet plane has a diameter of 8.0 cm. What would be the diameter of an output channel that would reduce the force by a factor of 10?

As Example 9.5 shows, we can relate forces produced by pistons directly to their diameters: $F_i = (d_i/d_o)^2 F_o$ or $F_o = (d_o/d_i)^2 F_i$. By making $d_o \gg d_i$, we can get huge factors of force multiplication, as is typical for hydraulic presses, jacks, and earth-moving equipment. (The shiny input piston rods are often visible on front loaders and backhoes.) Inversely, we can get a force reduction by making $d_i > d_o$, as in Follow-Up Exercise 9.5.

However, don't think that you are getting something for nothing with large force multiplications: Energy is still a factor, and it can never be multiplied by a machine. (Why not?) Looking at the work involved and assuming that the work output is equal to the work input, $W_o = W_i$ (an ideal condition—why?), we have, from Eq. 5.1,

$$F_o x_o = F_i x_i$$

or

$$F_o = \left(\frac{x_i}{x_o}\right) F_i$$

where x_o and x_i are the output and input distances moved by the respective pistons.

Thus, the output force can be much greater than the input force only if the input distance is much greater than the output distance. For example, if $F_o = 10F_i$, then $x_i = 10x_o$, and the input piston must travel 10 times the distance of the output piston. We say that *force is multiplied at the expense of distance.*

Pressure Measurement

Pressure can be measured by mechanical devices that are often spring loaded (such as a tire gauge). Another type of instrument, called a manometer, uses a liquid—usually mercury—to measure pressure. An *open-tube manometer* is illustrated in ▾Fig. 9.10a.

▼ **FIGURE 9.10 Pressure measurement (a)** For an open-tube manometer, the pressure of the gas in the container is balanced by the pressure of the liquid column and atmospheric pressure acting on the open surface of the liquid. The absolute pressure of the gas equals the sum of the atmospheric pressure (p_a) and $\rho g h$, the gauge pressure. **(b)** A tire gauge measures gauge pressure, the difference between the pressure in the tire and atmospheric pressure: $p_{gauge} = p - p_a$. Thus, if a tire gauge reads 200 kPa (30 lb/in^2), the actual pressure within the tire is 1 atm higher, or 300 kPa. **(c)** A barometer is a closed-tube manometer that is exposed to the atmosphere and thus reads only atmospheric pressure.

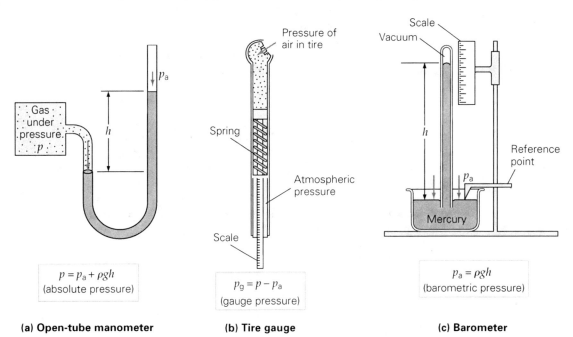

$p = p_a + \rho g h$
(absolute pressure)

$p_g = p - p_a$
(gauge pressure)

$p_a = \rho g h$
(barometric pressure)

(a) Open-tube manometer   **(b) Tire gauge**   **(c) Barometer**

Science Fundamentals

One end of the U-shaped tube is open to the atmosphere, and the other is connected to the container of gas whose pressure is to be measured. The liquid in the U-tube acts as a reservoir through which pressure is transmitted according to Pascal's principle.

The pressure of the gas (p) is balanced by the weight of the column of liquid (of height h, the difference in the heights of the columns) and the atmospheric pressure (p_a) on the open liquid surface:

$$p = p_a + \rho g h \tag{9.12}$$

The pressure p is called the **absolute pressure**.

You may have measured pressure using pressure gauges; a tire gauge used to measure air pressure in automobile tires is a common example (Fig. 9.10b). Such gauges, quite appropriately, measure **gauge pressure**: A pressure gauge registers only the pressure *above* (*or below*) atmospheric pressure. Hence, to get the absolute pressure (p), you have to add the atmospheric pressure (p_a) to the gauge pressure (p_g):

$$p = p_a + p_g$$

For example, suppose your tire gauge reads a pressure of 200 kPa ($\approx$ 30 lb/in^2). The absolute pressure within the tire is then $p = p_a + p_g = 101$ kPa + 200 kPa = 301 kPa, where normal atmospheric pressure is about 101 kPa (14.7 lb/in^2), as will be shown shortly.

The gauge pressure of a tire keeps the tire rigid or operational. In terms of the more familiar pounds per square inch (psi, or lb/in^2), a tire with a gauge pressure of 30 psi has an absolute pressure of about 45 psi (30 + 15, with atmospheric pressure $\approx$ 15 psi). Hence, the pressure on the inside of the tire is 45 psi, and that on the outside is 15 psi. The Δp of 30 psi keeps the tire inflated. If you open the valve or get a puncture, the internal and external pressures equalize and you have a flat!

Atmospheric pressure itself can be measured with a *barometer*. The principle of a mercury barometer is illustrated in Fig. 9.10c. The device was invented by Evangelista Torricelli (1608–1647), Galileo's successor as professor of mathematics at an academy in Florence. A simple barometer consists of a tube filled with mercury that is inverted into a reservoir. Some mercury runs from the tube into the reservoir, but a column supported by the air pressure on the surface of the reservoir remains in the tube. This device can be considered a *closed-tube manometer*, and the pressure it measures is just the atmospheric pressure, since the gauge pressure (the pressure *above* atmospheric pressure) is zero.

The atmospheric pressure is then equal to the pressure due to the weight of the column of mercury, or

$$p_a = \rho g h \tag{9.13}$$

A *standard atmosphere* is defined as the pressure supporting a column of mercury exactly 76 cm in height at sea level and at 0°C. (For a common biological atmospheric effect because of pressure changes, see Insight 9.2 on Possible Earaches.)

Changes in atmospheric pressure can be observed as changes in the height of a column of mercury. These changes are due primarily to high- and low-pressure air masses that travel across the country. Atmospheric pressure is commonly reported in terms of the height of the barometer column, and weather forecasters say that the barometer is rising or falling. That is,

1 atm (about 101 kPa) = 76 cm Hg = 760 mm Hg
= 29.92 in. Hg (about 30 in. Hg)

INSIGHT 9.2 AN ATMOSPHERIC EFFECT: POSSIBLE EARACHES

Variations in atmospheric pressure can have a common physiological effect: changes in pressure in the ears with changes in altitude. This "plugging up" and "popping" of the ears is frequently experienced in ascents and descents on mountain roads or on airplanes. The eardrum, so important to your hearing, is a membrane that separates the middle ear from the outer ear. [See Fig. 1 in the Chapter 14 (Sound) Insight 14.2 on Hearing, p. 475, to view the anatomy of the ear.] The middle ear is connected to the throat by the Eustachian tube, the end of which is normally closed. The tube opens during swallowing or yawning to permit air to escape, so the internal and external pressures are equalized.

However, when climbing relatively quickly in an airplane or in a car in a mountainous region, the air pressure outside the ear may be less than that in the middle ear. This difference in pressure forces the eardrum outward. If the outward pressure is not relieved, you will soon have an earache. The pressure is relieved by a "pushing" of air through the Eustachian tube into the throat, which produces a popping sound. We often swallow or yawn to assist this process. Similarly, when we descend, the higher outside pressure at lower altitudes needs to be equalized with the lower pressure in the middle ear. Swallowing allows air to flow into the middle ear in this case.

Nature takes care of us, but it is important to understand what is going on. If you have a throat infection, the opening of the Eustachian tube to the throat might be swollen, partially blocking the tube. You may be tempted to hold your nose and blow with your mouth closed in order to clear your ears. Don't do it! You could blow mucus into the inner ear and cause a painful inner-ear infection. Instead, swallow hard several times and give some big yawns to help open the Eustachian tube and equalize the pressure.

In honor of Torricelli, a pressure supporting 1 mm of mercury is given the name *torr*:

$$1 \text{ mm Hg} \equiv 1 \text{ torr}$$

and

$$1 \text{ atm} = 760 \text{ torr*}$$

Because mercury is highly toxic, it is sealed inside a barometer. A safer and less expensive device that is widely used to measure atmospheric pressure is the *aneroid* ("without fluid") *barometer*. In an aneroid barometer, a sensitive metal diaphragm on an evacuated container (something like a drumhead) responds to pressure changes, which are indicated on a dial. This is the kind of barometer you frequently find in homes in decorative wall mountings.

Since air is compressible, the atmospheric density and pressure are greatest at the Earth's surface and decrease with altitude. We live at the bottom of the atmosphere, but don't notice its pressure very much in our daily activities. Remember that our bodies are composed largely of fluids, which exert a matching outward pressure. Indeed, the external pressure of the atmosphere is so important to our normal functioning that we take it with us wherever we can. The pressurized suits worn by astronauts in space or on the Moon are needed not only to supply oxygen, but also to provide an external pressure similar to that on the Earth's surface.

A very important gauge pressure reading is discussed in Insight 9.3: Blood Pressure and Its Measurement on page 312. Read it before going on to Example 9.6.

---

*In the SI, one atmosphere has a pressure of 1.013×10^5 N/m², or about 10^5 N/m². Meteorologists use yet another unit of pressure called the *millibar* (mb). A *bar* is defined to be 10^5 N/m², and because a bar = 1000 mb, we have 1 atm ≈ 1 bar = 1000 mb. With 1000 mb, the small changes in atmospheric pressure are more easily reported.

INSIGHT   9.3   BLOOD PRESSURE AND ITS MEASUREMENT

Basically, a pump is a machine that transfers mechanical energy to a fluid, thereby increasing the pressure and causing the fluid to flow. One pump that is of interest to everyone is the heart, a muscular pump that drives blood throughout the body's circulatory network of arteries, capillaries, and veins. With each pumping cycle, the human heart's interior chambers enlarge and fill with freshly oxygenated blood from the lungs (Fig. 1).

The human heart contains two pairs of chambers: two ventricles and two atria. When the ventricles contract, blood is forced out through the arteries. Smaller and smaller arteries branch off from the main ones, until the very small capillaries are reached. There, oxygen and nutrients being carried by the blood are exchanged with the surrounding tissues, and carbon-dioxide (a waste gas) is picked up. The blood then flows into the veins to the lungs to expel carbon dioxide, back to the heart to complete the circuit.

When the ventricles contract, forcing blood into the arterial system, the pressure in the arteries increases sharply. The maximum pressure achieved during ventricular contraction is called the *systolic pressure*. When the ventricles relax, the arterial pressure drops, and the lowest pressure before the next contraction, called *diastolic pressure*, is reached. (These pressures are named after two parts of the pumping cycle, *systole* and *diastole*.)

The walls of the arteries have considerable elasticity and expand and contract with each pumping cycle. This alternating

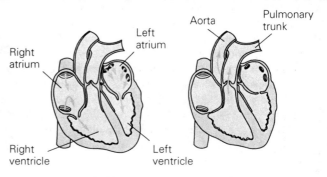

(a) Intake   **(b) Output**

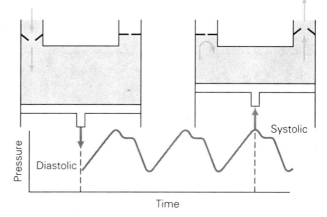

FIGURE 1 The heart as a pump The human heart is analogous to a mechanical force pump. Its pumping action, consisting of **(a)** intake and **(b)** output, gives rise to variations in blood pressure.

PHYSLET

Illustration 14.4 Pumping Water Up from a Well

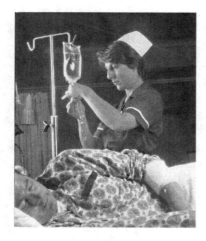

▲ **FIGURE 9.11** What height is needed? See Example 9.6.

Example 9.6 ■ An IV: A Gravity Assist

An IV (*intravenous injection*) is quite a different type of gravity assist from that discussed for space probes in Chapter 7. Consider a hospital patient who receives an IV under gravity flow, as shown in ◄Fig. 9.11. If the blood gauge pressure in the vein is 20.0 mm Hg, above what height should the bottle be placed for the IV blood transfusion to function properly?

Thinking It Through. The fluid gauge pressure at the bottom of the IV tube must be greater than the pressure in the vein and can be computed from Eq. 9.9. (The liquid is assumed to be incompressible.)

Solution.

Given: $p_v = 20.0$ mm Hg (vein gauge pressure)   *Find:* h (height for $p_v > 20$ mm Hg)
$\rho = 1.05 \times 10^3$ kg/m^3 (whole blood density from Table 9.2)

First, the common medical unit of mm Hg (or torr) needs to be changed to the SI unit of pascal (Pa, or N/m^2):

$$p_v = (20.0 \text{ mm Hg})[133 \text{ Pa}/(\text{mm Hg})] = 2.66 \times 10^3 \text{ Pa}$$

Then, for $p > p_v$,

$$p = \rho g h > p_v$$

or

$$h > \frac{p_v}{\rho g} = \frac{2.66 \times 10^3 \text{ Pa}}{(1.05 \times 10^3 \text{ kg/m}^3)(9.80 \text{ m/s}^2)} = 0.259 \text{ m} \ (\approx 26 \text{ cm})$$

Science Fundamentals

expansion and contraction can be felt as a *pulse* in an artery near the surface of the body. For example, the radial artery near the surface of the wrist is commonly used to measure a person's pulse. The pulse rate is equal to the ventricular contraction rate, and hence the pulse rate indicates the heart rate.

Taking a person's blood pressure involves measuring the pressure of the blood on the arterial walls. This is done with a *sphygmomanometer*. (The Greek word *sphygmo* means "pulse.") An inflatable cuff is inflated to shut off the blood flow temporarily. The cuff pressure is slowly released, and the artery is monitored with a stethoscope (Fig. 2). Soon blood is just forced through the constricted artery. This flow is turbulent and gives rise to a specific sound with each heartbeat. When the sound is first heard, the systolic pressure is noted on the gauge. When the turbulent beats disappear because blood begins to flow smoothly, the diastolic pressure is taken.

Blood pressure is commonly reported by giving the systolic and diastolic pressures, separated by a slash—for example, 120/80 (mm Hg, read as "120 over 80"). (The gauge in Fig. 2 is an aneroid type; older types of sphygmomanometers used a mercury column to measure blood pressure.) Normal blood pressure ranges are 120–139 for systolic and 80–89 for diastolic. (Blood pressure is a gauge pressure. Why?)

Away from the heart, blood vessels branch to smaller and smaller diameters. The pressure in the blood vessels decreases as their diameter decreases. In small arteries, such as those in the arm, the blood pressure is on the order of 10 to 20 mm Hg, and there is no systolic–diastolic variation.

High blood pressure is a common health problem. The elastic walls of the arteries expand under the hydraulic force of the blood pumped from the heart. Their elasticity may diminish with age, however. Cholesterol deposits can narrow and roughen the arterial passageways, impeding the blood flow and giving rise to a form of arteriosclerosis, or hardening of the arteries. Because of these defects, the driving pressure must increase to maintain a normal blood flow. The heart must work harder, which places a greater demand on the heart muscles. A relatively slight decrease in the effective cross-sectional area of a blood vessel has a rather large effect (an increase) on the flow rate, as will be shown in Section 9.4.

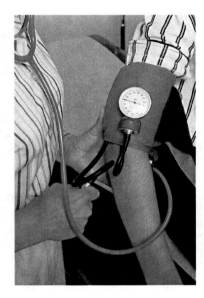

FIGURE 2 Measuring blood pressure The pressure is indicated on the gauge in millimeters Hg.

The IV bottle needs to be at least 26 cm above the injection site.

Follow-Up Exercise. The normal (gauge) blood pressure range is commonly reported as 120/80 (in millimeters Hg). Why is the blood pressure of 20 mm Hg in this Example so low?

9.3 Buoyancy and Archimedes' Principle

OBJECTIVES: To (a) relate the buoyant force to Archimedes' principle, and (b) tell whether an object will float in a fluid, on the basis of relative densities.

When placed in a fluid, an object will either sink or float. This is most commonly observed with liquids; for example, objects float or sink in water. But the same effect occurs in gases: A falling object sinks in the atmosphere, and other bodies float (▾Fig. 9.12).

Things float because they are buoyant, or are buoyed up. For example, if you immerse a cork in water and release it, the cork will be buoyed up to the surface and float there. From your knowledge of forces, you know that such motion requires an upward net force on the object. That is, there must be an upward force acting on the object that is greater than the downward force of its weight. The forces are equal when the object floats in equilibrium. The upward force resulting from an object being wholly or partially immersed in a fluid is called the **buoyant force**.

▲ **FIGURE 9.12** Fluid buoyancy
The air is a fluid in which objects
such as this dirigible floats. The
helium inside the blimps is less
dense than the surrounding air and
the blimp is supported by the
resulting buoyant force.

Illustration 14.3 Buoyant Force

How the buoyant force comes about can be seen by considering a buoyant
object being held under the surface of a fluid (▸Fig. 9.13a). The pressures on the
upper and lower surfaces of the block are $p_1 = \rho_f g h_1$ and $p_2 = \rho_f g h_2$, respectively, where ρ_f is the density of the fluid. Thus, there is a pressure difference
$\Delta p = p_2 - p_1 = \rho_f g (h_2 - h_1)$ between the top and bottom of the block, which
gives an upward force (the buoyant force) F_b. This force is balanced by the applied force and the weight of the block.

It is not difficult to derive an expression for the magnitude of the buoyant
force. We know that pressure is force per unit area. Thus, if both the top and bottom areas of the block are A, the magnitude of the net buoyant force in terms of the
pressure difference is

$$F_b = p_2 A - p_1 A = (\Delta p) A = \rho_f g (h_2 - h_1) A$$

Since $(h_2 - h_1) A$ is the volume of the block, and hence the volume of fluid displaced by the block, V_f, we can write the expression for F_b as

$$F_b = \rho_f g V_f$$

But $\rho_f V_f$ is simply the mass of the fluid displaced by the block, m_f. Thus, we can
write the expression for the buoyant force as $F_b = m_f g$: The magnitude of the
buoyant force is equal to the weight of the fluid displaced by the block (Fig. 9.13b).
This general result is known as **Archimedes' principle**:

A body immersed wholly or partially in a fluid experiences a buoyant force
equal in magnitude to the weight of the *volume of fluid* that is displaced:

$$F_b = m_f g = \rho_f g V_f \tag{9.14}$$

Archimedes (287 BCE–212 BCE) was given the task of determining whether a
gold crown made for the king was pure gold or contained a quantity of silver. Leg-
end has it that the solution to the problem came to him when he was in the bath
tub. (See the Physics Facts at the beginning of the chapter.) It is said that he was so
excited he jumped out of the tub and ran home through the streets of the city (un-
clothed) shouting "Eureka! Eureka!" (Greek for "I have found it"). Although
Archimedes' solution to the problem involved density and volume, it presumably
got him thinking about buoyancy.

Integrated Example 9.7 ■ Lighter Than Air: Buoyant Force

A spherical helium-filled weather balloon has a radius of 1.10 m. (a) Does the buoyant
force on the balloon depend on the density of (1) helium, (2) air, or (3) the weight of the
rubber "skin"? [$\rho_{air} = 1.29$ kg/m³ and $\rho_{He} = 0.18$ kg/m³.] (b) Compute the magnitude of
the buoyant force on the balloon. (c) The balloon's rubber skin has a mass of 1.20 kg. When
released, what is the magnitude of the balloon's initial acceleration if it carries a payload
with a mass of 3.52 kg?

(a) Conceptual Reasoning. The buoyant force has nothing to do with the helium or rubber
skin and is equal to the weight of the displaced air, which can be found from the balloon's
volume and the density of air. So the answer is (2).

(b, c) Quantitative Reasoning and Solution.

Given: $\rho_{air} = 1.29$ kg/m³
  $\rho_{He} = 0.18$ kg/m³
  $m_s = 1.20$ kg
  $m_p = 3.52$ kg
  $r = 1.10$ m

Find: (b) F_b (buoyant force)
  (c) a (initial acceleration)

(b) The volume of the balloon is

$$V = (4/3)\pi r^3 = (4/3)\pi(1.10\text{ m})^3 = 5.58\text{ m}^3$$

Then the buoyant force is equal to the weight of the air displaced:

$$F_b = m_{air}g = (\rho_{air}V)g = (1.29\text{ kg/m}^3)(5.58\text{ m}^3)(9.80\text{ m/s}^2) = 70.5\text{ N}$$

(c) Draw a free-body diagram. There are three weight forces downward—those of the helium, the rubber skin, and the payload—and the upward buoyant force. Sum these forces to find the net force, and then use Newton's second law to find the acceleration. The weights of the helium, rubber skin, and payload are as follows:

$$w_{He} = m_{He}g = (\rho_{He}V)g = (0.18\text{ kg/m}^3)(5.58\text{ m}^3)(9.80\text{ m/s}^2) = 9.84\text{ N}$$

$$w_s = m_sg = (1.20\text{ kg})(9.80\text{ m/s}^2) = 11.8\text{ N}$$

$$w_p = m_pg = (3.52\text{ kg})(9.80\text{ m/s}^2) = 35.5\text{ N}$$

Summing the forces (taking upward as positive),

$$F_{net} = F_b - w_{He} - w_s - w_p = 70.5\text{ N} - 9.84\text{ N} - 11.8\text{ N} - 35.5\text{ N} = 13.4\text{ N}$$

and

$$a = \frac{F_{net}}{m_{total}} = \frac{F_{net}}{m_{He} + m_s + m_p} = \frac{13.4\text{ N}}{0.994\text{ kg} + 1.20\text{ kg} + 3.52\text{ kg}} = 2.35\text{ m/s}^2$$

Follow-Up Exercise. As the balloon rises, it eventually stops accelerating and rises at a constant velocity for a short time, then starts sinking toward the ground. Explain this behavior in terms of atmospheric density and temperature. (*Hint*: Temperature and air density decreases with altitude. The pressure of a quantity of gas is directly proportional to temperature.)

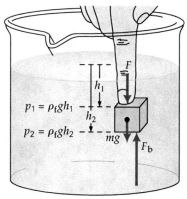

$$\Delta p = \rho_f g(h_2 - h_1)$$

(a)

Example 9.8 ■ Your Buoyancy in Air

Air is a fluid and our bodies displace air. And so, a buoyant force is acting on each of us. Estimate the magnitude of the buoyant force on a 75-kg person due to the air displaced.

Thinking It Through. The key word here is *estimate*, because not much data is given. We know that the buoyant force is $F_b = \rho_a g V$, where ρ_a is the density of air (which can be found in Table 9.2), and V is the volume of the air displaced, which is the same as the volume of the person. The question is, how do we find the volume of the person?

The mass is given, and if the density of the person were known, the volume could be found ($\rho = m/V$ or $V = m/\rho$). Here is where the estimate comes in. Most people can barely float in water, so the density of the human body is about that of water, $\rho = 1000\text{ kg/m}^3$. Using this estimate, the buoyant force can also be estimated.

Solution.

Given: $m = 75\text{ kg}$ *Find:* F_b (buoyant force)
$\rho_a = 1.29\text{ kg/m}^3$ (Table 9.2)
$\rho_p = 1000\text{ kg/m}^3$ (estimated density of person)

First, let's find the volume of the person,

$$V_p = \frac{m}{\rho_p} = \frac{75\text{ kg}}{1000\text{ kg/m}^3} = 0.075\text{ m}^3$$

Then,

$$F_b = \rho_a g V_p = \rho_a g\left(\frac{m}{\rho_p}\right) = (1.29\text{ kg/m}^3)(9.8\text{ m/s}^2)(0.075\text{ m}^3)$$

$$= 0.95\text{ N}\ (\approx 1.0\text{ N or }0.225\text{ lb})$$

Not much when you weigh yourself. But it does mean that your weight is ≈ 0.2 lb more than the scale reading.

Follow-Up Exercise. Estimate the buoyant force on a helium-filled weather balloon that has a diameter on the order of a meteorologist's arm span (arms held horizontally), and compare with the result in the Example.

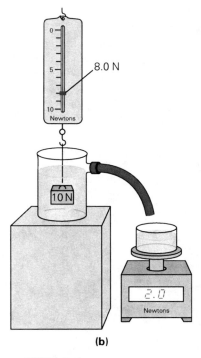

▲ **FIGURE 9.13 Buoyancy and Archimedes' principle (a)** A buoyant force arises from the difference in pressure at different depths. The pressure on the bottom of the submerged block (p_2) is greater than that on the top (p_1), so there is a (buoyant) force directed upward. (It is shifted for clarity.) **(b)** Archimedes' principle: The buoyant force on the object is equal to the weight of the volume of fluid displaced. (The scale is set to read zero when the container is empty.)

Exploration 14.2 Buoyant Force

Integrated Example 9.9 ■ Weight and Buoyant Force: Archimedes' Principle

A container of water with an overflow tube, similar to that shown in Fig. 9.13b, sits on a scale that reads 40 N. The water level is just below the exit tube in the side of the container. (a) An 8.0-N cube of wood is placed in the container. The water displaced by the floating cube runs out the exit tube into another container that is not on the scale. Will the scale reading then be (1) exactly 48 N, (2) between 40 N and 48 N, (3) exactly 40 N, or (4) less than 40 N? (b) Suppose you pushed down on the wooden cube with your finger such that the top surface of the cube was even with the water level. How much force would have to be applied if the wooden cube measured 10 cm on a side?

(a) Conceptual Reasoning. By Archimedes' principle, the block is buoyed upward with a force equal in magnitude to the weight of the water displaced. Since the block floats, the upward buoyant force must balance the weight of the cube and so has a magnitude of 8.0 N. Thus, a volume of water weighing 8.0 N is displaced from the container as 8.0 N of weight is added to the container. The scale still reads 40 N, so the answer is (3).

Note that the upward buoyant force and the block's weight act *on the block*. The reaction force (pressure) of the block *on the water* is transmitted to the bottom of the container (Pascal's principle) and is registered on the scale. (Make a sketch showing the forces on the cube.)

(b) Quantitative Reasoning and Solution. Here three forces are acting on the stationary cube: the buoyant force upward and the weight and the force applied by the finger downward. The weight of the cube is known, so to find the applied finger force, we need to determine the buoyant force on the cube.

Given: $\ell = 10 \text{ cm} = 0.10 \text{ m}$ (side length of cube) *Find:* downward applied force
  $w = 8.0 \text{ N}$ (weight of cube)   necessary to put cube even
      with water level

The summation of the forces acting on the cube is $\Sigma F_i = +F_b - w - F_f = 0$, where F_b is the upward buoyant force and F_f is the downward force applied by the finger. Hence, $F_f = F_b - w$. As we know, the magnitude of the buoyant force is equal to the weight of the water the cube displaces, which is given by $F_b = \rho_f g V_f$ (Eq. 9.14). The density of the fluid is that of water, which is known ($1.0 \times 10^3 \text{ kg/m}^3$, Table 9.2), so

$$F_b = \rho_f g V_f = (1.0 \times 10^3 \text{ kg/m}^3)(9.8 \text{ m/s}^2)(0.10 \text{ m})^3 = 9.8 \text{ N}$$

Thus,

$$F_f = F_b - w = 9.8 \text{ N} - 8.0 \text{ N} = 1.8 \text{ N}$$

Follow-Up Exercise. In part (a), would the scale still read 40 N if the object had a density greater than that of water? In part (b), what would the scale read?

Buoyancy and Density

We commonly say that helium and hot-air balloons float because they are lighter than air. To be technically correct, we should say they are *less dense than air*. An object's density will tell you whether it will sink or float in a fluid, as long as you also know the density of the fluid. Consider a solid uniform object that is totally immersed in a fluid. The weight of the object is

$$w_o = m_o g = \rho_o V_o g$$

The weight of the volume of fluid displaced, or the magnitude of the buoyant force, is

$$F_b = w_f = m_f g = \rho_f V_f g$$

If the object is *completely submerged*, $V_f = V_o$. Dividing the second equation by the first gives

$$\frac{F_b}{w_o} = \frac{\rho_f}{\rho_o} \quad \text{or} \quad F_b = \left(\frac{\rho_f}{\rho_o}\right)w_o \quad \textit{(object completely submerged)} \quad (9.15)$$

Thus, if ρ_o is less than ρ_f, then F_b will be greater than w_o, and the object will be buoyed to the surface and float. If ρ_o is greater than ρ_f, then F_b will be less than w_o, and the object will sink. If ρ_o equals ρ_f, then F_b will be equal to w_o, and the object will remain in equilibrium at any submerged depth (as long as the density of the fluid is constant). If the object is not uniform, so that its density varies over its volume, then the density of the object in Eq. 9.15 means average density.

Expressed in words, these three conditions are as follows:

An object will float in a fluid if the average density of the object is less than the density of the fluid ($\rho_o < \rho_f$).
An object will sink in a fluid if the average density of the object is greater than the density of the fluid ($\rho_o > \rho_f$).
An object will be in equilibrium at any submerged depth in a fluid if the average density of the object and the density of the fluid are equal ($\rho_o = \rho_f$).

See ▶Fig. 9.14 for an example of the last condition.

A quick look at Table 9.2 will tell you whether an object will float in a fluid, regardless of the shape or volume of the object. The three conditions just stated also apply to a fluid in a fluid, provided that the two are immiscible (do not mix). For example, you might think that cream is "heavier" than skim milk, but that's not so: Since cream floats on milk, it is less dense than milk.

In general, the densities of objects or fluids will be assumed to be uniform and constant in this book. (The density of the atmosphere does vary with altitude, but is relatively constant near the surface of the Earth.) In any event, in practical applications it is the *average* density of an object that often matters with regard to floating and sinking. For example, an ocean liner is, on average, less dense than water, even though it is made of steel. Most of its volume is occupied by air, so the liner's average density is less than that of water. Similarly, the human body has air-filled spaces, so most of us float in water. The surface depth at which a person floats depends on his or her density. (Why?)

In some instances, the overall density of an object is purposefully varied. For example, a submarine submerges by flooding its tanks with seawater (called "taking on ballast"), which increases its average density. When the sub is to surface, the water is pumped out of the tanks, so the average density of the sub becomes less than that of the surrounding seawater.

Similarly, many fish control their depths by using their *swim bladders* or *gas bladders*. A fish changes or maintains buoyancy by regulating the volume of gas in the gas bladder. Maintaining neutral buoyancy (neither rising or sinking) is important because it allows the fish to stay at a particular depth for feeding. Some fish may move up and down in the water in search of food. Instead of using up energy to swim up and down, the fish alters its buoyancy so as to go up and down.

This is accomplished by adjusting the quantities of gas in the gas bladder. Gas is transferred from the gas bladder to the adjoining blood vessels and back again. Deflating the bladder decreases the volume and increases the average density, and the fish sinks. Gas is forced into the surrounding blood vessels and carried away.

Conversely, to inflate the bladder, gases are forced into the bladder from the blood vessels, thereby increasing the volume and decreasing the average density, and the fish rises. These processes are complex, but Archimedes' principle is being applied in a biological setting.

PHYSLET

Exploration 14.1 Floating and Density

▲ **FIGURE 9.14 Equal densities and buoyancy** This soft drink contains colored gelatin beads that remain suspended for months with virtually no change. What is the density of the beads compared to the density of the drink?

Exploration 14.3 Buoyancy and Oil on Water

▲ **FIGURE 9.15 The tip of the iceberg** The vast majority of an iceberg's bulk is underneath the water as illustrated here.

Example 9.10 ■ Float or Sink? Comparison of Densities

A uniform solid cube of material 10 cm on each side has a mass of 700 g. (a) Will the cube float in water? (b) If so, how much of its volume would be submerged?

Thinking It Through. (a) The question is whether the density of the material the cube is made of is greater or less than that of water, so we compute the cube's density. (b) If the cube floats, then the buoyant force and the cube's weight are equal. Both of these forces are related to the cube's volume, so we can write them in terms of that volume and equate them.

Solution. It is sometimes convenient to work in cgs units in comparing small quantities. For densities in grams per cubic centimeter divide the values in Table 9.2 by 10^3, or drop the "$\times 10^3$" from the values given for solids and liquids, and replace with "$\times 10^{-3}$" for gases.

Given: $m = 700$ g
$L = 10$ cm
$\rho_{H_2O} = 1.00 \times 10^3$ kg/m³
$= 1.00$ g/cm³ (Table 9.2)

Find: (a) Whether the cube will float in water
(b) The percentage of the volume submerged if the cube does float

(a) The density of the cube is

$$\rho_c = \frac{m}{V_c} = \frac{m}{L^3} = \frac{700 \text{ g}}{(10 \text{ cm})^3} = 0.70 \text{ g/cm}^3 < \rho_{H_2O} = 1.00 \text{ g/cm}^3$$

Since ρ_c is less than ρ_{H_2O} the cube will float.

(b) The weight of the cube is $w_c = \rho_c g V_c$. When the cube is floating, it is in equilibrium, which means that its weight is balanced by the buoyant force. That is, $F_b = \rho_{H_2O} g V_{H_2O}$, where V_{H_2O} is the volume of water the submerged part of the cube displaces. Equating the expressions for weight and buoyant force gives

$$\rho_{H_2O} g V_{H_2O} = \rho_c g V_c$$

or

$$\frac{V_{H_2O}}{V_c} = \frac{\rho_c}{\rho_{H_2O}} = \frac{0.70 \text{ g/cm}^3}{1.00 \text{ g/cm}^3} = 0.70$$

Thus, $V_{H_2O} = 0.70 V_c$, and 70% of the cube is submerged.

Follow-Up Exercise. Most of an iceberg floating in the ocean (◄Fig. 9.15) is submerged. What is seen is the proverbial "tip of the iceberg." What percentage of an iceberg's volume is seen above the surface? [*Note:* Icebergs are frozen *fresh* water floating in salty sea water.]

A quantity called specific gravity is related to density. It is commonly used for liquids, but also applies to solids. The **specific gravity (*sp. gr.*)** of a substance is equal to the ratio of the density of the substance (ρ_s) to the density of water (ρ_{H_2O}) at 4°C, the temperature for maximum density:

$$sp. \ gr. = \frac{\rho_s}{\rho_{H_2O}}$$

Because it is a ratio of densities, specific gravity has no units. In cgs units, $\rho_{H_2O} = 1.00$ g/cm³, so

$$sp. \ gr. = \frac{\rho_s}{1.00} = \rho_s \quad (\rho_s \text{ in g/cm}^3 \text{ only})$$

That is, the specific gravity of a substance is equal to the numerical value of its density *in cgs units*. For example, if a liquid has a density of 1.5 g/cm³, its specific gravity is 1.5, which tells you that it is 1.5 times as dense as water. (As pointed out earlier, to get density values for solids and liquids in grams per cubic centimeter, divide the value in Table 9.2 by 10^3.)

9.4 Fluid Dynamics and Bernoulli's Equation

OBJECTIVES: To (a) identify the simplifications used in describing ideal fluid flow, and (b) use the continuity equation and Bernoulli's equation to explain common effects of ideal fluid flow.

In general, fluid motion is difficult to analyze. For example, think of trying to describe the motion of a particle (a molecule, as an approximation) of water in a rushing stream. The overall motion of the stream may be apparent, but a mathematical description of the motion of any one particle of it may be virtually impossible because of eddy currents (small whirlpool motions), the gushing of water over rocks, frictional drag on the stream bottom, and so on. A basic description of fluid flow is conveniently obtained by ignoring such complications and considering an *ideal fluid*. Actual fluid flow can then be approximated with reference to this simpler theoretical model.

In this simplified approach to fluid dynamics, it is customary to consider four characteristics of an **ideal fluid**. In such a fluid, flow is (1) *steady*, (2) *irrotational*, (3) *nonviscous*, and (4) *incompressible*.

> Condition 1: *Steady flow* means that all the particles of a fluid have the same velocity as they pass a given point.

Steady flow might be called smooth or regular flow. The path of steady flow can be depicted in the form of **streamlines** (▸Fig. 9.16a). Every particle that passes a particular point moves along a streamline. That is, every particle moves along the same path (streamline) as particles that passed by earlier. Streamlines never cross; if they did, a particle would have alternative paths and abrupt changes in its velocity, in which case the flow would not be steady.

Steady flow requires low velocities. For example, steady flow is approximated by the flow relative to a canoe that is gliding slowly through still water. When the flow velocity is high, eddies tend to appear, especially near boundaries, and the flow becomes turbulent as in Fig. 9.16b.

Streamlines also indicate the relative magnitude of the velocity of a fluid. The velocity is greater where the streamlines are closer together. Notice this effect in Fig. 9.16a. The reason for it will be explained shortly.

> Condition 2: *Irrotational flow* means that a fluid element (a small volume of the fluid) has no net angular velocity. This condition eliminates the possibility of whirlpools and eddy currents. (The flow is nonturbulent.)

Consider the small paddle wheel in Fig. 9.16a. With a zero net torque, the wheel does not rotate. Thus, the flow is irrotational.

> Condition 3: *Nonviscous flow* means that viscosity is negligible.

Viscosity refers to a fluid's internal friction, or resistance to flow. (For example, honey has a much greater viscosity than water.) A truly nonviscous fluid would flow freely with no internal energy loss within it. Also, there would be no frictional drag between the fluid and the walls containing it. In reality, when a liquid flows through a pipe, the speed is lower near the walls because of frictional drag and is higher toward the center of the pipe. (Viscosity is discussed in more detail in Section 9.5.)

> Condition 4: *Incompressible flow* means that the fluid's density is constant.

Liquids can usually be considered incompressible. Gases, by contrast, are quite compressible. Sometimes, however, gases approximate incompressible flow—for example, air flowing relative to the wings of an airplane traveling at low speeds. Theoretical or ideal fluid flow is not characteristic of most real situations, but the analysis of ideal flow provides results that approximate, or generally describe, a variety of applications. Usually, this analysis is derived, not from Newton's laws, but instead from two basic principles: conservation of mass and conservation of energy.

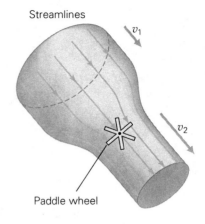

Streamlines

v_1

v_2

Paddle wheel

(a)

(b)

▲ **FIGURE 9.16 Streamline flow**
(a) Streamlines never cross and are closer together in regions of greater fluid velocity. The stationary paddle wheel indicates that the flow is irrotational, or without whirlpools and eddy currents. **(b)** The smoke from an extinguished candle begins to rise in nearly streamline flow, but quickly becomes rotational and turbulent.

▶ **FIGURE 9.17** Flow continuity
Ideal fluid flow can be described in terms of the conservation of mass by the equation of continuity.

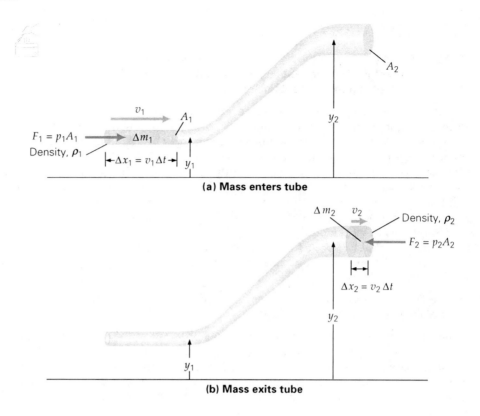

(a) Mass enters tube

(b) Mass exits tube

Equation of Continuity

PHYSLET

Illustration 15.1 The Continuity Equation

If there are no losses of fluid within a uniform tube, the mass of fluid flowing into the tube in a given time must be equal to the mass flowing out of the tube in the same time (by the conservation of mass). For example, in ▲Fig. 9.17a, the mass (Δm_1) entering the tube during a short time (Δt) is

$$\Delta m_1 = \rho_1 \Delta V_1 = \rho_1(A_1 \Delta x_1) = \rho_1(A_1 v_1 \Delta t)$$

where A_1 is the cross-sectional area of the tube at the entrance and, in a time Δt, a fluid particle moves a distance equal to $v_1 \Delta t$. Similarly, the mass leaving the tube in the same interval is (Fig. 9.17b)

$$\Delta m_2 = \rho_2 \Delta V_2 = \rho_2(A_2 \Delta x_2) = \rho_2(A_2 v_2 \Delta t)$$

Since the mass is conserved, $\Delta m_1 = \Delta m_2$, and it follows that

$$\rho_1 A_1 v_1 = \rho_2 A_2 v_2 \quad \text{or} \quad \rho A v = \text{constant} \qquad (9.16)$$

This general result is called the **equation of continuity**.

For an incompressible fluid, the density ρ is constant, so

$$A_1 v_1 = A_2 v_2 \quad \text{or} \quad A v = \text{constant} \quad \textit{(for an incompressible fluid)} \ (9.17)$$

This is sometimes called the **flow rate equation**. Av is called the *volume rate of flow*, and is the volume of fluid that passes by a point in the tube per unit time. (Av: $\text{m}^2 \cdot \text{m/s} = \text{m}^3/\text{s}$, volume per time.)

Note that the flow rate equation shows that the fluid velocity is greater where the cross-sectional area of the tube is smaller. That is,

$$v_2 = \left(\frac{A_1}{A_2}\right)v_1$$

▲ **FIGURE 9.18** Flow rate By the flow rate equation, the speed of a fluid is greater when the cross-sectional area of the tube through which the fluid is flowing is smaller. Think of a hose that is equipped with a nozzle such that the cross-sectional area of the hose is made smaller.

and v_2 is greater than v_1 if A_2 is less than A_1. This effect is evident in the common experience that the speed of water is greater from a hose fitted with a nozzle than from the same hose without a nozzle (◀Fig. 9.18).

The flow rate equation can be applied to the flow of blood in your body. Blood flows from the heart into the aorta. It then makes a circuit through the circulatory system, passing through arteries, arterioles (small arteries), capillaries, and venules (small veins) and back to the heart through veins. The speed is lowest in the capillaries. Is this a contradiction? No: The *total* area of the capillaries is much larger than that of the arteries or veins, so the flow rate equation is still valid.

Example 9.11 ■ Blood Flow: Cholesterol and Plaque

High cholesterol in the blood can cause fatty deposits called plaques to form on the walls of blood vessels. Suppose a plaque reduces the effective radius of an artery by 25%. How does this partial blockage affect the speed of blood through the artery?

Thinking It Through. The flow rate equation (Eq. 9.17) applies, but note that no values of area or speed are given. This indicates that we should use ratios.

Solution. Taking the unclogged artery to have a radius r_1, we can say that the plaque then reduces the effective radius to r_2.

Given: $r_2 = 0.75r_1$ (for a 25% reduction)   **Find:** v_2

Writing the flow rate equation in terms of the radii, we have

$$A_1v_1 = A_2v_2$$
$$(\pi r_1^2)v_1 = (\pi r_2^2)v_2$$

Rearranging and canceling,

$$v_2 = \left(\frac{r_1}{r_2}\right)^2 v_1$$

From the given information, $r_1/r_2 = 1/0.75$, so

$$v_2 = (1/0.75)^2 v_1 = 1.8v_1$$

Hence, the speed through the clogged artery increases by 80%.

Follow-Up Exercise. By how much would the effective radius of an artery have to be reduced to have a 50% increase in the speed of the blood flowing through it?

Example 9.12 ■ Speed of Blood in the Aorta

Blood flows at a rate of 5.00 L/min through an aorta with a radius of 1.00 cm. What is the speed of blood flow in the aorta?

Thinking It Through. It is noted that the flow rate is a volume flow rate, which implies the use of the flow rate equation (Eq. 9.17), Av = constant. Since the constant is in terms of volume/time, the given flow rate is the constant.

Solution. Listing the data:

Given: Flow rate = 5.00 L/min   **Find:** v (blood speed)
         $r = 1.00$ cm $= 10^{-2}$ m

Let's first find the cross-sectional area of the circular aorta.

$$A = \pi r^2 = (3.14)(10^{-2}\,\text{m})^2 = 3.14 \times 10^{-4}\,\text{m}^2$$

Then the (volume) flow rate needs to be put into standard units.

$$5.00\,\text{L/min} = (5.00\,\text{L/m})(10^{-3}\,\text{m}^3/\text{L})(1\,\text{min}/60\,\text{s}) = 8.33 \times 10^{-5}\,\text{m}^3/\text{s}$$

Using the flow rate equation, we have

$$v = \frac{\text{constant}}{A} = \frac{8.33 \times 10^{-5}\,\text{m}^3/\text{s}}{3.14 \times 10^{-4}\,\text{m}^2} = 0.265\,\text{m/s}$$

Follow-Up Exercise. Constrictions of the arteries occur with hardening of the arteries. If the radius of the aorta in this Example were constricted to 0.900 cm, what would be the percentage change in blood flow?

PHYSLET

Exploration 15.1 Blood Flow and the Continuity Equation

▶ **FIGURE 9.19 Flow rate and pressure** Taking the horizontal difference in flow heights to be negligible in a constricted pipe, we obtain, for Bernoulli's equation, $p + \frac{1}{2}\rho v^2 = $ constant. In a region of smaller cross-sectional area, the flow speed is greater (see flow rate equation); from Bernoulli's equation, the pressure in that region is lower than in other regions.

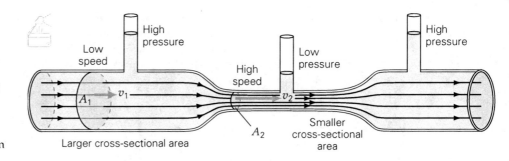

Exploration 15.2 Bernoulli's Equation

Bernoulli's Equation

The conservation of energy or the general work–energy theorem leads to another relationship that has great generality for fluid flow. This relationship was first derived in 1738 by the Swiss mathematician Daniel Bernoulli (1700–1782) and is named for him. Bernoulli's result was

$$W_{net} = \Delta K + \Delta U$$

$$\frac{\Delta m}{\rho}(p_1 - p_2) = \frac{1}{2}\Delta m(v_2^2 - v_1^2) + \Delta m g(y_2 - y_1)$$

where Δm is a mass increment as in the derivation of the continuity equation.

Note that in working with a fluid, the terms in Bernoulli's equation are work or energy per unit volume (J/m³). That is, $W = F\Delta x = p(A\Delta x) = p\Delta V$ and therefore $p = W/\Delta V$ (work/volume). Similarly, with $\rho = m/V$, we have $\frac{1}{2}\rho v^2 = \frac{1}{2}mv^2/V$ (energy/volume) and $\rho g y = mgy/V$ (energy/volume).

Canceling each Δm and rearranging gives the common form of **Bernoulli's equation**:

$$p_1 + \frac{1}{2}\rho v_1^2 + \rho g y_1 = p_2 + \frac{1}{2}\rho v_2^2 + \rho g y_2 \tag{9.18}$$

or

$$p + \frac{1}{2}\rho v^2 + \rho g y = \text{constant}$$

Note: Compare the derivation of Eq. 5.10 in Section 5.5.

Bernoulli's equation, or principle, can be applied to many situations. For example, for a fluid at rest ($v_2 = v_1 = 0$), Bernoulli's equation becomes

$$p_2 - p_1 = \rho g(y_1 - y_2)$$

This is the pressure–depth relationship derived earlier (Eq. 9.10). Also, if there is horizontal flow ($y_1 = y_2$), then $p + \frac{1}{2}\rho v^2 = $ constant, which indicates that the pressure decreases if the speed of the fluid increases (and vice versa). This effect is illustrated in ▲Fig. 9.19, where the difference in flow heights through the pipe is considered negligible (so the $\rho g y$ term drops out).

Chimneys and smokestacks are tall in order to take advantage of the more consistent and higher wind speeds at greater heights. The faster the wind blows over the top of a chimney, the lower the pressure, and the greater the pressure difference between the bottom and top of the chimney. Thus, the chimney draws exhaust out better. Bernoulli's equation and the continuity equation ($Av = $ constant) also tell you that if the cross-sectional area of a pipe is reduced, so that the velocity of the fluid passing through it is increased, then the pressure is reduced.

The Bernoulli effect (as it is sometimes called) gives a *simplistic* explanation for the lift of an airplane. Ideal airflow over an airfoil or wing is shown in ◀Fig. 9.20. (Turbulence is neglected.) The wing is curved on the top side and is angled relative to the incident streamlines. As a result, the streamlines above the wing are closer together than those below, which cause a higher air speed and lower pressure above the wing. With a higher pressure on the bottom of the wing, there is a net upward force, or *lift*.

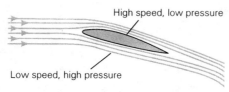

High speed, low pressure

Low speed, high pressure

▲ **FIGURE 9.20 Airplane lift— Bernoulli's principle in action** Because of the shape and orientation of an airfoil or airplane wing, the air streamlines are closer together, and the air speed is greater above the wing than below it. By Bernoulli's principle, the resulting pressure difference supplies part of the upward force called the lift.

This rather common explanation of lift is termed simplistic because Bernoulli's effect does not apply to the situation. Bernoulli's principle requires ideal fluid flow and energy conservation within the system, neither of which are satisfied in aircraft flying conditions. It is perhaps better to rely on Newton's laws, which always must be satisfied. Basically overall, the wing deflects the airflow downward, giving rise to a downward change in the airflow momentum and a downward force (Newton's second law). This results in an upward reaction force on the wing (Newton's third law). When this upward force exceeds the weight of the plane, you have enough lift for take off and flight.

PHYSLET

Illustration 15.4 Airplane Lift

Example 9.13 ■ Flow Rate from a Tank: Bernoulli's Equation

A cylindrical tank containing water has a small hole punched in its side below the water level, and water runs out (▼ Fig. 9.21). What is the approximate initial flow rate of water out of the tank?

PHYSLET

Illustration 15.2 Bernoulli's Principle at Work

Thinking It Through. Equation 9.17 ($A_1 v_1 = A_2 v_2$) is the flow rate equation, where Av has units of m^3/s, or volume/time. The v terms can be related by Bernoulli's equation, which also contains y, which can be used to find differences in height. The areas are not given, so relating the v terms might require some sort of approximation, as will be seen. (Note that the *approximate* initial flow rate is wanted.)

Solution.

PHYSLET

Exploration 15.3 Application of Bernoulli's Equation

Given: No specific values are given, so symbols will be used.   *Find* An expression for the approximate initial water flow rate from the hole

Bernoulli's equation,

$$p_1 + \tfrac{1}{2}\rho v_1^2 + \rho g y_1 = p_2 + \tfrac{1}{2}\rho v_2^2 + \rho g y_2$$

can be used. Recall that $y_2 - y_1$ is just the height of the surface of the liquid above the hole. The atmospheric pressures acting on the open surface and at the hole, p_1 and p_2, respectively, are essentially equal and cancel from the equation, as does the density, so we are left with

$$v_1^2 - v_2^2 = 2g(y_2 - y_1)$$

By the equation of continuity (the flow rate equation, Eq. 9.17), $A_1 v_1 = A_2 v_2$, where A_2 is the cross-sectional area of the tank and A_1 is that of the hole. Since A_2 is much greater than A_1, v_1 is much greater than v_2 (initially, $v_2 \approx 0$). So, to a good approximation,

$$v_1^2 = 2g(y_2 - y_1) \quad \text{or} \quad v_1 = \sqrt{2g(y_2 - y_1)}$$

The flow rate (volume/time) is then

$$\text{flow rate} = A_1 v_1 = A_1 \sqrt{2g(y_2 - y_1)}$$

Given the area of the hole and the height of the liquid above it, you can find the initial speed of the water coming from the hole and the flow rate. (What happens as the water level falls?)

Follow-Up Exercise. What would be the percentage change in the initial flow rate from the tank in this Example if the diameter of the small circular hole were increased by 30.0%?

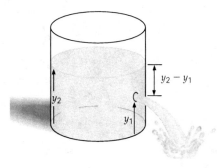

▲ **FIGURE 9.21** Fluid flow from a tank The flow rate is given by Bernoulli's equation. See Example 9.13.

Conceptual Example 9.14 ■ A Stream of Water: Smaller and Smaller

You have probably observed that a small steady stream of water flowing out of a kitchen faucet gets smaller the farther the water falls from the faucet. Why does that happen?

Reasoning and Answer. This effect can be explained by Bernoulli's principle. As the water falls, it accelerates and its speed increases. Then, by Bernoulli's principle, the liquid pressure inside the stream decreases. (See Fig. 9.19.) A pressure difference between that inside stream and the atmospheric pressure on the outside is thus created. As a result, there is an increasing inward force as the stream falls, so it becomes smaller. Eventually, the stream may get so thin that it breaks up into individual droplets.

Follow-Up Exercise. The equation of continuity can also be used to explain this stream effect. Give this explanation.

PHYSICS FACTS

- Daniel Gabriel Fahrenheit (1686–1736), a German instrument maker, constructed the first alcohol thermometer (1709) and mercury thermometer (1714). Fahrenheit used temperatures of 0° and 96° for reference points. The freezing and boiling points of water were then measured to be 32°F and 212°F.

- Anders Celsius (1701–1744), a Swedish astronomer, invented the Celsius temperature scale with a 100-degree interval between the freezing and boiling point of water (0°C and 100°C). Celsius' original scale was reversed, 100°C (freezing) and 0°C (boiling). This was later changed.

- The Celsius and Fahrenheit temperature scales have equal readings at −40°, that is −40°C = −40°F.

- The lowest possible temperature is absolute zero (−273.15°C). There is no known upper limit on temperature.

- The Golden Gate Bridge over San Francisco Bay varies in length by almost 1 m between summer and winter (thermal expansion).

- Almost all substances have positive coefficients of thermal expansion (expanding on heating). A few have negative coefficients (contraction on heating). Water does over a particular temperature range. The volume of a quantity of water decreases (contracts) on heating from 0°C to 4°C.

L ike sailboats, hot-air balloons are low-tech devices in a high-tech world. You can equip a balloon with the latest satellite-linked, computerized navigational system and attempt to fly across the Pacific. However, the basic principles that keep you aloft were known and understood centuries ago. As seen in the photo, air is heated and with an increase in temperature, the heated, less dense air rises. When enough hot air is in the balloon, it becomes buoyant and up you go.

Temperature and heat are frequent subjects of conversation, but if you had to tell what the words really mean, you might find yourself at a loss. We use various types of thermometers to measure temperatures, which provide an objective equivalent for our sensory experience of hot and cold. A temperature change generally results from the application or removal of heat. Temperature, therefore, is related to heat. But how? And what is heat? In this chapter, you'll find that the answers to such questions lead to an understanding of some far-reaching physical principles.

An early theory of heat considered it to be a fluidlike substance called *caloric* (from the Latin word *calor*, meaning "heat") that could be made to flow into and out of a body. Even though this theory has been abandoned, we still speak of heat as flowing from one object to another. Heat is now known to be energy in transit, and temperature and thermal properties are explained by considering the atomic and molecular behavior of substances. This and the next two chapters examine the nature of temperature and heat in terms of microscopic (molecular) theory and macroscopic observations. Here, you'll explore the nature of heat and the ways temperature is measured. You'll also encounter the gas laws, which explain not only the behavior of hot-air balloons, but also more important phenomena, such as how our lungs supply us with the oxygen we need to live.

338

10.1 Temperature and Heat

<u>OBJECTIVE:</u> To distinguish between temperature and heat.

A good way to begin studying thermal physics is with definitions of temperature and heat. **Temperature** is a relative measure, or indication, of hotness or coldness. A hot stove is said to have a high temperature and an ice cube to have a low temperature. An object that has a higher temperature than another object is said to be hotter or the other object colder. Note that *hot* and *cold* are relative terms, like *tall* and *short*. We can perceive temperature by touch. However, this temperature sense is somewhat unreliable, and its range is too limited to be useful for scientific purposes.

Heat is related to temperature and describes the process of energy transfer from one object to another. That is, **heat** is *the net energy transferred from one object to another because of a temperature difference*. Heat is energy in transit, so to speak. Once transferred, the energy becomes part of the total energy of the molecules of the object or system, that is, its **internal energy**. So heat (energy) transfers between objects can result in internal energy changes.*

On a microscopic level, temperature is associated with molecular motion. In kinetic theory (Section 10.5), which treats gas molecules as point particles, temperature is a measure of the average random *translational* kinetic energy of the molecules. However, diatomic molecules and other real substances, besides having such translational "temperature" energy, also may have kinetic energy due to vibrations and rotations, as well as potential energy due to the attractive forces between molecules. These energies do not contribute to the temperature of the gas but are part of its internal energy, which is the sum of all such energies (▾Fig. 10.1).

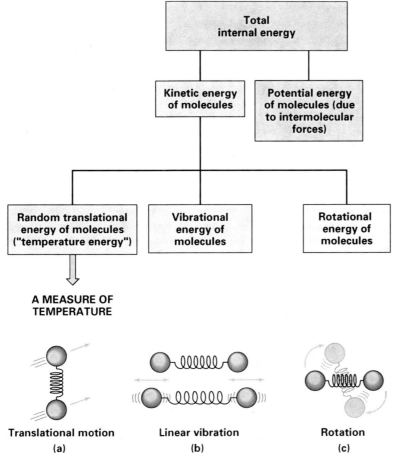

◄ **FIGURE 10.1** Molecular motions The total internal energy is made up of kinetic and potential energies. The kinetic energy has the following forms: **(a)** Temperature is associated with random translational motion of molecules. Neither the **(b)** linear vibrational motion and **(c)** rotation motion contribute to the temperature, nor does the intermolecular potential energy.

*Note: Some of the energy may go into doing work and not into internal energy (Section 12.2).

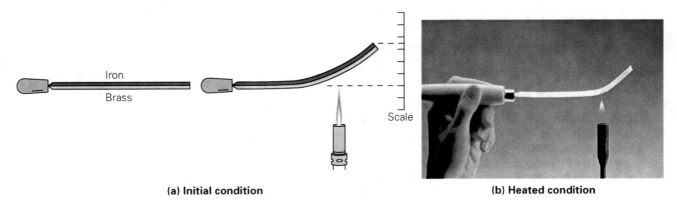

Iron

Brass

Scale

(a) Initial condition

(b) Heated condition

▲ **FIGURE 10.2** Thermal expansion (a) A bimetallic strip is made of two strips of different metals bonded together. (b) When such a strip is heated, it bends because of unequal expansions of the two metals. Here, brass expands more than iron, so the deflection is toward the iron. The deflection of the end of a strip could be used to measure temperature.

(a)

(b)

▲ **FIGURE 10.3** Bimetallic coil Bimetallic coils are used in (a) dial thermometers (the coil is in the center) and (b) household thermostats (the coil is to the right). Thermostats are used to regulate a heating or cooling system, turning off and on as the temperature of the room changes. The expansion and contraction of the coil causes the tilting of a glass vial containing mercury, which makes and breaks electrical contact.

Note that a higher temperature does not necessarily mean that one system has a greater internal energy than another. For example, in a classroom on a cold day, the air temperature is relatively high compared to that of the outdoor air. But all that cold air outside the classroom has far more internal energy than does the warm air inside, simply because there is so much *more* of it. If this were not the case, heat pumps would not be practical (Chapter 12). In other words, the internal energy of a system also depends on its mass, or the number of molecules in the system.

When heat is transferred between two objects, regardless of whether they are touching, the objects are said to be in *thermal contact*. When there is no longer a net heat transfer between objects in thermal contact, they have come to the same temperature and are said to be in *thermal equilibrium*.

10.2 The Celsius and Fahrenheit Temperature Scales

OBJECTIVES: To (a) explain how a temperature scale is constructed, and (b) convert temperatures from one scale to another.

A measure of temperature is obtained by using a **thermometer**, a device constructed to make use of some property of a substance that changes with temperature. Fortunately, many physical properties of materials change sufficiently with temperature to be used as the bases for thermometers. By far the most obvious and commonly used property is **thermal expansion** (Section 10.4), a change in the dimensions or volume of a substance that occurs when the temperature changes.

Almost all substances expand with increasing temperature, and do so to different extents. Most substances also contract with decreasing temperature. (Thermal expansion refers to both expansion and contraction; contraction is considered a negative expansion.) Because some metals expand more than others, a bimetallic strip (a strip made of two different metals bonded together) can be used to measure temperature changes. As heat is added, the composite strip will bend away from the side made of the metal that expands more (▲Fig. 10.2). Coils formed from such strips are used in dial thermometers and in common household thermostats (◄Fig. 10.3).

A common thermometer is the liquid-in-glass type, which is based on the thermal expansion of a liquid. A liquid in a glass bulb expands into a glass stem, rising in a capillary bore (a thin tube). Mercury and alcohol (usually dyed red to make it more visible) are the liquids used in most liquid-in-glass thermometers. These substances are chosen because of their relatively large thermal expansion and because they remain liquids over normal temperature ranges.

Thermometers are calibrated so that a numerical value can be assigned to a given temperature. For the definition of any standard scale or unit, two fixed reference points are needed. The ice point and the steam point of water at standard atmospheric pressure are two convenient fixed points. More commonly known as the freezing and boiling points, these are the temperatures at which pure water freezes and boils, respectively, under a pressure of 1 atm (standard pressure).

The two most familiar temperature scales are the **Fahrenheit temperature scale** (used in the United States) and the **Celsius temperature scale** (used in the rest of the world). As shown in ▸Fig. 10.4, the ice and steam points have values of 32°F and 212°F, respectively, on the Fahrenheit scale and 0°C and 100°C, respectively, on the Celsius scale. On the Fahrenheit scale, there are 180 equal intervals, or degrees (F°), between the two reference points; on the Celsius scale, there are 100 degrees (C°). Therefore, since $180/100 = 9/5 = 1.8$, a Celsius degree is almost twice as large as a Fahrenheit degree. (See margin note for the difference between °C and C°.)

A relationship for converting between the two scales can be obtained from a graph of Fahrenheit temperature (T_F) versus Celsius temperature (T_C), such as the one in ▾Fig. 10.5. The equation of the straight line (in slope–intercept form, $y = mx + b$) is $T_F = (180/100)T_C + 32$, and

$$T_F = \tfrac{9}{5}T_C + 32$$

or

Celsius-to-Fahrenheit conversion (10.1)

$$T_F = 1.8T_C + 32$$

where $\tfrac{9}{5}$ or 1.8 is the slope of the line and 32 is the intercept on the vertical axis. Thus, to change from a Celsius temperature (T_C) to its equivalent Fahrenheit temperature (T_F), you simply multiply the Celsius reading by $\tfrac{9}{5}$ and add 32.

The equation can be solved for T_C to convert from Fahrenheit to Celsius:

$$T_C = \tfrac{5}{9}(T_F - 32) \quad \textit{Fahrenheit-to-Celsius conversion} \quad (10.2)$$

 ▾ **FIGURE 10.5 Fahrenheit versus Celsius** A plot of Fahrenheit temperature versus Celsius temperature gives a straight line of the general form $y = mx + b$, where $T_F = \tfrac{9}{5}T_C + 32$.

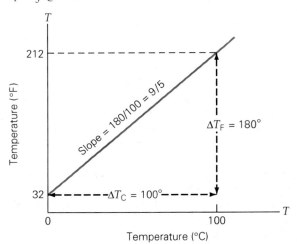

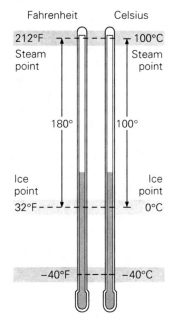

▲ **FIGURE 10.4** Celsius and Fahrenheit temperature scales Between the ice and steam fixed points, there are 100 degrees on the Celsius scale and 180 degrees on the Fahrenheit scale. Thus, a Celsius degree is 1.8 times as large as a Fahrenheit degree.

Note: For distinction, a particular temperature measurement, such as $T = 20°C$, is written with °C (pronounced 20 degrees Celsius), whereas a temperature interval, such as $\Delta T = 80°C - 60°C = 20$ C°, is written with C° (pronounced 20 Celsius degrees).

Example 10.1 ■ Converting Temperature Scale Readings: Fahrenheit and Celsius

What are (a) the typical room temperature of 20°C and a cold temperature of −18°C on the Fahrenheit scale; and (b) another cold temperature of −10°F and normal body temperature, 98.6°F, on the Celsius scale?

Thinking It Through. This is a direct application of Eqs. 10.1 and 10.2.

Solution.

Given: (a) $T_C = 20°C$ and $T_C = −18°C$ *Find:* for each temperature,
(b) $T_F = −10°F$ and $T_F = 98.6°F$ (a) T_F
                                                  (b) T_C

(a) Equation 10.1 is for changing Celsius readings to Fahrenheit:

$$20°C: \quad T_F = \tfrac{9}{5}T_C + 32 = \tfrac{9}{5}(20) + 32 = 68°F$$

$$−18°C: \quad T_F = \tfrac{9}{5}T_C + 32 = \tfrac{9}{5}(−18) + 32 = 0°F$$

(This typical room temperature of 20°C is a good one to remember.)

(b) Equation 10.2 changes Fahrenheit to Celsius:

$$−10°F: \quad T_C = \tfrac{5}{9}(T_F − 32) = \tfrac{5}{9}(−10 − 32) = −23°C$$

$$98.6°F: \quad T_C = \tfrac{5}{9}(T_F − 32) = \tfrac{5}{9}(98.6 − 32) = 37.0°C$$

From the last calculation, note that normal body temperature has a whole-number value on the Celsius scale. Keep in mind that a Celsius degree is 1.8 times (almost twice) as large as a Fahrenheit degree, so a temperature elevation of several degrees on the Celsius scale makes a big difference. For example, a temperature of 40.0°C represents an elevation of 3.0 C° over normal body temperature. However, on the Fahrenheit scale, this is an increase of 3.0 × 1.8 = 5.4 F°, or a temperature of 98.6 + 5.4 = 104.0°F.

Follow-Up Exercise. Convert the following temperatures: (a) −40°F to Celsius and (b) −40°C to Fahrenheit. *(Answers to all Follow-Up Exercises are at the back of the text.)*

Problem-Solving Hint

Because Eqs. 10.1 and 10.2 are so similar, it is easy to miswrite them. Since they are equivalent, you need to know only one of them—say, Celsius to Fahrenheit (Eq. 10.1, $T_F = \tfrac{9}{5}T_C + 32$). Solving this equation for T_C algebraically gives Eq. 10.2. A good way to make sure that you have written the conversion equation correctly is to test it with a known temperature, such as the boiling point of water. For example, $T_C = 100°C$, so

$$T_F = \tfrac{9}{5}T_C + 32 = \tfrac{9}{5}(100) + 32 = 212°F$$

Thus, we know the equation is correct.

Liquid-in-glass thermometers are adequate for many temperature measurements, but problems arise when highly accurate determinations are needed. A material may not expand uniformly over a wide temperature range. When calibrated to the ice and steam points, an alcohol thermometer and a mercury thermometer have the same readings at those points, but because alcohol and mercury have different expansion properties, the thermometers will not have exactly the same reading at an intermediate temperature, such as room temperature. For very sensitive temperature measurements and to define intermediate temperatures precisely, some other type of thermometer must be used. One such thermometer, a *gas thermometer*, is discussed next. But first, a couple of Insights on body temperatures—Insights 10.1 and 10.2.

INSIGHT 10.1 HUMAN BODY TEMPERATURE

We commonly take "normal" human body temperature to be 98.6°F (or 37.0°C). The source of this value is a study of human temperature readings done in 1868—more than 135 years ago. A more recent study, conducted in 1992, notes that the 1868 study used thermometers that were not as accurate as modern electronic (digital) thermometers. The new study has some interesting results.

The normal human body temperature from oral measurements varies among individuals over a range of about 96°F to 101°F, with an average temperature of 98.2°F. After strenuous exercise, the oral temperature can rise as high as 103°F. When the body is exposed to cold, oral temperatures can fall below 96°F. A rapid drop in temperature of 2 to 3 F° produces uncontrollable shivering. The skeletal muscles contract and so do the tiny muscles attached to the hair follicles. The result is "goose bumps."

Your body temperature is typically lowest in the morning, after you have slept and your digestive processes are at a low point. Normal body temperature generally rises during the day to a peak and then recedes. The 1992 study also indicated that women have a slightly higher average body temperature than do men (98.4°F versus 98.1°F).

What about the extremes? A fever temperature is typically between 102°F and 104°F. A body temperature above 106°F is extremely dangerous. At such temperatures, the enzymes that take part in certain chemical reactions in the body begin to be inactivated, and a total breakdown of body chemistry can result. On the cold side, decreased body temperature results in memory lapses and slurred speech, muscular rigidity, erratic heartbeats, and loss of consciousness. Below 78°F, death occurs due to heart failure. However, mild hypothermia (lower-than-normal body

temperature) can be beneficial. A decrease in body temperature slows down the body's chemical reactions, and cells use less oxygen than they normally do. This effect is applied in some surgeries (Fig. 1). A patient's body temperature may be lowered significantly to avoid damage to the brain and to the heart which must be stopped during some procedures.

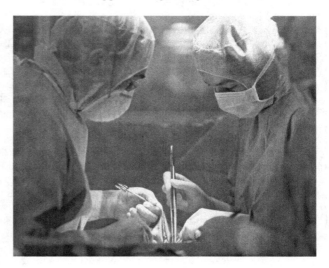

FIGURE 1 Lower than normal During some surgeries, the patient's body temperature is lowered to slow down the body's chemical reactions and to reduce the need for blood to supply oxygen to the tissues.

10.3 Gas Laws, Absolute Temperature, and the Kelvin Temperature Scale

OBJECTIVES: To (a) describe the ideal gas law, (b) explain how it is used to determine absolute zero, and (c) understand the Kelvin temperature scale.

Whereas different liquid-in-glass thermometers show slightly different readings for temperatures other than fixed points because of the liquids' different expansion properties, a thermometer that uses a gas gives the same readings regardless of the gas used. The reason is that at very low densities all gases exhibit the same expansion behavior.

The variables that describe the behavior of a given quantity (mass) of gas are pressure, volume, and temperature (p, V, and T). When temperature is held constant, the pressure and volume of a quantity of gas are related as follows:

$$pV = \text{constant} \quad \text{or} \quad p_1V_1 = p_2V_2 \quad \textit{(at constant temperature)} \quad (10.3)$$

That is, the product of pressure and volume is a constant. This relationship is known as *Boyle's law*, after Robert Boyle (1627–1691), the English chemist who discovered it.

When the pressure is held constant, the volume of a quantity of gas is related to the *absolute* temperature (to be defined shortly):

$$\frac{V}{T} = \text{constant} \quad \text{or} \quad \frac{V_1}{T_1} = \frac{V_2}{T_2} \quad \textit{(at constant pressure)} \quad (10.4)$$

INSIGHT 10.2 WARM-BLOODED VERSUS COLD-BLOODED

With few exceptions, all mammals and birds are warm-blooded and all fish, reptiles, amphibians, and insects are cold-blooded. The difference is that warm-blooded creatures try to maintain their bodies at a relatively constant temperature, while cold-blooded creatures take on the temperature of their surroundings (Fig. 1).

Warm-blooded creatures maintain a relatively constant body temperature by generating their own heat when in a cold environment and by cooling themselves when in a hot environment. To generate heat, warm-blooded animals convert food into energy. To stay cool on hot days, they sweat, pant, or get wet and thereby remove heat by water evaporation. Primates (humans, apes, monkeys, and so on) have sweat glands all over their bodies. Dogs and cats have sweat glands only in their feet. Pigs and whales have no sweat glands. Pigs generally rely on wallowing in mud for cooling, and whales can change water depths for temperature changes or seasonally migrate.

Also, some animals have fur coats for warmth in the winter and shed them to cool off. Warm-blooded animals can shiver to activate certain muscles to increase metabolism and thereby generate heat. Birds (and some people) migrate between colder and warmer regions.

The body temperature of cold-blooded creatures changes with the temperature of their environment. They are very active in warm environments and are sluggish when it is cold. This is because their muscle activity depends on chemical reactions that vary with temperature. Cold-blooded creatures often bask in the sun to warm up to increase their metabolism. Fish can change water depths or seasonally migrate. Frogs, toads, and lizards hibernate during winter. To stay warm, honeybees crowd together and rapidly flap their wings to generate heat.

Some animals do not fall into the strict definitions of being warm-blooded or cold-blooded. Bats, for example, are mammals that cannot maintain a constant body temperature, and they cool off when not active. Some warm-blooded animals, such as bears, groundhogs, and gophers, hibernate in winter. During the hibernation period, they live off stored body fat; their body temperatures may drop as much as 10 C° (18 F°).

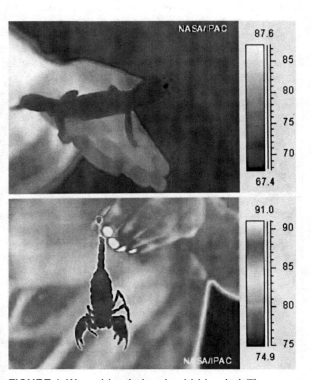

FIGURE 1 Warm-blooded and cold-blooded The infrared images show that cold-blooded creatures take on the temperature of their surroundings. Both the gecko and the scorpion are at the same temperature (color) as the air surrounding them. Notice the difference between these cold-blooded creatures and the warm-blooded humans holding them.

That is, the ratio of the volume to the temperature is a constant. This relationship is known as *Charles's law*, named for the French scientist Jacques Charles (1746–1823), who made early hot-air balloon flights and was therefore quite interested in the relationship between the volume and temperature of a gas. A popular demonstration of Charles's law is shown in ▶Fig. 10.6.

Low-density gases obey these laws, which may be combined into a single relationship. Since $pV = $ constant and $V/T = $ constant for a given quantity of gas, pV/T must also equal a constant. This relationship is the **ideal gas law**:

$$\frac{pV}{T} = \text{constant} \quad \text{or} \quad \frac{p_1 V_1}{T_1} = \frac{p_2 V_2}{T_2} \quad \textit{ideal gas law (ratio form)} \quad (10.5)$$

That is, the ratio pV/T at one time (t_1) is the same as at another time (t_2), or at any other time, as long as the quantity (number of molecules or mass) of gas does not change.

This relationship can be written in a more general form that applies not just to a given quantity of a single gas, but to any quantity of any low-pressure, dilute gas. With a quantity of gas determined by the number of molecules (N) in the gas (that is, $pV/T \propto N$), it follows that

$$\frac{pV}{T} = N k_B \quad \text{or} \quad pV = N k_B T \quad \textit{ideal gas law} \quad (10.6)$$

PHYSLET®

Exploration 20.3 Ideal Gas Law

where k_B is a constant of proportionality known as *Boltzmann's constant*:

$$k_B = 1.38 \times 10^{-23} \text{ J/K}$$

The K stands for temperature on the Kelvin scale, discussed shortly. (Can you show that the units are correct?) Note that the mass of the sample does not appear explicitly in Eq. 10.6. However, the number of molecules N in a sample of a gas is proportional to the total mass of the gas. The ideal gas law, sometimes called the *perfect gas law*, applies to real gases with low pressures and densities, and describes the behavior of most gases fairly accurately at normal densities.

Macroscopic Form of the Ideal Gas Law

Equation 10.6 is a *microscopic* (*micro* means extremely small) form of the ideal gas law in that it refers specifically to the number of molecules, N. However, the law can be rewritten in a *macroscopic* (*macro* means large) form, which involves quantities that can be measured with everyday laboratory equipment. In this form, we have

$$pV = nRT \quad \textit{ideal gas law} \tag{10.7}$$

using nR rather than Nk_B for convenience since $n \propto N$. Here, n is the number of moles (mol) of the gas, a quantity defined next, and R is called the *universal gas constant*: $R = 8.31 \text{ J/(mol·K)}$.

In chemistry, a **mole** (abbreviated mol) of a substance is defined as the quantity that contains **Avogadro's number** (N_A) of molecules:

$$N_A = 6.02 \times 10^{23} \text{ molecules/mol}$$

Thus, n and N in the two forms of the ideal gas law are related by $N = nN_A$. From Eq. 10.7, it can be shown that 1 mol of *any* gas occupies 22.4 L at 0°C and 1 atm. These conditions, 0°C and 1 atm, are known as *standard temperature and pressure* (STP).

It is important to note what these equations for the macroscopic (Eq. 10.7) and microscopic (Eq. 10.6) forms of the ideal gas law represent. For the macroscopic form of the ideal gas law, the constant $R = pV/(nT)$ has units of J/(mol·K). For the microscopic form of the law, $k_B = pV/(NT)$, with units of J/(molecule·K). Note that the difference between the macroscopic and microscopic forms of the ideal gas law is moles versus molecules, and we usually measure gas quantities in moles.

Equation 10.7 is a practical form of the ideal gas law, because (macroscopic or laboratory) quantities are measured in moles (n) of gases rather than the number of molecules (N). To use Eq. 10.7, we need to know the number of moles of a quantity of gas. This is done by finding the *formula mass* of a compound or element, which is the sum of the atomic masses given in the formula (for example, H_2O) of the substance. Because the masses are so small in relation to the SI standard kilogram, another unit, the *atomic mass unit* (u), is used:

$$1 \text{ atomic mass unit (u)} = 1.66054 \times 10^{-27} \text{ kg*}$$

The formula mass is determined from the chemical formula and the atomic masses of the atoms. (The latter are listed in Appendix IV and are commonly rounded to the nearest one half.) For example, water, H_2O, with two hydrogen atoms and one oxygen atom, has a formula mass of $2m_H + 1m_O = 2(1.0 \text{ u}) + 1(16.0 \text{ u}) = 18.0 \text{ u}$, because the atomic mass of each hydrogen atom is 1.0 u and that of an oxygen atom is 16.0 u. Then, 1 mol of water has a formula mass of 18.0. Similarly, the oxygen we breathe, O_2, has a formula mass of $2 \times 16.0 \text{ u} = 32.0 \text{ u}$. Hence, a mole of oxygen has a mass of 32.0 u. The mass of 1 mol of any substance is its formula mass expressed in grams. For example, 32.0 g of oxygen is one mole and would occupy 22.4 L at STP.

Note: The temperature T in the ideal gas law is absolute (Kelvin) temperature.

Note: N is the total number of molecules; N_A is Avogadro's number; $n = N/N_A$ is the number of moles.

(a)   (b)

▲ **FIGURE 10.6 Charles's law in action** Demonstrations of the relationship between the volume and the temperature of a quantity of gas. A weighted balloon, initially at room temperature, is placed in a beaker of water. **(a)** When ice is placed in the beaker and the temperature falls, the balloon's volume is reduced. **(b)** When the water is heated and the temperature rises, the balloon's volume increases.

*The atomic mass unit is based on assigning a carbon atom the value of exactly 12 u.

► **FIGURE 10.7 Constant-volume gas thermometer** Such a thermometer indicates temperature as a function of pressure, since, for a low-density gas, $p \propto T$. **(a)** At some initial temperature, the pressure reading has a certain value. **(b)** When the gas thermometer is heated, the pressure (and temperature) reading is higher, because, on average, the gas molecules are moving faster.

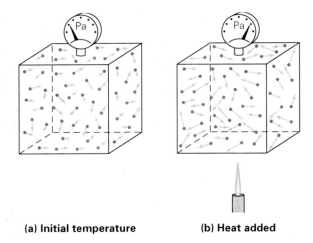

(a) Initial temperature   **(b) Heat added**

It is interesting to note that Avogadro's number allows you to compute the mass of a particular type of molecule. For example, suppose you want to know the mass of a water molecule (H_2O). As we have just seen, the formula mass of 1 mol of water is 18.0 g, or 18.0 g/mol. The *molecular mass* (m) is then given by

$$m = \frac{\text{formula mass (in kilograms)}}{N_A}$$

and, converting grams to kilograms, we have

$$m_{H_2O} = \frac{(18.0 \text{ g/mol})(10^{-3} \text{ kg/g})}{6.02 \times 10^{23} \text{ molecules/mol}} = 2.99 \times 10^{-26} \text{ kg/molecule}$$

Absolute Zero and the Kelvin Temperature Scale

The product of the pressure and the volume of a sample of ideal gas is directly proportional to the temperature of the gas: $pV \propto T$. This relationship allows a gas to be used to measure temperature in a *constant-volume gas thermometer*. Holding the volume of the gas constant, which can be done easily in a rigid container, means that $p \propto T$ (▲Fig. 10.7). Then using a constant-volume gas thermometer, one reads the temperature in terms of pressure. A plot of pressure versus temperature gives a straight line in this case (▼Fig. 10.8a).

▼ **FIGURE 10.8 Pressure versus temperature** **(a)** A low-density gas kept at a constant volume gives a straight line on a graph of p versus T, that is, $p = (Nk_B/V)T$. When the line is extended to the zero pressure value, a temperature of $-273.15°C$ is obtained, which is taken to be absolute zero. **(b)** Extrapolation of lines for all low-density gases indicates the same absolute zero temperature. The actual behavior of gases deviates from this straight-line relationship at low temperatures because the gases start to liquefy.

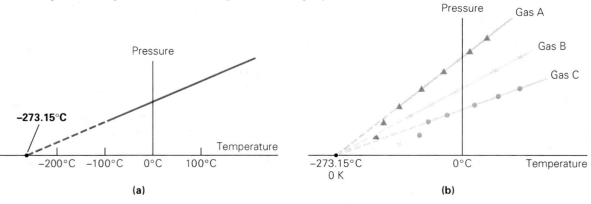

As can be seen in Fig. 10.8b, measurements of real gases (plotted data points) deviate from the values predicted by the ideal gas law at very low temperatures. This is because the gases liquefy at such temperatures. However, the relationship is linear over a large temperature range, and it looks as though the pressure might reach zero with decreasing temperature if the gas were to continue to be gaseous (ideal or perfect).

The absolute minimum temperature for an ideal gas is therefore inferred by extrapolating, or extending the straight line to the axis, as in Fig. 10.8b. This temperature is found to be −273.15°C and is designated as **absolute zero**. Absolute zero is believed to be the lower limit of temperature, but it has never been attained. In fact, there is a law of thermodynamics that says it never can be achieved (Section 12.5).* There is no known upper limit to temperature. For example, the temperatures at the centers of some stars are estimated to be greater than 100 million degrees (K or °C, take your choice).

Absolute zero is the foundation of the **Kelvin temperature scale**, named after the British scientist Lord Kelvin who proposed it in 1848.[†] On this scale, −273.15°C is taken as the zero point—that is, as 0 K (▼Fig. 10.9). The size of a single unit of Kelvin temperature is the same as that of the Celsius degree, so temperatures on these scales are related by

$$T_K = T_C + 273.15 \quad \textit{Celsius-to-Kelvin conversion} \qquad (10.8)$$

where T_K is the temperature in **kelvins** (*not* degrees Kelvin; for example, 300 kelvins). The kelvin is abbreviated as K (*not* °K). For general calculations, it is common to round the 273.15 in Eq. 10.8 to 273, that is,

$$T_K = T_C + 273 \quad \textit{(for general calculations)} \qquad (10.8a)$$

The absolute Kelvin scale is the official SI temperature scale; however, the Celsius scale is used in most parts of the world for everyday temperature readings. The absolute temperature in kelvins is used primarily in scientific applications.

◀ **FIGURE 10.9 The Kelvin temperature scale** The lowest temperature on the Kelvin scale (corresponding to −273.15°C) is absolute zero. A unit interval on the Kelvin scale, called a kelvin and abbreviated K, is equivalent to a temperature change of 1 C°; thus, $T_K = T_C + 273.15$. (The constant is usually rounded to 273 for convenience.) For example, a temperature of 0°C is equal to 273 kelvins.

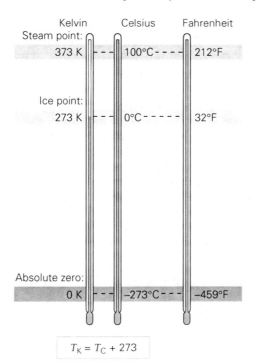

$$T_K = T_C + 273$$

---

*At the time of this writing, the lowest temperature scientists have been able to attain is 250×10^{-12} K, that is, 250 pK (picokelvins) above absolute zero.

[†]Lord Kelvin, born William Thomson (1824–1907), developed devices to improve telegraphy and the compass and was involved in the laying of the first transatlantic cable. When he received his title, it is said that he considered choosing Lord Cable or Lord Compass as the title, but decided on Lord Kelvin, after a river that runs near the University of Glasgow in Scotland, where he was a professor of physics for fifty years.

Problem-Solving Hint

Keep in mind that Kelvin temperatures *must* be used with the ideal gas law. It is a common mistake to use Celsius or Fahrenheit temperatures in that equation. Suppose you used a Celsius temperature of $T = 0°C$ in the gas law. You would have $pV = 0$, which makes no sense, since neither p nor V is zero at the freezing point of water.

Note that there can be no negative temperatures on the Kelvin scale if absolute zero is the lowest possible temperature. That is, the Kelvin scale doesn't have an arbitrary zero temperature somewhere within the scale as on the Fahrenheit and Celsius scales—zero K is absolute zero, period.

Example 10.2 ■ Deepest Freeze: Absolute Zero on the Fahrenheit Scale

What is absolute zero on the Fahrenheit scale?

Thinking It Through. This requires the conversion of 0 K to the Fahrenheit scale. But first a conversion to the Celsius scale is in order. (Why?)

Solution.

Given: $T_K = 0$ K   *Find:* T_F

Temperatures on the Kelvin scale are related directly to Celsius temperatures by $T_K = T_C + 273.15$ (Eq. 10.8), so first we convert 0 K to a Celsius value:

$$T_C = T_K - 273.15 = 0 - 273.15 = -273.15°C$$

(We use $-273.15°C$ for absolute zero to give a more accurate value of absolute zero on the Fahrenheit scale.) Then, converting to Fahrenheit (Eq. 10.1) gives

$$T_F = \tfrac{9}{5}T_C + 32 = \tfrac{9}{5}(-273.15) + 32 = -459.67°F$$

Thus, absolute zero is about $-460°F$.

Follow-Up Exercise. There is an absolute temperature scale associated with the Fahrenheit temperature scale called the Rankine scale. A Rankine degree is the same size as a Fahrenheit degree, and absolute zero is taken as 0°R (zero degrees Rankine). Write the conversion equations between (a) the Rankine and the Fahrenheit scales, (b) the Rankine and the Celsius scales, and (c) the Rankine and the Kelvin scales.

Initially, gas thermometers were calibrated by using the ice and steam points. The Kelvin scale uses absolute zero and a second fixed point adopted in 1954 by the International Committee on Weights and Measures. This second fixed point is the **triple point of water**, at which water coexists simultaneously in equilibrium as a solid (ice), liquid (water), and gas (water vapor). The triple point occurs at a unique set of values for temperature and pressure—a temperature of 0.01°C and a pressure of 4.58 mm Hg—and provides a reproducible reference temperature for the Kelvin scale. The temperature of the triple point on the Kelvin scale was assigned a value of 273.16 K. The SI kelvin unit is then defined as 1/273.16 of the temperature at the triple point of water.*

Now let's use the ideal gas law, which requires absolute temperatures.

Example 10.3 ■ The Ideal Gas Law: Using Absolute Temperatures

A quantity of low-density gas in a rigid container is initially at room temperature (20°C) and a particular pressure (p_1). If the gas is heated to a temperature of 60°C, by what factor does the pressure change?

Thinking It Through. A "factor" of change implies a ratio (p_2/p_1), so Eq. 10.5 should apply. Note that the container is rigid, which means that $V_1 = V_2$.

Solution.

Given: $T_1 = 20°C$ *Find:* p_2/p_1 (pressure ratio or factor)
$\quad\quad\quad$ $T_2 = 60°C$
$\quad\quad\quad$ $V_1 = V_2$

*The 273.16 value given here for the triple point temperature and the −273.15 value, as determined in Fig. 10.8, indicate different things. The −273.15°C is taken as 0 K. The 273.16 K (or 0.01°C) is a different reading on a different temperature scale.

Since the factor by which the pressure changes is wanted, we write p_2/p_1 as a ratio. For example, if $p_2/p_1 = 2$, then $p_2 = 2p_1$, or the pressure would change (increase) by a factor of 2. The ratio also indicates that we should use the ideal gas law in ratio form. The law requires *absolute* temperatures, so we first change the Celsius temperatures to kelvins:

$$T_1 = 20°C + 273 = 293 \text{ K}$$
$$T_2 = 60°C + 273 = 333 \text{ K}$$

Observe that a rounded value of 273 was used in Eq. 10.8 for convenience. Then, using the ideal gas law (Eq. 10.5) in the form $p_2 V_2/T_2 = p_1 V_1/T_1$, we have, with $V_1 = V_2$,

$$p_2 = \left(\frac{T_2}{T_1}\right)p_1 = \left(\frac{333 \text{ K}}{293 \text{ K}}\right)p_1 = 1.14p_1$$

So, p_2 is 1.14 times p_1; that is, the pressure increases by a factor of 1.14, or 14 percent. (What would the factor be if the Celsius temperatures were *incorrectly* used? It would be much larger: $60°C/20°C = 3$, or $p_2 = 3p_1$.)

Follow-Up Exercise. If the gas in this Example is heated from an initial temperature of 20°C (room temperature) so that the pressure increases by a factor of 1.26, what is the final Celsius temperature?

Note: *Always* use Kelvin (absolute) temperatures with the ideal gas law.

Because of its absolute nature, the Kelvin temperature scale has special significance. As will be seen in Section 10.5, the absolute temperature is directly proportional to the internal energy of an ideal gas and so can be used as an indication of that energy. There are no negative values on the absolute scale. Negative absolute temperatures would imply negative internal energy for the gas, a meaningless concept. Suppose you were asked to double the temperatures of, say, $-10°C$ and $0°C$. What would you do? The following Integrated Example should help.

Integrated Example 10.4 ■ Some Like It Hot: Doubling the Temperature

The evening weather report gives the day's high temperature as 10°C and predicts the next day's high to be 20°C. (a) A father tells his son that this means it will be twice as warm tomorrow, but the son says it does not. Do you agree with (1) the father or (2) the son? (b) Prove your result by using the absolute (Kelvin) temperature scale. Use a ratio.

(a) Conceptual Reasoning. Keep in mind that temperature gives a relative *indication* of hotness or coldness. Certainly, 20°C would be warmer than 10°C. But just because the numerical value of the higher temperature is twice as great (or greater by a factor of 2, because $20°C/10°C = 2$) does not necessarily mean it is twice as warm or there is twice the energy. It means that the air temperature is 10 degrees higher and therefore relatively warmer. So the son wins and the answer is (2).

(b) Quantitative Reasoning and Solution. The Kelvin temperatures can be computed directly from Eq. 10.8a, and a ratio of these temperatures will give the factor of increase based on internal energy.

Given: $T_{C_1} = 10°C$ *Find:* T_{K_2}/T_{K_1}
$T_{C_2} = 20°C$

The equivalent absolute temperatures are

$$T_{K_1} = T_{C_1} + 273 = 10°C + 273 = 283 \text{ K}$$
$$T_{K_2} = T_{C_2} + 273 = 20°C + 273 = 293 \text{ K}$$

and

$$\frac{T_{K_2}}{T_{K_1}} = \frac{293 \text{ K}}{283 \text{ K}} = 1.04$$

So there is an increase of 0.04, or 4% in temperature.

Follow-Up Exercise. The weather report gives the day's high temperature as 0°C. If the next day's temperature were double that, what would the temperature be in degrees Celsius? Would this be environmentally possible?

11 HEAT

PHYSICS FACTS

- With a skin temperature of 34°C (93.2°F), a person sitting in a room at 23°C (73.4°F) will lose about 100 J of heat per second, which is a power output approximately that which is a 100-W lightbulb. This is why a closed room full of people tends to get very warm.

- A couple of inches of fiberglass in the attic can cut heat loss by as much as 90% (see Example 11.7).

- If the Earth did not have an atmosphere (hence no greenhouse effect), its average surface temperature would be 30 C° (86 F°) lower than it is now. That would freeze liquid water and basically eliminate life as we know it.

- Most metals are excellent thermal conductors. However, iron and steel are relatively poor conductors; they conduct only about 12% as much as copper.

- Styrofoam is one of the best thermal insulators. It conducts only 25% as much as wool under similar conditions.

- During a race on a hot day, a professional cyclist can evaporate as much as seven liters of water in three hours in getting rid of the heat generated by this vigorous activity.

Heat is crucial to our existence. Our bodies must balance heat loss and gain to stay within the narrow temperature range necessary for life. This thermal balance is delicate and any disturbance can have serious consequences. Sickness can disrupt the balance and our bodies produce a chill or fever.

To maintain our health, we exercise by doing mechanical work such as lifting weights, riding bicycles, and so on. Our bodies convert food energy (chemical potential) to mechanical work; however, this process is not perfect. That is, the body cannot convert all the food energy into mechanical work—in fact, less than 20%, depending on which muscle groups are doing the work. The rest goes into heat. The leg muscles are the largest and most efficient in performing mechanical work; for example, cycling and running are relatively efficient processes. The arm and shoulder muscles are less efficient; hence, snow shoveling is a low-efficiency exercise. The body must have special cooling mechanisms to get rid of excess heat generated during intense exercise. The most efficient mechanism is through perspiring, or the evaporation of water. The Olympic marathon champion Gezahgne Abera tries to promote cooling and evaporation by pouring water over his head, as shown in the photograph.

On a larger scale, heat is important to our planet's ecosystem. The average temperature of the Earth, so critical to our environment and to the survival of the organisms that inhabit it, is maintained through a heat-exchange balance. Each day, a vast quantity of solar energy reaches our planet's atmosphere and surface. Scientists are concerned that a buildup of atmospheric "greenhouse" gases, a product of our industrial society, could significantly raise the Earth's average temperature. This change would undoubtedly have a negative effect on life on the Earth.

367

At a more practical level, most of us know to be very careful while handling anything that has recently been in contact with a flame or other source of heat. Yet while the copper bottom of a steel pot on the stove can be very hot, the steel pot handle is only warm to the touch. Sometimes direct contact isn't necessary for heat to be transmitted, but how was heat transferred? And why was the steel handle not nearly as hot as the pot? It has to do with thermal conduction as you will learn.

In this chapter, you'll learn what heat is and how it is measured. You will also study the various mechanisms by which heat is transferred from one object to another. This knowledge will allow you to explain many everyday phenomena, as well as provide a basis for understanding the conversion of thermal energy into useful mechanical work.

11.1 Definition and Units of Heat

OBJECTIVES: To (a) define heat, (b) distinguish the various units of heat, and (c) define the mechanical equivalent of heat.

Like work, heat involves a transfer of energy. In the 1800s, it was thought that heat described the amount of energy an object possessed, but this is not true. Rather, **heat** is the name used to describe a type of energy *transfer*. When we refer to "heat" or "heat energy," this is the amount of energy added to, or removed from, the total internal energy of an object due to temperature differences.

Because heat is energy *in transit*, it is measured in standard energy units. As usual, we use SI units (the joule), but for completeness, and define other commonly used units of heat. An important one is the **kilocalorie (kcal)** (▼ Fig. 11.1a):

> One kilocalorie (kcal) is defined as the amount of heat needed to raise the temperature of 1 kg of water by 1 C° (from 14.5°C to 15.5°C).

(This kilocalorie is technically known as the "15° kilocalorie.") The temperature range is specified because the energy needed varies slightly with temperature—a variation so small that it can be ignored at the temperature in question.

For smaller quantities, the **calorie (cal)** is sometimes used (1 kcal = 1000 cal). One calorie is the amount of heat needed to raise the temperature of 1 g of water by 1 C° (from 14.5°C to 15.5°C) (Fig. 11.1b).

A familiar use of the larger unit, the kilocalorie, is for specifying the energy values of foods. In this context, the word is usually shortened to *Calorie* (Cal). That is, people on diets really count kilocalories. This quantity refers to the food energy that is available for conversion to heat to be used, for mechanical movement, to maintain body temperature, or to increase body mass. (See Example 11.1.) The capital C distinguishes the larger kilogram-Calorie, or kilocalorie, from the smaller gram-calorie, or calorie. They are sometimes referred to as "big Calorie" and "little calorie." (In some countries, the joule is used for food values—see ▶Fig. 11.2.)

▶ **FIGURE 11.1 Units of heat (a)** A kilocalorie raises the temperature of 1 kg of water by 1 C°. **(b)** A calorie raises the temperature of 1 g of water by 1 C°. **(c)** A Btu raises the temperature of 1 lb of water by 1 F°. (Not drawn to scale.)

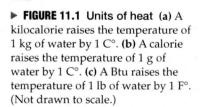

(a) 1 kilocalorie (kcal) or Calorie (Cal)

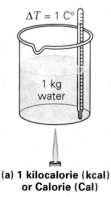

(b) 1 calorie (cal)

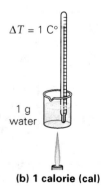

(c) 1 British thermal unit (Btu)

A unit of heat sometimes used in American industry is the **British thermal unit (Btu)**. One Btu is the amount of heat needed to raise the temperature of 1 lb of water by 1 F° (from 63°F to 64°F; Fig. 11.1c), and 1 Btu = 252 cal = 0.252 kcal. If you buy an air conditioner or an electric heater, you will find that it is rated in Btu, which is really Btu per hour—in other words, a power rating. For example, window air conditioners range from 4000 to 25000 Btu/h. This specifies the rate at which the appliance can remove heat.

The Mechanical Equivalent of Heat

The idea that heat is actually a transfer of energy is the result of work by many scientists. Some early observations were made by the American Benjamin Thompson (Count Rumford), 1753–1814, while he was supervising the boring of cannon barrels in Germany. Rumford noticed that water put into the bore of the cannon (to prevent overheating during drilling) boiled away and had to be replenished. The theory of heat at that time pictured it as a "caloric fluid," which flowed from hot objects to colder ones. Rumford did several experiments to detect "caloric fluid" by measuring changes in the weights of heated substances. Since no weight change was ever detected, he concluded that the mechanical work done by friction was actually responsible for the heating of the water.

This conclusion was later proven quantitatively by the English scientist James Joule (after whom the unit of energy is named, see Section 5.6). Using the apparatus illustrated in ▸Fig. 11.3, Joule demonstrated that when a given amount of mechanical work was done, the water was heated, as indicated by an increase in its temperature. He found that for every 4186 J of work done, the temperature of the water rose 1 C° per kg, or that 4186 J was equivalent to 1 kcal:

$$1 \text{ kcal} = 4186 \text{ J} = 4.186 \text{ kJ} \quad \text{or} \quad 1 \text{ cal} = 4.186 \text{ J}$$

This relationship is called the **mechanical equivalent of heat**. Example 11.1 illustrates an everyday use of these conversion factors.

▲ **FIGURE 11.2 It's a joule!** In Australia, diet drinks are labeled as being "low joule." In Germany, the labeling is a bit more specific: "Less than 4 kilojoules (1 kcal) in 0.3 Liter." How does this labeling compare to that for diet drinks in the United States?

Exploration 19.1 Mechanical Equivalent of Heat

Example 11.1 ■ Working Off That Birthday Cake: Mechanical Equivalent of Heat to the Rescue

At a birthday party, a student eats a piece of cake (food energy value of 400 Cal). To prevent this energy from being stored as fat, she takes a stationary-bicycle workout class right after the party. This exercise requires the body to do work at an average rate of 200 watts. How long must the student bicycle to achieve her goal of "working off" the cake's energy?

Thinking It Through. Power is the rate at which the student does work, and the watt (W) is its SI unit (1 W = 1 J/s, Section 5.6). To find the time to do this work, we express the food energy content in joules and use the definition of average power, $\overline{P} = W/t$ (work/time).

Solution. The work required to "burn up" the energy content of the cake is at least 400 Cal. Listing the data given and converting to SI units. (Remember that Cal means kcal.)

Given: $W = (400 \text{ kcal})\left(\dfrac{4186 \text{ J}}{\text{kcal}}\right) = 1.67 \times 10^6 \text{ J}$ *Find:* Time t to
$\overline{P} = 200 \text{ W} = 200 \text{ J/s}$ "burn up" 400 Cal

Rearranging the equation for average power,

$$t = \frac{W}{\overline{P}} = \frac{1.67 \times 10^6 \text{ J}}{200 \text{ J/s}} = 8.35 \times 10^3 \text{ s} = 139 \text{ min} = 2.32 \text{ h}$$

Follow-Up Exercise. If the 400 Cal in this Example were used to increase the student's gravitational potential energy, how high would she rise? (Assume her mass is 60 kg.) *(Answers to all Follow-Up Exercises are at the back of the text.)*

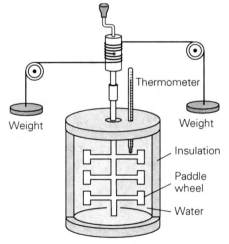

▲ **FIGURE 11.3 Joule's apparatus for determining the mechanical equivalent of heat** As the weights descend, the paddle wheels churn the water, and the mechanical energy, or work, is converted into heat energy, raising the temperature of the water. For every 4186 J of work done, the temperature of the water rises 1 C° per kilogram. Thus, 4186 J is equivalent to 1 kcal.

11.2 Specific Heat and Calorimetry

<u>OBJECTIVES:</u> To (a) define specific heat, and (b) explain how the specific heats of materials are measured using the technique of calorimetry.

PHYSLET

Illustration 19.1 Specific Heat

Specific Heats of Solids and Liquids

Recall from Chapter 10 that when heat is added to a solid or liquid, the energy may go toward increasing the average molecular kinetic energy (temperature change) and also toward increasing the potential energy associated with the molecular bonds. Different substances have different molecular configurations and bonding patterns. Thus, if equal amounts of heat are added to equal masses of different substances, the resulting temperature changes will *not* generally be the same.

The amount of heat (Q) required to change the temperature of a substance is proportional to the mass (m) of the substance and to the change in its temperature (ΔT). That is, $Q \propto m\Delta T$, or, in equation form, with a proportionality constant c,

$$Q = cm\Delta T \quad \text{or} \quad c = \frac{Q}{m\Delta T} \quad \textit{specific heat} \quad (11.1)$$

Here, $\Delta T = T_f - T_i$ is the temperature change of the object and c is the *specific heat capacity*, or simply its **specific heat**. The SI units of specific heat are $J/(kg \cdot K)$ or $J/(kg \cdot C°)$, because $1\,K = 1\,C°$. Specific heat is characteristic of the substance type. Thus, the specific heat gives us an indication of a material's internal molecular configuration and bonding.

Note that the specific heat physically means the heat (transfer) required to raise (or lower) the temperature of 1 kg of a substance by 1 C°. The specific heats of some common substances are given in Table 11.1. Specific heats vary slightly with temperature, but at everyday temperatures they can be considered constant.

The larger the specific heat of a substance, the more energy must be transferred to or taken from it (per kilogram of mass) to change its temperature by a given amount. That is, a substance with a higher specific heat requires more heat

TABLE 11.1	Specific Heats of Various Substances (Solids and Liquids) at 20°C and 1 atm	
	Specific Heat (c)	
Substance	J/(kg·C°)	kcal/(kg·C°) or cal/(g·C°)
Solids		
Aluminum	920	0.220
Copper	390	0.0932
Glass	840	0.201
Ice (−10°C)	2100	0.500
Iron or steel	460	0.110
Lead	130	0.0311
Soil (average)	1050	0.251
Wood (average)	1680	0.401
Human body (average)	3500	0.84
Liquids		
Ethyl alcohol	2450	0.585
Glycerin	2410	0.576
Mercury	139	0.0332
Water (15°C)	4186	1.000
Gas		
Water vapor (H_2O)	2000	0.48

for a given temperature change and mass than one with a lower specific heat. Table 11.1 shows that metals have specific heats considerably lower than that of water. Thus it takes only a small amount of heat to produce a relatively large temperature increase in a metal object, compared to the same mass of water.

Compared to most common materials, water has a large specific heat of 4186 J/(kg·C°), or 1.00 kcal/(kg·C°). You have been the victim of the high specific heat of water if you have ever burned your mouth on a baked potato or the hot cheese on a pizza. These foods have high water content and with its high specific heat, this means they don't cool off as quickly as some other drier foods do. The large specific heat of water is also responsible for the mild climate of places near large bodies of water. (See Section 11.4 for more details.)

Note from Eq. 11.1 that when there is a temperature increase, ΔT is positive ($T_f > T_i$) then Q is positive. This condition corresponds to energy being *added* to a system or object. Conversely, ΔT and Q are negative when energy is *removed from* a system or object. This sign convention will be used throughout this book.

Example 11.2 ■ Drinking Off That Birthday Cake: Specific Heat to the Rescue?

At a birthday party in Example 11.1, another student ate a piece of cake (400 Cal). To prevent this energy from being stored as fat, she decides to drink ice water at 0°C. She reasons that the ingested ice water will be warmed up to her normal body temperature of 37°C and absorb the energy. How much ice water would she have to drink to absorb the energy generated by metabolizing the birthday cake?

Thinking It Through. The heat to warm up a certain mass of ice water from 0°C to 37°C is equal to the 400 Cal of heat energy metabolized from the birthday cake. Since the heat, the specific heat, and the temperature change of the ice water are known, we can find the required mass of ice water using Eq. 11.1.

Solution. The heat required to warm up the ice water is 400 Cal. Listing the data given and converting to SI units. (Remember that Cal means kcal.)

Given: $Q = (400 \text{ kcal})\left(\dfrac{4186 \text{ J}}{\text{kcal}}\right) = 1.67 \times 10^6 \text{ J}$
$T_i = 0°C$
$T_f = 37°C$
$c = 4.186 \text{ kJ/(kg·C°)}$ (from Table 11.1)

Find: Mass m of water to "drink off" 400 Cal

From Eq. 11.1, $Q = cm\Delta T = cm(T_f - T_i)$. Solving for m gives

$$m = \frac{Q}{c\Delta T} = \frac{1.67 \times 10^6 \text{ J}}{[4186 \text{ J/(kg·C°)}](37°C - 0°C)} = 10.8 \text{ kg}$$

This mass of water occupies almost 3 gal or 12 L—quite a bit to drink. Don't try this, such an amount of water can be lethal.

Follow-Up Exercise. In this Example, how would the answer change if she drinks ice water at a temperature of 5°C rather than 0°C?

Integrated Example 11.3 ■ Cooking Class 101: Studying Specific Heats While Learning How to Boil Water

To prepare pasta, you bring a pot of water from room temperature (20°C) to its boiling point (100°C). The pot itself has a mass of 0.900 kg, is made of steel, and holds 3.00 kg of water. (a) Which of the following is true: (1) The pot requires more heat than the water, (2) the water requires more heat than the pot, or (3) they both require the same amount of heat? (b) Determine the required heat for both the water and the pot, and the ratio Q_w/Q_{pot}.

(a) **Conceptual Reasoning.** The temperature increase is the same for the water and the pot. Thus, the required heat is affected by the product of mass and specific heat. There is 3.0 kg of water to heat. This is more than three times the mass of the pot. From Table 11.1, the specific heat of water is about nine times larger than that of steel. Both factors together indicate that the water will require significantly more heat than the pot, so the answer is (2).

(continues on next page)

(b) Quantitative Reasoning and Solution. The heat needed can be found using Eq. 11.1, after looking up the specific heats. The temperature change is easily determined from the initial and final values.

Listing the data given:

Given: $m_{pot} = 0.900$ kg $\qquad$ *Find:* The required heat for the water and
$m_w = 3.00$ kg $\qquad\qquad\qquad\quad$ the pot, and the heat ratio Q_w/Q_{pot}
$c_{pot} = 460$ J/kg·C° (from Table 11.1)
$c_w = 4186$ J/kg·C° (from Table 11.1)
$\Delta T = T_f - T_i = 100°C - 20°C = 80$ C°

In general, the amount of heat is given by $Q = cm \, \Delta T$. The temperature increase (ΔT) for both objects is 80 C°. Thus, the heat for the water is

$$Q_w = c_w m_w \Delta T_w$$
$$= [4186 \text{ J}/(\text{kg} \cdot \text{C}°)](3.00 \text{ kg})(80 \text{ C}°) = 1.00 \times 10^6 \text{ J}$$

and the heat required for the pot is

$$Q_{pot} = c_{pot} m_{pot} \Delta T_{pot}$$
$$= [460 \text{ J}/(\text{kg} \cdot \text{C}°)](0.900 \text{ kg})(80 \text{ C}°) = 3.31 \times 10^4 \text{ J}$$

Because

$$\frac{Q_w}{Q_{pot}} = \frac{1.00 \times 10^6 \text{ J}}{3.31 \times 10^4 \text{ J}} = 30.2$$

water requires more than 30 times the heat, because it has more mass and a greater specific heat.

Follow-Up Exercise. (a) In this Example, if the pot were the same mass but instead made out of aluminum, would the heat ratio (water to pot) be smaller or larger than the answer for the steel pot? Explain. (b) Verify your answer.

Calorimetry

Calorimetry is a technique that quantitatively measures heat exchanges. Such measurements are made by using an instrument called a *calorimeter* (cal-oh-RIM-i-ter), usually an insulated container that allows little heat exchange with the environment (ideally none). A simple laboratory calorimeter is shown in ‹Fig. 11.4.

The specific heat of a substance can be determined by measuring the masses and temperature changes of the objects involved and using Eq. 11.1.* Usually the unknown is the unknown specific heat, c. Typically a substance of known mass and temperature is put into a quantity of water in a calorimeter. The water is at a different temperature from that of the substance, usually a lower one. The principle of the conservation of energy is then applied to determine the substance's specific heat, c. This procedure is called the *method of mixtures*. Example 11.4 illustrates the use of this procedure. Such heat-exchange problems are just a matter of "thermal accounting," involving the conservation of energy. The total of all the heat losses ($Q < 0$) must equal the total of all the heat gains ($Q > 0$). This means the algebraic sum of all the heat transfers must equal zero, or $\Sigma Q_i = 0$, assuming negligible heat exchange with the environment.

▲ **FIGURE 11.4** Calorimetry apparatus The calorimetry cup (center, with black insulating ring), goes into the larger container. The cover with the thermometer and stirrer is seen at the right. Metal shot or pieces of metal are heated in the small cup (with the handle) in the steam generator on the tripod.

Example 11.4 ■ Calorimetry Using the Method of Mixtures

Students in a physics lab are to determine the specific heat of copper experimentally. They place 0.150 kg of copper shot into boiling water and let it stay for a while, so as to reach a temperature of 100°C. Then they carefully pour the hot shot into a calorimeter cup (Fig. 11.4) containing 0.200 kg of water at 20.0°C. The final temperature of the mixture in the cup is measured to be 25.0°C. If the aluminum cup has a mass of 0.0450 kg, what is the specific heat of copper? (Assume that there is no heat exchange with the surroundings.)

*In this section, calorimetry will *not* involve phase changes, such as ice melting or water boiling. These effects are discussed in Section 11.3.

Thinking It Through. The conservation of heat energy is involved: $\Sigma Q_i = 0$, taking into account the correct positive and negative signs. In calorimetry problems, it is important to identify and label all of the quantities with proper signs. Identification of the heat gains and losses is crucial. You will probably use this method in the laboratory.

Solution. The subscripts Cu, w, and Al will be used to refer to the copper, water, and aluminum calorimeter cup, respectively. The subscripts h, i, and f to refer to the temperature of the *hot* metal shot, the water (and cup) *initially* at room temperature, and the *final* temperature of the system, respectively. With this notation,

Given: $m_{Cu} = 0.150$ kg   *Find:* c_{Cu} (specific heat)
        $m_w = 0.200$ kg
        $c_w = 4186$ J/(kg·C°) (from Table 11.1)
        $m_{Al} = 0.0450$ kg
        $c_{Al} = 920$ J/(kg·C°) (from Table 11.1)
        $T_h = 100°C$, $T_i = 20.0°C$, and $T_f = 25.0°C$

PHYSLET®

Exploration 19.3 Calorimetry

If there is no heat exchange with the surroundings, the system's total energy is conserved, $\Sigma Q_i = 0$, and

$$\Sigma Q_i = Q_w + Q_{Al} + Q_{Cu} = 0$$

Substituting the relationship in Eq. 11.1 for these heats,

$$c_w m_w \Delta T_w + c_{Al} m_{Al} \Delta T_{Al} + c_{Cu} m_{Cu} \Delta T_{Cu} = 0$$

or

$$c_w m_w (T_f - T_i) + c_{Al} m_{Al} (T_f - T_i) + c_{Cu} m_{Cu} (T_f - T_h) = 0$$

Here, the water and aluminum cup, initially at T_i, are heated to T_f, so $\Delta T_w = \Delta T_{Al} = (T_f - T_i)$. The copper initially at T_h is cooled to T_f, so $\Delta T_{Cu} = (T_f - T_h)$ and this is a negative quantity, indicating a temperature drop for the copper. Solving for c_{Cu} gives

$$c_{Cu} = -\frac{(c_w m_w + c_{Al} m_{Al})(T_f - T_i)}{m_{Cu}(T_f - T_h)}$$

$$= -\frac{\{[4186 \text{ J/(kg·C°)}](0.200 \text{ kg}) + [920 \text{ J/(kg·C°)}](0.0450 \text{ kg})\}(25.0°C - 20.0°C)}{(0.150 \text{ kg})(25.0°C - 100°C)}$$

$$= 390 \text{ J/(kg·C°)}$$

Notice that the proper use of signs resulted in a positive answer for c_{Cu}, as required. If, for example, the Q_{Cu} term had not had the correct sign, the answer would have been negative—a big clue that you had an initial sign error.

Follow-Up Exercise. In this example, what would the final equilibrium temperature be if the calorimeter (water and cup) initially had been at a warmer 30°C?

Specific Heat of Gases

When heat is added to or taken from most materials, they expand or contract. During expansion, for example, the materials would then do work on the atmosphere. For most solids and liquids, this work is negligible, because the volume changes are very small (Chapter 10). This is why this effect wasn't included in our discussion of specific heat of solids and liquids.

However, for gases, expansion and contraction *can* be significant. It is therefore important to specify the *conditions* under which heat is transferred when referring to a gas. If heat is added to a gas at constant volume (a *rigid* container), the gas does no work. (Why?) In this case, all of the heat goes into increasing the gas's internal energy and, therefore, to increasing its temperature. However, if the same amount of heat is added at constant pressure (a *nonrigid* container allowing a volume change), a portion of the heat is converted to work as the gas expands. Thus, not all of the heat will go into the gas's internal energy. This process results in a *smaller* temperature change than occurred during the constant-volume process.

To designate the physical quantities that are held constant while heat is added to or removed from a gas, we use a subscript notation: c_p means specific heat under conditions of constant pressure (p), and c_v means specific heat under conditions

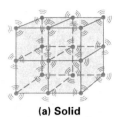

(a) Solid

(b) Liquid

(c) Gas

▲ **FIGURE 11.5 Three phases of matter** **(a)** The molecules of a solid are held together by bonds; consequently, a solid has a definite shape and volume. **(b)** The molecules of a liquid can move more freely, so a liquid has a definite volume and assumes the shape of its container. **(c)** The molecules of a gas interact weakly and are separated by relatively large distances; thus, a gas has no definite shape or volume, unless it is confined in a container.

Note: Solid, liquid, and gas are sometimes referred to as states of matter rather than phases of matter, but the *state* of a system has a different meaning in physics, as you will learn in Chapter 12.

of constant volume (v). The specific heat for water vapor (H_2O) given in Table 11.1 is the specific heat under constant pressure (c_p).

An important result is that for a particular gas, c_p is always greater than c_v. This is true because for a specific mass of gas, $c \propto Q/\Delta T$. Since for a given Q, ΔT_v is as large as it can be, and c_v will be less than c_p. In other words, $\Delta T_v > \Delta T_p$. Specific heats of gases play an important role in adiabatic thermodynamic processes. (See Section 12.3.)

11.3 Phase Changes and Latent Heat

OBJECTIVES: To **(a)** compare and contrast the three common phases of matter, and **(b)** relate latent heat to phase changes.

Matter normally exists in one of three *phases*: solid, liquid, or gas (◄Fig. 11.5). However, this division into three common phases is only approximate since there are other phases, such as a plasma phase and a superconducting phase. The phase that a substance is in depends on the substance's internal energy (as indicated by its temperature) and the pressure on it. However, it is likely that you think of adding or removing heat as the way to change the phase of a substance.

In the **solid phase**, molecules are held together by attractive forces, or bonds (Fig. 11.5a). Adding heat causes increased motion about the molecular-equilibrium positions. If enough heat is added to provide sufficient energy to break the intermolecular bonds, most solids undergo a phase change and become liquids. The temperature at which this phase change occurs is called the **melting point**. The temperature at which a liquid becomes a solid is called the **freezing point**. In general, these temperatures are the same for a given substance, but they can differ slightly.

In the **liquid phase**, molecules of a substance are relatively free to move and a liquid assumes the shape of its container (Fig. 11.5b). In certain liquids, there may be some locally ordered structure, giving rise to liquid crystals, such as those used in LCDs (liquid crystal displays) of calculators and computer displays (Chapter 24).

Adding even more heat increases the motion of the molecules of a liquid. When they have enough energy to become separated, the liquid changes to the **gaseous (or vapor) phase***. This change may occur slowly, by *evaporation* (p. 379), or rapidly, at a particular temperature called the **boiling point**. The temperature at which a gas condenses into a liquid is the **condensation point**.

Some solids, such as dry ice (solid carbon dioxide), mothballs, and certain air fresheners, change directly from the solid to the gaseous phase at standard pressure. This process is called **sublimation**. Like the rate of evaporation, the rate of sublimation increases with temperature. A phase change from a gas to a solid is called *deposition*. Frost, for example, is solidified water vapor (gas) deposited on grass, car windows, and other objects. Frost is *not* frozen dew (liquid water), as is sometimes mistakenly assumed.

Latent Heat

In general, when heat is transferred to a substance, its temperature increases as the average kinetic energy per molecule increases. However, when heat is added (or removed) during a phase change, the temperature of the substance does *not* change. For example, if heat is added to a quantity of ice at −10°C, the temperature of the ice increases until it reaches its melting point of 0°C. At this point, the addition of more heat does not increase the ice's temperature, but causes it to melt, or change phase. (The heat must be added slowly so that the ice and melted water remain in thermal equilibrium, otherwise, the ice water can warm above 0°C even though the ice remains at 0°C.) Only after the ice is completely melted does adding more heat cause

---

*The terms *vapor* and *vapor phase* are sometimes used interchangeably with the term *gaseous phase*. Strictly speaking, *vapor* refers to the gaseous phase of a substance in contact with its liquid phase.

the temperature of the water to rise. A similar situation occurs during the liquid–gas phase change at the boiling point. Adding more heat to boiling water only causes more vaporization. A temperature increase occurs only *after* the water is completely boiled, resulting in *superheated steam*.

During a phase change, the heat goes into breaking the attractive bonds and separating molecules (increasing their potential, rather than kinetic, energies) rather than into increasing the temperature. The heat required for a phase change is called the **latent heat (L)***, which is defined as the magnitude of the heat needed per unit mass to induce a phase change:

$$L = \frac{|Q|}{m} \quad \textit{latent heat} \tag{11.2}$$

where m is the mass of the substance. Latent heat has SI units of joules per kilogram (J/kg), or kilocalories per kilogram (kcal/kg).

The latent heat for a solid–liquid phase change is called the **latent heat of fusion** (L_f), and that for a liquid–gas phase change is called the **latent heat of vaporization** (L_v.) These quantities are often referred to as simply the *heat of fusion* and the *heat of vaporization*. The latent heats of some substances, along with their melting and boiling points, are given in Table 11.2. (The latent heat for the less common solid–gas phase change is called the *latent heat of sublimation* and is symbolized by L_s.) As you might expect, the latent heat (in joules per kilogram) is the amount of energy per kilogram *given up* when the phase change is in the opposite direction, that is, from liquid to solid or gas to liquid.

A more useful form of Eq. 11.3 is given by solving for Q and including a positive/negative sign for the two possible directions of heat flow:

$$Q = \pm mL \quad \textit{(signs with latent heat)} \tag{11.3}$$

This equation is more practical for problem solving because in calorimetry problems, you are typically interested in applying conservation of energy in the form of $\Sigma Q_i = 0$. The positive/negative sign ($\pm$) must be explicitly expressed because heat can flow either into ($+$) or out of ($-$) the object or system of interest.

When solving calorimetry problems involving phase changes, you must be careful to use the correct sign for those terms, in agreement with our sign conventions (▼Fig. 11.6). For example, if water is condensing from steam into liquid droplets, *removal* of heat is involved, necessitating the choice of the *negative* sign.

Note: Keep in mind that ice can be colder than 0°C and steam can be hotter than 100°C.

TABLE 11.2 Temperatures of Phase Changes and Latent Heats for Various Substances (at 1 atm)

Substance	Melting Point	L_f		Boiling Point	L_v	
		J/kg	kcal/kg		J/kg	kcal/kg
Alcohol, ethyl	−114°C	1.0×10^5	25	78°C	8.5×10^5	204
Gold	1063°C	0.645×10^5	15.4	2660°C	15.8×10^5	377
Helium†	—	—	—	−269°C	0.21×10^5	5
Lead	328°C	0.25×10^5	5.9	1744°C	8.67×10^5	207
Mercury	−39°C	0.12×10^5	2.8	357°C	2.7×10^5	65
Nitrogen	−210°C	0.26×10^5	6.1	−196°C	2.0×10^5	48
Oxygen	−219°C	0.14×10^5	3.3	−183°C	2.1×10^5	51
Tungsten	3410°C	1.8×10^5	44	5900°C	48.2×10^5	1150
Water	0°C	3.33×10^5	80	100°C	22.6×10^5	540

†Not a solid at a pressure of 1 atm; melting point is −272°C at 26 atm.

Latent is Latin for "hidden".

▶ **FIGURE 11.6 Phase changes and latent heats (a)** At 0°C, 3.33×10^5 J must be added to 1 kg of ice or removed from 1 kg of liquid water to change its phase. **(b)** At 100°C, 22.6×10^5 J must be added to 1 kg of liquid water or removed from 1 kg of steam to change its phase.

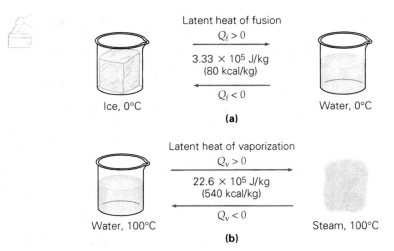

Latent heat of fusion
$Q_f > 0$
3.33×10^5 J/kg
(80 kcal/kg)
$Q_f < 0$

Ice, 0°C   Water, 0°C
(a)

Latent heat of vaporization
$Q_v > 0$
22.6×10^5 J/kg
(540 kcal/kg)
$Q_v < 0$

Water, 100°C   Steam, 100°C
(b)

Problem-Solving Hint

Recall in Section 11.2 that where there were no phase changes, the expression for heat $Q = cm\Delta T$ automatically gave the correct sign for Q from the sign of ΔT. But there is no ΔT during a phase change. *Choosing the correct sign is up to you.*

For water, the latent heats of fusion and vaporization are
$$L_f = 3.33 \times 10^5 \text{ J/kg}$$
$$L_v = 22.6 \times 10^5 \text{ J/kg}$$

The accompanying Learn by Drawing, numerically expressed in Example 11.5, shows explicitly the two types of heat terms (specific heat and latent heat) that must be employed in the general situation when any of the objects undergo a temperature change *and* a phase change.

Example 11.5 ■ From Cold Ice to Hot Steam

Heat is added to 1.00 kg of cold ice at −10°C. How much heat is required to change the cold ice to hot steam at 110°C?

Thinking It Through. Five steps are involved: (1) heating ice to its melting point (specific heat of ice), (2) melting ice to ice water at 0°C (latent heat, a phase change), (3) heating liquid water (specific heat of liquid water), (4) vaporizing water at 100°C (latent heat, a phase change), and (5) heating steam (specific heat of water vapor). The key idea here is that the temperature does not change during a phase change. [Refer to Learn by Drawing on page 377.]

Solution.

Given: $m = 1.00$ kg   *Find:* Q_{total} (total heat)
$T_i = -10°C$
$T_f = 110°C$
$L_f = 3.33 \times 10^5$ J/kg (from Table 11.2)
$L_v = 22.6 \times 10^5$ J/kg (from Table 11.2)
$c_{ice} = 2100$ J/(kg·C°) (from Table 11.1)
$c_{water} = 4186$ J/(kg·C°) (from Table 11.1)
$c_{steam} = 2000$ J/(kg·C°) (from Table 11.1)

(1) $Q_1 = c_{ice}m\Delta T_1 = [2100 \text{ J/(kg·C°)}](1.00 \text{ kg})[0°C - (-10°C)]$ *(heating ice)*
     $= +2.10 \times 10^4$ J

(2) $Q_2 = +mL_v = (1.00 \text{ kg})(3.33 \times 10^5 \text{ J/kg}) = +3.33 \times 10^5$ J *(melting ice)*

(3) $Q_3 = c_w m\Delta T_2 = [4186 \text{ J/(kg·C°)}](1.00 \text{ kg})(100°C - 0°C)$ *(heating water)*
     $= +4.19 \times 10^5$ J

(4) $Q_4 = +mL_v = (1.00 \text{ kg})(22.6 \times 10^5 \text{ J/kg}) = +2.26 \times 10^6$ J *(vaporizing water)*

(5) $Q_5 = c_{steam}m\Delta T_3 = [2000 \text{ J/(kg·C°)}](1.00 \text{ kg})(110°C - 100°C)$ *(heating steam)*
     $= +2.00 \times 10^4$ J

Science Fundamentals

The total heat required is

$$Q_{\text{total}} = \Sigma Q_i = 2.1 \times 10^4 \, \text{J} + 3.33 \times 10^5 \, \text{J} + 4.19 \times 10^5 \, \text{J} + 2.26 \times 10^6 \, \text{J} + 2.00 \times 10^4 \, \text{J}$$
$$= 3.05 \times 10^6 \, \text{J}$$

The latent heat of vaporization is, by far, the largest. It is actually greater than the sum of the other four terms.

Follow-Up Exercise. How much heat must a freezer remove from liquid water (initially at 20°C) to create 0.250 kg of ice at −10°C?

Problem-Solving Hint

Note that you must compute the latent heat at each phase change. It is a common error to use the specific-heat equation with a temperature interval *that includes* a phase change. Also, you cannot assume a complete phase change until you have checked for it numerically. (See Example 11.6.)

LEARN BY DRAWING   FROM COLD ICE TO HOT STEAM

It can be helpful to focus on the fusion and vaporization of water graphically. To heat up a piece of cold ice at −10°C all the way to hot steam at 110°C, five separate specific heat and latent heat calculations are necessary. (Most freezers are at a temperature of about −10°C.) At the phase change (0°C and 100°C) heat is added without a tempera-ture change. Once each phase change is complete, adding more heat causes the temperature to increase. The slopes of the lines in the drawings are not all the same, which in-dicates that the specific heats of the various phases are not the same. (Why do different slopes mean different specific heats?) The numbers come from Example 11.5

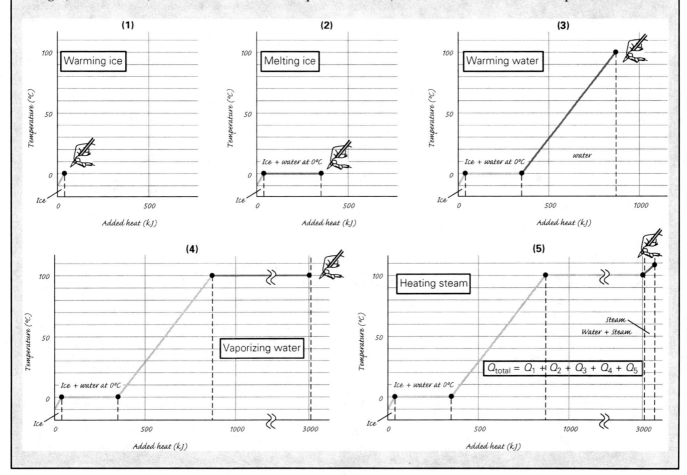

Technically the freezing and boiling points of water (0°C and 100°C, respectively) apply only at 1 atm of pressure. Phase-change temperatures generally vary with pressure. For example, the boiling point of water decreases with decreasing pressure. At high altitudes, where there is lower atmospheric pressure, the boiling point of water is lowered. For example, at Pikes Peak, Colorado, at an elevation of about 4300 m, the atmospheric pressure is about 0.79 atm and water boils at about 94°C rather than at 100°C. The lower temperature lengthens the cooking time of food. Conversely, some cooks use a pressure cooker to *reduce* cooking time—by increasing the pressure, a pressure cooker raises the boiling point.

The freezing point of water actually *decreases* with increasing pressure. This inverse relationship is characteristic of only a very few substances, including water (Section 10.4), that expand when they freeze.

Example 11.6 ■ Practical Calorimetry: Using Phase Changes to Save a Life

Organ transplants are becoming commonplace. Many times, the procedure involves removing a healthy organ from a deceased person and flying it to the recipient. During that time, to prevent its deterioration, the organ is packed in ice in an insulated container. Assume that a liver has a mass of 0.500 kg and is initially at 29°C. The specific heat of the human liver is 3500 J/(kg·C°). The liver is surrounded by 2.00 kg of ice initially at −10°C. Calculate the final equilibrium temperature.

Thinking It Through. Clearly, the liver will cool, and the ice will warm. However, it is not clear what temperature the ice will reach. If it gets to the freezing point, it will begin to melt, and a phase change must be considered. If all of it melts, then additional heat required to warm that water to a temperature above 0°C must be considered. Thus, care must be taken, since it *cannot* be assumed that all the ice melts, or even that the ice reaches its melting point. Hence, the calorimetry equation (conservation of energy) cannot be written down until the terms in it are determined. First we need to review the *possible* heat transfers. Only then can the final temperature be determined.

Solution. Listing the data given and the information obtained from tables,

Given: $m_l = 0.500$ kg   *Find:* The final temperature of the system
$m_{ice} = 2.00$ kg
$c_l = 3500$ J/(kg·C°)
$c_{ice} = 2100$ J/(kg·C°)   (from Table 11.1)
$L_f = 3.33 \times 10^5$ J/(kg·C°) (from Table 11.2)

The amount of heat required to bring the ice to 0°C from −10°C is

$$Q_{ice} = c_{ice}m_{ice}\Delta T_{ice} = [2100 \text{ J/(kg·C°)}](2.00 \text{ kg})(+10 \text{ C°}) = +4.20 \times 10^4 \text{ J}$$

Since this heat must come from the liver, the *maximum* heat available from the liver needs to be calculated; that is, if its temperature drops all the way from 29°C to 0°C:

$$Q_{l,max} = c_l m_l \Delta T_{l,max} = [3500 \text{ J/(kg·C°)}](0.500 \text{ kg})(-29 \text{ C°}) = -5.08 \times 10^4 \text{ J}$$

This *is* enough to bring the ice to 0°C. If 4.20×10^4 J of heat flows into the ice (bringing it to 0°C), the liver is still not at 0°C. Then how much ice melts? This depends on how much more heat can be transferred from the liver.

How much more heat Q' would be extracted from the liver if its temperature were to drop to 0°C? This value is just the maximum amount minus the heat that went into warming the ice, or

$$Q' = |Q_{l,max}| - 4.20 \times 10^4 \text{ J}$$
$$= 5.08 \times 10^4 \text{ J} - 4.20 \times 10^4 \text{ J} = 8.8 \times 10^3 \text{ J}$$

Compare this with the magnitude of the heat needed to melt the ice completely ($|Q_{melt}|$) to decide whether this can, in fact, happen. The heat required to melt *all* the ice is

$$|Q_{melt}| = +m_{ice}L_{ice} = +(2.00 \text{ kg})(3.33 \times 10^5 \text{ J/kg}) = +6.66 \times 10^5 \text{ J}$$

Since this amount of heat is much larger than the amount available from the liver, only part of the ice melts. In the process, the liver has dropped to 0°C, and the remainder of the ice is at 0°C. Since everything in the "calorimeter" is at the same temperature, heat flow stops, and the final system temperature is 0°C. Thus the final result is that the liver is in a container with ice and some liquid water, all at 0°C. Since the container is a very good insulator, it will prevent any inward heat flow that might raise the liver's temperature. It is therefore expected that the liver will arrive at its destination in good shape.

Follow-Up Exercise. (a) In this Example, how much of the ice melts? (b) If the ice originally had been at its melting point (0°C), what would the equilibrium temperature have been?

Problem-Solving Hint

Notice in Example 11.6 that numbers were *not* plugged directly into the $\Sigma Q_i = 0$ equation, which is equivalent to assuming that all the ice melts. In fact, if this step had been done, we would have been on the wrong track. For calorimetry problems *involving phase changes*, a careful step-by-step numerical "accounting" procedure should be followed until all of the pieces of the system are at the same temperature. At that point, the problem is over, because no more heat exchanges can happen.

Evaporation

The **evaporation** of water from an open container becomes evident only after a relatively long period of time. This phenomenon can be explained in terms of the kinetic theory (Section 10.5). The molecules in a liquid are in motion at different speeds. A faster-moving molecule near the surface may momentarily leave the liquid. If its speed is not too large, the molecule will return to the liquid, because of the attractive forces exerted by the other molecules. Occasionally, however, a molecule has a large enough speed to leave the liquid entirely. The higher the temperature of the liquid, the more likely this phenomenon is to occur.

The escaping molecules take their energy with them. Since those molecules with greater-than-average energy are the ones most likely to escape, the average molecular energy, and thus the temperature of the remaining liquid, will be reduced. That is, *evaporation is a cooling process* for the object from which the molecules escape. You have probably noticed this phenomenon when drying off after a bath or shower. You can read more about this in Insight 11.1 on page 380 on Physiological Regulation of Body Temperature.

PHYSLET
Illustration 20.4 Evaporative Cooling

11.4 Heat Transfer

OBJECTIVES: To (a) describe the three mechanisms of heat transfer, and (b) give practical applications of each.

The transfer of heat is an important topic and has many practical applications. Heat can move from place to place by three different mechanisms: conduction, convection, and radiation.

Conduction

You can keep a pot of coffee hot on an electric stove because heat is conducted through the bottom of the coffeepot from the hot metal burner. The process of **conduction** results from molecular interactions. Molecules at a higher-temperature region on an object move relatively rapidly. They collide with, and transfer some of their energy to, the less energetic molecules in a nearby cooler part of the object. In this way, energy is conductively transferred from a higher-temperature region to a lower-temperature region—transfer as a result of a temperature difference.

Solids can be divided into two general categories: metals and nonmetals. Metals are generally good conductors of heat, or **thermal conductors**. Metals have a large number of electrons that are free to move around (not permanently bound to a particular molecule or atom). These free electrons (rather than the interaction between adjacent atoms) are primarily responsible for the good heat conduction in metals. Nonmetals, such as wood and cloth, have relatively few free electrons. The absence of this transfer mechanism makes them poor heat conductors relative to metals. A poor heat conductor is called a **thermal insulator**.

PHYSLET
Illustration 19.2 Heat Transfer, Conduction

INSIGHT 11.1 PHYSIOLOGICAL REGULATION OF BODY TEMPERATURE

Being warm-blooded, humans must maintain a narrow range of body temperature. (See Insight 10.1, page 343.) The generally accepted value for the average normal body temperature is 37.0°C (98.6°F). However, it can be as low as 35.5°C (96°F) in the early-morning hours on a cold day and as high as 39.5°C (103°F) during intense exercise on a hot day. For females, the body temperature at rest rises very slightly after ovulation as a result of a rise in the hormone progesterone. This can be used to predict on which day ovulation will occur in the next cycle.

When the ambient temperature is lower than the body temperature, the body loses heat. If the body loses too much heat, a circulatory mechanism causes a reduction of blood flow to the skin in order to reduce heat loss. A physiological response to this mechanism through shivering is to increase heat generation (and thus warm the body) by "burning" the body's reserves of carbohydrate or fat. If the body temperature drops below 33°C (91.4°F), *hypothermia* may result, which can cause severe thermal injuries to organs and even death.

At the other extreme, if the body is subjected to ambient temperatures higher than the body temperature, along with intense exercise, the body can overheat. *Heat stroke* is a prolonged elevation of body temperature above 40°C (104°F). If the body becomes overheated, the blood vessels to the skin dilate, carrying more warm blood to the skin, enabling the interior of the body and organs to remain cooler. (The person's face may turn red.)

Usually, radiation, conduction, natural convection (discussed later in Section 11.4), and possibly slight evaporation of perspiration on the skin are sufficient to maintain a heat loss at a rate that keeps our body temperature in the safe range. However, when the ambient temperature becomes too high, these mechanisms cannot do the job completely. To avoid heat stroke, as a last resort (and the most efficient one), the body produces heavy perspiration. The evaporation of water from our skin removes a lot of heat, thanks to the large value of latent heat of vaporization of water.

Evaporation lowers the temperature of the perspiration on our bodies, which can then draw heat from our skin and thus cool our bodies. The removal of a minimum of 2.26×10^6 J of heat from the body is required to evaporate each kilogram (liter) of water.* For the body of a 75-kg person, which is mainly composed of water, the heat loss due to evaporation of 1 kg of water could lower the body temperature as much as

$$\Delta T = \frac{Q}{cm} = \frac{2.26 \times 10^6 \text{ J}}{[4186 \text{ J}/(\text{kg} \cdot \text{C}°)](75 \text{ kg})} = 7.2 \text{ C}°$$

On a hot day's race, a professional cyclist can evaporate as much as 7.0 kg of water in 3.5 h. This heat loss through sweat is the mechanism that enables the body to keep its temperature in the safe range.

On a summer day, a person may stand in front of a fan and remark how "cool" the blowing air feels. But the fan is merely blowing hot air from one place to another. The air *feels* cool because it is relatively drier (has low humidity compared to the sweaty body) and therefore its flow promotes evaporation, which removes latent-heat energy.

---

*The actual latent heat of vaporization of perspiration is about 2.42×10^6 J (greater than the 2.26×10^6 J value used here for temperature at 100°C).

In general, the ability of a substance to conduct heat depends on the substance's phase. Gases are poor thermal conductors; their molecules are relatively far apart, and collisions are therefore infrequent. Liquids and solids are better thermal conductors than gases, because their molecules are closer together and can interact more readily.

Heat conduction is usually described using the *time rate* of heat flow ($\Delta Q/\Delta t$) in a material for a given temperature difference (ΔT), as illustrated in ►Fig. 11.7. Experiment has established that the rate of heat flow through a substance depends on the temperature difference between its boundaries. Heat conduction also depends on the size and shape of the object as well as its composition. In our analysis of heat flow, we will use uniform slabs for simplicity.

Experimentally, it is found that the heat flow rate ($\Delta Q/\Delta t$ in J/s or W) through a slab of material is directly proportional to the material's surface area (A) and the temperature difference across its ends (ΔT), and inversely proportional to its thickness (d). That is,

$$\frac{\Delta Q}{\Delta t} \propto \frac{A \Delta T}{d}$$

Using a constant of proportionality k allows us to write the relation as an equation:

$$\frac{\Delta Q}{\Delta t} = \frac{kA \Delta T}{d} \quad \text{(conduction only)} \quad (11.4)$$

The constant k, called the **thermal conductivity**, characterizes the heat-conducting ability of a material and depends only on the type of material. The

TABLE 11.3	Thermal Conductivities of Some Substances	

Substance	Thermal Conductivity, k	
	J/(m·s·C°) *or* W/(m·C°)	kcal/(m·s·C°)
Metals		
Aluminum	240	5.73×10^{-2}
Copper	390	9.32×10^{-2}
Iron and steel	46	1.1×10^{-2}
Silver	420	10×10^{-2}
Liquids		
Transformer oil	0.18	4.3×10^{-5}
Water	0.57	14×10^{-5}
Gases		
Air	0.024	0.57×10^{-5}
Hydrogen	0.17	4.1×10^{-5}
Oxygen	0.024	0.57×10^{-5}
Other Materials		
Brick	0.71	17×10^{-5}
Concrete	1.3	31×10^{-5}
Cotton	0.075	1.8×10^{-5}
Fiberboard	0.059	1.4×10^{-5}
Floor tile	0.67	16×10^{-5}
Glass (typical)	0.84	20×10^{-5}
Glass wool	0.042	1.0×10^{-5}
Goose down	0.025	0.59×10^{-5}
Human tissue (average)	0.20	4.8×10^{-5}
Ice	2.2	53×10^{-5}
Styrofoam	0.042	1.0×10^{-5}
Wood, oak	0.15	3.6×10^{-5}
Wood, pine	0.12	2.9×10^{-5}
Vacuum	0	0

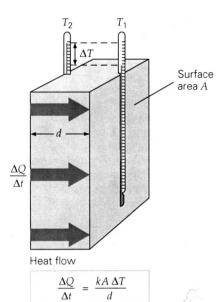

$$\frac{\Delta Q}{\Delta t} = \frac{kA\,\Delta T}{d}$$

▲ **FIGURE 11.7 Thermal conduction** Heat conduction is characterized by the time rate of heat flow ($\Delta Q/\Delta t$) in a material with a temperature difference across it of ΔT. For a slab of material, $\Delta Q/\Delta t$ is directly proportional to the cross-sectional area (A) and the thermal conductivity (k) of the material; it is inversely proportional to the thickness of the slab (d).

▼ **FIGURE 11.8 Copper-bottomed pots** Copper is used on the bottoms of some stainless steel pots and saucepans. The high thermal conductivity of copper ensures the rapid and even spread of heat from the burner; the low thermal conductivity of stainless steel retains the heat in the pot and keeps the handle not too hot to touch. (The thermal conductivity of stainless steel is only 12% that of copper.)

greater the value of k for a material, the better it will conduct heat, all other factors being equal. The units of k are J/(m·s·C°) = W/(m·C°). The thermal conductivities of various substances are listed in Table 11.3. These values vary slightly with temperature, but can be considered constant over normal temperature ranges.

Compare the relatively large thermal conductivities of the good thermal conductors, the metals, with the relatively small thermal conductivities of some good thermal insulators, such as Styrofoam and wood. Some stainless steel cooking pots have copper bottoms (▶Fig. 11.8). Being a good conductor of heat, the copper conducts heat faster to the food being cooked and also promotes the distribution of heat over the bottom of a pot for even cooking. Conversely, Styrofoam is a good insulator, mainly because it contains small, trapped pockets of air, thus reducing conduction and convection losses (p. 383). When you step on a tile floor with one bare foot and on an adjacent rug with the other bare foot, you feel that the tile is "colder" than the rug. However, both the tile and rug are actually at the same temperature. The reason is that the tile is a much better thermal conductor, so it removes or conducts heat from your foot better than the rug, making your foot on tile feel colder.

▶ **FIGURE 11.9** Insulation and thermal conductivity (a), (b) Attics should be insulated to prevent loss of heat by the mechanism of conduction. See Example 11.7 and Insight 11.2 (page 384) on Physics, the Construction Industry, and Energy Conservation. (c) This thermogram of a house allows us to visualize the house's heat loss. Blue represents the areas that have the lowest rate of heat leaking; white, pink, and red indicate areas with increasingly larger heat losses. (Red areas have the most loss). What recommendations would you make to the owner of this house to save both money and energy? (Compare this figure with Fig. 11.15.)

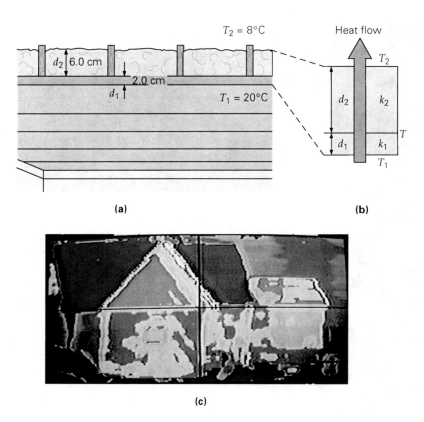

(a) (b)

(c)

Exploration 19.4 Heat Balance

Example 11.7 ■ Thermal Insulation: Helping Prevent Heat Loss

A room with a pine ceiling that measures 3.0 m by 5.0 m and is 2.0 cm thick has a layer of glass-wool insulation above it that is 6.0 cm thick (▲ Fig. 11.9a). On a cold day, the temperature inside the room at ceiling height is 20°C, and the temperature in the attic above the insulation layer is 8°C. Assuming that the temperatures remain constant with a steady heat flow, how much energy does the layer of insulation save in 1.0 h? Assume that losses are due to conduction only.

Thinking It Through. Here we have two materials, so we must consider Eq. 11.4 for two different thermal conductivities (k). We want to find $\Delta Q/\Delta t$ for the combination so that we can get ΔQ for $\Delta t = 1.0$ h. The situation is a bit complicated, because the heat flows through two materials. But we know that at a steady rate, *the heat flows must be the same through both* (why?). To find the energy saved in 1.0 h, we need to compute how much heat is conducted in this time with and without the layer of insulation.

Solution. Computing some of the quantities in Eq. 11.4 and making conversions as we list the data,

Given: $A = 3.0 \text{ m} \times 5.0 \text{ m} = 15 \text{ m}^2$ *Find:* Energy saved in one hour
$d_1 = 2.0 \text{ cm} = 0.020 \text{ m}$
$d_2 = 6.0 \text{ cm} = 0.060 \text{ m}$
$\Delta T = T_1 - T_2 = 20°C - 8.0°C = 12 \text{ C}°$
$\Delta t = 1.0 \text{ h} = 3.6 \times 10^3 \text{ s}$
$k_1 = 0.12 \text{ J/(m·s·C°)(wood, pine)}$
$k_2 = 0.042 \text{ J/(m·s·C°)(glass wool)}$ } (from Table 11.3)

(In working such problems with several given quantities, it is especially important to label all the data correctly.)

First, let's consider how much heat would be conducted in one hour through the wooden ceiling with no insulation present. Since we know Δt, we can rearrange Eq. 11.4*

*Equation 11.4 can be extended to any number of layers or slabs of materials: $\Delta Q/\Delta t = A(T_2 - T_1)/\Sigma(d_i/k_i)$. (See Insight 11.2 involving insulation in building construction, p. 384).

to find ΔQ_c (heat conducted through the wooden ceiling alone, assuming the same ΔT):

$$\Delta Q_c = \left(\frac{k_1 A \Delta T}{d_1}\right)\Delta t = \left\{\frac{[0.12 \text{ J}/(\text{m}\cdot\text{s}\cdot\text{C}°)](15 \text{ m}^2)(12 \text{ C}°)}{0.020 \text{ m}}\right\}(3.6 \times 10^3 \text{ s}) = 3.9 \times 10^6 \text{ J}$$

Now we need to find the heat conducted through the ceiling *and* the insulation layer together. Let T be the temperature at the interface of the materials and T_1 and T_2 be the warmer and cooler temperatures, respectively (Fig. 11.9b). Then

$$\frac{\Delta Q_1}{\Delta t} = \frac{k_1 A(T_1 - T)}{d_1} \quad \text{and} \quad \frac{\Delta Q_2}{\Delta t} = \frac{k_2 A(T - T_2)}{d_2}$$

We don't know T, but when the conduction is steady, the flow rates are the same for both materials; that is, $\Delta Q_1/\Delta t = \Delta Q_2/\Delta t$, or

$$\frac{k_1 A(T_1 - T)}{d_1} = \frac{k_2 A(T - T_2)}{d_2}$$

The A's cancel, and solving for T gives

$$T = \frac{k_1 d_2 T_1 + k_2 d_1 T_2}{k_1 d_2 + k_2 d_1}$$

$$= \frac{[0.12 \text{ J}/(\text{m}\cdot\text{s}\cdot\text{C}°)](0.060 \text{ m})(20.0°C) + [0.042 \text{ J}/(\text{m}\cdot\text{s}\cdot\text{C}°)](0.020 \text{ m})(8.0°C)}{[0.12 \text{ J}/(\text{m}\cdot\text{s}\cdot\text{C}°)](0.060 \text{ m}) + [0.042 \text{ J}/(\text{m}\cdot\text{s}\cdot\text{C}°)](0.020 \text{ m})}$$

$$= 18.7°C$$

Since the flow rate is the same through the wood and the insulation, we can use the expression for either material to calculate it. Let's use the expression for the wood ceiling. Here, care must be taken to use the correct ΔT. The temperature at the wood–insulation interface is 18.7°C; thus,

$$\Delta T_{\text{wood}} = |T_1 - T| = |20°C - 18.7°C| = 1.3°C$$

Therefore, the heat flow rate is

$$\frac{\Delta Q_1}{\Delta t} = \frac{k_1 A |\Delta T_{\text{wood}}|}{d_1} = \frac{[0.12 \text{ J}/(\text{m}\cdot\text{s}\cdot\text{C}°)](15 \text{ m}^2)(1.3 \text{ C}°)}{0.020 \text{ m}} = 1.2 \times 10^2 \text{ J/s (or W)}$$

In 1.0 h, the heat loss with insulation in place is

$$\Delta Q_1 = \frac{\Delta Q_1}{\Delta t} \times \Delta t = (1.2 \times 10^2 \text{ J/s})(3600 \text{ s}) = 4.3 \times 10^5 \text{ J}$$

This value represents a decreased heat loss of

$$\Delta Q_c - \Delta Q_1 = 3.9 \times 10^6 \text{ J} - 4.3 \times 10^5 \text{ J} = 3.5 \times 10^6 \text{ J}$$

This amount represents a savings of $\dfrac{3.5 \times 10^6 \text{ J}}{3.9 \times 10^6 \text{ J}} \times (100\%) = 90\%.$

Follow-Up Exercise. Verify that the heat flow rate is the same through the insulation as through the wood (1.2×10^2 J/s) in this Example.

Convection

In general, compared with solids, liquids and gases are not good thermal conductors. However, the mobility of molecules in fluids permits heat transfer by another process—convection. (A fluid is a substance that can flow, and hence includes both liquids and gases.) **Convection** is heat transfer as a result of mass transfer, which can be natural or forced.

Natural convection cycles occur in liquids and gases. For example, when cold water is in contact with a hot object, such as the bottom of a pot on a stove, the object transfers heat to the water adjacent to the pot by conduction. But the water carries the heat away with it by natural convection, and a cycle is set up in which upper, colder (more dense) water replaces the rising warm (less dense) water. Such cycles are also

INSIGHT 11.2 PHYSICS, THE CONSTRUCTION INDUSTRY, AND ENERGY CONSERVATION

In the last few decades, many homeowners have found it cost-effective to provide their homes with better insulation. To quantify the insulating properties of various materials, the insulation and construction industries do not use thermal conductivity k. Rather, they use a quantity called *thermal resistance*, which is related to the *inverse* of k.

To see how these two quantities are related, consider Eq. 11.4 rewritten as

$$\frac{\Delta Q}{\Delta t} = \left(\frac{k}{d}\right)A\Delta T = \left(\frac{1}{R_t}\right)A\Delta T$$

where the *thermal resistance* is $R_t = d/k$. Note that R_t depends not only on the material's properties (expressed in the thermal conductivity k), but also on its thickness d. R_t is a measure of how "resistant" to heat flow the slab of material is.

The heat flow rate is proportional to the area of the material and to the temperature difference. More area means more heat conduction, and temperature differences are the fundamental cause of the heat flow in the first place. But note that the heat flow rate $\Delta Q/\Delta t$ is inversely related to the thermal resistance: More thermal resistance results in less heat flow. More resistance is attained using *thicker* material with a *low* conductivity.

For homeowners, the lesson is clear. To reduce heat flow (and thus minimize heat loss in the winter and heat gain in the summer), they should reduce areas of low thermal resistance, such as windows, or at least increase the window's resistance by switching to double or triple panes. Similarly for walls, increasing the thermal resistance by adding or upgrading insulation is the way to go. Lastly, changing interior temperature requirements (changing $\Delta T = |T_{\text{exterior}} - T_{\text{interior}}|$) can make a big difference. In summer, homeowners should raise the thermostat setting on air conditioning (lowering ΔT by increasing T_{interior}), and in winter, they should lower the thermostat setting on the heating system (lowering ΔT by decreasing T_{interior}).

Insulation and building materials are classified according to their *R-values*—that is, their thermal resistance values. In the United States, the units of R_t are $\text{ft}^2 \cdot \text{h} \cdot \text{F}°/\text{Btu}$. While these units may seem awkward, the important point is that they are proportional to the thermal resistance of the material. Thus, wall insulation with a value of R-31 (meaning $R_t = 31\ \text{ft}^2 \cdot \text{h} \cdot \text{F}°/\text{Btu}$) is about 1.6 times (or 31/19) as resistive (0.6 times, or 19/31, as conductive) as insulation with a value of R-19. A comparison photo of various types of insulation is shown in Fig. 1.

FIGURE 1 Differences in R-values For insulation blankets made of identical materials, the R-values are proportional to the materials' thickness.

important in atmospheric processes, as illustrated in ▾Fig. 11.10. During the day, the ground heats up more quickly than do large bodies of water, as you may have noticed if you have been to the beach. This phenomenon occurs both because the water has a higher specific heat than land and because convection currents disperse the absorbed heat throughout the larger volume of water. The air in contact with the warm ground is heated and expands, becoming less dense. As a result, the warm air rises (air currents) and, to fill the space, other air moves horizontally (winds)—creating a sea breeze near a large body of water. Cooler air descends, and a thermal convection cycle is set up, which transfers heat away from the land. At night, the ground loses its heat more quickly than the water, and the surface of the water is warmer than the land. As a result, the cycle is reversed. Since the prevailing jet streams over the Northern

▶ **FIGURE 11.10 Convection cycles** During the day, natural convection cycles give rise to sea breezes near large bodies of water. At night, the pattern of circulation is reversed, and the land breezes blow. The temperature differences between land and water are the result of their specific-heat differences. Water has a much larger specific heat, so the land warms up more quickly during the day. At night, the land cools more quickly, while the water remains warmer, because of its larger specific heat.

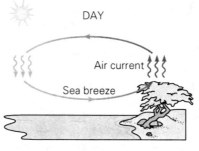

DAY

Air current

Sea breeze

Land warmer than water

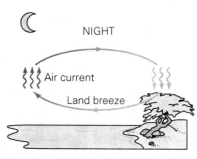

NIGHT

Air current

Land breeze

Water warmer than land

Hemisphere are mostly from west to east, west coasts usually have milder climate than east coasts. The winds move the ocean air with more constant temperature toward the west coasts. On a smaller scale, there is usually a smaller temperature fluctuation on the west coasts than a few miles inland, where desert conditions prevail.

In *forced convection*, the fluid is moved mechanically. This condition results in transfer without a temperature difference. In fact, we can transfer heat energy from a low-temperature region to a high-temperature region this way, as in the case of the forced convection of a refrigerator coolant removing energy from the cooler interior of the refrigerator. (The circulating coolant carries heat energy from the inside of the refrigerator, and this heat is given up to the environment, as we will see in Section 12.5.)

Common examples of forced convection systems are forced-air heating systems in homes (▸Fig. 11.11), the human circulatory system, and the cooling system of an automobile engine. The human body does not use all of the energy obtained from food; a great deal is lost in the form of heat. (There's usually a temperature difference between your body and your surroundings.) So that body temperature will stay normal, the internally generated heat is transferred close to the surface of the skin by blood circulation. From the skin, the energy is conducted to the air or lost by radiation (the other heat-transfer mechanism, to be discussed shortly). This circulatory system is highly adjustable; blood flow can be increased or decreased to specific areas depending on needs.

Water or some other coolant is circulated (pumped) through most automobile cooling systems. (Some smaller engines are air-cooled.) The coolant carries engine heat to the radiator (a form of *heat exchanger*), where forced-air flow produced by the fan and car movement carries it away. The *radiator* of an automobile is actually misnamed—most of the heat is transferred from it by forced convection rather than by radiation.

Conceptual Example 11.8 ■ Foam Insulation: Better Than Air?

Polymer foam insulation is sometimes blown into the space between the inner and outer walls of a house. Since air is a better thermal insulator than foam, why is the foam insulation needed: (a) To prevent loss of heat by conduction, (b) to prevent loss of heat by convection, or (c) for fireproofing?

Reasoning and Answer. Polymer foams will generally burn, so (c) isn't likely to be the answer. Air is a poor thermal conductor, even poorer than plastic foam (Styrofoam—see Table 11.3), so the answer can't be (a). However, as a gas, the air is subject to convection *within the wall space*. In the winter, the air near the warm inner wall is heated and rises, thus setting up a convection cycle in the space and transferring heat to the cold outer wall. In the summer, with air conditioning, the heat-loss cycle is reversed. Foam blocks the movement of air and thus stops such convection cycles. Hence, the answer is (b).

Follow-Up Exercise. Thermal underwear and thermal blankets are loosely knit with lots of small holes. Wouldn't they be more effective if the material were closely knit?

Radiation

Conduction and convection require some material as a transport medium. The third mechanism of heat transfer needs no medium; it is called **radiation**, which refers to energy transfer by electromagnetic waves (Chapter 20). Heat is transferred to the Earth from the Sun through empty space by radiation. Visible light and other forms of electromagnetic radiation are commonly referred to as *radiant energy*.

You have experienced heat transfer by radiation if you've ever stood near an open fire (▾Fig. 11.12). You can feel the heat on your exposed hands and face. This heat transfer is not due to convection or conduction, since heated air rises and air is a poor conductor. Visible radiation is emitted from the burning material, but most of the heating effect comes from the invisible **infrared radiation** emitted by the glowing embers or coals. You feel this radiation because it is absorbed by water molecules in your skin. (Body tissue is about 85% water.) The water molecule has an internal vibration whose frequency coincides with that of infrared radiation, which is therefore readily absorbed. (This effect is called *resonance absorption*. The electromagnetic wave

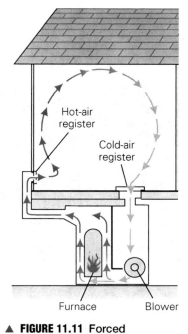

▲ **FIGURE 11.11 Forced convection** Houses are commonly heated by forced convection. Registers or gratings in the floors or walls allow heated air to enter and cooler air to return to the heat source. (Can you explain why the registers are located near the floor?) In older homes, hot water runs through pipes along the wall baseboards, and natural convection distributes the heat vertically upward.

Note: Resonance is discussed in Section 13.5.

▶ **FIGURE 11.12** Heating by conduction, convection, and radiation The hands on top of the flame are warmed by the convection of rising hot air (and some radiation). The gloved hand is warmed by conduction. The hands to the right of the flame are warmed by radiation.

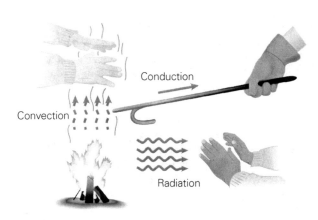
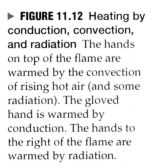

drives the molecular vibration, and energy is transferred to the molecule, somewhat like pushing a swing. See Chapter 13 on oscillations for more details.) Heat transfer by radiation can play a practical role in daily living (◀Fig. 11.13).

Infrared radiation is sometimes referred to as "heat radiation" or thermal radiation. You may have noticed the reddish infrared lamps used to keep food warm in cafeterias. Heat transfer by infrared radiation is also important in maintaining our planet's warmth by a mechanism known as the *greenhouse effect.* This important environmental topic is discussed in Insight 11.3 on page 388 on The Greenhouse Effect.

Although infrared radiation is invisible to the human eye, it can be detected by other means. Infrared detectors can measure temperature remotely (▼Fig. 11.14). Also, some cameras can use special infrared film. A picture taken with this film is an image consisting of contrasting light and dark areas, corresponding to regions of higher and lower temperatures, respectively. Special instruments that apply such *thermography* are used in industry and medicine; the images they produce are called *thermograms* (▶Fig. 11.15).

A new application of thermograms is for security. The system consists of an infrared camera and a computer that identifies an individual by means of the unique heat pattern emitted by the facial blood vessels. The camera takes a picture of the radiation from a person's face, which is compared with an earlier image stored in the computer memory.

The rate at which an object radiates energy has been found to be proportional to the fourth power of the object's absolute temperature (T^4). This relationship is expressed in an equation known as **Stefan's law**, expressed as

$$P = \frac{\Delta Q}{\Delta t} = \sigma A e T^4 \quad \text{(radiation only)} \tag{11.5}$$

▲ **FIGURE 11.13** A practical application of heat transfer by radiation A Tibetan teakettle is heated by focusing sunlight, using a metal reflector.

Illustration 19.3 Heat Transfer, Radiation

▶ **FIGURE 11.14** Detecting SARS Infrared thermometers were used to measure body temperature during the Severe Acute Respiratory Syndrome (SARS) outbreak in 2003.

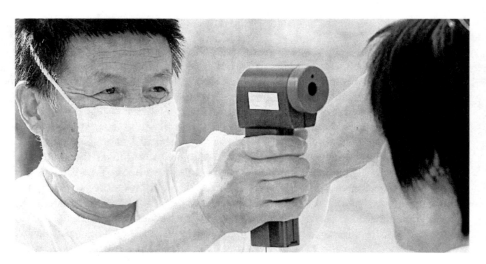

where P is the power radiated in watts (W), or joules per second (J/s). A is the object's surface area and T is its temperature in Kelvin. The symbol σ (the Greek letter sigma) is the *Stefan–Boltzmann constant*: $\sigma = 5.67 \times 10^{-8} \, \text{W}/(\text{m}^2 \cdot \text{K}^4)$. The **emissivity** ($e$) is a unitless number between 0 and 1 that is characteristic of the material. Dark surfaces have emissivities close to 1, and shiny surfaces have emissivities close to 0. The emissivity of human skin is about 0.70.

Dark surfaces not only are better emitters of radiation, but they are also good absorbers. This must be the case because to maintain a constant temperature, the incident energy absorbed must equal the emitted energy. *Thus, a good absorber is also a good emitter.* An ideal, or perfect, absorber (and emitter) is referred to as a **black body** ($e = 1.0$). Shiny surfaces are poor absorbers, since most of the incident radiation is reflected. This fact can be demonstrated easily, as shown in ▾Fig. 11.16. (Can you see why it is better to wear light-colored clothes in the summer and dark-colored clothes in the winter?)

When an object is in thermal equilibrium with its surroundings, its temperature is constant; thus, it must be emitting and absorbing radiation at the same rate. However, if the temperatures of the object and its surroundings are different, there will be a net flow of radiant energy. If an object is at a temperature T and its surroundings are at a temperature T_s, the net rate of energy loss or gain per unit time (power) is given by

$$P_{\text{net}} = \sigma A e (T_s^4 - T^4) \tag{11.6}$$

Note that if T_s is less than T, then P (or $\Delta Q/\Delta t$) will be negative, indicating a net heat energy loss, in keeping with our heat-flow sign convention. Keep in mind that the temperatures used in calculating radiated power are the absolute temperatures in kelvins.

You may have noticed in Chapter 10 that heat was defined as the net thermal energy transfer due to temperature differences. The word *net* here is important. It is possible to have energy transfer between an object and its surroundings, or between objects, at the same temperature. Note that if $T_s = T$ (that is, there is no temperature difference), there is a continuous exchange of radiant energy (Eq. 11.6 still holds), but there is no *net* change of the internal energy of the object.

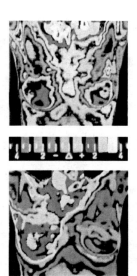

▲ **FIGURE 11.15 Applied thermography** Thermograms can be used to detect breast cancer by detecting tumor regions that are higher in temperature than normal. The upper photo shows a thermogram scan of a woman without breast cancer. The lower photo shows the result for a woman with breast cancer. The "hot spots" in this scan tells the physician where the cancer resides.

Example 11.9 ■ Body Heat: Radiant-Heat Transfer

Suppose that your skin has an emissivity of 0.70, a temperature of 34°C, and a total area of 1.5 m². How much net energy per second will be radiated from your skin if the ambient room temperature is 20°C?

Thinking It Through. Everything is given for us to find P_{net} from Eq. 11.6. The net radiant-energy transfer is between the skin and the surroundings. We must remember to work with temperatures in kelvins.

Solution.

Given: $T_s = 20°C + 273 = 293 \, \text{K}$ *Find:* P_{net} (net power)
$T = 34°C + 273 = 307 \, \text{K}$
$e = 0.70$
$A = 1.5 \, \text{m}^2$
$\sigma = 5.67 \times 10^{-8} \, \text{W}/(\text{m}^2 \cdot \text{K}^4) \text{(known)}$

Using Eq. 11.6 directly,

$$P_{\text{net}} = \sigma A e (T_s^4 - T^4)$$
$$= [5.67 \times 10^{-8} \, \text{W}/(\text{m}^2 \cdot \text{K}^4)](1.5 \, \text{m}^2)(0.70)[(293 \, \text{K})^4 - (307 \, \text{K})^4]$$
$$= -90 \, \text{W} \ (\text{or} -90 \, \text{J/s})$$

Thus, 90 J of energy is radiated, or *lost* (as indicated by the minus sign), each second. That is, the human body loses heat at a rate that is close to that of a 100-W lightbulb! No wonder a room full of people can get warm!

Follow-Up Exercise. (a) In this Example, suppose the skin had been exposed to an ambient room temperature of only 10°C. What would the rate of heat loss be? (b) Elephants have huge body masses and large daily caloric food intakes. Can you explain how their huge ear flaps (large surface area) might help stabilize their body temperature?

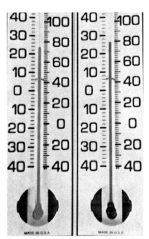

▲ **FIGURE 11.16 Good absorber** Black objects are generally good absorbers of radiation. The bulb of the thermometer on the right has been painted black. Note the difference in temperature readings.

INSIGHT 11.3 THE GREENHOUSE EFFECT

The *greenhouse effect* helps regulate the Earth's long-term average temperature, which has been fairly constant for some centuries. By this natural phenomenon, a portion of the solar radiation (mostly visible) reaches and warms the Earth's surface. The Earth, in turn, reradiates energy in the form of infrared (IR) radiation. The balance between absorption and radiation is a major factor in stabilizing the Earth's temperature.

This balance is affected by the concentration of atmospheric *greenhouse* gases—primarily water vapor, carbon dioxide (CO_2), and methane. As the reradiated infrared radiation passes back through the atmosphere, some of the radiation is absorbed by the greenhouse gases. These gases are selective absorbers: They absorb radiation at certain IR wavelengths but not at others (Fig. 1a).

If IR radiation is absorbed, the atmosphere warms, and in turn the Earth is warmed. Without the atmosphere absorbing the IR radiation, life on the Earth would probably not exist because, the average surface temperature would be a cold $-18°C$, rather than the present $15°C$.

Why is this phenomenon called the *greenhouse effect*? The reason is that the atmosphere functions somewhat like the glass in a greenhouse. That is, the absorption and transmission properties of glass are similar to those of the atmospheric greenhouse gases—in general, visible radiation is transmitted, but infrared radiation is selectively absorbed (Fig. 1b). We have all observed the warming effect of sunlight passing through glass—for example, in a closed car on a sunny but cold day. Similarly, a greenhouse heats up by trapping the reradiated infrared radiation inside. Thus, it is quite warm in a greenhouse on a sunny day, even in winter. (The glass enclosure also keeps warm air from escaping upward. In practice, this elimination of heat loss by convection is the chief factor in maintaining an elevated temperature in a greenhouse.)

The problem on Earth is that human activities since the beginning of the industrial age have been accentuating greenhouse warming. With the combustion of hydrocarbon fuels (gas, oil, coal, and so on) for heating and industrial processes, vast amounts of CO_2 and other greenhouse gases are vented into the atmosphere, where they trap increasingly more IR radiation. There is grave concern that the result of this trend will be—and in fact already is—increased *global warming*, an increase in the Earth's average temperature. Such an increase could dramatically affect the environment. For example, some detailed calculations indicate that the climate in many parts of the globe would be altered, with agricultural production and world food supplies affected in ways that are very difficult to predict. A general rise in temperature would cause partial melting of the polar ice caps. Sea levels would rise, flooding low-lying regions and endangering coastal ports and population centers.

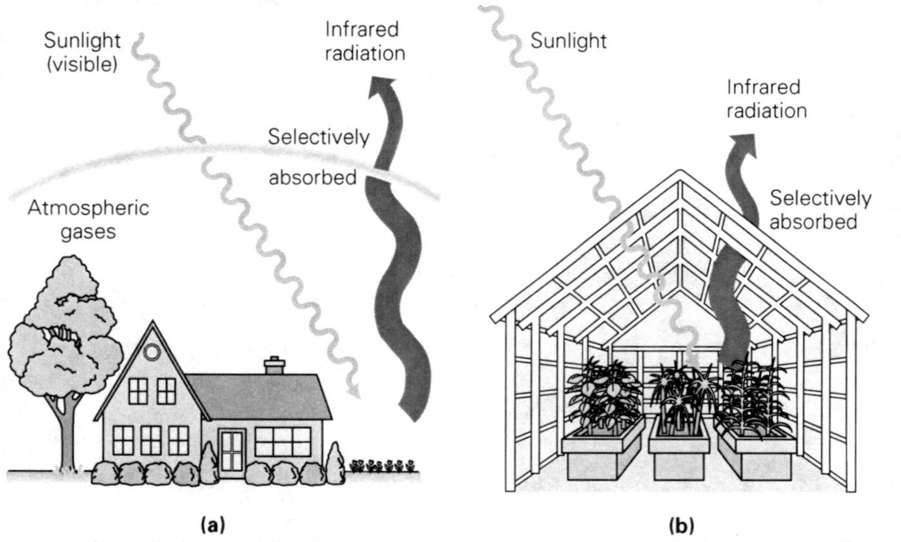

(a)

(b)

FIGURE 1 The greenhouse effect **(a)** The greenhouse gases of the atmosphere, particularly water vapor, methane, and carbon dioxide, are selective absorbers with absorption properties similar to those of the glass used in greenhouses. Visible light is transmitted and heats the Earth's surface, while some of the infrared radiation that is re-emitted is absorbed and trapped in the Earth's atmosphere. **(b)** A greenhouse operates in a similar way.

Problem-Solving Hint

Note that in Example 11.9, the fourth powers of the temperatures were found first, and then their difference was found. It is *not* correct to find the temperature difference and then raise it to the fourth power: $T_s^4 - T^4 \neq (T_s - T)^4$.

Let's consider a practical example of heat transfer that is becoming more commonplace as energy costs rise—solar panels.

Conceptual Example 11.10 ■ Solar Panels: Reducing the Heat Transfer

Solar panels are used to collect solar energy to heat water, which may then be direct-ly to heat a home at night. The panel boxes have black interiors (why?) through which the piping runs to carry the water, and the top is covered with glass. However, ordinary glass absorbs a lot of the Sun's ultraviolet radiation. This absorption reduces the heating effect. Wouldn't it be better to leave the glass off the panel boxes?

Reasoning and Answer. Some energy is absorbed by the glass, but the glass serves a use-ful purpose and saves a lot more energy than it absorbs. As the black interior and piping of the panel box heat up, there could be heat loss by radiation (infrared) and convection. The glass prevents this loss from occurring via the greenhouse effect. It absorbs much of the infrared radiation and also keeps the convection currents *inside* the solar-panel box. (See the Insight on The Greenhouse Effect.)

Follow-Up Exercise. Is there any practical reason for window drapes (other than privacy)?

Let's look at a few more real-life examples of heat transfer. In the spring, a late frost could kill the buds on fruit trees in an orchard. To reduce heat transfer, some growers spray water on the trees to form ice before a hard frost occurs. Using ice to save buds? Ice is a relatively poor (and inexpensive) thermal conductor, so it has an insulating effect. It will maintain the buds' temperature at 0°C, not going below that value, and therefore protects the buds.

Another method to protect orchards from freezing is the use of smudge pots, containers in which material is burned to create a dense cloud of smoke. At night, when the Sun-warmed ground cools off by radiation, the cloud absorbs this heat and reradiates it back to the ground. Thus, the ground takes longer to cool, hopefully without reaching freezing temperatures before the Sun comes up. (Recall that frost is the direct condensation of water vapor in the air to ice—not frozen dew.)

A Thermos bottle (►Fig. 11.17) keeps cold beverages cold and hot ones hot. It con-sists of a double-walled, partially evacuated container with silvered walls (mirrored interior). The bottle is constructed to minimize all three mechanisms of heat transfer. The double-walled and partially evacuated container counteracts conduction and convection because both processes depend on a medium to transfer the heat (the double walls are more for holding the partially evacuated region than for reducing conduction and convection). The mirrored interior minimizes loss by radiation. The stopper on top of the thermos stops convection off the top of the liquid as well.

Look at ▼Fig. 11.18. Why would anyone wear a dark robe in the desert? We have learned that dark objects absorb radiation (Fig. 11.16). Wouldn't a white robe be better? A dark robe definitely absorbs more radiant energy and warms the air

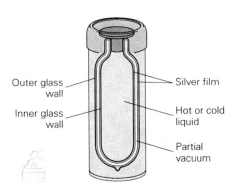

Outer glass wall
Inner glass wall
Silver film
Hot or cold liquid
Partial vacuum

▲ **FIGURE 11.17 Thermal insulation** The Thermos bottle minimizes all three mechanisms of heat transfer.

◄ **FIGURE 11.18 A dark robe in the desert?** Dark objects absorb more radiation than do lighter ones, and they become hotter. What's going on here? See the text for an explanation.

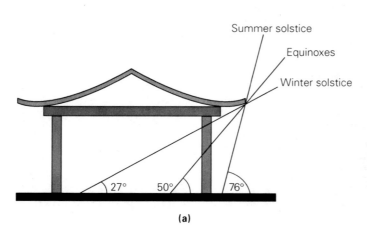

(a)   (b)

▲ **FIGURE 11.19 Aspects of passive solar design in ancient China (a)** In summer, with the sun angle high, the overhangs provide shade to the building. The brick and mud walls are thick to reduce conductive heat flow to the interior. In winter, the sun angle is low so the sunlight streams into the building, especially with the help of the upward curved overhangs. The leaves of nearby deciduous trees provide additional shade in the summer but allow sunlight in when they have dropped their leaves in the winter. **(b)** A photo of such a building in Beijing, China, in December.

inside near the body. But note that the robe is open at the bottom. The warm air rises (since it is less dense) and exits at the neck area, and outside cooler air enters the robe at the bottom—a natural-convection air circulation.

Finally, consider some of the thermal factors involved in "passive" solar house design used as far back as in ancient China (▲ Fig. 11.19). The term *passive* means that the design elements require no active use of energy to conserve energy. In Beijing, China, for example, the angles of the sunlight are 76°, 50°, and 27° above the horizon at the summer solstice, the spring and fall equinoxes, and the winter solstice, respectively. With a proper combination of column height and roof overhang length, maximum sunlight is allowed *into* the building in the winter, but most of the sunlight will *not* reach the inside of the building in the summer. The overhangs of the roofs are also curved upward, not just for good looks, but also for letting the maximum amount of light into the building in the winter. Trees planted on the south side of the building can also play important roles in both summer and winter. In the summer, the leaves block and filter the sunlight; in the winter, the dropped leaves will let sunlight through.

PHYSICS FACTS

- Waves (of different types) can travel through solids, liquids, gases, and vacuum.

- Disturbances set up waves. Soldiers marching across older wooden bridges are told to break step and not march at a periodic cadence. This might correspond to a natural frequency of the bridge, resulting in resonance and large oscillations that could damage the bridge and even cause it to collapse.

- *Brain waves* are tiny oscillating electrical voltages in the brain. These are measured by attaching electrodes on the scalp hooked to an EEG (*electroencephalograph*) to get a recording (*graph*) of electrical signals (*electro*) from the brain (*encephalo*). Electrical signals from the brain are displayed in the form of brain waves, the frequency of which depends on the brain's activity.

- *Tidal waves* are not related to tides. More appropriate is the Japanese name *tsunami*, which means "harbor wave." The effects of a tsunami are intensified in the confined spaces of bays and harbors. The waves are generated by subterranean earthquakes and can race across the ocean at speeds up to 960 km/h, with little surface evidence. When a tsunami reaches the shallow coast, friction slows the wave down, at the same time causing it to roll up into a 5- to 30-m-high wall of water that crashes down on the shoreline.

The photograph depicts what a lot of people probably first think of when they hear the word *wave*. We're all familiar with ocean waves or their smaller relatives, the ripples that form on the surface of a lake or pond when something disturbs the surface. Yet in many ways, the waves that are most important to us, as well as most interesting to physicists, either are invisible or don't look like waves. Sound, for example, is a wave. Perhaps most surprisingly, light is a wave. In fact, all electromagnetic radiations are waves—radio waves, microwaves, X-rays, and so on. Whenever you peer through a microscope, put on a pair of glasses, or look at a rainbow, you are experiencing wave energy in the form of light. In Chapter 28, you'll learn how even moving particles have wavelike properties. But first we need to look at the basic description of waves.

In general, waves are related to vibrations or oscillations—back-and-forth motion—such as that of a mass on a spring or a swinging pendulum, and fundamental to such motions are restoring forces or torques. In a material medium, the restoring force is provided by intermolecular forces. If a molecule is disturbed, restoring forces exerted by its neighbors tend to return the molecule to its original position, and it begins to oscillate. In so doing, it affects adjacent molecules, which are in turn set into oscillation. This is referred to as *propagation*. This raises the question, "What is propagated by the molecules in a material?" The answer is *energy*. A single disturbance, which happens when you give the end of a stretched rope a quick shake, gives rise to a *wave pulse*. A continuous, repetitive disturbance gives rise to a continuous propagation of energy that we call *wave motion*. But before looking at waves in media, it is helpful to analyze the oscillations of a single mass.

433

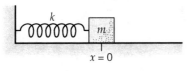

(a) Equilibrium

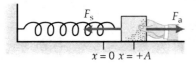

(b) $t = 0$ Just before release

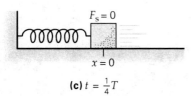

(c) $t = \frac{1}{4}T$

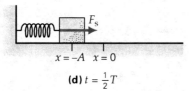

(d) $t = \frac{1}{2}T$

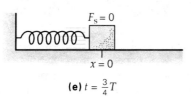

(e) $t = \frac{3}{4}T$

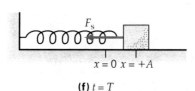

(f) $t = T$

▲ **FIGURE 13.1** Simple harmonic motion (SHM) When an object on a spring **(a)** is displaced from its equilibrium position, $x = 0$, and **(b)** is released, the object undergoes SHM (assuming no frictional losses). The time it takes to complete one cycle is the period of oscillation (T). (Here, F_s is the spring force and F_a is the applied force.) **(c)** At $t = T/4$, the object is back at its equilibrium position; **(d)** at $t = T/2$, it is at $x = -A$. **(e)** During the next half cycle, the motion is to the right; **(f)** at $t = T$, the object is back at its initial ($t = 0$) starting position as in (b).

13.1 Simple Harmonic Motion

OBJECTIVES: To (a) describe simple harmonic motion, and (b) describe how energy and speed vary in such motion.

The motion of an oscillating object depends on the restoring force that makes the object go back and forth. It is convenient to begin to study such motion by considering the simplest type of force acting along the x-axis: a force that is directly proportional to the object's displacement from equilibrium. A common example is the (ideal) spring force, described by **Hooke's law** (Section 5.2),

$$F_s = -kx \tag{13.1}$$

where k is the spring constant. Recall from Chapter 5 that the minus sign indicates that the force is always in the direction opposite that of the displacement. That is, the force always tends to *restore* the object to the spring's equilibrium position.

Suppose that an object on a horizontal frictionless surface is connected to a spring as shown in ◄Fig. 13.1. When the object is displaced to one side of its equilibrium position and released, it will move back and forth—that is, it will vibrate, or oscillate. Here, an oscillation or a vibration is clearly a *periodic motion*—a motion that repeats itself again and again along the same path. For linear oscillations, like those of an object attached to a spring, the path may be back and forth or up and down. For the angular oscillation of a pendulum, the path is back and forth along a circular arc.

Motion under the influence of the type of force described by Hooke's law is called **simple harmonic motion (SHM)**, because the force is the simplest restoring force and because the motion can be described by harmonic functions (sines and cosines), as you will see later in the chapter. The directed distance of an object in SHM from its equilibrium position is the object's **displacement**. Note in Fig. 13.1 that the displacement can be either positive or negative, which indicates direction. The maximum displacements are $+A$ and $-A$ (Fig. 13.1b, d). The magnitude of the maximum displacement, or the maximum distance of an object from its equilibrium position, is called the object's **amplitude (A)**, a scalar quantity that expresses the distance of both extreme displacements from the equilibrium position.

Besides the amplitude, two other important quantities used in describing an oscillation are its period and frequency. The **period (T)** is the time it takes the object to complete one cycle of motion. A cycle is a *complete* round trip, or motion through a complete oscillation. For example, if an object starts at $x = A$ (Fig. 13.1b), then when it returns to $x = A$ (as in Fig. 13.1f), it will have completed one cycle in a time we call one period. If an object were initially at $x = 0$ when disturbed, then its second return to this point would mark a cycle. (Why a *second* return?) In either case, the object would travel a distance of $4A$ during one cycle. Can you show this?

The **frequency (f)** is the number of cycles per second. The frequency and the period are related by

$$f = \frac{1}{T} \quad \textit{frequency and period} \tag{13.2}$$

SI unit of frequency: hertz (Hz), or cycle per second (cycle/s)

The inverse relationship is reflected in the units. The period is the number of seconds per cycle, and the frequency is the number of cycles per second. For example, if $T = \frac{1}{2}$ s/cycle, then it completes 2 cycles each second or $f = 2$ cycles/s.

The standard unit of frequency is the **hertz (Hz)**, which is one cycle per second.[*] From Eq. 13.2, frequency has the unit inverse seconds (1/s, or s^{-1}),

---

[*]The unit is named for Heinrich Hertz (1857–1894), a German physicist and early investigator of electromagnetic waves.

TABLE 13.1	Terms Used to Describe Simple Harmonic Motion

displacement—the directed distance of an object ($\pm x$) from its equilibrium position.

amplitude (A)—the magnitude of the maximum displacement, or the maximum distance, of an object from its equilibrium position.

period (T)—the time for one complete cycle of motion.

frequency (f)— the number of cycles per second (in hertz or inverse seconds, where $f = 1/T$).

since the period is a measure of time. Although cycle is not really a unit, you might find it convenient at times to express frequency in cycles per second to help with unit analysis. This is similar to the way the radian (rad) is used in the description of circular motion in Sections 7.1 and 7.2.

The preceding terms used to describe SHM are summarized in Table 13.1.

Energy and Speed of a Mass–Spring System in SHM

Recall from Chapter 5 that the potential energy stored in a spring that is stretched or compressed a distance $\pm x$ from equilibrium (chosen to be $x = 0$) is

$$U = \tfrac{1}{2}kx^2 \tag{13.3}$$

The *change* in potential energy of an object oscillating on a spring is related to the work done by the spring force. An object with mass m oscillating on a spring also has kinetic energy. The kinetic and potential energies together give the total mechanical energy E of the system:

$$E = K + U = \tfrac{1}{2}mv^2 + \tfrac{1}{2}kx^2 \tag{13.4}$$

When the object is at one of its maximum displacements, $+A$ or $-A$, it is instantaneously at rest, $v = 0$ (▼Fig. 13.2). Thus, all the energy is in the form of potential energy (U_{max}) at this location; that is,

$$E = \tfrac{1}{2}m(0)^2 + \tfrac{1}{2}k(\pm A)^2 = \tfrac{1}{2}kA^2$$

or

$$E = \tfrac{1}{2}kA^2 \quad \begin{array}{l} \textit{total energy of an object} \\ \textit{in SHM on a spring} \end{array} \tag{13.5}$$

This outcome is a general result for SHM:

The total energy of an object in simple harmonic motion is directly proportional to the square of the amplitude.

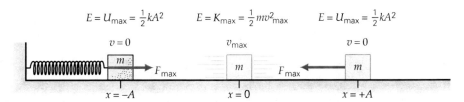

$E = U_{max} = \tfrac{1}{2}kA^2 \qquad E = K_{max} = \tfrac{1}{2}mv^2_{max} \qquad E = U_{max} = \tfrac{1}{2}kA^2$

$v = 0 \qquad\qquad v_{max} \qquad\qquad v = 0$

$F_{max} \qquad\qquad F_{max}$

$x = -A \qquad\qquad x = 0 \qquad\qquad x = +A$

▲ **FIGURE 13.2 Oscillations and energy** For a mass oscillating in SHM on a spring (on a frictionless surface), the total energy at the amplitude positions ($\pm A$) is all potential energy (U_{max}), and $E = \tfrac{1}{2}kx^2 = \tfrac{1}{2}kA^2$, which is the total energy of the system. At the center position ($x = 0$), the total energy is all kinetic energy ($E = \tfrac{1}{2}mv^2_{max}$, where m is the mass of the block). How is the total energy divided at locations somewhere between $x = 0$ and $x = \pm A$?

Demonstration/activity: Demonstrate simple harmonic motion with a mass hung on a spring or a light spring connected to a glider on an air track. Motion on a horizontal surface, such as the air track, is better, to avoid having to consider gravitational potential energy. Discuss points where the potential energy is a maximum and points where the kinetic energy is a maximum. Discuss the location where the potential and kinetic energies are equal by considering the shaded area on the force–displacement graph.

Illustration 16.3 Energy and Simple Harmonic Motion

Note: This discussion will be limited to light springs, the mass of which can be considered negligible.

Equation 13.5 allows us to express the velocity of an object oscillating on a spring as a function of position:

$$E = K + U \quad \text{or} \quad \tfrac{1}{2}kA^2 = \tfrac{1}{2}mv^2 + \tfrac{1}{2}kx^2$$

Solving for v^2 and taking the square root:

$$v = \pm\sqrt{\frac{k}{m}(A^2 - x^2)} \quad \text{velocity of an object in SHM} \tag{13.6}$$

where the positive and negative signs indicate the direction of the velocity. Note that at $x = \pm A$ the velocity is zero, since the object is instantaneously at rest at its maximum displacement from equilibrium.

Note also that when the oscillating object passes through its equilibrium position ($x = 0$), its potential energy is zero. At that instant, the energy is all kinetic, and the object is traveling at its maximum speed v_{max}. The expression for the energy in this case is

$$E = \tfrac{1}{2}kA^2 = \tfrac{1}{2}mv_{max}^2$$

and,

$$v_{max} = \sqrt{\frac{k}{m}}\,A \quad \begin{array}{l}\textit{maximum speed}\\ \textit{of mass on a spring}\end{array} \tag{13.7}$$

In the next Example, as well as in the accompanying Learn by Drawing, you can visualize the continuous trade-off between kinetic and potential energy.

Example 13.1 ■ A Block and a Spring: Simple Harmonic Motion

A block with a mass of 0.25 kg sitting on a frictionless surface is connected to a light spring that has a spring constant of 180 N/m (see Fig. 13.1). If the block is displaced 15 cm from its equilibrium position and released, what are (a) the total energy of the system and (b) the speed of the block when it is 10 cm from its equilibrium position?

Thinking It Through. The total energy depends on the spring constant (k) and the amplitude (A), which are given. At $x = 10$ cm, the speed should be less than the maximum speed. (Why?)

Solution. First we list the given data, as usual, and what is to be found. The initial displacement is the amplitude. (Why?)

Given: $m = 0.25$ kg   *Find:* (a) E (total energy)
$k = 180$ N/m   (b) v (speed)
$A = 15$ cm $= 0.15$ m
$x = 10$ cm $= 0.10$ m

(a) The total energy is given by Eq. 13.5:

$$E = \tfrac{1}{2}kA^2 = \tfrac{1}{2}(180 \text{ N/m})(0.15 \text{ m})^2 = 2.0 \text{ J}$$

(b) The instantaneous speed of the block at a distance 10 cm from the equilibrium position is given by Eq. 13.6 without directional signs:

$$v = \sqrt{\frac{k}{m}(A^2 - x^2)} = \sqrt{\frac{180 \text{ N/m}}{0.25 \text{ kg}}[(0.15 \text{ m})^2 - (0.10 \text{ m})^2]} = \sqrt{9.0 \text{ m}^2/\text{s}^2} = 3.0 \text{ m/s}$$

What would the speed be at $x = -10$ cm?

Follow-Up Exercise. In part (b) of this Example, the block at $x = 10$ cm is at two thirds, or 67%, of its maximum displacement. Is its speed at that position therefore 67% of its maximum speed? Justify your answer mathematically. (*Answers to all Follow-Up Exercises are at the back of the text.*)

LEARN BY DRAWING   OSCILLATING IN A PARABOLIC POTENTIAL WELL

A way to visualize the conservation of energy in simple harmonic motion is shown in Fig. 1. The potential energy of a mass–spring system can be sketched on a plot of energy (E) versus position (x). Since $U = \frac{1}{2}kx^2 \propto x^2$, the graph is a *parabola*.

In the absence of nonconservative forces, the total energy of the system, E, is constant. But E is the sum of the kinetic and potential energies. During the oscillations, there is a continuous trade-off between the two types of energies, but their sum remains constant. Mathematically, this relationship is written as $E = K + U$. In Fig. 2, U (indicated by a blue arrow) is represented by the vertical distance from the x-axis.

Since E is constant and independent of x, it is plotted as a horizontal line (shown in green). The kinetic energy is the part of the total energy that is *not* potential energy; that is, $K = E - U$. It can be graphically interpreted (purple arrow) as the vertical distance between the potential-energy parabola and the horizontal green total-energy line. As the object oscillates on the x-axis, the energy trade-offs can be visualized as the lengths of the two arrows change.

A general location, x_1, is shown in Fig. 2. Neither the kinetic energy nor the potential energy is at its maximum value of E there. These maximum values occur instead at $x = 0$ and $x = \pm A$, respectively. The motion cannot exceed $x = \pm A$, because that would imply a negative kinetic energy, which is physically impossible. (Why?) The amplitude positions are sometimes called the *endpoints* of the motion, because they are the locations where the speed is instantaneously zero and the object reverses direction.

Try using the graphical approach to answer the following questions (and make up some of your own): What do you have to do to E to increase the amplitude of oscillation, and how might you do this? What happens to the amplitude of a real-life system in SHM in the presence of a force such as friction when E decays with time?

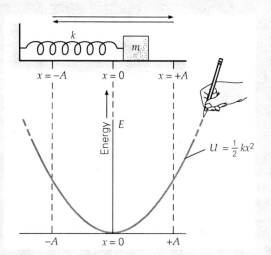

FIGURE 1 The potential-energy "well" of a spring–mass system The potential energy of a spring that is stretched or compressed from its equilibrium position ($x = 0$) is a parabola, since $U \propto x^2$. At $x = \pm A$, all of the system's energy is potential.

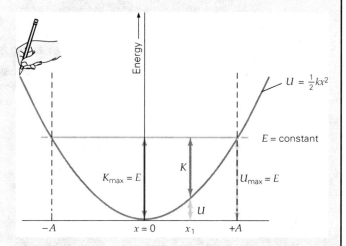

FIGURE 2 Energy transfers as the spring–mass system oscillates The vertical distance from the x-axis to the parabola is the system's potential energy. The remainder—the vertical distance between the parabola and the horizontal line representing the system's constant total energy E—is the system's kinetic energy (K).

The spring constant is commonly determined by placing an object of known mass on the end of a spring and letting it settle vertically to a new equilibrium position. The next Example shows some typical results.

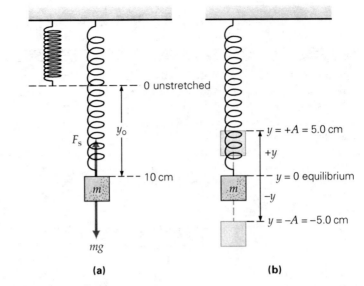

▲ **FIGURE 13.3 Determination of the spring constant** **(a)** When an object suspended on a spring is in equilibrium, the two forces on the object cancel, so that $F_s = w$, or $ky_o = mg$. Thus, the spring constant k can be computed: $k = mg/y_o$. **(b)** The zero reference point of an object in SHM and suspended on a spring is conveniently taken to be the new equilibrium position, as the motion is symmetric about that point. (See Example 13.2.)

Example 13.2 ■ The Spring Constant: Experimental Determination

When a 0.50-kg mass is suspended from a spring, the spring stretches a distance of 10 cm to a new equilibrium position (▲ Fig. 13.3a). (a) What is the spring constant of the spring? (b) The mass is then pulled down another 5.0 cm and released. What is the highest position of the oscillating mass?

Thinking It Through. At the equilibrium position, the net force on the mass is zero because $a = 0$. In part (b), negative y will be used to designate "downward," as is customary in problems involving vertical motion.

Solution.

Given: $m = 0.50 \text{ kg}$ **Find:**   (a) k (spring constant)
                $y_o = 10 \text{ cm} = 0.10 \text{ m}$ (b) A (amplitude)
                $y = -5.0 \text{ cm} = -0.050 \text{ m}$
                    (new reference point)

(a) When the suspended mass is in equilibrium (Fig. 13.3a), the net force on the mass is zero. Thus, the weight of the mass and the spring force are equal and opposite. Then, equating their magnitudes,

$$F_s = w$$

or

$$ky_o = mg$$

Hence,

$$k = \frac{mg}{y_o} = \frac{(0.50 \text{ kg})(9.8 \text{ m/s}^2)}{0.10 \text{ m}} = 49 \text{ N/m}$$

(b) Once set into motion, the mass oscillates up and down through the equilibrium position. Since the motion is symmetric about this point, it is convenient to designate it as the zero reference point of the oscillation (Fig. 13.3b). The initial displacement is $-A$, so the highest position of the mass will be 5.0 cm above the equilibrium position $(+A)$.

Follow-Up Exercise. How much more potential energy does the spring in this Example have at the bottom of its oscillation than at the top?

13.2 Equations of Motion

OBJECTIVES: To (a) understand the equation of SHM, and (b) explain what is meant by phase and phase differences.

The equation that gives the object's position as a function of time is referred to as the **equation of motion**. For example, the equation of motion with a constant linear acceleration is $x = x_o + v_o t + \frac{1}{2}at^2$, where v_o is the initial velocity (Chapter 2). However, the acceleration is not constant in simple harmonic motion, so the kinematic equations of Chapter 2 do not apply to this case.

The equation of motion for an object in SHM can be found from a relationship between simple harmonic and uniform circular motions. SHM can be simulated by a component of uniform circular motion, as illustrated in ▾Fig. 13.4. As the illuminated object moves in uniform circular motion (with constant angular speed ω) in a vertical plane, its shadow moves back and forth vertically, following the same path as the object on the spring, which is in simple harmonic motion. Since the shadow and the object have the same position at any time, it follows that the equation of motion for the shadow of the object in circular motion is the same as the equation of motion for the oscillating object on the spring.

From the reference circle in Fig. 13.4b, the y-coordinate (position) of the object is given by

$$y = A \sin \theta$$

But the object moves with a constant angular velocity of magnitude ω. In terms of the angular distance θ, assuming that $\theta = 0°$ at $t = 0$, we have $\theta = \omega t$, so

$$y = A \sin \omega t \quad \begin{array}{l}\textit{(SHM for } y_o = 0,\\ \textit{initial upward motion)}\end{array} \qquad (13.8)$$

Note that as t increases from zero, y increases in the positive direction, so the equation describes initial upward motion.

With Eq. 13.8 as the equation of motion, the mass *must* always be initially at $y_o = 0$. But what if the mass on the spring were initially at the amplitude position $+A$? In that case, the sine equation would not describe the motion, because it does

Illustration 16.1 Representations of Simple Harmonic Motion

▾ **FIGURE 13.4 Reference circle for vertical motion** (a) The shadow of an object in uniform circular motion has the same vertical motion as an object oscillating on a spring in simple harmonic motion. (b) The motion can be described by $y = A \sin \theta = A \sin \omega t$ (assuming that $y = 0$ at $t = 0$).

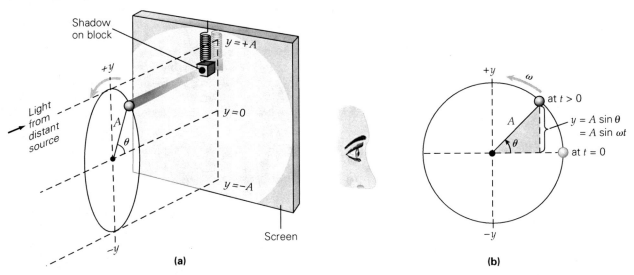

▶ **FIGURE 13.5** Sinusoidal equation
of motion As time passes, the
oscillating object traces out a
sinusoidal curve on the moving
paper. In this case, $y = A \cos \omega t$,
because the object's initial
displacement is $y_o = +A$.

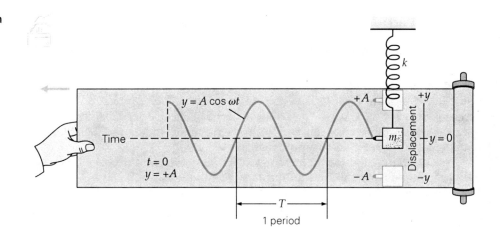

not describe the *initial condition*—that is, $y_o = +A$ at $t_o = 0$. So another equation of
motion is needed, and $y = A \cos \omega t$ applies. By this equation, at $t_o = 0$, the mass is
at $y_o = A \cos \omega t = A \cos \omega(0) = +A$, and the cosine equation correctly describes
the initial conditions (▲ Fig. 13.5):

$$y = A \cos \omega t \qquad \begin{array}{l} \textit{(initial downward motion} \\ \textit{with } y_o = +A) \end{array} \qquad (13.9)$$

Here, the initial motion is downward, because, for times shortly after $t_o = 0$, the
value of y decreases. If the amplitude were $-A$, the mass would initially be at the
bottom and the initial motion would be upward.

Thus, the equation of motion for an oscillating object may be either a sine or a
cosine function. Both of these functions are referred to as being *sinusoidal*. That is,
simple harmonic motion is described by a sinusoidal function of time.

The angular speed ω (in rad/s) of the *reference circle object* (Fig. 13.4) is called
the *angular frequency* of the oscillating object, since $\omega = 2\pi f$, where f is the frequency of revolution or rotation of the object (Section 7.2). Figure 13.4 shows that
the frequency of the "orbiting" object is the same as the frequency of oscillation of
the object on the spring. Thus, using $f = 1/T$, we can write Eq. 13.8 as

$$y = A \sin(2\pi f t) = A \sin\left(\frac{2\pi t}{T}\right) \qquad \begin{array}{l} \textit{(SHM for } y_o = 0, \\ \textit{initial upward motion)} \end{array} \qquad (13.10)$$

Note that this equation is for initial upward motion, because after $t_o = 0$, the value
of y increases positively. For initial downward motion, the amplitude term would
be $-A$.

Equations 13.8 and 13.10 give three equivalent forms of the equation of motion for an object in SHM. Any one of them can be used for convenience, depending on the known parameters. For example, suppose you are given the time t in
terms of the period T—say, $t_o = 0$, $t_1 = T/4$, and $t_2 = 3T/4$—and are asked to find
the position of an object in SHM at these times. In this case, it is convenient to use
Eq. 13.10, and

$$t_o = 0 \qquad y_o = A \sin[2\pi(0)/T] = A \sin 0 = 0$$

$$t_1 = \frac{T}{4} \qquad y_1 = A \sin[2\pi(T/4)/T] = A \sin \pi/2 = A$$

$$t_2 = \frac{3T}{4} \qquad y_2 = A \sin[2\pi(3T/4)/T] = A \sin 3\pi/2 = -A$$

The results tell us that the object was initially at $y = 0$ (equilibrium), as we
knew. One quarter of a period later, it was at $y = A$, or the amplitude of its oscillation; and at a time of three quarters of a period ($3T/4$), it was at the $-A$ position, which is to be expected, since the motion is periodic. (Where would the
object be at $T/2$ and T?)

Hence, we may write in general,

$$y = \pm A \sin \omega t = \pm A \sin(2\pi f t) = \pm A \sin\left(\frac{2\pi t}{T}\right)$$ (+ *for initial motion upward with* $y_o = 0$; – *for initial motion downward with* $y_o = 0$) (13.8a)

By a similar development, Eq. 13.9 has the general form

$$y = \pm A \cos \omega t = \pm A \cos(2\pi f t) = \pm A \cos\left(\frac{2\pi t}{T}\right)$$ (+ *for initial motion downward with* $y_o = +A$; – *for initial motion upward with* $y_o = -A$) (13.9b)

To show the convenience of the reference circle, let us use it to compute the period of the spring–object system. Note that the time for the object in the reference circle to make one complete "orbit" is exactly the time it takes for the oscillating object to make one complete cycle. (See Fig. 13.4.) Thus, all we need is the time for one orbit around the reference circle, and we have the period of oscillation. Because the object "orbiting" the reference circle is in uniform circular motion at a constant speed equal to the maximum speed of oscillation v_{max}, the object travels a distance of one circumference in one period. Then $t = d/v$, where $t = T$, the circumference is d, and v is v_{max} given by Equation 13.7; that is,

$$T = \frac{d}{v_{max}} = \frac{2\pi A}{\sqrt{k/m}\, A}$$

or

$$T = 2\pi \sqrt{\frac{m}{k}} \quad \begin{array}{l}period\ of\ object\\ oscillating\ on\ a\ spring\end{array}$$ (13.11)

Because the amplitudes canceled out in Eq. 13.11, *the period (and frequency) are independent of the amplitude of the motion*. This statement is a general feature of simple harmonic oscillators—that is, oscillators driven by a linear restoring force, such as a spring obeying Hooke's law.

Note: Period and frequency are independent of amplitude in SHM.

We see from Eq. 13.11 that the greater the mass, the longer the period, and the greater the spring constant (or the stiffer the spring), the shorter the period. It is the *ratio* of mass to stiffness that determines the period. Thus, you can offset an increase in mass by using a stiffer spring.

Since $f = 1/T$,

$$f = \frac{1}{2\pi} \sqrt{\frac{k}{m}} \quad \begin{array}{l}frequency\ of\ mass\\ oscillating\ on\ a\ spring\end{array}$$ (13.12)

PHYSLET

Illustration 16.2 The Simple Pendulum and Spring Motion

Thus, the greater the spring constant (the stiffer the spring), the more frequently the system vibrates, as you might expect.

Also, note that since $\omega = 2\pi f$, we may write

$$\omega = \sqrt{\frac{k}{m}} \quad \begin{array}{l}angular\ frequency\ of\ mass\\ oscillating\ on\ a\ spring\end{array}$$ (13.13)

PHYSLET

Exploration 16.1 Spring and Pendulum Motion

As another example, a simple pendulum (a small, heavy object on a string) will undergo simple harmonic motion for small angles of oscillation. The period of a simple pendulum oscillating through a small angle $\theta \lesssim 10°$ is given, to a good approximation, by

$$T = 2\pi \sqrt{\frac{L}{g}} \quad period\ of\ a\ simple\ pendulum$$ (13.14)

where L is the length of the pendulum and g is the acceleration due to gravity. A pendulum-driven clock that is not properly rewound and is running down would still keep correct time, because the period would remain unchanged as the amplitude decreased. As shown by Eq. 13.14, the period is independent of amplitude.

An important difference between the period of the mass–spring system and that of the pendulum is that the latter is independent of the mass of the bob. (See Eq. 13.11 and Eq. 13.14.) Can you explain why? Think about what supplies the restoring force for the pendulum's oscillations. It is gravity. Hence, the acceleration (along with the velocity and period) is expected to be independent of mass. That is, the gravitational force automatically provides the same acceleration to different bob masses on pendulums with the same length. We have seen that similar effects occur in free fall (Chapter 2) and with blocks sliding and cylinders rolling down inclines (Chapters 4 and 8, respectively). The next Example demonstrates the usage of the equation of motion for SHM.

Example 13.3 ■ An Oscillating Mass: Applying the Equation of Motion

A mass on a spring oscillates vertically with an amplitude of 15 cm, a frequency of 0.20 Hz, and an equation of motion given by Eq. 13.8, with $y_o = 0$ at $t_o = 0$ and initial upward motion. (a) What are the position and direction of motion of the mass at $t = 3.1$ s? (b) How many oscillations (cycles) does the mass make in a time of 12 s?

Thinking It Through. Part (a) is a straightforward application of Eq. 13.8. In part (b), the number of oscillations means the number of cycles, and recall that frequency is sometimes expressed in cycles per second. Hence, multiplying the frequency by the time would give the number of cycles or oscillations.

Solution.

Given: $A = 15$ cm $= 0.15$ m   *Find:* (a) y (position and direction of motion)
$f = 0.20$ Hz   (b) n (number of oscillations or cycles)
$y = A \sin \omega t$ (Eq. 13.8)
(a) $t = 3.1$ s   (b) $t = 12$ s

(a) First, since the frequency f is given, it is convenient to use the equation of motion in the form $y = A \sin 2\pi f t$ (Eq. 13.10). As can be seen from the equation, at $t_o = 0$, $y_o = 0$, so initially the mass is at the zero (equilibrium) position. Then, at $t = 3.1$ s,

$$y = A \sin 2\pi f t$$
$$= (0.15 \text{ m}) \sin[2\pi(0.20 \text{ s}^{-1})(3.1 \text{ s})]$$
$$= (0.15 \text{ m}) \sin(3.9 \text{ rad}) = -0.10 \text{ m}$$

So the mass is at $y = -0.10$ m at $t = 3.1$ s. But what is its direction of motion? Let's look at the period (T) and see what part of its cycle the mass is in. By Eq. 13.2,

$$T = \frac{1}{f} = \frac{1}{0.20 \text{ Hz}} = 5.0 \text{ s}$$

In $t = 3.1$ s, the mass has gone through 3.1 s/5.0 s $= 0.62$, or 62%, of a period or cycle, so it is moving downward. [The motion is up $\left(\frac{1}{4}\text{cycle}\right)$ and back $\left(\frac{1}{4}\text{ cycle}\right)$ to $y_o = 0$ in $\frac{1}{2}$, or 50%, of the cycle, and therefore downward during the next $\frac{1}{4}$ cycle].

(b) The number of oscillations (cycles) is equal to the product of the frequency (cycles/s) and the elapsed time (s), both of which are given:

$$n = ft = (0.20 \text{ cycles/s})(12 \text{ s}) = 2.4 \text{ cycles}$$

or with $f = 1/T$,

$$n = \frac{t}{T} = \frac{12 \text{ s}}{5.0 \text{ s}} = 2.4 \text{ cycles}$$

(Note that *cycle* is not a unit and is used only for convenience.)

Thus, the mass has gone through two complete cycles and 0.4 of another, which means that it is on its way back to $y_o = 0$ from its amplitude position of $+A$. (Why?)

Follow-Up Exercise. Find what is asked for in this Example at times (1) $t = 4.5$ s and (2) $t = 7.5$ s.

Problem-Solving Hint

Note that in the calculation in part (a) of Example 13.3, where we have sin 3.9, the angle is in radians, *not* degrees. Don't forget to set your calculator to radians (rather than degrees) when finding the value of a trigonometric function in equations for simple harmonic or circular motion.

Example 13.4 ■ Fun with a Pendulum: Frequency and Period

A helpful older brother takes his sister to play on the swings in the park. He pushes her from behind on each return. Assuming that the swing behaves as a simple pendulum with a length of 2.50 m, (a) what would be the frequency of the oscillations, and (b) what would be the interval between the brother's pushes?

Thinking It Through. (a) The period is given by Eq. 13.14, and the frequency and period are inversely related: $f = 1/T$. (b) Since the brother pushes from one side on each return, he must push once every cycle that is completed, so the time between his pushes is equal to the swing's period.

Solution.

Given: $L = 2.50 \text{ m}$ Find: (a) f (frequency)
                                            (b) T (period)

(a) We can take the reciprocal of Eq. 13.14 to solve directly for the frequency:

$$f = \frac{1}{T} = \frac{1}{2\pi}\sqrt{\frac{g}{L}} = \frac{1}{2\pi}\sqrt{\frac{9.80 \text{ m/s}^2}{2.50 \text{ m}}} = 0.315 \text{ Hz}$$

(b) The period is then found from the frequency:

$$T = \frac{1}{f} = \frac{1}{0.315 \text{ Hz}} = 3.17 \text{ s}$$

The brother must push every 3.17 s to maintain a steady swing (and to keep his sister from complaining).

Follow-Up Exercise. In this Example, the older brother, a physics buff, carefully measures the period of the swing to be 3.18 s, not 3.17 s. If the length of 2.50 m is accurate, what is the acceleration due to gravity at the location of the park? Considering this accurate value of g, do you think the park is at sea level?

Initial Conditions and Phase

You may be wondering how to decide whether to use a sine or cosine function to describe a particular case of simple harmonic motion. In general, the form of the function is determined by the initial displacement and velocity of the object: the *initial conditions* of the system. These initial conditions are the values of the displacement and velocity at $t = 0$; taken together, they tell how the system is initially set into motion.

Let's look at four special cases. If an object in vertical SHM has an initial displacement of $y = 0$ at $t = 0$ and moves initially upward, the equation of motion is $y = A \sin \omega t$ (▾Fig. 13.6a). Note that $y = A \cos \omega t$ does not satisfy the initial condition, because $y_o = A \cos \omega t = A \cos \omega(0) = A$, since $\cos 0 = 1$.

Suppose that the object is initially released ($t = 0$) from its positive amplitude position ($+A$), as in the case of the object on a spring shown in Fig. 13.5. Here, the equation of motion is $y = A \cos \omega t$ (Fig. 13.6b). This expression satisfies the initial condition: $y_o = A \cos \omega(0) = A$.

The other two cases are (1) $y = 0$ at $t = 0$, with motion initially downward (for an object on a spring) or in the negative direction (for horizontal SHM), and (2) $y = -A$ at $t = 0$, meaning that the object is initially at its negative-amplitude position. These motions are described by $y = -A \sin \omega t$ and $y = -A \cos \omega t$, respectively, as illustrated in Figs. 13.6c and d.

Only these four initial conditions will be considered in our study. Should y_o have a value other than 0 or $\pm A$, the equation of motion is somewhat complicated. Note in Fig. 13.6 that if the curves are extended in the negative direction of the horizontal axis (dashed purple lines), they all have the same shape, but have been "shifted," so to speak. In (a) and (b), one curve is ahead of the other by 90°, or $\frac{1}{4}$ cycle. That is, the two curves are shifted by a quarter cycle with respect to one another. The oscillations are then said to have a *phase difference* of 90°. In (a) and (c), the curves are shifted 180° and are 180° out of phase. (Note in this case that the oscillations are opposite: When one mass is going up, the other is going down.) What about the oscillations in (a) and (d)?

Note: Initial conditions include both the displacement y_o and velocity v_o at $t = 0$.

▶ **FIGURE 13.6 Initial conditions and equations of motion** The initial conditions (y_o and t_o) determine the form of the equation of motion—for the cases shown here, either a sine or a cosine. For $t_o = 0$, the initial displacements are **(a)** $y_o = 0$, **(b)** $y_o = +A$, **(c)** $y_o = 0$, and **(d)** $y_o = -A$. The equations of motion must match the initial conditions. (See text for description.)

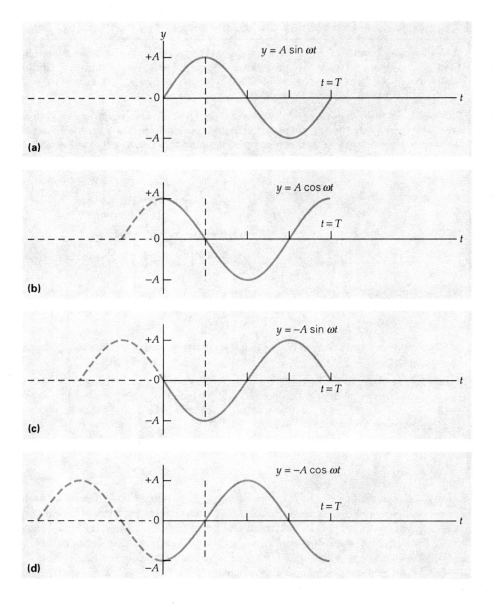

A figure with a 360° (or 0°) phase shift is not shown, because this would be the same as that in (a). When two objects in SHM have the same equation of motion, they are said to be oscillating *in phase*, which means that they are oscillating together with identical motions. Objects with a 180° phase shift or difference are said to be *completely out of phase* and will always be going in opposite directions and be at opposite amplitudes at the same time.

Velocity and Acceleration in SHM

Expressions for the velocity and acceleration of an object in SHM can also be obtained. Using calculus, one can show that $v = \Delta y/\Delta t = \Delta(A \sin \omega t)/\Delta t$ in the limit as Δt goes to zero gives the following expression for the instantaneous velocity:

Note: Maximum speed $v = \omega A$.

$$v = \omega A \cos \omega t \qquad \begin{array}{l}\textit{(vertical velocity if } v_o \textit{ is upward} \\ t_o = 0, y_o = 0)\end{array} \qquad (13.15)$$

Here, the signs indicating direction are given by the cosine function.

The acceleration can be found by using Newton's second law with the spring force $F_s = -ky$:

$$a = \frac{F_s}{m} = \frac{-ky}{m} = -\frac{k}{m} A \sin \omega t$$

Since $\omega = \sqrt{k/m}$,

$$a = -\omega^2 A \sin \omega t = -\omega^2 y \quad \begin{array}{l}\textit{(vertical acceleration if } v_o \textit{ is}\\ \textit{upward at } t_o = 0, y_o = 0)\end{array} \quad (13.16)$$

Note: Maximum acceleration magnitude $a = \omega^2 A$.

Note that the functions for the velocity and acceleration are out of phase with that for the displacement. Since the velocity is 90° out of phase with the displacement, the speed is greatest when $\cos \omega t = \pm 1$ at $y = 0$, that is, when the oscillating object is passing through its equilibrium position. The acceleration is 180° out of phase with the displacement (as indicated by the minus sign on the right-hand side of Eq. 13.16). Therefore, the magnitude of the acceleration is a maximum when $\sin \omega t = \pm 1$ at $y = \pm A$, that is, when the displacement is a maximum, or when the object is at an amplitude position. At any position except the equilibrium position, the directional sign of the acceleration is opposite that of the displacement, as it should be for an acceleration resulting from a restoring force. At the equilibrium position, both the displacement and acceleration are zero. (Can you see why?)

Note also that the acceleration in SHM is not constant with time. Hence, the kinematic equations for acceleration (Chapter 2) *cannot* be used, since they describe constant acceleration.

Damped Harmonic Motion

Simple harmonic motion with constant amplitude implies that there are no losses of energy, but in practical applications there are always some frictional losses. Therefore, to maintain a constant amplitude motion, energy must be added to a system by some external driving force, such as someone pushing a swing. Without a driving force, the amplitude and the energy of an oscillator decrease with time, giving rise to **damped harmonic motion** (▼Fig. 13.7a). The time required for the

▼ **FIGURE 13.7 Damped harmonic motion (a)** When a driving force adds energy to a system in an amount equal to the energy losses of the system, the oscillation is steady with a constant amplitude. When the driving force is removed, the oscillations decay (that is, they are damped), and the amplitude decreases nonlinearly with time. **(b)** In some applications, damping is desirable and even promoted, as with shock absorbers in automobile suspension systems. Otherwise, the passengers would be in for a bouncy ride.

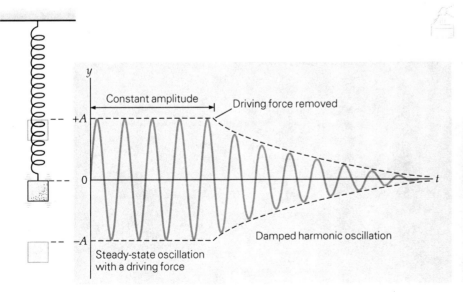

(a)

(b)

PHYSLET®

Illustration 16.4 Forced and Damped Motion

oscillations to cease, or damp out, depends on the magnitude and type of the damping force (such as air resistance).

In many applications involving continuous periodic motion, damping is unwanted and necessitates an energy input. However, in some instances, damping is desirable. For example, the dial in a spring-operated bathroom scale oscillates briefly before stopping at a weight reading. If not properly damped, these oscillations would continue for some time, and you would have to wait before you could read your weight. Shock absorbers provide damping in the suspension systems of automobiles (Fig. 13.7b; also see Fig. 9.9b). Without "shocks" to dissipate energy after hitting a bump, the ride would be bouncy. In California, many new buildings incorporate damping mechanisms (giant shock absorbers) to dampen their oscillatory motion after they are set in motion by earthquake waves.

PHYSLET®

Illustration 18.1 Representation of Two-Dimensional Waves

13.3 Wave Motion

OBJECTIVES: To (a) describe wave motion in terms of various parameters, and (b) identify different types of waves.

The world is full of waves of various types; some examples are water waves, sound waves, waves generated by earthquakes, and light waves. All waves result from a disturbance, the source of the wave. In this chapter, we will be concerned with mechanical waves—those that are propagated in some medium. (Light waves, which do not require a propagating medium, will be considered in more detail in later chapters.)

When a medium is disturbed, energy is imparted to it. Suppose that energy is added to a material mechanically, such as by impact or (in the case of a gas) by compression. The addition of the energy sets some of the particles in the medium vibrating. Because the particles are linked by intermolecular forces, the oscillation of each particle affects that of its neighbors. The added energy propagates, or spreads, by means of interactions among the particles of the medium. An analogy to this process is shown in ◄Fig. 13.8, where the "particles" are dominoes. As each domino falls, it topples the one next to it. Thus, energy is transferred from domino to domino, and the disturbance propagates through the medium—the energy travels, not the medium.

In this case, there is no restoring force between the dominoes, so they do not oscillate, as do particles in a continuous material medium. Therefore, the disturbance moves in space, but it does not repeat itself in time at any one location.

Similarly, if the end of a stretched rope is given a quick shake, the disturbance transfers energy from the hand to the rope, as illustrated in ▼Fig. 13.9. The forces acting

▲ FIGURE 13.8 Energy transfer The propagation of a disturbance, or a transfer of energy through space, is seen in a row of falling dominoes.

▶ FIGURE 13.9 Wave pulse The hand disturbs the stretched rope in a quick up-and-down motion, and a wave pulse propagates along the rope. (The red arrows represent the velocities of the hand and of pieces of the rope at different times and locations.) The rope "particles" move up and down as the pulse passes. The energy in the pulse is thus *both* kinetic (elastic) and potential (gravitational).

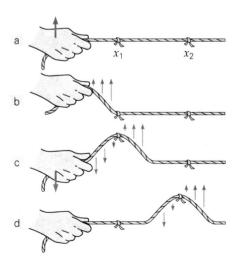

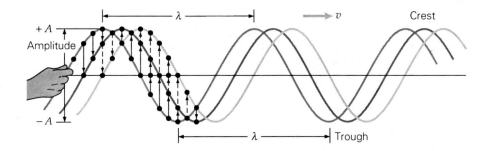

continuous harmonic disturbance can set up a sinusoidal wave in a stretched rope, and the wave travels down the rope with wave speed v. Note that the "particles" in the rope oscillate vertically in simple harmonic motion. The distance between two successive points that are in phase (for example, at two crests) on the waveform is the wavelength λ of the wave. Can you tell how much time has elapsed, as a fraction of the period T, between the first (red) and last (blue) waves?

between the "particles" in the rope cause them to move in response to the motion of the hand, and a *wave pulse* travels down the rope. Each "particle" goes up and then back down as the pulse passes by. This motion of individual particles and the propagation of the wave pulse as a whole can be observed by tying pieces of ribbon onto the rope (at x_1 and x_2 in the figure). As the disturbance passes point x_1, the ribbon rises and falls, as do the rope's "particles." Later, the same happens to the ribbon at x_2, which indicates that the energy disturbance is propagating, or traveling, along the rope.

In a continuous material medium, particles interact with their neighbors, and restoring forces cause them to oscillate when they are disturbed. Thus, a disturbance not only propagates through space, but may be repeated over and over in time at each position. Such a regular, rhythmic disturbance in both time and space is called a **wave**, and the transfer of energy is said to take place by means of **wave motion**.

A continuous wave motion, or *periodic wave*, requires a disturbance from an oscillating source (▲Fig. 13.10). In this case, the particles move up and down continuously. If the driving source is such that a constant amplitude is maintained (the source oscillates in simple harmonic motion), the resulting particle motion is also simple harmonic.

Such periodic wave motion will have sinusoidal forms (sine or cosine) in both time and space. Being *sinusoidal in space* means that if you took a photograph of the wave at any instant ("freezing" it in time), you would see a sinusoidal waveform (such as one of the curves in Fig. 13.10). However, if you looked at a single point in space as a wave passed by, you would see a particle of the medium oscillating up and down *sinusoidally with time,* like the mass on a spring discussed in Section 13.2. (For example, imagine looking through a thin slit at a fixed location on the moving paper in Fig. 13.5. The wave trace would be seen rising and falling like a particle.)

Note: A wave is a combination of oscillations in space and time.

Wave Characteristics

Specific quantities are used to describe sinusoidal waves. As with a particle in simple harmonic motion, the **amplitude (A)** of a wave is the magnitude of the maximum displacement, or the maximum distance, from the particle's equilibrium position (Fig. 13.10). This quantity corresponds to the height of a wave crest or the depth of a trough. Recall from Section 13.2 that, in SHM, the total energy of the oscillator is proportional to the square of the amplitude. Similarly, the energy *transported* by a wave is proportional to the square of its amplitude ($E \propto A^2$). Note the difference, though: A wave is one way of *transmitting* energy through space, whereas an oscillator's energy is localized in space.

For a periodic wave, the distance between two successive crests (or troughs) is called the **wavelength (λ)** (Fig. 13.10). Actually, it is the distance between any two successive parts of the wave that are in phase (that is, that are at identical points on the waveform). The crest and trough positions are usually used for convenience. Note that a wavelength corresponds spatially to one cycle. Keep in mind that the wave, not the medium or material, is traveling.

The **frequency (f)** of a periodic wave is the number of cycles per second— that is, the number of complete waveforms, or wavelengths, that pass by a given point during each second. The frequency of the wave is the same as the frequency of the SHM source that created it.

Illustration 17.2 Wave Functions

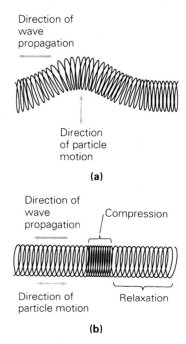

Direction of wave propagation

Direction of particle motion

(a)

Direction of wave propagation

Compression

Direction of particle motion

Relaxation

(b)

▲ **FIGURE 13.11 Transverse and longitudinal waves** (Wave pulses shown here for simplicity) **(a)** In a transverse wave, the motion of the particles is perpendicular to the direction of the wave velocity, as shown here in a spring for a wave moving to the left. A transverse wave is sometimes called a *shear wave*, because it supplies a force that tends to shear the medium. Transverse shear waves can propagate only in solids. (Why?) **(b)** In a longitudinal wave, the particle motion is parallel to (or *along*) the direction of the wave velocity. Here, a wave pulse also moves to the left. A longitudinal wave is sometimes called a *compressional wave*, because the force tends to compress the medium. Longitudinal compressional waves can propagate in all media—solid, liquid, and gas. Can you explain the motion of the wave *source* for both types of waves?

A periodic wave is said to possess a **period (T)**. The period $T = 1/f$ is the time for one complete waveform (a wavelength) to pass by a given point. Since a wave moves, it also has a **wave speed (v)** (or velocity if the wave's direction is specified). Any particular point on the wave (such as a crest) travels a distance of one wavelength λ in a time of one period T. Then, since $v = d/t$ and $f = 1/T$, we have

$$v = \frac{\lambda}{T} = \lambda f \quad \textit{wave speed} \tag{13.17}$$

Note that the dimensions of v are correct (length/time). In general, the wave speed depends on the nature of the medium, in addition to the source frequency f.

Example 13.5 ■ Dock of the Bay: Finding Wave Speed

A person on a pier observes a set of incoming waves that have a sinusoidal form with a distance of 1.6 m between the crests. If a wave laps against the pier every 4.0 s, what are (a) the frequency and (b) the speed of the waves?

Thinking It Through. Knowing the period and wavelength, the definition of frequency and Eq. 13.17 for wave speed can be used.

Solution. The distance between crests is the wavelength, so we have the following information:

Given: $\lambda = 1.6$ m   *Find:*   (a) f (frequency)
         $T = 4.0$ s   (b) v (wave speed)

(a) The lapping indicates the arrival of a wave crest; hence, 4.0 s is the wave period—the time it takes to travel one wavelength (the crest-to-crest distance). Then

$$f = \frac{1}{T} = \frac{1}{4.0 \text{ s}} = 0.25 \text{ s}^{-1} = 0.25 \text{ Hz}$$

(b) The frequency or the period can be used in Eq. 13.17 to find the wave speed:

$$v = \lambda f = (1.6 \text{ m})(0.25 \text{ s}^{-1}) = 0.40 \text{ m/s}$$

Alternatively,

$$v = \frac{\lambda}{T} = \frac{1.6 \text{ m}}{4.0 \text{ s}} = 0.40 \text{ m/s}$$

Follow-Up Exercise. On another day, the person measures the speed of sinusoidal water waves at 0.25 m/s. (a) How far does a wave crest travel in 2.0 s? (b) If the distance between successive crests is 2.5 m, what is the frequency of these waves?

Types of Waves

In general, waves may be divided into two types, based on the direction of the particles' oscillations relative to that of the wave velocity. In a **transverse wave**, the particle motion is perpendicular to the direction of the wave velocity. The wave produced in a stretched string (Fig. 13.10) is an example of a transverse wave, as is the wave shown in ◄Fig. 13.11a. A transverse wave is sometimes called a *shear wave*, because the disturbance supplies a force that tends to shear the medium—to separate layers of that medium at a right angle to the direction of the wave velocity. Shear waves can propagate only in solids, since a liquid or a gas cannot support a shear. That is, a liquid or a gas does not have sufficient restoring forces between its particles to propagate a transverse wave.

In a **longitudinal wave**, the particle oscillation is parallel to the direction of the wave velocity. A longitudinal wave can be produced in a stretched spring by moving the coils back and forth along the spring axis (Fig. 13.11b). Alternating pulses of compression and relaxation travel along the spring. A longitudinal wave is sometimes called a *compressional wave*.

Sound waves in air are another example of longitudinal waves. A periodic disturbance produces compressions in the air. Between the compressions are *rarefactions*—regions where the density of the air is reduced, or rarefied. A loudspeaker oscillating

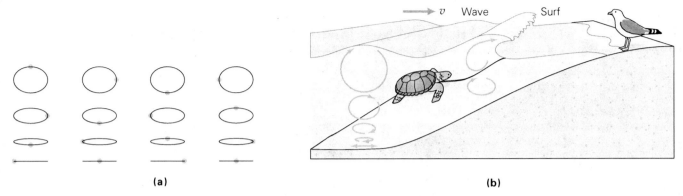

▲ **FIGURE 13.12 Water waves** Water waves are a combination of longitudinal and transverse motions. **(a)** At the surface, the water particles move in circles, but their motions become more longitudinal with depth. **(b)** When a wave approaches the shore, the lower particles are forced into steeper paths until, finally, the wave breaks or falls over to form surf.

back and forth, for example, can create these compressions and rarefactions, which travel out into the air as sound waves. (Sound is discussed in detail in Chapter 14.)

Longitudinal waves can propagate in solids, liquids, and gases, because all phases of matter can be compressed to some extent. The propagations of transverse and longitudinal waves in different media give information about the Earth's interior structure, as discussed in Insight 13.1 on Earthquakes, Seismic Waves, and Seismology, page 450.

The sinusoidal profile of water waves might make you think that they are transverse waves. Actually, they reflect a combination of longitudinal and transverse motions (▲Fig. 13.12). The particle motion may be nearly circular at the surface and becomes more elliptical with depth, eventually longitudinal. A hundred meters or so below the surface of a large body of water, the wave disturbances have little effect. For example, a submarine at these depths is undisturbed by large waves on the ocean's surface. As a wave approaches shallower water near shore, the water particles have difficulty completing their elliptical paths. When the water becomes too shallow, the particles can no longer move through the bottom parts of their paths, and the wave breaks. Its crest falls forward to form breaking surf as the waves' kinetic energy is transformed into potential energy—a water "hill" that eventually topples over.

PHYSLET

Illustration 17.1 Wave Types

INSIGHT 13.1 EARTHQUAKES, SEISMIC WAVES, AND SEISMOLOGY

The structure of the Earth's interior is something of a mystery. The deepest mine shafts and drillings extend only a few kilometers into the Earth, compared with a depth of about 6400 km to the Earth's center. Using waves to probe the Earth's structure is one way to investigate it further. Waves generated by earthquakes have proved to be especially useful for this purpose. Seismology is the study of these waves, called *seismic waves*.

Earthquakes are caused by the sudden release of built-up stress along cracks and faults, such as the famous San Andreas Fault in California (Fig. 1). According to the geological theory of plate tectonics, the outer layer of the Earth consists of rigid plates—huge slabs of rock that move very slowly relative to one another. Stresses continuously build up, particularly along boundaries between plates.

When slippage of plates finally occurs, the energy from this stress-relieving event propagates outward as (seismic) waves from a site below the surface called the *focus*. The point on the Earth's surface directly above the focus is called the *epicenter*, and receives the greatest impact of a quake. Seismic waves are of two general types: surface waves and body waves. *Surface waves*, which move along the Earth's surface, account for most earthquake damage (Fig. 2). *Body waves* travel through the Earth and are both longitudinal and transverse waves. The compressional (longitudinal) waves are called *P waves*, and the shear (transverse) waves are called *S waves* (Fig. 3).

P and S stand for *primary* and *secondary* and indicate the waves' relative speeds (actually, their arrival times at monitoring stations). In general, primary waves travel through materials faster than do secondary waves and are detected first. An earthquake's rating on the Richter scale is related to the energy released in the form of seismic waves.

Seismic stations around the world monitor P and S waves with sensitive detecting instruments called *seismographs*. From the data gathered, we can map the paths of the waves through the Earth and thereby learn about the structure of the interior of our planet. The Earth's interior seems to be divided into three general regions: the crust, the mantle, and the core, which itself has a solid inner region and a liquid outer region.*

The locations of these regions' boundaries are determined in part by *shadow zones*, regions where no waves of a particular type are detected. These zones appear because, although longitudinal

*In most places, the crust is about 24–30 km (15–20 mi) thick; the mantle is 2900 km (1800 mi) thick; and the core has a radius of 3450 km (2150 mi). The solid inner core has a radius of about 1200 km (750 mi).

FIGURE 2 Bad vibrations Earthquake damage caused by the surface waves of a major shock that struck Kobe, Japan, in January 1995.

waves can travel through solids *or* liquids, transverse waves can travel only through solids. When an earthquake occurs, P waves are detected on the side of the Earth opposite the focus, but S waves are not. (See Fig. 3.) The absence of S waves in a shadow zone leads to the conclusion that the Earth must have a region near its center that is in the liquid phase.

When the transmitted P waves enter and leave the liquid region, they are refracted (bent). This refraction gives rise to a P-wave shadow zone, which indicates that only the outer part of the core is liquid. As you will learn in Chapter 19, the combination of a liquid outer core and the Earth's rotation may be responsible for the Earth's magnetic field.

FIGURE 1 The San Andreas Fault A small section of the fault, which runs through the San Francisco Bay area as well as across the more rural regions of California, is shown here.

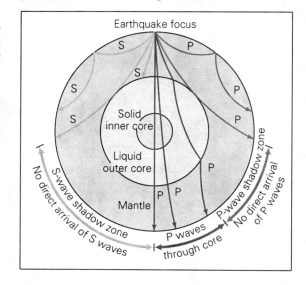

FIGURE 3 Compressional and shear waves Earthquakes produce waves that travel through the Earth. Because transverse (S) waves are not detected on the opposite side of the Earth, scientists believe that at least part of the Earth's core is a viscous liquid under high pressures and temperatures. The waves bend continuously, or refract, because their speed varies with depth.

14

SOUND

PHYSICS FACTS

- Sound is (a) the physical propagation of a disturbance (energy) in a medium, and (b) the physiological and psychological response generally to pressure waves in air. (For example, see the discussion of a tree falling in the forest in the chapter introduction.)

- Humans cannot hear sounds with frequencies below 20 Hz—infrasound. Both elephants and rhinoceroses communicate by infrasound. Infrasound is produced by avalanches, meteors, tornadoes, earthquakes, and ocean waves. Some migratory birds are able to hear infrasounds produced when ocean waves break, which allows them to orient themselves with the coastline.

- The normal audible frequency range of human hearing is between 20 Hz and 20 kHz.

- The visible part of the outer ear is called the *pinna* or ear flap. Many animals move the ear flap in order to focus their hearing in a certain direction. Humans cannot do so.

- Ultrasound (frequency > 20 kHz) is used to make fetal images—"baby's first picture."

- Loud noise exposure—for example, from rock bands—is a common cause of tinnitus, or ringing in the ears.

Good vibrations, clearly! We owe a lot to sound waves. Not only do they provide us with one of our main sources of enjoyment in the form of music, but they also bring us a wealth of vital information about our environment, from the chime of a doorbell to the warning shrill of a police siren to the song of a mockingbird. Indeed, sound waves are the basis for our major form of communication: speech. These waves can also constitute a highly irritating distraction (noise). But sound waves become music, speech, or noise only when our ears perceive them. Physically, sound is simply waves that propagate in solids, liquids, and gases. Without a medium, there can be no sound; in a vacuum such as outer space, there is utter silence.

This distinction between the sensory and physical meanings of sound gives you a way to answer the old philosophical question: If a tree falls in the forest where there is no one to hear it, does it make a sound? The answer depends on how sound is defined—it is no if we are thinking in terms of sensory hearing, but yes if we are considering only the physical waves. Since sound waves are all around us most of the time, we are exposed to many interesting sound phenomena. You'll explore some of the most important of these in this chapter.

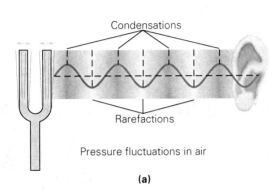

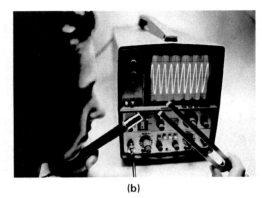

(a) **(b)**

PHYSLET

Illustration 18.2 *Molecular View of a Sound Wave*

▲ **FIGURE 14.1** **Vibrations make waves** **(a)** A vibrating tuning fork disturbs the air, producing alternating high-pressure regions (condensations) and low-pressure regions (rarefactions), which form sound waves. **(b)** After being picked up by a microphone, the pressure variations are converted to electrical signals. When these signals are displayed on an oscilloscope, the sinusoidal waveform is evident.

14.1 Sound Waves

OBJECTIVES: To (a) define sound, and (b) explain the sound frequency spectrum.

For sound waves to exist there must be a disturbance or vibrations in some medium. This disturbance may be the clapping of hands or the skidding of tires as a car comes to a sudden stop. Under water, you can hear the click of rocks against one another. If you put your ear to a thin wall, you can hear sounds from the other side of the wall. **Sound waves** in gases and liquids (both are fluids) are primarily longitudinal waves. However, sound disturbances moving through solids can have both longitudinal and transverse components. The intermolecular interactions in solids are much stronger than in fluids and allow transverse components to propagate.

The characteristics of sound waves can be visualized by considering those produced by a tuning fork, essentially a metal bar bent into a U shape (▲ Fig. 14.1). The prongs, or tines, vibrate when struck. The fork vibrates at its fundamental frequency (with an antinode at the end of each tine), so a single tone is heard. (A *tone* is sound with a definite frequency.) The vibrations disturb the air, producing alternating high-pressure regions called *condensations* and low-pressure regions called *rarefactions*. Assuming the fork steadily vibrates, the disturbances propagate outward, and a series of them can be described by a sinusoidal wave.

When the disturbances traveling through the air reach the ear, the eardrum (a thin membrane) is set into vibration by the pressure variations. On the other side of the eardrum, tiny bones (the hammer, anvil, and stirrup) carry the vibrations to the inner ear, where they are picked up by the auditory nerve. (See Insight 14.2 on the ear on page 475.)

Characteristics of the ear limit the perception of sound. Only sound waves with frequencies between about 20 Hz and 20 kHz (kilohertz) initiate nerve impulses that are interpreted by the human brain as sound. This frequency range is called the **audible region** of the **sound frequency spectrum** (◀Fig. 14.2). Hearing is most acute in the 1000–10000 Hz range, with speech mainly in the 1000–4000 Hz range.

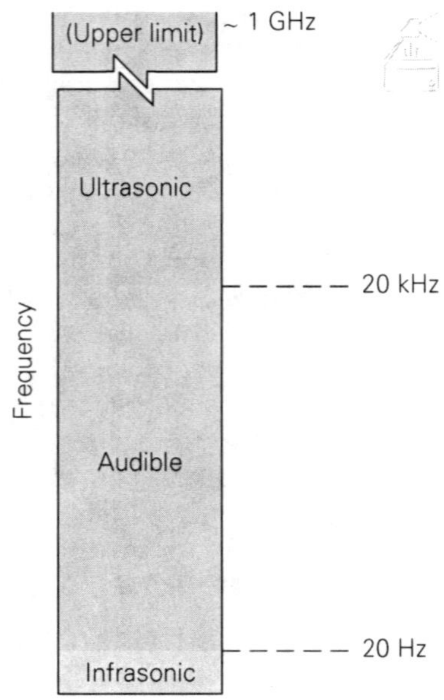

▲ **FIGURE 14.2** **Sound frequency spectrum** The audible region of sound for humans lies between about 20 Hz and 20 kHz. Below this is the infrasonic region, and above it is the ultrasonic region. The upper limit is about 1 GHz, because of the elastic limitations of materials.

Infrasound

Frequencies lower than 20 Hz are in the **infrasonic region**. Waves in this region, which humans are unable to hear, are found in nature. Longitudinal waves generated by earthquakes have infrasonic frequencies, and these waves are used to study the Earth's interior (see Insight 13.1, p. 450). Infrasonic waves, or *infrasound*, are also generated by wind and weather patterns. Elephants and cattle have hearing responses in the infrasonic region and may even give early warnings of earthquakes and weather disturbances, such as tornadoes. (Elephants can detect sounds with frequencies as low as 1 Hz, but the pigeon takes the infrasound hearing prize, being able to detect sound frequencies as low as 0.1 Hz.) It has been found that the vortex of a tornado produces infrasound. Also, the frequency changes, with low frequencies when the vortex is small and higher frequencies when the vortex is large. Infrasound can be detected miles away from a tornado, and so may be a method for gaining increased warning times for tornado approaches.

There are infrasound listening stations. Nuclear explosions produce infrasound, and after the Nuclear Test Ban Treaty of 1963, infrasound listening stations were set up to detect possible violations. Now these stations can be used to detect other sources such as earthquakes and tornadoes.

Ultrasound

Above 20 kHz is the **ultrasonic region**. Ultrasonic waves can be generated by high-frequency vibrations in crystals. Ultrasonic waves, or *ultrasound*, cannot be detected by humans, but can be by other animals. The audible region for dogs extends to about 40 kHz, so ultrasonic or "silent" whistles can be used to call dogs without disturbing people. Cats and bats have even higher audible ranges, up to about 70 kHz and 100 kHz, respectively.

There are many practical applications of ultrasound. Since ultrasound can travel for kilometers in water, it is used in sonar to detect underwater objects and their ranges, much like radar uses radio waves. Sound pulses generated by the sonar apparatus are reflected by underwater objects, and the resulting echoes are picked up by a detector. The time required for a sound pulse to make one round trip, together with the speed of sound in water, gives the distance or range of the object. Sonar also is widely used by fishermen to detect schools of fish, and in a similar manner, ultrasound is used in autofocus cameras. Distance measurement allows focal adjustments to be made.

There are applications of ultrasonic sonar in nature. Sonar appeared in the animal kingdom long before it was developed by human engineers. On their nocturnal hunting flights, bats use a kind of natural sonar to navigate in and out of their caves and to locate and catch flying insects (▼Fig. 14.3a). The bats emit pulses of ultrasound and track their prey by means of the reflected echoes. The technique is known as *echolocation*. The auditory system and data-processing capabilities of bats are truly amazing. (Note the size of the bat's ears in Fig. 14.3b.)

On the basis of the intensity of the echo, a bat can tell how big an insect is—the smaller the insect, the less intense is the echo. The direction of motion of an insect is sensed by the frequency of the echo. If an insect is moving away from the bat, the returning echo will have a lower frequency. If the insect is moving toward the bat, the

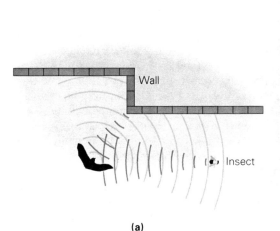

(a)

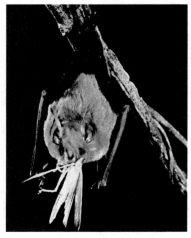

(b)

◀ **FIGURE 14.3** Echolocation **(a)** With the aid of their own natural sonar systems, bats hunt flying insects. The bats emit pulses of ultrasonic waves, which lie within their audible region, and use the echoes reflected from their prey to guide their attack. **(b)** Note the size of the ears—good for ultrasonic hearing. Do you know why bats roost hanging upside down? See text for answer.

INSIGHT 14.1 ULTRASOUND IN MEDICINE

Probably the best known applications of ultrasound are in medicine. For instance, ultrasound is used to obtain an image of a fetus, avoiding potentially dangerous X-rays. Ultrasonic generators (transducers) made of piezoelectric materials produce high-frequency pulses that are used to scan the designated region of the body.* When the pulses encounter a boundary between two tissues that have different densities, the pulses are reflected. These reflections are monitored by a receiving transducer, and a computer constructs an image from the reflected signals. Images of the fetus are recorded several times each second as the transducer is scanned across the mother's abdomen. A still shot or "echogram" of a fetus is shown in Fig. 1. A developing fetus,

*When an electric field is applied to a piezoelectric material, it undergoes mechanical distortion. Periodic applications allow the generation of ultrasonic waves. Conversely, when the material experiences mechanical pressure, an electric voltage develops. This allows the detection of ultrasonic waves.

which is surrounded by a sac containing the amniotic fluid, can be distinguished from other anatomical features, and the position, size, sex, and possible abnormalities may be detected.

Ultrasound can be used to assess stroke risk. Plaque deposits may accumulated on the inner walls of blood vessels and restrict blood flow. One of the major causes of stroke is the obstruction of the carotid artery in the neck, which directly affects the blood supply to the brain. The presence and severity of such obstructions may be detected by using ultrasound (Fig. 2). An ultrasonic generator is placed on the neck, and the reflections from blood cells moving through the artery are monitored to determine the rate of blood flow, thereby providing an indication of the severity of any blockage. This procedure involves shifting the frequency of the reflected waves, as described by the *Doppler effect*. (There will be more on this effect in Section 14.5, along with more on Doppler "flow meters.")

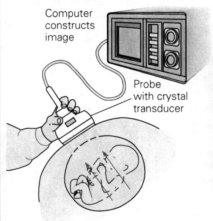

Computer constructs image

Probe with crystal transducer

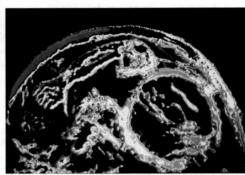

FIGURE 1 Ultrasound in use
Ultrasound generated by transducers, which convert electrical oscillations into mechanical vibrations and vice versa, is transmitted through tissue and is reflected from internal structures. The reflected waves are detected by the transducers, and the signals are used to construct an image, or echogram, shown here for a well-developed fetus.

echo will have a higher frequency. The change in frequency is known as the *Doppler effect*, which is presented in more detail in Section 14.5. Dolphins also use ultrasonic sonar to locate objects. This is very efficient since sound travels almost five times as fast in water as in air.

The bat, the only mammal to have evolved true flight, is a much maligned and feared creature. However, because they feed on tons of insects yearly, bats save the environment from a lot of insecticides. "Blind as a bat" is a common expression, yet bats have fairly good vision, which complements their use of echolocation. Finally, do you know why bats roost and hang upside down (Fig. 14.3b)? That is their take-off position. Unlike birds, bats can't launch themselves from the ground. Their wings don't produce enough lift to allow takeoff directly from the ground, and their legs are so small and underdeveloped that they can't run to build up takeoff speed. So they use their claws to hang, and fall into flight when they are ready to fly.

Ultrasound is used to clean teeth with ultrasonic toothbrushes. In industrial and home applications, ultrasonic baths are used to clean metal machine parts, dentures, and jewelry. The high-frequency (short-wavelength) ultrasound vibrations loosen particles in otherwise inaccessible places. Perhaps the best known medical application of ultrasound is to view a fetus without exposing it to harmful X-rays. (See Insight 14.1 on Ultrasound in Medicine.) Also, ultrasound is used to diagnosis gallstones and kidney stones, and can be used to break these up by a technique called *lithotripsy* (Greek, "stone breaking").

Science Fundamentals

Another widely used ultrasonic device is the ultrasonic scalpel, which uses ultrasonic energy for both precise cutting and coagulation. Vibrating at about 55 kHz, the scalpel makes small incisions, at the same time causing a protein clot to form that seals blood vessels—"bloodless" surgery, so to speak. The ultrasonic scalpel has been used in gynecological procedures such as the removal of fibroid tumors, in tonsillectomies, and many other types of surgical procedures.[†]

In cases of uncontrolled bleeding, such as blunt trauma resulting from a car accident or severe wounds received in com-

[†]One of the most remarkable and complicated inventions of nature is the blood clot. It can be life-saving–when it magically forms and stops a site of bleeding, or it can be life-threatening–when it blocks an artery in the heart or the brain.

bat, rapid hemostasis (termination of bleeding) is essential. Solutions being investigated and developed include the use of diagnostic ultrasound to detect the site of bleeding and high-intensity focused ultrasound (HIFU) to induce hemostasis by ultrasonic cauterization. In China, ultrasound-guided HIFU has been used successfully for several years and is becoming the treatment of choice for many forms of cancer.

Note: Adapted from the plenary lecture given by Dr. Lawrence A. Crum at the 18th International Congress on Acoustics in Kyoto, Japan, in the summer of 2004. Professor Crum is at the Applied Physics Laboratory at the University of Washington in Seattle, Washington.

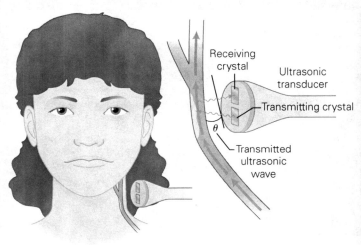
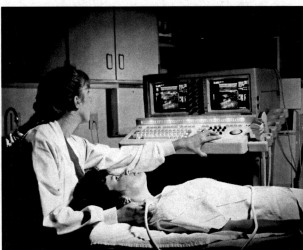

FIGURE 2 Carotid artery blockage? Ultrasound is used to measure the blood flow through the carotid artery to see if there is a blockage. See text for description.

Ultrasonic frequencies extend into the megahertz (MHz) range, but the sound frequency spectrum does not continue indefinitely. There is an upper limit of about 10^9 Hz, or 1 GHz (gigahertz), which is determined by the upper limit of the elasticity of the materials through which the sound propagates.

14.2 The Speed of Sound

OBJECTIVES: To (a) tell how the speed of sound differs in different media, and (b) describe the temperature dependence of the speed of sound in air.

In general, the speed at which a disturbance moves through a medium depends on the elasticity and density of the medium. For example, as you learned in Chapter 13, the wave speed in a stretched string is given by $v = \sqrt{F_T/\mu}$, where F_T is the tension in the string and μ is the linear mass density of the string.

Similar expressions describe wave speeds in solids and liquids, for which the elasticity is expressed in terms of moduli (Chapter 9). In general, the speed of sound in a solid and in a liquid is given by $v = \sqrt{Y/\rho}$ and $v = \sqrt{B/\rho}$, respectively, where Y is Young's modulus, B is the bulk modulus, and ρ is the density. The speed of sound in a gas is inversely proportional to the square root of the molecular mass, but the equation will not be presented here.

TABLE 14.1

Speed of Sound in Various Media (typical values)

Medium	Speed (m/s)
Solids	
Aluminum	5100
Copper	3500
Iron	4500
Glass	5200
Polystyrene	1850
Zinc	3200
Liquids	
Alcohol, ethyl	1125
Mercury	1400
Water	1500
Gases	
Air (0°C)	331
Air (100°C)	387
Helium (0°C)	965
Hydrogen (0°C)	1284
Oxygen (0°C)	316

Solids are generally more elastic than liquids, which in turn are more elastic than gases. In a highly elastic material, the restoring forces between the atoms or molecules cause a disturbance to propagate faster. Thus, the speed of sound is generally about two to four times as fast in solids as in liquids and about ten to fifteen times as fast in solids as in gases such as air (Table 14.1).

Although not expressed explicitly in the preceding equations, the speed of sound generally depends on the temperature of the medium. In dry air, for example, the speed of sound is 331 m/s (about 740 mi/h) at 0°C. As the temperature increases, so does the speed of sound. For *normal environmental temperatures*, the speed of sound in air increases by about 0.6 m/s for each degree Celsius above 0°C. Thus, a good approximation of the speed of sound in air for a particular (environmental) temperature is given by

$$v = (331 + 0.6T_C) \text{ m/s} \quad \textit{speed of sound in dry air} \quad (14.1)$$

where T_C is the air temperature in degrees Celsius.* Although not written explicitly, the units associated with the factor 0.6 are meters per second per Celsius degree $[\text{m/(s} \cdot \text{C}°)]$.

Let's take a comparative look at the speed of sound in different media.

Example 14.1 ■ Solid, Liquid, Gas: Speed of Sound in Different Media

From their material properties, find the speed of sound in (a) a solid copper rod, (b) liquid water, and (c) air at room temperature (20°C).

Thinking It Through. We know that the speed of sound in a solid or a liquid depends on the elastic modulus and the density of the solid or liquid. These values are available in Tables 9.1 and 9.2. The speed of sound in air is given by Eq. 14.1.

Solution.

Given:
$Y_{Cu} = 11 \times 10^{10} \text{ N/m}^2$
$B_{H_2O} = 2.2 \times 10^9 \text{ N/m}^2$
$\rho_{Cu} = 8.9 \times 10^3 \text{ kg/m}^3$
$\rho_{H_2O} = 1.0 \times 10^3 \text{ kg/m}^3$
(all values from Tables 9.1 and 9.2)
$T_C = 20°C$ (for air)

Find: (a) v_{Cu} (speed in copper)
(b) v_{H_2O} (speed in water)
(c) v_{air} (speed in air)

(a) To find the speed of sound in a copper rod, we use the expression $v = \sqrt{Y/\rho}$:

$$v_{Cu} = \sqrt{\frac{Y}{\rho}} = \sqrt{\frac{11 \times 10^{10} \text{ N/m}^2}{8.9 \times 10^3 \text{ kg/m}^3}} = 3.5 \times 10^3 \text{ m/s}$$

(b) For water, $v = \sqrt{B/\rho}$:

$$v_{H_2O} = \sqrt{\frac{B}{\rho}} = \sqrt{\frac{2.2 \times 10^9 \text{ N/m}^2}{1.0 \times 10^3 \text{ kg/m}^3}} = 1.5 \times 10^3 \text{ m/s}$$

(c) For air at 20°C, by Eq. 14.1, we have

$$v_{air} = (331 + 0.6T_C) \text{ m/s} = [331 + 0.6(20)] \text{ m/s} = 343 \text{ m/s} = 3.43 \times 10^2 \text{ m/s}$$

Follow-Up Exercise. In this Example, how many times faster is the speed of sound in copper (a) than in water and (b) than in air (at room temperature)? Compare your results with the values given at the beginning of the section. (*Answers to all Follow-Up Exercises are at the back of the text.*)

---

*A better approximation of these and higher temperatures is given by the expression

$$v = \left(331\sqrt{1 + \frac{T_C}{273}}\right) \text{ m/s}$$

In Table 14.1, see v for air at 100°C, which is outside the normal environmental temperature range.

A generally useful approximate value for the speed of sound in air is $\frac{1}{3}$ km/s (or $\frac{1}{5}$ mi/s). Using this value, you can, for example, estimate how far away lightning is by counting the number of seconds between the time you observe the flash and the time you hear the associated thunder. Because the speed of light is so fast, you see the lightning flash almost instantaneously. The sound waves of the thunder travel relatively slowly, at about $\frac{1}{3}$ km/s. For example, if the interval between the two events is measured to be 6 s (often by counting "one thousand one, one thousand two, ... "), the lightning stroke was about 2 km away $\left(\frac{1}{3}\text{ km/s} \times 6\text{ s} = 2\text{ km, or } \frac{1}{5}\text{ mi/s} \times 6\text{ s} = 1.2\text{ mi}\right)$.

You may also have noticed the delay in the arrival of sound relative to that of light at a baseball game. If you're sitting in the outfield stands, you see the batter hit the ball before you hear the crack of the bat.

Example 14.2 ■ Good Approximations?

(a) Show how good the approximations of $\frac{1}{3}$km/s and $\frac{1}{5}$mi/s are for the speed of sound. Use room temperature and dry air conditions. (b) Find the percent error of each.

Thinking It Through. Taking the actual speed of sound to be given by Eq. 14.1, and converting $\frac{1}{3}$km/s and $\frac{1}{5}$mi/s to m/s, comparisons can be made.

Solution. Listing what is given, along with the calculation of the speed of sound:

Given: $T_C = 20°C$ (room temperature) **Find:** (a) How approximations compare to
$v = (331 + 0.6T_C)$ m/s   actual value
$= [331 + 0.6(20)]$ m/s $= 343$ m/s (b) Percent errors
$v_{km} = \frac{1}{3}$ km/s
$v_{mi} = \frac{1}{5}$ mi/s

(a) Then, doing the conversions:

$$v_{km} = \tfrac{1}{3}\text{ km/s } (10^3\text{ m/km}) = 333\text{ m/s}$$

$$v_{mi} = \tfrac{1}{5}\text{ mi/s } (1609\text{ m/mi}) = 322\text{ m/s}$$

The approximations are somewhat reasonable, with v_{km} being the better.

(b) The percent error is given by the absolute difference of the values, divided by the accepted value times 100%. So, (where units cancel)

$v_{km} = \frac{1}{3}$ km/s   % error $= \dfrac{|343 - 333|}{343} \times 100\% = \dfrac{10}{343} \times 100\% = 2.9\%$

$v_{mi} = \frac{1}{5}$ mi/s   % error $= \dfrac{|343 - 322|}{343} \times 100\% = \dfrac{21}{343} \times 100\% = 6.1\%$

so the kilometers per second approximation is considerably better.

Follow-Up Exercise. Suppose the thunderstorm and lightning occurs on a very hot day with a dry-air temperature of 38°C. Would the percent errors in the Example increase or decrease? Justify your answer.

The speed of sound in air depends on various factors. Temperature is the most important, but there are other considerations, such as the homogeneity and composition of the air. For example, the air composition may not be "normal" in a polluted area. These effects are relatively small and will not be considered, except conceptually in the next Example.

Conceptual Example 14.3 ■ Speed of Sound: Sound Traveling Far and Wide

Note that the speed of sound in *dry* air for a given temperature is given to a good approximation by Eq. 14.1. However, the moisture content of the air (humidity) varies, and this variation affects the speed of sound. At the same temperature, would sound travel faster in (a) dry air or (b) moist air?

Reasoning and Answer. According to an old folklore saying, "Sound traveling far and wide, a stormy day will betide." This saying implies that sound travels faster on a highly humid day, when a storm or precipitation is likely. But is the saying true?

Near the beginning of this section, we learned that the speed of sound in a gas is inversely proportional to the square root of the molecular mass of the gas. So at constant pressure, is moist air more or less dense than dry air?

In a volume of moist air, a large number of water (H_2O) molecules occupy the space normally occupied by either nitrogen (N_2) or oxygen (O_2) molecules, which make up 98% of the air. Water molecules are less massive than both nitrogen and oxygen molecules. [From Section 10.3, the molecular (formula) masses are H_2O, 18 g; N_2, 28 g; and O_2, 32 g.] Thus, the average molecular mass of a volume of moist air is less than that of dry air, and the speed of sound is greater in moist air.

We can look at this situation another way: Since water molecules are less massive, they have less inertia and respond to the sound wave faster than nitrogen or oxygen molecules do. The water molecules therefore propagate the disturbance faster.

Follow-Up Exercise. Considering only molecular masses, would you expect the speed of sound to be greatest in nitrogen, oxygen, or helium (at the same temperature and pressure)? Explain.

Note: Humidity was included here as an interesting consideration for the speed of sound in air. However, henceforth, in computing the speed of sound in air at a certain temperature, we will consider only dry air (Eq. 14.1) unless otherwise stated.

Always keep in mind that our discussion generally assumes ideal conditions for the propagation of sound. Actually, the speed of sound depends on many things, one of which is humidity, as the preceding Conceptual Example shows. A variety of other properties affect the propagation of sound. As an example, let's ask the question, "Why do ships' foghorns have such a low pitch or frequency?" The answer is that low-frequency sound waves travel farther than high-frequency ones under identical conditions. This effect is explained by a couple of characteristics of sound waves. First, sound waves are attenuated (that is, they lose energy) because of the viscosity of the air (Section 9.5). Second, sound waves tend to interact with oxygen and water molecules in the air. The combined result of these two properties is that the total attenuation of sound in air depends on the frequency of the sound: the higher the frequency, the more the attenuation and the shorter the distance traveled. It turns out that the attenuation increases as the *square* of the frequency. For example, a 200-Hz sound will travel 16 times as far as an 800-Hz sound to obtain the same attenuation. So, low-frequency foghorns are used. With a shock wave dependence on frequency, you might notice that when a storm's lightning is farther away, the thunder you generally hear is a low-frequency rumble. (See Insight 14.2 for more on the ear and hearing.)

14.3 Sound Intensity and Sound Intensity Level

OBJECTIVES: To (a) define sound intensity and explain how it varies with distance from a point source, and (b) calculate sound intensity levels on the decibel scale.

Wave motion involves the propagation of energy. The rate of energy transfer is expressed in terms of **intensity**, which is the energy transported per unit time across a unit area. Since energy divided by time is power, intensity is power divided by area:

$$\text{intensity} = \frac{\text{energy/time}}{\text{area}} = \frac{\text{power}}{\text{area}} \qquad \left[I = \frac{E/t}{A} = \frac{P}{A} \right]$$

The standard units of intensity (power/area) are watts per square meter (W/m^2).

INSIGHT 14.2 THE PHYSIOLOGY AND PHYSICS OF THE EAR AND HEARING

The ear consists of three basic parts: the outer ear, the middle ear, and the inner ear (Fig. 1). The visible part of the ear is the *pinna* (or ear flap), and it collects and focuses sound waves. Many animals can move the ear flap in order to focus their hearing in a particular direction; humans have generally lost this ability and must turn the head. The sound enters the ear and travels through the *ear canal* to the *eardrum* of the middle ear.

The eardrum is a membrane that vibrates in response to the pressure of impinging sound waves. The vibrations are transmitted through the middle ear by an intricate set of three bones called the *malleus*, or hammer; the *incus*, or anvil; and the *stapes*, or stirrup. These bones form a linkage to the *oval window*, the opening to the inner ear. The eardrum transmits sound vibrations to the bones of the middle ear, which in turn transmits the vibrations through the oval window to the fluid of the inner ear.

The inner ear consists of the *semicircular canals*, the *cochlea*, and the *auditory nerve*. The semicircular canals and the cochlea are filled with a water-like liquid. The liquid and the nerve cells in the semicircular canal play no role in the process of hearing but serve to detect rapid movements and assist in maintaining balance.

The inner surface of the cochlea, a snail-shaped organ, is lined with more than 25 000 hairlike nerve cells. These nerve cells differ from each other slightly in length and have different degrees of resiliency to the fluid waves passing through the cochlea. Different hair cells have sensitivity to particular frequencies of waves. When the frequency of a compressional wave matches the natural frequency of hair cells, the cells resonate (Section 13.5) with a larger amplitude of vibration. This causes the release of electrical impulses from the nerve cells, which are transmitted to the auditory nerve. The auditory nerve carries the signals to the brain, where they are interpreted as sound.

The hair cells of the cochlea are very critical to hearing. Damage to those cells can give rise to *tinnitus*, or "ringing in the ears." Exposure to loud noises is a common cause of tinnitus and often leads to hearing loss as well. After a loud rock concert in an enclosed room, people often hear a temporary ringing in the ears and some slight loss of hearing. Hair cells can be damaged by loud noises temporarily or permanently. Over time, loud sounds can cause permanent injury because hair cells are lost. Because the hair cells are (resonance) frequency specific, a person may be unable to hear sounds at particular frequencies.

In a quiet room, put both thumbs in your ears firmly and listen. Do you hear a low pulsating sound? You are hearing the sound, at about 25 Hz, made by the contracting and relaxing of the muscle fibers in your hands and arms. Although in the audible range, these sounds are not normally heard, because the human ear is relatively insensitive to low-frequency sounds.

The middle ear is connected to the throat by the Eustachian tube, the end of which is normally closed. It opens during swallowing and yawning to permit air to enter and leave, so that internal and external pressures are equalized. You have probably experienced a "stopping up" of your ears with a sudden change in atmospheric pressure (e.g., during rapid ascents or descents in elevators or airplanes). Swallowing opens the Eustachian tubes and relieves the excess pressure difference on the middle ear. (See Insight 9.2, An Atmospheric Effect: Possible Earaches, p. 311.)

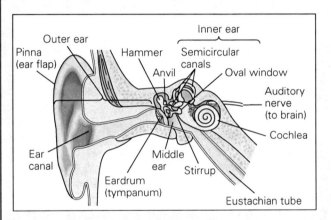

FIGURE 1 Anatomy of the human ear The ear converts pressure waves in the air into electrical nerve impulses that are interpreted as sounds by the brain.

Consider a point source that sends out spherical sound waves, as shown in ▾Fig. 14.4. If there are no losses, the sound intensity at a distance R from the source is

$$I = \frac{P}{A} = \frac{P}{4\pi R^2} \quad \text{(point source only)} \tag{14.2}$$

where P is the power of the source and $4\pi R^2$ is the area of a sphere of radius R, through which the sound energy passes perpendicularly.

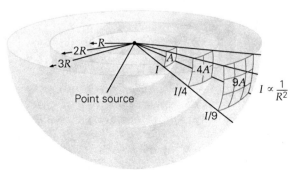

◀ **FIGURE 14.4 Intensity of a point source** The energy emitted from a point source spreads out equally in all directions. Since intensity is power divided by area, $I = P/A = P/(4\pi R^2)$, where the area is that of a spherical surface. The intensity then decreases with the distance from the source as $1/R^2$ (figure not to scale).

The intensity of a point source of sound is therefore *inversely proportional to the square of the distance from the source* (an inverse-square relationship). Two intensities at different distances from a point source of constant power can be compared as a ratio:

$$\frac{I_2}{I_1} = \frac{P/(4\pi R_2^2)}{P/(4\pi R_1^2)} = \frac{R_1^2}{R_2^2}$$

or

$$\frac{I_2}{I_1} = \left(\frac{R_1}{R_2}\right)^2 \quad \text{(point source only)} \tag{14.3}$$

Suppose that the distance from a point source is doubled; that is, $R_2 = 2R_1$, or $R_1/R_2 = \frac{1}{2}$. Then

$$\frac{I_2}{I_1} = \left(\frac{R_1}{R_2}\right)^2 = \left(\frac{1}{2}\right)^2 = \frac{1}{4}$$

and

$$I_2 = \frac{I_1}{4}$$

Since the intensity decreases by a factor of $1/R^2$, doubling the distance decreases the intensity to a quarter of its original value.

A good way to understand this inverse-square relationship intuitively is to look at the geometry of the situation. As Fig. 14.4 shows, the greater the distance from the source, the larger the area over which a given amount of sound energy is spread, and thus the lower its intensity. (Imagine having to paint two walls of different areas. If you had the same amount of paint to use on each, you'd have to spread it more thinly over the larger wall.) Since this area increases as the square of the radius R, the intensity decreases accordingly—that is, as $1/R^2$.

Sound intensity is perceived by the ear as **loudness**. On the average, the human ear can detect sound waves (at 1 kHz) with an intensity as low as 10^{-12} W/m². This intensity (I_0) is referred to as the *threshold of hearing*. Thus, for us to hear a sound, it must not only have a frequency in the audible range, but also be of sufficient intensity. As the intensity is increased, the perceived sound becomes louder. At an intensity of 1.0 W/m², the sound is uncomfortably loud and may be painful to the ear. This intensity (I_p) is called the *threshold of pain*.

Note that the thresholds of pain and hearing differ by a factor of 10^{12}:

$$\frac{I_p}{I_0} = \frac{1.0 \text{ W/m}^2}{10^{-12} \text{ W/m}^2} = 10^{12}$$

That is, the intensity at the threshold of pain is a *trillion* times that at the threshold of hearing. Within this enormous range, the perceived loudness is not directly proportional to the intensity. That is, if the intensity is doubled, the perceived loudness does not double. In fact, a doubling of perceived loudness corresponds approximately to an increase in intensity by a factor of 10. For example, a sound with an intensity of 10^{-5} W/m² would be perceived to be twice as loud as one with an intensity of 10^{-6} W/m². (The smaller the negative exponent, the larger the intensity.)

Sound Intensity Level: The Bel and the Decibel

It is convenient to compress the large range of sound intensities by using a logarithmic scale (base 10) to express *intensity levels* (not to be confused with sound intensity in W/m²). The intensity level of a sound must be referenced to a standard intensity, which is taken to be that of the threshold of hearing, $I_0 = 10^{-12}$ W/m². Then, for any intensity I, the intensity level is the logarithm (or log) of the ratio of I to I_o, that is, $\log I/I_o$. For example, if a sound has an intensity of $I = 10^{-6}$ W/m²,

$$\log \frac{I}{I_o} = \log \frac{10^{-6} \text{ W/m}^2}{10^{-12} \text{ W/m}^2} = \log 10^6 = 6 \text{ B}$$

(Recall that $\log_{10} 10^x = x$.)* The exponent of the power of 10 in the final log term is taken to have a unit called the **bel (B)**. Thus, a sound with an intensity of 10^{-6} W/m² has an intensity level of 6 B on this scale. That way, the intensity range from 10^{-12} W/m² to 1.0 W/m² is compressed into a scale of intensity levels ranging from 0 B to 12 B.

A finer intensity scale is obtained by using a smaller unit, the **decibel (dB)**, which is a tenth of a bel. The range from 0 to 12 B corresponds to 0 to 120 dB. In this case, the equation for the relative **sound intensity level**, or **decibel level (β)**, is

$$\beta = 10 \log \frac{I}{I_o} \qquad (\text{where } I_o = 10^{-12} \text{ W/m}^2) \qquad (14.4)$$

Note that the sound intensity level (in decibels, which are dimensionless) is *not* the same as the sound intensity (in watts per square meter).

The decibel intensity scale and familiar sounds at some intensity levels are shown in ▼Fig. 14.5. Sound intensities can have detrimental effects on hearing, and because of this, the U.S. government has set occupational noise-exposure limits.

Note: The bel was named in honor of Alexander Graham Bell, the inventor of the telephone.

▼ **FIGURE 14.5 Sound intensity levels and the decibel scale** The intensity levels of some common sounds on the decibel (dB) scale.

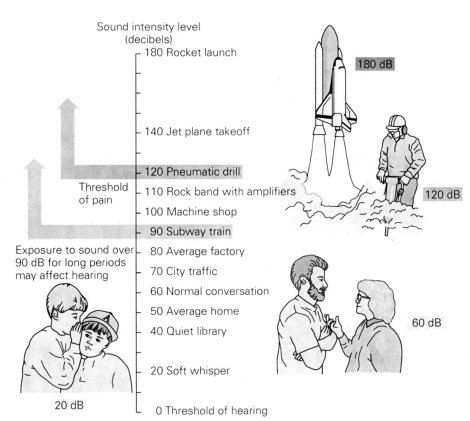

*A review of logarithms is given in Appendix I.

Example 14.4 ■ Sound Intensity Levels: Using Logarithms

What are the intensity levels of sounds with intensities of (a) 10^{-12} W/m^2 and (b) 5.0×10^{-6} W/m^2?

Thinking It Through. The sound intensity levels can be found by using Eq. 14.4.

Solution.

Given: (a) $I = 10^{-12}$ W/m^2 *Find:* (a) β (sound intensity level)
          (b) $I = 5.0 \times 10^{-6}$ W/m^2 (b) β

(a) Using Eq. 14.4, we have

$$\beta = 10 \log \frac{I}{I_o} = 10 \log \left(\frac{10^{-12}\,\text{W/m}^2}{10^{-12}\,\text{W/m}^2} \right) = 10 \log 1 = 0\,\text{dB}$$

The intensity 10^{-12} W/m^2 is the same as that at the threshold of hearing. (Recall that $\log 1 = 0$, since $1 = 10^0$ and $\log 10^0 = 0$.) Note that an intensity level of 0 dB does not mean that there is no sound.

(b) $\beta = 10 \log \dfrac{I}{I_o} = 10 \log \left(\dfrac{5.0 \times 10^{-6}\,\text{W/m}^2}{10^{-12}\,\text{W/m}^2} \right)$

$= 10 \log(5.0 \times 10^6) = 10(\log 5.0 + \log 10^6) = 10(0.70 + 6.0) = 67\,\text{dB}$

Follow-Up Exercise. Note in this Example that the intensity of 5.0×10^{-6} W/m^2 is halfway between 10^{-6} and 10^{-5} (or 60 and 70 dB), yet this intensity does not correspond to a midway value of 65 dB. (a) Why? (b) What intensity *does* correspond to 65 dB? (Compute it to three significant figures.)

Example 14.5 ■ Intensity Level Differences: Using Ratios

(a) What is the difference in the intensity levels if the intensity of a sound is doubled? (b) By what factors does the intensity increase for intensity level *differences* of 10 dB and 20 dB?

Thinking It Through. (a) If the intensity is doubled, then $I_2 = 2I_1$, or $I_2/I_1 = 2$. We can then use Eq. 14.4 to find the intensity difference. Recall that $\log a - \log b = \log a/b$. (b) Here, it is important to note that these values are intensity level *differences*, $\Delta\beta = \beta_2 - \beta_1$, *not* intensity *levels*. The equation developed in part (a) will work. (Why?)

Solution. Listing the data,

Given: (a) $I_2 = 2I_1$ *Find:* (a) $\Delta\beta$ (intensity level difference)
          (b) $\Delta\beta = 10$ dB   (b) I_2/I_1 (factors of increase)
              $\Delta\beta = 20$ dB

(a) Using Eq. 14.4 and the relationship $\log a - \log b = \log a/b$, we have, for the difference, $\Delta\beta = \beta_2 - \beta_1 = 10[\log(I_2/I_o) - \log(I_1/I_o)] = 10 \log[(I_2/I_o)/(I_1/I_o)] = 10 \log I_2/I_1$. Then,

$$\Delta\beta = 10 \log \frac{I_2}{I_1} = 10 \log 2 = 3\,\text{dB}$$

Thus, doubling the intensity increases the intensity level by 3 dB (such as an increase from 55 dB to 58 dB).

(b) For a 10-dB difference,

$$\Delta\beta = 10\,\text{dB} = 10 \log \frac{I_2}{I_1} \quad \text{and} \quad \log \frac{I_2}{I_1} = 1.0$$

Since $\log 10^1 = 1$, the intensity ratio is 10:1 because

$$\frac{I_2}{I_1} = 10^1 \quad \text{and} \quad I_2 = 10\,I_1$$

Similarly, for a 20-dB difference,

$$\Delta \beta = 20 \text{ dB} = 10 \log \frac{I_2}{I_1} \quad \text{and} \quad \log \frac{I_2}{I_1} = 2.0$$

Since $\log 10^2 = 2$,

$$\frac{I_2}{I_1} = 10^2 \quad \text{and} \quad I_2 = 100 \, I_1$$

Thus, an intensity-level difference of 10 dB corresponds to changing (increasing or decreasing) the intensity by a factor of 10. An intensity-level difference of 20 dB corresponds to changing the intensity by a factor of 100.

You should be able to guess the factor that corresponds to an intensity-level difference of 30 dB. In general, the factor of the intensity change is $10^{\Delta \beta}$, where $\Delta \beta$ is the difference in levels of bels. Since 30 dB = 3 B and $10^3 = 1000$, the intensity changes by a factor of 1000 for an intensity level difference of 30 dB.

Follow-Up Exercise. A $\Delta \beta$ of 20 dB and a $\Delta \beta$ of 30 dB correspond to factors of 100 and 1000, respectively, in intensity changes. Does a $\Delta \beta$ of 25 dB correspond to an intensity-change factor of 500? Explain.

Example 14.6 ■ Combined Sound Levels: Adding Intensities

Sitting at a sidewalk restaurant table, a friend talks to you in normal conversation (60 dB). At the same time, the intensity level of the street traffic reaching you is also 60 dB. What is the total intensity level of the combined sounds?

Thinking It Through. It is tempting simply to add the two sound intensity levels together and say that the total is 120 dB. But intensity levels in decibels are logarithmic, so you can't add them in the normal way. However, intensities (I) can be added arithmetically, since energy and power are scalar quantities. Then the combined intensity level can be found from the sum of the intensities.

Solution. We have the following information:

Given: $\beta_1 = 60$ dB   *Find:* Total β
$\qquad \beta_2 = 60$ dB

Let's find the intensities associated with the intensity levels:

$$\beta_1 = 60 \text{ dB} = 10 \log \frac{I_1}{I_o} = 10 \log \left(\frac{I_1}{10^{-12} \text{ W/m}^2} \right)$$

By inspection, we have

$$I_1 = 10^{-6} \text{ W/m}^2$$

Similarly, $I_2 = 10^{-6}$ W/m^2, since both intensity levels are 60 dB. So the total intensity is

$$I_{\text{total}} = I_1 + I_2 = 1.0 \times 10^{-6} \text{ W/m}^2 + 1.0 \times 10^{-6} \text{ W/m}^2 = 2.0 \times 10^{-6} \text{ W/m}^2$$

Then, converting back to intensity level, we get

$$\beta = 10 \log \frac{I_{\text{total}}}{I_o} = 10 \log \left(\frac{2.0 \times 10^{-6} \text{ W/m}^2}{10^{-12} \text{ W/m}^2} \right) = 10 \log(2.0 \times 10^6)$$

$$= 10(\log 2.0 + \log 10^6) = 10(0.30 + 6.0) = 63 \text{ dB}$$

This value is a long way from 120 dB! Notice that the combined intensities doubled the intensity value, and the intensity level increased by 3 dB, in agreement with our finding in part (a) of Example 14.5.

Follow-Up Exercise. In this Example, suppose the added noise gave a total that *tripled* the sound intensity level of the conversation. What would be the total combined intensity level in this case?

▲ **FIGURE 14.6 Protect your hearing** Continuous loud sounds can damage hearing, so our ears may need protection as shown here. Note in Table 14.2 that the intensity level of lawn mowers is on the order of 90 dB.

Protect Your Hearing

Hearing may be damaged by excessive noise, so our ears sometimes need protection from continuous loud sounds (▲Fig. 14.6). Hearing damage depends on the sound intensity level (decibel level) and the exposure time. The exact combinations vary for different people, but a general guide to noise levels is given in Table 14.2. Studies have shown that sound levels of 90 dB and above will damage receptor nerves in the ear, resulting in a loss of hearing. At 90 dB, it takes eight hours or less for damage to occur. In general, if the sound level is increased by 5 decibels, the safe exposure time is cut in half. For example, if a sound level of 95 dB (that of a very loud lawn mower or motorcycle) takes four hours to damage your hearing, then a sound level of 105 dB takes only one hour to do damage.

TABLE 14.2 Sound Intensity Levels and Ear Damage Exposure Times

	Decibels (dB)	Examples	Damage Can Occur with Nonstop Exposure
Faint	30	Quiet library, whispering	
Moderate	60	Normal conversation, sewing machine	
Very loud	80	Heavy traffic, noisy restaurant, screaming child	10 hours
	90	Lawn mower, motorcycle, loud party	Less than 8 hours
	100	Chainsaw, subway train, snowmobile	Less than 2 hours
Extremely loud	110	Stereo headset at full blast, rock concert	30 minutes
	120	Dance clubs, car stereos, action movies, some musical toys	15 minutes
	130	Jackhammer, loud computer games, loud sporting events	Less than 15 minutes
Painful	140	Boom stereos, gunshot blast, firecrackers	Any length (for example, hearing loss can occur from a few shots of a high-powered gun if protection is not worn)

Courtesy of The EAR Foundation.

15

ELECTRIC CHARGE, FORCES, AND FIELDS

PHYSICS FACTS

- Charles Augustin de Coulomb (1736–1806), a French scientist and the discoverer of the force law between charged objects, had a diverse career. In addition, he made significant contributions in hospital reform, the cleanup of the Parisian water supply, Earth magnetism, soils engineering, and the construction of forts, the latter two while he served in the military.

- The Taser stun gun, as used by law enforcement agencies, works by generating a large electric charge separation and applying it to parts of the body, disrupting the normal electrical signals and causing temporary incapacity. The stun gun needs to physically contact the body with its two electrodes, and the shock can be delivered even through thick clothing. A long-distance version of the Taser works by firing barbed electrodes with trailing wires.

- The electric eel (which can grow up to 6 feet in length and is actually a fish) acts electrically in a similar way to a Taser. More than 80% of the eel's body is tail, with its vital organs located behind its small head. It uses the electric field it creates for both locating prey and stunning them before eating.

- Home air purifiers use the electric force to reduce dust, bacteria, and other particulates in the air. The electric force removes electrons from the pollutants, making them positively charged. These particles are attracted to negatively charged plates, where they stay until manually removed. When working properly, these purifiers can reduce the particulate level by more than 99%.

Few natural processes deliver such an enormous amount of energy in a fraction of a second as a lightning bolt. Yet most people have never experienced its power at close range; luckily, only a few hundred people per year are struck by lightning in the United States.

It might surprise you to realize that you have almost certainly had a similar experience, at least in a physics context. Have you ever walked across a carpeted room and gotten a shock when you reached for a metallic doorknob? Although the scale is dramatically different, the physical process involved (static electricity discharge) is much the same as being struck by lightning—mini-lightning, so to speak.

Electricity sometimes gives rise to dramatic effects such as sparking electrical outlets or lightning strikes. We know that electricity can sometimes be dangerous, but we also know that electricity can be "domesticated." In the home or office, its usefulness is taken for granted. Indeed, our dependence on electric energy becomes evident only when the power goes off unexpectedly, providing a dramatic reminder of the role that it plays in our daily lives. Yet less than a century ago there were no power lines crossing the country, no electric lights or appliances—none of the electrical applications that are all around us today.

Physicists now know that the electric force is related to the magnetic force (see Chapter 20). Together they are called the "electromagnetic force," which is one of the four fundamental forces in nature. (Gravity [Chapter 7] and two types of short-range nuclear forces discussed in Chapters 29 and 30 are the other three.) We begin here by studying the electric force and its properties. Eventually (Chapter 20) the magnetic and electric forces will be interconnected.

505

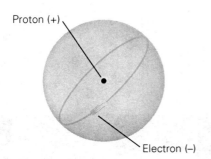

Proton (+)

Electron (–)

(a) Hydrogen atom

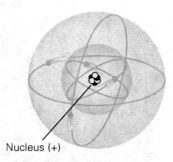

Nucleus (+)

(b) Beryllium atom

▲ **FIGURE 15.1 Simplistic model of atoms** The so-called solar system model of **(a)** a hydrogen atom and **(b)** a beryllium atom views the electrons (negatively charged) as orbiting the nucleus (positively charged), analogously to the planets orbiting the Sun. The electronic structure of atoms is actually much more complicated than this.

Note: Recall the discussion of Newton's third law in Section 4.4.

▶ **FIGURE 15.2 The charge–force law, or law of charges (a)** Like charges repel. **(b)** Unlike charges attract.

15.1 Electric Charge

OBJECTIVES: To **(a)** distinguish between the two types of electric charge, **(b)** state the charge–force law that operates between charged objects, and **(c)** understand and use the law of charge conservation.

What is *electricity*? One simple answer is that it is a term describing phenomena associated with the electricity we have in our homes. But fundamentally it really involves the study of the interaction between *electrically charged* objects. To demonstrate this, our study will start with the simplest situation, electro*statics*, when electrically charged objects are *at rest*.

Like mass, **electric charge** is a fundamental property of matter (Chapter 1). Electric charge is associated with particles that make up the atom: the electron and the proton. The simplistic solar system model of the atom, as illustrated in ◀Fig. 15.1, likens its structure to that of the planets orbiting the Sun. The *electrons* are viewed as orbiting a nucleus, a core containing most of the atom's mass in the form of *protons* and electrically neutral particles called *neutrons*. As seen in Section 7.5, the centripetal force that keeps the planets in orbit about the Sun is supplied by gravity. Similarly, the force that keeps the electrons in orbit around the nucleus is the electrical force. However, there are important distinctions between gravitational and electrical forces.

One difference is that there is only one type of mass and gravitational forces are only attractive. Electric charge, however, comes in two types, distinguished by the labels positive ($+$) and negative ($-$). Protons carry a positive charge, and electrons carry a negative charge. Different combinations of the two types of charge can produce *either* attractive *or* repulsive electrical forces.

The directions of the electric forces when charges interact with one another are given by the following principle, called the **law of charges** or the **charge–force law**:

| Like charges repel, and unlike charges attract. |

That is, two negatively charged particles or two positively charged particles repel each other, whereas particles with opposite charges attract each other (▼Fig. 15.2). The repulsive and attractive forces are equal and opposite, and act on different objects, in keeping with Newton's third law (action–reaction).

The charge on an electron and that on a proton are equal in magnitude, but opposite in sign. The magnitude of the charge on an electron is abbreviated as *e* and is the fundamental unit of charge, because it is the smallest charge observed in nature.* The SI unit of charge is the **coulomb (C)**, named for the French physicist/engineer Charles A. de Coulomb (1736–1806), who discovered a relationship between electric force and charge (Section 15.3). The charges and masses of the electron, proton, and

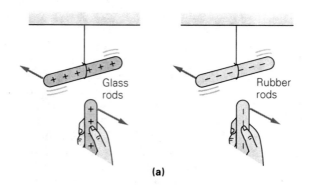

Glass rods

Rubber rods

(a)

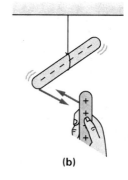

(b)

*Protons, as well as neutrons and other particles, are now known to be made up of more fundamental particles called *quarks*, which carry charges of $\pm\frac{1}{3}$ and $\pm\frac{2}{3}$ of the electronic charge. There is experimental evidence of the existence of quarks within the nucleus, but free quarks have not been detected. Current theory implies that direct detection of quarks may, in principle, be impossible (Chapter 30).

TABLE 15.1	Sub-atomic Particles and Their Electric Charge	
Particle	Electric Charge*	Mass*
Electron	-1.602×10^{-19} C	$m_e = 9.109 \times 10^{-31}$ kg
Proton	$+1.602 \times 10^{-19}$ C	$m_p = 1.673 \times 10^{-27}$ kg
Neutron	0	$m_n = 1.675 \times 10^{-27}$ kg

*Even though the values are displayed to four significant figures, we will usually use only two or three in our calculations.

neutron are given in Table 15.1, where we see that $e = 1.602 \times 10^{-19}$ C. Our general symbol for charge will be q or Q. The charge on the electron is written as $q_e = -e = -1.602 \times 10^{-19}$ C, and that on the proton as $q_p = +e = +1.602 \times 10^{-19}$ C.

Other terms are frequently used when discussing charged objects. Saying that an object has a **net charge** means that the object has an excess of either positive or negative charges. (It is common, however, to ask about the "charge" of an object when we really mean the net charge.) As you will see in Section 15.2, excess charge is most commonly produced by a transfer of electrons, *not* protons. (Protons are bound in the nucleus and, under most common situations, do not leave.) For example, if an object has a (net) charge of $+1.6 \times 10^{-18}$ C, then it has had electrons removed from it. Specifically it has a deficiency of *ten* electrons, because $10 \times 1.6 \times 10^{-19}$ C $= 1.6 \times 10^{-18}$ C. That is, the total number of electrons on the object no longer completely cancels the positive charge of all the protons—resulting in a net positive charge. On an atomic level, some of the atoms that compose the object are deficient in electrons. Such positively charged atoms are termed *positive ions*. Atoms with an excess of electrons are *negative ions*.

Since the charge of the electron is such a tiny fraction of a coulomb, an object having a net charge on the order of one coulomb is rarely seen in everyday situations. Therefore, it is common to express amounts of charge using *microcoulombs* (μC, or 10^{-6} C), *nanocoulombs* (nC, or 10^{-9} C), and *picocoulombs* (pC, or 10^{-12} C).

Because the (net) electric charge on an object is caused by either a deficiency or an excess of electrons, it must always be an integer multiple of the charge on an electron. A plus sign or a minus sign will indicate whether the object has a deficiency or an excess of electrons respectively. Thus, for the (net) charge of an object, we may write

$$q = \pm ne \qquad (15.1)$$
SI unit of charge: coulomb (C)

where $n = 1, 2, 3, \ldots$. It is sometimes said that charge is "quantized," which means that it occurs only in integral multiples of the fundamental electronic charge.

In dealing with any electrical phenomena, another important principle is **conservation of charge**:

| The net charge of an isolated system remains constant. |

That is, the net charge remains constant even though it may not be zero. Suppose, for example, that a system consists initially of two electrically neutral objects, and one million electrons are transferred from one to the other. The object with the added electrons will then have a net negative charge, and the object with the reduced number of electrons will have a net positive charge of equal magnitude. (See Example 15.1.) But the net charge of the *system* remains zero. If the universe is considered as a whole, conservation of charge means that the net charge *of the universe* is constant.

Note that this principle doesn't prohibit the creation or destruction of charged particles. In fact, physicists have known for a long time that charged particles can be created and destroyed on the atomic and nuclear levels. However, because of charge conservation, charged particles are created or destroyed only in pairs with equal and opposite charges.

Science Fundamentals

Integrated Example 15.1 ▪ On the Carpet: Conservation of Quantized Charge

You shuffle across a carpeted floor on a dry day and the carpet acquires a net positive charge (for details on this mechanism, see Section 15.2). (a) Will you have a (1) deficiency or (2) an excess of electrons? (b) If the charge the carpet acquired has a magnitude of 2.15 nC, how many electrons were transferred?

(a) Conceptual Reasoning. (a) Since the carpet has a net positive charge, it must have lost electrons and you must have gained them. Thus, your charge is negative, indicating an excess of electrons, and the correct answer is (2).

(b) Quantitative Reasoning and Solution. Because the charge of one electron is known, we can quantify the excess of electrons. Express the charge in coulombs, and state what is to be found.

Given: $q_c = +(2.15 \text{ nC})\left(\dfrac{10^{-9}\,\text{C}}{1\,\text{nC}}\right)$ *Find:* n, number of transferred electrons

$= +2.15 \times 10^{-9}\,\text{C}$

$q_e = -1.60 \times 10^{-19}\,\text{C}$ (from Table 15.1)

The net charge on you is

$$q = -q_c = -2.15 \times 10^{-9}\,\text{C}$$

Thus

$$n = \frac{q}{q_e} = \frac{-2.15 \times 10^{-9}\,\text{C}}{-1.60 \times 10^{-19}\,\text{C/electron}} = 1.34 \times 10^{10} \text{ electrons}$$

As can be seen, net charges, even in everyday situations, can involve huge numbers of electrons (here, more than 13 billion), because the charge of any one electron is very small.

Follow-Up Exercise. In this Example, if your mass is 80 kg, by what percentage has your mass increased due to the excess electrons? (*Answers to all Follow-Up Exercises are at the back of the text.*)

ELECTRIC CURRENT AND RESISTANCE

PHYSICS **FACTS**

- André Marie Ampère (1775–1836) was a French physicist/mathematician known for his work with electric currents. His name is used for the SI unit of current, the ampere (usually shortened to *amp*). He also worked in chemistry, being involved in the classification of the elements and the discovery of fluorine. In physics, Ampère is famous for being one of the first to attempt a combined theory of electricity and magnetism. Ampere's law, which describes the *magnetic* field created by a flow of *electric* charge, is one of the four fundamental equations of classical electromagnetism.

- In a metal wire, the electric *energy* travels at the speed of light (in the wire), which is much faster than the speed of the charge carriers themselves. The speed of the latter is only several millimeters per second.

- The SI unit of electrical resistance, the ohm (Ω), is named after Georg Simon Ohm (1789–1854), a German mathematician and physicist. A quantity called electrical conductivity, proportional to the *inverse* of resistance, is named, appropriately enough, the mho—his last name spelled backwards.

- Using a voltage of up to 600 volts, electric eels and rays can, for brief times, discharge as much as 1 ampere of current through flesh. The energy is delivered at a rate of 600 J/s, or about three-fourths of a horsepower.

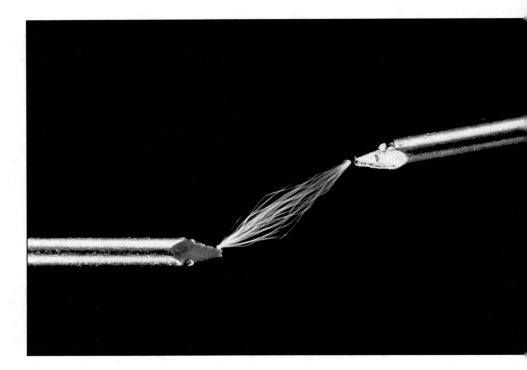

If you were asked to think of electricity and its uses, many favorable images would probably come to mind, including such diverse applications as lamps, television remote controls, computers, and electric leaf blowers. You might also think of some unfavorable images, such as dangerous lightning, a shock, or sparks you may have experienced from an overloaded electric outlet.

Common to all of these images is the concept of electric energy. For an electric appliance, energy is supplied by electric current in wires; for lightning or a spark, it is conducted through the air. In either case, the light, heat, or mechanical energy given off is simply electric energy converted to a different form. In the photograph, for example, the light given off by the spark is emitted by air molecules.

In this chapter, we are concerned with the fundamental principles governing electric circuits. These principles will enable us to answer questions such as the following: What is electric current and how does it travel? What causes an electric current to move through an appliance when we flip a switch? Why does the electric current cause the filament in a bulb to glow brightly, but not affect the connecting wires in the same way? We can apply electrical principles to gain an understanding of a wide range of phenomena, from the operation of household appliances to the workings of Nature's spectacular fireworks—lightning.

568

17.1 Batteries and Direct Current

OBJECTIVES: To (a) introduce the properties of a battery, (b) explain how a battery produces a direct current in a circuit, and (c) learn various circuit symbols for sketching schematic circuit diagrams.

After studying electric force and energy in Chapters 15 and 16, you can probably guess what is required to produce an *electric current*, or a flow of charge. Here are some analogies to help. Water naturally flows downhill, from higher to lower gravitational potential energy—that is, because there is a *difference* in gravitational potential energy. Heat flows naturally because of temperature *differences*. In electricity, a flow of electric charge is caused by an *electric* potential *difference*—what we call "voltage."

In solid conductors, particularly metals, some of the outer electrons of atoms are relatively free to move. (In liquid conductors and charged gases called *plasmas*, positive and negative ions as well as electrons can move.) Energy is required to move electric charge. Electric energy is generated through the conversion of other forms of energy, giving rise to a potential difference, or voltage. Any device that can produce and maintain a potential difference is called by the general name of a *power supply*.

Battery Action

One common type of power supply is the battery. A **battery** converts stored *chemical* potential energy into electrical energy. The Italian scientist Alessandro Volta constructed one of the first practical batteries. A simple battery consists of two unlike metal *electrodes* in an *electrolyte*, a solution that conducts electricity. With the appropriate electrodes and electrolyte, a potential difference develops across the electrodes as a result of chemical action (▸Fig. 17.1).

When a complete circuit is formed, for example, by connecting a lightbulb and wires (Fig. 17.1), electrons from the more negative electrode (B) will move through the wire and bulb to the less negative electrode (A).* The result is a flow of electrons in the wire. As electrons move through the bulb's filament, colliding with and transferring energy to its atoms (typically tungsten), the filament reaches a sufficient temperature to give off visible light (glow). Since electrons move to regions of higher potential, electrode A is at a higher potential than B. Thus the battery action has created a potential *difference* (V) across its terminals. Electrode A is the **anode** and labeled with a plus (+) sign. Electrode B is the **cathode** and labeled as negative (−). It is easy to keep track of this sign convention because the negatively charged electrons will move through the wire from B (−) to A (+).

For the study of circuits, we can just picture a battery as a "black box" that maintains a constant potential difference across its terminals. Inserted into a circuit, a battery can do work on, and transfer energy to, electrons in the wire (at the expense of its own internal chemical energy), which in turn delivers that energy to external circuit elements. In these elements, the energy is converted into other forms, such as mechanical motion (as in electric fans), heat (as in immersion heaters), and light (as in flashlights). Other sources of voltage, such as generators and photocells, will be considered later.

To help better visualize the role of a battery, consider the gravitational analogy in ▸Fig. 17.2. A gasoline-fueled pump (analogous to the battery) does work on the water as it lifts it. The increase in the water's gravitational potential energy comes at the expense of the chemical potential energy of the gasoline molecules. The water then returns to the pump by flowing down the trough (analogous to the wire) into the pond. On the way down, the water does work on the wheel, resulting in rotational kinetic energy, analogous to the electrons transferring energy to a lightbulb.

---

*As we shall see soon, a *complete circuit* is any complete loop consisting of wires and electrical devices (such as batteries and lightbulbs).

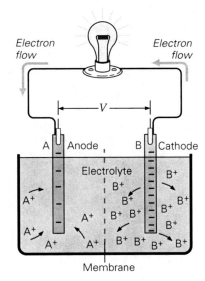

▲ **FIGURE 17.1 Battery action in a chemical battery or cell** Chemical processes involving an electrolyte and two unlike metal electrodes cause ions of both metals to dissolve into the solution at different rates. Thus, one electrode (the cathode) becomes more negatively charged than the other (the anode). The anode is at a higher potential than the cathode. By convention, the anode is designated the positive terminal and the cathode the negative. This potential difference (V) can cause a current, or a flow of charge (electrons), in the wire. The positive ions migrate as shown. (A membrane is necessary to prevent mixing of the two types of ion; why?)

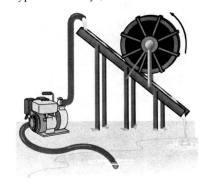

▲ **FIGURE 17.2 Gravitational analogy to a battery and lightbulb** A gasoline-powered pump lifts water from the pond, increasing the potential energy of the water. As the water flows downhill, it transfers energy to (or does work on) a waterwheel, causing the wheel to spin. This action is analogous to the delivery of energy to a lightbulb by an electrical current (for example, as in Fig. 17.1).

▶ **FIGURE 17.3** Electromotive force (emf) and terminal voltage **(a)** The emf ($\mathcal{E}$) of a battery is the maximum potential difference across its terminals. This maximum occurs when the battery is not connected to an external circuit. **(b)** Because of internal resistance (r), the terminal voltage V when the battery is in operation is less than the emf $\mathcal{E}$. Here, R is the resistance of the lightbulb.

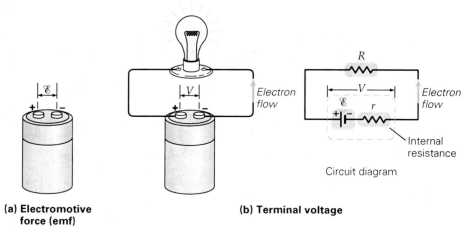

(a) Electromotive force (emf)

(b) Terminal voltage

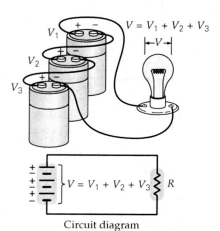

Circuit diagram

(a) Batteries in series

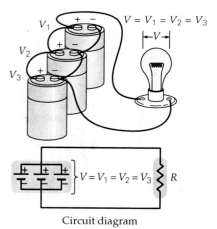

Circuit diagram

(b) Batteries in parallel (equal voltages)

▲ **FIGURE 17.4** Batteries in series and in parallel **(a)** When batteries are connected in series, their voltages add, and the voltage across the resistance R is the sum of the voltages. **(b)** When batteries of the same voltage are connected in parallel, the voltage across the resistance is the same, as if only a single battery were present. In this case, each battery supplies part of the total current.

Battery EMF and Terminal Voltage

The potential difference across the terminals of a battery *when it is not connected* to a circuit is called the battery's **electromotive force (emf)**, symbolized by $\mathcal{E}$. The name is misleading, because emf is *not* a force, but a potential difference, or voltage. To avoid confusion with force, we will call electromotive force just *emf*. Thus a battery's emf represents the work done by the battery *per coulomb* of charge that passes through it. If a battery does 1 joule of work on 1 coulomb of charge, then its emf is 1 joule per coulomb ($1\ \text{J/C}$), or 1 volt ($1\ \text{V}$).

The emf actually represents the maximum potential difference across the terminals (▲Fig. 17.3a). Under practical circumstances, when a battery is in a circuit and charge flows, the voltage across the terminals is always slightly *less* than the emf. This "operating voltage" (V) of a battery (the battery symbol is the pair of unequal-length parallel lines in Fig. 17.3b) is called its **terminal voltage**. Because batteries in actual operation are of most interest, it is the terminal voltage that is important.

Under many conditions, the emf and terminal voltage are essentially the same. Any difference is due to the battery's *internal resistance* (r), shown explicitly in the circuit diagram in Fig. 17.3b. (Resistance, defined in Section 17.3, is a quantitative measure of the opposition to charge flow.) Internal resistances are typically small, so the terminal voltage of a battery is essentially the same as the emf, that is, $V \approx \mathcal{E}$. However, when a battery supplies a large current or when its internal resistance is high (older batteries), the terminal voltage may drop appreciably below the emf. The reason is that it takes some voltage just to produce a current in the internal resistance itself. Mathematically, the terminal voltage is related to the emf, current, and internal resistance by $V = \mathcal{E} - Ir$ where I is the *electric current* (Section 17.2) in the battery.

For example, most modern cars have a battery "voltage readout." Upon startup, the 12-V battery's voltage typically reads only 10 V (this value is normal). Because of the enormous current required at startup, the Ir term (2 V) reduces the emf by about 2 V to the measured terminal voltage of 10 V. When the engine is running and supplying most of the electric energy to run the car's functions, the current required from the battery is essentially zero and the battery readout rises back to normal voltage levels. Thus, the terminal voltage, and not the emf, is a true indication of the state of the battery. Unless otherwise specified, we will assume negligible internal resistance, so that $V \approx \mathcal{E}$.

There is a wide variety of batteries in use. One of the most common is the 12-V automobile battery, consisting of six 2-V cells connected in *series*.* That is, the positive terminal of each cell is connected to the negative terminal of the next (see the three cells in ◀Fig. 17.4a). When batteries or cells are connected in this fashion, their voltages add. If cells are connected in *parallel*, their positive terminals are connected to each other, as are the negative ones (Fig. 17.4b). When identical batteries are connected this way, the potential difference or terminal

---

*Chemical energy is converted to electrical energy in a chemical *cell*. The term *battery* generally refers to a collection, or "battery," of cells.

voltage is the same for all of them. However, each supplies only a fraction of the current to the circuit. For example, if you have three batteries with equal voltages connected in parallel, each supplies one third of the total current. A parallel connection of two batteries is the main method for "jump-starting" a car. For such a start, the weak (high r) battery is connected in parallel to a normal (low r) battery, which delivers most of the current to start the car.

Note: Recall that *voltage* is used to mean "difference in electric potential."

Circuit Diagrams and Symbols

To help analyze and visualize circuits, it is common to draw *circuit diagrams* that are schematic representations of the wires, batteries, appliances, and so on. Each element in the circuit is represented by its own symbol in such a diagram. As in Fig. 17.3b and Fig. 17.4, the battery symbol is two parallel lines, the longer representing the positive terminal and the shorter the negative terminal. Any element (such as a lightbulb or appliance) that *opposes* the flow of charge is represented by the symbol —⋀⋀—. (Electrical resistance is defined in Section 17.3; here we merely introduce the symbol.) Connecting wires are unbroken lines and assumed, unless stated otherwise, to have negligible resistance. Where lines cross, it is assumed that they do *not* contact one another, unless they have a dot at their intersection. Lastly, switches are shown as "drawbridges," capable of going up (to open the circuit and stop the current) and down (closed to complete the circuit and allow current). These symbols, along with that of the capacitor (from Chapter 16), are summarized in the accompanying Learn by Drawing. An example of the use of these symbols and circuit diagrams to understand circuits conceptually is shown in the next example.

Conceptual Example 17.1 ■ Asleep at the Switch?

▸Fig. 17.5 shows a circuit diagram that represents two identical batteries (each with a terminal voltage V) connected in parallel to a lightbulb (represented by a resistor). Because it is assumed that the wires have no resistance, we know that before switch S_1 is opened, the voltage across the lightbulb equals V (that is, $V_{AB} = V$). What happens to the voltage across the lightbulb when S_1 is opened? (a) The voltage remains the same (V) as before the switch was opened. (b) The voltage drops to $V/2$, because only one battery is now connected to the bulb. (c) The voltage drops to zero.

Reasoning and Answer. It might be tempting to choose answer (b), because there is now just one battery. But look again. The remaining battery is still connected to the lightbulb. This means that there must be *some* voltage across the lightbulb, so the answer certainly cannot be (c). But it also means that the answer cannot be (b), because the remaining battery itself will maintain a voltage of V across the bulb. Hence, the answer is (a).

Follow-Up Exercise. In this Example, what would the correct answer be if, in addition to opening S_1, switch S_2 were also opened? Explain your answer and reasoning. *(Answers to all Follow-Up Exercises are at the back of the text.)*

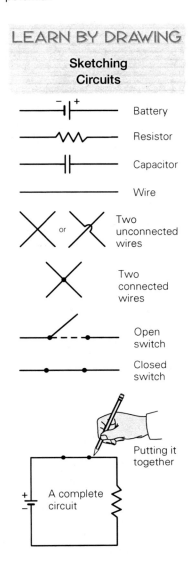

LEARN BY DRAWING

Sketching Circuits

Battery

Resistor

Capacitor

Wire

Two unconnected wires   or

Two connected wires

Open switch

Closed switch

Putting it together

A complete circuit

17.2 Current and Drift Velocity

OBJECTIVES: To (a) define electric current, (b) distinguish between electron flow and conventional current, and (c) explain the concept of drift velocity and electric energy transmission.

As we have just seen, to sustain an electric current requires a voltage source and a **complete circuit**—the name given to a continuous conducting path. Most practical circuits include a switch to "open" or "close" the circuit. An open switch eliminates the continuous part of the path, thereby stopping the flow of charge in the wires.

Electric Current

Because it is the electrons that move in any circuit's wires, the charge flow is away from the negative terminal of the battery. Historically, however, circuit analysis has been done in terms of **conventional current**. The conventional current's direction is

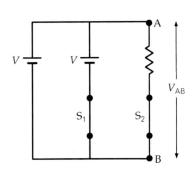

▲ **FIGURE 17.5 What happens to the voltage?** See Example 17.1.

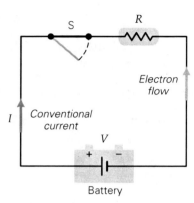

▲ **FIGURE 17.6 Conventional current** For historical reasons, circuit analysis is usually done with conventional current. Conventional current is in the direction in which positive charges would flow, or opposite to the electron flow.

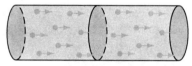

▲ **FIGURE 17.7 Electric current** Electric current (I) in a wire is defined as the rate at which the net charge (q) passes through the wire's cross-sectional area: $I = q/t$. The units of I are amperes (A), or *amps* for short.

that in which positive charges would flow, that is, *opposite* the actual electron flow (◄Fig. 17.6). (Some situations do exist in which a positive charge flow *is* responsible for the current—for example, in semiconductors.)

The battery is said to *deliver* current to a circuit or a component of that circuit (a circuit element). Alternatively, we sometimes say that a circuit (or its components) *draws* current from the battery. The current then returns to the battery. A battery can produce a current in only one direction. One-directional charge flow is called **direct current (dc)**. (Note if the current changes direction and/or magnitude, it is *alternating current*. We will study this type of situation in detail in Chapter 21.)

Quantitatively, the **electric current (I)** is the time rate of flow of net charge. We will be concerned primarily with steady charge flow. In this case, if a net charge q passes through a cross-sectional area in a time interval t (◄Fig. 17.7), the electric current is defined as

$$I = \frac{q}{t} \quad electric\ current \tag{17.1}$$

SI unit of current: coulomb per second (C/s) or ampere (A)

The coulomb per second is designated the **ampere (A)** in honor of the French physicist André Ampère (1775–1836), an early investigator of electrical and magnetic phenomena. In everyday usage, the ampere is commonly shortened to *amp.* Thus, a current of 10 A is read as "ten amps." Small currents are routinely expressed in *milliamperes* (mA, or 10^{-3} A), *microamperes* (μA, or 10^{-6} A), or *nanoamperes* (nA, or 10^{-9} A). These are usually shortened to *milliamps, microamps,* and *nanoamps,* respectively. In a typical household circuit, it is not unusual for the wires to carry several amps of current. To understand the relationship between charge and current, consider the next example.

Example 17.2 ■ Counting Electrons: Current and Charge

Suppose there is a steady current of 0.50 A in a flashlight bulb lasting for 2.0 min. How much charge passes through the bulb during this time? How many electrons does this represent?

Thinking It Through. The current and time elapsed are given; therefore, the definition of current (Eq. 17.1) allows us to find the charge q. Since each electron carries a charge of magnitude 1.6×10^{-19} C, then q can be converted into the number of electrons.

Solution. Listing the data given and converting the time into seconds:

Given: $I = 0.50$ A $\qquad$ *Find:* q (amount of charge)
$\quad\quad\quad t = 2.0$ min $= 1.2 \times 10^2$ s $\qquad\quad n$ (number of electrons)

By Eq. 17.1, $I = q/t$, so the magnitude of the charge is

$$q = It = (0.50\ \text{A})(1.2 \times 10^2\ \text{s}) = (0.50\ \text{C/s})(1.2 \times 10^2\ \text{s}) = 60\ \text{C}$$

Solving for the number of electrons (n), we have

$$n = \frac{q}{e} = \frac{60\ \text{C}}{1.6 \times 10^{-19}\ \text{C/electron}} = 3.8 \times 10^{20}\ \text{electrons}$$

(It takes a lot of electrons.)

Follow-Up Exercise. Many sensitive laboratory instruments can measure currents in the nanoamp range or smaller. How long, in years, would it take for 1.0 C of charge to flow past a given point in a wire that carries a current of 1.0 nA?

Drift Velocity, Electron Flow, and Electric Energy Transmission

Although we frequently mention charge flow in analogy to water flow, electric charge traveling in a conductor does not flow the same way that water flows in a pipe. In the absence of a potential difference across the ends of a metal wire, the free electrons move randomly at high speeds, colliding many times per second with the metal atoms. As a result, there is no net flow of charge, because equal amounts of charge pass through a given cross-sectional area in opposite directions during a specific time interval.

However, when a potential difference (voltage) *is* applied across the wire (such as by a battery), an electric field appears in the wire in one direction. A flow of electrons then begins *opposite* that direction (why?). This does *not* mean the electrons move directly from one end of the wire to the other. They still move in all directions as they collide with the atoms of the conductor but there is now an *added* component (in one direction) to their velocities (▸Fig. 17.8). The result is that their velocities are now, on average, more toward the positive terminal of the battery than away.

This net electron flow is characterized by an average velocity called the **drift velocity**. The drift velocity is much smaller than the random (thermal) velocities of the electrons themselves. Typically the magnitude of the drift velocity is on the order of 1 mm/s. At that speed, it would take an electron about 17 min to travel 1 m along a wire. Yet a lamp comes on almost instantaneously when the switch is closed (completing the circuit), and the electronic signals carrying telephone conversations travel almost instantaneously over miles of wire. How can that be?

Evidently, *something* must be moving faster than the "drifting" electrons. Indeed, this something is the electric field. When a potential difference is applied, the associated electric field in the conductor travels at a speed close to that of light (in the material, roughly 10^8 m/s). Thus the electric field influences the electrons *throughout the conductor* almost instantaneously. This means that the current starts everywhere in the circuit essentially simultaneously. You don't have to wait for electrons to "get there" from a distant place (say, near the switch). Thus in the light bulb, the electrons that are *already* in its filament begin to move almost immediately, delivering energy and creating light with no noticeable delay.

This effect is analogous to toppling a row of standing dominos. When you tip a domino at one end, that *signal* (or energy) is transmitted rapidly down the row. Very quickly, at the other end, the last domino topples (and delivers energy). Note that the domino delivering the signal or energy is *not* the one you pushed. It was the energy, not the dominos, that traveled down the row.

17.3 Resistance and Ohm's Law

OBJECTIVES: To (a) define electrical resistance and explain what is meant by an ohmic resistor, (b) summarize the factors that determine resistance, and (c) calculate the effect of these factors in simple situations.

If you place a voltage (potential difference) across the ends of any conducting material, what factors determine the current? As might be expected, usually the greater the voltage, the greater the current. However, another factor also influences current. Just as internal friction (viscosity; see Chapter 9) affects fluid flow in pipes, the resistance of the wire's material will affect the flow of charge. Any object that offers significant resistance to electrical current is called a *resistor* and is represented by the zigzag symbol (Section 17.1). This symbol is used to represent all types of resistors, from the cylindrical color-coded ones on printed circuit boards to electrical devices and appliances such as hair dryers and lightbulbs (▸Fig. 17.9).

But how is resistance quantified? We know, for example, that if a large voltage applied across an object produces only a small current, then that object has a high resistance. Thus, the **resistance (R)** of any object should be related to the ratio of the voltage across the object to the resulting current through that object. Resistance is therefore defined as

$$R = \frac{V}{I} \quad electrical\ resistance \qquad (17.2a)$$

SI unit of resistance: volt per ampere (V/A), or ohm (Ω)

The units of resistance are volts per ampere (V/A), called the **ohm** (Ω) in honor of the German physicist Georg Ohm (1789–1854), who investigated the relationship between current and voltage. Large values of resistance are commonly expressed as kilohms (kΩ) and megohms (MΩ). A schematic circuit diagram

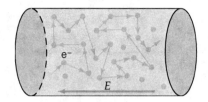

Drift velocity v_d

▲ **FIGURE 17.8 Drift velocity** Because of collisions with the atoms of the conductor, electron motion is random. However, when the conductor is connected, for example, to a battery to form a complete circuit, there is a small net motion in the direction opposite the electric field [toward the high-potential (positive) terminal, or anode]. The speed and direction of this net motion form the drift velocity of the electrons.

Note: *Resistor* is a generic term for any object that possesses significant electrical resistance.

Note: Remember, *V* stands for ΔV.

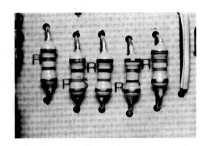

▲ **FIGURE 17.9 Resistors in use** A printed circuit board, typically used in computers, includes resistors of different values. The large, striped cylinders are resistors; their four-band color code indicates their resistance in ohms.

Note: *Ohmic* means "having a constant resistance."

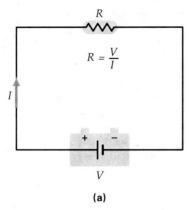

$$R = \frac{V}{I}$$

(a)

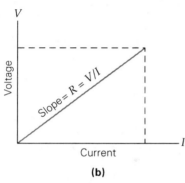

(b)

▲ **FIGURE 17.10 Resistance and Ohm's law (a)** In principle, any object's electrical resistance can be determined by dividing the voltage across it by the current through it. **(b)** If the object obeys Ohm's law (applicable only to a constant resistance), then a plot of voltage versus current is a straight line with a slope equal to R, the element's resistance. (Its resistance does not change with voltage.)

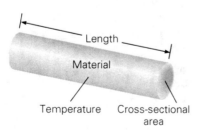

▲ **FIGURE 17.11 Resistance factors** Factors directly affecting the electrical resistance of a cylindrical conductor are the type of material it is made of, its length (L), its cross-sectional area (A), and its temperature (T).

showing how, in principle, resistance is determined is illustrated in ◄Fig. 17.10a. (In Chapter 18, we will study the instruments that are used to measure electrical currents and voltages, called *ammeters* and *voltmeters*, respectively.)

For some materials, the resistance may be constant over a range of voltages. A resistor that exhibits constant resistance is said to obey **Ohm's law**, or to be *ohmic*. The law was named after Ohm, who found materials possessing this property. A plot of voltage versus current for a material with an ohmic resistance gives a straight line with a slope equal to its resistance R (Fig. 17.10b). A common and practical form of Ohm's law is

$$V = IR \quad \text{(Ohm's law)} \quad \text{(17.2b)}$$

(or $I \propto V$, only when $R =$ constant)

Ohm's law is *not* a fundamental law in the same sense as, for example, the law of conservation of energy. There is no "law" that states that materials *must* have constant resistance. Indeed, many of our advances in electronics are based on materials such as semiconductors, which have *nonlinear* (nonohmic) voltage–current relationships.

Unless specified otherwise, we will assume resistor to be ohmic. Always remember, however, that many materials are nonohmic. For instance, the tungsten filaments in lightbulbs have resistance that increases with temperature, being much larger at their operating temperature than at room temperature. The following Example shows how the resistance of the human body can make the difference between life and death.

Example 17.3 ■ Danger in the House: Human Resistance

Any room in the house that is exposed to water and electrical voltage can present hazards. (See the discussion of electrical safety in Section 18.5.) For example, suppose a person steps out of a shower and inadvertently touches an exposed 120-V wire (perhaps a frayed cord on a hair dryer) with a finger. The human body, when wet, can have an electrical resistance as low as 300 Ω. Using this value, estimate the current in that person's body.

Thinking It Through. The wire is at an electrical potential of 120 V above the floor, which is "ground" and taken to be at 0 V. Therefore the voltage (or potential difference) across the body is 120 V. To determine the current, we can use Eq. 17.2, the definition of resistance.

Solution. Listing the data,

Given: $V = 120$ V   *Find:* I (current in the body)
         $R = 300$ Ω

From Eq. 17.2, we have

$$I = \frac{V}{R} = \frac{120 \text{ V}}{300 \text{ Ω}} = 0.400 \text{ A} = 400 \text{ mA}$$

While this is a small current by everyday standards, it is a large current for the human body. A current over 10 mA can cause severe muscle contractions, and currents on the order of 100 mA can stop the heart. So this current is potentially deadly. (See Insight 18.2 on Electricity and Personal Safety, Table 1, in Chapter 18 on page 614.)

Follow-Up Exercise. When the human body is dry, its resistance (over its length) can be as high as 100 kΩ. What voltage would be required to produce a current of 1.0 mA (the value that a person can barely feel)?

Factors That Influence Resistance

On the atomic level, resistance arises when electrons collide with the atoms that make up a material. Thus, resistance partially depends on the type of material of which an object is composed. However, geometrical factors also influence resistance. In summary, the resistance of an object of uniform cross-section, such as a length of wire, depends on four properties: (1) the type of material, (2) its length, (3) its cross-sectional area, and (4) its temperature (◄Fig. 17.11).

As you might expect, the resistance of an object (such as a piece of wire) is *inversely* proportional to its cross-sectional area (A), and *directly* proportional to its length (L); that is, $R \propto L/A$. For example, a uniform metal wire 4 m long offers twice as much resistance as a similar wire 2.0 m long, but a wire with a cross-sectional area of 0.50 mm^2 has only half the resistance of one with an area of 0.25 mm^2. These geometrical resistance conditions are analogous to those for liquid flow in a pipe. The longer the pipe, the more is its resistance (drag), but the larger its cross-sectional area, the more liquid it can carry per second. To see an interesting use of the dependence of resistance on length and area by living organisms, read Insight 17.1 on The "Bio-Generation" of High Voltage on this page.

Illustration 30.5 Ohm's "Law"

INSIGHT 17.1 THE "BIO-GENERATION" OF HIGH VOLTAGE

From the discussion of battery action in Section 17.1, you know that two different metals in acid can generate a constant separation of charge (a voltage) and thus can produce electric current. However, living organisms can also create voltages by a process sometimes called "bio-generation." Electric eels (see Insight 15.2 on page 527), in particular, can generate 600 V, more than enough to kill humans. But how do they accomplish this? As we shall see, the process has similarities both to regular "dry cells" and to nerve signal transmission.

Eels have three organs related to its electrical activities. The Sachs' organ generates low-voltage pulsations for navigation. The others, named the Hunter organ and the Main organ, are sources of high voltage (Fig. 1). In these organs, cells called *electrocytes*, or *electroplates*, are arranged in a stack. Each cell has a flat, disklike shape. The electroplate stack is a series connection similar to that in a car battery, in which there are six cells at 2 V each, producing a total of 12 V. Each electroplate is capable of producing a voltage of only about 0.15 V, but four or five thousand in series can add up to a voltage of 600 V. The electroplates are electrically similar to muscle cells in that they, like muscle cells, receive nerve impulses by synaptic connection. However, these nerve impulses do not cause movement. Instead they trigger voltage generation by the following mechanism.

Each electroplate has the same structure. The top and bottom membranes behave similarly to nerve membranes (see Insight 16.1 on page 552). Under resting conditions, the Na$^+$ ions cannot penetrate the membrane. To equilibrate their concentrations on both sides, the ions reside near the outside surface. This, in turn, attracts the (interior) negatively charged proteins to the interior surface. As a result, the interior is at a potential of 0.08 V lower than the outside. Therefore, under resting conditions, the outside

top (toward the head, or anterior) surface and the outside bottom (posterior) surface of *all* the electroplates are positive (one is shown in Fig. 2a) and exhibit no voltage ($\Delta V_1 = 0$). Thus, under resting conditions a series stack has no voltage ($\Delta V_{total} = \sum \Delta V_i = 0$) from top to bottom (Fig. 2b).

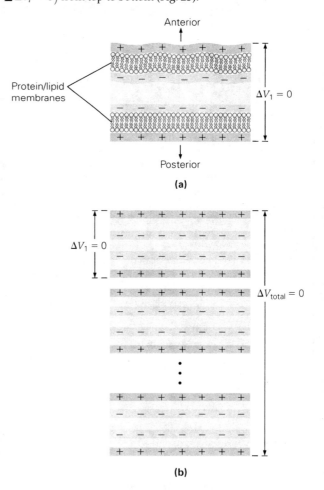

FIGURE 2 (a) A single, resting electroplate One of the thousands of electroplates in the eel's electric organs has, under resting conditions, equal amounts of positive charge at its top and bottom, resulting in no voltage. (b) Resting electroplates in series Several thousand electroplates in series under resting conditions have a total voltage of zero.

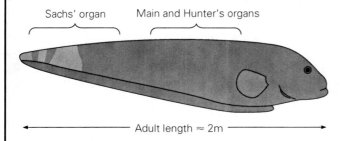

FIGURE 1 Anatomy of an electric eel 80% of an electric eel's body is devoted to voltage generation. Most of that portion contains the two organs (Main and Hunter's) responsible for the high voltage associated with killing of prey. The Sachs' organ produces a lower pulsating voltage used for navigation.

(continues on next page)

However, when an eel locates prey, the eel's brain sends a signal along a neuron *to only the bottom membrane* of each electroplate (one cell is shown in Fig. 3a). A chemical (*acetylcholine*) diffuses across the synapse onto the membrane, briefly opening the ion channels and allowing in Na^+. *For a few milliseconds the lower membrane polarity is reversed*, creating a voltage across one cell of $\Delta V_1 \approx 0.15$ V. The whole stack does this simultaneously, causing a large voltage across the ends of the stack ($\Delta V_{total} \approx 4000 \ \Delta V_1 = 600$ V; see Fig. 3b). When the eel touches the prey with the stack ends, the resulting current pulse through the prey (about 0.5 A) delivers enough energy to kill or at least stun.

An interesting biological "wiring" arrangement enables all electroplates to be triggered simultaneously—a requirement crucial for generation of the maximum voltage. Since each electroplate is a different distance from the brain, the action potential traveling down the neurons must be carefully timed. To do this, the neurons attached to the top of the stack (closest to the brain) are longer and thinner than those attached to the bottom. From what you know about resistance (see, for example, the discussion of Eq. 17.3 and $R \propto L/A$), it should be clear that both a reduction in area and increase in length of the neurons serve to increase neuron resistance compared with those attached to more distant electroplates. Increased resistance means that the action potential travels slower through the closer neurons, thus enabling the closer electroplates to receive their signal at the same time as the more distant ones—a very interesting and practical use of physics (from the eel's perspective, not the prey's).

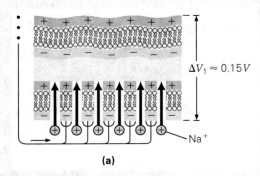

(a)

FIGURE 3 (a) An electroplate in action Upon location of prey, a signal is sent from the eel's brain to each electroplate along a neuron attached only to the bottom of the plate. This triggers a brief opening of the ion channel allowing Na^+ ions to the interior, temporarily reversing the polarity of the lower membrane. This creates a temporary electric potential difference (voltage) between the top and bottom membranes. Each electroplate voltage is typically a few tenths of a volt. **(b) A series stack of electroplates in action** When each electroplate in the stack is triggered into action by the lower neuron signal, this results in a large voltage between the top and bottom of the stack, typically on the order of 600 V. This large voltage enables the eel to deliver a pulse of current on the order of a few tenths of an ampere through the prey. The energy deposited in the prey is usually enough to stun or kill it.

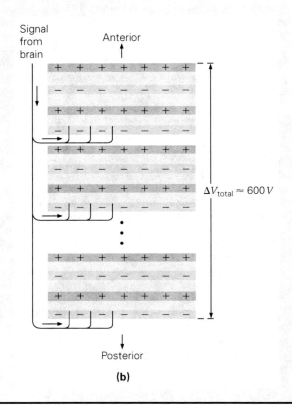

(b)

Resistivity

Note: Do not confuse resistivity with mass density, which has the same symbol (ρ).

The resistance of an object is partly determined by its material's atomic properties, quantitatively described by that material's **resistivity (ρ)**. The resistance of uniform cross-section object is given by

$$R = \rho \left(\frac{L}{A} \right) \tag{17.3}$$

SI unit of resistivity: ohm-meter ($\Omega \cdot m$)

The units of resistivity (ρ) are ohm-meters ($\Omega \cdot m$). (You should show this.) Thus, knowing its resistivity (the material type) and using Eq. 17.3, the resistance of any

TABLE 17.1   Resistivities (at 20°C) and Temperature Coefficients of Resistivity for Various Materials*

	$\rho\,(\Omega \cdot m)$	$\alpha\,(1/C°)$		$\rho\,(\Omega \cdot m)$	$\alpha\,(1/C°)$
Conductors			*Semiconductors*		
Aluminum	2.82×10^{-8}	4.29×10^{-3}	Carbon	3.6×10^{-5}	-5.0×10^{-4}
Copper	1.70×10^{-8}	6.80×10^{-3}	Germanium	4.6×10^{-1}	-5.0×10^{-2}
Iron	10×10^{-8}	6.51×10^{-3}	Silicon	2.5×10^{2}	-7.0×10^{-2}
Mercury	98.4×10^{-8}	0.89×10^{-3}			
Nichrome (alloy of nickel and chromium)	100×10^{-8}	0.40×10^{-3}	*Insulators*		
Nickel	7.8×10^{-8}	6.0×10^{-3}	Glass	10^{12}	
Platinum	10×10^{-8}	3.93×10^{-3}	Rubber	10^{15}	
Silver	1.59×10^{-8}	4.1×10^{-3}	Wood	10^{10}	
Tungsten	5.6×10^{-8}	4.5×10^{-3}			

*Values for semiconductors are general ones, and resistivities for insulators are typical orders of magnitude.

constant-area object can be calculated, as long as its length and cross-sectional area is known.

The values of the resistivities of some conductors, semiconductors, and insulators are given in Table 17.1. The values apply at 20°C, because resistivity can depend on temperature. Most common wires are composed of copper or aluminum with cross-sectional areas on the order of 10^{-6} m² or 1 mm². For a length of 1.5 m, you should be able to show that the resistance of a copper wire with this area is about 0.025 Ω (= 25 mΩ). This explains why wire resistances are neglected in circuits—their values are much less than most household devices.

An interesting and potentially important medical application involves the measurement of human body resistance and its relationship to body fat. (See Insight 17.2 on Bioelectrical Impedance Analysis on page 578.) To get a feeling for the magnitudes of these quantities in living tissue, consider the following Example.

Example 17.4 ■ Electric Eels: Cooking with Bio-Electricity?

Suppose an electric eel touches the head and tail of a cylindrically shaped fish and applies a voltage of 600 V across it. (See Insight 17.1 on page 575.) If a current of 0.80 A results (likely killing the prey), estimate the average resistivity of the fish's flesh, assuming it is 20 cm long and 4.0 cm in diameter.

Thinking It Through. With cylindrical geometry, we know its length and can find its cross-sectional area from the given dimensions. From the voltage and current, its resistance can be determined. Lastly, its resistivity can be estimated using Eq. 17.3.

Solution. Listing the data:

Given: $L = 20$ cm $= 0.20$ m   *Find:* f (resistivity)
$d = 4.0$ cm $= 4.0 \times 10^{-2}$ m
$V = 600$ V
$I = 0.80$ A

The cross-sectional area of the fish is

$$A = \pi r^2 = \pi \left(\frac{d}{2}\right)^2 = \frac{\pi(2.0 \times 10^{-2}\,\text{m})^2}{4} = 3.1 \times 10^{-4}\,\text{m}^2$$

(continues on next page)

We also know that the fish's overall resistance is $R = \dfrac{V}{I} = \dfrac{600 \text{ V}}{0.80 \text{ A}} = 7.5 \times 10^2 \, \Omega$. From Eq. 17.3, we have

$$\rho = \frac{RA}{L} = \frac{(7.5 \times 10^2 \, \Omega)(3.1 \times 10^{-4} \text{ m}^2)}{0.20 \text{ m}} = 1.2 \, \Omega \cdot \text{m or about } 120 \, \Omega \cdot \text{cm}$$

Comparing this to the values in Table 17.1, you can see that, as expected, the fish's flesh is much more resistive than metals, but certainly not a great insulator. The value is on the order of the resistivities measured for different human tissues; for example, cardiac muscle has a resistivity of about 175 $\Omega \cdot$ cm and liver on the order of 200 $\Omega \cdot$ cm. Clearly our answer is an average over the whole fish and tells us nothing about different regions of the fish.

Follow-Up Exercise. Suppose for its next meal, the eel in this Example chooses a different species of fish. The next fish has twice the average resistivity, half the length, and half the diameter of the first fish. What current would be expected in this fish if the eel applied 400 V across its body?

For many materials, especially metals, the temperature dependence of resistivity is nearly linear if the temperature change is not too great. That is, the resistivity at a temperature T after a temperature change $\Delta T = T - T_o$ is given by

$$\rho = \rho_o(1 + \alpha \Delta T) \qquad \text{\textit{temperature variation} of resistivity} \qquad (17.4)$$

where α is a constant (usually only over a certain temperature range) called the **temperature coefficient of resistivity** and ρ_o is a reference resistivity at T_o (usually 20°C). Equation 17.4 can be rewritten as

$$\Delta \rho = \rho_o \alpha \Delta T \qquad (17.5)$$

Note: Compare the form of Eq. 17.5 with Eq. 10.10 for the linear expansion of a solid.

where $\Delta \rho = \rho - \rho_o$ is the change in resistivity that occurs when the temperature changes by ΔT. The ratio $\Delta \rho / \rho_o$ is dimensionless, so α has units of inverse Celsius degrees, written as $1/\text{C}°$. Physically, α represents the fractional change in resistivity ($\Delta \rho / \rho_o$) per Celsius degree. The temperature coefficients of resistivity for some materials are listed in Table 17.1. These coefficients are assumed to be constant over normal temperature ranges. Notice that for semiconductors and insulators the coefficients are generally orders of magnitude and are usually not constant.

INSIGHT · 17.2 BIOELECTRICAL IMPEDANCE ANALYSIS (BIA)

Traditional methods for estimating body-fat percentages involve the use of buoyancy tanks (for density measurements, see Chapter 9) or calipers to pinch the flesh. However, in recent years, electrical resistance experiments have been designed to measure the body fat of the human body.[*] In theory, these measurements—termed *bioelectrical impedance analysis* (BIA)—have the potential to determine, with more accuracy than traditional methods, a patient's total water content, fat-free mass, and body fat (*adipose tissue*).

The principle of BIA is based on the water content of the human body. Water in the human body is a relatively good conductor of electric current, due to the presence of ions such as potassium (K^+) and sodium (Na^+). Because muscle tissue holds more water per kilogram than fat holds, it is a better conductor than fat. Thus for a given voltage, the difference in currents should be a good indicator of the fat-to-muscle percentage.

In practice, one electrode of a low-voltage power supply is connected to the wrist and the other to the opposite ankle during a BIA test. The current is kept below 1 mA for safety, with typical currents being about 800 μA. The subject cannot feel this small

[*]Technically, this technique measures the body's *impedance*, which includes effects of capacitance and magnetic effects as well as resistance. (See Chapter 21.) However, these contributions are about 10% of the total. Hence, the word *resistance* is used here.

current. Typical resistance values are about 250 Ω. From Ohm's law, the required voltage is $V = IR = (8 \times 10^{-4} \text{ A})(250 \, \Omega) = 0.200 \text{ V}$, or about 200 mV. In actuality, the voltage alternates in polarity at a frequency of 50 kHz, because this frequency is known *not* to trigger electrically excitable tissues, such as nerves and cardiac muscle.

From what has been presented in this chapter (for example, Eq. 17.3), you should be able to understand some of the factors involved in interpreting the results of human resistance measurements. The measured resistance is the total resistance. However, the current travels not through a uniform material but rather through the arm, trunk, and leg. Not only does each of these body parts have a different fat-to-muscle ratio, which affects resistivity (ρ), but also they differ widely in length (L) and cross-sectional area (A). The arm and the leg, usually dominated by muscle and with a small cross-sectional area, offer the most resistance. The trunk, which usually contains a relatively high percentage of fat and has a large cross-sectional area, has low resistance.

By subjecting BIAs to statistical analysis, researchers hope to understand how the wide range of physical and genetic parameters present in humans affects resistance measurements. Among these parameters are height, weight, body type, and ethnicity. Once the correlations are understood, BIA may well become a valuable medical tool in routine physicals and in the diagnosis of various diseases.

Resistance is directly proportional to resistivity (Eq. 17.3). This means that an object's resistance has the same dependence on temperature as its resistivity (Eqs. 17.3 and 17.4). The resistance of an object of uniform cross section varies with temperature:

$$R = R_0(1 + \alpha\Delta T) \quad \text{or} \quad \Delta R = R_0\alpha\Delta T \qquad \begin{matrix} \textit{temperature variation} \\ \textit{of resistance} \end{matrix} \qquad (17.6)$$

Here, $\Delta R = R - R_0$, the change in resistance relative to its reference value R_0, usually taken to be at 20°C. The variation of resistance with temperature provides a means of measuring temperature in the form of an *electrical resistance thermometer*, as illustrated in the next Example.

Example 17.5 ■ An Electrical Thermometer: Variation of Resistance with Temperature

A platinum wire has a resistance of 0.50 Ω at 0°C. It is placed in a water bath, where its resistance rises to a final value of 0.60 Ω. What is the temperature of the bath?

Thinking It Through. From the temperature coefficient of resistivity for platinum from Table 17.1, ΔT can be found from Eq. 17.6 and added to 0°C, the initial temperature, to find the temperature of the bath.

Solution.

Given: $T_0 = 0°C$ *Find:* T (temperature of the bath)
        $R_0 = 0.50\ \Omega$
        $R = 0.60\ \Omega$
        $\alpha = 3.93 \times 10^{-3}/C°$ (Table 17.1)

The ratio $\Delta R/R_0$ is the fractional change in the initial resistance R_0 (at 0°C). We solve Eq. 17.6 for ΔT, using the given values:

$$\Delta T = \frac{\Delta R}{\alpha R_0} = \frac{R - R_0}{\alpha R_0} = \frac{0.60\ \Omega - 0.50\ \Omega}{(3.93 \times 10^{-3}/C°)(0.50\ \Omega)} = 51\ C°$$

Thus, the bath is at $T = T_0 + \Delta T = 0°C + 51\ C° = 51°C$.

Follow-Up Exercise. In this Example, if the material had been copper with $R_0 = 0.50\ \Omega$, rather than platinum, what would its resistance be at 51°C? From this, you should be able to explain which material makes the more "sensitive" thermometer, one with a high temperature coefficient of resistivity or one with a low value.

Superconductivity

Carbon and other semiconductors have negative temperature coefficients of resistivity. However, many materials, including most metals, have positive temperature coefficients, which means that their resistances increase as temperature increases. You might wonder how far electrical resistance can be reduced by lowering the temperature. In certain cases, the resistance can reach zero—not just close to zero, but, as accurately as can be measured, *exactly* zero. This phenomenon is called **superconductivity** (first discovered in 1911 by Heike Kamerlingh Onnes, a Dutch physicist). Currently the required temperatures are about 100 K or below. Thus its current usage is restricted to high-tech laboratory apparatus and research equipment.

However, it does have the potential for important new everyday applications, especially if materials can be found whose superconducting temperature is near room temperature. Among the applications are superconducting magnets (already in use in labs and small-scale naval propulsion units). In the absence of resistance, high currents and very high magnetic fields are possible (Chapter 19). Used in motors or engines, superconducting electromagnets would be more efficient, providing more power for the same energy input. Superconductors might also be used as electrical transmission lines with no resistive losses. Some envision superfast superconducting computer memories. The absence of electrical resistance opens almost endless possibilities. You're likely to hear more about superconductor applications in the future as new materials are developed.

22

REFLECTION AND REFRACTION OF LIGHT

PHYSICS FACTS

- Due to total internal reflection, optical fibers allow signals to travel for long distances without repeaters (amplifiers), to compensate for reductions in signal strength. Fiber-optic repeaters are currently about 100 km (about 62 mi) apart, compared to about 1.5 km (about 1 mi) for electrical (wire-based) systems.

- Every day installers lay enough new fiber-optic cables for computer networks to circle the Earth three times. Optical fibers can be drawn to smaller diameters than copper wire. Fibers can be as small as 10 microns in diameter. In comparison, the average human hair is about 25 microns in diameter.

- Most camera lenses are coated with a thin film to reduce light loss due to reflection. For a typical seven-element camera lens, about 50% of the light would be lost due to reflection if the lens were not coated with thin films.

- In 1998, scientists at MIT made a perfect mirror, a mirror with 100% reflection. A tube lined with this type of mirror would transmit light over long distances better than optical fibers.

We live in a visual world, surrounded by eye-catching images such as that refractive image of the turtle shown in the photo. How these images are formed is something taken largely for granted—until we see something that can't be easily explained. *Optics* is the study of light and vision. Human vision requires *visible light* of wavelength from 400 nm to 700 nm (see Fig. 20.23). Optical properties, such as reflection and refraction, are shared by all electromagnetic waves. Light acts as a wave in its propagation (Chapter 24) and as a particle (photon) when it interacts with matter (Chapter 27–30).

In this chapter, we will investigate the basic optical phenomena of reflection, refraction, total internal reflection, and dispersion. The principles that govern reflection explain the behavior of mirrors, while those that govern refraction explain the properties of lenses. With the aid of these and other optical principles, we can understand many optical phenomena experienced every day—why a glass prism spreads light into a spectrum of colors, what causes mirages, how rainbows are formed, and why the legs of a person standing in a lake or swimming pool seem to shorten. Some less familiar but increasingly useful territory, including the fascinating field of fiber optics will also be explored.

A simple geometrical approach involving straight lines and angles can be used to investigate many aspects of the properties of light, especially how light propagates. For these purposes, we need not be concerned with the physical (wave) nature of electromagnetic waves described in Chapter 20. The principles of geometrical optics will be introduced here and applied in greater detail in the study of mirrors and lenses in Chapter 23.

705

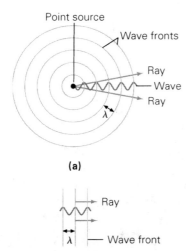

(a)

(b)

▲ **FIGURE 22.1 Wave fronts and rays** A wave front is defined by adjacent points on a wave that are in phase, such as those along wave crests or troughs. A line perpendicular to a wave front in the direction of the wave's propagation is called a ray. **(a)** Near a point source, the wave fronts are circular in two dimensions and spherical in three dimensions. **(b)** Very far from a point source, the wave fronts are approximately linear or planar and the rays nearly parallel.

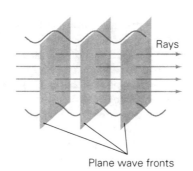

▲ **FIGURE 22.2 Light rays** A plane wave travels in a direction perpendicular to its wave fronts. A beam of light can be represented by a group of parallel rays (or by a single ray).

22.1 Wave Fronts and Rays

OBJECTIVE: To define and explain the concepts of wave fronts and rays.

Waves, electromagnetic or otherwise, are conveniently described in terms of wave fronts. A **wave front** is the line or surface defined by adjacent portions of a wave that are in phase. If an arc is drawn along one of the crests of a circular water wave moving out from a point source, all the particles on the arc will be in phase (◄Fig. 22.1a). An arc along a wave trough would work equally well. For a three-dimensional spherical wave, such as a sound or light wave emitted from a point source, the wave front is a spherical surface rather than a circle.

Very far from the source, the curvature of a short segment of a circular or spherical wave front is extremely small. Such a segment may be approximated as a *linear wave front* (in two dimensions) or a **plane wave front** (in three dimensions), just as we take the surface of the Earth to be locally flat (Fig. 22.1b). A plane wave front can also be produced directly by a large luminous flat surface. In a uniform medium, wave fronts propagate outward from the source at a speed characteristic of the medium. This was seen for sound waves in Chapter 14, and the same occurs for light, although at a much faster speed. The speed of light is greatest in a vacuum: $c = 3.00 \times 10^8$ m/s. The speed of light in air, for all practical purposes, is the same as that in vacuum.

The geometrical description of a wave in terms of wave fronts tends to neglect the fact that the wave is actually oscillating, like those studied in Chapter 13. This simplification is carried a step further with the concept of a ray. As illustrated in Fig. 22.1, a line drawn perpendicular to a series of wave fronts and pointing in the direction of propagation is called a **ray**. Note that a ray points in the direction of the energy flow of a wave. A plane wave is assumed to travel in a straight line in a medium in the direction of its rays, perpendicular to its plane wave fronts. A beam of light can be represented by a group of rays or simply as a single ray (◄Fig. 22.2). The representation of light as rays is adequate and convenient for describing many optical phenomena.

How do we see things and objects around us? We see them because rays from the objects, or rays that appear to come from the objects, enter our eyes (▼Fig. 22.3). In the eyes rays form images of the objects on the retina. The rays could be coming directly from the objects as in the case of light sources or could be reflected or refracted by the objects or other optical systems. Our eyes and brain working together, however, cannot tell whether the rays actually come from the objects or only *appear* to come from the objects. This is one way magicians can fool our eyes with seemingly impossible illusions.

The use of the geometrical representations of wave fronts and rays to explain phenomena such as the reflection and refraction of light is called **geometrical optics**. However, certain other phenomena, such as the interference of light, cannot be treated in this manner and must be explained in terms of actual wave characteristics. These phenomena will be considered in Chapter 24.

▶ **FIGURE 22.3 How we see things** We see things because **(a)** rays from the objects or **(b)** rays appearing to come from the objects enter our eyes.

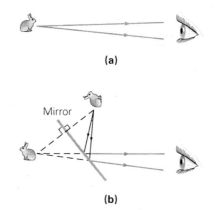

(a)

(b)

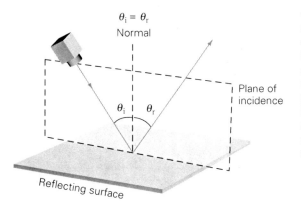

$\theta_i = \theta_r$
Normal

Plane of incidence

θ_i θ_r

Reflecting surface

◀ **FIGURE 22.4 The law of reflection** According to the law of reflection, the angle of incidence (θ_i) is equal to the angle of reflection (θ_r). Note that the angles are measured relative to a normal (a line perpendicular to the reflecting surface). The normal and the incident and reflected rays always lie in the same plane.

22.2 Reflection

OBJECTIVES: To (a) explain the law of reflection, and (b) distinguish between regular (specular) and irregular (diffuse) reflection.

The reflection of light is an optical phenomenon of enormous importance: If light were not reflected to our eyes by objects around us, we wouldn't see the objects at all. **Reflection** involves the absorption and re-emission of light by means of complex electromagnetic vibrations in the atoms of the reflecting medium. However, the phenomenon is easily described by using rays.

A light ray incident on a surface is described by an **angle of incidence (θ_i)**. This angle is measured relative to a *normal*—a line perpendicular to the reflecting surface (▲ Fig. 22.4). Similarly, the reflected ray is described by an **angle of reflection (θ_r)**, also measured from the normal. The relationship between these angles is given by the **law of reflection**: The angle of incidence is equal to the angle of reflection, or

$$\theta_i = \theta_r \quad \textit{law of reflection} \quad (22.1)$$

Two other attributes of reflection are that the incident ray, the reflected ray, and the normal all lie in the same plane, which is sometimes called the plane of incidence, and that the incident and the reflected rays are on opposite sides of the normal.

When the reflecting surface is smooth and flat, the reflected rays from parallel incident rays are also parallel (▶Fig. 22.5a). This type of reflection is called **specular**, or **regular**, **reflection**. The reflection from a highly polished flat mirror is an example of specular (regular) reflection (Fig. 22.5b). If the reflecting surface is rough, however, the reflected rays are not parallel, because of the irregular nature of the surface (▶Fig. 22.6). This type of reflection is termed **diffuse**, or **irregular**, **reflection**. The reflection of light from this page is an example of diffuse reflection because the paper is microscopically rough. Insight 22.1 on A Dark, Rainy Night on page 709, discusses more about the difference between specular and diffuse reflection in a real-life situation.

Note in Fig. 22.5a and Fig. 22.6 that the law of reflection still applies locally to both specular and diffuse reflection. However, the type of reflection involved determines whether we see images from a reflecting surface. In specular reflection, the reflected, parallel rays produce an image when they are viewed by an optical system such as an eye or a camera. Diffuse reflection does not produce an image, because the light is reflected in various directions.

Experience with friction and direct investigations show that all surfaces are rough on a microscopic scale. What, then, determines whether reflection is specular or diffuse? In general, if the dimensions of the surface irregularities are greater than the wavelength of the light, the reflection is diffuse. Therefore, to make a good mirror, glass (with a metal coating) or metal must be polished at least until the surface

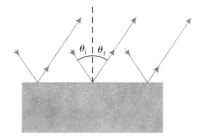

θ_i θ_r

(a) Specular (regular) reflection (diagram)

(b) Specular (regular) reflection (photo)

▲ **FIGURE 22.5 Specular (regular) reflection (a)** When a light beam is reflected from a smooth surface and the reflected rays are parallel, the reflection is said to be specular or regular. **(b)** Specular (regular) reflection from a smooth water surface produces an almost perfect mirror image of salt mounds at this Australian salt mine.

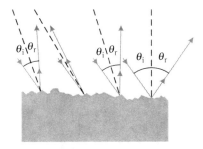

θ_i θ_r θ_i θ_r θ_i θ_r

▲ **FIGURE 22.6 Diffuse (irregular) reflection** Reflected rays from a relatively rough surface, such as this page, are not parallel; the reflection is said to be diffuse or irregular. (Note that the law of reflection still applies locally to each individual ray.)

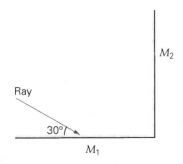

Ray

30°

M_1

M_2

▲ **FIGURE 22.7 Trace the ray** See Example 22.1.

Note: Drawing diagrams like these is extremely important in the study of geometrical optics.

LEARN BY DRAWING

**Tracing
the Reflected Rays**

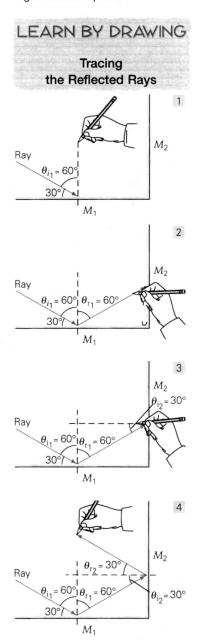

irregularities are about the same size as the wavelength of light. Recall from Chapter 20 that the wavelength of visible light is on the order of 10^{-7} m. (You will learn more about reflection from a mirror in the Learn by Drawing presented in Example 22.1.)

Diffuse reflection enables us to see illuminated objects, such as the Moon. If the Moon's spherical surface were smooth, only the reflected sunlight from a small region would come to an observer on the Earth, and only that small illuminated area would be seen. Also, you can see the beam of light from a flashlight or spotlight because of diffuse reflection from dust and particles in the air.

Example 22.1 ■ Tracing the Reflected Ray

Two mirrors, M_1 and M_2, are perpendicular to each other, with a light ray incident on one of the mirrors as shown in ◄Fig. 22.7. (a) Sketch a diagram to trace the path of the reflected light ray. (b) Find the direction of the ray after it is reflected by M_2.

Thinking It Through. The law of reflection can be used to determine the direction of the ray after it leaves the first and then the second mirror.

Solution.

Given: $\theta = 30°$ (angle relative to M_1)   *Find:* (a) Sketch a diagram tracing the light ray
                                                             (b) θ_{r_2} (angle of reflection from M_2)

Follow steps 1–4 in Learn by Drawing:

(a) 1. Since the incident and reflected rays are measured from the normal (a line perpendicular to the reflecting surface), we draw the normal to mirror M_1 at the point the incident ray hits M_1. From geometry, it can be seen that the angle of incidence on M_1 is $\theta_{i_1} = 60°$.
   2. According to the law of reflection, the angle of reflection from M_1 is also $\theta_{r_1} = 60°$. Next, draw this reflected ray with an angle of reflection of 60°, and extend it until it hits M_2.
   3. Draw another normal to M_2 at the point where the ray hits M_2. Also from geometry (focus on the triangle in the diagram), the angle of incidence on M_2 is $\theta_{i_2} = 30°$. (Why?)

(b) 4. The angle of reflection off M_2 is $\theta_{r_2} = \theta_{i_2} = 30°$. This is the final direction of the ray reflected after both mirrors.
   What if the directions of the rays are reversed? In other words, if a ray is first incident on M_2, in the direction opposite that of the one drawn for part (b), will all the rays reverse their directions? Draw another diagram to prove that this is indeed the case. Light rays are reversible.

Follow-Up Exercise. When following an eighteen-wheel truck, you may see a sign on the back stating, "If you can't see my mirror, I can't see you." What does this mean? (*Answers to all Follow-Up Exercises are at the back of the text.*)

22.3 Refraction

OBJECTIVES: To (a) explain refraction in terms of Snell's law and the index of refraction, and (b) give examples of refractive phenomena.

Refraction refers to the change in direction of a wave at a boundary where the wave passes from one transparent medium into another. In general, when a wave is incident on a boundary between media, some of the wave's energy is reflected and some is transmitted. For example, when light traveling in air is incident on a transparent material such as glass, it is partially reflected and partially transmitted (▶Fig. 22.8). But the direction of the transmitted light is different from the direction of the incident light, so the light is said to have been refracted; in other words, it has changed direction.

This change in direction is caused by the fact that light travels with different speeds in different media. Intuitively, you might expect the passage of light to take longer through a medium with more atoms per volume, and the

INSIGHT 22.1 A DARK, RAINY NIGHT

When you drive on a dry night, you can clearly see the road and the street signs ahead of you from your headlights. However, here is a familiar scene on a dark, rainy night: Even with headlights, you can hardly see the road ahead. When a car approaches, the situation becomes even worse. You see the reflections of the approaching car's headlights from the surface of the road, and they appear brighter than usual. Often nothing can be seen except the reflective glare of the oncoming headlights.

What causes these conditions? When the road surface is dry, the reflection of light off the road is diffuse (irregular), because the surface is rough. Light from your headlights hits the road in front of you and reflects in all directions. Some of it reflects back, and

you can see the road clearly (just as you can read this page because the paper is microscopically rough). However, when the road surface is wet, water fills the crevices, turning the road into a relatively smooth reflecting surface (Fig. 1a). Light from the headlights then reflects ahead. The normally diffuse reflection is gone and is replaced by specular reflection. Reflected images of lighted buildings and road lights form, blurring the view of the surface, and the specular reflection of oncoming cars' headlights may make it difficult for you to see the road (Fig. 1b).

Besides wet, slippery surfaces, specular reflection is a major cause of accidents on rainy nights. Thus, extra caution is advised under such conditions.

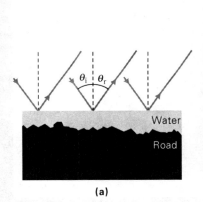

(a)

(b)

FIGURE 1 Diffuse to specular (a) The diffuse reflection from a dry road is turned into specular reflection by water on the road's surface. (b) Instead of seeing the road, a driver sees the reflected images of lights, buildings, and so on.

---

speed of light is, in fact, generally less in denser media. For example, the speed of light in water is about 75% of that in air or a vacuum. ▾Fig. 22.9a shows the refraction of light at an air–water boundary.

The change in the direction of wave propagation is described by the **angle of refraction**. In Fig. 22.9b, θ_1 is the angle of incidence and θ_2 is the angle of refraction. We use notations of θ_1 and θ_2 for the angles of incidence and refraction to avoid confusion with θ_i and θ_r for the angles of incidence and reflection. Willebrord Snell (1580–1626), a Dutch physicist, discovered a relationship between the angles (θ) and the speeds (v) of light in two media (Fig. 22.9b):

$$\frac{\sin \theta_1}{\sin \theta_2} = \frac{v_1}{v_2} \quad \textit{Snell's law} \tag{22.2}$$

This expression is known as **Snell's law**. Note that θ_1 and θ_2 are always taken with respect to the normal.

Thus, light is refracted when passing from one medium into another because the speed of light is different in the two media. The speed of light is greatest in a vacuum, and it is therefore convenient to compare the speed of light in other

▲ **FIGURE 22.8 Reflection and refraction** A beam of light is incident on a trapezoidal prism from the left. Part of the beam is reflected, and part is refracted. The refracted beam is partially reflected and partially refracted at the bottom glass–air surface.

▶ **FIGURE 22.9 Refraction (a)** Light changes direction on entering a different medium. **(b)** The refracted ray is described by the angle of refraction, θ_2, measured from the normal.

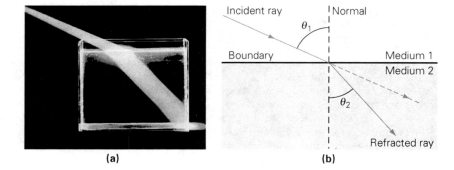

(a)   **(b)**

Illustration 34.1 *Huygen's Principle and Refraction*

Note: When light is refracted,
- its speed and wavelength are changed;
- its frequency remains unchanged.

media with this constant value (c). This is done by defining a ratio called the **index of refraction (n)**:

$$n = \frac{c}{v}\left(\frac{\text{speed of light in a vacuum}}{\text{speed of light in a medium}}\right) \qquad (22.3)$$

As a ratio of speeds, the index of refraction is a unitless quantity. The indices of refraction of several substances are given in Table 22.1. Note that these values are for a specific wavelength of light. The wavelength is specified because v, and consequently n, are slightly different for different wavelengths. (This is the cause of dispersion, to be discussed later in the chapter.) The values of n given in the table will be used in examples and exercises in this chapter for all wavelengths of light in the visible region, unless otherwise noted. Observe that n is always greater than 1, because the speed of light in a vacuum is greater than the speed of light in any material ($c > v$).

The frequency (f) of light does not change when the light enters another medium, but the wavelength of light in a material (λ_m) differs from the wavelength of that light in a vacuum (λ), as can be easily shown:

$$n = \frac{c}{v} = \frac{\lambda f}{\lambda_m f}$$

or

$$n = \frac{\lambda}{\lambda_m} \qquad (22.4)$$

The wavelength of light in the medium is then $\lambda_m = \lambda/n$. Since $n > 1$, it follows that $\lambda_m < \lambda$.

TABLE 22.1

Indices of Refraction (at $\lambda = 590$ nm)*

Substance	n
Air	1.00029
Water	1.33
Ice	1.31
Ethyl alcohol	1.36
Fused quartz	1.46
Human eye	1.336–1.406
Polystyrene	1.49
Oil (typical value)	1.50
Glass (by type)†	1.45–1.70
crown	1.52
flint	1.66
Zircon	1.92
Diamond	2.42

*One nanometer (nm) is 10^{-9} m.

†Crown glass is a soda–lime silicate glass; flint glass is a lead–alkali silicate glass. Flint glass is more dispersive than crown glass (Section 22.5).

Example 22.2 ■ The Speed of Light in Water: Index of Refraction

Light from a laser with a wavelength of 632.8 nm travels from air into water. What are the speed and wavelength of the laser light in water?

Thinking It Through. If we know the index of refraction (n) of a medium, the speed and wavelength of light in the medium can be obtained from Eq. 22.3 and Eq. 22.4.

Solution.

Given: $n = 1.33$ (from Table 22.1)   *Find:* v and λ_m (speed and wavelength
      $\lambda = 632.8$ nm   of light in water)
      $c = 3.00 \times 10^8$ m/s (speed of light in air)

Since $n = c/v$,

$$v = \frac{c}{n} = \frac{3.00 \times 10^8 \text{ m/s}}{1.33} = 2.26 \times 10^8 \text{ m/s}$$

Note that $1/n = v/c = 1/1.33 = 0.75$; therefore, v is 75% of the speed of light in a vacuum. Also, $n = \lambda/\lambda_m$, so

$$\lambda_m = \frac{\lambda}{n} = \frac{632.8 \text{ nm}}{1.33} = 475.8 \text{ nm}$$

Follow-Up Exercise. The speed of light of wavelength 500 nm (in air) in a particular liquid is 2.40×10^8 m/s. What is the index of refraction of the liquid and the wavelength of light in the liquid?

The index of refraction, n, is a measure of the speed of light in a transparent material, or technically, a measure of the *optical density* of the material. For example, the speed of light in water is less than that in air, so water is said to be optically denser than air. (Optical density in general correlates with mass density. However, in some instances, a material with a greater optical density than another can have a lower mass density.) Thus, the greater the index of refraction of a material, the greater is the material's optical density and the smaller is the speed of light in the material.

For practical purposes, the index of refraction is measured in air rather than in a vacuum, since the speed of light in air is very close to c, and

$$n_{air} = \frac{c}{v_{air}} \approx \frac{c}{c} = 1$$

(From Table 22.1, $n_{air} = 1.00029$, and we will usually assume $n_{air} = 1$.)

A more practical form of Snell's law can be rewritten as

$$\frac{\sin \theta_1}{\sin \theta_2} = \frac{v_1}{v_2} = \frac{c/n_1}{c/n_2} = \frac{n_2}{n_1}$$

or

$$n_1 \sin \theta_1 = n_2 \sin \theta_2 \quad \begin{matrix} \textit{Snell's law} \\ \textit{(another form)} \end{matrix} \quad (22.5)$$

where n_1 and n_2 are the indices of refraction for the first and second media, respectively.

Note that Eq. 22.5 can be used to measure the index of refraction. If the first medium is air, then $n_1 \approx 1$ and $n_2 \approx \sin \theta_1 / \sin \theta_2$. Thus, only the angles of incidence and refraction need to be measured to determine the index of refraction of a material experimentally. On the other hand, if the index of refraction of a material is known, it can be used in Snell's law to find the angle of refraction for any angle of incidence.

Note also that the sine of the refraction angle is inversely proportional to the index of refraction: $\sin \theta_2 \approx \sin \theta_1 / n_2$. Hence, for a given angle of incidence, the greater the index of refraction, the smaller is $\sin \theta_2$ and the smaller is the angle of refraction, θ_2.

More generally, the following relationships hold:

- If the second medium is more optically dense than the first medium ($n_2 > n_1$), the ray is refracted *toward* the normal ($\theta_2 < \theta_1$), as illustrated in ▾Fig. 22.10a.
- If the second medium is less optically dense than the first medium ($n_2 < n_1$), the ray is refracted *away from* the normal ($\theta_2 > \theta_1$), as illustrated in Fig. 22.10b.

Exploration 34.4 Fermat's Principle and Snell's Law

Note: During refraction the product of $n \sin \theta$ remains a constant from medium to medium.

▾ **FIGURE 22.10** Index of refraction and ray deviation **(a)** When the second medium is more optically dense than the first ($n_2 > n_1$), the ray is refracted toward the normal, as in the case of light entering water from air. **(b)** When the second medium is less optically dense than the first ($n_2 < n_1$), the ray is refracted away from the normal. [This is the case if the ray in part (a) is traced in reverse, going from medium 2 to medium 1.]

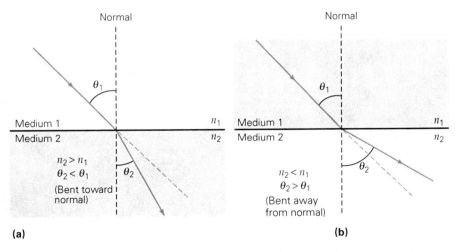

(a)   **(b)**

Integrated Example 22.3 ■ Angle of Refraction: Snell's Law

Light in water is incident on a piece of crown glass at an angle of 37° (relative to the normal). (a) Will the transmitted ray be (1) bent toward the normal, (2) bent away from the normal, or (3) not bent at all? Use a diagram to illustrate. (b) What is the angle of refraction?

(a) Conceptual Reasoning. We can use Table 22.1 to look up the indices of refraction of water and crown glass. According to the alternative form of Snell's law (Eq. 22.5), $n_1 \sin \theta_1 = n_2 \sin \theta_2$, (1) is the correct answer. Since $n_2 > n_1$, the angle of refraction must be smaller than the angle of incidence ($\theta_2 < \theta_1$). Because both θ_1 and θ_2 are measured from the normal, the refracted ray will bend toward the normal. The ray diagram in this case is identical to Fig. 22.10a.

(b) Quantitative Reasoning and Solution. Again, the alternative form of Snell's law (Eq. 22.5) is most practical in this case. (Why?) Listing the given quantities,

Given: $\theta_1 = 37°$ **Find:** (b) θ_2 (angle of refraction)
$n_1 = 1.33$ (water, from Table 22.1)
$n_2 = 1.52$ (crown glass, from Table 22.1)

The angle of refraction is found by using Eq. 22.5,

$$\sin \theta_2 = \frac{n_1 \sin \theta_1}{n_2} = \frac{(1.33)(\sin 37°)}{1.52} = 0.53$$

and

$$\theta_2 = \sin^{-1}(0.53) = 32°$$

Follow-Up Exercise. It is found experimentally that a beam of light entering a liquid from air at an angle of incidence of 37° exhibits an angle of refraction of 29° in the liquid. What is the speed of light in the liquid?

Example 22.4 ■ A Glass Tabletop: More about Refraction

A beam of light traveling in air strikes the glass top of a coffee table at an angle of incidence of 45° (▼ Fig. 22.11). The glass has an index of refraction of 1.5. (a) What is the angle of refraction for the light transmitted into the glass? (b) Prove that the emergent beam is parallel to the incident beam—that is, that $\theta_4 = \theta_1$. (c) If the glass is 2.0 cm thick, what is the lateral displacement between the ray entering and the ray emerging from the glass (the perpendicular distance between the two rays—d in the figure)?

Thinking It Through. Since two refractions are involved in this example, we use Snell's law in parts (a) and (b), and then some geometry and trigonometry in part (c).

Solution. Listing the data:

Given: $\theta_1 = 45°$ **Find:** (a) θ_2 (angle of refraction)
$n_1 = 1.0$ (air)   (b) Show that $\theta_4 = \theta_1$
$n_2 = 1.5$ (c) d (lateral displacement)
$y = 2.0$ cm

▶ **FIGURE 22.11 Two refractions** In the glass, the refracted ray is displaced laterally (sideways) a distance d from the incident ray, and the emergent ray is parallel to the original ray. (See Example 22.4.)

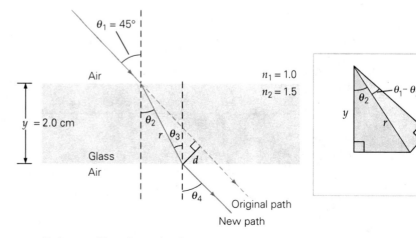

(a) Using the practical form of Snell's law, Eq. 22.5, with $n_1 = 1.0$ for air gives

$$\sin \theta_2 = \frac{n_1 \sin \theta_1}{n_2} = \frac{(1.0) \sin 45°}{1.5} = \frac{0.707}{1.5} = 0.47$$

Thus,

$$\theta_2 = \sin^{-1}(0.47) = 28°$$

Note that the beam is refracted toward the normal.

(b) If $\theta_1 = \theta_4$, then the emergent ray is parallel to the incident ray. Then applying Snell's law to the beam at both surfaces,

$$n_1 \sin \theta_1 = n_2 \sin \theta_2$$

and

$$n_2 \sin \theta_3 = n_1 \sin \theta_4$$

From the figure, $\theta_2 = \theta_3$. Therefore,

$$n_1 \sin \theta_1 = n_1 \sin \theta_4$$

or

$$\theta_1 = \theta_4$$

Thus, the emergent beam is parallel to the incident beam but displaced laterally or perpendicularly to the incident direction at a distance d.

(c) It can be seen from the inset in Fig. 22.11 that, to find d, we need to first find r from the known information in the pink right triangle. Then,

$$\frac{y}{r} = \cos \theta_2 \quad \text{or} \quad r = \frac{y}{\cos \theta_2}$$

In the yellow right triangle, $d = r \sin(\theta_1 - \theta_2)$. Substituting r from the previous step yields

$$d = \frac{y \sin(\theta_1 - \theta_2)}{\cos \theta_2} = \frac{(2.0 \text{ cm}) \sin(45° - 28°)}{\cos 28°} = 0.66 \text{ cm}$$

Follow-Up Exercise. If the glass in this Example had $n = 1.6$, would the lateral displacement be the same, larger, or smaller? Explain your answer conceptually, and then calculate the actual value to verify your reasoning.

Conceptual Example 22.5 ■ The Human Eye: Refraction and Wavelength

A simplified representation of the crystalline lens in a human eye shows it to have a cortex (an outer layer) of $n_{cortex} = 1.386$ and a nucleus (core) of $n_{nucleus} = 1.406$. (See Fig. 25.1b.) Note that both refraction indices are within the range listed for the human eye in Table 22.1. If a beam of monochromatic (single-frequency or -wavelength) light of wavelength 590 nm is directed from air through the front of the eye and into the crystalline lens, qualitatively compare and list the frequency, speed, and wavelength of light in air, the cortex, and the nucleus. First do the comparison without numbers, and then calculate the actual values to verify your reasoning.

Reasoning and Answer. First, the relative magnitudes of the indices of refraction are needed, where $n_{air} < n_{cortex} < n_{nucleus}$.

As learned earlier in this section, the frequency (f) of light is the same in all three media: air, the cortex, and the nucleus. Thus, the frequency can be calculated by using the speed and the wavelength of light in any of these materials, but it is easiest in air. (Why?) From the wave relationship $c = \lambda f$ (Eq. 13.17),

$$f = f_{air} = f_{cortex} = f_{nucleus} = \frac{c}{\lambda} = \frac{3.00 \times 10^8 \text{ m/s}}{590 \times 10^{-9} \text{ m}} = 5.08 \times 10^{14} \text{ Hz}$$

The speed of light in a medium depends on its index of refraction, since $v = c/n$. The smaller the index of refraction, the higher the speed. Therefore, the speed of light is the highest in air ($n = 1.00$) and lowest in the nucleus ($n = 1.406$).

The speed of light in the cortex is

$$v_{cortex} = \frac{c}{n_{cortex}} = \frac{3.00 \times 10^8 \text{ m/s}}{1.386} = 2.16 \times 10^8 \text{ m/s}$$

(continues on next page)

and the speed of light in the nucleus is

$$v_{nucleus} = \frac{3.00 \times 10^8 \text{ m/s}}{1.406} = 2.13 \times 10^8 \text{ m/s}$$

We also know that the wavelength of light in a medium depends on the index of refraction of the medium ($\lambda_m = \lambda/n$). The smaller the index of refraction, the longer the wavelength. Therefore, the wavelength of light is the longest in air ($n = 1.00$ and $\lambda = 590$ nm) and shortest in the nucleus ($n = 1.406$).

The wavelength in the cortex can be calculated from Eq. 22.4:

$$\lambda_{cortex} = \frac{\lambda}{n_{cortex}} = \frac{590 \text{ nm}}{1.386} = 426 \text{ nm}$$

and the wavelength in the nucleus is

$$\lambda_{nucleus} = \frac{590 \text{ nm}}{1.406} = 420 \text{ nm}$$

Finally, a table can be constructed to compare more easily the index of refraction, frequency, speed, and wavelength of light in the three media:

	Index of refraction	Frequency (Hz)	Speed (m/s)	Wavelength (nm)
Air	1.00	5.08×10^{14}	3.00×10^8	590
Cortex	1.386	5.08×10^{14}	2.16×10^8	426
Nucleus	1.406	5.08×10^{14}	2.13×10^8	420

Follow-Up Exercise. A light source of a single frequency is submerged in water in a special fish tank. The beam travels in the water, through double glass panes at the side of the tank (each glass pane has a different n), and into air. In general, what happens to (a) the frequency and (b) the wavelength of the light when it emerges into the outside air?

Refraction is common in everyday life and explains many things we observe. Let's look at refraction in action.

Mirage: A common example of this phenomenon sometimes occurs on a highway on a hot summer day. The refraction of light is caused by layers of air that are at different temperatures (the layer closer to the road is at a higher temperature, lower density, and lower index of refraction). This variation in indices of refraction gives rise to the observed "wet" spot and an inverted image of an object such as a car (▼Fig. 22.12a). The

▼ **FIGURE 22.12 Refraction in action** (a) An inverted car on a "wet" road, a mirage. (b) The mirage is formed when light from the object is refracted by layers of air at different temperatures near the surface of the road.

(a)

(b)

INSIGHT 22.2 NEGATIVE INDEX OF REFRACTION AND THE "PERFECT" LENS

In 1968 physicists predicted the existence of a material with a negative index of refraction. They expected that, in the presence of such a negative-index material, nearly all known wave propagation and optical phenomena would be substantially altered. Negative-index materials were not known to exist at the time, however.

At the beginning of the twenty-first century, a new class of artificially structured materials was created that were found to have negative indices of refraction. Moreover, a natural ferroelastic material called a *"twinned" alloy* (containing yttrium, vanadium, and oxygen) has also displayed a negative index of refraction (Fig. 1).

Figure 2 illustrates the difference between materials with positive and negative indices of refraction. In Fig. 2a, light incident on a positive-index material is refracted to the other side of the normal to the interface. However, if the material has a negative index of refraction, the same incident light is refracted to the same side of the normal to the interface (Fig. 2b). Due to

this "abnormal" refraction, negative-index slab materials with flat surfaces can even focus light as shown in Fig. 2c, resulting in a new class of lenses (to be discussed in Chapter 23). If a light source is placed on one side of a slab with a refractive index $n = -1$, the light rays are refracted in such a way as to produce a focal point inside the material and then another just outside the material. The "focal length" of such a lens would depend on both the object distance and the thickness of the slab.

The undesirable characteristics of lenses made of materials with a positive index of refraction are energy loss due to reflection, aberrations, and low resolution due to diffraction limit (more on this in Chapter 24). The latest experiments provide strong evidence that negative-index materials have an important future in imaging. This is because negative-index lenses offer a new degree of flexibility that could lead to more compact lenses with reduced lens aberration. The diffraction limit—which is the most fundamental limitation to image resolution—may be circumvented by negative-index materials. Furthermore, total negative refraction—that is, absence of a reflection—has been observed in materials with a negative index of refraction. Such a lens would truly be a "perfect lens."

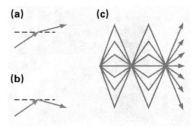

FIGURE 1 Material with a negative index of refraction This artificial material made from grids of rings and wires has a negative index of refraction.

FIGURE 2 Reflection in positive-index versus negative-index materials **(a)** Light incident on the interface between air and a positive-index material is bent toward the other side of the normal, **(b)** whereas in a negative-index material light is bent toward the same side of the normal. **(c)** If a light source is placed on one side of a slab with a refractive index of $n = -1$, the waves are refracted in such a way as to produce a focus inside the material and then another just outside the material.

term *mirage* generally brings to mind a thirsty person in the desert "seeing" a pool of water that really isn't there. This optical illusion plays tricks on the mind, with the image usually seen as in a pool of water and our eye's past experience unconsciously leading us to conclude that there is water on the road.

In Fig. 22.12b, there are two ways for light to get to our eyes from the car. First, the horizontal rays come directly from the car to our eyes, so we see the car above the ground. Also, the rays from the car that travel toward the road surface will be gradually refracted by the layered air. After hitting the surface, these rays will be refracted again and travel toward our eyes. (See the inset in the figure.) Cooler air has a higher density and so a higher index of refraction. A ray traveling toward the road surface will be gradually refracted with increasing angle of refraction until it hits the surface. It will then be refracted again with decreasing angle of refraction, going toward our eyes. As a consequence, we also see an inverted image of the car, below the road surface. In other words, the surface of the road acts almost as a mirror.

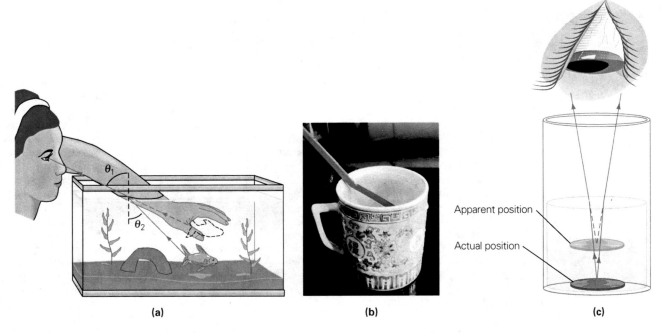

(a)　　　　　　　　　(b)　　　　　　　　　(c)

▲ **FIGURE 22.13 Refractive effects**
(a) The light is refracted, and because we tend to think of light as traveling in straight lines, the fish is below where we think it is.
(b) The chopstick appears bent at the air–water boundary. If the cup is transparent, we see a different refraction. (See Exercise 21.)
(c) Because of refraction, the coin appears to be closer than it actually is.

The "pool of water" is actually sky light being refracted—an image of the sky. This layering of air of different temperatures, creating different indices of refraction, causes us to "see" the rising hot air as a result of continually changing refraction.

The opposite of this is the mirage at sea (looming effect). At the sea, the air above is warmer than below. This causes the light to be refracted opposite as in Fig. 22.12b, causing objects to be seen in the air above sea.

Not where it should be: You may have experienced a refractive effect while trying to reach for something underwater, such as a fish (▲Fig. 22.13a). We are used to light traveling in straight lines from objects to our eyes, but the light reaching our eyes from a submerged object has a directional change at the air–water interface. (Note in the figure that the ray is refracted away from the normal.) As a result, the object appears closer to the surface than it actually is, and therefore we tend to miss the object when reaching for it. For the same reason, a chopstick in a cup appears bent (Fig. 22.13b), a coin in a glass of water will appear closer than it really is (Fig. 22.13c), and the legs of a person standing in water seem shorter than their actual length. The relationship between the true depth and the apparent depth can be calculated. (See Exercise 37.)

Atmospheric effects: The Sun on the horizon sometimes appears flattened, with its horizontal dimension greater than its vertical dimension (▼Fig. 22.14a). This effect is the result of temperature and density variations in the denser air along the horizon. These variations occur predominantly vertically, so light from the top and bottom portions of the Sun are refracted differently as the two sets of beams pass through different atmospheric densities with different indices of refraction.

Atmospheric refraction lengthens the day, so to speak, by allowing us to see the Sun (or the Moon, for that matter) just before it actually rises above the horizon and

▶ **FIGURE 22.14 Atmospheric effects (a)** The Sun on the horizon commonly appears flattened as a result of atmospheric refraction. **(b)** Before rising and after setting, the Sun can be seen briefly also because of atmospheric refraction. (Exaggerated for illustration).

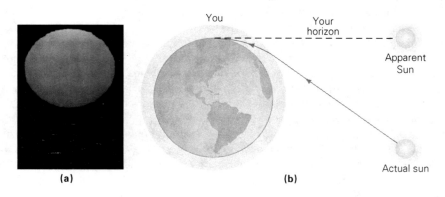

(a)　　　　　　　　　(b)

Science Fundamentals

just after it actually sets below the horizon (as much as 20 min on both ends). The denser air near the Earth refracts the light over the horizon toward us (Fig. 22.14b).

The twinkling of stars is due to atmospheric turbulence, which distorts the light from the stars. The turbulences refract light in random directions and cause the stars to appear to "twinkle." Stars on the horizon will appear to twinkle more than stars directly overhead, because the light has to pass through more of the Earth's atmosphere. However, planets do not "twinkle" as much. This is because stars are much farther away than planets, so they appear as point sources. Outside the Earth's atmosphere, the stars don't twinkle.

23

MIRRORS AND LENSES

PHYSICS FACTS

- The largest refracting optical lens in the world measures 1.827 m (5.99 ft) in diameter. It was constructed by a team at the Optics Shop of the Optical Sciences Center of the University of Arizona in Tucson, Arizona, and completed in January 2000.

- The largest mirror under development for the European Space Agency's Herschel Space Observatory is 3.5 m (11.5 ft) in diameter. It is made from silicon carbide, which reduces its mass by a factor of 5 compared with traditional materials.

- A typical camera lens actually has more than one element (lens) inside. Many camera lenses have seven or more compensating elements to reduce or eliminate various types of lens aberrations. A single lens would produce distorted images.

What would life be like if there were no mirrors in bathrooms or cars, and if eyeglasses did not exist? Imagine a world without optical images of any kind—no photographs, no movies, no TV. Think about how little we'd know about the universe if there were no telescopes to observe distant planets and stars—or how little we'd know about biology and medicine if there were no microscopes to see bacteria and cells. It is often forgotten how dependent we are on mirrors and lenses.

The first mirror was probably the reflecting surface of a pool of water. Later, people discovered that polished metals and glass also have reflective properties. They must also have noticed that when they looked at things through glass, the objects looked different than when viewed directly, depending on the shape of the glass. In some cases, the objects appeared to be reduced or inverted, as the flower in the photo. In time, people learned to shape glass purposefully into lenses, paving the way for the eventual development of the many optical devices we now take for granted.

The optical properties of mirrors and lenses are based on the principles of reflection and refraction of light, as introduced in Chapter 22. In this chapter, you'll learn the principles of mirrors and lenses. Among other things, you'll discover why the images in the photo are upside down and reduced, whereas your image in an ordinary flat mirror is right side up—but the image doesn't seem to comb your hair with the same hand you use!

729

23.3 Lenses

OBJECTIVES: To (a) distinguish between converging and diverging lenses, (b) describe their images and their characteristics, and (c) find image locations and characteristics by using ray diagrams and the thin-lens equation.

The word *lens* is from the Latin *lentil*, which is a round, flattened, edible seed of a pea-like plant. Its shape is similar to that of a lens. An optical **lens** is made from transparent material (most commonly glass, but sometimes plastic or crystal). One or both surfaces usually have a spherical contour. *Biconvex* spherical lenses (with both surfaces convex) and *biconcave* spherical lenses (with both surfaces concave) are illustrated in ▾Fig. 23.11. Lenses can form images by refracting the light that passes through them.

A biconvex lens is an example of a **converging lens**. Incident light rays parallel to the axis of the lens converge at a focal point (F) on the opposite side of the lens (▾Fig. 23.12a). This fact provides a way to experimentally determine the focal length of a converging lens. You may have focused the Sun's rays with a magnifying glass (a biconvex, or converging, lens) and thereby witnessed the concentration of radiant energy that results (Fig. 23.12b).

A biconcave lens is an example of a **diverging lens**. Incident parallel rays emerge from the lens as though they emanated from a focal point on the incident side of the lens (▸Fig. 23.13).

▸ **FIGURE 23.11** Spherical lenses
Spherical lenses have surfaces defined by two spheres, and the surfaces are either convex or concave. **(a)** Biconvex and **(b)** biconcave lenses are shown here. If $R_1 = R_2$, a lens is spherically symmetric.

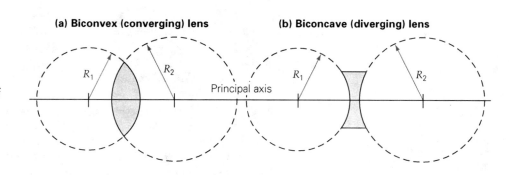

(a) Biconvex (converging) lens   **(b) Biconcave (diverging) lens**

▸ **FIGURE 23.12** Converging lens
(a) For a thin biconvex lens, rays parallel to the axis converge at the focal point F. **(b)** A magnifying glass (converging lens) can be used to focus the Sun's rays to a spot—with incendiary results. Do not try this at home!

Illustration 35.1 Lenses and the Thin-Lens Approximation

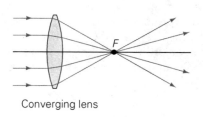

Converging lens

(a) Biconvex (converging) lens

(b)

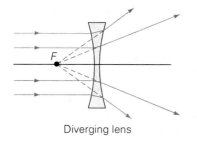

Biconcave (diverging) lens

◀ **FIGURE 23.13** Diverging lens
Rays parallel to the axis of a
biconcave, or diverging, lens
appear to diverge from a focal point
on the incident side of the lens.

There are several types of converging and diverging lenses (▼Fig. 23.14).
Convex and concave meniscus lenses are the type most commonly used for corrective eyeglasses. In general, a converging lens is thicker at its center than at its
periphery, and a diverging lens is thinner at its center than at its periphery. This
discussion will be limited to spherically symmetric biconvex and biconcave lenses, for which both surfaces have the same radius of curvature.

When light passes through a lens, it is refracted and displaced laterally
(Example 22.4 and Fig. 22.11). If a lens is thick, this displacement may be fairly large
and can complicate analysis of the lens's characteristics. This problem does not arise
with thin lenses, for which the refractive displacement of transmitted light is negligible. Our discussion will be limited to thin lenses. A thin lens is a lens for which the
thickness of the lens is assumed to be negligible compared with the lens's focal length.

A lens with spherical geometry has, *for each lens surface*, a center of curvature (C),
a radius of curvature (R), a focal point (F), and a focal length (f). The focal points
are at equal distances on either side of a thin lens. However, for a spherical lens,
the focal length is *not* simply related to R by $f = R/2$ as it is for spherical mirrors.
Because the focal length also depends on the lens's index of refraction, the focal
length of a lens is usually specified, rather than its radius of curvature. This will be
discussed in Section 23.4.

The general rules for drawing ray diagrams for lenses are similar to those for
spherical mirrors. But some modifications are necessary, since light passes
through a lens. Opposite sides of a lens are generally distinguished as the *object
side* and the *image side*. The object side is the side on which an object is positioned,
and the image side is the *opposite* side of the lens (where a real image would be
formed). The three rays from a point on an object are drawn as follows (see Learn
by Drawing for Example 23.5 on page 743):

1. A **parallel ray** is a ray that is parallel to the lens's optic axis on incidence and,
   after refraction, either (a) passes through the focal point on the image side of a
   converging lens *or* (b) appears to diverge from the focal point on the object
   side of a diverging lens.

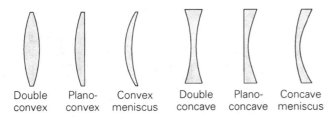

| Double convex | Plano- convex | Convex meniscus | Double concave | Plano- concave | Concave meniscus |

Converging lenses   **Diverging lenses**

▲ **FIGURE 23.14** Lens shapes Lens shapes vary widely and are normally categorized as
converging or diverging. In general, a converging lens is thicker at its center than at the
periphery, and a diverging lens is thinner at its center than at the periphery.

Exploration 35.2 Ray Diagrams

2. A **chief ray**, or **central ray**, is a ray that passes through the center of the lens and is undeviated because the lens is "thin."

3. A **focal ray** is a ray that (a) passes through the focal point on the object side of a converging lens *or* (b) appears to pass through the focal point on the image side of a diverging lens and, after refraction, is parallel to the lens's optic axis.

As with spherical mirrors, only two rays are needed to determine the image; we will normally use the parallel and chief rays. (As in the case of mirrors, however, it is generally a good idea to include a third ray, the focal ray, in your diagrams as a check.)

Example 23.5 ■ Learn by Drawing: A Lens Diagram

An object is placed 30 cm in front of a thin biconvex lens of focal length 20 cm. (a) Use a ray diagram to locate the image. (b) Discuss the characteristics of the image.

Thinking It Through. Follow the steps for lens ray diagrams, as given previously.

Solution.

Given: $d_o = 30$ cm   **Find:** (a) location of the image (using a ray diagram)
          $f = 20$ cm   (b) the image's characteristics

(a) Since we have been asked to use a ray diagram to locate the image (see the accompanying Learn by Drawing), the first thing to decide is a scale for the drawing. In this example, a scale of 1 cm to represent 10 cm is used. That way, the object would be 3.00 cm in front of the mirror in our drawing.

First the optic axis, the lens, the object (a lighted candle), and the focal points (F) are drawn. A vertical dashed line through the center of the lens is drawn because, for simplicity, the refraction is depicted as if it occurs at the center of each lens. In reality, it would occur at the air–glass and glass–air surfaces of each lens.

Follow steps 1–4 in the accompanying Learn by Drawing:

1. The first ray drawn is the parallel ray (① in the drawing). From the tip of the flame, draw a horizontal ray (parallel to the optic axis). After passing through the lens, this ray goes through the focal point F on the image side.

2. Then draw the chief ray (② in the drawing). From the tip of the flame, draw a ray passing through the center of the lens. This ray will go undeviated through the thin lens to the image side.

3. It can be clearly seen that these two rays intersect on the image side. The point of intersection is the image point of the tip of the candle. From this point, draw the image by extending the tip of the flame to the optic axis.

4. Only two rays are needed to locate the image. However, if you draw the third ray, in this case the focal ray (③ in the drawing), it must go through the same point on the image at which the other two rays intersect (if you are drawing the diagram carefully). The ray from the tip of the flame passing through the focal point F on the object side will travel parallel to the optic axis on the image side.

(b) From the ray diagram in part (a), the image is real (because the rays intersect or converge on the image side). As a result, this real image could be seen on a screen (for example, a piece of white paper) that is positioned at a distance d_i from the converging lens. The image is also inverted (the image of the candle points downward) and is larger than the object.

In this case, $d_o = 30$ cm and $f = 20$ cm, so $2f > d_o > f$. Using similar ray diagrams, you can prove that for any d_o in this range, the image is always real, enlarged, and inverted. Actually, the overhead projector in your classroom uses this particular arrangement.

Follow-Up Exercise. In this Example, what does the image look like if the object is 10 cm in front of the lens? Locate the image graphically and discuss the characteristics of the image.

LEARN BY DRAWING

A LENS RAY DIAGRAM (SEE EXAMPLE 23.5)

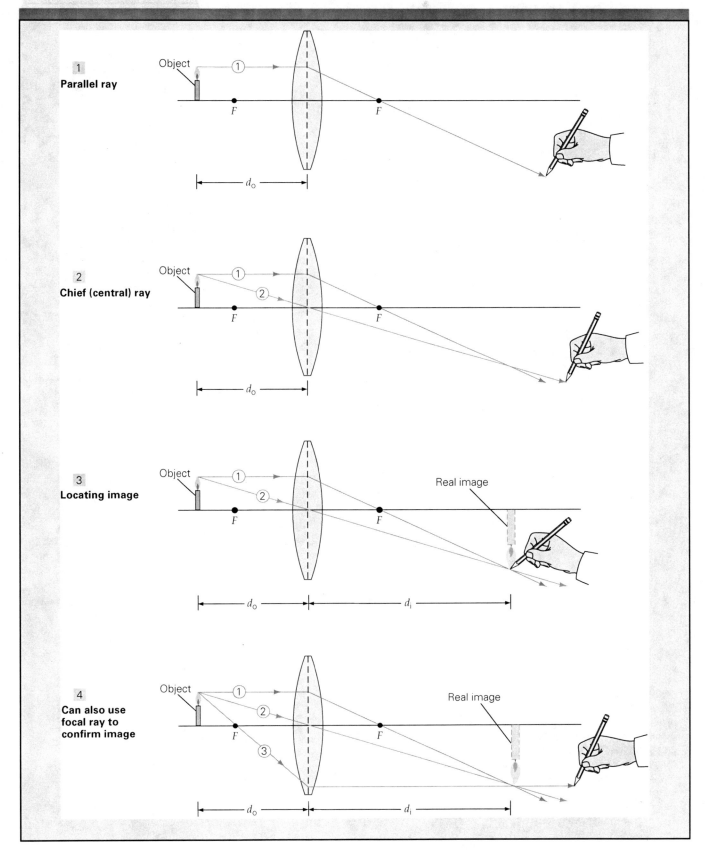

1
Parallel ray

Object

d_o

2
Chief (central) ray

Object

d_o

3
Locating image

Object

Real image

d_o d_i

4
Can also use focal ray to confirm image

Object

Real image

d_o d_i

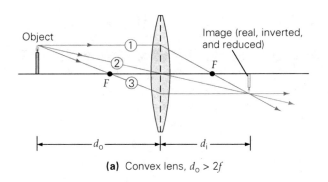

(a) Convex lens, $d_o > 2f$

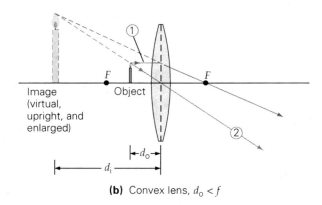

(b) Convex lens, $d_o < f$

▲ **FIGURE 23.15 Ray diagrams for lenses (a)** A converging biconvex lens forms a real object when $d_o > 2f$. The image is real, inverted, and reduced. **(b)** Ray diagram for a converging lens with $d_o < f$. The image is virtual, upright, and magnified. Practical examples are shown for both cases.

To illustrate these procedures, ▲Fig. 23.15 shows other ray diagrams with different object distances for a converging lens, along with real-life applications. The image of an object is real when it is formed on the side of the lens *opposite* the object's side (see Fig. 23.15a). A virtual image is said to be formed on the same side of the lens as the object (see Fig. 23.15b).

Regions could be similarly defined for the object distance for a converging lens as was done for a converging mirror in Fig. 23.7a. Here, an object distance of $d_o = 2f$ for a converging lens has significance similar to that of $d_o = R = 2f$ for a converging mirror (▼Fig. 23.16).

The ray diagram for a diverging lens will be discussed shortly. Like diverging mirrors, diverging lenses can form only virtual images of real objects.

▶ **FIGURE 23.16 Convex lens** For a convex, or converging, lens, the object is located within one of three regions defined by the focal distance (f) and twice the focal distance ($2f$) or at one of these two points. For $d_o > 2f$, the image is real, inverted, and reduced (Fig. 23.15a). For $2f > d_o > f$, the image will also be real and inverted, but enlarged, or magnified, as shown by the ray diagrams in Example 23.5. For $d_o < f$, the image will be virtual, upright, and enlarged (Fig. 23.15b).

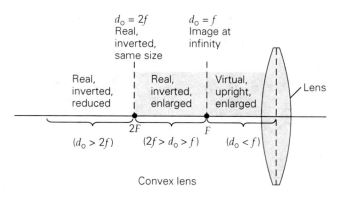

TABLE 23.3	Sign Conventions for Thin Lenses

Focal length (f)

Converging lens (sometimes called a *positive* lens)	f is positive
Diverging lens (sometimes called a *negative* lens)	f is negative

Object distance (d_o)

Object is in front of the lens (real object)	d_o is positive
Object is behind the lens (virtual object)*	d_o is negative

Image distance (d_i) and Image type

Image is formed on the image side of the lens—opposite to the object (real image)	d_i is positive
Image is formed on the object side of the lens—same side as the object (virtual image)	d_i is negative

Image orientation (M)

Image is upright with respect to the object	M is positive
Image is inverted with respect to the object	M is negative

*In a combination of two (or more) lenses, the image formed by the first lens is taken as the object of the second lens (and so on). If this image–object falls behind the second lens, it is referred to as a virtual object, and the object distance is taken to be negative ($-$).

PHYSLET

Exploration 35.3 Moving a Lens

The image distances and characteristics for a spherical lens can also be found analytically. The equations for thin lenses are identical to those for spherical mirrors. The **thin-lens equation** is

$$\frac{1}{d_o} + \frac{1}{d_i} = \frac{1}{f} \quad \text{thin-lens equation} \tag{23.5}$$

As in the case for spherical mirrors, an alternative form of the thin-lens equation,

$$d_i = \frac{d_o f}{d_o - f} \tag{23.5a}$$

gives a quick and easy way to find d_i.

The **magnification factor**, like that for spherical mirrors, is given by

$$M = -\frac{d_i}{d_o} \tag{23.6}$$

The sign conventions for these thin-lens equations are given in Table 23.3.

Just as when you are working with mirrors, it is helpful to sketch a ray diagram before working a lens problem analytically.

Example 23.6 ■ Three Images: Behavior of a Converging Lens

A biconvex lens has a focal length of 12 cm. For an object (a) 60 cm, (b) 15 cm, and (c) 8.0 cm from the lens, where is the image formed, and what are its characteristics?

Thinking It Through. With the focal length (f) and the object distances (d_o), we can apply Eq. 23.5 to find the image distances (d_i) and Eq. 23.6 to determine the image characteristics. Sketch ray diagrams first to get an idea of the image characteristics. The diagrams should be in good agreement with the calculations.

Solution.

Given: f = 12 cm
(a) d_o = 60 cm
(b) d_o = 15 cm
(c) d_o = 8.0 cm

Find: d_i and the image characteristics for all three cases

(continues on next page)

(a) The object distance is greater than twice the focal length $(d_o > 2f)$. Using Eq. 23.5,

$$\frac{1}{d_o} + \frac{1}{d_i} = \frac{1}{f}$$

or

$$\frac{1}{d_i} = \frac{1}{f} - \frac{1}{d_o} = \frac{1}{12\ \text{cm}} - \frac{1}{60\ \text{cm}} = \frac{5}{60\ \text{cm}} - \frac{1}{60\ \text{cm}} = \frac{4}{60\ \text{cm}} = \frac{1}{15\ \text{cm}}$$

Then

$$d_i = 15\ \text{cm} \quad \text{and} \quad M = -\frac{d_i}{d_o} = -\frac{15\ \text{cm}}{60\ \text{cm}} = -0.25$$

The image is real (positive d_i), inverted (negative M), and one-fourth the object's size $\left(|M| = 0.25\right)$. A camera uses this arrangement when the object distance is greater than $2f(d_o > 2f)$.

(b) Here, $2f > d_o > f$. Using Eq. 23.5,

$$\frac{1}{d_i} = \frac{1}{12\ \text{cm}} - \frac{1}{15\ \text{cm}} = \frac{5}{60\ \text{cm}} - \frac{4}{60\ \text{cm}} = \frac{1}{60\ \text{cm}}$$

Then

$$d_i = 60\ \text{cm} \quad \text{and} \quad M = -\frac{d_i}{d_o} = -\frac{60\ \text{cm}}{15\ \text{cm}} = -4.0$$

The image is real (positive d_i), inverted (negative M), and four times the object's size $\left(|M| = 4.0\right)$. This situation applies to the overhead projector and slide projector $(2f > d_o > f)$.

(c) For this case, $d_o < f$. Using the alternative form (Eq. 23.5a),

$$d_i = \frac{d_o f}{d_o - f} = \frac{(8.0\ \text{cm})(12\ \text{cm})}{8.0\ \text{cm} - 12\ \text{cm}} = -24\ \text{cm}$$

Then

$$M = -\frac{d_i}{d_o} = -\frac{(-24\ \text{cm})}{8.0\ \text{cm}} = +3.0$$

The image is virtual (negative d_i), upright (positive M), and three times the object's size $(|M| = 3.0)$. This situation is an example of a simple microscope or magnifying glass $(d_o < f)$.

As you can see, a converging lens is versatile. Depending on the object distance (relative to the focal length), the lens can be used as a camera, projector, or magnifying glass.

Follow-Up Exercise. If the object distance of a convex lens is allowed to vary, at what object distance does the real image change from being reduced to being magnified?

PHYSLET°

Exploration 35.1 Image Formation

Conceptual Example 23.7 ■ Half an Image?

A converging lens forms an image on a screen, as shown in ▸Fig. 23.17a. Then the lower half of the lens is blocked, as shown in Fig. 23.17b. As a result, (a) only the top half of the original image will be visible on the screen; (b) only the bottom half of the original image will be visible on the screen; or (c) the entire image will be visible.

Reasoning and Answer. At first thought, you might imagine that blocking off half of the lens would eliminate half of the image. However, rays from *every* point on the object pass through *all parts* of the lens. Thus, the upper half of the lens can form a total image (as could the lower half), so the answer is (c).

You might confirm this conclusion by drawing a chief ray in Fig. 23.17b. Or you might use the scientific method and experiment—particularly if you wear eyeglasses. Block off the bottom part of your glasses, and you will find that you can still read through the top part (unless you wear bifocals).

Follow-Up Exercise. Can you think of any property of the image that *would* be affected by blocking off half of the lens? Explain.

Science Fundamentals

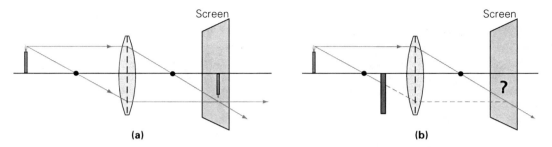

▲ **FIGURE 23.17** Half a lens, half an image? **(a)** A converging lens forms an image on a screen.
(b) The lower half of the lens is blocked. What happens to the image? See Conceptual Example 23.7.

Integrated Example 23.8 ■ **Time for a Change: Behavior of a Diverging Lens**

An object is 24 cm in front of a diverging lens that has a focal length of −15 cm. (a) Use a ray diagram to determine whether the image is (1) real and magnified, (2) virtual and reduced, (3) real and upright, or (4) upright and magnified. (b) Find the location and characteristics of the image with the thin-lens equations.

(a) Conceptual Reasoning. (See the sign conventions in Table 23.3.) Use a scale of 1 cm (in our drawing of ▶Fig. 23.18) to represent 10 cm. The object will be 2.4 cm in front of the lens in our drawing. Draw the optic axis, the lens, the object (in this case, a lighted candle), the focal point (F), and a vertical dashed line through the center of the lens.

The parallel ray ① starts from the tip of the flame, travels parallel to the optic axis, diverges from the lens after refraction, and appears to diverge from the F on the object side. The chief ray ② originates from the tip of the flame and goes through the center of the lens, with no direction change. We see that these two rays, after refraction, diverge and do not intersect. However, they appear to come from in front of the lens (object side), and that apparent intersection is the image point of the tip of the flame. We can also draw the focal ray ③ to verify that these rays appear to come from the same image point. The focal ray appears to go through the focal point on the image side and travels parallel to the optic axis after refraction from the lens.

This image is virtual (why?), upright, and smaller than the object, so the answer is (2): virtual and reduced. Measuring from the diagram (keeping in mind the drawing scale we are using), we find that $d_i \approx -9$ cm (virtual image) and $M = \dfrac{h_i}{h_o} \approx \dfrac{0.5 \text{ cm}}{1.4 \text{ cm}} = +0.4$.

(b) Quantitative Reasoning and Solution.

Given: $d_o = 24$ cm   *Find:* d_i, M, and image characteristics
$f = -15$ cm (diverging lens)

Note that the focal length is negative for a diverging lens. (See Table 23.3.) From Eq. 23.5,

$$\frac{1}{24 \text{ cm}} + \frac{1}{d_i} = \frac{1}{-15 \text{ cm}} \quad \text{or} \quad \frac{1}{d_i} = \frac{1}{-15 \text{ cm}} - \frac{1}{24 \text{ cm}} = -\frac{13}{120 \text{ cm}}$$

so

$$d_i = -\frac{120 \text{ cm}}{13} = -9.2 \text{ cm}$$

Then

$$M = -\frac{d_i}{d_o} = -\frac{(-9.2 \text{ cm})}{24 \text{ cm}} = +0.38$$

Thus, the image is virtual (d_i is negative) and upright (M is positive), and it is 0.38 times the height of the object. Due to the fact that f is negative for a diverging lens, d_i is always negative for any positive value of d_o, so the image of an object is always virtual.

Follow-Up Exercise. A diverging lens always forms a virtual image of a real object. What general statements can be made about the image's orientation and magnification?

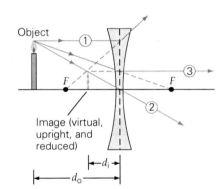

▲ **FIGURE 23.18** Diverging lens Ray diagram of a diverging lens. Here, the image is virtual and in front of the lens, upright, and smaller than the object. See Integrated Example 23.8.

PHYSLET

Illustration 35.2 Image from a Diverging Lens

A special type of lens that you may have encountered is discussed in Insight 23.2 on Fresnel Lenses, on page 748.

INSIGHT 23.2 FRESNEL LENSES

To focus parallel light or to produce a large beam of parallel light rays, a sizable converging lens is sometimes necessary. The large mass of glass necessary to form such a lens is bulky and heavy. Moreover, a thick lens absorbs some of the light and is likely to show distortions. A French physicist named Augustin Fresnel (Fray-nel', 1788–1827) developed a solution to this problem for the lenses used in lighthouses. Fresnel recognized that the refraction of light takes place at the surfaces of a lens. Hence, a lens could be made thinner—and almost flat—by removing glass from the interior, as long as the refracting properties of the surfaces were not changed.

This can be accomplished by cutting a series of concentric grooves in the surface of the lens (Fig. 1a). Note that the surface of each remaining curved segment is nearly parallel to the corresponding surface of the original lens. Together, the concentric segments refract light as does the original biconvex converging lens (Fig. 1b). In effect, the lens has simply been slimmed down by the removal of unnecessary glass between the refracting surfaces.

A lens with a series of concentric curved surfaces is called a *Fresnel lens*. Such lenses are widely used in overhead projectors and in beacons (Fig. 1c). A Fresnel lens is very thin and therefore much lighter in weight than a conventional biconvex lens with the same optical properties. Also, Fresnel lenses are easily molded from plastic—often with one flat side (plano-convex) so that the lens can be attached to a glass surface.

One disadvantage of Fresnel lenses is that concentric circles are visible when an observer is looking through such a lens and when an image produced by the lens is projected on a screen, as when we use an overhead projector.

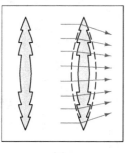

(a)

(b)

(c)

FIGURE 1 Fresnel lens
(a) The focusing action of a lens comes from refraction at its surfaces. It is therefore possible to reduce the thickness of a lens by cutting away glass in concentric grooves, leaving a set of curved surfaces with the same refractive properties as the lens from which they were derived. **(b)** A flat Fresnel lens with concentric curved surfaces magnifies like a biconvex converging lens. **(c)** An array of Fresnel lenses produces focused beams in this Boston Harbor light. (Fresnel lenses were, in fact, developed for use in lighthouses.)

PHYSLET®

Exploration 35.4 What is Behind the Curtain?

Combinations of Lenses

Many optical instruments, such as microscopes and telescopes (Chapter 25), use a combination of lenses, or a compound-lens system. When two or more lenses are used in combination, we can determine the overall image produced by considering the lenses individually in sequence. That is, the image formed by the first lens becomes the object for the second lens, and so on. For this reason, we present the principles of lens combinations before considering the specifics of their real-life applications.

If the first lens produces an image in front of the second lens, that image is treated as a real object (d_o is positive) for the second lens (▸Fig. 23.19a). If, however, the lenses are close enough so that the image from the first lens is *not* formed before the rays pass through the second lens (Fig. 23.19b), then a modification must be made in the sign conventions. In this case, the image from the first lens is treated as a *virtual* object for the second lens. The virtual object distance is taken to be *negative* in the lens equation (Table 23.3).

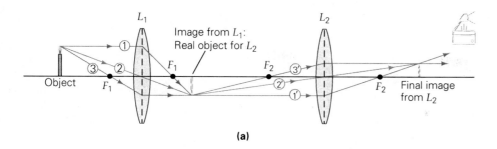

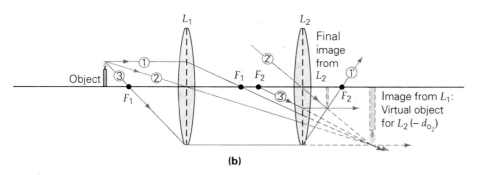

(a)

(b)

◀ **FIGURE 23.19 Lens combinations**
The final image produced by a compound-lens system can be found by treating the image of one lens as the object for the adjacent lens. **(a)** If the image of the first lens (L_1) is formed in front of the second lens (L_2), the object for the second lens is said to be real. (Note that rays 1', 2', and 3' are the parallel, chief, and focal rays, respectively, for L_2. They are *not* continuations of rays 1, 2, and 3— the parallel, chief, and focal rays, respectively, for L_1.) **(b)** If the rays pass through the second lens before the image is formed, the object for the second lens is said to be virtual, and the object distance for the second lens is taken to be negative.

It can be shown that the total magnification (M_{total}) of a compound-lens system is the product of the individual magnification factors of the component lenses. For example, for a two-lens system, as in Fig. 23.19,

$$M_{total} = M_1 M_2 \qquad (23.7)$$

The conventional signs for M_1 and M_2 carry through the product to indicate, from the sign of M_{total}, whether the final image is upright or inverted. (See Exercise 83.)

Example 23.9 ■ A Special Offer: A Lens Combo and a Virtual Object

Consider two lenses similar to those illustrated in Fig. 23.19b. Suppose the object is 20 cm in front of lens L_1, which has a focal length of 15 cm. Lens L_2, with a focal length of 12 cm, is 26 cm from L_1. What is the location of the final image, and what are its characteristics?

Thinking It Through. This is a double application of the thin-lens equation. The lenses are treated successively. The image of lens L_1 becomes the object of lens L_2. We must keep the quantities distinctly labeled and the distances appropriately referenced (with signs!).

Solution. We have

Given: $d_{o_1} = +20$ cm   *Find:* d_{i_2} and image characteristics
$\quad\quad f_1 = +15$ cm
$\quad\quad f_2 = +12$ cm
$\quad\quad D = 26$ cm (distance between lenses)

The first step is to apply the thin-lens equation (Eq. 23.5) and the magnification factor for thin lenses (Eq. 23.6) to L_1:

$$\frac{1}{d_{i_1}} = \frac{1}{f_1} - \frac{1}{d_{o_1}} = \frac{1}{15 \text{ cm}} - \frac{1}{20 \text{ cm}} = \frac{4}{60 \text{ cm}} - \frac{3}{60 \text{ cm}} = \frac{1}{60 \text{ cm}}$$

or

$$d_{i_1} = 60 \text{ cm (real image from } L_1)$$

and

$$M_1 = -\frac{d_{i_1}}{d_{o_1}} = -\frac{60 \text{ cm}}{20 \text{ cm}} = -3.0 \text{ (inverted and magnified)}$$

The image from lens L_1 becomes the object for lens L_2. This image is then $d_{i_1} - D = 60 \text{ cm} - 26 \text{ cm} = 34 \text{ cm}$ on the right, or image, side of L_2. Therefore, it is a *virtual* object (see Table 23.3), and $d_{o_2} = -34$ cm. (Remember that d_o for virtual objects is taken to be negative.)

(continues on next page)

Then applying the equations to the second lens, L_2:

$$\frac{1}{d_{i_1}} = \frac{1}{f_2} - \frac{1}{d_{o_1}} = \frac{1}{12 \text{ cm}} - \frac{1}{(-34 \text{ cm})} = \frac{23}{204 \text{ cm}}$$

or

$$d_{i_2} = 8.9 \text{ cm (real image)}$$

and

$$M_2 = -\frac{d_{i_1}}{d_{o_2}} = -\frac{8.9 \text{ cm}}{(-34 \text{ cm})} = 0.26 \text{ (upright and reduced)}$$

(*Note*: The virtual object for L_2 was inverted, and thus the term *upright* means that the *final* image is also inverted.) The total magnification M_{total} is then

$$M_{\text{total}} = M_1 M_2 = (-3.0)(0.26) = -0.78$$

The sign is carried through with the magnifications. We determine that the final real image is located at 8.9 cm on the right (image) side of L_2 and that it is inverted (negative sign) relative to the initial object and reduced.

Follow-Up Exercise. Suppose the object in Fig. 23.19b were located 30 cm in front of L_1. Where would the final image be formed in this case, and what would be its characteristics?

PHYSICS FACTS

- Some sources say Thomas Young, who first demonstrated the wave nature of light, could read by age 2 and read the Bible twice in his early years.

- The track-to-track distance is 0.74 μm on a DVD-ROM and 1.6 μm on a CD-ROM. In comparison, the diameter of human hair is on the order of 50–150 μm. DVD-ROM and CD-ROM tracks really split hairs.

- AM radio can be heard better in some areas than FM radio. This is because the longer AM waves are more easily diffracted around buildings and other obstacles.

- Skylight is partially polarized. It is believed that some insects, such as bees, use polarized skylight to determine navigational directions relative to the Sun.

- To an observer on Earth, the "red planet" Mars appears reddish because the surface material contains iron oxide. The rusting of iron on Earth produces iron oxide.

It's always intriguing to see brilliant colors produced by objects that we know don't have any color of their own. The glass of a prism, for example, which is clear and transparent by itself, nevertheless gives rise to a whole array of colors when white light passes through it. Prisms, like the water droplets that produce rainbows, don't create color. They merely separate the different colors that make up white light.

The phenomena of reflection and refraction are conveniently analyzed by using geometrical optics (Chapter 22). Ray diagrams (Chapter 23) show what happens when light is reflected from a mirror or passed through a lens. However, other phenomena involving light, such as the interference patterns of the soap bubble in the photo, cannot be adequately explained or described using the ray concept, since this technique ignores the wave nature of light. Other wave phenomena include diffraction and polarization.

Physical optics, or **wave optics**, takes into account wave properties that geometrical optics ignores. The wave theory of light leads to satisfactory explanations of those phenomena that cannot be analyzed with rays. Thus, in this chapter, the wave nature of light must be used to analyze phenomena such as interference and diffraction.

Wave optics must be used to explain how light propagates around small objects or through small openings. We see this in our everyday life with the narrow grooves in CDs, DVDs, and other items. An object or opening is considered small if it is in the order of magnitude of the wavelength of light.

24.1 Young's Double-Slit Experiment

OBJECTIVES: To (a) explain how Young's experiment demonstrated the wave nature of light, and (b) compute the wavelength of light from experimental results.

It has been stated that light behaves like a wave, but no proof of this assertion has been discussed. How would you go about demonstrating the wave nature of light? One method that involves the use of interference was first devised in 1801 by the English scientist Thomas Young (1773–1829). **Young's double-slit experiment** not only demonstrates the wave nature of light, but also allows the measurement of its wavelengths. Essentially, light can be shown to be a wave if it exhibits wave properties such as interference and diffraction.

Recall from the discussion of wave interference in Sections 13.4 and 14.4 that superimposed waves may interfere constructively or destructively. Constructive interference occurs when two crests are superimposed. If a crest and a trough are superimposed, then destructive interference occurs. Interference can be easily observed with water waves, for which constructive and destructive interference produce obvious interference patterns (▸Fig. 24.1).

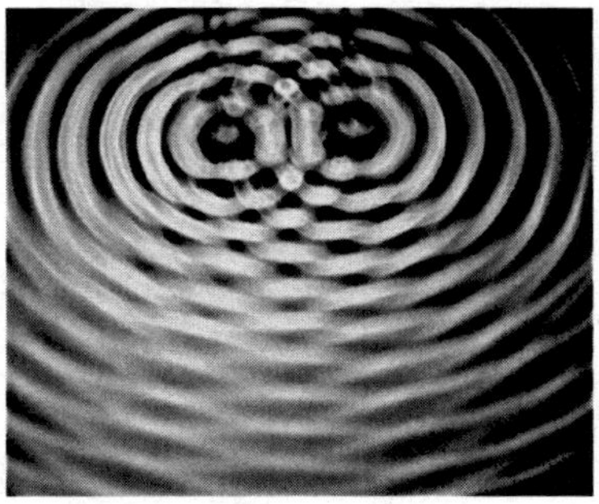

▲ **FIGURE 24.1 Water-wave interference** The constructive and destructive interference of water waves from two coherent sources in a ripple tank produces interference patterns.

Note: Compare Fig. 24.1 with Fig. 14.8a.

The interference of (visible) light waves is not as easily observed, because of their relatively short wavelengths ($\approx 10^{-7}$ m) and the fact that they usually are not really monochromatic (single frequency). Also, stationary interference patterns are produced only with *coherent sources*—sources that produce light waves having a constant phase relationship to one another. For example, for constructive interference to occur at some point, the waves meeting at that point must be in phase. As the waves meet, a crest must *always* overlap a crest, and a trough must *always* overlap a trough. If a phase difference develops between the waves over time, the interference pattern changes, and a stable or stationary pattern will not be established.

In an ordinary light source, the atoms are excited randomly, and the emitted light waves fluctuate in amplitude and frequency. Thus, light from two such sources is *incoherent* and cannot produce a stationary interference pattern. Interference does occur, but the phase difference between the interfering waves changes so fast that the interference effects are not discernible. To obtain the equivalent of two coherent sources, a barrier with one narrow slit is placed in front of a single light source, and a barrier with two very narrow slits is positioned symmetrically in front of the first barrier (▾Fig. 24.2a).

PHYSLET®

Illustration 37.1 Ripple Tank

Waves propagating out from the single slit are in phase, and the double slits then act as two coherent sources by separating each wave into two parts. Any random changes in the light from the original source will thus occur for the light passing through both slits, and the phase difference will be constant. The modern laser beam, a coherent light source, makes the observation of a stable interference pattern much

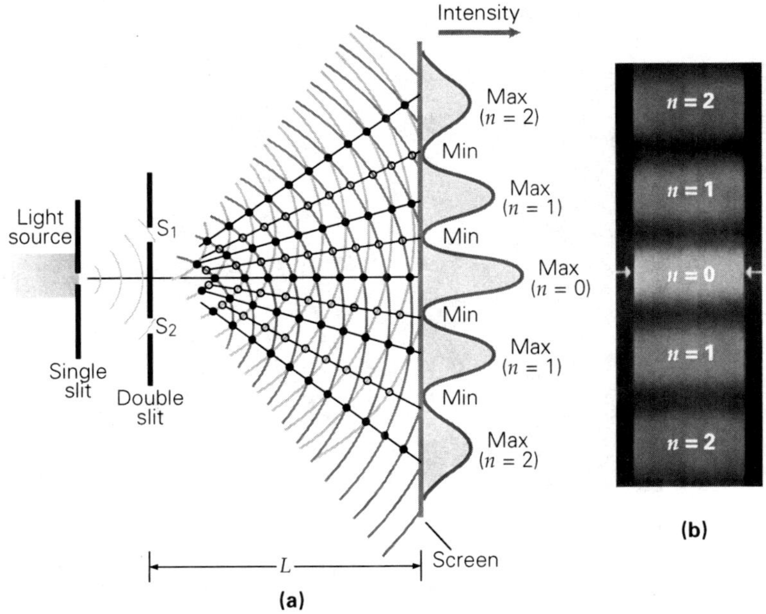

◂ **FIGURE 24.2 Double-slit interference (a)** The coherent waves from two slits are shown in blue (top slit) and red (bottom slit). The waves spread out as a result of diffraction from narrow slits. The waves interfere, producing alternating maxima and minima, on the screen. **(b)** An interference pattern. Note the symmetry of the pattern about the central maximum (n = 0).

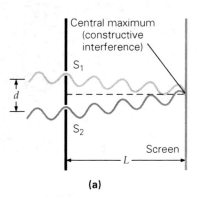

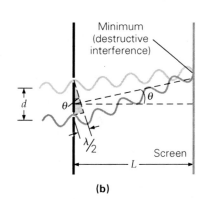

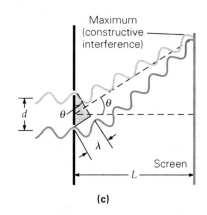

(a)   (b)   (c)

▲ **FIGURE 24.3 Interference** The interference that produces a maximum or minimum depends on the difference in the path lengths of the light from the two slits. **(a)** The path-length difference at the position of the central maximum is zero, so the waves arrive in phase and interfere constructively. **(b)** At the position of the first minimum, the path-length difference is $\lambda/2$, and the waves interfere destructively. **(c)** At the position of the first maximum, the path-length difference is λ, and the interference is constructive.

easier. A series of maxima or bright positions can be observed on a screen placed relatively far from the slits (Fig. 24.2b).

To help analyze Young's experiment, let's imagine that light with a single wavelength (monochromatic light) is used. Because of diffraction (see Sections 13.4 and 14.4 and, in this chapter, Section 24.3), or the spreading of light as it passes through a slit, the waves spread out and interfere as illustrated in Fig. 24.2a. Coming from two coherent "sources," the interfering waves produce a stable interference pattern on the screen. The pattern consists of a bright central maximum (▲Fig. 24.3a) and a series of symmetrical side minima (Fig. 24.3b) and maxima (Fig. 24.3c), which mark the positions at which destructive and constructive interference occur. The existence of this interference pattern clearly demonstrates the wave nature of light. The intensities of each side maxima decrease with distance from the central maximum.

Measuring the wavelength of light requires us to look at the geometry of Young's experiment, as shown in ▼ Fig. 24.4. Let the screen be a distance L from the slits and P be an arbitrary point on the screen. P is located a distance y from the center of the central maximum and at an angle θ relative to a normal line between the slits. The slits S_1 and S_2 are separated by a distance d. Note that the light path from slit S_2 to P is longer than the path from slit S_1 to P. As the figure shows, the path-length difference (ΔL) is approximately

$$\Delta L = d \sin \theta$$

The fact that the angle in the small shaded triangle is almost equal to θ can be shown by a simple geometrical argument involving similar triangles when $d \ll L$, as described in the caption of Fig. 24.4.

▶ **FIGURE 24.4 Geometry of Young's double-slit experiment** The difference in the path lengths for light traveling from the two slits to a point P is $r_2 - r_1 = \Delta L$, which forms a side of the small shaded triangle. Because the barrier with the slits is parallel to the screen, the angle between r_2 and the barrier (at S_2, in the small shaded triangle) is equal to the angle between r_2 and the screen. When L is much greater than y, that angle is almost identical to the angle between the screen and the dashed line, which is an angle in the large shaded triangle. The two shaded triangles are then almost exactly similar, and the angle at S_1 in the small triangle is almost exactly equal to θ. Thus, $\Delta L = d \sin \theta$. (Not drawn to scale. Assume that $d \ll L$.)

The relationship of the phase difference of two waves to their path-length difference was discussed in Chapter 14 for sound waves. These conditions hold for any wave, including light. Constructive interference occurs at any point where the path-length difference between the two waves is an integral number of wavelengths:

$$\Delta L = n\lambda \qquad \text{for } n = 0, 1, 2, 3, \ldots \qquad \textit{condition for constructive interference} \qquad (24.1)$$

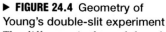

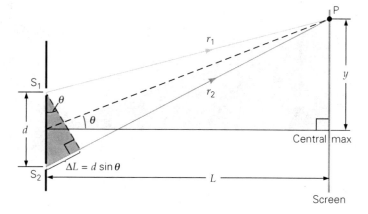

Similarly, for destructive interference, the path-length difference is an odd number of half-wavelengths:

$$\Delta L = \frac{m\lambda}{2} \quad \text{for } m = 1, 3, 5, \ldots \quad \begin{array}{l}\textit{condition for} \\ \textit{destructive interference}\end{array} \quad (24.2)$$

Thus, in Fig. 24.4, the maxima (constructive interference) satisfy

$$d \sin \theta = n\lambda \quad \text{for } n = 0, 1, 2, 3, \ldots \quad \begin{array}{l}\textit{condition for} \\ \textit{interference maxima}\end{array} \quad (24.3)$$

where n is called the *order number*. The zeroth order ($n = 0$) corresponds to the central maximum; the first order ($n = 1$) is the first maximum on either side of the central maximum; and so on. As the path-length difference varies from point to point, so does the phase difference and the resulting type of interference (constructive or destructive).

The wavelength can therefore be determined by measuring d and θ for a maximum of a particular order (other than the central maximum), because Eq. 24.3 can be solved as $\lambda = (d \sin \theta)/n$.

The angle θ locates a maximum relative to the central maximum. This can be measured from a photograph of the interference pattern, such as shown in Fig. 24.2b. If θ is small ($y \ll L$), $\sin \theta \approx \tan \theta = y/L$. Substituting this y/L for $\sin \theta$ into Eq. 24.3 and solving for y gives a good approximation of the distance of the nth maximum (y_n) from the central maximum on either side:

$$y_n \approx \frac{nL\lambda}{d} \quad \text{for } n = 0, 1, 2, 3, \ldots \quad \begin{array}{l}\textit{lateral distance to} \\ \textit{maxima for small } \theta \textit{ only}\end{array} \quad (24.4)$$

A similar analysis gives the locations of the minima. (See Exercise 12a.)

From Eq. 24.3, we see that, except for the zeroth order, $n = 0$ (the central maximum), the positions of the maxima depend on wavelength—different wavelengths (λ) give different values of $\sin \theta$ and therefore of θ and y. Hence, when we use white light, the central maximum is white because all wavelengths are at the same location, but the other orders become a "spread out" spectrum of colors. Because y is proportional to λ ($y \propto \lambda$), we observed, in a given order, that red is farther out than blue or that red has a longer wavelength than blue.

By measuring the positions of the color maxima within a particular order, Young was able to determine the wavelengths of the colors of visible light. Note also that the size or "spread" of the interference pattern, y_n, depends inversely on the slit separation d. The smaller d, the more spread out the pattern. For large d, the interference pattern is so compressed that it appears to us as a single white spot (all maxima together at center).

In this analysis, the word *destructive* does *not* imply that energy is destroyed. Destructive interference is simply a description of a physical fact—that if light energy is not present at a particular location, by energy conservation, it *must* be somewhere else. The mathematical description of Young's double-slit experiment tells you that there is no light energy at the minima. The light energy is redistributed and located at the maxima. This is also observed with sound waves as well.

PHYSLET
Exploration 37.1 Varying Numbers and Orientations of Sources

PHYSLET
Exploration 37.2 Changing the Separation Between Sources

Integrated Example 24.1 ■ Measuring the Wavelength of Light: Young's Double-Slit Experiment

In a lab experiment similar to the one shown in Fig. 24.4, monochromatic light (only one wavelength or frequency) passes through two narrow slits that are 0.050 mm apart. The interference pattern is observed on a white wall 1.0 m from the slits, and the second-order maximum is at an angle of $\theta_2 = 1.5°$. (a) If the slit separation decreases, the second-order maximum will be seen at an angle of (1) greater than 1.5°, (2) 1.5°, (3) less than 1.5°. Explain. (b) What is the wavelength of the light and what is the distance between the second-order and third-order maxima? (c) if $d = 0.040$ mm, what is θ_2?

(a) Conceptual Reasoning. According to the condition for constructive interference, $d \sin \theta = n\lambda$, the product of d and $\sin \theta$ is a constant, for a given wavelength λ and order number n. Therefore, if d decreases, $\sin \theta$ will increase and so will θ. Thus the answer is (1).

(continues on next page)

(b) and (c) Quantitative Reasoning and Solution. Eq. 24.3 can be used to find the wavelength. Since $L \gg d$, that is, 1.0 m $\gg 0.050$ mm, then θ is small. We could compute y_2 and y_3 from Eq. 24.4 and determine the distance between the second-order and third-order maxima $(y_3 - y_2)$. However, the maxima for a given wavelength of light are evenly spaced (for a small θ). That is, the distance between adjacent maxima is a constant.

Given: $L = 1.0$ m   **Find:**   (b) λ (wavelength) and $y_3 - y_2$
              $n = 2$ (distance between $n = 2$ and $n = 3$)
       (b) $\theta_2 = 1.5°$ (c) θ_2 if $d = 0.040$ mm
            $d = 0.050$ mm $= 5.0 \times 10^{-5}$ m
       (c) $d = 4.0 \times 10^{-5}$ m

(b) Using Eq. 24.3 gives

$$\lambda = \frac{d \sin \theta}{n} = \frac{(5.0 \times 10^{-5} \text{ m}) \sin 1.5°}{2} = 6.5 \times 10^{-7} \text{ m} = 650 \text{ nm}$$

This value is 650 nm, which is the wavelength of orange-red light (see Fig. 20.23). Using a general approach for n and $n + 1$, we get

$$y_{n+1} - y_n = \frac{(n + 1)L\lambda}{d} - \frac{nL\lambda}{d} = \frac{L\lambda}{d}$$

In this case, the distance between successive fringes is

$$y_3 - y_2 = \frac{L\lambda}{d} = \frac{(1.0 \text{ m})(6.5 \times 10^{-7} \text{ m})}{5.0 \times 10^{-5} \text{ m}} = 1.3 \times 10^{-2} \text{ m} = 1.3 \text{ cm}$$

(c) $\sin \theta_2 = \dfrac{n\lambda}{d} = \dfrac{(2)(650 \times 10^{-9} \text{ m})}{(4.0 \times 10^{-5} \text{ m})} = 0.0325$ so $\theta_2 = \sin^{-1}(0.0325) = 1.9° > 1.5°$.

Follow-Up Exercise. Suppose white light were used instead of monochromatic light in this Example. What would be the separation distance of the red ($\lambda = 700$ nm) and blue ($\lambda = 400$ nm) components in the second-order maximum? *(Answers to all Follow-Up Exercises are at the back of the text.)*

24.2 Thin-Film Interference

OBJECTIVES: To (a) describe how thin films can produce colorful displays, and (b) give some examples of practical applications of thin-film interference.

Have you ever wondered what causes the rainbowlike colors when white light is reflected from a thin film of oil or a soap bubble? This effect—known as *thin-film interference*—is a result of the interference of light reflected from opposite surfaces of the film and may be understood in terms of wave interference.

First, however, you need to know how the phase of a light wave is affected by reflection. Recall from Chapter 13 that a wave pulse on a rope undergoes a 180° phase change [or a *half wave shift* ($\lambda/2$)], when reflected from a rigid support and no phase shift when reflected from a free support (▼Fig. 24.5). Similarly, as the figure shows, the phase change for the reflection of light waves at a boundary depends on the indices of refraction (n) of the two materials:

- A light wave undergoes a 180° phase change on reflection if $n_1 < n_2$.
- There is no phase change on reflection if $n_1 > n_2$.

▼ **FIGURE 24.5 Reflection and phase shifts** The phase changes that light waves undergo on reflection are analogous to those for pulses in strings. **(a)** The phase of a pulse in a string is shifted by 180° on reflection from a fixed end, and so is the phase of a light wave when it is reflected from a more optically dense medium. **(b)** A pulse in a string has a phase shift of zero (it is not shifted) when reflected from a free end. Analogously, a light wave is not phase shifted when reflected from a less optically dense medium.

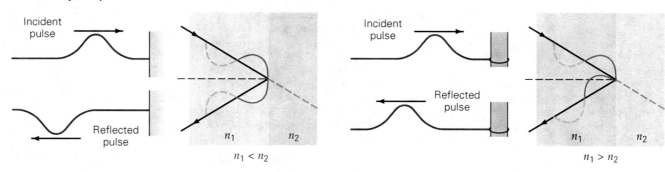

(a) Fixed end: 180° phase shift   **(b)** Free end: zero phase shift

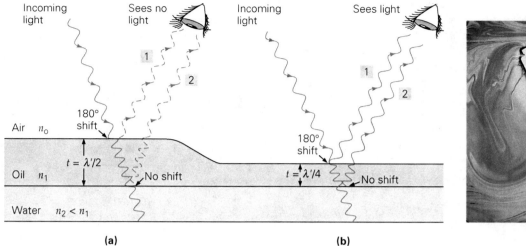

(a)   (b)   (c)

▲ **FIGURE 24.6 Thin-film interference** For an oil film on water, there is a 180° phase shift for light reflected from the air–oil interface and a zero phase shift at the oil–water interface. λ' is the wavelength in the oil. **(a)** Destructive interference occurs if the oil film has a minimum thickness of $\lambda'/2$ for normal incidence. (Waves are displaced and angled for clarity.) **(b)** Constructive interference occurs with a minimum film thickness of $\lambda'/4$. **(c)** Thin-film interference in an oil slick. Different film thicknesses give rise to the reflections of different colors.

To understand why you see colors from a soap bubble or an oil film (for example, floating on water or on a wet road), consider the reflection of monochromatic light from a thin film in ▲Fig. 24.6. The path length of the wave in the film depends on the angle of incidence (why?), but for simplicity, we will assume normal (perpendicular) incidence for the light, even though the rays are drawn at an angle in the figure, for clarity.

The oil film has a greater index of refraction than that of air, and the light reflected from the air–oil interface (wave 1 in the figure) undergoes a 180° phase shift. The transmitted waves pass through the oil film and are reflected at the oil–water interface. In general, the index of refraction of oil is greater than that of water (see Table 22.1)—that is, $n_1 > n_2$—so a reflected wave in this instance (wave 2) does *not* have the phase shift.

You might think that if the path length of the wave in the oil film ($2t$, twice the thickness—down and back) were an integral number of wavelengths—for example, if $2t = 2(\lambda'/2)$ in Fig. 24.6a, where $\lambda' = \lambda/n$ is the wavelength in the oil—then the waves reflected from the two surfaces would interfere constructively. But keep in mind that the wave reflected from the top surface (wave 1) undergoes a 180° phase shift. The reflected waves from the two surfaces are therefore actually *out of phase* and would interfere destructively for this condition. This means that no reflected light for this wavelength would be observed. (The light would be transmitted.)

Similarly, if the path length of the waves in the film were an odd number of half-wavelengths [$2t = 2(\lambda'/4) = \lambda'/2$] in Fig. 24.6b, again where λ' is the wavelength in the oil, then the reflected waves would actually be *in phase* (as a result of a 180° phase shift of wave 1) and would interfere constructively. Reflected light for this wavelength would be observed from above the oil film.

Because oil and soap films generally have different thicknesses in different regions, particular wavelengths (colors) of white light interfere constructively in different regions after reflection. As a result, a vivid display of various colors appears (Fig. 24.6c). This may also change if the film thickness changes with time. Thin-film interference may be seen when two glass slides are stuck together with an air film between them (▼Fig. 24.7a). The bright colors of a peacock, an example of colorful interference in nature, are a result of layers of fibers in its feathers. Light reflected from successive layers interferes constructively, giving bright colors, even though the feather has no pigment of its own. Since the condition for constructive interference depends on the angle of incidence, the color pattern changes somewhat with the viewing angle and motion of the bird (Fig. 24.7b).

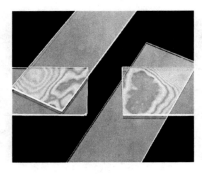

(a)

(b)

▲ **FIGURE 24.7 Thin-film interference (a)** A thin air film between microscope slides gives colorful patterns. **(b)** Multilayer interference in a peacock's feathers gives rise to bright colors. The brilliant throat colors of hummingbirds are produced in the same way.

A practical application of thin-film interference is nonreflective coatings for lenses. (See Insight 24.1, on page 768, on Nonreflecting Lenses.) In this situation, a film coating is used to create destructive interference between the reflected waves so as to *increase the light transmission* into the glass (▾Fig. 24.8). The index of refraction of the film has a value between that of air and glass ($n_0 < n_1 < n_2$). Consequently, phase shifts of incident light take place at the surfaces of both the film and the glass.

In such a case, the condition for constructive interference of the reflected light is

$$\Delta L = 2t = m\lambda' \text{ or } t = \frac{m\lambda'}{2} = \frac{m\lambda}{2n_1} \quad m = 1, 2, \ldots \quad \begin{array}{l}\text{condition for con-}\\ \text{structive interference}\\ \text{when } n_0 < n_1 < n_2\end{array} \quad (24.5)$$

and the condition for destructive interference is

$$\Delta L = 2t = \frac{m\lambda'}{2} \text{ or } t = \frac{m\lambda'}{4} = \frac{m\lambda}{4n_1} \quad m = 1, 3, 5, \ldots \quad \begin{array}{l}\text{condition for de-}\\ \text{structive interference}\\ \text{when } n_0 < n_1 < n_2\end{array} \quad (24.6)$$

The *minimum* film thickness for destructive interference occurs when $m = 1$, so

$$t_{min} = \frac{\lambda}{4n_1} \quad \begin{array}{l}\text{minimum film thickness}\\ \text{(for } n_0 < n_1 < n_2)\end{array} \quad (24.7)$$

If the index of refraction of the film is greater than that of air and glass, then only the reflection at the air–film interface has the 180° phase shift. Therefore, $2t = m\lambda'$ will actually create destructive interference and $2t = m\lambda'/2$ constructive interference. (Why?)

Example 24.2 ■ Nonreflective Coatings: Thin-Film Interference

A glass lens ($n = 1.60$) is coated with a thin, transparent film of magnesium fluoride ($n = 1.38$) to make the lens nonreflecting. (a) What is the minimum film thickness for the lens to be nonreflecting for normally incident light of wavelength 550 nm? (b) Will a film thickness of 996 nm make the lens nonreflecting?

Thinking It Through. (a) Equation 24.7 can be used directly to get an idea of the minimum film thickness for a nonreflective coating. (b) We need to determine whether 996 nm satisfies the condition in Eq. 24.6.

Solution.

Given: $n_0 = 1.00$ (air) **Find:** (a) t_{min} (minimum film thickness)
$n_1 = 1.38$ (for film)   (b) determine whether $t = 996$ nm
$n_2 = 1.60$ (for lens)   gives a nonreflecting lens
$\lambda = 550$ nm

(a) Because $n_2 > n_1 > n_0$,

$$t_{min} = \frac{\lambda}{4n_1} = \frac{550 \text{ nm}}{4(1.38)} = 99.6 \text{ nm}$$

which is quite thin ($\approx 10^{-5}$ cm). In terms of atoms, which have diameters on the order of 10^{-10} m, or 10^{-1} nm, the film is 10^3 atoms thick.

Illustration 37.2 Dielectric Mirrors

▶ **FIGURE 24.8 Thin-film interference** For a thin film on a glass lens, there is a 180° phase shift at each interface when the index of refraction of the film is less than that of the glass. The waves reflected off the top and bottom surfaces of the film interfere. For clarity, the angle of incidence is drawn to be large, but, in reality, it is almost zero.

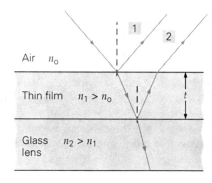

(b)

$$t = 996 \text{ nm} = 10(99.6 \text{ nm}) = 10t_{\text{min}} = 10\left(\frac{\lambda}{4n_1}\right) = 5\left(\frac{\lambda}{2n_1}\right)$$

This means that this film thickness does *not* satisfy the nonreflective condition (destructive interference). Actually, it satisfies the requirement for constructive interference (Eq. 24.5) with $m = 5$. Such a coating specific for infrared radiation on car and house windows could be useful in hot climates, because it maximizes reflection and minimizes transmission.

Follow-Up Exercise. For the glass lens in this Example to reflect, rather than transmit, the incident light through the lens, what would be the minimum film thickness?

Optical Flats and Newton's Rings

The phenomenon of thin-film interference can be used to check the smoothness and uniformity of optical components such as mirrors and lenses. *Optical flats* are made by grinding and polishing glass plates until they are as flat and smooth as possible. (The surface roughness is usually in the order of $\lambda/20$.) The degree of flatness can be checked by putting two such plates together at a slight angle so that a very thin air wedge is between them (▸Fig. 24.9a). The reflected waves off the bottom of the top plate (wave 1) and top of the bottom plate (wave 2) interfere. Note that wave 2 has a 180° phase shift as it is reflected from an air–plate interface, whereas wave 1 does not. Therefore, at certain points from where the plates touch (point O), the condition for constructive interference is $2t = m\lambda/2$ ($m = 1, 3, 5, \dots$), and the condition for destructive interference is $2t = m\lambda$ ($m = 0, 1, 2, \dots$). The thickness t determines the type of interference (constructive or destructive). If the plates are smooth and flat, a regular interference pattern of bright and dark bands appears (Fig. 24.9b). This pattern is a result of the uniformly varying differences in path lengths between the plates. Any irregularity in the pattern indicates an irregularity in at least one plate. Once a good optical flat is verified, it can be used to check the flatness of a reflecting surface, such as that of a precision mirror.

Direct evidence of the 180° phase shift can be clearly seen in Fig. 24.9. At the point where the two plates touch ($t = 0$), we see a *dark* band. If there were no phase shift, $t = 0$ would correspond to $\Delta L = 0$, and we would expect a bright band to appear. The fact that it is a dark band proves that there is a phase shift in reflection from a more optically dense material.

A similar technique is used to check the smoothness and symmetry of lenses. When a curved lens is placed on an optical flat, a radially symmetric air wedge is formed between the lens and the optical flat (▾Fig. 24.10a). Since the thickness of the air wedge again determines the condition for constructive and destructive interference, the regular interference pattern in this case is a set of concentric circular bright and dark rings (Fig. 24.10b). They are called *Newton's rings*, after Isaac Newton, who first

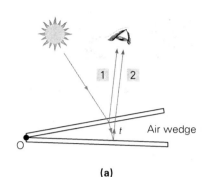

(a)

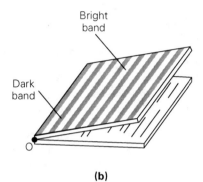

(b)

▲ **FIGURE 24.9 Optical flatness** **(a)** An optical flat is used to check the smoothness of a reflecting surface. The flat is placed so that there is an air wedge between it and the surface. The waves reflected from the two plates interfere, and the thickness of the air wedge at certain points determines whether bright or dark bands are seen. **(b)** If the surface is smooth, a regular or symmetrical interference pattern is seen. Note that a dark band is at point O where $t = 0$.

◄ **FIGURE 24.10 Newton's rings** **(a)** A lens placed on an optical flat forms a ring-shaped air wedge, which gives rise to interference of the waves reflected from the top (wave 1) and the bottom (wave 2) of the air wedge. **(b)** The resulting interference pattern is a set of concentric rings called *Newton's rings*. Note that at the center of the pattern is a dark spot. Lens irregularities produce a distorted pattern.

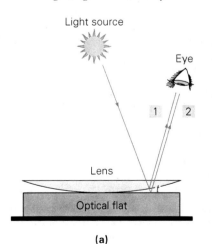

(a)

(b)

INSIGHT 24.1 NONREFLECTING LENSES

You may have noticed the blue-purple tint of the coated optical lenses used in cameras and binoculars. The coating makes the lenses almost "nonreflecting." If a lens is a nonreflecting type, then the incident light is mostly transmitted through the lens. Maximum transmission of light is desirable for the exposure of photographic film and for viewing objects with binoculars.

For a typical (reflecting) air–glass interface, about 4% of the light is reflected and 96% is transmitted. A modern camera lens is actually made up of a group of lenses (elements) in order to improve image quality. For instance, a 35-mm–70-mm zoom lens might consist of up to 13 elements, thus having 26 reflective surfaces.

After one reflection, 0.96 = 96% of the light is transmitted. After two reflections, or one element, the transmitted light is only $0.96 \times 0.96 = 0.96^2 = 0.92$, or 92%, of the incident light. Thus after 26 reflections, the transmitted light is only $0.96^{26} = 0.35$, or 35%, of the incident light, if lenses are not coated. Therefore, almost all modern lenses are coated with nonreflecting film.

A lens is made nonreflecting by coating it with a thin-film material with an index of refraction between the indices of refraction of air and glass (Fig. 24.8). If the coating is a quarter-wavelength ($\lambda'/4$) thick, the difference in path length between the reflected rays is $\lambda'/2$, where λ' is the wavelength of light in the coating. In this case, both reflected waves undergo a phase shift, and therefore they are out of phase for a path-length difference of $\lambda'/2$ and interfere destructively. That is, the incident light is transmitted, and the coated lens is nonreflecting.

Note that the actual thickness of a quarter-wavelength thickness of film is specific to the particular wavelength of light. The thickness is usually chosen to be a quarter-wavelength of yellow-green light ($\lambda \approx 550$ nm), to which the human eye is most sensitive. The wavelengths at the red and blue ends of the visible region are still partially reflected, giving the coated lens its bluish-purple tint (Fig. 1). Sometimes other quarter-wavelength thicknesses are chosen, giving rise to other hues, such as amber or reddish purple, depending on the application of the lens.

Nonreflective coatings are also applied to the surfaces of solar cells, which convert light into electrical energy (Chapter 27). Because the thickness of such a coating is wavelength dependent, the losses due to reflection can be decreased from around 30% to only 10%. Even so, the process improves the cell's efficiency.

FIGURE 1 Coated lenses The nonreflective coating on binocular and camera lenses generally produces a characteristic bluish-purple hue. (Why?)

described this interference effect. Note that at the point where the lens and the optical flat touch ($t = 0$), there is, once again, a dark spot. (Why?) Lens irregularities give rise to a distorted fringe pattern, and the radii of these rings can be used to calculate the radius of curvature of the lens.

24.3 Diffraction

OBJECTIVES: To (a) define diffraction, and (b) give examples of diffractive effects.

In geometrical optics, light is represented by rays and pictured as traveling in straight lines. If this model were to represent the real nature of light, however, there would be no interference effects in Young's double-slit experiment. Instead, there would be only two bright images of slits on the screen, with a well-defined shadow area where no light enters. But we *do* see interference patterns, which means that the light must deviate from a straight-line path and enter the regions that would otherwise be in shadow. The waves actually "spread out" as they pass through the slits. This spreading is called **diffraction**. Diffraction generally occurs when waves pass through small openings or around sharp edges or corners. The diffraction of water waves is shown in ◄Fig. 24.11. (See also Fig. 13.18.)

As Fig. 13.18 shows, the amount of diffraction depends on the wavelength in relation to the size of the opening or object. In general, *the longer the wavelength compared to the width of the opening or object, the greater the diffraction*. This effect is also shown in ►Fig. 24.12. For example, in Fig. 24.12a, the width of the opening w is much greater than the wavelength ($w \gg \lambda$), and there is little diffraction—the wave keeps traveling without much spreading. (There is also *some* degree of diffraction due to the edges of the opening.) In Fig. 24.12b, with the wavelength and opening

▼ **FIGURE 24.11 Water-wave diffraction** This photograph of a beach dramatically shows single-slit diffraction of ocean waves through the barrier openings. Note that the beach has been shaped by the circular wave fronts.

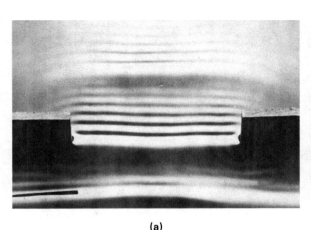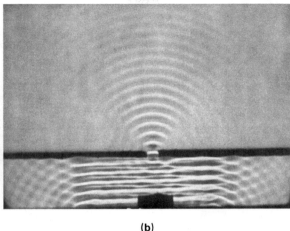

(a)   **(b)**

▲ **FIGURE 24.12 Wavelength and opening dimensions** In general, the narrower the opening compared to the wavelength, the greater the diffraction. **(a)** Without much diffraction ($w \gg \lambda$), the wave would keep traveling in its original direction. **(b)** With noticeable diffraction ($w \approx \lambda$), the wave bends around the opening and spreads out.

width the same order of magnitude ($w \approx \lambda$), there is noticeable diffraction—the wave spreads out and deviates from its original direction. Part of the wave keeps traveling in its original direction but the rest bends *around* the opening and clearly spreads out.

The diffraction of sound is quite evident (Chapter 14). Someone can talk to you from another room or around the corner of a building, and even in the absence of reflections, you can easily hear the person. Recall that audible sound wavelengths are on the order of centimeters to meters. Thus, the widths of ordinary objects and openings are about the same as or narrower than the wavelengths of sound, and diffraction will readily occur under these conditions.

Visible light waves, however, have wavelengths on the order of 10^{-7} m. Therefore diffraction phenomena for these waves often go unnoticed, especially through large openings such as doors where sound readily diffracts. However, close inspection of the area around a sharp razor blade will show a pattern of bright and dark bands (▶Fig. 24.13). Diffraction can lead to interference, and thus these interference patterns are evidence of the diffraction of the light around the edge of the blade.

As an illustration of "single-slit" diffraction, consider a slit in a barrier (▼Fig. 24.14). Suppose that the slit (width w) is illuminated with monochromatic light. A diffraction pattern consisting of a bright central maximum and a symmetrical array of maxima (regions of constructive interference) on both sides is observed on a screen at a distance L from the slit (we will assume $L \gg w$).

Thus a diffraction pattern results from the fact that various points on the wave front passing through the slit can be considered to be small point sources of light. The interference of those waves gives rise to the *diffraction* maxima and minima.

The fairly complex analysis is not done here; however, from geometry, it can be proven that the minima (regions of destructive interference) satisfy the relationship

$$w \sin \theta = m\lambda \qquad \text{for } m = 1, 2, 3, \ldots \quad \textit{condition for minima} \qquad (24.8)$$

where θ is the angle of a particular minimum, designated by $m = 1, 2, 3, \ldots$, on either side of the central maximum and m is called the order number. (There is no $m = 0$. Why?)

Although this result is similar in form to that for Young's double-slit experiment (Eq. 24.3), it is extremely important to realize that for the single-slit experiment, minima, rather than maxima, are analyzed. Also, note that the width of the slit (w) is used in diffraction. Physically, this is diffraction from a single slit, *not* interference from two slits.

The small-angle approximation, $\sin \theta \approx y/L$, can be made when $y \ll L$. In this case, the distances of the minima relative to the center of the central maximum are given by

$$y_m = m\left(\frac{L\lambda}{w}\right) \qquad \text{for } m = 1, 2, 3, \ldots \quad \textit{location for minima} \qquad (24.9)$$

Illustration 38.1 Single Slit Diffraction

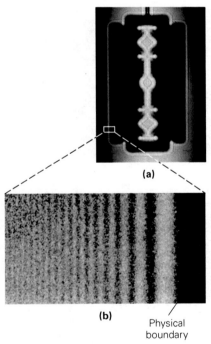

(a)

(b)

Physical boundary

▲ **FIGURE 24.13 Diffraction in action**
(a) Diffraction patterns produced by a razor blade. **(b)** A close-up view of the diffraction pattern formed at the edge of the blade.

▶ **FIGURE 24.14 Single-slit diffraction** The diffraction of light by a single slit gives rise to a diffraction pattern consisting of a large and bright central maximum and a symmetric array of side maxima. The order number m corresponds to the minima or dark positions. (See text for description.)

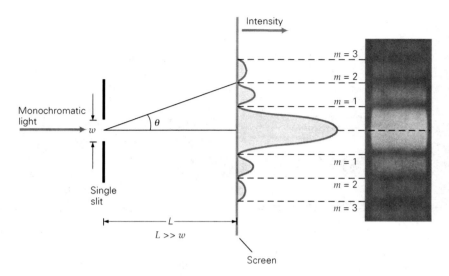

The qualitative predictions from Eq. 24.9 are interesting and instructive:

- For a given slit width (w), the longer the wavelength (λ), the wider (more "spread out") the diffraction pattern.
- For a given wavelength (λ) the narrower the slit width (w), the wider the diffraction pattern.
- The width of the central maximum is twice the width of any side maximum.

Let's look in detail at these results. As the slit is made narrower, the central maximum and the side maxima spread out and become larger. Equation 24.9 is not applicable to very small slit widths (because of the small-angle approximation). If the slit width is decreased until it is of the same order of magnitude as the wavelength of the light, then the central maximum spreads out over the whole screen. That is, diffraction becomes dramatically evident when the width of the slit is about the same as the wavelength of the light used. Diffraction effects are most easily observed when $\lambda/w \approx 1$, or $w \approx \lambda$.

Conversely, if the slit is made wider for a given wavelength, then the diffraction pattern becomes less spread out. The maxima move closer together and eventually become difficult to distinguish when w is much wider than λ ($w \gg \lambda$). The pattern then appears as a fuzzy shadow around the central maximum, which is the illuminated image of the slit. This type of pattern is observed for the image produced by sunlight entering a dark room through a hole in a curtain. Such an observation led early experimenters to investigate the wave nature of light. The acceptance of this concept was, in large part, due to the explanation of diffraction offered by physical optics.

The central maximum is twice as wide as any of the side maxima. Taking the width of the central maximum to be the distance between the bounding minima on each side ($m = 1$), or a value of $2y_1$, we obtain, from Eq. 24.9 with $y_1 = L\lambda/w$,

$$2y_1 = \frac{2L\lambda}{w} \quad \textit{width of central maximum} \quad (24.10)$$

Similarly, the width of the side maximum on the sides is given by

$$y_{m+1} - y_m = (m + 1)\left(\frac{L\lambda}{w}\right) - m\left(\frac{L\lambda}{w}\right) = \frac{L\lambda}{w} = y_1 \quad (24.11)$$

Thus, the width of the central maximum is twice that of the side maxima.

Conceptual Example 24.3 ■ Diffraction and Radio Reception

While you drive through a city or mountainous areas, the quality of your radio reception varies sharply from place to place, with stations seeming to fade out and reappear. Could diffraction be a cause of this? Which of the following bands would you expect to be least affected by it: (a) Weather (162 MHz); (b) FM (88–108 MHz); or (c) AM (525–1610 kHz)?

Reasoning and Answer. Radio waves, like visible light, are electromagnetic waves and so tend to travel in straight lines when they are long distances from their sources. They can be blocked by objects in their path—especially if the objects are massive (such as hills and buildings).

However, because of diffraction, radio waves can also "wrap around" obstacles or "fan out" as they pass through obstacles and openings, *provided* their wavelength is at least roughly the size of the obstacle or opening. The longer the wavelength, the greater the amount of diffraction, and so the *less likely* the radio waves are to be obstructed.

To determine which band benefits most by such diffraction, we need the wavelengths that correspond to the given frequencies, as given by $c = \lambda f$. AM radio waves, with $\lambda = 186–571$ m, are the longest of the three bands (by a factor of about 100). Thus AM broadcasts are more likely to be diffracted around such objects as buildings or mountains or through the openings between them, and the answer is (c).

Follow-Up Exercise. Woodwind instruments, such as the clarinet and the flute, usually have smaller openings than brass instruments, such as the trumpet and trombone. During halftime at a football game, when a marching band faces you, you can easily hear both the woodwind instruments and the brass instruments. Yet when the band marches away from you, the brass instruments sound muted, but you can hear the woodwinds quite well. Why?

Integrated Example 24.4 ■ **Width of the Central Maximum: Single-Slit Diffraction**

Monochromatic light passes through a slit whose width is 0.050 mm. (a) The general spreadout of the diffraction pattern, in general, is (1) larger for longer wavelengths, (2) larger for shorter wavelengths, (3) the same for all wavelengths. Explain. (b) At what angle will the third minimum be seen and what is the width of the central maximum on a screen located 1.0 m from the slit, for $\lambda = 400$ nm and 550 nm, respectively?

(a) Conceptual Reasoning. The general size of the diffraction pattern can be characterized by the position of a particular maximum or minimum. From Eq. 24.8, it can be seen that for a given width w and order number m, the position of a minimum $\sin \theta$ is directly proportional to the wavelength λ. Therefore, a longer wavelength will correspond to a greater $\sin \theta$ or a greater θ, and the answer is (1).

(b) Quantitative Reasoning and Solution. This part is a direct application of Eq. 24.8 and Eq. 24.10.

Given: $\lambda_1 = 400$ nm $= 4.00 \times 10^{-7}$ m   **Find:** θ_3 and $2y_1$ (width of central maximum)
   $\lambda_2 = 550$ nm $= 5.50 \times 10^{-7}$ m
   $w = 0.050$ mm $= 5.0 \times 10^{-5}$ m
   $m = 3$
   $L = 1.0$ m

For $\lambda = 400$ nm:
   From Eq. 24.8, we have

$$\sin \theta_3 = \frac{m\lambda}{w} = \frac{3(4.00 \times 10^{-7} \text{ m})}{5.0 \times 10^{-5} \text{ m}} = 0.024 \quad \text{so} \quad \theta_3 = \sin^{-1} 0.024 = 1.4°$$

Equation 24.10 gives

$$2y_1 = \frac{2L\lambda}{w} = \frac{2(1.0 \text{ m})(4.00 \times 10^{-7} \text{ m})}{5.0 \times 10^{-5} \text{ m}} = 1.6 \times 10^{-2} \text{ m} = 1.6 \text{ cm}$$

For $\lambda = 700$ nm:

$$\sin \theta_3 = \frac{m\lambda}{w} = \frac{3(5.50 \times 10^{-7} \text{ m})}{5.0 \times 10^{-5} \text{ m}} = 0.033 \quad \text{so} \quad \theta_3 = \sin^{-1} 0.033 = 1.9°$$

$$2y_1 = \frac{2L\lambda}{w} = \frac{2(1.0 \text{ m})(5.50 \times 10^{-7} \text{ m})}{5.0 \times 10^{-5} \text{ m}} = 2.2 \times 10^{-2} \text{ m} = 2.2 \text{ cm}$$

Follow-Up Exercise. By what factor would the width of the central maximum change if red light ($\lambda = 700$ nm) were used instead of 550 nm?

▶ **FIGURE 24.15 Diffraction grating**
A diffraction grating produces a sharply defined interference/diffraction pattern. Two parameters define a grating: the slit separation d and the slit width w. The combination of multiple-slit interference and single-slit diffraction determine the intensity distribution of the various orders of maxima.

Illustration 38.2 Application of Diffraction Gratings

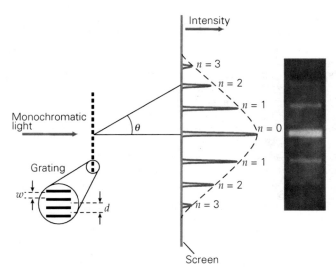

Diffraction Gratings

We have seen that maxima and minima result from diffraction followed by interference when monochromatic light passes through a set of double slits. As the number of slits is increased, the maxima become sharper (narrower) and the minima wider. The sharp maxima are very useful in optical analysis of light sources and other applications. ▲Fig. 24.15 shows a typical experiment with monochromatic light incident on a **diffraction grating**, which consists of large numbers of parallel, closely spaced slits. Two parameters define a diffraction grating: the slit separation between successive slits, d, and the individual slit width, w. The resulting pattern of interference and diffraction is shown in ▼Fig. 24.16.

Diffraction gratings were first made of fine strands of wire. They produce effects similar to what can be seen by viewing a candle flame through a feather held close to the eye. Better gratings have a large number of fine lines or grooves on glass or metal surfaces. If light is transmitted through a grating, it is called a *transmission grating*. However, *reflection gratings* are also common. The closely spaced grooves of a compact disc or a DVD act as a reflection grating, giving rise to their familiar iridescent sheen (▶Fig. 24.17). Commercial master gratings are made by depositing a thin film of aluminum on an optically flat surface and then removing some of the reflecting metal by cutting regularly spaced, parallel lines. Precision diffraction gratings

▶ **FIGURE 24.16 Intensity distribution of interference and diffraction** (a) Interference determines the positions of the interference maxima:
$d \sin \theta = n\lambda, n = 0, 1, 2, 3, \ldots$.
(b) Diffraction locates the positions of the diffraction minima:
$w \sin \theta = m\lambda, m = 1, 2, 3, \ldots$, and the relative intensity of the maxima.
(c) The combination (product) of interference and diffraction determine the overall intensity distribution.

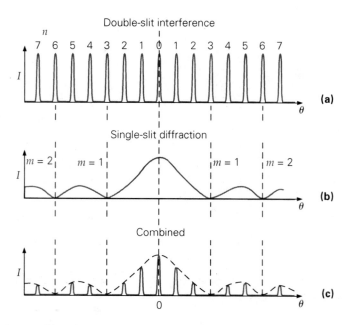

are made using two coherent laser beams that intersect at an angle. The beams expose a layer of photosensitive material, which is then etched. The spacing of the grating lines is determined by the intersection angle of the beams. Precision gratings may have 30 000 lines per centimeter or more and are therefore expensive and difficult to fabricate. Most gratings used in laboratory instruments are *replica gratings*, which are plastic castings of high-precision master gratings.

It can be shown that the condition for interference maxima for a grating illuminated with monochromatic light is identical to that for a double slit. The expression is

$$d \sin \theta = n\lambda \qquad \text{for } n = 0, 1, 2, 3, \dots \quad \textit{interference maxima} \qquad (24.12)$$

where n is called the *order-of-interference maximum* and θ is the angle at which that maximum occurs for a particular wavelength. The zeroth-order maximum is coincident with the central maximum. The spacing between adjacent slits (d) is obtained from the number of lines or slits per unit length of the grating: $d = 1/N$. For example, if $N = 5000$ lines/cm, then

$$d = \frac{1}{N} = \frac{1}{5000/\text{cm}} = 2.0 \times 10^{-4} \text{ cm}$$

If the light incident on a grating is white light (polychromatic), then the maxima are multicolored (▼Fig. 24.18a). There is no deviation of the components of the light for the zeroth order ($\sin \theta = 0$ for all wavelengths), so the central maximum is white. However, the colors separate for higher orders, since the position of the maximum depends on wavelength (Eq. 24.12). With the longer wavelength having a larger θ, this produces a spectrum. Note that it is possible for higher orders produced by a diffraction grating to overlap. That is, the angles for different orders may be the same for two different wavelengths.

Only a limited number of spectral orders can be obtained using a diffraction grating. The number depends on the wavelength of the light and on the grating's spacing (d). From Eq. 24.12, because θ cannot exceed 90° (that is, $\sin \theta \leq 1$), we have

$$\sin \theta = \frac{n\lambda}{d} \leq 1 \qquad \text{or} \qquad n_{\text{max}} \leq \frac{d}{\lambda}$$

Diffraction gratings have almost completely replaced prisms in spectroscopy. The creation of a spectrum and the measurement of wavelengths by a grating depend only on geometrical measurements such as lengths and/or angles. Wavelength determination using a prism, in contrast, depends on the dispersive characteristics of the material of which the prism is made. Thus, it is crucial to know precisely how the index of refraction depends on the wavelength of light. In contrast to a prism, which deviates red light least and violet light most, a diffraction grating produces the smallest angle for violet light

▲ **FIGURE 24.17 Diffraction effects** The narrow grooves of compact discs (CDs) act as reflection diffraction gratings, producing colorful displays.

Note: d is the distance between adjacent slits.

Exploration 38.2 Diffraction Grating

▼ **FIGURE 24.18 Spectroscopy** **(a)** In each side maximum, components of different wavelengths (R = red and V = violet) are separated, because the deviation depends on wavelength: $\theta = \sin^{-1}(n\lambda/d)$. **(b)** As a result, gratings are used in spectrometers to determine the wavelengths present in a beam of light by measuring their angles of diffraction and to separate the various wavelengths for further analysis.

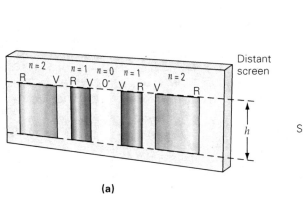

(a)

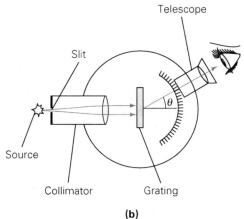

(b)

(short λ) and the greatest for red light (long λ). Notice that a prism disperses white light into a single spectrum. A diffraction grating, however, produces a number of spectra, one for each order other than $n = 0$, and the higher the order, the more spread out.

The sharp spectra produced by gratings are used in instruments called *spectrometers* (Fig. 24.18b). Using a spectrometer, materials can be illuminated with light of various wavelengths to find which wavelengths are strongly transmitted or reflected. Their absorption can then be measured and material characteristics determined.

Example 24.5 ■ A Diffraction Grating: Line Spacing and Spectral Orders

A particular diffraction grating produces an $n = 2$ spectral order at an angle of 30° for light with a wavelength of 500 nm. (a) How many lines per centimeter does the grating have? (b) At what angle can the $n = 3$ spectral order be seen?

Thinking It Through. (a) To find the number of lines per centimeter (N) the grating has, we need to know the grating spacing (d), since $N = 1/d$. With the given data, we can find d from Eq. 24.12. (b) Using Eq. 24.12 again, we can find θ for $n = 3$.

Solution.

Given: $\lambda = 500\,\text{nm} = 5.00 \times 10^{-7}\,\text{m}$ *Find:* (a) N (lines/cm)
     $n = 2$ (b) θ for $n = 3$
     $\theta = 30°$ for $n = 2$

(a) Using Eq. 24.12, we get the grating spacing:

$$d = \frac{n\lambda}{\sin \theta} = \frac{2(5.00 \times 10^{-7}\,\text{m})}{\sin 30°} = 2.00 \times 10^{-6}\,\text{m} = 2.00 \times 10^{-4}\,\text{cm}$$

Then

$$N = \frac{1}{d} = \frac{1}{2.00 \times 10^{-4}\,\text{cm}} = 5000\,\text{lines/cm}$$

(b)

$$\sin \theta = \frac{n\lambda}{d} = \frac{3(5.00 \times 10^{-7}\,\text{m})}{2.00 \times 10^{-6}\,\text{m}} = 0.75$$

so

$$\theta = \sin^{-1} 0.75 = 48.6°$$

Follow-Up Exercise. If white light of wavelength ranging from 400 to 700 nm were used, what would be the angular width of the spectrum for the second order?

X-Ray Diffraction

In principle, the wavelength of any electromagnetic wave can be determined by using a diffraction grating with the appropriate spacing. Diffraction was used to determine the wavelengths of X-rays early in the twentieth century. Experimental evidence indicated that the wavelengths of X-rays were probably around 10^{-10} m or 0.1 nm, but it is impossible to construct a diffraction grating with this spacing. Around 1913, Max von Laue (1879–1960), a German physicist, suggested that the regular spacing of the atoms in a crystalline solid might make the crystal act as a diffraction grating for X-rays, since the atomic spacing is on the order of 0.1 nm (▶Fig. 24.19). When X-rays were directed at crystals, diffraction patterns were indeed observed. (See Fig. 24.19b.)

Figure 24.19a illustrates diffraction by the planes of atoms in a crystal such as sodium chloride. The path-length difference is $2d \sin \theta$, where d is the distance between the crystal's internal planes. Thus, the condition for constructive interference is

$$2d \sin \theta = n\lambda \qquad \text{for } n = 1, 2, 3, \ldots \qquad \begin{array}{l} \textit{constructive interference} \\ \textit{X-ray diffraction} \end{array} \qquad (24.13)$$

This relationship is known as **Bragg's law**, after W. L. Bragg (1890–1971), the British physicist who first derived it. Note that θ is *not* measured from the normal, as is the convention in optics.

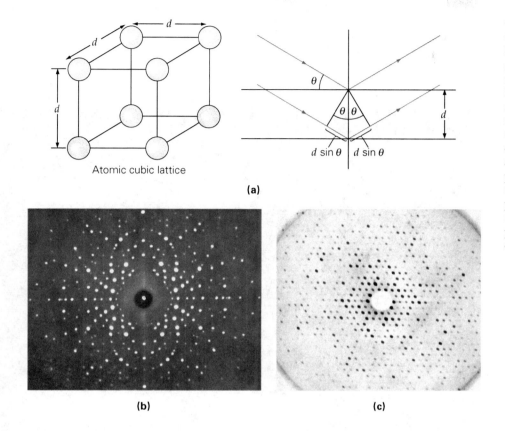

Atomic cubic lattice

(a)

(b)

(c)

◀ **FIGURE 24.19** Crystal diffraction
(a) The array of atoms in a crystal-lattice structure acts as a diffraction grating, and X-rays are diffracted from the planes of atoms. With a lattice spacing of d, the path-length difference for the X-rays diffracted from adjacent planes is $2d \sin \theta$.
(b) X-ray diffraction pattern of a crystal of potassium sulfate. By analyzing the geometry of such patterns, investigators can deduce the structure of the crystal and the position of its various atoms.
(c) X-ray diffraction pattern of the protein hemoglobin, which carries oxygen in blood.

X-ray diffraction is now routinely used to investigate the internal structure not only of simple crystals, but also of large, complex biological molecules such as proteins and DNA (Fig. 24.19c). Because of their short wavelengths, which are comparable with interatomic distances *within* a molecule, X-rays provide a method for investigating atomic structures within molecules.

25

VISION AND OPTICAL INSTRUMENTS

PHYSICS FACTS

- About 80% of the refracting power of a human eye comes from the cornea while the other 20% comes from the crystalline lens. The crystalline lens can change shape to accommodate close or far focusing by means of the ciliary muscles.

- The human eye collects a lot of information. If it were compared to a digital camera, the human eye would be equivalent to 500 megapixels. A common digital camera has 2 to 10 megapixels.

- A red blood cell has a diameter of about $7\,\mu m$ (7×10^{-6} m). When viewed with a compound microscope at $1000\times$, it appears to be 7 mm (7×10^{-3} m).

- Some cameras on satellites have excellent resolution. From space they can read the license plates on cars.

Vision is one of our chief means of acquiring information about the world around us. However, the images seen by many eyes are not always clear or in focus, and glasses or some other remedy are needed. Great progress has been made in the last decade in contact lens therapy and surgical correction of vision defects. A popular procedure is laser surgery, as shown in the photo. Laser surgery can be used for such procedures as repairing torn retinas, destroying eye tumors, and stopping abnormal growth of blood vessels that can endanger vision.

Optical instruments, the basic function of which is to improve and extend the power of observation beyond that of the human eye, augment our vision. Mirrors and lenses are used in a variety of optical instruments, including microscopes and telescopes.

The earliest magnifying lenses were drops of water captured in a small hole. By the seventeenth century, artisans were able to grind fair-quality lenses for simple microscopes or magnifying glasses, which were used primarily for botanical studies. (These early lenses also found a use in spectacles.) Soon, the basic compound microscope, which uses two lenses, was developed. Modern compound microscopes, which can magnify an object up to 200 times, extended our vision into the microbe world.

Around 1609, Galileo used lenses to construct an astronomical telescope that allowed him to observe valleys and mountains on the Moon, sunspots, and the four largest moons of Jupiter. Today, huge telescopes that use lenses and mirrors have extended our vision far into the past as we look at farther, and therefore, younger, galaxies.

What would our knowledge be if these instruments had never been invented? Bacteria would still be unknown, and planets, stars, and galaxies would have remained nothing but mysterious points of light.

Mirrors and lenses were discussed in terms of geometrical optics in Chapter 23, and the wave nature of light was investigated in Chapter 24. These principles can be applied to the study of vision and optical instruments. In this chapter, you will learn about our fundamental optical instrument—the human eye, without which all others would be of little use. Also microscopes and telescopes will be discussed, along with the factors that limit their viewing.

25.1 The Human Eye

OBJECTIVES: To (a) describe the optical workings of the eye, and (b) explain some common vision defects and how they are corrected.

The human eye is the most important of all optical instruments, because without it we would know little about our world and the study of optics would not exist. The human eye is analogous to a simple camera in several respects (▼Fig. 25.1). A simple camera consists of a converging lens, which is used to focus images on light-sensitive film (traditional camera) or *charge coupled device*, CCD, (in digital cameras) at the back of the camera's interior chamber. (Recall from Chapter 23 that for relatively distant objects, a converging lens produces a small, inverted, real image.) There is an adjustable diaphragm opening, or aperture, and a shutter to control the amount of light entering the camera.

The eye, too, focuses images onto a light-sensitive lining (the retina) on the rear surface of the eyeball. The eyelid might be thought of as a shutter; however, the shutter of a camera, which controls the exposure time, is generally opened only for a fraction of a second, while the eyelid is normally open for continuous exposure. The human nervous system actually performs a function analogous to a shutter by analyzing image signals from the eye at a rate of 20 to 30 times per second.

Note: Image formation by a converging lens is discussed in Section 23.3; see Figure 23.15a.

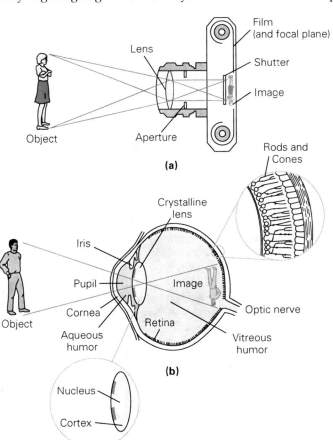

(a)

(b)

◀ **FIGURE 25.1 Camera and eye analogy** In some respects, **(a)** a simple camera is similar to **(b)** the human eye. An image is formed on the film in a camera and on the retina of the eye. (The complex refractive properties of the eye are not shown here, because multiple refractive media are involved.) See text for a comparative description.

PHYSLET

Illustration 36.2 *Camera*

PHYSLET

Exploration 36.1 *Camera*

The eye might therefore be better likened to a movie or video camera, which exposes a similar number of frames (images) per second.

Although the optical functions of the eye are relatively simple, its physiological functions are quite complex. As Fig. 25.1b shows, the eyeball is a nearly spherical chamber. It has an internal diameter of about 1.5 cm and is filled with a transparent jellylike substance called the *vitreous humor*. The eyeball has a white outer covering called the *sclera*, part of which is visible as the "white" of the eye. Light enters the eye through a curved, transparent tissue called the *cornea* and passes into a clear fluid known as the *aqueous humor*. Behind the cornea is a circular diaphragm, the *iris*, whose central opening is the *pupil*. The iris contains the pigment that determines eye color. Through muscle action, the area of the pupil can change (from 2 to 8 mm in diameter), thereby controlling the amount of light entering the eye.

Behind the iris is a *crystalline lens*, a converging lens composed of microscopic glassy fibers. (See Conceptual Example 22.5 on page 713 about the internal elements, the nucleous and cortex, inside the crystalline lens.) When tension is exerted on the lens by attached muscles, the glassy fibers slide over each other, causing the shape, and therefore focal length, of the lens to change, to help in focusing the image on the retina properly. Notice that this is an *inverted* image (Fig. 25.1b). We do not see an inverted image, however, because the brain reinterprets this image as being right-side-up.

On the back interior wall of the eyeball is a light-sensitive surface called the **retina**. From the retina, the optic nerve relays retinal signals to the brain. The retina is composed of nerves and two types of light receptors, or photosensitive cells, called **rods** and **cones**, because of their shapes. The rods are more sensitive to light than are the cones and distinguish light from dark in low light intensities (twilight vision). The cones can distinguish frequency ranges but require brighter light. The brain interprets these different frequencies as colors (color vision). Most of the cones are clustered in a central region of the retina called the *macula*. The rods, which are more numerous than the cones, are outside this region and are distributed nonuniformly over the retina.

The focusing adjustment of the eye differs from that of a simple camera. A camera lens has a constant focal length, and the image distance is varied by moving the lens relative to the film to produce sharp images for different object distances. In the eye, the image distance is constant, and the focal length of the lens is varied (as the attached muscles change the lens's shape) to produce sharp images on the retina, regardless of object distance. When the eye is focused on distant objects, the muscles are relaxed, and the crystalline lens is thinnest with a power of about 20 D (diopters). Recall from Chapter 23 that the power (P) of a lens in diopters (D), which is the reciprocal of its focal length *in meters*. So 20 D corresponds to a focal length of $f = 1/(20 \text{ D}) = 0.050$ m $= 5.0$ cm. When the eye is focused on closer objects, the lens becomes thicker. Then its radius of curvature and hence its focal length are decreased. For close-up vision, the lens power may increase to 30 D ($f = 0.033$ m), or even more in young children. The adjustment of the focal length of the crystalline lens is called *accommodation*. (Look at a nearby object and then at an object in the distance, and notice how fast accommodation takes place. It's practically instantaneous.)

The distance extremes over which sharp focus is possible are known as the *far point* and the *near point*. The *far point* is the greatest distance at which the eye can see objects clearly and is infinity for a normal eye. The *near point* is the position closest to the eye at which objects can be seen clearly. This position depends on the extent to which the lens can be deformed (thickened) by accommodation. The range of accommodation gradually diminishes with age as the crystalline lens loses its elasticity. Generally, in the normal eye the near point gradually recedes with age. The approximate positions of the near point at various ages are listed in Table 25.1.

Children can see sharp images of objects that are within 10 cm of their eyes, and the crystalline lens of a normal young-adult eye can do the same for objects as close as 12 to 15 cm. However, adults at about age 40 normally experience a shift in the near point to beyond 25 cm. You may have noticed middle-aged people holding reading material fairly far from their eyes so as to move it out to be within the range of accommodation. When the print becomes too small (or the arms too short), corrective reading glasses are one solution. The recession of the near point with age is not considered an abnormal defect. Since it proceeds at about the same rate in most normal eyes, it is considered mainly a part of the normal "aging" process.

TABLE 25.1

Approximate Near Points of the Normal Eye at Different Ages

Age (years)	Near Point (centimeters)
10	10
20	12
30	15
40	25
50	40
60	100

Note: The relationship between lens power in diopters and focal length is presented in Eq. 23.9, in Section 23.4.

Note: The eye sees clearly between its far point and near point.

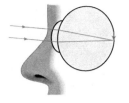
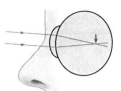
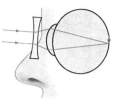
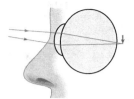
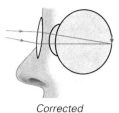

Uncorrected   *Corrected*   *Uncorrected*   *Corrected*

(a) Normal   **(b) Nearsightedness (myopia)**   **(c) Farsightedness (hyperopia)**

Vision Defects

The existence of a "normal" eye (▲Fig. 25.2a) implies that some eyes must have defects. This is indeed the case, as is quite apparent from the number of people who wear corrective glasses or contact lenses. Many people have eyes that cannot accommodate within the normal range (25 cm to infinity). These people usually have one of the two most common visual defects: nearsightedness (myopia) or farsightedness (hyperopia). Both of these conditions can usually be corrected with glasses, contact lenses, or surgery.

Nearsightedness (or *myopia*) is the ability to see nearby objects clearly, but not distant objects. That is, the far point is less than infinity. When an object is beyond the far point, the rays focus in *front* of the retina (Fig. 25.2b). As a result, the image on the retina is blurred, or out of focus. As the object is moved closer, its image moves back toward the retina. When the object reaches the far point for that eye, a sharp image is formed on the retina.

Nearsightedness usually arises because the eyeball is too long or the curvature of the cornea is too great. Whatever the reason, the eyeball overconverges the light from distant objects to a spot in front of the retina. Appropriate diverging lenses correct this condition. Such a lens causes the rays to diverge before reaching the cornea. The eye thus focuses the image farther back on the retina.

Farsightedness (or *hyperopia*) is the ability to see distant objects clearly, but not nearby ones. That is, the near point is farther from the eye than normal. The image of an object that is closer than the near point is formed behind the retina (Fig. 25.2c). Farsightedness arises because the eyeball is too short, because of insufficient curvature of the cornea or because of insufficient elasticity of the crystalline lens. If this occurs as part of the aging process as previously discussed, it is called *presbyopia*.

Farsightedness is usually corrected with appropriate converging lenses. Such a lens causes the rays to converge on the retina, and the eye is then able to focus the image on the retina. Converging lenses are also used in middle-aged people to correct presbyopia, a vision condition in which the crystalline lens of the eye loses its flexibility, which makes it difficult to focus on close objects.

▲ **FIGURE 25.2** Nearsightedness and farsightedness
(a) The normal eye produces sharp images on the retina for objects located between its near point and its far point. The image is real, inverted, and always smaller than the object. (Why?) Here, the object is a distant, upward-pointing arrow (not shown) and the light rays come from its tip. (b) In a nearsighted eye, the image of a *distant* object is focused *in front of* the retina. This defect is corrected with a diverging lens. (c) In a farsighted eye, the image of a *nearby* object is focused *behind* the retina. This defect is corrected with a converging lens. (Not drawn to scale.)

PHYSLET®

Illustration 36.1 The Human Eye

Integrated Example 25.1 ■ Correcting Nearsightedness: Use of Diverging Lenses

(a) An optometrist has a choice to give a patient either regular glasses or contact lenses to correct nearsightedness (▼Fig. 25.3). Usually, regular glasses sit a few centimeters in front of the eye and contact lenses right on the eye. Should the power of the contact lenses prescribed be (1) the same as, (2) greater than, or (3) less than that of the regular glasses? Explain. (b) A certain nearsighted person cannot see objects clearly when they are more than 78.0 cm from either eye. What power must corrective lenses have, for both regular glasses and contact lenses, if this person is to see distant objects clearly? Assume that the glasses are 3.00 cm in front of the eye.

(a) Conceptual Reasoning. For nearsightedness, the corrective lens is a diverging one (Fig. 25.3). The lens must effectively put the image of a distant object ($d_o = \infty$) at the far point of the eye, that is, d_f from the eye. The image, which acts as an object for the eye, is then within the range of accommodation. Because the image distance is *measured from the lens*, a contact lens will have a *longer* image distance. For a contact lens, $d_i = -(d_f)$. For regular glasses, $d_i = -|d_f - d|$, where d is the distance between the regular glasses and the eye. A minus sign and absolute values are used for the image distance because the image is virtual, being on the object side of the lens. (You may recall from Chapter 23 that diverging lenses can form only virtual images.)

Note: Review Example 23.6 and 23.8.

Note: Image formation by a diverging lens is discussed in Section 23.3; see Figure 23.18.

(continues on next page)

▶ **FIGURE 25.3** Correcting nearsightedness A diverging lens is used. See Integrated Example 25.1. Only regular glasses are shown. For contact lenses, the lens is immediately in front of the eye ($d = 0$).

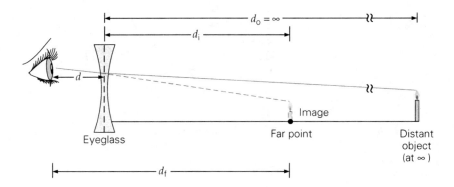

Note that d_i is negative. Recall that the power of a lens is $P = 1/f$ (Eq. 23.9). We can use the thin-lens equation (Eq. 23.5) to find P if we can determine the object and image distances, d_o and d_i:

$$P = \frac{1}{f} = \frac{1}{d_o} + \frac{1}{d_i} = \frac{1}{\infty} + \frac{1}{d_i} = \frac{1}{d_i} = -\frac{1}{|d_i|}$$

That is, a longer $|d_i|$ will yield a smaller P, so the contact lenses should have a lower power than the regular glasses. Thus, the answer is (3).

(b) Quantitative Reasoning and Solution. Once we understand how corrective lenses work, the calculation for part (b) is straightforward.

Given: $d_f = 78$ cm $= 0.780$ m (far point) **Find:** P (in diopters) for regular glasses
$d = 3.0$ cm $= 0.0300$ m P (in diopters) for contact lenses

For regular glasses,

$$|d_i| = |d_f - d| = 0.780 \text{ m} - 0.0300 \text{ m} = 0.750 \text{ m}$$

(See Fig 25.3, which is not drawn to scale.) So, $d_i = -0.750$ m.

Then, using the thin-lens equation, we get

$$P = \frac{1}{f} = \frac{1}{d_o} + \frac{1}{d_i} = \frac{1}{\infty} + \frac{1}{-0.750 \text{ m}} = -\frac{1}{0.750 \text{ m}} = -1.33 \text{ D}$$

A negative, or diverging, lens with a power of 1.33 D is needed.

For contact lenses,

$$|d_i| = |d_f| = 0.780 \text{ m}$$

($d = 0$.) So, $d_i = -0.78$ m.

Then, using the thin-lens equation, we get

$$P = \frac{1}{\infty} + \frac{1}{-0.780 \text{ m}} = -\frac{1}{0.780 \text{ m}} = -1.28 \text{ D}$$

Follow-Up Exercise. Suppose a mistake was made for regular glasses in this Example such that a "corrective" lens of +1.33 D were used. What happens to the image of objects at infinity? *(Answers to all Follow-Up Exercises are at the back of the text.)*

If the far point for a nearsighted person is changed using diverging lenses (see Integrated Example 25.1), the near point will be affected as well. This causes the close-up vision to worsen, but *bifocal lenses* can be used in this situation to address the problem. Bifocals were invented by Benjamin Franklin, who glued two lenses together. They are now made by grinding or molding lenses with different curvatures in two different regions. Both nearsightedness and farsightedness can be treated at the same time with bifocals. Trifocals are also available, with lenses having three different curvatures. The top lens is for far vision and the bottom lens for near vision. The middle lens is for intermediate vision and is sometimes referred to as a lens for "computer" vision.

More modern techniques involve contact lens therapy or the use of a laser to correct nearsightedness. These are discussed in detail in Insight 25.1, Cornea "Orthodontics" and Surgery, on accompanying page. The purpose of either technique is to change the shape the exposed surface of the cornea, which changes its refractive characteristics. The result, for the nearsighted case, is to make the image of a distant object fall on the retina.

INSIGHT 25.1 CORNEA "ORTHODONTICS" AND SURGERY

The imperfect shape of the cornea of the human eye often causes refractive errors that result in vision defects. For example, a cornea that is curved too much can cause nearsightedness; a flatter-than-normal cornea can cause farsightedness. A cornea that is not spherical can cause astigmatism (Section 23.4).

Recently, a nonsurgical contact lens treatment to improve vision in a matter of hours was developed. This procedure, called *orthokeratology*, or *Ortho-K*, is achieved in a unique way, with the wearing of custom-designed contact lenses. These contact lenses slowly change the shape of the cornea by means of gentle pressure to improve vision safely and quickly. The best analogy to describe Ortho-K is by calling it "orthodontics for the eye."

Laser surgery is also used to reshape the cornea. The surgical procedure corrects the defective shape or irregular surface of the cornea so that it can better focus light on the retina, thereby reducing or even eliminating vision defects (Fig. 1).

In corneal laser surgery, first, a very precise instrument called a *microkeratome* is used to create a thin corneal flap with a hinge on one side of the cornea (Fig. 2a). Once the flap is folded back, a tightly focused ultraviolet pulsed laser is used to reshape the cornea. Each laser pulse accurately removes a microscopic layer of the inner cornea in the targeted area, thus reshaping the cornea to correct vision defects (Fig. 2b). The flap is then placed back in its original position without the need for stitches (Fig. 2c). The procedure is usually painless, and patients typically have only minimal discomfort. Some patients achieve corrected vision within a day after this procedure.

Even more exciting advances in vision correction are on the horizon. For example, researchers have developed techniques for replacing a damaged cornea with freshly bioengineered tissues. If the patient has one healthy eye, stem cells are harvested from it. The cells grow into a sturdy layer of tissue that surgeons can use to replace the bad corneal tissues of the other eye by stitching the new tissue onto that damaged eye. If both of the patient's eyes are damaged, donor tissues may be collected from a close relative.

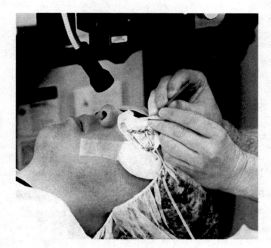

FIGURE 1 Eye surgery Laser surgery is performed to reshape the cornea. Notice that the surgeon is wearing no latex gloves. The fine chalk dust used as a lubricant on the gloves could contaminate the eye.

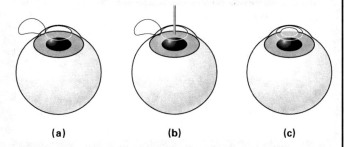

(a) (b) (c)

FIGURE 2 Cornea reshaping (a) A flap is made on the corneal surface. **(b)** A laser beam is used to reshape the cornea. **(c)** The flap is placed back.

Integrated Example 25.2 ■ Correcting Farsightedness: Use of a Converging Lens

A farsighted person has a near point of 75 cm for the left eye and a near point of 100 cm for the right one. (a) If the person is prescribed contact lenses, the power of the left lens should be (1) greater than, (2) the same as, (3) less than the power of the right lens. Explain. (b) What powers should contact lenses have to allow the person to see an object clearly at a distance of 25 cm?

(a) Conceptual Reasoning. The normal eye's near point is 25 cm. For farsightedness, the corrective lens must be converging and form the image at its eye's near point of an object at the normal eye's near point. Since the near point of the left eye (75 cm) is closer to the 25-cm normal position than the right eye, the left lens should have less power so the answer is (3).

(b) Quantitative Reasoning and Solution. Let us label the two different eyes as L (left) and R (right). The image distances are negative. (Why?)

Given: $d_{i_L} = -75 \text{ cm} = -0.75 \text{ m}$ *Find:* P_L and P_R (lens power for each eye)
$d_{i_R} = -100 \text{ cm} = -1.0 \text{ m}$
$d_o = 25 \text{ cm} = 0.25 \text{ m}$

The optics of these two eyes are usually different (as is typical), as in this problem, and a different lens prescription is usually required for each eye. In this case, each lens is to form an image at its eye's near point of an object that is at a distance (d_o) of 0.25 m. The

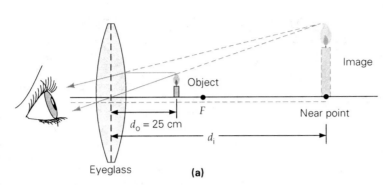

(a) **(b)**

▲ **FIGURE 25.4** Reading glasses and correcting farsightedness **(a)** When an object at the normal near point (25 cm) is viewed through reading glasses with converging lenses, the image is formed farther away, but within the eye's range of accommodation (beyond the receded near point). See Integrated Example 25.2. **(b)** Small print as viewed through the lens of reading glasses. The camera used to take this picture is focused past this page onto where the virtual image is.

image will then act as an object within the eye's range of accommodation. This situation is similar to a person wearing reading glasses (▲ Fig. 25.4). (For the sake of clarity, the lens in Fig. 25.4a is not in contact with the eye.)

The image distances are negative, because the images are virtual (that is, the image is on the same side as the object). With contact lenses, the distance from the eye to the object and the distance from the lens to the object are the same. Then

$$P_L = \frac{1}{f_L} = \frac{1}{d_o} + \frac{1}{d_{i_L}} = \frac{1}{0.25 \text{ m}} - \frac{1}{0.75 \text{ m}} = \frac{2}{0.75 \text{ m}} = +2.7 \text{ D}$$

and

$$P_R = \frac{1}{f_R} = \frac{1}{d_o} + \frac{1}{d_{i_R}} = \frac{1}{0.25 \text{ m}} - \frac{1}{1.0 \text{ m}} = \frac{3}{1.0 \text{ m}} = +3.0 \text{ D}$$

Note that the left lens has less power than the right lens, as expected.

Follow-Up Exercise. A mistake is made in grinding or molding the corrective lenses in this Example such that the left lens is made to the prescription intended for the right eye, and vice versa. Discuss what happens to the images of an object at a distance of 25 cm.

Another common defect of vision is **astigmatism**, which is usually due to a refractive surface, normally the cornea or crystalline lens, being out of round (nonspherical). As a result, the eye has different focal lengths in different planes (▼Fig. 25.5a). Points may appear as lines, and the image of a line may be distinct in one direction and blurred in another or blurred in both directions. A test for astigmatism is given in Fig. 25.5b.

Astigmatism can be corrected with lenses that have greater curvature in the plane in which the cornea or crystalline lens has deficient curvature (Fig. 25.5c). Astigmatism is lessened in bright light, because the pupil of the eye becomes smaller, so only rays near the axis are entering the eye, thus avoiding the outer edges of the cornea.

You have probably heard of *20/20 vision*. But what is it? *Visual acuity* is a measure of how vision is affected by object distance. This quantity is commonly determined by using a chart of letters placed at a given distance from the eyes. The result is usually expressed as a fraction: The *numerator* is the distance at which the test eye sees a standard symbol, such as the letter E, clearly; the *denominator* is the distance at which the letter is seen clearly by a *normal* eye. A 20/20 (test/normal) rating, which is sometimes called "perfect" vision, means that at a distance of 20 ft, the eye being tested can see standard-sized letters as clearly as can a normal eye.

▼ **FIGURE 25.5** Astigmatism When one of the eye's refracting components is not spherical, the eye has different focal lengths in different planes. **(a)** The effect occurs because rays in the vertical plane (red) and horizontal plane (blue) are focused at different points: F_v and F_h, respectively. **(b)** To someone with eyes that are astigmatic, some or all of the lines in this diagram will appear blurred. **(c)** Nonspherical lenses, such as plano-convex cylindrical lenses, are used to correct astigmatism.

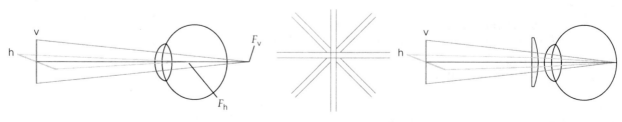

(a) Uncorrected astigmatism   **(b) Test for astigmatism**   **(c) Corrected by lens**

25.4 Diffraction and Resolution

OBJECTIVES: To (a) describe the relationship of diffraction and resolution, and (b) state and explain Rayleigh's criterion.

The diffraction of light places a limitation on our ability to distinguish objects that are close together when we use microscopes or telescopes. This effect can be understood by considering two point sources located far from a narrow slit of width w (▼Fig. 25.15). The sources could represent distant stars, for example. In the absence of diffraction, two bright spots, or images, would be observed on a screen. As you know from Section 24.3, however, the slit diffracts the light, and each image consists of a central maximum with a pattern of weaker bright and dark fringes on either side. If the sources are close together, the two central maxima may overlap. In this case, the images cannot be distinguished, or are said to be *unresolved*. For the images to be *resolved*, the central maxima must not overlap appreciably.

In general, images of two sources can be resolved if the central maximum of one falls at or beyond the first minimum of the other. This limiting condition for the **resolution** of two images—that is, the ability to distinguish them as separate—was first proposed by Lord Rayleigh (1842–1919), a British physicist. The condition is known as the **Rayleigh criterion**:

> Two images are said to be just resolved when the central maximum of one image falls on the first minimum of the diffraction pattern of the other image.

The Rayleigh criterion can be expressed in terms of the angular separation (θ) of the sources. (See Fig. 25.15.) The first minimum ($m = 1$) for a single-slit diffraction pattern satisfies this relationship:

$$w \sin \theta = m\lambda = \lambda \quad \text{or} \quad \sin \theta = \frac{\lambda}{w}$$

According to Fig. 25.15, this is the minimum angular separation for two images to be just resolved according to the Rayleigh criterion. In general, for visible

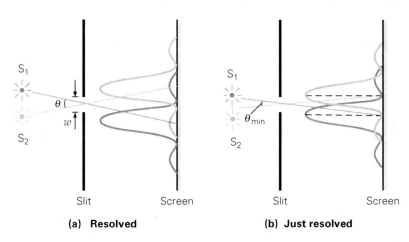

(a) Resolved   **(b) Just resolved**

◀ **FIGURE 25.15 Resolution** Two light sources in front of a slit produce diffraction patterns. **(a)** When the angle subtended by the sources at the slit is large enough for the diffraction patterns to be distinguishable, the images are said to be resolved. **(b)** At smaller angles, the central maxima are closer together. At θ_{min}, the central maximum of one image's diffraction pattern falls on the first dark fringe of the other image's pattern, and the images are said to be just resolved. For smaller angles, the patterns are unresolved.

INSIGHT 25.2 TELESCOPES USING NONVISIBLE RADIATION

The word *telescope* usually brings to mind visual observations. However, the visible region is only a very small part of the electromagnetic spectrum, and celestial objects emit many other types of radiation, including radio waves. This fact was discovered accidentally in 1931 by an American electrical engineer named Carl Jansky while he was working on static interference with intercontinental radio communications. Jansky found an annoying static hiss that came from a fixed direction in space, apparently from a celestial source. It was soon clear that radio waves could be another valuable source of astronomical information, and radio telescopes were built to investigate this source.

A radio telescope operates similarly to a reflecting visible light telescope. A reflector with a large area collects and focuses the radio waves at a point where a detector picks up the signal (Fig. 1). The parabolic collector, called a *dish*, is covered with metal wire mesh or metal plates. Since the wavelengths of radio waves range from a few millimeters to several meters, wire mesh is "smooth" enough and a good reflecting surface for such waves.

Radio telescopes supplement optical telescopes and provide some definite advantages over them. For instance, radio waves pass freely through the huge clouds of dust that hide a large part of our galaxy from visual observation. Also, radio waves easily penetrate the Earth's atmosphere, which reflects and scatters a large percentage of the incoming visible light.

Infrared light is also affected by the Earth's atmosphere. For example, water vapor is a strong absorber of infrared radiation. Thus, observations with infrared telescopes are sometimes made from high-flying aircraft or from orbiting spacecraft, beyond the influence of atmospheric water vapor. The first *orbiting* infrared observatory was launched in 1983. Not only is atmospheric interference eliminated in space, but the telescope may be cooled to a very low temperature without becoming coated with condensed water vapor. Cooling the telescope helps eliminate the interference of infrared radiation generated by the telescope itself. The orbiting infrared telescope launched

FIGURE 1 Radio telescopes Several of the dish antennae that make up the Very Large Array (VLA) radio telescope near Socorro, New Mexico. There are 27 movable dishes, each 25 m in diameter, forming the array along a Y-shaped railway network. The data from all the antennae are combined to produce a single radio image. In this way, it is possible to attain a resolution equivalent to that of one giant radio dish (a couple hundred feet in diameter).

in 1983 was cooled with liquid helium to about 10 K; it carried out an infrared survey of the entire sky.

The atmosphere is virtually opaque to ultraviolet radiation, X-rays, and gamma rays, so telescopes that detect these types of radiation cannot be Earth based. Orbiting satellites with telescopes sensitive to these types of radiation have mapped out portions of the sky, and other surveys are planned. Observatories by orbiting satellites in the visible region are not affected by air turbulence or refraction. Perhaps in the not-too-distant future, a permanently staffed orbiting observatory carrying a variety of telescopes will replace the uncrewed Hubble Telescope and help expand our knowledge of the universe.

---

light, the wavelength is much smaller than the slit width ($\lambda < w$), so θ is small and $\sin \theta \approx \theta$. In this case, the limiting, or **minimum angle of resolution (θ_{min})** for a slit of width w is

$$\theta_{min} = \frac{\lambda}{w} \quad \begin{array}{l}\textit{minimum angle of resolution}\\ \textit{(for a slit)}\end{array} \qquad (25.7)$$

(Note that θ_{min} is a pure number and is therefore in radians.) Thus, the images of two sources will be *distinctly* resolved if the angular separation of the sources is greater than λ/w.

The apertures (openings) of cameras, microscopes, and telescopes are generally circular. Thus, there is a *circular* diffraction pattern around the central maximum, in the form of a bright circular disk (▸Fig. 25.16). Detailed analysis shows that the **minimum angle of resolution for a circular aperture** for the images of two objects to be just resolved is similar to, but slightly different from, Eq. 25.7. It is

$$\theta_{min} = \frac{1.22\lambda}{D} \quad \begin{array}{l}\textit{minimum angle of resolution}\\ \textit{(for a circular aperture)}\end{array} \qquad (25.8)$$

where D is the diameter of the aperture and θ_{min} is in radians.

Equation 25.8 applies to the objective lens of a microscope or telescope, or the iris of the eye, all of which may be considered to be circular apertures for light. According to Eqs. 25.7 and 25.8, the smaller θ_{min}, the better the resolution. The minimum angle of resolution, θ_{min}, should be small so that objects close together can be resolved; therefore, the aperture should be as *large* as possible. This is yet another reason for using large lenses (and mirrors) in telescopes.

Example 25.7 ■ The Eye and Telescope: Evaluating Resolution with the Rayleigh Criterion

Determine the minimum angle of resolution by the Rayleigh criterion for (a) the pupil of the eye (daytime diameter of about 4.0 mm) for visible light with a wavelength of 660 nm; (b) the European Southern Observatory refracting telescope (diameter of 8.2 m), for visible light of the same wavelength as in part (a); and (c) a radio telescope 25 m in diameter for radiation with a wavelength of 21 cm.

Thinking It Through. This is a comparison of θ_{min} for apertures with different diameters—a direct application of Eq. 25.8.

Solution.

Given: (a) $D = 4.0\text{ mm} = 4.0 \times 10^{-3}\text{ m}$ **Find:** (a) θ_{min} (minimum angles
$\quad\quad\quad \lambda = 660\text{ nm} = 6.60 \times 10^{-7}\text{ m}$ of resolution)
$\quad\quad$ (b) $D = 8.2\text{ m}$ (b) θ_{min}
$\quad\quad\quad \lambda = 660\text{ nm} = 6.60 \times 10^{-7}\text{ m}$ (c) θ_{min}
$\quad\quad$ (c) $D = 25\text{ m}$
$\quad\quad\quad \lambda = 21\text{ cm} = 0.21\text{ m}$

(a) For the eye,

$$\theta_{min} = \frac{1.22\lambda}{D} = \frac{1.22(6.60 \times 10^{-7}\text{ m})}{4.0 \times 10^{-3}\text{ m}} = 2.0 \times 10^{-4}\text{ rad}$$

(b) For the light telescope,

$$\theta_{min} = \frac{1.22(6.60 \times 10^{-7}\text{ m})}{8.2\text{ m}} = 9.8 \times 10^{-8}\text{ rad}$$

(*Note:* The resolution of Earth-bound telescopes with large-diameter objectives is usually not limited by diffraction, but rather by other effects, such as atmospheric turbulence. Thus, in actuality, Earth-bound telescopes have a θ_{min} on the order of 10^{-6} rad, or resolution one tenth as good as without the atmosphere.)

(c) For the radio telescope,

$$\theta_{min} = \frac{1.22(0.21\text{ m})}{25\text{ m}} = 0.010\text{ rad}$$

The smaller the angular separation, the better the resolution. What do the results tell you?

Follow-Up Exercise. As noted in Section 25.3, the Hubble Space Telescope has a mirror diameter of 2.4 m. How does its resolution compare with that of the largest Earth-bound telescopes? (See the note in part (b) of this Example.)

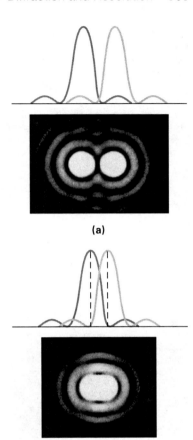

(a)

(b)

▲ **FIGURE 25.16 Circular-aperture resolution (a)** When the angular separation of two objects is large enough, the images are well resolved. (Compare with Fig. 25.15a.) **(b)** Rayleigh criterion: The central maximum of the diffraction pattern of one image falls on the first minimum of the diffraction pattern of the other image. (Compare with Fig. 25.15b.) The images of objects with smaller angular separations cannot be clearly distinguished as individual images.

For a microscope, it is more convenient to specify the actual separation (s) between two point sources. Since the objects are usually near the focal point of the objective, to a good approximation,

$$\theta_{min} = \frac{s}{f} \quad\text{or}\quad s = f\theta_{min}$$

where f is the focal length of the lens and θ_{min} is expressed in radians. (Here, s is taken as the arc length subtended by θ_{min}, and $s = r\theta_{min} = f\theta_{min}$.) Then, using Eq. 25.8, we get

$$s = f\theta_{min} = \frac{1.22\lambda f}{D} \quad\quad \textit{resolving power of a microscope} \quad\quad (25.9)$$

This minimum distance between two points whose images can be just resolved is called the **resolving power** of the microscope. Note that s is directly proportional to λ, so shorter wavelength gives better resolution. In practice, the resolving power of a microscope indicates the ability of the objective to distinguish fine detail in specimens' structures. For another real-life example of resolution, see ▼Fig. 25.17.

▶ **FIGURE 25.17** Real-life resolution (a), (b), (c) A sequence of an approaching automobile's headlights. In (a), the headlights are almost unresolved through the circular aperture of the camera (or your eye). As the automobile moves closer, the headlights are resolved.

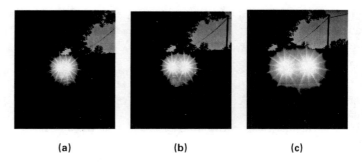

(a)   (b)   (c)

Conceptual Example 25.8 ■ Viewing from Space: The Great Wall of China

The Great Wall of China was originally about 2400 km (1500 mi) long, with a base width of about 6.0 m and a top width of about 3.7 m. Several hundred kilometers of the wall remain intact (◀Fig. 25.18). It is sometimes said that the wall is the only human construction that can be seen with the unaided eye by an astronaut orbiting the Earth. Using the result from part (a) of Example 25.7, see if it is visible. (Neglect any atmospheric effects.)

Reasoning and Answer. Despite the length of the wall, it would not be visible from space unless its *width* subtends the minimum angle of resolution for the eye of an observing astronaut ($\theta_{min} = 2.0 \times 10^{-4}$ rad from Example 25.7). Actually, guard towers with roofs as wide as 7.0 m were located every 180 m along the Wall. Let's take the maximum observable width to be 7.0 m. (Actually, it is the circular arc length that subtends the angle, but at such a long radius, the chord length is very nearly equal to the circular arc length. Refer to Example 7.2, and make yourself a sketch.)

Let's assume that the astronaut is just able to distinguish the guard roof. Recall that $s = r\theta$ (Eq. 7.3), where s is the maximum observable width of the wall and r is the radial (height) distance. Then, the astronaut would have to be at, or closer than, a distance of

$$r = \frac{s}{\theta} = \frac{7.0 \text{ m}}{2.0 \times 10^{-4} \text{ (rad)}} = 3.5 \times 10^4 \text{ m} = 35 \text{ km} \ (= 22 \text{ mi})$$

So above 35 km, the wall would *not* be able to be seen with the unaided eye. Orbiting satellites are about 300 km (190 mi) or more above the Earth. The statement about the ability to see the wall from space is false.

Follow-Up Exercise. What would be the minimum diameter of the objective of a telescope that would allow an astronaut orbiting the Earth at an altitude of 300 km to actually see the Great Wall? (Take all conditions to be the same as stated in this Example, and assume that the wavelength of light is 550 nm.)

▲ **FIGURE 25.18 The Great Wall** The walkway of the Great Wall of China, which was built as a fortification along China's northern border.

Note: The relationship between wavelength and index of refraction is given in Section 22.3; see Eq. 22.4.

Note from Eq. 25.8 that higher resolution can be gained by using radiation of a shorter wavelength. Thus, a telescope with an objective of a given size will have greater resolution with violet light than with red light. For microscopes, it is possible to increase resolving power by shortening the wavelengths of the light used to create the image. This can be done with a specialized objective called an *oil immersion lens*. When such a lens is used, a drop of transparent oil fills the space between the objective and the specimen. Recall that the wavelength of light in oil is $\lambda' = \lambda/n$, where n is the index of refraction of the oil and λ is the wavelength of light in air. For values of n about 1.50 or higher, the wavelength is significantly reduced, and the resolving power is increased proportionally.

QUANTUM PHYSICS

PHYSICS FACTS

- Theoretically, a hot sample of hydrogen gas can give off many different wavelengths. Of those, only four are in the visible range.

- It takes on the order of a million years for the high-energy gamma and X-ray photons released by nuclear fusion at the Sun's center to make their way to the surface of the Sun. This long trip is caused by the many random collisions that result in a reduction of photon energy down into the visible-light range. The trip to Earth from the solar surface takes only about 8 minutes.

- Helium was first discovered in the Sun's atmosphere using its characteristic photon absorption energies. Helium does not exist naturally in the Earth's atmosphere. We have significant amounts of it because it is trapped in deep wells with natural gas.

- Laser beams are so well defined spatially that bouncing them off a mirror located on the Moon (the Apollo astronauts placed the mirrors there in the early 1970s) enables us to determine the distance to the Moon to within a few meters.

asers are used in a variety of everyday applications—in bar code scanners at store checkout counters, in computer printers, in various types of surgery, and in laboratory situations, such as the one shown in the chapter-opening photo. You own a laser yourself if you have a CD or DVD player.

The laser is a practical application of principles that revolutionized physics. These principles were first developed in the early twentieth century, one of the most productive eras in the history of physics. For example, special relativity (Chapter 26) helped resolve problems faced by classical (Newtonian) relativity in describing objects moving at speeds near that of light. However, there were other troublesome areas in which classical theories did not agree with experimental results. To address these issues, scientists devised new hypotheses based on nontraditional approaches and ushered in a profound revolution in our understanding of the physical world. Chief among these new theories was the idea that light is *quantized* into discrete amounts of energy. This concept and others like it led to the formulation of a new set of principles and a new branch of physics called *quantum mechanics*.

Quantum theory demonstrated that particles often exhibit wave properties and that waves frequently behave as particles. Thus was born the *wave–particle duality* of matter. As a result of quantum theory, calculations in the realm of the very small—dimensions the sizes of atoms and smaller—must deal with *probabilities* rather than in the precisely determined values associated with classical theory.

A detailed treatment of quantum mechanics requires extremely complex mathematics. However, a general overview of the important results is essential to an understanding of physics as it is known today. Thus, the important developments of "quantum" physics are presented in this chapter, and an introduction to quantum mechanics is provided in Chapter 28.

851

27.1 Quantization: Planck's Hypothesis

OBJECTIVES: To (a) define blackbody radiation and use Wien's law, and (b) understand how Planck's hypothesis paved the way for quantum ideas.

One of the problems scientists faced at the end of the nineteenth century was how to explain the spectra of electromagnetic radiation emitted by hot objects—solids, liquids, and dense gases. This radiation is sometimes called **thermal radiation**. You learned in Chapter 11 that the total intensity of the emitted radiation from such objects is proportional to the fourth power of the absolute Kelvin temperature (T^4) of the object. Thus, all objects emit thermal radiation to some degree.

However, at everyday temperatures, this radiation is almost all in the infrared (IR) region and not visible to our eyes. However, at temperatures of about 1000 K, a solid object will begin to emit an appreciable amount of radiation in the long-wavelength end of the visible spectrum, observed as a reddish glow. A red-hot electric stove burner is a good example of this. Still-higher temperatures cause the radiation to shift to shorter wavelengths and the color to change to yellow-orange. Above a temperature of about 2000 K, an object glows yellowish-white, like the filament of a light bulb, and gives off appreciable amounts of all the visible colors, but with different percentages.

Although we observe a dominant color with our eyes, in actuality there is a *continuous spectrum*. A spectrum shows how the intensity of emitted energy depends on wavelength, as illustrated in ▾Fig. 27.1a for a hot object. Notice that practically all wavelengths are present, but there is a dominant color (wavelength region), which depends on the object's temperature.

Note: The concept of a blackbody was introduced in Section 11.4.

The curves shown in Fig. 27.1a are for an ideal **blackbody**. An ideal blackbody is an ideal object that absorbs all radiation that is incident on it. Although such a blackbody is not attainable, it can be experimentally approximated by a small hole that leads to a cavity inside a block of material (Fig. 27.1b). Radiation falling on the hole enters the cavity and is reflected back and forth off the cavity walls. If the hole is very small, only a small fraction of the incident radiation will make its way back out of the hole. Since nearly all the radiation incident on the hole is absorbed, as viewed from the outside the hole approximates a blackbody.

Teaching tip: Point out the relationship between the *frequency* of the maximum-intensity blackbody radiation and the absolute temperature.

Two things happen to the spectrum as the temperature increases (Fig. 27.1a). As expected, more radiation is emitted at every wavelength, but also the wavelength

▶ **FIGURE 27.1 Thermal radiation**
(a) Intensity-versus-wavelength curves for the thermal radiation from a blackbody at different temperatures. The wavelength associated with the maximum intensity (λ_{max}) becomes shorter with increasing temperature. **(b)** A blackbody can be approximated by a small hole leading to an interior cavity in a block of material.

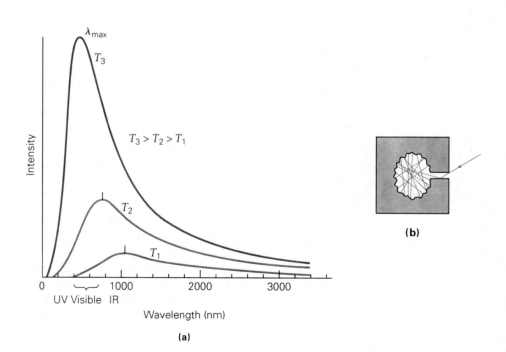

of the maximum-intensity component (λ_{max}) becomes shorter. This wavelength shift is described experimentally by **Wien's displacement law**,

$$\lambda_{max}T = 2.90 \times 10^{-3} \text{ m} \cdot \text{K} \qquad (27.1)$$

where λ_{max} is the wavelength of the radiation (in meters) at which maximum intensity occurs and T is the temperature of the body (in kelvins).

Wien's law can be used to determine the wavelength of the maximum spectral component if the temperature of the emitter is known, or the temperature of the emitter if the wavelength of the strongest emission is known. Thus, it can be used to estimate the temperatures of stars (dense gases) from their radiation spectrum, as the following Example shows.

Example 27.1 ■ Solar Colors: Using Wien's Law

The visible surface of our Sun is the gaseous photosphere from which radiation escapes. At the top of the photosphere, the temperature is 4500 K; at a depth of about 260 km, the temperature is 6800 K. Assuming the Sun radiates energy as if it were a blackbody, (a) what are the wavelengths of the radiation of maximum intensity for these temperatures, and (b) to what colors do these wavelengths correspond?

Thinking It Through. Wien's displacement law (Eq. 27.1) enables us to determine the wavelengths.

Solution.

Given: $T_1 = 4500$ K *Find:* (a) λ_{max} (for the two different temperatures)
$T_2 = 6800$ K (b) Colors corresponding to these λ_{max} values

(a) At the top of the photosphere,

$$\lambda_{max} = \frac{2.90 \times 10^{-3} \text{ m} \cdot \text{K}}{4500 \text{ K}} = (6.44 \times 10^{-7} \text{ m})(10^9 \text{ nm/m}) = 644 \text{ nm}$$

and at the 260-km depth,

$$\lambda_{max} = \frac{2.90 \times 10^{-3} \text{ m} \cdot \text{K}}{6800 \text{ K}} = (4.26 \times 10^{-7} \text{ m})(10^9 \text{ nm/m}) = 426 \text{ nm}$$

(b) As the temperature increases with depth, the wavelength of the radiation of maximum intensity shifts from red toward the blue end of the spectrum. Thus the Sun's surface is orange-red and shifts towards the blue since temperature increases with depth. (For a discussion of the visible spectrum and color in relation to wavelength, see Section 20.4 and Fig. 20.23.) Combining all the depths and temperatures, we have a spectrum that shows all wavelengths (colors), but is dominated by yellow. Notice that some of the emitted radiation will be in the ultraviolet region, some of which is absorbed by the ozone layer in the Earth's atmosphere.

Follow-Up Exercise. What would be the dominant wavelengths (and corresponding colors) associated with the radiation emitted from the surface of the following stars: (a) Betelgeuse, with an average surface temperature of 3.00×10^3 K; (b) Rigel, with an average surface temperature of 1.00×10^4 K? *(Answers to all Follow-Up Exercises are at the back of the text.)*

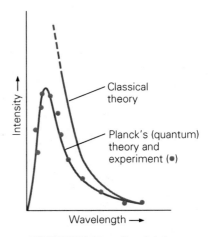

▲ **FIGURE 27.2 The ultraviolet catastrophe** Classical theory predicts that the intensity of thermal radiation emitted by a blackbody should be inversely related to the wavelength of the emitted radiation. If this were true, the intensity would become infinite as the wavelength approaches zero. In contrast, Planck's quantum theory agrees with the observed radiation distribution (solid dots).

The Ultraviolet Catastrophe and Planck's Hypothesis

Classically, thermal radiation results from the oscillations of electric charges associated with the atoms near the surface of an object. Since these charges oscillate at different frequencies, a continuous spectrum of emitted radiation is expected.

Classical calculations describing the radiation spectrum emitted by a blackbody predict an intensity that is inversely related to wavelength (actually $I \propto 1/\lambda^4$). At long wavelengths, the classical theory agrees fairly well with experimental data. However, at short wavelengths, the agreement disappears. Contrary to experimental observations, the classical theory predicts that the radiation intensity should increase without bound as the wavelength gets smaller. This is illustrated in ▶Fig. 27.2. The classical prediction is sometimes called the *ultraviolet catastrophe—ultraviolet* because the difficulty occurs for wavelengths shorter than that associated with violet, and *catastrophe* because it predicts that the emitted energy grows without limits at these wavelengths.

The failure of classical electromagnetic theory to explain the characteristics of thermal radiation led Max Planck (1858–1947), a German physicist, to re-examine the phenomenon. In 1900, Planck formulated a theory that correctly predicted the observed distribution of the blackbody radiation spectrum. (Compare the solid blue curve with the data points in Fig. 27.2.) However, his theory depended upon a radical idea. He had to assume that the thermal oscillators (the atoms emitting the radiation) have only *discrete*, or particular, amounts of energy rather than a continuous distribution of energies. Only with this assumption did his theory agree with experiment.

Planck found that these discrete amounts of energy were related to the frequency f of the atomic oscillations by

$$E_n = n(hf) \qquad \text{for } n = 1, 2, 3, \ldots \qquad \text{\textit{Planck's quantization hypothesis}} \qquad (27.2)$$

Note: As with other fundamental constants, we will take h to be *exact* at 6.63×10^{-34} J·s, for calculation purposes.

That is, the oscillator energy occurs only in integral multiples of hf. The symbol h is a constant called **Planck's constant**. Its experimental value (to three significant figures) is

$$h = 6.63 \times 10^{-34} \text{ J·s}$$

The idea expressed in Eq. 27.2 is called **Planck's hypothesis**. Rather than allowing the oscillator energy to have any value, Planck's hypothesis states that the energy is *quantized*; that is, it occurs only in discrete amounts. The smallest possible amount of oscillator energy, according to Eq. 27.2 with $n = 1$, is

$$E_1 = hf \qquad (27.3)$$

All other values of the energy are integral multiples of hf. The quantity hf is called a **quantum** of energy (from the Latin *quantus*, meaning "how much"). As a result, the energy of an atom can change only by the absorption or emission of energy in discrete, or *quantum*, amounts.

Although the theoretical predictions agreed with experiment, Planck himself was not convinced of the validity of his quantum hypothesis. However, the concept of quantization was extended to explain other phenomena that could not be explained classically. Despite Planck's hesitation, the quantum hypothesis earned him a Nobel Prize in 1918.

27.2 Quanta of Light: Photons and the Photoelectric Effect

OBJECTIVES: To (a) describe the photoelectric effect, (b) explain how it can be understood by assuming that light energy is carried by particles, and (c) summarize the properties of photons.

The concept of the quantization of light energy was introduced in 1905 by Albert Einstein in a paper concerning light absorption and emission, at about the same time he published his famous paper on special relativity. Einstein reasoned that energy quantization should be a fundamental property of electromagnetic waves (light). He suggested that if the energy of the thermal oscillators in a hot substance is quantized, then it necessarily followed that, to conserve energy, *the emitted radiation should also be quantized*. For example, suppose an atom initially had an energy of $3hf$ ($n = 3$ in Eq. 27.2) and ended up with a final (lower) energy of $2hf$ ($n = 2$ in Eq. 27.2). Einstein proposed that the atom *must* emit a specific amount (or *quantum*) of light energy—in this case, $3hf - 2hf = hf$. He named this quantum, or package, of light energy the **photon**. Each photon has a definite amount of energy E that depends on the frequency f of the light according to

$$E = hf \qquad \text{\textit{photon energy and light frequency}} \qquad (27.4)$$

This idea suggests that light can behave as discrete quanta (plural of "quantum"), or "particles," of energy rather than as a wave. One way to interpret Eq. 27.4 is as a mathematical "connection" between the *wave nature* of light (a wave of frequency f) and the *particle nature* of light (photons each with an energy E). Given light of a certain frequency or wavelength, Eq. 27.4 enables us to calculate the energy in each photon, or vice versa.

Einstein used the photon concept to explain the **photoelectric effect**, another phenomenon for which the classical description was inadequate. Certain metallic materials are *photosensitive*; that is, when light strikes their surface, electrons may be emitted. The radiant energy supplies the energy necessary to free the electrons from the material. A schematic representation of a photoelectric-effect experiment is shown in ▸Fig. 27.3a. A variable voltage (say by a variable battery or power supply) is maintained between the anode and the cathode. When light strikes the cathode (maintained at ground or zero voltage) which is photosensitive, electrons are emitted. Because they are released by absorption of light energy, these emitted electrons are called *photoelectrons*. They are collected at the anode, which is maintained initially at some positive voltage V to attract the photoelectrons. Thus, in the complete circuit a current is registered on the ammeter.

When a photocell is illuminated with monochromatic (single-wavelength) light of different intensities, characteristic curves are obtained as a function of the applied voltage (Fig. 27.3b). For positive voltages, the anode attracts the electrons. Under these conditions, the *photocurrent* I_p is the flow rate of the photoelectrons, which does *not* vary with voltage. This is because under a positive voltage the electrons are attracted to the anode and *all* the electrons reach it. As expected classically, I_p is proportional to the incident light intensity—the greater the intensity ($I_2 > I_1$ in Fig. 27.3b), the more energy is available to free electrons.

The kinetic energy of the photoelectrons can be measured by *reversing* the voltage across the electrodes, that is, reversing the battery terminals and making $V < 0$, and creating *retarding-voltage* conditions. Now the electrons are repelled from, instead of being attracted to, the anode. The electrons' initial kinetic energies are converted into electric potential energy as they approach the now negatively charged anode. As the retarding voltage is made more and more negative, the photocurrent decreases. This is because (by energy conservation) only electrons with initial kinetic energies greater than $e|V|$ can be collected at the negative anode and thus produce a photocurrent. At some value of retarding voltage, with a magnitude of V_o, called the **stopping potential**, the photocurrent drops to zero. No electrons are collected at that voltage or greater (more negative)—because even the fastest photoelectrons are turned around before reaching the anode. Hence, the maximum kinetic energy (K_{max}) of the photoelectrons is related to the magnitude of the stopping potential (V_o) by

$$K_{max} = eV_o \qquad (27.5)$$

Experimentally, when the frequency of the incident light is varied, this maximum kinetic energy increases linearly with the frequency (▾Fig. 27.4). No emission of electrons is observed for light with a frequency below a certain *cutoff frequency* f_o. Even if the light intensity is very low, the current begins essentially instantaneously with no observable time delay, as long as a material is being illuminated by light with a frequency $f > f_o$.

The important characteristics of the photoelectric effect are summarized in Table 27.1. Notice that only one of the characteristics is predicted correctly by classical wave theory, whereas Einstein's photon concept explains all of the results. When an electron absorbs a quantum of light energy, some of the photon's energy goes to free the electron, with the remainder showing up as kinetic energy. The work required to free the electron is designated by ϕ. So, when a photon of energy E is absorbed, conservation of energy requires that $E = K + \phi$, or, using Eq. 27.4 to replace E, we have

$$hf = K + \phi \qquad (27.6)$$

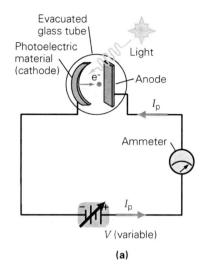

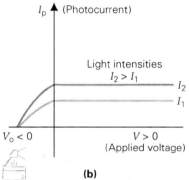

▲ **FIGURE 27.3 The photoelectric effect and characteristic curves** (a) Incident monochromatic light on the photoelectric material in a photocell (or phototube) causes the emission of electrons, which results in a current in the circuit. The applied voltage is variable. (b) As the plots of photocurrent versus voltage for two intensities of light show, the current stays constant as the voltage is increased. However, for negative voltages (using the battery with reversed polarity), the current goes to zero when the stopping potential has a magnitude of $|V_o|$, which, for a fixed frequency, depends only on the type of material, but is independent of intensity.

Note: Recall from Eq. 16.2 that $\Delta U_e = qV$.

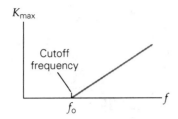

▲ **FIGURE 27.4 Maximum kinetic energy versus light frequency in the photoelectric effect** The maximum kinetic energy (K_{max}) of the photoelectrons is a linear function of the incident-light frequency. Below a certain cutoff frequency f_o, no photoemission occurs, regardless of the intensity of the light.

Teaching tip: Make sure that students have a clear understanding as to why classical theories *cannot* account for the photoelectric effect.

LEARN BY DRAWING

The Photoelectric Effect and Energy Conservation

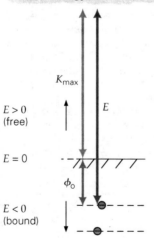

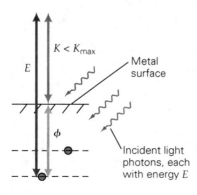

TABLE 27.1	Characteristics of the Photoelectric Effect

Characteristic	Predicted by wave theory?
1. The photocurrent is proportional to the intensity of the light.	Yes
2. The maximum kinetic energy of the emitted electrons depends on the frequency of the light, but not on its intensity.	No
3. No photoemission occurs for light with a frequency below a certain cutoff frequency f_o, regardless of the light intensity.	No
4. A photocurrent is observed immediately when the light frequency is greater than f_o, even if the light intensity is extremely low.	No

Since the energies are very small, the commonly used energy unit is the electron-volt (eV; see Chapter 16). Recall that $1.00\ \text{eV} = 1.60 \times 10^{-19}\ \text{J}$.

The least tightly bound electron will have the maximum kinetic energy K_{max}. (Why?) The energy needed to free this electron is called the **work function (ϕ_o)** of the material. For this situation, Eq. 27.6 becomes

$$\underset{\substack{incident\ photon \\ energy}}{hf} = \underset{\substack{maximum\ kinetic \\ energy\ of\ freed \\ electron}}{K_{max}} + \underset{\substack{minimum\ work \\ needed\ to\ free \\ the\ electron}}{\phi_o} \qquad (27.7)$$

Other electrons require more energy than the minimum to be freed, so their kinetic energy will be less than K_{max}. This concept is explored visually in the Learn by Drawing feature on this page. Some typical numerical values are shown in the next Example.

Example 27.2 ■ The Photoelectric Effect: Electron Speed and Stopping Potential

The work function of a particular metal is known to be 2.00 eV. If the metal is illuminated with light of wavelength 550 nm, what will be (a) the maximum kinetic energy of the emitted electrons and (b) their maximum speed? (c) What is the stopping potential?

Thinking It Through. (a) By energy conservation (Eq. 27.7), the maximum kinetic energy is the difference between the incoming photon energy and the work function. (b) Speed can be determined from kinetic energy, since the mass of an electron is known ($m = 9.11 \times 10^{-31}$ kg). (c) The stopping potential is found by requiring that all of the kinetic energy be converted to electric potential energy (Eq. 27.5).

Solution. First, converting the data into SI units.

Given: $\phi_o = (2.00\ \text{eV})(1.60 \times 10^{-19}\ \text{J/eV})$ **Find:** (a) K_{max} (maximum kinetic energy)
$\qquad\quad = 3.20 \times 10^{-19}\ \text{J}$ (b) v_{max} (maximum speed)
$\qquad\ \lambda = 550\ \text{nm} = 5.50 \times 10^{-7}\ \text{m}$ (c) V_o (stopping potential)

(a) Using $\lambda f = c$, we find that the photon energy of light with the given wavelength is

$$E = hf = \frac{hc}{\lambda} = \frac{(6.63 \times 10^{-34}\ \text{J} \cdot \text{s})(3.00 \times 10^{8}\ \text{m/s})}{5.50 \times 10^{-7}\ \text{m}} = 3.62 \times 10^{-19}\ \text{J}$$

Then

$$K_{max} = E - \phi_o = 3.62 \times 10^{-19}\ \text{J} - 3.20 \times 10^{-19}\ \text{J}$$

$$= (4.20 \times 10^{-20}\ \text{J})\left(\frac{1\ \text{eV}}{1.60 \times 10^{-19}\ \text{J}}\right) = 0.263\ \text{eV}$$

(b) v_{max} can be found from $K_{max} = \frac{1}{2}mv_{max}^2$:

$$v_{max} = \sqrt{\frac{2K_{max}}{m}} = \sqrt{\frac{2(4.20 \times 10^{-20}\ \text{J})}{9.11 \times 10^{-31}\ \text{kg}}} = 3.04 \times 10^{5}\ \text{m/s}$$

(c) The stopping potential is related to K_{max} by $K_{max} = eV_o$; therefore,

$$V_o = \frac{K_{max}}{e} = \frac{0.420 \times 10^{-19}\,\text{J}}{1.60 \times 10^{-19}\,\text{C}} = 0.23\,\text{V}$$

Follow-Up Exercise. In this Example, suppose that a different wavelength of light is used and the new stopping voltage is found to be 0.50 V. What is the wavelength of this new light? Explain why this wavelength requires a larger stopping voltage.

Einstein's photon model of light is, in fact, consistent with *all* the experimental results of the photoelectric effect. In the photon model, an increase in light intensity means an increase in the number of photons and therefore in the number of photoelectrons (that is, the photocurrent). However, an increase in intensity would *not* mean a change in the energy of any one photon, since that energy depends only on the light frequency ($E = hf$). Therefore, K_{max} should be independent of intensity, but linearly dependent on the frequency of the incident light—as is observed experimentally.

Einstein's quantum theory of light also explains the existence of a cutoff frequency. In his interpretation, since photon energy depends on frequency, this means that below a certain (cutoff) frequency (f_o) the photons simply don't have enough energy to dislodge even the most loosely bound electrons. Therefore, no current is observed for those frequencies. Since, at the cutoff frequency, no electrons are emitted, the cutoff frequency can be found by setting $K_{max} = 0$ in Eq. 27.7:

$$hf_o = K_{max} + \phi_o = 0 + \phi_o$$

or

$$f_o = \frac{\phi_o}{h} \qquad \begin{matrix}\textit{threshold, or}\\ \textit{cutoff, frequency}\end{matrix} \qquad (27.8)$$

Note: A photon of energy hf_o will barely free an electron from a solid, but the electron will have essentially no kinetic energy.

The cutoff frequency f_o is sometimes called the **threshold frequency**. It represents the minimum frequency of light necessary to create photoelectrons. Below the threshold frequency, the binding energy of the least-bound electron exceeds the photon energy. Although the electron may absorb the photon energy, it will not have enough energy to be freed from the material and become a photoelectron. (How would you explain this, using a sketch such as the one in the accompanying Learn by Drawing?)

Example 27.3 ■ The Photoelectric Effect: Threshold Frequency and Wavelength

What are the threshold frequency and corresponding wavelength for the metal described in Example 27.2?

Thinking It Through. Example 27.2 gives the work function, so Eq. 27.8 allows us to determine the threshold frequency. The threshold wavelength can then be computed from $\lambda = c/f$.

Solution. Listing the data, we have

Given: $\phi_o = 2.00$ eV $= 3.20 \times 10^{-19}$ J (from Example 27.2)

Find: f_o (threshold frequency) λ_o (wavelength at threshold frequency)

Solving for the threshold frequency f_o from $\phi_o = hf_o$ (Eq. 27.8), we get

$$f_o = \frac{\phi_o}{h} = \frac{3.20 \times 10^{-19}\,\text{J}}{6.63 \times 10^{-34}\,\text{J}\cdot\text{s}} = 4.83 \times 10^{14}\,\text{Hz}$$

The wavelength (the threshold wavelength) corresponding to this frequency is

$$\lambda_o = \frac{c}{f_o} = \frac{3.00 \times 10^8\,\text{m/s}}{4.83 \times 10^{14}\,\text{Hz}} = 6.21 \times 10^{-7}\,\text{m} = 621\,\text{nm}$$

Any frequency lower than 4.83×10^{14} Hz, or, alternatively, any wavelength longer than 621 nm, would not yield photoelectrons. Since this wavelength lies in the red-orange end of the electromagnetic spectrum, yellow light, for example, would dislodge electrons, but deep-red light would not.

Follow-Up Exercise. In this Example, what would be the stopping voltage if the frequency of the light were twice the cutoff frequency?

Demonstration/activity: Demonstrate the photoelectric effect by using a UV light source to knock electrons off a negatively charged electroscope. Then, while covering the UV light with glass (which absorbs most of the UV), show that the same source's visible light does not knock electrons off.

▶ **FIGURE 27.5** Photoelectric applications: The electric eye **(a)** A diagram of an electric-eye circuit. When light strikes a photocell material (any photosensitive material), it frees electrons from their atoms (but not from the solid as a whole). In effect this lowers the material's resistance by enabling it to conduct current. The result is a current in the circuit. Interruption of the light beam opens the circuit in the relay (a magnetic switch) that controls the particular device. **(b)** Electric-eye circuits are used in automatic garage-door openers. When the door starts to move downward, any interruption of the electric-eye beam (usually IR light) causes the door to stop, protecting anything that may be under the descending door.

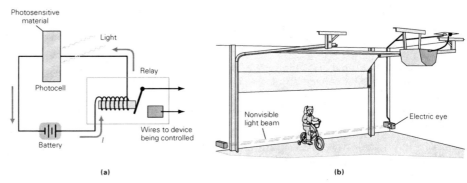

(a)

(b)

Problem-Solving Hint

In photon calculations, the wavelength of the light is often given rather than the frequency. Typically, what is needed is the photon *energy*. Instead of first calculating the frequency $(f = c/\lambda)$, then the energy in joules $(E = hf)$, and finally converting to electron-volts, this all can be done in one step. To do so, combine these two equations to form $E = hf = hc/\lambda$ and express the product hc in electron-volts times nanometers, or eV·nm. The value of this useful product is

$$hc = (6.63 \times 10^{-34}\ \text{J·s})(3.00 \times 10^{8}\ \text{m/s}) = 1.99 \times 10^{-25}\ \text{J·m}$$
$$= \frac{(1.99 \times 10^{-25}\ \text{J·m})(10^{9}\ \text{nm/m})}{1.60 \times 10^{-19}\ \text{J/eV}}$$
$$= 1.24 \times 10^{3}\ \text{eV·nm}$$

This shortcut can save time and effort in working problems and allows quick estimation of the photon energy associated with light of a given wavelength (or vice versa). Thus, if orange light ($\lambda = 600$ nm) is used, you need only divide in your head to realize that each photon carries approximately 2 eV of energy. A more exact result could be calculated if needed, as $E = \dfrac{hc}{\lambda} = \dfrac{1.24 \times 10^{3}\ \text{eV·nm}}{600\ \text{nm}} = 2.07\ \text{eV}.$

(a)

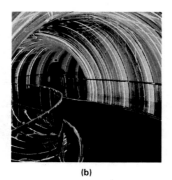

(b)

▲ **FIGURE 27.7** Gas-discharge tubes **(a)** These luminous glass tubes are gas-discharge tubes, in which atoms of various gases emit light when electrically excited. Each gas radiates its own characteristic wavelengths. **(b)** Only some "neon lights" actually contain neon, which glows with a red hue; other gases produce other colors.

There are many applications of the photoelectric effect. The fact that the current produced by photocells is proportional to the intensity of the light makes them ideal for use in photographers' light meters. Photocells are also used in solar-energy applications to convert sunlight to electricity.

Another common application of the photocell is the electric eye (▲Fig. 27.5a). As long as light strikes the photocell, there is current in the circuit. Blocking the light opens the circuit in the relay (magnetic switch), which in turn controls some device. A common application of the electric eye is to turn on streetlights automatically at night. A safety application of the electric eye is shown in Fig. 27.5b. Note that in many of these applications (including the garage-door safety mechanism) the IR light photons do not actually free the electrons from the *material*. All is required is that they free them from the *atoms* in the material—thus the electrons stay in the material but are free to move through the material. Once they are freed, the external voltage causes them to flow, resulting in an electrical current that can be detected and put to appropriate use depending on the application.

27.4 The Bohr Theory of the Hydrogen Atom

OBJECTIVES: To (a) understand how the Bohr model of the hydrogen atom explains that atom's emission and absorption spectra, (b) calculate the energies and wavelengths of emitted and absorbed photons for transitions in atomic hydrogen, and (c) understand how the generalized concept of atomic energy levels can explain other atomic phenomena.

In the 1800s, much experimental work was done with gas-discharge tubes—for example, those containing hydrogen, neon, and mercury vapor. Common neon "lights" are actually gas-discharge tubes (▲Fig. 27.7). Recall that light from an incandescent source, such as a lightbulb's hot filament, exhibits a *continuous spectrum* in which all wavelengths are present. However, when light emissions from gas-discharge tubes were

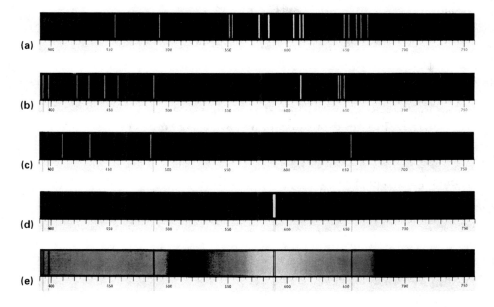

◀ **FIGURE 27.8** Emission and
absorption spectra of gases
When a gas is excited by heat or
electricity, the light it emits can be
separated into its various
wavelengths by a prism or
diffraction grating; the result is a
bright-line, or emission, spectrum,
such as the ones shown here from
(a) barium, **(b)** calcium,
(c) hydrogen, and **(d)** sodium, each
with its own characteristic pattern.
(e) When a continuous spectrum
from a hot solid or dense gas is
viewed after passing through a cool
gas, a dark-line, or absorption,
spectrum is observed. Each line
represents a particular wavelength
the gas has absorbed. The
absorption spectrum of the Sun
provided here shows several
prominent absorption lines
produced by the gases of the solar
atmosphere before the sunlight
makes it to the Earth. In fact, the
inert gas helium was first
discovered to exist on the Sun by
this very method.

analyzed, discrete spectra with only certain wavelengths present were observed
(▲Fig. 27.8). The spectrum of light coming from such a tube is called a *bright-line spectrum*, or **emission spectrum**. In general, the wavelengths present in an emission spectrum are characteristic of the individual atoms or molecules of the particular gas.

Atoms can absorb light as well as emit it. If white light is passed through a cool
gas, the energy at certain frequencies or wavelengths is absorbed. The result is a *dark-
line spectrum*, or **absorption spectrum**—a series of dark lines superimposed on a continuous spectrum (Fig. 27.8e). Just as in emission spectra, the missing wavelengths are
uniquely related to the type of atom or molecule doing the absorbing. By determining
the pattern of emitted and/or absorbed wavelengths, the type of atoms or molecules
present in a sample can be identified. This method is called *spectroscopic analysis* and is
widely used in physics, astrophysics, biology, and chemistry. For example, the element helium was first discovered on the Sun when scientists found that an absorp-
tion-line pattern in the sunlight did not match any known pattern on the Earth. That
unknown pattern belonged to the helium atom.

Although the reason for line spectra was not understood in the 1800s, they
provided an important clue to the electron structure of atoms. Hydrogen, with its
relatively simple visible spectrum, received much of the attention. It is also the
simplest atom, consisting of only one electron and one proton. In the late nineteenth century, the Swiss physicist J. J. Balmer found an empirical formula that
gives the wavelengths of the four spectral lines of hydrogen in the visible region:

$$\frac{1}{\lambda} = R\left(\frac{1}{2^2} - \frac{1}{n^2}\right) \quad \text{for } n = 3, 4, 5, \text{ and } 6 \qquad \begin{array}{l}\textit{visible spectrum} \\ \textit{of hydrogen}\end{array} \qquad (27.10)$$

R is called the *Rydberg constant*, named after the Swedish physicist Johannes Rydberg
(1854–1919), who also studied atomic emission lines. R has an experimental value of
$1.097 \times 10^{-2} \text{ nm}^{-1}$. The four spectral lines of hydrogen in the visible region (note
four values for n in Eq. 27.10), are part of the **Balmer series**. There wavelengths fit the
formula, but it was not understood why. Similar formulas were found to fit other
spectral-line series that were completely in the ultraviolet and infrared regions.

An explanation of the spectral lines was given in a theory of the hydrogen
atom put forth in 1913 by the Danish physicist Niels Bohr (1885–1962). Bohr assumed that the electron of the hydrogen atom orbits the proton in a circular orbit
analogous to a planet orbiting the Sun. The attractive electrical force between the
electron and proton supplies the necessary centripetal force for the circular motion. Recall that the centripetal force is given by $F_c = mv^2/r$, where v is the electron's orbital speed, m is its mass, and r is the radius of its orbit. The force between
the proton and electron is given by Coulomb's law as $F_e = kq_1q_2/r^2 = ke^2/r^2$, where

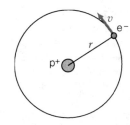

▲ FIGURE 27.9 The Bohr model of the hydrogen atom The electron is pictured as revolving around the much more massive proton in a circular orbit. The electric force of attraction provides the centripetal force.

e is the magnitude of the charge of the proton and the electron (◄Fig. 27.9). Equating these two forces, we have

$$\frac{mv^2}{r} = \frac{ke^2}{r^2} \tag{27.11}$$

The total energy of the atom is the sum of its kinetic and potential energies. Recall from Chapter 16 that the electric potential energy of two point charges is given by $U_e = kq_1q_2/r$. Since the electron and proton are oppositely charged, $U_e = -ke^2/r$. Thus, the expression for the total energy becomes

$$E = K + U_e = \tfrac{1}{2}mv^2 - \frac{ke^2}{r}$$

From Eq. 27.11, the kinetic energy can be written as $\tfrac{1}{2}mv^2 = ke^2/2r$. With this relationship, the total energy becomes

$$E = \frac{ke^2}{2r} - \frac{ke^2}{r} = -\frac{ke^2}{2r} \tag{27.12}$$

Note that E is negative, indicating that the system is bound. As the radius gets very large, E approaches zero. With $E = 0$, the electron would no longer be bound to the proton, and the atom, having lost its electron, would be *ionized*.

Up to this point, only classical principles had been applied. At this step in the theory, Bohr made a radical assumption—radical in the sense that he introduced a quantum concept to attempt to explain atomic line spectra:

Bohr assumed that the angular momentum of the electron was quantized and could have only discrete values that were integral multiples of $h/2\pi$, where h is Planck's constant.

Recall that in a circular orbit of radius r, the angular momentum L of an object of mass m is given by mvr (Eq. 8.14). Therefore, Bohr's assumption translates into

$$mvr = n\left(\frac{h}{2\pi}\right) \qquad \text{for } n = 1, 2, 3, 4, \ldots \tag{27.13}$$

The integer n is an example of a *quantum number*. Specifically, n is the atom's **principal quantum number.*** With this assumption, the orbital speed of the electron (v) can be found. Its (quantized) values are

$$v_n = \frac{nh}{2\pi mr} \qquad \text{for } n = 1, 2, 3, 4, \ldots$$

Putting this expression for v into Eq. 27.11 and solving for r, we obtain

$$r_n = \left(\frac{h^2}{4\pi^2 ke^2 m}\right) n^2 \qquad \text{for } n = 1, 2, 3, 4, \ldots \tag{27.14}$$

Here, the subscript n on r is used to indicate that only certain radii are possible—that is, the size of the orbit is also quantized. The energy for an orbit can be found by substituting this expression for r into Eq. 27.12, which gives

$$E_n = -\left(\frac{2\pi^2 k^2 e^4 m}{h^2}\right)\frac{1}{n^2} \qquad \text{for } n = 1, 2, 3, 4, \ldots \tag{27.15}$$

where the energy is also written with a subscript of n to show its dependence on n. The quantities in the parentheses on the right-hand sides of Eqs. 27.14 and 27.15 are constants and can be evaluated numerically. Because the radii are so small, they are typically expressed in nanometers (nm); similarly, energies are expressed in electron-volts (eV):

$$r_n = 0.0529n^2 \text{ nm} \qquad \text{for } n = 1, 2, 3, 4, \ldots \qquad \begin{array}{l}\textit{orbital radii and energies}\\ \textit{for the hydrogen atom}\end{array} \tag{27.16}$$

$$E_n = \frac{-13.6}{n^2} \text{ eV} \qquad \text{for } n = 1, 2, 3, 4, \ldots \tag{27.17}$$

The use of these expressions is shown in the next Example.

*The principal quantum number is only one of four quantum numbers necessary to completely describe each electron in an atom. See Chapter 28.

Example 27.5 ■ A Bohr Orbit: Radius and Energy

Find the orbital radius and energy of an electron in a hydrogen atom characterized by the principal quantum number $n = 2$.

Thinking It Through. Equations 27.16 and 27.17 are used with $n = 2$.

Solution. For $n = 2$,

$$r_2 = 0.0529n^2 \text{ nm} = 0.0529(2)^2 \text{ nm} = 0.212 \text{ nm}$$

and

$$E_2 = \frac{-13.6}{n^2} \text{ eV} = \frac{-13.6}{2^2} \text{ eV} = -3.40 \text{ eV}$$

Follow-Up Exercise. In this Example, what is (a) the speed and (b) the kinetic energy of the orbiting electron?

However, there was still a problem with Bohr's theory. Classically, any accelerating charge should radiate electromagnetic energy (light). For the Bohr circular orbits, the electron is accelerating centripetally. Thus, the orbiting electron should lose energy and spiral into the nucleus. Clearly, this doesn't happen in the hydrogen atom, so Bohr had to make another nonclassical assumption. He postulated that:

> The hydrogen electron does *not* radiate energy when it is in a bound, discrete orbit. It radiates energy only when it makes a *downward transition* to an orbit of lower energy. It makes an *upward transition* to an orbit of higher energy by absorbing energy.

Energy Levels

The "allowed" orbits of the electron in a hydrogen atom are commonly expressed in terms of their energy (▼Fig. 27.10). In this context, the electron is referred to as being in a particular "energy level" or state. The principal quantum number labels the particular energy level. The lowest energy level ($n = 1$) is the **ground state**. The energy levels above the ground state are called **excited states**. For example, $n = 2$ is the *first excited state* (see Example 27.5), and so on.

The electron is normally in the ground state and must be given enough energy to raise it to an excited state. Since the energy levels have specific energies, it follows that the electron can be excited only by absorbing certain discrete amounts of energy. The energy levels can be thought of as the rungs of a ladder.* A person who goes up and down a ladder changes his or her gravitational potential energy by discrete amounts. Similarly, an electron goes up and down its own "energy ladder" in discrete steps. Notice, however, that the energy levels of the hydrogen atom are not evenly spaced, as they are on a ladder (Fig. 27.10).

Note: Review the concept of potential-energy wells, presented in Sections 5.4 and 7.5. (See Figs. 5.14 and 7.18.)

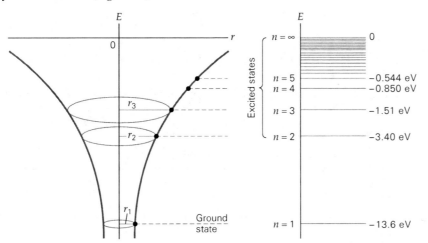

◀ **FIGURE 27.10 Orbits and energy levels of the hydrogen electron** The Bohr theory predicts that the hydrogen electron can occupy only certain orbits having discrete radii. Each allowed orbit has a corresponding total energy, conveniently displayed as an energy-level diagram. The lowest energy level ($n = 1$) is the ground state; the levels above it ($n > 1$) are excited states. The orbits are shown on the left, plotted in the $1/r$ electrical potential of the proton. The electron in the ground state is deepest in the potential-energy well, analogous to the gravitational potential-energy well of Fig. 7.18. (Neither r nor the energy levels are drawn to scale—can you tell why?)

---

*Care must be taken with this. As we step down or up a ladder, our gravitational potential energy takes on all values in between the end values. However, in an electron's "quantum" jump, it *never* has any intermediate energy value. That is, it has an energy to start and one to end, emitting or absorbing a quantum of energy in making the transition, but it never takes on an energy value in between the initial and final values.

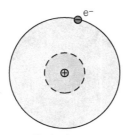

Excited atom

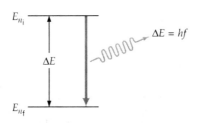

Emitted photon

De-excitation

E_{n_i}

ΔE

E_{n_f}

$\Delta E = hf$

▲ **FIGURE 27.11** Electron transitions and photon emission When a hydrogen atom emits light, its electron makes a downward transition to a lower orbit (with less energy), and a photon is emitted. The photon's energy is equal to the energy difference between the two levels.

If enough energy is absorbed, it is possible for the electron to no longer be bound to the atom; that is, it is possible for the atom to be *ionized*. For example, to ionize a hydrogen atom initially in its ground state requires a minimum of 13.6 eV of energy. This minimum process makes the final energy of the electron zero (since it is free), and it has a principal quantum number of $n = \infty$. However, if the electron is initially in an excited state, then less energy is needed to ionize the atom. Since the energy of the electron in any state is E_n, the energy needed to free it from the atom is $-E_n$. This energy is called the **binding energy** of the electron. Note that $-E_n$ is positive and represents the energy required to ionize the atom if the electron initially is in a state with a principal quantum number of n.

An electron generally does not remain in an excited state for long; it decays, or makes a downward transition to a lower energy level, in a very short time. The time an electron spends in an excited state is called the **lifetime** of the excited state. For many states, the lifetime is about 10^{-8} s. In making a transition to a lower state, the electron emits a quantum of light energy in the form of a photon (◄Fig. 27.11). The energy ΔE of the photon is equal in magnitude to the energy *difference* of the levels:

$$\Delta E = E_{n_i} - E_{n_f} = \left[\frac{-13.6}{n_i^2} \text{ eV}\right] - \left[\frac{-13.6}{n_f^2} \text{ eV}\right]$$

or

$$\Delta E = 13.6\left(\frac{1}{n_f^2} - \frac{1}{n_i^2}\right)\text{eV} \qquad \begin{array}{l}\textit{photon energy (in eV)} \\ \textit{emitted by an H atom}\end{array} \qquad (27.18)$$

Here, the subscripts i and f refer to the initial and final states, respectively. According to the Bohr theory, this energy difference is emitted as a photon with an energy E. Therefore, $E = \Delta E = hc/\lambda$, or $\lambda = hc/\Delta E$. Thus only particular wavelengths of light are emitted. These particular wavelengths (or alternatively, frequencies) correspond to the various transitions between energy levels and explain the existence of an emission spectrum.

The final principal quantum number n_f refers to the energy level in which the electron ends up during the emission process. The original *Balmer emission series* in the visible region corresponds to $n_f = 2$ and $n_i = 3, 4, 5$ and 6. There is only one emission series entirely in the ultraviolet range, called the *Lyman series*, in which all the transitions end in the $n_f = 1$ state (the ground state). There are many series entirely in the infrared region, most notably the *Paschen series*, which ends with the electron in the second excited state, $n_f = 3$. (These series take their names from their discoverers.)

Usually, the wavelength of the light is what is measured during the emission process. Since photon energy and light wavelength are related by Einstein's equation (Eq. 27.4), the wavelength of the emitted light, λ, can be obtained from

$$\lambda \text{ (in nm)} = \frac{hc}{\Delta E} = \frac{1.24 \times 10^3 \text{ eV} \cdot \text{nm}}{\Delta E \text{ (in eV)}} \qquad (27.19)$$

(See the Problem-Solving Hint on page 858.) Consider Example 27.6.

Example 27.6 ■ Investigating the Balmer Series: Visible Light from Hydrogen

What is the wavelength (and color) of the emitted light when an electron in a hydrogen atom undergoes a transition from the $n = 3$ energy level to the $n = 2$ energy level?

Thinking It Through. The emitted photon has an energy equal to the energy difference between the two energy levels (Eq. 27.18). The wavelength of the light can then be obtained by using Eq. 27.19.

Solution.

Given: $n_i = 3$ *Find:* λ (wavelength of emitted light)
        $n_f = 2$

The energy of the emitted photon is equal to the magnitude of the atom's change in energy. Thus,

$$\Delta E = 13.6\left(\frac{1}{n_f^2} - \frac{1}{n_i^2}\right)\text{eV} = 13.6\left(\frac{1}{4} - \frac{1}{9}\right)\text{eV} = 1.89 \text{ eV}$$

Using Eq. 27.19 (and making sure that ΔE is expressed in electron-volts), we obtain

$$\lambda = \frac{1.24 \times 10^3 \text{ eV} \cdot \text{nm}}{\Delta E} = \frac{1.24 \times 10^3 \text{ eV} \cdot \text{nm}}{1.89 \text{ eV}} = 656 \text{ nm}$$

which is in the red portion of the visible spectrum. Refer to Fig. 27.8c and note the emission line right around 660 nm for hydrogen. The transition in this example is what gives rise to this red line.

Follow-Up Exercise. Light of what wavelength would be just sufficient to ionize a hydrogen atom if it started in its first excited state? Classify this type of light. Is it visible, UV, or IR?

In summary, since the Bohr model of hydrogen requires that the electron make transitions only between discrete energy levels, the atom emits photons of discrete energies (or light of discrete wavelengths), which results in emission spectra. This process is summarized in ▼Fig. 27.12.

Integrated Example 27.7 ■ The Balmer Series: Entirely Visible?

We know that four wavelengths of the Balmer series are in the visible range (Fig. 27.12). (a) There are more than just these four in this series. What type of light are they likely to be: (1) infrared, (2) visible, or (3) ultraviolet? (b) What is the longest wavelength of nonvisible light in the Balmer series?

(a) Conceptual Reasoning. The Balmer series of emission lines is given off when the electron ends in the first excited state, that is, $n_f = 2$ (Fig. 27.12). There are four distinct visible wavelengths, corresponding to $n_i = 3, 4, 5,$ and 6. Any other lines in this series must start with $n_i = 7$ or higher and therefore represent a larger energy difference than those for the visible lines. This means that these photons carry more energy than visible-light photons, and the light will have a shorter wavelength than visible light. Wavelengths smaller than visible are UV. Thus the answer is (3); the other Balmer lines must be in the ultraviolet region.

(b) Thinking It Through. The longest nonvisible Balmer series wavelength corresponds to the smallest photon energy above the $n = 6 \rightarrow 2$ transition. (Why?). Hence, we are talking about $n_i = 7$ and $n_f = 2$. The energy difference can be computed from Eq. 27.18. Then λ can be calculated from Eq. 27.19.

Given: The Balmer emission series for hydrogen   *Find:* The longest nonvisible wavelength in the Balmer series

From Eq. 27.18,

$$\Delta E = 13.6\left(\frac{1}{n_f^2} - \frac{1}{n_i^2}\right)\text{eV} = 13.6\left(\frac{1}{4} - \frac{1}{49}\right)\text{eV} = 3.12 \text{ eV}$$

This energy difference corresponds to light of wavelength

$$\lambda = \frac{1.24 \times 10^3 \text{ eV} \cdot \text{nm}}{\Delta E} = \frac{1.24 \times 10^3 \text{ eV} \cdot \text{nm}}{3.12 \text{ eV}} = 397 \text{ nm}$$

This is just below the lower limit of the visible spectrum, which ends at 400 nm.

Follow-Up Exercise. In hydrogen, what is the longest wavelength of light emitted in the Lyman series? In what region of the spectrum is this light?

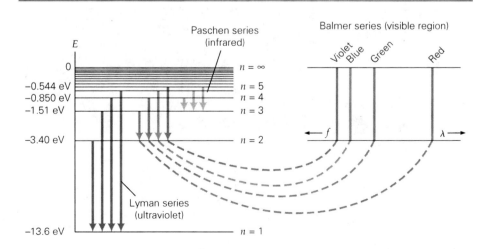

◄ **FIGURE 27.12 Hydrogen spectrum** Transitions may occur between two or more energy levels as the electron returns to the ground state. Transitions to the $n = 2$ state give spectral lines with wavelengths in the visible region (the Balmer series). Transitions to other levels give rise to other series (not in the visible region), as shown.

Conceptual Example 27.8 ■ Up and Down in the Hydrogen Atom: Absorbed and Emitted Photons

Assume that a hydrogen atom, initially in its ground state, absorbs a photon. In general, how many emitted photons would you expect to be associated with the de-excitation process back to the ground state? Can there be (a) more than one photon, or must there be (b) only one photon?

Reasoning and Answer. Since the difference between light emission and absorption is the direction of the transition (down for emission, up for absorption), you might be tempted to answer (b), because only one photon was required for the excitation process. However, if you look at the details of the two processes, you will realize that they are not necessarily symmetrical. In absorbing a photon's energy, a hydrogen atom will jump from its ground state to an excited state—let's say from $n = 1$ to $n = 4$. This process requires a single photon of a unique energy (that is, light of a unique wavelength).

However, in dropping back to the ground state, the atom may take any one of *several* possible routes. For example, the atom could go from the $n = 4$ state to the $n = 3$ state, followed by a transition to the ground state ($n = 1$). This process would involve the emission of two photons. Therefore, the answer is (a). In general, following the absorption of a single photon, several photons can be emitted.

Follow-Up Exercise. (a) How many different-energy photons may a hydrogen atom emit in de-exciting from the third excited state to the ground state? (b) Starting from the ground state, which excitation transition *must* result in only one emitted photon when the hydrogen atom de-excites? Explain your reasoning.

Bohr's theory gave excellent agreement with experiment for hydrogen gas as well as for other ions with just one electron, such as singly ionized helium. However, it could not successfully describe multielectron atoms. Bohr's theory was incomplete in the sense that it patched new quantum ideas into a basically classical framework. The theory contains some correct concepts, but a complete description of the atom did not come until the development of quantum mechanics (Chapter 28). Nevertheless, the idea of discrete energy levels in atoms enables us to qualitatively understand phenomena such as fluorescence.

In **fluorescence**, an electron in an excited state returns to the ground state in two or more steps, like a ball bouncing down a flight of stairs. At each step, a photon is emitted. Each such step represents a smaller energy transition than the original energy required for the upward transition. Therefore, each emitted photon must have a lower energy and a longer wavelength than the original exciting photon. For example, the atoms of many minerals can be excited by absorbing ultraviolet (UV) light and *fluoresce*, or glow, in the visible region when they de-excite (▼Fig. 27.13). A variety of living organisms, from corals to butterflies, manufacture fluorescent pigments that emit visible light.

(a) Visible illumination

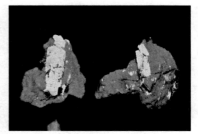

(b) UV illumination

▲ **FIGURE 27.13** Fluorescence Many minerals emit light of visible wavelengths when illuminated by invisible ultraviolet light (so-called black light). The visible light is produced when atoms excited by the UV light de-excite to lower energy levels in several smaller steps, yielding photons of less energy and longer (visible) wavelengths.

28

QUANTUM MECHANICS AND ATOMIC PHYSICS

PHYSICS FACTS

- Louis de Broglie's full name was Prince Louis-Victor Pierre Raymond de Broglie. Besides winning the Nobel Prize in physics in 1929 for his discovery of "the wave nature of the electron," he also excelled as a teacher/lecturer. In 1952 the first Kalinga Prize was awarded to him by UNESCO for his efforts to explain aspects of modern physics to laypeople.

- Hitler rose to power in Germany in 1933, the same year that Werner Heisenberg was awarded the Nobel Prize for his contributions to the creation of quantum mechanics. Heisenberg is associated with one of the most famous principles in modern physics: the Heisbenberg uncertainty principle. Protected by the Nobel Prize, Heisenberg became a spokesman for modern physics in Germany and remained there throughout World War II. He was not a Nazi, but he was a German citizen, and felt it his duty to preserve some of German science.

- All elementary particles have associated *antiparticles*. For the familiar electron, the antiparticle is the positive electron, or simply the positron. If electron and positron meet, they annihilate into gamma radiation, the result of converting their mass (energy) into electromagnetic (light) energy. Many of the properties of a particle and its antiparticle are opposite, such as electric charge. However, antiparticles have "regular" mass; that is, they are attracted downward to the Earth, not repelled.

J ust a few decades ago, if someone had claimed to have a photograph of an atom, people would have laughed. Today, a device called the scanning tunneling microscope (STM) routinely produces images such as shown in the photograph. The blue shapes represent iron atoms, neatly arranged on a copper surface.

The STM operates on a quantum-mechanical phenomenon called *tunneling*. Tunneling reflects some of the fundamental features of the subatomic realm: the probabilistic character of quantum processes and the wave nature of particles. These features explain how particles may turn up in places where, according to classical notions, they should not be.

In the 1920s, a new kind of physics, based on the synthesis of wave and quantum ideas, was introduced. This new theory, called **quantum mechanics**, combined the wave–particle duality of matter into a single consistent description. It revolutionized scientific thought and provides the basis of our understanding of phenomena that occur on the scale of molecular sizes and smaller.

In this chapter, some of the basic ideas of quantum mechanics are presented in order to show how they describe matter. Practical applications made possible by the quantum-mechanical view of nature, such as the electron microscope and magnetic resonance imaging (MRI), are also discussed.

877

28.2 The Schrödinger Wave Equation

OBJECTIVES: To understand qualitatively (a) the reasoning that underlies the Schrödinger wave equation, and (b) the equation's use in finding particle wave functions.

De Broglie's hypothesis predicts that moving particles have associated waves that somehow govern their behavior. However, it does not tell us the *form* of these waves, only their wavelengths. To have a useful theory, an equation that will give the mathematical form of these matter waves is needed. We also need to know how these waves govern particle motion. In 1926, Erwin Schrödinger, an Austrian physicist, presented a general equation that describes the de Broglie matter waves and their interpretation.

A traveling de Broglie wave varies with location and time in a similar way to everyday wave motion (Section 13.2). The de Broglie wave is denoted by ψ (the Greek letter psi, pronounced "sigh") and is called the **wave function** ψ, and is associated with the particle's kinetic, potential, and total energy. Recall that for a conservative mechanical system (Section 5.5), the total mechanical energy E, which is the sum of the kinetic and potential energies, is a constant; that is $K + U = E$. Schrödinger proposed a similar equation for the de Broglie matter waves, involving the wave function ψ. **Schrödinger's wave equation*** has the general form

$$(K + U)\psi = E\psi \qquad (28.4)$$

Equation 28.4 can be solved for ψ, but doing so involves complex mathematical operations well beyond the scope of this text. For us, the more important question is related to the physical significance of ψ. During the early development of quantum mechanics, it was not at all clear how ψ should be interpreted. After much thought and investigation, Schrödinger and his colleagues hypothesized the following:

Note: More precisely, the square of the absolute value of the wave-function solution to Schrödinger's equation, $|\psi|^2$, gives the probability of finding a particle at a location.

> The square of a particle's wave function is proportional to the probability of finding that particle at a given location.

The interpretation of ψ^2 as a *probability* altered the idea that the electron in a hydrogen atom could be found only in orbits at discrete distances from the nucleus, as described in the Bohr theory. When the Schrödinger equation was solved for the hydrogen atom, there was a nonzero probability of finding the electron at almost any distance from the nucleus. The relative probability of finding an electron [in the ground state ($n = 1$)] at a given distance from the proton is shown in ▾Fig. 28.3a.

The *maximum* probability coincides with the Bohr radius of 0.0529 nm, but it is possible that, for instance, the electron could even be inside the nucleus. Notice that,

▶ **FIGURE 28.3 Electron probability for hydrogen-atom orbits (a)** The square of the wave function is the probability of finding the hydrogen electron at a particular location. Here, it is assumed to be in the ground state ($n = 1$), and its probability is plotted as a function of radial distance from the proton. The electron has the greatest probability of being at a distance of 0.0529 nm, which matches the radius of the first Bohr orbit. **(b)** The probability distribution gives rise to the idea of an electron probability cloud around the nucleus. The cloud's density reflects the probability density.

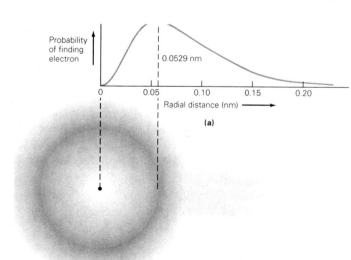

(a)

(b) Electron "cloud"

*Although Eq. 28.4 looks like a multiplication of $E = K + U$ by ψ, it is much more complex. For example, K is no longer $\frac{1}{2}mv^2$, but is instead replaced by a quantity (called an *operator*) that enables us to *extract* the kinetic energy from ψ.

although the ground-state wave function exists for distances well beyond 0.20 nm from the proton, there is little chance of finding an electron beyond this distance. The probability density distribution gives rise to the idea of an *electron cloud* around the nucleus (Fig. 28.3b). This cloud is actually a probability density cloud, meaning that the electron can be found in many different locations with varying probabilities.

An interesting quantum-mechanical result that runs counter to our everyday experiences is *tunneling*. In classical physics, there are regions forbidden to particles by energy considerations. These regions are areas where a particle's potential energy would be greater than its total energy. Classically, the particle is not allowed in such regions because it would have a negative kinetic energy there $(E - U = K < 0)$, which is impossible. In such situations, we say that the particle's location is limited by a *potential-energy barrier*.

In certain instances, however, quantum mechanics predicts a small, but finite, probability of the particle's wave function penetrating the barrier and thus of the particle being found on the other side of the barrier. Thus, there is a certain probability (which is practically zero for everyday objects) of the particle "tunneling" through the barrier, especially on the atomic level, where the wave nature of particles is exhibited. Such tunneling forms the basis of the scanning tunneling microscope (STM; see the accompanying Insight 28.2 on The Scanning Tunneling Microscope), which creates images with a resolution on the order of the size of a single atom. Barrier penetration also explains certain nuclear decay processes (Chapter 29).

INSIGHT 28.2 THE SCANNING TUNNELING MICROSCOPE (STM)

The *scanning tunneling microscope* (STM) was invented in the late 1970s and promptly revolutionized the field of surface physics. STMs use quantum-mechanical tunneling to produce stunning images of atoms, such as this chapter's opening photograph.

The STM produces atomic-sized images by positioning its sharp tip very close (about 1 nm) to a surface. A voltage is applied between the tip and the surface, causing electron tunneling through the vacuum gap (Fig. 1). This tunneling current is extremely sensitive to the separation distance. A feedback circuit monitors this current and moves the probe vertically to keep the current constant. The separation distance is digitized, recorded, and processed by computers for display. When the probe is passed over the surface of the specimen in successive nearby parallel movements, a three-dimensional image of the surface can be displayed. Typical vertical resolution for STMs is 0.001 nm, and lateral resolutions are about 0.1 nm. Because the diameters of individual atoms are on the order of several tenths of a nanometer, STMs allow detailed images of atoms to be created. Figure 2 shows the result of a surface scan on gallium arsenide, a semiconductor material.

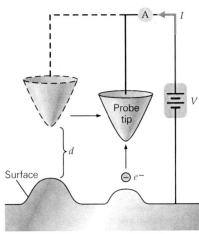

FIGURE 1 Schematic representation of the STM The tip of a probe is moved across the contours of a specimen's surface. A small voltage applied between the probe and the surface causes electrons to tunnel across the vacuum gap. The tunneling current is extremely sensitive to the separation distance between the probe tip and the surface. A feedback circuit (not shown) moves the probe up and down so as to keep constant the tunneling current as measured by the ammeter shown as (A). Thus, when the probe is scanned across the sample, surface features smaller than atoms (up to 0.001 nm vertically) can be detected. When the probe is passed over the surface in many successive and nearby parallel paths, the resulting data can be processed to produce three-dimensional images.

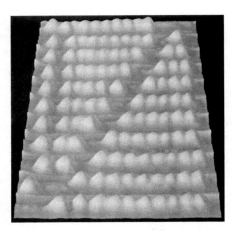

FIGURE 2 Scanning tunneling microscopy results Atoms of the semiconductor gallium arsenide.

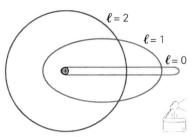

▲ **FIGURE 28.4 The orbital quantum number (ℓ)** The orbits of an electron are shown for the second excited state in hydrogen. For the principal quantum number $n = 3$, there are three different values of angular momentum (corresponding to the three differently shaped orbits and three different values of ℓ), but they all have the same total energy. The circular orbit has the maximum angular momentum; the narrowest orbit would actually pass through the proton classically and thus has zero angular momentum.

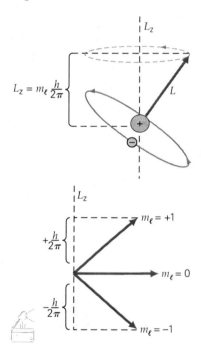

▲ **FIGURE 28.5 The magnetic quantum number m_ℓ** Here, $\vec{L}$ is the vector angular momentum associated with the orbit of the electron. Because the energy of an orbit is independent of the orientation of its plane, orbits with the same ℓ that differ only in m_ℓ have the same energy. There are $2\ell + 1$ possible orientations for a given ℓ. The value of m_ℓ tells the *component* of the angular-momentum vector in a given direction, as shown (below) for $\ell = 1$.

28.3 Atomic Quantum Numbers and the Periodic Table

OBJECTIVE: To understand the structure of the periodic table in terms of quantum-mechanical electron orbits and the Pauli exclusion principle.

The Hydrogen Atom

When the Schrödinger equation was solved for the hydrogen atom, the results predicted the energy levels to be the same as those from the Bohr theory (Section 27.4). Recall that the Bohr-model energy values depended only on the **principal quantum number** n. However, in addition, the solution to the Schrödinger equation gave two other quantum numbers, designated as ℓ and m_ℓ. Three quantum numbers are needed because the electron can move in three dimensions.

The quantum number ℓ is called the **orbital quantum number**. It is associated with the orbital angular momentum of the electron. For each value of n, the ℓ quantum number has integer values from zero up to a maximum value of $n - 1$. For example, if $n = 3$, the three possible values of ℓ are 0, 1, and 2. ◄Figure 28.4 shows three orbits with different angular momenta, but the same energy. The number of different ℓ values for a given n value is equal to n. In the hydrogen atom, the energy of the electron depends only on n. Thus, orbits with the same n value, but different ℓ values, have the same energy and are said to be *degenerate*.

The quantum number m_ℓ is called the **magnetic quantum number**. The name originated from experiments in which an external *magnetic* field was applied to a sample. They showed that a particular energy level (one with given values of n and ℓ) of a hydrogen atom actually consists of several orbits that differ slightly in energy *only when in a magnetic field*. Thus, in the absence of a field, there was additional energy degeneracy. Clearly, there must be more to the description of the orbit than just n and ℓ. The quantum number m_ℓ was introduced to enumerate the number of levels that existed for a given orbital quantum number ℓ. Under zero-magnetic-field conditions, the energy of the atom does not depend on either of these quantum numbers.

The magnetic quantum number m_ℓ is associated with the orientation of the orbital angular-momentum vector $\vec{L}$ in space (◄Fig. 28.5). If there is no external magnetic field, then all orientations of $\vec{L}$ have the same energy. For each value of ℓ, m_ℓ is an integer that can range from zero to 6ℓ. That is, $m_\ell = 0, 61, 62, \ldots, 6\ell$. For example, an orbit described by $n = 3$ and $\ell = 2$ can have m_ℓ values of -2, -1, 0, $+1$, and $+2$. In this case, the orbital angular-momentum vector $\vec{L}$ has five possible orientations, all with the same energy if no magnetic field is present. In general, for a given value of ℓ, there are $2\ell + 1$ possible values of m_ℓ. For example, with $\ell = 2$, there are five values of m_ℓ, since $2\ell + 1 = (2 \times 2) + 1 = 5$.

However, this finding was not the end of the story. The use of high-resolution optical spectrometers showed that each emission line of hydrogen is, in fact, two very closely spaced lines. Thus, each emitted wavelength is actually two. This splitting is called *spectral fine structure*. Hence, a fourth quantum number was necessary in order to describe each atomic state completely. This number is called the **spin quantum number m_s** of the electron. It is associated with the *intrinsic* angular momentum of the electron. This property, called *electron spin*, is sometimes described by analogy to the angular momentum associated with a spinning object (▸Fig. 28.6). Because each energy level is split into only two levels, the electron's intrinsic angular momentum (or, more simply, its "spin") can possess only two orientations, called "spin up" and "spin down."

Thus, the fine structure of an atom's energy levels results from the electron spin's having two orientations with respect to the atom's *internal* magnetic field, produced by the electron's orbital motion. Analogous to a magnetic moment (such as a compass) in a magnetic field, the atom possesses slightly less energy when its electron's spin is "lined up" with the field than when the spin is aligned opposite to the field. However, keep in mind that spin is fundamentally a purely quantum-mechanical concept; it is not really analogous to a spinning top. This is because, as far as we know now, the electron possesses no size—that is, it is truly a point particle.

TABLE 28.1	Quantum Numbers for the Hydrogen Atom		
Quantum Number	Symbol	Allowed Values	Number of Allowed Values
Principal	n	$1, 2, 3, \ldots$	no limit
Orbital angular momentum	ℓ	$0, 1, 2, 3, \ldots, (n-1)$	n (for each n)
Orbital magnetic	m_ℓ	$0, \pm 1, \pm 2, \pm 3, \ldots, \pm \ell$	$2\ell + 1$ (for each ℓ)
Spin	m_s	$\pm \frac{1}{2}$	2 (for each m_ℓ)

Thus, for the excited state of hydrogen with $n = 3$ and $\ell = 2$, each value of m_ℓ also has two possible spin orientations. For example, when $m_\ell = +1$, there are two possible sets of the four quantum numbers: $n = 3$, $\ell = 2$, and $m_\ell = +1$, with $m_s = +\frac{1}{2}$; and $n = 3$, $\ell = 2$, and $m_\ell = +1$, with $m_s = -\frac{1}{2}$. Both sets would have nearly the same energy. The orbit's energy is therefore almost independent of the electron's spin direction. This condition results in yet another (approximate) energy degeneracy. In summary, the energy of the various states of the hydrogen atom are, to a very high degree, determined solely by the primary quantum number n.

The four quantum numbers for the hydrogen atom are summarized in Table 28.1. Other particles, such a protons, neutrons, and composites of them called *atomic nuclei* also possess spin. A particularly useful property of the spin of a proton, and of atomic nuclei in general, is discussed in Insight 28.3 on Magnetic Resonance Imaging (MRI) on page 884.

Multielectron Atoms

The Schrödinger equation cannot be solved exactly for atoms with more than one electron (multielectron atoms). However, a solution can be found, to a workable approximation, in which each electron occupies a state characterized by a set of quantum numbers similar to those for hydrogen. Because of the repulsive forces between the electrons, the description of a multielectron atom is much more complicated. For one, the energy depends not only on the principal quantum number n, but also on the orbital quantum number ℓ. This condition gives rise to a subdivision (or "splitting") of the degeneracy seen in hydrogen atoms. In multielectron atoms, the energies of the atomic levels generally depend on all four quantum numbers.

It is common to refer to all the electron levels that share the same n value as making up a **shell** and to all the electron levels that share the same ℓ values within that shell as **subshells**. That is, electron levels with the same n value are said to be "in the same shell." Similarly, electrons with the same n and ℓ values are said to be "in the same subshell."

The ℓ subshells can be designated by integers; however, it is common to use letters instead. The letters $s, p, d, f, g, \ldots$ correspond to the values of $\ell = 0, 1, 2, 3, 4, \ldots$ respectively. After f, the letters go alphabetically (Table 28.2).

Because in multielectron atoms an electron's energy depends on both n and ℓ, both quantum numbers are used to label atomic energy levels (a shell and subshell, respectively). The labeling convention is as follows: n is written as a number, followed by the letter that stands for the value of ℓ. For example, $1s$ denotes an energy level with $n = 1$ and $\ell = 0$; $2p$ is for $n = 2$ and $\ell = 1$; $3d$ is for $n = 3$ and $\ell = 2$; and so on. Also, it is common to refer to the m_ℓ values as representing *orbitals*. For example, a $2p$ energy level has three orbitals, corresponding to the m_ℓ values of $-1, 0$, and $+1$ (because $\ell = 1$).

The hydrogen atom energy levels are not evenly spaced, but do increase sequentially. In multielectron atoms, not only are the energy levels unevenly spaced, but their numerical sequence is also, in general, out of order. The shell–subshell ($n - \ell$ notation) energy-level sequence for a multielectron atom is shown in ▾Fig. 28.7a. Notice, for example, that the $4s$ level is, energywise, below the $3d$ level. Such variations result in part from electrical forces between the electrons. Furthermore, note

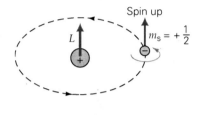

Spin up

$m_s = +\frac{1}{2}$

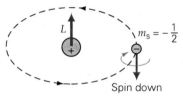

$m_s = -\frac{1}{2}$

Spin down

▲ **FIGURE 28.6** The electron-spin quantum number (m_s) The electron spin can be either up or down. Electron spin is strictly a quantum mechanical property and should not be identified with the physical spin of a macroscopic body, except with respect to conceptual reasoning.

Note: The n quantum number designates orbital shells; the ℓ quantum number designates orbital subshells.

TABLE 28.2	
Subshell Designations	
Value of ℓ	Designation
$\ell = 0$	s
$\ell = 1$	p
$\ell = 2$	d
$\ell = 3$	f
$\ell = 4$	g
$\ell = 5$	h
$\ldots$	$\ldots$

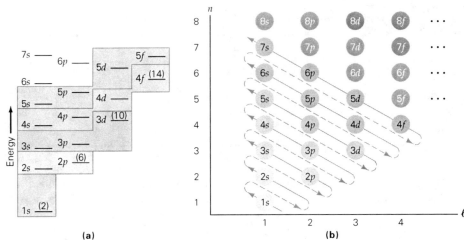

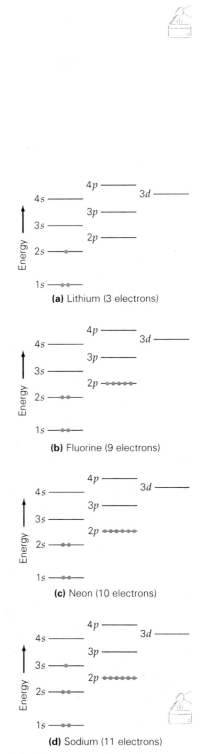

(a) Lithium (3 electrons)

(b) Fluorine (9 electrons)

(c) Neon (10 electrons)

(d) Sodium (11 electrons)

▲ **FIGURE 28.8** Filling subshells
The electron subshell distributions for several unexcited atoms (in their ground state) according to the Pauli exclusion principle. Because of spin, any s subshell can hold a maximum of two electrons, and any p subshell can hold a maximum of six electrons. What can you say about the d subshells?

▲ **FIGURE 28.7** Energy levels of a multielectron atom **(a)** The shell–subshell $(n-\ell)$ sequence shows that the energy levels are not evenly spaced and that the sequence of energy levels has numbers out of order. For example, the 4s level lies below the 3d level. The maximum number of electrons for a subshell, $2(2\ell + 1)$, is shown in parentheses on representative levels. (The vertical energy differences may not be drawn to scale.) **(b)** A convenient way to remember the energy-level order of a multielectron atom is to list the n-versus-ℓ values as shown here. The diagonal lines then give the energy levels in ascending order.

that the electrons in the outer orbits are "shielded" from the attractive force of the nucleus by the electrons that are closer to the nucleus. For example, consider the highly elliptical orbit (Fig. 28.4) of an electron in the 4s ($\ell = 0$) orbit. The electron clearly spends more time near the nucleus, and hence is more tightly bound, than if it were in the more circular 3d ($\ell = 2$) orbit. A convenient way to remember the order of the levels is given in Fig. 28.7b.

The ground state of a multielectron atom has some similarities to that of the hydrogen atom, with its one electron in the 1s, or lowest energy, level. In a multielectron atom, the ground state still has the lowest total energy, but is a combination of energy levels in this case. That is, the electrons are in the lowest possible energy levels. But to identify how the electrons fill these levels, we must know how many electrons can occupy a particular energy level. For example, the lithium (Li) atom has three electrons. Can they all be in the 1s level? As we shall see, the answer, given by the Pauli exclusion principle, is no.

The Pauli Exclusion Principle

Exactly how the electrons of a multielectron atom distribute themselves in the ground-state energy levels is governed by a principle set forth in 1928 by the Austrian physicist Wolfgang Pauli. The **Pauli exclusion principle** states the following:

No two electrons in an atom can have the same set of quantum numbers (n, ℓ, m_ℓ, m_s). That is, no two electrons in an atom can be in the same quantum state.

This principle limits the number of electrons that can occupy a given energy level. For example, the 1s ($n = 1$ and $\ell = 0$) level can have only one m_ℓ value, $m_\ell = 0$, along with only two m_s values, $m_s = 6\frac{1}{2}$. Thus, there are only two unique sets of quantum numbers (n, ℓ, m_ℓ, m_s) for the 1s level—$\left(1, 0, 0, +\frac{1}{2}\right)$ and $\left(1, 0, 0, -\frac{1}{2}\right)$—so only two electrons can occupy the 1s level. If this situation is indeed the case, then we say that such a shell is *full*; all other electrons are excluded from it by Pauli's principle. Thus, for a Li atom, with three electrons, the third electron must occupy the next higher level (2s) when the atom is in the ground state. This case is illustrated in ◄Fig. 28.8, along with the ground-state energy levels for some other atoms.

Integrated Example 28.3 ■ The Quantum Shell Game:
How Many States?

(a) How does the number of possible electron states compare between the $2p$ and the $4p$ subshells: (1) The number of states in the $2p$ subshell is greater than that in the $4p$ subshell; (2) the number of states in the $2p$ subshell is less than that in the $4p$ subshell; or (3) the number of states in the $2p$ subshell is the same as that in the $4p$ subshell? (b) Compare the number of possible electron states in the $3p$ subshell to the number in the $4d$ subshell.

(a) Conceptual Reasoning. The term *subshell* refers to the states that share the same ℓ quantum number within a shell. That is, they all have the same principal quantum number n. All that matters is that their ℓ values are the same. Therefore, the number of states in the two subshells is the same, so the correct answer is (3).

(b) Thinking It Through. This part is a matter of following the quantum-mechanical counting rules. Also remember that each letter stands for a specific value of ℓ. The p level means that $\ell = 1$, and the d level means that $\ell = 2$. In each subshell, we replace the letter designation for ℓ by its number. Thus, the data given are as follows:

Given: $3p$ level means $n = 3$ and $\ell = 1$ **Find:** the number of quantum states in
$4d$ level means $n = 4$ and $\ell = 2$ the $3p$ subshell as compared with the number in the $4d$ subshell

For a particular subshell, the ℓ value determines the number of states. Recall that there are $(2\ell + 1)$ possible m_ℓ values for a given ℓ. Thus, for $\ell = 1$, there are $[(2 \times 1) + 1] = 3$ values for m_ℓ. (They are $+1, 0,$ and -1.) Each of these values can have two m_s values $\left(6\frac{1}{2}\right)$, making six different combinations of (n, ℓ, m_ℓ, m_s), or six states.

In general, the number of possible states for a given value of ℓ is $2(2\ell + 1)$, taking into account the two possible "spin states" for each orbital state:

Number of electron states for $\ell = 1$ is $2(2\ell + 1) = 2[(2 \times 1) + 1] = 6$
Number of electron states for $\ell = 2$ is $2(2\ell + 1) = 2[(2 \times 2) + 1] = 10$

Comparison shows that the d subshell has more possible electron states than does the p subshell, regardless of which shell they are in (that is, their n value).

These results are summarized in Table 28.3. Notice that the total number of states in a given *shell* (designated by n) is $2n^2$. For example, for the $n = 2$ shell, the total number of states for its combined s and p subshells ($\ell = 0, 1$) is $2n^2 = 2(2)^2 = 8$. This means that up to eight electrons can be accommodated in the $n = 2$ shell: two in the $2s$ subshell and six in the $2p$ subshell.

Follow-Up Exercise. How many electrons could be accommodated in the $3d$ subshell if there were no spin quantum number?

TABLE 28.3 Possible Sets of Quantum Numbers and States

Electron Shell n	Subshell ℓ	Subshell Notation	Orbitals (m_ℓ)	Number of Orbitals (m_ℓ) in Subshell $= (2\ell + 1)$	Number of States m_s in Subshell $= 2(2\ell + 1)$	Total Electron States for Shell $= 2n^2$
1	0	$1s$	0	1	2	2
2	0	$2s$	0	1	2	8
	1	$2p$	$1, 0, -1$	3	6	
3	0	$3s$	0	1	2	18
	1	$3p$	$1, 0, -1$	3	6	
	2	$3d$	$2, 1, 0, -1, -2$	5	10	
4	0	$4s$	0	1	2	32
	1	$4p$	$1, 0, -1$	3	6	
	2	$4d$	$2, 1, 0, -1, -2$	5	10	
	3	$4f$	$3, 2, 1, 0, -1, -2, -3$	7	14	

INSIGHT 28.3 MAGNETIC RESONANCE IMAGING (MRI)

Magnetic resonance imaging, or MRI, has become a common and important medical technique for the noninvasive examination of the human body (Fig. 1). Originally known as NMR (for *nuclear magnetic resonance*), MRI is based on the quantum-mechanical concept of spin.

A current-carrying loop in a magnetic field experiences a torque that tends to orient the loop's magnetic moment parallel to the field, much like a compass (Chapter 20). Electrons possess an intrinsic angular momentum called *spin*. This condition gives rise to a *spin magnetic moment*, which aligns in a similar manner to the compass. When atoms are placed in a magnetic field, each of their energy levels is split into two levels (for the two possible spin orientations—parallel and antiparallel to the magnetic field), each with a slightly different energy, which results in the fine structure in the atoms' emission spectra.

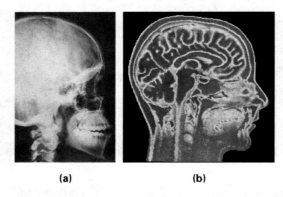

(a)   **(b)**

FIGURE 1 Diagnostic images (a) An X-ray of a human head. **(b)** A magnetic resonance image (MRI) of a human head. The amount of detail captured, especially in the soft tissues of the brain, makes such images very useful for medical diagnosis.

Nuclei exhibit similar spin effects when placed in magnetic fields. Because neutrons and protons possess spin, nuclei, which are composed of neutrons and protons, also possess magnetic moments. To understand the basics of MRI, let us concentrate on the simplest atom, hydrogen, with a nucleus composed of a single proton. The magnetic resonance of hydrogen is commonly measured in an MRI apparatus, since hydrogen is the most abundant element in the human body. The spin angular momentum of the proton can take on only two values, similar to that of electron spin, called "spin up" and "spin down." These values describe the orientation of the proton's magnetic moment relative to the direction of an external magnetic field (Fig. 2a). With spin up, the magnetic moment is parallel to the field, with spin down, it points opposite to the field. The spin-down orientation has a slightly higher energy, and the energy difference ΔE between the two levels is proportional to the magnitude of the magnetic field. The transition to the higher energy level can be made by allowing the proton to absorb a photon with energy equal to ΔE.

In a typical MRI apparatus, the sample (usually a region of the human body) is placed in a magnetic field $\vec{B}$. The magnitude of the field determines the energy E (or light frequency f) of the photon needed to cause a transition. This is because the photon energy absorption requires that $E = hf = \Delta E$, which is proportional to the strength of the magnetic field, B. The photons that trigger this transition are supplied by a pulsed beam of radio-frequency (RF) radiation applied to the sample. If the frequency of the radiation is adjusted so that the photon energy equals the energy level difference, many nuclei will absorb the photon energy and be excited into the higher energy level. The frequency that creates such excitation is known as the *resonance frequency* ($f = \Delta E/h$), hence the name magnetic *resonance* imaging.

Figure 3 shows a typical MRI device. Large coils produce the magnetic field. (Notice the solenoid arrangement in Fig. 3a.) Other coils produce the RF signals ("RF photons") that cause the nuclei to

Electron Configurations The electron structure of the ground state of atoms can be determined, so to speak, by putting an increasing number of electrons in the lower energy subshells [hydrogen (H), 1 electron; helium (He), 2 electrons; lithium (Li), 3 electrons; and so on], as was done for four elements in Fig. 28.8. However, rather than drawing diagrams, a shorthand notation called the **electron configuration** is widely used.

In this notation, the subshells are written in order of increasing energy, and the number of electrons in each subshell designated with a superscript. For example, $3p^5$ means that a $3p$ subshell is occupied by five electrons. The electron configurations for the atoms shown in Fig. 28.8 can thus be written as follows:

Li	(3 electrons)	$1s^2 2s^1$
F	(9 electrons)	$1s^2 2s^2 2p^5$
Ne	(10 electrons)	$1s^2 2s^2 2p^6$
Na	(11 electrons)	$1s^2 2s^2 2p^6 3s^1$

In writing an electron configuration, when one subshell is filled, you go on to the next higher one. The total of all the superscripts in any configuration must add up to the number of electrons in the atom.

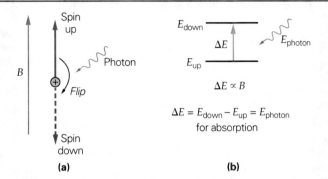

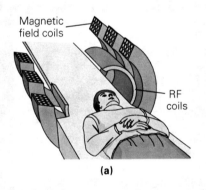

FIGURE 2 Nuclear spin (a) In a uniform magnetic field, the spin angular momentum, or spin magnetic moment, of a hydrogen nucleus (a proton) can have only two values—called "spin up" and "spin down," in reference to the direction of the external magnetic field. (b) This condition gives rise to two energy levels for the nucleus. Energy must be absorbed in order to "flip" the proton spin.

"flip their spin"—that is, to be excited from the lower to the upper energy level. The resulting absorption of energy is detected, as is emitted radiation coming from a return transition to the lower state. Regions that produce the greatest absorption (or re-emission) are those with the greatest concentration of the particular nucleus to which the apparatus is "tuned" by the choice of B and f. (Other nuclei besides hydrogen have their own characteristic intrinsic spins and can be imaged by tuning the frequency to match their resonance frequency.) Images are produced by means of computerized tomography, similar to that used in X-ray CT scans (see Section 20.4). The result is a two- or three-dimensional image (Fig. 1b) that can provide a great deal of diagnostic medical information.

Although a variety of atomic nuclei exhibit nuclear magnetic resonance, most MRI work is done with hydrogen, because body tissues vary in water content. For example, muscle tissue has more water than does fatty tissue, so there is a distinct contrast in the radiation intensity of the two materials. Similarly, fatty deposits in blood vessels are perceived distinctly from the tissue of the vessel walls. A tumor with a water content different than that of the surrounding tissue would also show up in an MRI image.

FIGURE 3 MRI (a) A diagram and (b) a photograph of the apparatus used for magnetic resonance imaging.

The energy spacing between adjacent subshells is not uniform, as Figs. 28.7a and 28.8 show. In general, there are relatively large energy gaps between the s subshells and the subshells immediately below them. (Compare the 4s subshell with the 3p one in Fig. 28.7a.) The subshells just below the s subshells are usually p subshells, with the exception of the lowest subshell—the 1s subshell is below the 2s subshell. The gaps between other subshells—for example, between the 3s subshell and the 3p subshell above it, or between the 4d and 5p subshells—are considerably smaller.

This unevenness in energy differences gives rise to periodic large energy gaps, represented by vertical lines between certain subshells in the electron configuration:

$$1s^2|2s^22p^6|3s^23p^6|4s^23d^{10}4p^6|5s^24d^{10}5p^6|6s^24f^{14}5d^{10}6p^6|\ldots$$

(number of states) (2) (8) (8) (18) (18) (32)

The subshells *between* the lines have only slightly different energies. The grouping of subshells (for example, $2s^22p^6$) that have about the same energy is referred to as an **electron period**.

Electron periods are the basis of the periodic table of elements. With your present knowledge of electron configurations, you are now in a position to understand the periodic table better than the person who originally developed it.

The Periodic Table of Elements

By 1860, more than sixty chemical elements had been discovered. Several attempts had been made to classify the elements into some orderly arrangement, but none were satisfactory. It had been noted in the early 1800s that the elements could be listed in such a way that similar chemical properties recurred periodically throughout the list. With this idea, in 1869, a Russian chemist, Dmitri Mendeleev (pronounced men-duh-*lay*-eff), created an arrangement of the elements, based on this periodic property. The modern version of his **periodic table of elements** is used today and can be seen on the walls of just about every science building (▸Fig. 28.9).

Mendeleev arranged the known elements in rows, called **periods**, in order of increasing atomic mass. When he came to an element that had chemical properties similar to those of one of the previous elements, he put this element below the previous similar one. In this manner, he formed both horizontal rows of elements and vertical columns called **groups**, or families of elements with similar chemical properties. The table was later rearranged in order of increasing atomic, or proton, number (the number of protons in the nucleus of an atom is the number at the top left of each of the element boxes in Fig. 28.9) in order to resolve some inconsistencies. Notice that if atomic masses were used, cobalt and nickel, atomic numbers 27 and 28, respectively, would fall in reversed columns.

With only 65 elements known at the time, there were vacant spaces in Mendeleev's table. The elements for these spaces were yet to be discovered. Because the missing elements were part of a sequence and had properties similar to those of other elements in a group, Mendeleev could predict their masses and chemical properties. Less than 20 years after Mendeleev devised his table, which showed chemists what to look for in order to find the undiscovered elements, three of the missing elements were, in fact, discovered.

The periodic table puts the elements into seven horizontal rows, or periods. The first period has only two elements. Periods 2 and 3 each have 8 elements, and periods 4 and 5 each have 18 elements. Recall that the s, p, d, and f subshells can contain a maximum of 2, 6, 10, and 14 electrons $[2(2\ell + 1)]$, respectively. You should begin to see a correlation between these numbers and the arrangements of elements in the periodic table.

The periodicity of the periodic table can be understood in terms of the electron configurations of the atoms. For $n = 1$, the electrons are in one of two s states ($1s$); for $n = 2$, electrons can fill the $2s$ and $2p$ states, which gives a total of 10 electrons; and so on. Thus, the period number for a given element is equal to the highest n shell containing electrons in the atom. Notice the electron configurations for the elements in Fig. 28.9. Also, compare the electron periods given earlier, as defined by energy gaps, and the periods in the periodic table (▾Fig. 28.10). There is a one-to-one correlation, so the periodicity comes from energy-level considerations in atoms.

Chemists refer to *main group elements* as elements in which the last (least bound) electron enters an s or p subshell. In *transition elements*, the last electron enters a d subshell; and in *inner transition elements*, the last electron enters an f subshell. So that the periodic table is not unmanageably wide, the f subshell elements are usually placed in two rows at the bottom of the table. Each of the two rows is given a name—the *lanthanide series* and the *actinide series*—based on its position within the period.

Finally, we can also understand why elements in vertical columns, or groups, have similar chemical properties. The chemical properties of an atom, such as its ability to react and form compounds, depend almost entirely on the atom's outermost electrons—that is, those electrons in the outermost *unfilled* shell. It is these electrons, called *valence electrons*, that form chemical bonds with other atoms. Because of the way in which the elements are arranged in the table, the outermost electron configurations of all the atoms in any one group are similar. The atoms in such a group would thus be expected to have similar chemical properties, and they do. For example, notice the first two groups at the left of the table. They have one and two outermost electrons in an s subshell, respectively. These elements are all highly reactive metals that form compounds that have many similarities. The group at the far right,

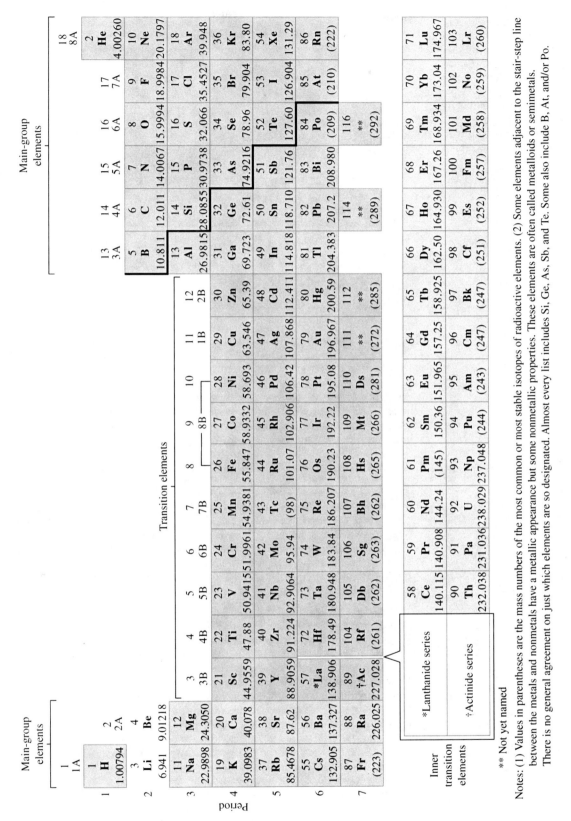

▲ **FIGURE 28.9 The periodic table of elements** The elements are arranged in order of increasing atomic, or proton, number. Horizontal rows are called *periods*, and vertical columns are called *groups*. The elements in a group have similar chemical properties. Each atomic mass represents an average of that element's isotopes, weighted to reflect their relative abundance in our immediate environment. The masses have been rounded to two decimal places; more precise values are given in Appendices IV and V. (A value in parentheses represents the mass number of the best-known or longest-lived isotope of an unstable element. See Appendix IV for an alphabetical listing of elements.

▶ **FIGURE 28.10 Electron periods**
The periods of the periodic table are related to electron configurations. The last n shell to be filled is equal to the period number. The electron periods and the corresponding periods of the table are defined by relatively large energy gaps between successive subshells (such as between 4s and 3p) of the atoms.

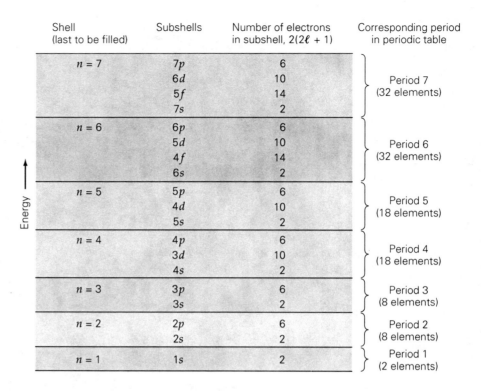

Shell (last to be filled)	Subshells	Number of electrons in subshell, $2(2\ell + 1)$	Corresponding period in periodic table
$n = 7$	7p	6	Period 7 (32 elements)
	6d	10	
	5f	14	
	7s	2	
$n = 6$	6p	6	Period 6 (32 elements)
	5d	10	
	4f	14	
	6s	2	
$n = 5$	5p	6	Period 5 (18 elements)
	4d	10	
	5s	2	
$n = 4$	4p	6	Period 4 (18 elements)
	3d	10	
	4s	2	
$n = 3$	3p	6	Period 3 (8 elements)
	3s	2	
$n = 2$	2p	6	Period 2 (8 elements)
	2s	2	
$n = 1$	1s	2	Period 1 (2 elements)

(Energy ↑)

the noble gases, includes elements with completely filled subshells (and thus a full shell). These elements are at the ends of electron periods, or just before a large energy gap. These gases are nonreactive and can form compounds (by chemical bonding) only under very special conditions.

Conceptual Example 28.4 ■ Combining Atoms: Performing Chemistry on the Periodic Table

Combinations of atoms, called *molecules*, can form if atoms come together and share outer electrons. This sharing process is called *covalent bonding*. In this "shared-custody" scheme, both atoms find it energetically beneficial (that is, they lower their combined total energies) to have the equivalent of a filled outer shell of electrons, if only on a part-time basis. Using your knowledge of electron shells and the periodic chart, determine which of the following atoms would most likely form a covalent arrangement with oxygen: (a) neon (Ne); (b) calcium (Ca); or (c) hydrogen (H).

Reasoning and Answer. Choice (a), neon, with a total of 10 electrons, can be eliminated immediately, because it has a full outer shell of 8 electrons and, as such, has nothing to be gained by losing or adding electrons. Looking at the periodic table, we see that oxygen, with 6 outer-shell electrons, is 2 electrons shy of having a full complement of 8 electrons. It *could* occasionally have those 2 electrons by sharing electrons with another atom or atoms. Choice (b), calcium, with its 20 electrons, is 2 electrons beyond the previous full shell of 10. You might think, therefore, that calcium is a possible covalent partner. However, you must remember that the covalent arrangement is a two-way street. In other words, the arrangement would also require calcium sometimes to have two *more* electrons than normal.

This situation would put the calcium atom in the awkward position of being 4 electrons beyond the full shell of 10 and 14 electrons away from the next complete shell. Hence, even though this attempt at covalent bonding might seem to work for oxygen, it certainly won't work well for calcium. The two species do, however, combine to form calcium oxide (CaO). The bonding that keeps calcium oxide together is based on the electrical attraction between the positive calcium ion, Ca^{+2}, and the negative oxygen ion, O^{-2}. In this type of bonding, the two atoms permanently exchange two electrons, making each a doubly charged ion of opposite signs. This bond is called an *ionic bond* and is *not* covalent. Thus, answer (b), calcium, is not correct.

The remaining candidate, hydrogen, has one electron fewer than a full shell of two. Thus, if a hydrogen atom could add one electron, it would attain an electron configuration like that of the lightest inert gas, helium. Since each hydrogen atom needs to share only one electron, two of them can accomplish this by sharing with a single oxygen atom. Part of the time, the hydrogen atoms must share their electrons with the oxygen atom in order to create the latter's full outer shell of eight electrons. So, the correct answer is (c)—two hydrogen atoms covalently bound to a single oxygen atom. This combination has the molecular formula H_2O—water.

Follow-Up Exercise. In this Example, (a) what would be the electron configuration of the oxygen in the water molecule at some instant when it has "custody" of the electrons from both hydrogen atoms? (b) What would be the net charge on the oxygen in this case?

29

THE NUCLEUS

PHYSICS FACTS

- Spent nuclear fuel rods from nuclear reactors are laden with radioactive nuclei. Many of these are chemically separated and used in medical and industrial applications.

- Many fission fragments are potentially harmful to living things if ingested at high levels. For example, I-131, used as a diagnostic tool for thyroid cancer, can actually cause thyroid cancer at high levels of exposure.

- The radioactive nuclide americium-241, used in most smoke detectors, is actually created artificially. None exists naturally as its half-life is only about 400 years.

- A lengthy plane flight at high altitude can expose passengers to the amount of radiation energy dosage (from cosmic rays) comparable to that of a chest X-ray.

- Of the yearly "dose" of radiation, more than half is due to natural background radiation, the rest from sources such as medical X-rays.

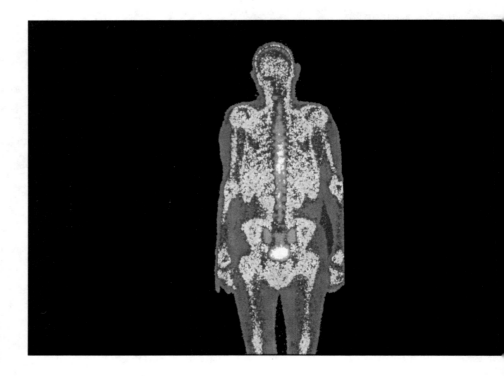

The skeletal image (a bone scan) in the chapter-opening photograph was created by radiation from a radioactive source. *Radiation* and *radioactivity* are words that sometimes produce anxiety, but the beneficial uses of radiation are often overlooked. For instance, exposure to high-energy radiation can cause cancer—yet precisely the same sort of radiation, in relatively small doses, can be useful in the diagnosis and treatment of cancer.

The bone scan in the chapter-opening photo was created by radiation released when unstable nuclei spontaneously broke apart after being administered to and taken up by the body—a process we call *radioactive decay*. But what makes some nuclei stable, while others decay? What determines the rate at which they break down and the particles that they emit? These are some of the questions that will be explored in this chapter. We'll also learn how radiation is detected and measured, as well as more about its dangers and uses.

In addition, the study of radioactivity and nuclear stability helps us understand the nature of the nucleus, its structure, its energy, and how this energy can be released. Nuclear energy is one of our major energy sources. In this chapter we concentrate on understanding the nucleus itself.

902

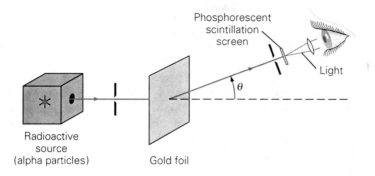

◀ **FIGURE 29.1** Rutherford's scattering experiment A beam of alpha particles from a radioactive source was scattered by gold nuclei in a thin foil, and the scattering was observed as a function of the scattering angle θ. The observer detects the light (viewed through a lens) given off by a phosphorescent scintillation screen.

29.1 Nuclear Structure and the Nuclear Force

OBJECTIVES: To (a) distinguish between the Thomson and Rutherford–Bohr models of the atom, (b) specify some of the basic properties of the strong nuclear force, and (c) understand nuclear notation.

It is evident from the emission of electrons from heated filaments (called *thermionic emission*) and the photoelectric effect that atoms contain electrons. Since an atom is normally electrically neutral, it must contain a positive charge equal in magnitude to the total charge of its electrons. Since the electron's mass is small compared with the mass of even the lightest of atoms, most of an atom's mass appears to be associated with that positive charge.

Based on these observations, J. J. Thomson (1856–1940), a British physicist who had experimentally proven the existence of the electron in 1897, proposed a model of the atom. In his model, the electrons are uniformly distributed within a continuous sphere of positive charge. It was called a "plum pudding" model, because the electrons in the positive charge are analogous to raisins in a plum pudding. The region of positive charge was assumed to have a radius on the order of 10^{-10} m, or 0.1 nm, roughly the diameter of an atom.

As you probably know, our modern model of the atom is quite different. This model concentrates all the positive charge, and practically all of the mass, in a central *nucleus*, surrounded by orbiting electrons. The existence of such a nucleus was first proposed by British physicist Ernest Rutherford (1871–1937). Combining this idea with the Bohr theory of electron orbits (Section 27.4) led to the simplistic "solar system" model, or **Rutherford–Bohr model**, of the atom.

Rutherford's insight came from the results of alpha-particle scattering experiments performed in his laboratory about 1911. An alpha (α) particle is a doubly positively charged particle ($q_\alpha = +2e$) that is naturally emitted from some radioactive materials. (See Section 29.2.) A beam of these particles was directed at a thin gold-foil "target," and the deflection angles and percentage of scattered particles were observed (▲Fig. 29.1).

An alpha particle is more than 7000 times as massive as an electron. Thus, the Thomson model predicts only tiny deflections—the result of collisions with the light electrons as an alpha particle passes through such a model of a gold atom (▶Fig. 29.2). Surprisingly, however, Rutherford observed alpha particles scattered at appreciable angles. In about 1 in every 8000 scatterings, the alpha particles were actually *backscattered*; that is, they were scattered through angles greater than 90° (▼Fig. 29.3).

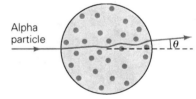

▲ **FIGURE 29.2** The plum pudding model In Thomson's plum pudding model of the atom, massive alpha particles were expected to be only slightly deflected by collisions with the electrons (blue dots) in the atom. The experimental results were quite different.

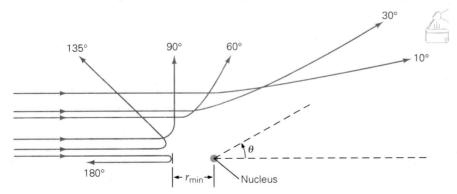

◀ **FIGURE 29.3** Rutherford scattering A compact, dense atomic nucleus with a positive charge accounts for the observed scattering. An alpha particle in a head-on collision with the nucleus would be scattered directly backward ($\theta = 180°$) after coming within a distance r_{min} of the nucleus. At this scale, the electron orbits (about the nucleus) are too far away to be seen.

Calculations showed that the probability of backscattering in the Thomson model was minuscule—certainly much, much less than 1 in 8000. As Rutherford described the backscattering, "It was almost as incredible as if you had fired a 15-inch shell at a piece of tissue paper and it came back and hit you."

The experimental results led Rutherford to the concept of a nucleus: "On consideration, I realized that this scattering backward must be the result of a single collision, and when I made calculations I saw that it was impossible to get anything of that order of magnitude unless you took a system in which the greater part of the mass of the atom was concentrated in a minute nucleus. It was then that I had the idea of an atom with a minute massive center carrying a charge."

If all of the positive charge of a target atom were concentrated in a small region, then an alpha particle coming close to this region would experience a large deflecting (electrical repulsion) force. The mass of this positive "nucleus" would be larger than that of the alpha particle, and in this model backscattering is much more likely to occur than in the plum pudding model.

A simple estimate can give an idea of the approximate size of a nucleus. It is during a head-on collision that an alpha particle comes closest to the nucleus (a distance labeled as r_{min} in Fig. 29.3). That is, the alpha particle approaching the nucleus stops at r_{min} and is accelerated back along its original path. Assuming a spherical charge distribution, the electric potential energy of the alpha particle (α) and nucleus (n) when separated by a center-to-center distance r is $U = kq_\alpha q_n/r = k(2e)(Ze)/r$ (Eq. 16.5). Here, Z is the **atomic number**, or the number of protons in the nucleus. Therefore the charge of the nucleus is $q_n = +Ze$. By conservation of energy, the kinetic energy of the incoming alpha particle is completely converted into electric potential energy at the turnaround point, r_{min}. Using $q_\alpha = +2e$, we equate the two energies, which results in

$$\tfrac{1}{2}mv^2 = \frac{k(2e)Ze}{r_{min}}$$

or, solving for r_{min}, we obtain

$$r_{min} = \frac{4kZe^2}{mv^2} \tag{29.1}$$

In Rutherford's experiment, the kinetic energy of the alpha particles from the particular source had been measured, and Z was known to be 79 for gold. Using these values, along with the constants in Eq. 29.1, Rutherford found r_{min} to be on the order of 10^{-14} m.

Although the nuclear model of the atom is useful, the nucleus is much more than a volume of positive charge. The nucleus is actually composed of two types of particles—protons and neutrons—collectively referred to as **nucleons**. The nucleus of the hydrogen atom is a single proton. Rutherford suggested that the hydrogen nucleus be named *proton* (from the Greek meaning "first") after he became convinced that no nucleus could be less massive than the hydrogen nucleus. A **neutron** is an electrically neutral particle with a mass slightly greater than that of a proton. The existence of the neutron was not experimentally verified until 1932.

The Nuclear Force

Of the forces in the nucleus, there is certainly the attractive gravitational force between nucleons. But in Chapter 15, this gravitational force was shown to be negligible compared with the repulsive electrical force between the positive protons. Taking only these repulsive forces into account, it would be predicted that the nucleus should fly apart. Yet the nuclei of many atoms are stable. Therefore, there must be an *attractive* force between nucleons that overcomes the electrical repulsion and thereby holds the nucleus together. This strong attractive force is called the **strong nuclear force**, or simply the *nuclear force*.

The exact expression for the nuclear force is extremely complex. However, some general features of it are as follows:

• The nuclear force is strongly attractive and much larger in magnitude than both the electrostatic force and the gravitational force between nucleons.

• The nuclear force is very short-ranged; that is, a nucleon interacts only with its nearest neighbors, over distances on the order of 10^{-15} m.

• The nuclear force is independent of electric charge; that is, it acts between *any* two nucleons—two protons, a proton and a neutron, or two neutrons.

Thus, nearby protons repel each other electrically, but attract each other (and nearby neutrons) by the strong force, with the latter winning the battle. Having no electric charge, neutrons only attract nearby protons and neutrons.

Nuclear Notation

To describe the nuclei of different atoms, it is convenient to use the notation illustrated in ▶Fig. 29.4a. The chemical symbol of the element is used with subscripts and a superscript. The subscript on the left is called the *atomic number* (Z), which indicates the number of protons in the nucleus. A more descriptive name for the symbol Z is **proton number**, which will be used in this book. For electrically neutral atoms, Z is equal to the number of orbital electrons. (Why?)

The number of protons in the nucleus of an atom determines the species of the atom—that is, the element to which the atom belongs. In Fig. 29.4b, the proton number $Z = 6$ indicates that the nucleus belongs to a carbon atom. The proton number thus defines which chemical symbol is used. Electrons can be removed from (or added to) an atom to form an ion, *but this does not change the atom's species*. For example, a nitrogen atom with an electron removed, N^+, is still nitrogen—a nitrogen *ion*. It is the proton number, rather than the electron number, that determines the species of atom.

The superscript to the left of the chemical symbol is called the **mass number (A)**—the total number of protons and neutrons in the nucleus. Since protons and neutrons have roughly equal masses, the mass numbers of nuclei give a relative comparison of nuclear masses. For the carbon nucleus in Fig. 29.4b, the mass number is $A = 12$, because there are six protons and six neutrons. The number of neutrons, called the **neutron number (N)**, is sometimes indicated by a subscript on the right side of the chemical symbol. However, this subscript is usually omitted, because it can be calculated from A and Z; that is, $N = A - Z$. Similarly, the proton number is routinely omitted, because the chemical symbol uniquely specifies the value of Z.

Even though the atoms of an element all have the same number of protons in their nuclei, they may have different numbers of neutrons. For example, nuclei of different carbon atoms $(Z = 6)$ may contain six, seven, or eight neutrons. In nuclear notation, these atoms would be written as $^{12}_{6}C_{6}$, $^{13}_{6}C_{7}$, and $^{14}_{6}C_{8}$, respectively. Atoms whose nuclei have the same number of protons, but different numbers of neutrons, are called **isotopes**. The three atoms we just listed are three isotopes of carbon.

Isotopes are like members of a family. They all have the same Z number and the same surname (element name), but they are distinguishable by the number of neutrons in their nuclei and, therefore by their mass. Isotopes are referred to by their mass numbers; for example, these isotopes of carbon are called *carbon-12*, *carbon-13*, and *carbon-14*, respectively. There are other isotopes of carbon that are unstable: ^{11}C, ^{15}C, and ^{16}C. A particular nuclear species or isotope of any element is also called a **nuclide**. So far, we have mentioned six nuclides of carbon. Generally, only a few isotopes of a given species are stable. But this number can vary from none to several or more. In fact, in our carbon example, ^{14}C is unstable, although it is long lived. Only ^{12}C and ^{13}C, in fact, are truly stable isotopes of carbon.

Another important family of isotopes is that of hydrogen, which has three isotopes: ^{1}H, ^{2}H, and ^{3}H. These isotopes are given special names. ^{1}H is called *ordinary hydrogen*, or simply *hydrogen*; ^{2}H is called *deuterium*. Deuterium, which is stable, is sometimes known as *heavy hydrogen*. It can combine with oxygen to form heavy water (written D_2O). The third isotope of hydrogen, ^{3}H, called *tritium*, is unstable.

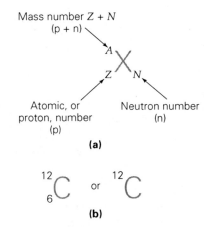

▲ **FIGURE 29.4 Nuclear notation**
(a) The composition of a nucleus is shown by the chemical symbol of the element with the mass number A (sum of protons and neutrons) as a left superscript and the proton (atomic) number Z as a left subscript. The neutron number N may be shown as a right subscript, but both Z and N are routinely omitted, because the letter symbol tells you Z, and $N = A - Z$. **(b)** The two most common nuclear notations for a nucleus of one of the stable isotopes of carbon—carbon-12.

Note: All the isotopes in one family have almost the same orbital-electron structure and thus very similar chemical properties.

29.2 Radioactivity

OBJECTIVES: To (a) define the term *radioactivity*; (b) distinguish among alpha, beta, and gamma decay; and (c) write nuclear-decay equations.

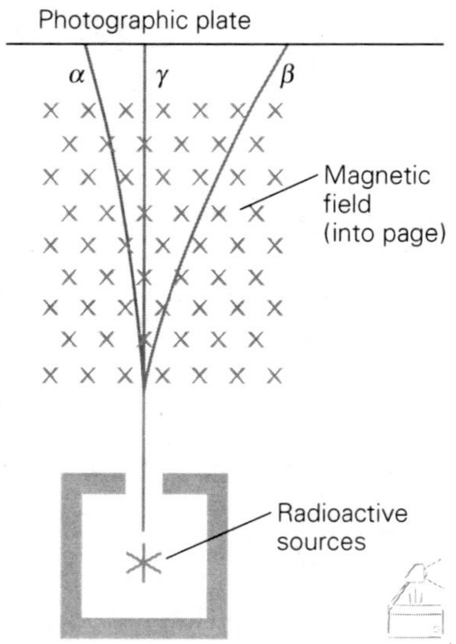

▲ FIGURE 29.5 Nuclear radiation
Different types of radiation from radioactive sources can be distinguished by passing them through a magnetic field. Alpha and beta particles are deflected. From the right-hand magnetic-force rule, alpha particles are positively charged and beta particles are negatively charged. The radii of curvature (not drawn to scale) allow the particles to be distinguished by mass. Gamma rays are not deflected and thus are uncharged; they are quanta of electromagnetic energy.

Most elements have at least one stable isotope. It is atoms with stable nuclides with which we are most familiar in the environment. However, some nuclei are unstable and disintegrate spontaneously (or decay), emitting energetic particles and photons. Unstable isotopes are said to be *radioactive* or to exhibit **radioactivity**. For example, tritium ($^3_1$H) has a radioactive nucleus. Of all the unstable nuclides, only a small number occur naturally. Others can be produced artificially (Chapter 30).

Radioactivity is unaffected by normal physical or chemical processes, such as heat, pressure, and chemical reactions. Processes such as these simply do *not* affect the source of the radioactivity—the nucleus. Nor can nuclear instability be explained by a simple imbalance of attractive and repulsive forces within the nucleus. This is because, experimentally, nuclear disintegrations (of a given isotope) occur at a fixed rate. That is, the nuclei in a given sample do not all decay at the same time. According to classical theories, identical nuclei *should* decay at the same time. Therefore, radioactive decay suggests that the probability effects of quantum mechanics might be in play.

The discovery of radioactivity is credited to the French scientist Henri Becquerel. In 1896, while studying the fluorescence of a uranium compound, he discovered that a photographic plate near a sample had been darkened, even though the compound had not been activated by exposure to light and was not fluorescing. Apparently, this darkening was caused by some new type of radiation emitted from the compound itself. In 1898, Pierre and Marie Curie announced the discovery of two radioactive elements, radium and polonium, which they had isolated from uranium pitchblende ore.

Experiment shows that the radiation emitted by radioactive isotopes is of three different kinds. When a radioactive isotope is placed in a chamber so that the emitted radiation passes through a magnetic field to a photographic plate (◄Fig. 29.5), the various types of radiation expose the plate, producing characteristic spots by which the types of radiation may be identified. The positions of the spots show that some isotopes emit radiation that is deflected to the left; some emit radiation that is deflected to the right; and some emit radiation that is undeflected. These spots are characteristic of what came to be known as *alpha, beta,* and *gamma* radiations.

From the opposite deflections of two of the types of radiation in the magnetic field, it is evident that positively charged particles are associated with alpha decay and that negatively charged particles are emitted during beta decay. Because of their much smaller deflection, alpha particles must be considerably more massive than beta particles. The undeflected gamma radiation must be electrically neutral. (Why?)

Detailed investigations of the three different radiation types revealed the following:

- **Alpha particles** are actually doubly charged ($+2e$) particles that contain two protons and two neutrons. They are identical to the nucleus of the helium atom ($^4_2$He).
- **Beta particles** are electrons (positive electrons or *positrons* were discovered later).
- **Gamma rays** are high-energy quanta of electromagnetic energy (photons).

For a few radioactive elements, two spots are found on the film, indicating that the elements decay by two different modes. Let's now look at some details of each of these three modes of decay.

Alpha Decay

When an alpha particle is ejected from a radioactive nucleus, the nucleus loses two protons and two neutrons, so the mass number (A) is decreased by four ($\Delta A = -4$). The proton number (Z) is also decreased by two ($\Delta Z = -2$). Because the *parent nucleus* (the original nucleus) loses two protons, the *daughter nucleus* (the resulting nucleus) is the nucleus of a different element, defined by the new proton number. Thus, the **alpha-decay** process is one of nuclear *transmutation*, in which the nuclei of one element change into the nuclei of a lighter element.

An example of an isotope, or nuclide, that undergoes alpha decay is polonium-214. The decay process is represented as a nuclear equation (usually written without neutron numbers):

$$\underset{polonium}{^{214}_{84}\text{Po}} \rightarrow \underset{lead}{^{210}_{82}\text{Pb}} + \underset{\substack{alpha\ particle \\ (helium\ nucleus)}}{^{4}_{2}\text{He}}$$

Notice that both the mass-number and proton-number totals are equal on each side of the equation: $(214 = 210 + 4)$ and $(84 = 82 + 2)$, respectively. This condition reflects the experimental facts that *two conservation laws apply to all nuclear processes*. The first is the **conservation of nucleons**:

| The total number of nucleons (A) remains constant in any nuclear process. |

The second is the familiar **conservation of charge**:

| The total charge remains constant in any nuclear process. |

These conservation laws allow us to predict the composition of the daughter nucleus, as the following Example illustrates.

Example 29.1 ■ Uranium's Daughter: Alpha Decay

A $^{238}_{92}\text{U}$ nucleus undergoes alpha decay. What is the resulting daughter nucleus?

Thinking It Through. Nucleon conservation allows the prediction of the daughter's proton number. From that, the element's name can be determined from the periodic table.

Solution. Since $\Delta Z = -2$ for alpha decay, the parent uranium-238 (^{238}U) nucleus loses two protons, and the daughter nucleus has a proton number $Z = 92 - 2 = 90$, which is thorium's proton number (see the periodic table, Fig. 28.9). The equation for this decay can therefore be written as

$$^{238}_{92}\text{U} \rightarrow {}^{234}_{90}\text{Th} + {}^{4}_{2}\text{He} \quad \text{or} \quad {}^{238}_{92}\text{U} \rightarrow {}^{234}_{90}\text{Th} + {}^{4}_{2}\alpha$$

where the helium nucleus is finally written as $^{4}_{2}\alpha$ (sometimes just α).

Follow-Up Exercise. Using high-energy accelerators, it is possible to *add* an alpha particle to a nucleus—essentially the reverse of the reaction in this Example. Write the equation for this nuclear reaction, and predict the identity of the resulting nucleus if an alpha particle is added to a ^{12}C nucleus. (*Answers to all Follow-Up Exercises are at the back of the text.*)

From experiments, it is found that the kinetic energies of alpha particles from radioactive sources are typically a few MeV. (See Section 16.2.) For example, the energy of the alpha particle from the decay of ^{214}Po is about 7.7 MeV, and that from ^{238}U decay is about 4.14 MeV. Alpha particles from such sources were used in the scattering experiments that led to the Rutherford nuclear model.

Outside the nucleus, the repulsive electric force increases as an alpha particle approaches the nucleus. Inside the nucleus, however, the strongly attractive nuclear force dominates. These conditions are depicted in ▸Fig. 29.6, which shows a graph of the potential energy U as a function of r, the distance from the center of the nucleus. Consider alpha particles (with kinetic energy of 7.7 MeV) from a ^{214}Po source incident on ^{238}U (Fig. 29.6). The alpha particles don't have enough kinetic energy to overcome the *electric potential-energy "barrier,"* whose height exceeds 7.7 MeV. Thus, Rutherford scattering occurs. On the other hand, we do know that the ^{238}U nucleus does undergo alpha decay, emitting an alpha particle with an energy of 4.4 MeV, which is below the height of the barrier. How can these lower-energy alpha particles cross a barrier from the inside to the outside, when higher-energy alpha particles cannot cross from outside to the inside? According to classical theory, this is impossible, since it violates the conservation of energy. However, quantum mechanics offers an explanation.

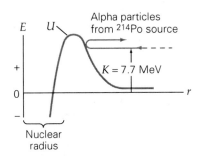

▲ **FIGURE 29.6 Potential-energy barrier for alpha particles** Alpha particles from radioactive polonium with energies of 7.7 MeV do not have enough energy to overcome the electrostatic potential-energy barrier of the ^{238}U nucleus and are scattered.

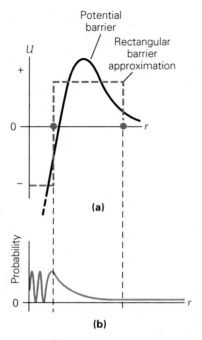

▲ FIGURE 29.7 Tunneling or barrier penetration (a) The potential-energy barrier presented by a nucleus to an alpha particle can be approximated by a rectangular barrier. **(b)** The probability of finding the alpha particle at a given location, according to quantum-mechanical calculations, is shown. If the particle is initially inside the nucleus, it has a likelihood of "tunneling" through the barrier and appearing outside the nucleus. Typically, this event has a very small, but nonzero, probability of occurring for elements above lead on the periodic table.

Note: Remember that the positron or electron emitted during β^6 decay is *not* initially present in the neutron or proton that decays. Among other things, its presence before decay would violate conservation of energy, the uncertainty principle, and conservation of angular momentum. The electron or positron is *created at the time of the decay* and does not exist before that. See Chapter 30 for further details.

Quantum mechanics predicts a nonzero probability of an alpha particle, initially inside the nucleus, to be found *outside* the nucleus (◄Fig 29.7). This phenomenon is called **tunneling**, or **barrier penetration**, since the alpha particle has a certain probability of tunneling through the barrier. (As an example, recall that electrons do this in the scanning tunneling microscope [STM], in Chapter 28.)

Beta Decay

The emission of an electron (a beta particle) in a nuclear-decay process might seem contradictory to the proton–neutron model of the nucleus. Note, however, that the electron emitted in **beta decay** is *not* part of the original nucleus. *The electron is created during the decay.* There are several types of beta decay. When a negative electron is emitted, the process is called β^- **decay**. An example of this type of beta decay is that of ^{14}C:

$$\underset{carbon}{^{14}_{6}\text{C}} \rightarrow \underset{nitrogen}{^{14}_{7}\text{N}} + \underset{\substack{beta\ particle\\(electron)}}{^{0}_{-1}\text{e}}$$

The parent nucleus (carbon-14) has six protons and eight neutrons, whereas the daughter nucleus (nitrogen) has seven protons and seven neutrons. Notice that the electron symbol has a nucleon number of zero (because the electron is not a nucleon) and a charge number of -1. Thus, both nucleon number (14) and electric charge ($+6$) are conserved.

In this type of beta decay, the neutron number of the parent nucleus decreases by one, and the proton number of the daughter nucleus increases by one. Thus, the nucleon number remains unchanged. In essence, it would appear that *a neutron within such an unstable nucleus decays into a proton and an electron (which is then emitted)*:

$$\underset{neutron}{^{1}_{0}\text{n}} \rightarrow \underset{proton}{^{1}_{1}\text{p}} + \underset{electron}{^{0}_{-1}\text{e}} \quad (basic\ \beta^-\ decay)$$

Beta decay generally happens when a nucleus is unstable because of having too many neutrons compared to protons. (See Section 29.5, which discusses nuclear stability.) The most massive stable isotope of carbon is ^{13}C, with only seven neutrons. But ^{14}C has too many neutrons for a nucleus with six protons and is unstable. Since beta decay simultaneously decreases the neutron number *and* increases the proton number, the product is more stable. In this case, the product nucleus is ^{14}N, which is stable. For completeness, we note that another elementary particle, called a *neutrino*, is emitted in beta decay. For simplicity, it will not be shown in the nuclear-decay equations here. Its important role in beta decay will be discussed more fully in Chapter 30.

There are actually two modes of beta decay, β^- and β^+, as well as a third process called *electron capture*. Whereas β^- decay involves the emission of an electron, $\boldsymbol{\beta^1}$ **decay**, or *positron decay*, involves the emission of a positron. The positron is a positive electron—the antiparticle of the electron (see Section 28.5). A positron is symbolized as $^{0}_{+1}\text{e}$. Nuclei that undergo β^+ decay have too many protons relative to the number of neutrons. The net effect of β^+ decay is to convert a proton into a neutron. As in β^- decay, this process serves to create a more stable daughter nucleus. An example of β^+ decay is the following:

$$\underset{oxygen}{^{15}_{8}\text{O}_7} \rightarrow \underset{nitrogen}{^{15}_{7}\text{N}_8} + \underset{positron}{^{0}_{+1}\text{e}}$$

Positron emission is also accompanied by a neutrino (but a different type from that associated with β^- decay), which we will also discuss in Chapter 30.

A process that competes with β^+ decay is called **electron capture** (abbreviated as **EC**). This process involves the absorption of *orbital* electrons by a nucleus. The net result is the same daughter nucleus that would have been produced by positron decay—hence describes as *competing*. That is, there is usually a certain probability that *both* can happen. A specific example of electron capture is as follows:

$$\underset{\text{orbital electron}}{_{-1}^{0}\text{e}} + \underset{\text{beryllium}}{_{4}^{7}\text{Be}} \rightarrow \underset{\text{lithium}}{_{3}^{7}\text{Li}}$$

As in β^+ decay, a proton changes into a neutron, but no beta particle is emitted in electron capture.

Gamma Decay

In **gamma decay**, the nucleus emits a gamma (γ) ray, a high-energy photon of electromagnetic energy. The emission of a gamma ray by a nucleus in an excited state is analogous to the emission of a photon by an excited atom. Most commonly, the nucleus emitting the gamma ray is a daughter nucleus left in an excited state after alpha decay, beta decay, or electron capture.

Nuclei possess energy levels analogous to those of atoms. However, nuclear energy levels are much farther apart and more complicated than those of an atom. The nuclear energy levels are typically separated by *kilo*electron-volts (keV) and *mega*electron-volts (MeV), rather than the few electron-volts (eV) that separate energy levels in atoms. As a result, gamma rays are very energetic, having energies larger than those of visible light and, thus, gamma rays have extremely short wavelengths. It is common to indicate a nucleus in an excited state with a superscript asterisk. For example, the decay of ^{61}Ni from an excited nuclear state (indicated by the asterisk) to one of lesser energy would be written as follows:

$$\underset{\substack{\text{nickel}\\(\text{excited})}}{_{28}^{61}\text{Ni}^*} \rightarrow \underset{\text{nickel}}{_{28}^{61}\text{Ni}} + \underset{\text{gamma ray}}{\gamma}$$

Note that *in gamma decay, the mass and proton numbers do not change.* The daughter nucleus is simply the parent nucleus with less energy. As an example of gamma emission following beta decay, consider the following Integrated Example.

Integrated Example 29.2 ■ Two for One: Beta Decay and Gamma Decay

Naturally occurring cesium has only one stable isotope, $^{133}_{55}$Cs. However, the unstable isotope $^{137}_{55}$Cs is a common nucleus found in used nuclear fuel rods at power plants after their original uranium fuel has become depleted. (See Chapter 30.) When $^{137}_{55}$Cs decays, its daughter nucleus is sometimes left in an excited state. After the initial decay, the daughter emits a gamma ray to produce a final stable nucleus. (a) Does $^{137}_{55}$Cs first decay by (1) β^+ decay, (2) β^- decay, or (3) electron capture? Explain. (b) Find the final daughter product by writing the chain of decay equations. Show all the steps leading to the final stable nucleus.

(a) Conceptual Reasoning. The $^{137}_{55}$Cs isotope has too many neutrons to be stable, as $^{133}_{55}$Cs, with four fewer neutrons, is stable. Choices (1) and (3) both increase the number of neutrons relative to the number of protons. Lowering the number of neutrons calls for β^- decay, so the correct choice is (2), β^- decay.

(b) Thinking It Through. Since we know that $^{137}_{55}$Cs must decay by emitting a β^- particle, its daughter (in an excited state) can be determined from charge and nucleon conservation. The final state of the daughter will result after a gamma-ray photon is emitted.

The data is as follows:

Given: Initial nucleus of $^{137}_{55}$Cs   *Find:* The decay schemes that lead to the stable nucleus

During β^- decay, the proton number increases by one; thus, the daughter will be barium ($Z = 56$). (See the periodic table, Fig. 28.9.) The decay equation should indicate that barium is left in an excited state that is ready to decay via gamma emission. (As usual in this chapter, the neutrino is omitted.) Thus, the decay equation is

$$\underset{\text{cesium}}{_{55}^{137}\text{Cs}} \rightarrow \underset{\substack{\text{barium}\\(\text{excited})}}{_{56}^{137}\text{Ba}^*} + \underset{\text{electron}}{_{-1}^{0}\text{e}}$$

(continues on next page)

This process is then quickly followed by the emission of a gamma ray from the excited barium nucleus:

$$^{137}_{55}\text{Ba*} \quad \rightarrow \quad ^{137}_{55}\text{Ba} \quad + \quad \gamma$$

barium   *barium*   *gamma ray*
(excited)

Sometimes this process is written as a combined equation to show the sequential behavior:

$$^{137}_{55}\text{Cs} \quad \rightarrow \quad ^{137}_{56}\text{Ba*} \quad + \quad ^{0}_{-1}\text{e}$$

cesium   *barium (excited)*   *electron*

$$\downarrow$$

$$^{137}_{56}\text{Ba} \quad + \quad \gamma$$

barium   *gamma ray*

Follow-Up Exercise. An unstable isotope of sodium, ^{22}Na, can be produced in nuclear reactors. The only stable isotope of sodium is ^{23}Na. ^{22}Na is known to decay by one type of beta decay. (a) Which type of beta decay is it? Explain. (b) Write down the beta-decay scheme, and predict the daughter nucleus.

Radiation Penetration

The absorption, or degree of penetration, of nuclear radiation is an important consideration in many modern applications. A familiar use of radiation is the radioisotope treatment of cancer. Radiation penetration is also important, for example, in determining the amount of nuclear shielding needed around a nuclear reactor. In our food industry, gamma radiation is now used to penetrate some foods in order to kill bacteria and thus sterilize the food. In industry, the absorption of radiation is used to monitor and control the thickness of metal and plastic sheets in fabrication processes.

The three types of radiation (alpha, beta, and gamma) are absorbed quite differently. As they move along their penetration paths, the electrically charged alpha and beta particles interact with the electrons of the atoms of a material and may ionize some of them. The charge and speed of the particle determine the rate at which it loses energy along its path (remember that ionizing an atom takes energy) and, thus, the degree of penetration. The degree of penetration also depends on properties of the material, such as its density. In general, what happens when the various particles enter a material is as follows:

• Alpha particles are doubly charged, have a relatively large mass, and move relatively slowly. Thus a few centimeters of air or a sheet of paper will usually completely stop them.

• Beta particles are much less massive and are singly charged. They can travel a few meters in air or a few millimeters in aluminum before being stopped.

• Gamma rays are uncharged and are therefore more penetrating than alpha and beta particles. A significant portion of a beam of high-energy gamma rays can penetrate a centimeter or more of a dense material, such as lead. Lead is commonly used as shielding against harmful X-rays and gamma rays. Photons can lose energy or be removed from a beam of gamma rays by a combination of Compton scattering, the photoelectric effect, and pair production (the latter occurs only for photon energies above about 1 MeV). (See Ch. 27.)

Radiation passing through matter can do considerable damage. Structural materials can become brittle and lose their strength when exposed to strong radiation, such as can happen in nuclear reactors (Chapter 30) and to space vehicles exposed to cosmic radiation. In biological tissue, the radiation damage is chiefly due to ionizations in living cells (Section 29.5). We are continually exposed to normal background radiation from radioisotopes in the environment and cosmic radiation from outer space. The energy we absorb and the damage inflicted to cells from exposure to everyday levels of such radiation is usually too low to be harmful. However, concern has been expressed about the radiation exposure of

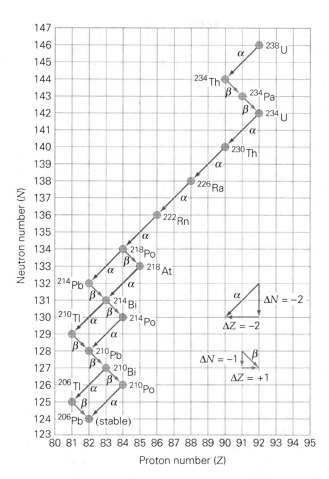

◄ **FIGURE 29.8 Decay series of uranium-238** On this plot of N versus Z, a diagonal transition from right to left is an alpha-decay process, and a diagonal transition from left to right is a β^--decay process. (How can you tell?) The decay series continues until the stable nucleus ^{206}Pb is reached.

people employed in jobs in which radiation levels may be considerably higher. For example, workers at nuclear power plants are constantly monitored for absorbed radiation and subject to strict rules that govern the amount of time for which they can work in a given period. Also, airplane flight crews who spend many hours aboard high-flying jet aircraft may receive significant exposure to radiation from cosmic rays. (Cosmic rays are discussed in more detail on page 915.)

Of the many unstable nuclides, only a small number occur naturally. Most of the radioactive nuclides found in nature are products of the decay series of heavy nuclei. There is continual radioactive decay progressing in a series into successively lighter elements. For example, the ^{238}U decay series (or "chain") is shown in ▲Fig. 29.8. It stops when the stable isotope of lead, ^{206}Pb, is reached. Note that some nuclides in the series decay by two modes and that radon (^{222}Rn) is part of this decay series. This radioactive gas has received a great deal of attention in the last few decades because it can accumulate in significant amounts in poorly ventilated buildings.

Note: See also Figs. 29.20 (^{237}Np) and 29.21 (^{239}Pu).

29.3 Decay Rate and Half-Life

OBJECTIVES: To (a) explain the concepts of activity, decay constant, and half-life of a radioactive sample; and (b) use radioactive decay to find the age of objects.

The nuclei in a sample of radioactive material do *not* decay all at once, but rather do so randomly at a rate characteristic of the particular nucleus and unaffected by external influences. It is impossible to tell exactly when a *particular* unstable nucleus will decay. What can be determined, however, is how many nuclei in a sample will decay during a given period of time.

The **activity (R)** of a sample of radioactive nuclide is defined as the number of nuclear disintegrations, or decays, per second. For a given amount of material, activity decreases with time, as fewer and fewer radioactive nuclei remain. Each nuclide has its own characteristic rate of decrease. The rate at which the number of parent nuclei (N) decreases is proportional to the number present, or $\Delta N/\Delta t \propto N$. This can be rewritten in equation form (using a constant of proportionality called λ) as follows:

$$\frac{\Delta N}{\Delta t} = -\lambda N$$

where the constant λ is called the **decay constant**. This quantity has SI units of s^{-1} (why?) and depends on the particular nuclide. The larger the decay constant λ, the greater is the rate of decay. The minus sign in the previous equation indicates that N is decreasing. The activity (R) of a radioactive sample is the magnitude of $\Delta N/\Delta t$, or the *decay rate*, expressed in decays per second, but without the minus sign (see the usage in Example 29.3):

Note: Activity = number of decays per second = $|\Delta N/\Delta t|$ and is a positive number.

$$R = \text{activity} = \left|\frac{\Delta N}{\Delta t}\right| = \lambda N \qquad (29.2)$$

Using calculus, Eq. 29.2 (with the minus sign put back in) can be solved for the number of the remaining (or undecayed) parent nuclei (N) at any time t compared with the number N_o present at $t = 0$. The result is:

$$N = N_o e^{-\lambda t} \qquad (29.3)$$

Thus the number of undecayed (parent) nuclei expressed as a fraction of the number initially present (N/N_o) decreases *exponentially* with time, as illustrated in ▼Fig. 29.9. This graph follows an exponentially decaying function $e^{-\lambda t}$. (Remember that $e \approx 2.718$ is the base of natural logarithms and should be available on your calculator.)

The decay rate of a nuclide is commonly expressed in terms of its *half-life* rather than the decay constant. The **half-life ($t_{1/2}$)** is defined as the time it takes for half of the radioactive nuclei in a sample to decay. This is the time corresponding to $N/N_o = \frac{1}{2}$ in Fig. 29.9. In the same amount of time, activity (decays per second) also is cut in half, since the activity is proportional to the number of undecayed nuclei present. Because of this proportionality, the decay rate is usually measured to determine half-life. In other words, what is usually measured is the rate at which the decay particles are emitted, and the time for that rate to drop in half.

For example, by plotting measured decay rates, ►Fig. 29.10 illustrates that the half-life of strontium-90 (^{90}Sr) can be determined to be 28 years. An alternative way to view the concept of half-life is to consider the mass of parent material. Thus, if there were initially 100 micrograms (μg) of ^{90}Sr, only 50 μg of ^{90}Sr would remain after 28 years. The other 50 μg would have decayed by the following beta-decay process:

$$\underset{\text{strontium}}{^{90}_{38}\text{Sr}} \longrightarrow \underset{\text{yttrium}}{^{90}_{39}\text{Y}} + \underset{\text{electron}}{^{0}_{-1}\text{e}}$$

► **FIGURE 29.9 Radioactive decay** The fraction of the remaining parent nuclei (N/N_o) in a radioactive sample plotted as a function of time follows an exponential-decay curve. The curve's shape and steepness depend on the decay constant λ or the half-life $t_{1/2}$.

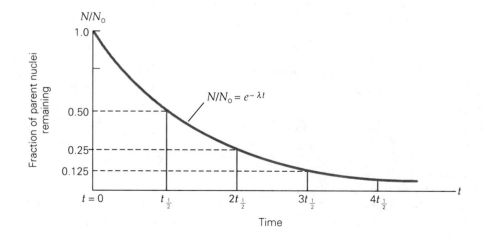

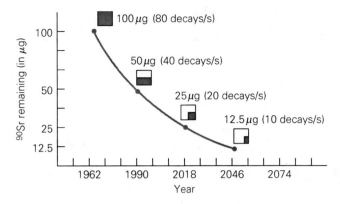

Thus, the sample would contain a mixture of both strontium and yttrium (and any decay products of yttrium). After another 28 years, half of these strontium nuclei would decay, leaving only 25 μg of ^{90}Sr, and so on.

The half-lives of radioactive nuclides vary greatly, as Table 29.1 shows. Nuclides with very short half-lives are generally created in nuclear reactions (Chapter 30). If these nuclides had existed when the Earth was formed (about 5 billion years ago), they would have long since decayed. In fact, this is the case for technetium (Tc) and promethium (Pm, not shown in Table 29.1). These elements do *not* exist naturally, as they have no stable configurations and their half-lives are short. However, they can be produced in laboratories. Conversely, the half-life of the naturally occurring ^{238}U isotope is about 4.5 billion years. This means that about half of the original ^{238}U present when the Earth was formed exists today. The longer the half-life of a nuclide, the more slowly it decays and the smaller is the decay constant λ. Thus the half-life and the decay constant have an inverse relationship, or $t_{1/2} \propto 1/\lambda$. To show the numerical relationship, consider Eq. 29.3. When $t = t_{1/2}$, then $N/N_0 = \frac{1}{2}$. Therefore,

$$\frac{N}{N_0} = \frac{1}{2} = e^{-\lambda t_{1/2}}$$

TABLE 29.1	The Half-Lives of Some Radioactive Nuclides (in Order of Increasing Half-Life)	
Nuclide	*Primary Decay Mode*	*Half-Life of Decay Mode*
Beryllium-8 ($^{8}_{4}$Be)	α	1×10^{-16} s
Polonium-213 ($^{213}_{84}$Po)	α	4×10^{-16} s
Oxygen-19 ($^{19}_{8}$O)	β^-	27 s
Fluorine-17 ($^{17}_{9}$F)	β^+, EC	66 s
Polonium-218 ($^{218}_{84}$Po)	α, β^-	3.05 min
Technetium-104 ($^{104}_{43}$Tc)	β^-	18 min
Iodine-123 ($^{123}_{53}$I)	EC	13.3 h
Krypton-76 ($^{76}_{36}$Kr)	EC	14.8 h
Magnesium-28 ($^{28}_{12}$Mg)	β^-	21 h
Radon-222 ($^{222}_{86}$Rn)	α	3.82 days
Iodine-131 ($^{131}_{53}$I)	β^-	8.0 days
Cobalt-60 ($^{60}_{27}$Co)	β^-	5.3 y
Strontium-90 ($^{90}_{38}$Sr)	β^-	28 y
Radium-226 ($^{226}_{88}$Ra)	α	1600 y
Carbon-14 ($^{14}_{6}$C)	β^-	5730 y
Plutonium-239 ($^{239}_{94}$Pu)	α	2.4×10^4 y
Uranium-238 ($^{238}_{92}$U)	α	4.5×10^9 y
Rubidium-87 ($^{87}_{37}$Rb)	β^-	4.7×10^{10} y

But because $e^{-0.693} \approx \frac{1}{2}$ (check this on your calculator), we can compare the exponents and determine (to three significant figures) the following result:

$$t_{1/2} = \frac{0.693}{\lambda} \tag{29.4}$$

The concept of half-life is important in medical applications, as is shown in Example 29.3.

Example 29.3 ■ An "Active" Thyroid: Half-Life and Activity

The half-life of iodine-131 (^{131}I), used in thyroid treatments, is 8.0 days. At a certain time, about 4.0×10^{14} iodine-131 nuclei are in a hospital patient's thyroid gland. (a) What is the ^{131}I activity in the thyroid at that time? (b) How many ^{131}I nuclei remain after 1.0 day?

Thinking It Through. (a) Equation 29.4 enables us to determine the decay constant λ from the half-life, and then use Eq. 29.2 to find the initial activity. (b) To get N, Eq. 29.3 can be used in connection with the e^x button on a calculator.

Solution. Listing the data and converting the half-life into seconds,

Given: $t_{1/2} = 8.0$ days $= 6.9 \times 10^5$ s   **Find:**   (a) R_0 (activity at $t = 0$)
$N_0 = 4.0 \times 10^{14}$ nuclei (initially)   (b) N (number of undecayed nuclei
$t = 1.0$ day   after 1.0 day)

(a) The decay constant is determined from its relationship to the half-life (Eq. 29.4) as follows:

$$\lambda = \frac{0.693}{t_{1/2}} = \frac{0.693}{6.9 \times 10^5 \text{ s}} = 1.0 \times 10^{-6} \text{ s}^{-1}$$

Using the initial number of undecayed nuclei, N_0, we find that the initial activity R_0 is

$$R_0 = \left| \frac{\Delta N}{\Delta t} \right| = \lambda N_0 = (1.0 \times 10^{-6} \text{ s}^{-1})(4.0 \times 10^{14}) = 4.0 \times 10^8 \text{ decays/s}$$

(b) With $t = 1.0$ day and $\lambda = 0.693/t_{1/2} = 0.693/8.0$ days $= 0.087$ day^{-1},

$$N = N_0 e^{-\lambda t} = (4.0 \times 10^{14} \text{ nuclei})e^{-(0.087 \text{ day}^{-1})(1.0 \text{ day})}$$
$$= (4.0 \times 10^{14} \text{ nuclei})e^{-0.087} = (4.0 \times 10^{14} \text{ nuclei})(0.917) = 3.7 \times 10^{14} \text{ nuclei}$$

The e^x-function calculator button is sometimes labeled as the inverse of the ln x function. Become familiar with it. Here we have $e^{-0.087} \approx 0.917$ to three significant figures.

Follow-Up Exercise. In this Example, suppose that the attending physician will not allow the patient to go home until the activity is $\frac{1}{64}$ of its original level. (a) How long would the patient have to remain in observation? (b) In practice, the amount of time is much shorter than your answer to part (a). Can you think of a possible biological reason(s) for this?

By the "strength" of a radioactive sample we really mean its activity R. A common unit of radioactivity is named in honor of Pierre and Marie Curie.* One **curie (Ci)** is defined as

$$1 \text{ Ci} \equiv 3.70 \times 10^{10} \text{ decays/s}$$

This definition is historical and is based on the known activity of 1.00 g of pure radium. However, the modern SI unit is the **becquerel (Bq)**, which is defined as

$$1 \text{ Bq} \equiv 1 \text{ decay/s}$$

Therefore,

$$1 \text{ Ci} = 3.70 \times 10^{10} \text{ Bq}$$

Even with the present-day emphasis on SI units, the "strengths" of radioactive sources are still commonly specified in curies. The curie is a relatively large unit, however, so the *millicurie* (mCi), the *microcurie* (μCi), and even smaller multiples such as the *nanocurie* (nCi) and *picocurie* (pCi) are used. Teaching laboratories, for

*Marie Sklodowska Curie (1867–1934) was born in Poland and studied in France, where she met and married physicist Pierre Curie (1859–1906). In 1903, Madame Curie (as she is commonly known) and Pierre shared the Nobel Prize in physics with Henri Becquerel (1852–1908) for their work on radioactivity. She was also awarded the Nobel Prize in chemistry in 1911 for the discovery of radium.

example, typically use samples with activities of one microcurie or less. The strength of a source is calculated in the following Example.

Example 29.4 ■ Declining Source Strength: Get a Half-Life!

A ^{90}Sr beta source has an initial activity of 10.0 mCi. How many decays per second will be taking place after 84.0 years?

Thinking It Through. Table 29.1 lists the half-life for the source. In this Example, we can use the fact that in each successive half-life, the activity decreases by half from what it was at the start of that interval. Thus, Eq. 29.3 need not be used, because the elapsed time is exactly three half-lives. (This approach is advisable only when the elapsed time is an integral multiple of the half-life, as it is here.)

Solution.

Given: Initial activity = 10.0 mCi   *Find:* R (activity after 84.0 years)
         $t = 84.0$ y
         $t_{1/2} = 28.0$ y (from Table 29.1)

Since 84 years is exactly three half-lives, the activity after that amount of time has elapsed will be one-eighth as great $\left(\frac{1}{2} \times \frac{1}{2} \times \frac{1}{2} = \frac{1}{8}\right)$, and the strength of the source will then be

$$R = \left|\frac{\Delta N}{\Delta t}\right| = 10.0 \text{ mCi} \times \frac{1}{8} = 1.25 \text{ mCi} = 1.25 \times 10^{-3} \text{ Ci}$$

In terms of decays per second, or becquerels, we have

$$R = \left|\frac{\Delta N}{\Delta t}\right| = (1.25 \times 10^{-3} \text{ Ci})\left(3.70 \times 10^{10}\frac{\text{decays/s}}{\text{Ci}}\right)$$
$$= 4.63 \times 10^7 \text{ decays/s} = 4.63 \times 10^7 \text{ Bq}$$

Follow-Up Exercise. For the material in this Example, suppose a radiation safety officer tells you that this sample can go into the low-level waste disposal only when its activity drops to one millionth of its initial activity. Estimate, to two significant figures, how long the sample must be kept before it can be disposed. [*Hint:* Your calculator may save some time: 2 raised to what power produces about a million?]

Radioactive Dating

Because their decay rates are constant, radioactive nuclides can be used as nuclear clocks. In the previous Example, the half-life of a radioactive nuclide was used to determine how much of the sample will exist in the future. Similarly, by using the half-life to calculate backward in time, scientists can determine the age of objects that contain known radioactive nuclides. As you might surmise, some idea of initial amount of the nuclide present must be known.

To illustrate the principle of radioactive dating, let's look at how it is done with ^{14}C, a very common method used in archeology. **Carbon-14 dating** is used on materials that were once part of living things and on the remnants of objects made from or containing such materials (such as wood, bone, leather, or parchment). The process depends on the fact that living things (including yourself) contain a known amount of radioactive ^{14}C. The concentration is very small—about one ^{14}C atom for every 7.2×10^{11} atoms of ordinary ^{12}C. Even so, the ^{14}C present in our bodies *cannot* be due to ^{14}C that was present when the Earth was formed. This is because the half-life of ^{14}C is $t_{1/2} = 5730$ yr, which is very short in comparison with the age of the Earth.

The ^{14}C nuclei that exist in living things are there because that isotope is continuously being produced in the atmosphere by cosmic rays. *Cosmic rays* are high-speed charged particles that reach us from various sources such as the Sun and nearby exploding stars called supernovae. These "rays" are actually primarily protons. When they enter our upper atmosphere they can cause reactions that produce neutrons (▸Fig. 29.11). These neutrons are then absorbed by the nuclei of the nitrogen atoms of the air, which, in turn, decay by emitting a proton (written as p or $^1_1$H) to produce ^{14}C by the reaction

$$^{14}_7\text{N} + ^1_0\text{n} \rightarrow ^{14}_6\text{C} + ^1_1\text{H}$$

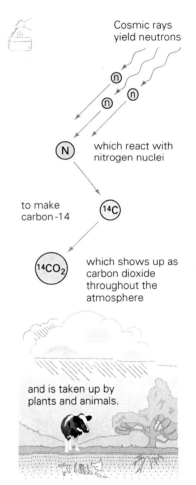

Cosmic rays yield neutrons

which react with nitrogen nuclei

to make carbon-14

which shows up as carbon dioxide throughout the atmosphere

and is taken up by plants and animals.

But when an organism dies, no fresh carbon-14 replaces the carbon-14 decaying in its tissues, and the carbon-14 radioactivity decreases by half every 5730 years.

▲ **FIGURE 29.11** Carbon-14 radioactive dating The formation of carbon-14 in the atmosphere and its entry into the biosphere.

Note: The cosmic-ray production of ^{14}C is an example of a nuclear reaction that induces a nuclear transmutation. Such reactions will be studied in more detail in Chapter 30.

^{14}C eventually decays by β^- decay ($^{14}_{6}$C $\rightarrow$ $^{14}_{7}$N $+$ $^{0}_{-1}$e), because it is neutron rich. Although the intensity of incident cosmic rays may not be exactly constant over time, the concentration of ^{14}C in the atmosphere is relatively constant, because of atmospheric mixing and the fixed decay rate.

The ^{14}C atoms are oxidized into carbon dioxide (CO_2), so a small fraction of the CO_2 molecules in the air is radioactive. Plants take in this radioactive CO_2 by photosynthesis, and animals ingest the plant material. As a result, the concentration of ^{14}C in living organic matter is the same as the concentration in the atmosphere, one part in 7.2×10^{11}. However, once an organism dies, the ^{14}C in that organism is *no longer* replenished, and thus the ^{14}C concentration decreases. *Thus, the concentration of ^{14}C in dead matter relative to that in living things can be used to establish when the organism died.* Since radioactivity is generally measured in terms of activity, the ^{14}C activity in organisms now alive must somehow be found. The following Example shows how this is done.

Example 29.5 ■ Living Organisms: Natural Carbon-14 Activity

For ^{14}C, determine the average activity R in decays per minute per gram of natural carbon, found in living organisms, if the concentration of ^{14}C in the organisms is the same as that in the atmosphere.

Thinking It Through. From the previous discussion, we know the concentration of ^{14}C relative to that of ^{12}C. To calculate the ^{14}C activity, we need the decay constant (λ), which can be computed from the half-life of ^{14}C ($t_{1/2}$ = 5730 years; see Table 29.1) and the number of ^{14}C atoms (N) per gram. Carbon has an atomic mass of 12.0, so N can be found from Avogadro's number (recall that N_A = 6.02×10^{23} atoms/mole) and the number of moles, n = N/N_A (see Section 10.3).

Solution. Listing the known ratio and the half-life from Table 29.1 (and converting the half-life into minutes), we have

Given: $\dfrac{^{14}C}{^{12}C} = \dfrac{1}{7.2 \times 10^{11}} = 1.4 \times 10^{-12}$ *Find:* Average activity R per gram

$t_{1/2}$ = (5730 years)(5.26×10^5 min/year)
$\quad\quad$ = 3.01×10^9 min

Carbon has 12.0 g per mole.

From the half-life, the decay constant is

$$\lambda = \frac{0.693}{t_{1/2}} = \frac{0.693}{3.01 \times 10^9 \text{ min}} = 2.30 \times 10^{-10} \text{ min}^{-1}$$

For 1.0 g of carbon, the number of moles is n = 1.0 g/(12 g/mol) = $\frac{1}{12}$ mol, so the number of atoms (N) is

$$N = nN_A = \left(\frac{1}{12}\text{mol}\right)(6.02 \times 10^{23} \text{ C nuclei/mol}) = 5.0 \times 10^{22} \text{ C nuclei (per gram)}$$

The number of ^{14}C nuclei per gram is given by the concentration factor

$$N\left(\frac{^{14}C}{^{12}C}\right) = (5.0 \times 10^{22} \text{ C nuclei/g})\left(1.4 \times 10^{-12} \frac{^{14}\text{C nuclei}}{\text{C nuclei}}\right) = 7.0 \times 10^{10} \text{ (}^{14}\text{C nuclei/g)}$$

The activity in decays per gram of carbon per minute (to two significant figures) is

$$\left|\frac{\Delta N}{\Delta t}\right| = \lambda N = (2.30 \times 10^{-10} \text{ min}^{-1})(7.0 \times 10^{10} \text{ }^{14}\text{C/g}) = 16 \frac{^{14}\text{C decays}}{\text{g} \cdot \text{min}}$$

Thus, if an artifact such as a bone or a piece of cloth has a current activity of 8.0 decays per gram of carbon per minute, then the original living organism would have died about one half-life, or about 5700 years, ago. This would put the date of the artifact near 3700 B.C.

Follow-Up Exercise. Suppose that your instruments could measure ^{14}C beta emissions only down to 1.0 decays/min. How far back (to two significant figures) could you estimate the ages of dead organisms?

Now consider how the activity calculated in Example 29.5 can be used to date ancient organic finds.

Example 29.6 ■ Old Bones: Carbon-14 Dating

A bone is unearthed in an archeological dig. Laboratory analysis determines that there are 20 beta emissions per minute from 10 g of carbon in the bone. What is the approximate age of the bone?

Thinking It Through. Since the initial activity of a living sample is known (Example 29.5), we can work backward to determine the amount of time elapsed.

Solution. For comparison purposes, the activity *per gram* is the relevant number.

Given: Activity = 20 decays/min in 10 g of carbon   *Find:* Age of the bone
            = 2.0 decays/g·min

Assuming that the bone had the normal concentration of ^{14}C when the organism died, the ^{14}C activity at the time of death would have been 16 decays/g·min (Example 29.5). Afterward, the decay rate would decrease by half for each half-life:

$$16 \xrightarrow{t_{1/2}} 8 \xrightarrow{t_{1/2}} 4 \xrightarrow{t_{1/2}} 2 \text{ decay/g·min}$$

So, with an observed activity of 2.0 decays/g·min, the ^{14}C in the bone has gone through approximately three half-lives. Thus, the bone is three half-lives old, or, to two significant figures,

$$\text{Age} \approx 3.0t_{1/2} = (3.0)(5730 \text{ y}) = 1.7 \times 10^4 \text{ y}$$
$$\approx 17\,000 \text{ y}$$

Follow-Up Exercise. Studies indicate that on Earth the stable isotope ^{39}K represents about 93.2% of all the potassium. A long-lived (but unstable) nuclide, ^{40}K, represents only about 0.010%. ^{40}K has a half-life of 1.28×10^9 y. (a) The remainder of the existing potassium (6.8%) is all one other isotope of potassium. What isotope is this most likely to be? (b) What would the percentage ^{40}K abundance have been when the Earth was first formed, assumed to be 4.7×10^9 years ago?

The limit of radioactive carbon dating depends on the ability to measure the very low activity in old samples. Current techniques give an age-dating limit of about 40 000–50 000 years, depending on the sample size. After about ten half-lives, the radioactivity is barely measurable (less than two decays per gram per *hour*).

Another radioactive dating process uses lead-206 (^{206}Pb) and uranium-238 (^{238}U). This dating method is used extensively in geology, because of the long half-life of ^{238}U. Lead-206 is the stable end isotope of the ^{238}U decay series. (See Fig. 29.8.) If a rock sample contains both of these isotopes, the lead is assumed to be a decay product of the uranium that was there when the rock first formed. Thus, the ratio of $^{206}Pb/^{238}U$ can be used to determine the age of the rock.

29.5 Radiation Detection, Dosage, and Applications

OBJECTIVES: To (a) gain insight into the operating principles of various nuclear-radiation detectors, (b) investigate the medical and biological effects of radiation exposure, and (c) study some of the practical uses and applications of radiation.

Detecting Radiation

Since, in general, our senses cannot detect radioactive decay directly, detection must be accomplished through indirect means. For example, people who work with radioactive materials or in nuclear reactors usually wear film badges that indicate cumulative exposure to radiation by the degree of darkening of the film when developed. If more immediate ("real time") and quantitative methods are needed to detect radiation, a variety of instruments is available.

These instruments, as a group, are known as **radiation detectors**. Fundamentally, they are all based on the ionization or excitation of atoms, a phenomenon caused by the passage of energetic particles through matter. The electrically charged alpha and beta particles transfer energy to atoms by electrical interactions, removing electrons and creating ions. Gamma-ray photons can produce ionization by the photoelectric effect and Compton scattering (Section 27.3). They may also produce electrons and positrons by pair production (Section 28.5), if their energy is large enough. Regardless of the source, the particles produced by these interactions, not the actual radiated particles, are the objects "detected" by a radiation detector.

One of the most common radiation detectors is the *Geiger counter*, developed by Hans Geiger (1882–1945), a student and then colleague of Ernest Rutherford. The principle of the Geiger counter is illustrated in ▼Fig. 29.15. A voltage of about 1000 V is applied across the wire electrode and outer electrode (a metallic tube) of the Geiger tube that contains a gas (such as argon) at low pressure. When an ionizing particle enters the tube through a thin window, the particle ionizes some gas atoms. The freed electrons are accelerated toward the positive anode. On their way, they strike and ionize other atoms. This process snowballs, and the resulting "avalanche" produces a current pulse. The pulse is amplified and sent to an electronic counter that counts the pulses, or the number of particles detected. The pulses are sometimes used to drive a loudspeaker so that particle detection is heard as a click.

► **FIGURE 29.15 The Geiger counter** Incident radiation ionizes a gas atom, freeing an electron that is, in turn, accelerated toward the central (positive) electrode. On the way, this electron produces additional electrons through ionization, resulting in a current pulse that is detected as a voltage across the external resistor *R*.

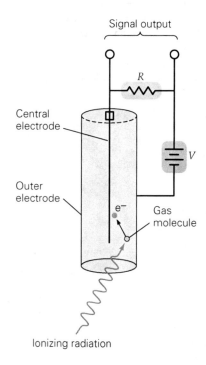

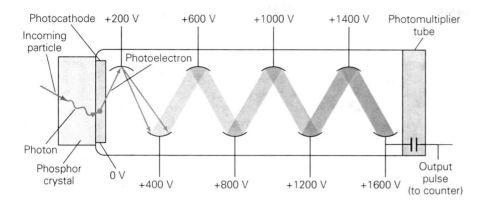

▲ **FIGURE 29.16** The scintillation counter A photon emitted by a phosphor atom excited by an incoming particle causes the emission of a photoelectron from the photocathode. Accelerated through a difference in potential in a photomultiplier tube, the photoelectrons free secondary electrons when they collide with successive electrodes at higher potentials. After several steps, a relatively weak scintillation is converted into a measurable electric pulse.

Another method of detection is the *scintillation counter* (▲Fig. 29.16). Here, the atoms of a phosphor material [such as sodium iodide (NaI)] are excited by an incident particle. A visible-light pulse is emitted when the atoms return to their ground state. The light pulse is converted to an electrical pulse by a photoelectric material. The pulse is then amplified in a *photomultiplier tube*, which consists of a series of electrodes of successively higher potential. The photoelectrons are accelerated toward the first electrode and acquire sufficient energy to cause several secondary electrons from ionization to be emitted when they strike the electrode. This process continues, and relatively weak scintillations are converted into sizable electrical pulses, which are then counted electronically.

In a *solid-state*, or *semiconductor, detector*, charged particles passing through a semiconductor material produce electrons, because of ionization. When a voltage is applied across the material, the electrons are collected as an electric current, which can be amplified and counted.

The three previous detectors determine the number of particles that interact in their material. Other different methods allow the actual trajectory, or "tracks," of charged particles to be seen and/or recorded. Among this type of detector are the cloud chamber, the bubble chamber, and the spark chamber. In the first two, vapors and liquids are supercooled and superheated, respectively, by suddenly varying the volume and pressure.

The *cloud chamber* was developed early in the 1900s by C. T. R. Wilson, a British atmospheric physicist. In the chamber, supercooled vapor condenses into droplets on the sites of ionized molecules created along the path of an energetic particle. When the chamber is illuminated, the droplets scatter the light, making the path visible (▼Fig. 29.17).

▲ **FIGURE 29.17** Cloud-chamber tracks The circular track in this photograph of a cloud chamber was made by a positron in a strong magnetic field. (Can you explain the approximately circular path of the particle in terms of the orientation of the magnetic field relative to the positron's velocity?)

The *bubble chamber*, which was invented by the American physicist D. A. Glazer in 1952, uses a similar principle. A reduction in pressure causes a liquid to be superheated and able to boil. Ions produced along the path of an energetic particle become sites for bubble formation, and a trail of bubbles is created. Since the bubble chamber uses a liquid, commonly liquid hydrogen, the density of atoms in it is much greater than in the vapor of a cloud chamber. Thus, tracks are more readily observable in bubble chambers, and hence bubble chambers have largely replaced cloud chambers.

In a *spark chamber*, the path of a charged particle is registered by a series of sparks. The charged particle passes between a pair of electrodes that have a high difference in potential and are immersed in an inert (noble) gas. The charged particle causes the ionization of gas molecules, giving rise to a visible spark (flash of light) between the electrodes as the released electrons travel to the positive electrode. A spark chamber is merely an array of such electrodes in the form of parallel plates or wires. A series of sparks, which can be photographed, then marks the particle's path.

Once the particle's trajectory is displayed, the particle's energy can be determined. Typically, a magnetic field is applied across the chamber, any charged particles are deflected, and the energy of a particle can be calculated from the radius of curvature of its path. Gamma rays, of course, will not leave visible tracks in any of these detectors. However, their presence can be detected indirectly because they are able to produce electrons by such processes as the photoelectric effect and pair production. The gamma-ray energy can be determined from the measured energy of these electrons.

Biological Effects and Medical Applications of Radiation

In medicine, nuclear radiation can be used beneficially in the diagnosis and treatment of some diseases, but it also is potentially harmful if not handled and administered properly. Nuclear radiation and X-rays can penetrate human tissue without pain or any other sensation. However, early investigators quickly learned that large doses or repeated small doses can lead to reddened skin, lesions, and other conditions. It is now known that certain types of cancers can be caused by excessive exposure to radiation.

The chief hazard of radiation is damage to living cells, due primarily to ionization. Ions, particularly complex ions or radicals produced by radiation, may be highly reactive (for example, a hydroxyl ion [OH^-] produced from water). Such reactive ions interfere with the normal chemical operations of the cell. If enough cells are damaged or killed, cell reproduction might not be fast enough, and the irradiated tissue could eventually die. In other instances, genetic damage, or mutation, may occur in a chromosome in the cell nucleus. If the affected cells are sperm or egg cells (or their precursors), any children that they produce may have various birth defects. If the damaged cells are ordinary body cells, they may become cancerous, reproducing in a rapid and uncontrolled manner and eventually becoming a malignant tumor. The human cells most susceptible to radiation damage are those of the reproductive organs, bone marrow, and lymph nodes. To begin our discussion of radiation damage and applications, let us investigate how the radiation "dose" is quantified.

Radiation Dosage   An important consideration in radiation therapy and radiation safety is the amount, or *dose*, of radiation energy absorbed. Several quantities are used to describe this amount in terms of *exposure, absorbed dose,* or *equivalent dose.* The earliest unit of dosage, the **roentgen (R)**, based on exposure and defined in terms of ionization produced in air. One roentgen is the quantity of X-rays or gamma rays required to produce an ionization charge of 2.58×10^{-4} C/kg in air.

The **rad** (radiation absorbed dose) is an *absorbed dose* unit. One rad is an absorbed dose of radiation energy of 10^{-2} J/kg of absorbing *material*. Note that the rad is based on energy absorbed from the radiation rather than simply ionization caused by the radiation in air (as the roentgen is). As such, it is more directly related to the biological damage caused by the radiation. Because of this characteristic, the rad has largely replaced the roentgen.

The rad is not an SI unit. The SI unit for absorbed dose is the **gray (Gy)**, defined as

$$1 \text{ Gy} = 1 \text{ J/kg} = 100 \text{ rad}$$

Note: The gray was named in honor of Louis Harold Gray, a British radiobiologist whose studies laid the foundation for measuring absorbed dose.

TABLE 29.4	Typical Relative Biological Effectiveness (RBE) Values of Various Types of Radiations

Type	RBE (or QF)
X-rays and gamma rays	1
Beta particles	1.2
Slow neutrons	4
Fast neutrons and protons	10
Alpha particles	20

However, the most meaningful assessment of the effects of radiation must involve measuring the *biological damage* produced, because it is well known that equal doses (in rads) of different types of radiation produce *different* effects. For example, a relatively massive alpha particle with a charge of $+2e$ moves through the tissue rather slowly, with a great deal of electrical interaction. The ionizing collisions thus occur close together along a short penetration path and are more localized. Therefore, potentially more dangerous damage is done by alpha particles than by electrons or gamma rays.

This *effective dose* is measured in terms of the **rem** (**r**ad equivalent **m**an). The various degrees of effectiveness of different particles are characterized by a factor called **relative biological effectiveness (RBE)**, or *quality factor* (QF), which has been tabulated for various particles in Table 29.4. (Note in Table 29.4 that X-rays and gamma rays have, by definition, an RBE of 1.)

The effective dose is given by the product of the dose in rads and the appropriate RBE:

$$\text{effective dose (in rems)} = \text{dose (in rads)} \times \text{RBE} \qquad (29.6)$$

Thus, 1 rem of *any* type of radiation does approximately the same amount of biological damage. For example, a 20-rem effective dose of alpha particles does the same amount of damage as a 20-rem effective dose of X-rays. However, note that to administer these doses, 20 rad of X-rays is needed, compared with only 1 rad of alpha particles.

Remember that the SI unit of *absorbed dose* is the gray. The SI unit of *effective dose* is the **sievert (Sv)**:

$$\text{effective dose (in sieverts)} = \text{dose (in grays)} \times \text{RBE} \qquad (29.7)$$

Since 1 Gy = 100 rad, it follows that 1 Sv = 100 rem.

It is difficult to set a maximum permissible radiation dosage, but the general standard for humans is an average dose of 5 rem/yr after age 18, with no more than 3 rem in any three-month period. In the United States, the normal average annual dose per capita is about 200 mrem (millirem). About 125 mrem comes from the natural background of cosmic rays and naturally occurring radioactive isotopes in soil, building materials, and so on. The remainder is chiefly from diagnostic medical applications, mostly X-rays.

Medical Treatment Using Radiation Some radioactive isotopes can be used for medical treatment, typically for cancerous conditions. Since a radioactive isotope, or a *radioisotope* as it is sometimes called, behaves chemically like a stable isotope of the element, it can participate in chemical reactions associated with normal bodily functions. One such radioisotope, used to treat thyroid cancer, is ^{131}I. Under usual conditions, the thyroid gland absorbs normal iodine. However, if ^{131}I is absorbed in a large enough dose, it can kill cancer cells. To see how a dose of radiation to the thyroid from ^{131}I can be estimated, consider Example 29.9. For a discussion of further uses of radioisotopes, see Insight 29.1 on Biological and Medical Applications of Radiation (page 923).

Example 29.9 ■ Radiation Dosage: Iodine-131 and Thyroid Cancer

One method of treating a cancerous thyroid is to administer a hefty amount of the radioactive isotope ^{131}I. The thyroid absorbs this iodine, and the iodine's gamma rays kill cells in the thyroid. (For data on ^{131}I, see Example 29.3.) (a) Write down the decay scheme of ^{131}I, and predict the identity of the daughter nucleus, which, in this case, is stable after emitting a gamma ray. (b) The charged particle (part (a) tells the type) has an average kinetic energy of 200 keV. Assume that the patient was given 0.0500 mCi of ^{131}I and that the thyroid absorbs only 25% of this. Further assume that only 40% of that 25% actually decays in the thyroid. If all of the energy carried by the charged particles is deposited in the thyroid, estimate the dose received by the thyroid (50.0 g) due to the ionization created by the charged particle radiation only. (Do not include the effect of the gamma rays.)

Thinking It Through. (a) The decay will be β^- decay, because the initial nucleus contains too many neutrons (78 neutrons compared with the 74 for stable iodine). The daughter nucleus is determined by its proton number. The daughter is left in an excited state and emits a gamma ray in order to become stable. (b) The dose depends on the energy deposited per kilogram of thyroid. Hence, we need to know how many β^- particles are emitted (and therefore absorbed). This number is determined by the initial number of ^{131}I nuclei that are actually present in the thyroid. The effective dose will depend on the RBE for β^- particles, found in Table 29.4.

Solution.

Given: 0.0500 mCi of ^{131}I ingested   *Find:* (a) the decay scheme for ^{131}I
25% of the ^{131}I makes it to the thyroid   (b) the dose (in rem) from
40% of the ^{131}I that makes it to   the emitted particles
the thyroid decays there
$\overline{K}_\beta = 200$ keV
$m = 50.0$ g $= 0.0500$ kg
RBE (see Table 29.4)

(a) Looking up the element with $Z = 54$, we find that it is xenon (Xe). The decay scheme is therefore

$$^{131}_{53}\text{I} \quad \rightarrow \quad ^{131}_{54}\text{Xe}^* \quad + \quad \beta^-$$
$$\text{iodine} \qquad \text{xenon} \qquad \text{beta}$$
$$\text{(excited)}$$
$$\downarrow$$
$$^{131}_{54}\text{Xe} \quad + \quad \gamma$$
$$\text{xenon} \qquad \text{gamma ray}$$

(b) Of the 0.0500 mCi, only 0.0125 mCi makes it to the thyroid. Of that, only 40%, or 0.00500 mCi $(5.00 \times 10^{-6}$ Ci), actually decays in the thyroid. From this information and Eq. 29.2 the number of ^{131}I nuclei that decay in the thyroid can be found. From Example 29.3, the decay constant for ^{131}I is $\lambda = 1.0 \times 10^{-6}$ s^{-1}. Thus, the number of ^{131}I nuclei, N, that decays in the thyroid is

$$N = \frac{R}{\lambda} = \frac{(5.00 \times 10^{-6}\ \text{Ci})\left(3.7 \times 10^{10}\ \dfrac{\text{nuclei/s}}{\text{Ci}}\right)}{1.0 \times 10^{-6}\ \text{s}^{-1}} = 1.85 \times 10^{11}\ ^{131}\text{I nuclei}$$

Each ^{131}I nucleus releases one β^- particle, with an average kinetic energy of 200 keV. Remembering that there is 1.60×10^{-19} J/eV, or 1.60×10^{-16} J/keV, we find that the energy, E, deposited in the thyroid is

$$E = (1.85 \times 10^{11}\ ^{131}\text{I nuclei})\left(200\ \frac{\text{keV}}{^{131}\text{I nuclei}}\right)\left(1.60 \times 10^{-16}\ \frac{\text{J}}{\text{keV}}\right)$$
$$= 5.92 \times 10^{-3}\ \text{J}$$

The absorbed dose is

$$\text{absorbed dose} = \frac{5.92 \times 10^{-3}\ \text{J}}{0.0500\ \text{kg}} = 0.118\ \frac{\text{J}}{\text{kg}}$$
$$= 0.118\ \text{Gy or } 11.8\ \text{rad}$$

The effective dose (in sieverts and rems) is this multiplied by the RBE for beta particles (1.2):

$$\text{effective dose} = (0.118\ \text{Gy})(1.2) = 0.142\ \text{Sv} = 14.2\ \text{rem}$$

Follow-Up Exercise. In this Example, determine the absorbed and effective dose from the gamma rays, assuming that 10% of the gamma rays are absorbed in the thyroid tissue and that their energy is 364 keV. Compare these results with the dose from the β^- radiation.

INSIGHT 29.1 BIOLOGICAL AND MEDICAL APPLICATIONS OF RADIATION

Radiation has always been a double-edged sword. We know of its potentially harmful side, yet sources of radiation can also provide solutions to problems. Exposure to high levels of gamma radiation is now an approved method of food sterilization in the United States. Chicken and beef are commonly sterilized this way, thus reducing the threat of *Salmonella* and *E. coli* contamination. In the aftermath of the terrorist attacks on the United States in the fall of 2001, some of this gamma-radiation technology is being retooled so that it can kill anthrax spores and other weapons based on organisms.

External radiation sources such as ^{60}Co are also used to treat cancer. ^{60}Co emits energetic gamma rays with energies of 1.17 and 1.33 MeV. Thus a sample of ^{60}Co, with its relatively long half-life, can provide an inexpensive and convenient source of penetrating radiation. Essentially, all you need is the ^{60}Co sample in a lead box with a hole to allow gamma rays to exit in one direction. One problem, however, with this "single-beam" method is that the gamma rays deposit energy in the healthy flesh both in front of and behind the targeted tumor.

An improved version of ^{60}Co treatment, called the *gamma knife,* is in use at several research hospitals (Fig. 1). Once the tumor is located, beams of gamma rays from ^{60}Co sources arranged in a ring are accurately aimed at it. Any one source is relatively weak and thus does not do too much damage outside the tumor itself. However, where the beams meet at the tumor site, a lot of energy is

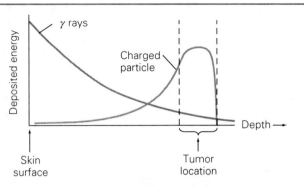

FIGURE 2 A comparison of the energy deposited for a gamma-ray beam with that of a charged particle, such as a negative pion, passing through tissue.

deposited. Thus, a large dose can be deposited at the tumor, with minimal damage to surrounding tissue. This instrument requires careful computer calculations and is still under development.

Even more exotic techniques are being tested in an effort to kill inoperable tumors. One such method is *pion therapy.* A pion is an unstable elementary particle (Chapter 30) that can be produced in accelerators by bombarding a target, such as carbon, with high-energy protons. Of medical interest are the negatively charged pions π^- (positive and neutral ones exist also). Pions of a specific kinetic energy can be selected and focused by magnetic fields onto a region of the body where a tumor exists. Unlike photons (gamma rays and X-rays), charged particles create most of their ionization "damage" at the end of their path, when they are moving slowly. By adjusting their kinetic energy, researchers can end the pion's path right at the tumor site (Fig. 2), thus causing maximum damage to the cancer cells. As a bonus, since the pions are unstable, they give off gamma rays that will do even more damage from inside the tumor (Fig. 3). Research on this technology-intensive technique is ongoing, with some success.

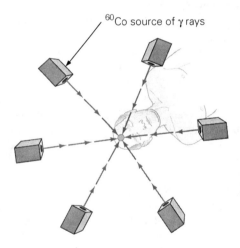

FIGURE 1 The gamma knife consists of many relatively weak beams of gamma rays (usually from ^{60}Co) that are calculated to converge on the location of an inoperable tumor. Thus, unlike in the traditional single-beam treatment, much more of the energy ends up at the tumor site, and less damage is done in front of or behind the tumor.

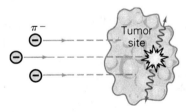

FIGURE 3 Pionic cancer therapy consists of focusing a beam of negative pions onto a tumor. Unlike energy from beams of gamma rays, most of the pion energy is deposited at the tumor site. In addition, when pions decay, gamma rays are released at the tumor, causing further destruction of cancer cells.

Medical Diagnosis Applications That Use Radiation Besides theraputic use, such as that previously described for iodine-131, radioactive isotopes can be used for diagnostic procedures. Since the radioisotope behaves chemically like a stable isotope, attaching radioisotopes to molecules enables the molecules to be used as tracers as they travel to different organs and regions of the body.

Many bodily functions can be studied by monitoring the location and activity of tracer molecules as they are absorbed during body processes. For example, the

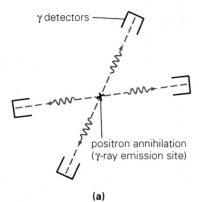

γ detectors

positron annihilation
(γ-ray emission site)

(a)

(b)

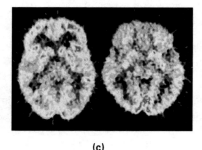

(c)

▶ **FIGURE 29.18** PET scan **(a)** and **(b)** A PET scanner can, for example, monitor brain activity after the administration of glucose-containing radioactive isotopes. Note the use of an array of detectors for the gamma radiation produced when a positron is annihilated. Any one detector pair pinpoints a line on which the source of the gamma emission was located. With many such pairs working together, the site can be determined to an accuracy of about a centimeter. **(c)** PET scans of a normal brain (left) and the brain of a schizophrenic patient (right).

activity of the thyroid gland can be determined by monitoring its iodine uptake with small amounts of radioactive iodine-123. This isotope emits gamma rays and has a half-life of 13.3 h. The uptake of radioactive iodine by a person's thyroid can be monitored by a gamma detector and compared with the function of a normal thyroid to check for abnormalities. Similarly, radioactive solutions of iodine and gold are quickly absorbed by the liver.

One of the most commonly used diagnostic tracers is technetium-99 (^{99}Tc). It has a convenient half-life of 6 h, emits gamma rays, and combines with a large variety of compounds. When injected into the bloodstream, ^{99}Tc will not be absorbed by the brain, because of the blood–brain barrier. However, tumors do not have this barrier, and brain tumors readily absorb the ^{99}Tc. These tumors then show up as gamma-ray emitting sites using detectors external to the body. Similarly, other areas of the body can be scanned and unusual activities noted and measured.

It is possible to image gamma-ray activity in a single plane, or "slice," through the body. A gamma detector is moved around the patient to measure the emission intensity from many angles. A complete image can then be constructed by using computer-assisted tomography, as in X-ray CT. This process is referred to as *single-photon emission tomography* (SPET). Another technique, *positron emission tomography* (PET), uses tracers that are positron emitters, such as ^{11}C and ^{15}O. When a positron is emitted, it is quickly annihilated, and two gamma rays are produced that travel in opposite directions. The gamma rays are recorded simultaneously by a ring of detectors surrounding the patient (◀Fig. 29.18).

In a common application, PET technology is used to detect fast-growing cancer cells. The positron emitter ^{18}F is chemically attached to glucose molecules and administered to the patient. Actively growing cells absorb glucose, but *very* active cancer cells absorb considerably more. By comparing the emissions coming from a given region on a potentially sick patient to that from a normal, healthy person, these "overactive" cancer cells can be detected. Such PET scans are now routinely done, for example, as a follow-up to chemotherapy treatment of lymphoma (cancer of the lymph system). A PET scan can detect even tiny leftover active tumors that can then be targeted for further treatment.

Domestic and Industrial Applications of Radiation

A common application of radioactivity in the home is the smoke detector. In this detector, a weak radioactive source ionizes air molecules. The freed electrons and the positive ions are collected using the voltage of a battery, thus setting up a small current in the detector circuit. If smoke enters the detector, the ions there become attached to the smoke particles, causing a reduction in the current. The drop in current is sensed electronically, which triggers an alarm (▶Fig. 29.19).

Industry also makes good use of radioactive isotopes. Radioactive tracers are used to determine flow rates in pipes, to detect leaks, and to study corrosion and wear. Also, it is possible to radioactivate certain compounds at a particular stage in a process by irradiating them with particles, generally neutrons. This technique is called **neutron activation analysis** and is an important method of identifying elements in a sample. Before the development of this procedure, the chief methods of identification were chemical and spectral analyses. In both of these methods, a fairly large amount of a sample has to be destroyed during the procedure. As a result, a sample may not be large enough for analysis, or small traces of elements in a sample may go undetected. Neutron activation analysis has the advantage over these methods on both scores. Only minute samples are needed, and the method can detect very minute trace amounts of an element.

A typical neutron activation process might start with californium-252, an unstable neutron emitter that can be produced artificially:

$$^{252}_{98}\text{Cf} \rightarrow ^{251}_{98}\text{Cf} + ^{1}_{0}\text{n}$$
(source)

These neutrons are used to bombard a sample and create characteristic gamma rays. A common target is nitrogen, consisting mostly of ^{14}N. When ^{14}N absorbs a neutron, the ^{15}N nucleus is usually created in an excited state. The excited nitrogen-15

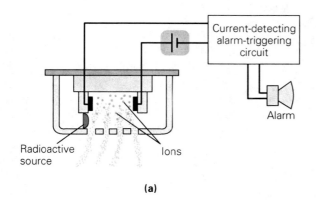

(a)

(b)

◄ FIGURE 29.19 Smoke detector **(a)** A weak radioactive source ionizes the air and sets up a small current. Smoke particles that enter the detector attach to some of the ionized electrons, thereby reducing the current, causing an alarm to sound. **(b)** Inside a real smoke detector, the ionization chamber is the aluminum "can" containing the americium-241. The slots allow airflow, and the can acts as one of the charged plates. Inside is a ceramic holder that contains the oppositely charged plate. Under that plate is the americium-241 source. Even though the activity of the source is small, caution should be taken never to touch the source if the detector is opened like this.

nucleus decays with the emission of a gamma ray with a distinctive energy. This reaction is shown as follows:

$$\ce{^{1}_{0}n} + \ce{^{14}_{7}N} \rightarrow \ce{^{15}_{7}N^*} \rightarrow \ce{^{15}_{7}N} + \gamma$$

(excited nucleus)   (gamma ray)

When an energy-sensitive gamma-ray detector is placed to the side of the sample, the presence of nitrogen can be determined.

Nitrogen activation is commonly used as an important antiterrorist tool at airports. Virtually all explosives contain nitrogen. Thus, by using neutron activation and analyzing the energy of any gamma-ray emission coming from a suitcase, we can check for an explosive device in the suitcase. Other materials in the suitcase may contain nitrogen too, so manual checks are made to confirm any suspicious findings.

Recently, the U.S. government has given permission for the use of gamma radiation in the processing of poultry. The radiation kills bacteria, helps preserve the food, and in no way makes the food radioactive. There are, however, continuing concerns with this process from food health professionals. Even though the gamma-ray emission cannot make the meat radioactive, it *can* change some of the *chemical* bonding through ionization effects. This possibility has prompted enough concerns about whether this process can affect the chemical structure of the meat—making it unsafe to eat—to warrant further study.

Chemistry

CHAPTER 1

INTRODUCTION: MATTER AND MEASUREMENT

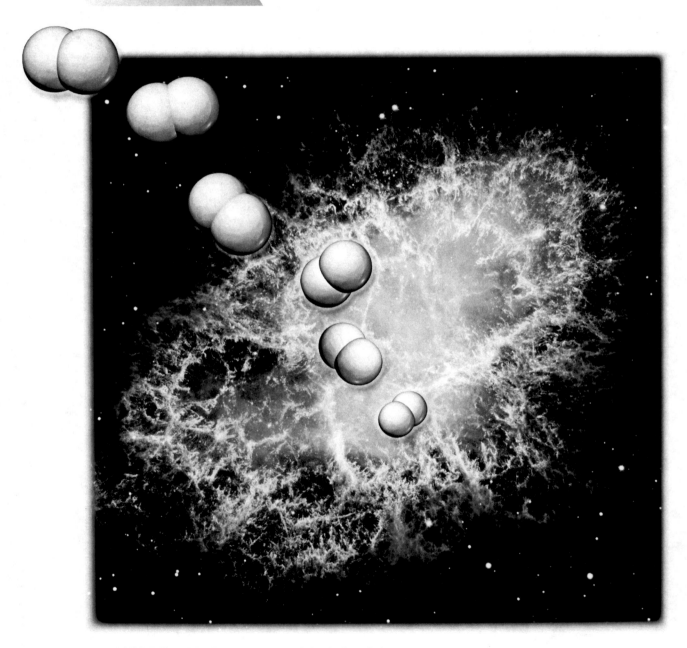

HUBBLE SPACE TELESCOPE IMAGE of the Crab Nebula, a 6-light-year-wide expanding remnant of a star's supernova explosion. The orange filaments are the tattered remains of the star and consist mostly of hydrogen, the simplest and most plentiful element in the universe. Hydrogen occurs as molecules in cool regions, as atoms in hotter regions, and as ions in the hottest regions. The processes that occur within stars are responsible for creating other chemical elements from hydrogen.

Science Fundamentals

HAVE YOU EVER WONDERED why ice melts and water evaporates? Why do leaves turn colors in the fall, and how does a battery generate electricity? Why does keeping foods cold slow their spoilage, and how do our bodies use food to maintain life?

Chemistry answers these questions and countless others like them. **Chemistry** is the study of materials and the changes that materials undergo. One of the joys of learning chemistry is seeing how chemical principles operate in all aspects of our lives, from everyday activities like lighting a match to more far-reaching matters like the development of drugs to cure cancer. Chemical principles also operate in the far reaches of our galaxy (chapter-opening photo) as well as within and around us.

This first chapter lays a foundation for our study of chemistry by providing an overview of what chemistry is about and dealing with some fundamental concepts of matter and scientific measurements. The list above, entitled "What's Ahead," gives a brief overview of the organization of this chapter and some of the ideas that we will consider. As you study, keep in mind that the chemical facts and concepts you are asked to learn are not ends in themselves; they are tools to help you better understand the world around you.

1

1.1 THE STUDY OF CHEMISTRY

Before traveling to an unfamiliar city, you might look at a map to get some sense of where you are heading. Because chemistry may be unfamiliar to you, it's useful to get a general idea of what lies ahead before you embark on your journey. In fact, you might even ask why you are taking the trip.

The Atomic and Molecular Perspective of Chemistry

Chemistry is the study of the properties and behavior of matter. **Matter** is the physical material of the universe; it is anything that has mass and occupies space. A **property** is any characteristic that allows us to recognize a particular type of matter and to distinguish it from other types. This book, your body, the clothes you are wearing, and the air you are breathing are all samples of matter. Not all forms of matter are so common or so familiar. Countless experiments have shown that the tremendous variety of matter in our world is due to combinations of only about 100 very basic, or elementary, substances called **elements**. As we proceed through this text, we will seek to relate the properties of matter to its composition, that is, to the particular elements it contains.

Chemistry also provides a background to understanding the properties of matter in terms of **atoms**, the almost infinitesimally small building blocks of matter. Each element is composed of a unique kind of atom. We will see that the properties of matter relate to both the kinds of atoms the matter contains (*composition*) and to the arrangements of these atoms (*structure*).

Atoms can combine to form **molecules** in which two or more atoms are joined together in specific shapes. Throughout this text you will see molecules represented using colored spheres to show how their component atoms connect to each other (Figure 1.1 ▼). The color provides a convenient and easy way to distinguish between the atoms of different elements. For examples, compare the molecules of ethanol and ethylene glycol in Figure 1.1. Notice that these molecules have different compositions and structures. Ethanol contains only one oxygen atom, which is depicted by one red sphere. In contrast, ethylene glycol has two atoms of oxygen.

Even apparently minor differences in the composition or structure of molecules can cause profound differences in their properties. Ethanol, also called grain alcohol, is the alcohol in beverages such as beer and wine. Ethylene glycol, on the other hand, is a viscous liquid used as automobile antifreeze. The properties of these two substances differ in many ways, including the temperatures at which they freeze and boil. The biological activities of the two molecules are also quite different. Ethanol is consumed throughout the world, but you should *never* consume ethylene glycol because it is highly toxic. One of the challenges that chemists undertake is to alter the composition or structure of molecules in a controlled way, creating new substances with different properties.

Every change in the observable world—from boiling water to the changes that occur as our bodies combat invading viruses—has its basis in the world of atoms and molecules. Thus, as we proceed with our study of chemistry, we will find ourselves thinking in two realms: the *macroscopic* realm

▼ Figure 1.1 **Molecular models.** The white, dark gray, and red spheres represent atoms of hydrogen, carbon, and oxygen, respectively.

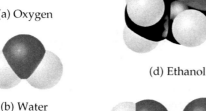

(a) Oxygen

(b) Water

(c) Carbon dioxide

(d) Ethanol

(e) Ethylene glycol

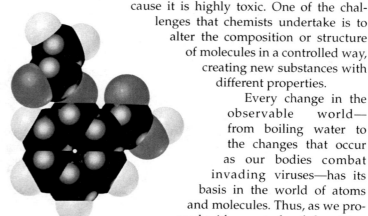

(f) Aspirin

of ordinary-sized objects (*macro* = large) and the *submicroscopic* realm of atoms and molecules. We make our observations in the macroscopic world—in the laboratory and in our everyday surroundings. To understand that world, however, we must visualize how atoms and molecules behave at the submicroscopic level. Chemistry is the science that seeks to understand the properties and behavior of matter by studying the properties and behavior of atoms and molecules.

⚠ GIVE IT SOME THOUGHT

(a) In round numbers, about how many elements are there? **(b)** What submicroscopic particles are the building blocks of matter?

Why Study Chemistry?

Chemistry provides important understanding of our world and how it works. It is an extremely practical science that greatly impacts our daily lives. Indeed, chemistry lies near the heart of many matters of public concern: improvement of health care; conservation of natural resources; protection of the environment; and provision of our everyday needs for food, clothing, and shelter. Using chemistry, we have discovered pharmaceutical chemicals that enhance our health and prolong our lives. We have increased food production through the use of fertilizers and pesticides, and we have developed plastics and other materials that are used in almost every facet of our lives. Unfortunately, some chemicals also have the potential to harm our health or the environment. As educated citizens and consumers, it is in our best interest to understand the profound effects, both positive and negative, that chemicals have on our lives and to strike an informed balance about their uses.

Most of you are studying chemistry, however, not merely to satisfy your curiosity or to become more informed consumers or citizens, but because it is an essential part of your curriculum. Your major might be biology, engineering, pharmacy, agriculture, geology, or some other field. Why do so many diverse subjects share an essential tie to chemistry? The answer is that chemistry, by its very nature, is the *central science*, central to a fundamental understanding of other sciences and technologies. For example, our interactions with the material world raise basic questions about the materials around us. What are their compositions and properties? How do they interact with us and our environment? How, why, and when do they undergo change? These questions are important whether the material is part of high-tech computer chips, a pigment used by a Renaissance painter, or the DNA that transmits genetic information in our bodies (Figure 1.2 ▼).

By studying chemistry, you will learn to use the powerful language and ideas that have evolved to describe and enhance our understanding of matter. The language of chemistry is a universal scientific language that is widely used

▼ Figure 1.2 **Chemistry helps us better understand materials.** (a) A microscopic view of an EPROM (Erasable Programmable Read-Only Memory) silicon microchip. (b) A Renaissance painting, *Young Girl Reading*, by Vittore Carpaccio (1472–1526). (c) A long strand of DNA that has spilled out of the damaged cell wall of a bacterium.

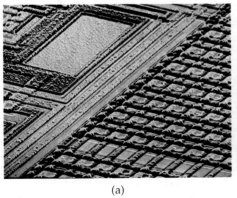

(a)   (b)   (c)

Chemistry Put to Work CHEMISTRY AND THE CHEMICAL INDUSTRY

Many people are familiar with common household chemicals such as those shown in Figure 1.3▶, but few realize the size and importance of the chemical industry. Worldwide sales of chemicals and related products manufactured in the United States total approximately $550 billion annually. The chemical industry employs more than 10% of all scientists and engineers and is a major contributor to the US economy.

Vast amounts of chemicals are produced each year and serve as raw materials for a variety of uses, including the manufacture of metals, plastics, fertilizers, pharmaceuticals, fuels, paints, adhesives, pesticides, synthetic fibers, microprocessor chips, and numerous other products. Table 1.1▼ lists the top eight chemicals produced in the United States. We will discuss many of these substances and their uses as the course progresses.

People who have degrees in chemistry hold a variety of positions in industry, government, and academia. Those who work in the chemical industry find positions as laboratory chemists, carrying out experiments to develop new products (research and development), analyzing materials (quality control), or assisting customers in using products (sales and service). Those with more experience or training may work as managers or company directors. A chemistry degree also can prepare you for alternate careers in teaching, medicine, biomedical research, information science, environmental work, technical sales, work with government regulatory agencies, and patent law.

▲ Figure 1.3 **Household chemicals.** Many common supermarket products have very simple chemical compositions.

Rank	Chemical	Formula	2006 Production (billions of pounds)	Principal End Uses
1	Sulfuric acid	H_2SO_4	79	Fertilizers, chemical manufacturing
2	Ethylene	C_2H_4	55	Plastics, antifreeze
3	Lime	CaO	45	Paper, cement, steel
4	Propylene	C_3H_6	35	Plastics
5	Phosphoric acid	H_3PO_4	24	Fertilizers
6	Ammonia	NH_3	23	Fertilizers
7	Chlorine	Cl_2	23	Bleaches, plastics, water purification
8	Sodium hydroxide	NaOH	18	Aluminum production, soap

TABLE 1.1 ■ The Top Eight Chemicals Produced by the Chemical Industry in 2006[a]

[a]Most data from *Chemical and Engineering News*, July 2, 2007, pp. 57, 60.

in other disciplines. Furthermore, an understanding of the behavior of atoms and molecules provides powerful insights into other areas of modern science, technology, and engineering.

1.2 CLASSIFICATIONS OF MATTER

Let's begin our study of chemistry by examining some fundamental ways in which matter is classified and described. Two principal ways of classifying matter are according to its physical state (as a gas, liquid, or solid) and according to its composition (as an element, compound, or mixture).

States of Matter

A sample of matter can be a gas, a liquid, or a solid. These three forms of matter are called the **states of matter**. The states of matter differ in some of their simple observable properties. A **gas** (also known as *vapor*) has no fixed volume or shape; rather, it conforms to the volume and shape of its container. A gas can be compressed to occupy a smaller volume, or it can expand to occupy a larger one. A **liquid** has a distinct volume independent of its container but has no specific shape. A liquid assumes the shape of the portion of the container that it occupies. A **solid** has both a definite shape and a definite volume. Neither liquids nor solids can be compressed to any appreciable extent.

The properties of the states of matter can be understood on the molecular level (Figure 1.4▶). In a gas the molecules are far apart and are moving at high speeds, colliding repeatedly with each other and with the walls of the container. Compressing a gas decreases the amount of space between molecules, increases the frequency of collisions between molecules, but does not alter the size or shape of the molecules. In a liquid the molecules are packed closely together but still move rapidly. The rapid movement allows the molecules to slide over each other; thus, a liquid pours easily. In a solid the molecules are held tightly together, usually in definite arrangements in which the molecules can wiggle only slightly in their otherwise fixed positions.

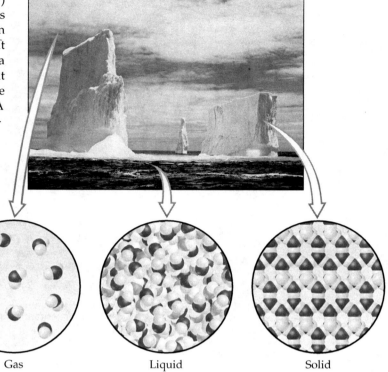

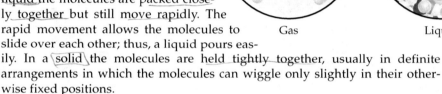

Gas   Liquid   Solid

▲ Figure 1.4 **The three physical states of water—water vapor, liquid water, and ice.** In this photo we see both the liquid and solid states of water. We cannot see water vapor. What we see when we look at steam or clouds is tiny droplets of liquid water dispersed in the atmosphere. The molecular views show that the molecules in the gas are much further apart than those in the liquid or solid. The molecules in the liquid do not have the orderly arrangement seen in the solid.

Pure Substances

Most forms of matter that we encounter—for example, the air we breathe (a gas), gasoline for cars (a liquid), and the sidewalk on which we walk (a solid)—are not chemically pure. We can, however, resolve, or separate, these forms of matter into different pure substances. A **pure substance** (usually referred to simply as a *substance*) is matter that has distinct properties and a composition that does not vary from sample to sample. Water and ordinary table salt (sodium chloride), the primary components of seawater, are examples of pure substances.   NaCl

All substances are either elements or compounds. **Elements** cannot be decomposed into simpler substances. On the molecular level, each element is composed of only one kind of atom [Figure 1.5(a and b)▼]. **Compounds** are

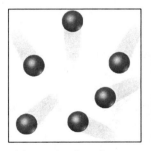

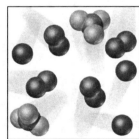

(a) Atoms of an element

(b) Molecules of an element

(c) Molecules of a compound

(d) Mixture of elements and a compound

▲ Figure 1.5 **Molecular comparison of element, compounds, and mixtures.** Each element contains a unique kind of atom. Elements might consist of individual atoms, as in (a), or molecules, as in (b). Compounds contain two or more different atoms chemically joined together, as in (c). A mixture contains the individual units of its components, shown in (d) as both atoms and molecules.

▶ Figure 1.6 **Relative abundances of elements.** Elements in percent by mass in (a) Earth's crust (including oceans and atmosphere) and (b) the human body.

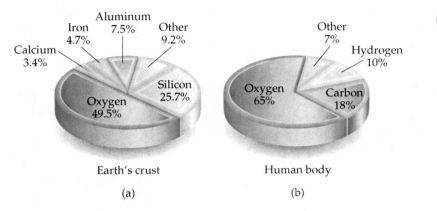

Earth's crust

(a)

Human body

(b)

substances composed of two or more elements; they contain two or more kinds of atoms [Figure 1.5(c)]. Water, for example, is a compound composed of two elements: hydrogen and oxygen. Figure 1.5(d) shows a mixture of substances. **Mixtures** are combinations of two or more substances in which each substance retains its own chemical identity.

Elements

Currently, 117 elements are known. These elements vary widely in their abundance, as shown in Figure 1.6▲. For example, only five elements—oxygen, silicon, aluminum, iron, and calcium—account for over 90% of Earth's crust (including oceans and atmosphere). Similarly, just three elements—oxygen, carbon, and hydrogen—account for over 90% of the mass of the human body.

Some of the more common elements are listed in Table 1.2▼, along with the chemical abbreviations, or chemical *symbols*, used to denote them. The symbol for each element consists of one or two letters, with the first letter capitalized. These symbols are mostly derived from the English name for the element, but sometimes they are derived from a foreign name instead (last column in Table 1.2). You will need to know these symbols and learn others as we encounter them in the text.

All the known elements and their symbols are listed on the front inside cover of this text. The table in which the symbol for each element is enclosed in a box is called the *periodic table*. In the periodic table the elements are arranged in vertical columns so that closely related elements are grouped together. We describe the periodic table in more detail in Section 2.5.

 GIVE IT SOME THOUGHT

Which element is most abundant in both Earth's crust and in the human body? What is the symbol for this element?

Compounds

Most elements can interact with other elements to form compounds. For example, consider the fact that when hydrogen gas burns in oxygen gas, the

TABLE 1.2 ■ Some Common Elements and Their Symbols					
Carbon	C	Aluminum	Al	Copper	Cu (from *cuprum*)
Fluorine	F	Bromine	Br	Iron	Fe (from *ferrum*)
Hydrogen	H	Calcium	Ca	Lead	Pb (from *plumbum*)
Iodine	I	Chlorine	Cl	Mercury	Hg (from *hydrargyrum*)
Nitrogen	N	Helium	He	Potassium	K (from *kalium*)
Oxygen	O	Lithium	Li	Silver	Ag (from *argentum*)
Phosphorus	P	Magnesium	Mg	Sodium	Na (from *natrium*)
Sulfur	S	Silicon	Si	Tin	Sn (from *stannum*)

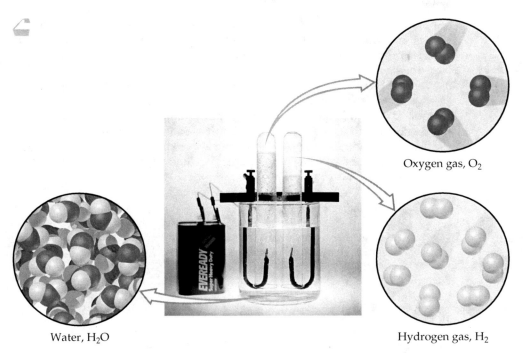

Oxygen gas, O$_2$

Water, H$_2$O

Hydrogen gas, H$_2$

▲ Figure 1.7 **Electrolysis of water.** Water decomposes into its component elements, hydrogen and oxygen, when a direct electrical current is passed through it. The volume of hydrogen, which is collected in the right tube of the apparatus, is twice the volume of oxygen, which is collected in the left tube.

elements hydrogen and oxygen combine to form the compound water. Conversely, water can be decomposed into its component elements by passing an electrical current through it, as shown in Figure 1.7▲. Pure water, regardless of its source, consists of 11% hydrogen and 89% oxygen by mass. This macroscopic composition corresponds to the molecular composition, which consists of two hydrogen atoms combined with one oxygen atom:

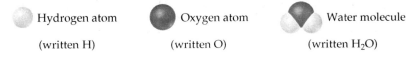

Hydrogen atom   Oxygen atom   Water molecule

(written H)   (written O)   (written H$_2$O)

The elements hydrogen and oxygen themselves exist naturally as diatomic (two-atom) molecules:

Oxygen molecule   (written O$_2$)

Hydrogen molecule   (written H$_2$)

As seen in Table 1.3▼, the properties of water bear no resemblance to the properties of its component elements. Hydrogen, oxygen, and water are each a unique substance, a consequence of the uniqueness of their respective molecules.

TABLE 1.3 ■ Comparison of Water, Hydrogen, and Oxygen			
	Water	**Hydrogen**	**Oxygen**
State[a]	Liquid	Gas	Gas
Normal boiling point	100 °C	−253 °C	−183 °C
Density[a]	1000 g/L	0.084 g/L	1.33 g/L
Flammable	No	Yes	No

[a]At room temperature and atmospheric pressure. (See Section 10.2.)

The observation that the elemental composition of a pure compound is always the same is known as the **law of constant composition** (or the **law of definite proportions**). French chemist Joseph Louis Proust (1754–1826) first put forth the law in about 1800. Although this law has been known for 200 years, the general belief persists among some people that a fundamental difference exists between compounds prepared in the laboratory and the corresponding compounds found in nature. However, a pure compound has the same composition and properties regardless of its source. Both chemists and nature must use the same elements and operate under the same natural laws. When two materials differ in composition and properties, we know that they are composed of different compounds or that they differ in purity.

GIVE IT SOME THOUGHT

Hydrogen, oxygen, and water are all composed of molecules. What is it about a molecule of water that makes it a compound, whereas hydrogen and oxygen are elements?

Mixtures

Most of the matter we encounter consists of mixtures of different substances. Each substance in a mixture retains its own chemical identity and its own properties. In contrast to a pure substance that has a fixed composition, the composition of a mixture can vary. A cup of sweetened coffee, for example, can contain either a little sugar or a lot. The substances making up a mixture (such as sugar and water) are called *components* of the mixture.

Some mixtures do not have the same composition, properties, and appearance throughout. Both rocks and wood, for example, vary in texture and appearance throughout any typical sample. Such mixtures are *heterogeneous* [Figure 1.8(a) ▼]. Mixtures that are uniform throughout are *homogeneous*. Air is a homogeneous mixture of the gaseous substances nitrogen, oxygen, and smaller amounts of other substances. The nitrogen in air has all the properties that pure nitrogen does because both the pure substance and the mixture contain the same nitrogen molecules. Salt, sugar, and many other substances dissolve in water to form homogeneous mixtures [Figure 1.8(b)]. Homogeneous mixtures are also called **solutions**. Although the term solution conjures an image of a liquid in a beaker or flask, solutions can be solids, liquids, or gases. Figure 1.9 ▶ summarizes the classification of matter into elements, compounds, and mixtures.

▶ Figure 1.8 **Mixtures.** (a) Many common materials, including rocks, are heterogeneous. This close-up photo is of malachite, a copper mineral.
(b) Homogeneous mixtures are called solutions. Many substances, including the blue solid shown in this photo (copper sulfate), dissolve in water to form solutions.

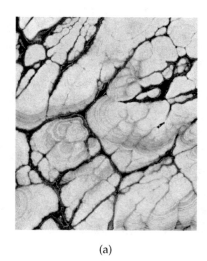

(a)   (b)

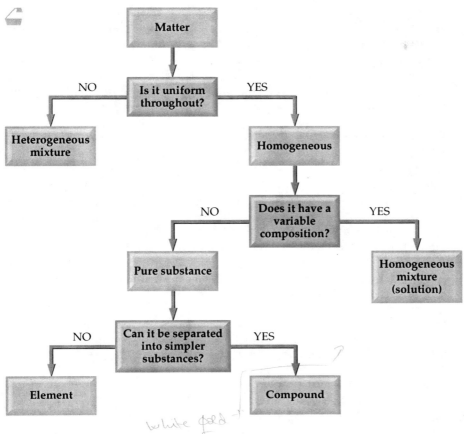

◀ Figure 1.9 **Classification of matter.** At the chemical level all matter is classified ultimately as either elements or compounds.

(handwritten annotations) white gold →

(handwritten annotations) white gold ⌈gold⌉ differ (weight)
⌊white⌋
uniform in composition

■ **SAMPLE EXERCISE 1.1** | Distinguishing Among Elements, Compounds, and Mixtures

"White gold," used in jewelry, contains gold and another "white" metal such as palladium. Two different samples of white gold differ in the relative amounts of gold and palladium that they contain. Both samples are uniform in composition throughout. Without knowing any more about the materials, use Figure 1.9 to classify white gold.

SOLUTION

Because the material is uniform throughout, it is homogeneous. Because its composition differs for the two samples, it cannot be a compound. Instead, it must be a homogeneous mixture.

■ **PRACTICE EXERCISE**

Aspirin is composed of 60.0% carbon, 4.5% hydrogen, and 35.5% oxygen by mass, regardless of its source. Use Figure 1.9 to characterize and classify aspirin.
Answer: It is a compound because it has constant composition and can be separated into several elements.

1.3 PROPERTIES OF MATTER

Every substance has a unique set of properties. For example, the properties listed in Table 1.3 allow us to distinguish hydrogen, oxygen, and water from one another. The properties of matter can be categorized as physical or chemical. **Physical properties** can be observed without changing the identity and composition of the substance. These properties include color, odor, density, melting point, boiling point, and hardness. **Chemical properties** describe the way a substance may change, or *react,* to form other substances. A common chemical property is flammability, the ability of a substance to burn in the presence of oxygen.

Some properties, such as temperature, melting point, and density, are called **intensive properties**. They do not depend on the amount of the sample being examined and are particularly useful in chemistry because many of these properties can be used to *identify* substances. **Extensive properties** of substances depend on the quantity of the sample, with two examples being mass and volume. Extensive properties relate to the *amount* of substance present.

Physical and Chemical Changes

As with the properties of a substance, the changes that substances undergo can be classified as either physical or chemical. During a **physical change** a substance changes its physical appearance but not its composition. (That is, it is the same substance before and after the change.) The evaporation of water is a physical change. When water evaporates, it changes from the liquid state to the gas state, but it is still composed of water molecules, as depicted earlier in Figure 1.4. All **changes of state** (for example, from liquid to gas or from liquid to solid) are physical changes.

In a **chemical change** (also called a **chemical reaction**) a substance is transformed into a chemically different substance. When hydrogen burns in air, for example, it undergoes a chemical change because it combines with oxygen to form water. The molecular-level view of this process is depicted in Figure 1.10▼.

Chemical changes can be dramatic. In the account that follows, Ira Remsen, author of a popular chemistry text published in 1901, describes his first

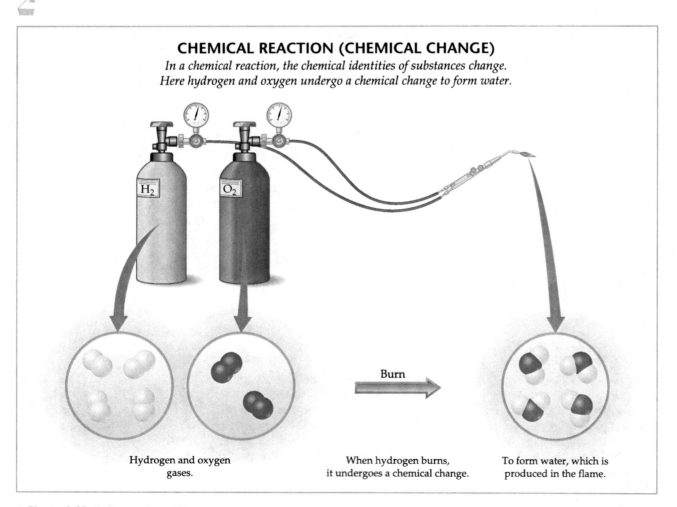

CHEMICAL REACTION (CHEMICAL CHANGE)
In a chemical reaction, the chemical identities of substances change.
Here hydrogen and oxygen undergo a chemical change to form water.

Burn

Hydrogen and oxygen gases.

When hydrogen burns, it undergoes a chemical change.

To form water, which is produced in the flame.

▲ Figure 1.10 **A chemical reaction.**

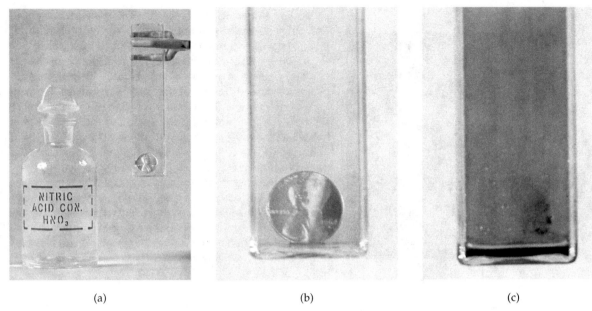

(a)   (b)   (c)

▲ Figure 1.11 **The chemical reaction between a copper penny and nitric acid.** The dissolved copper produces the blue-green solution; the reddish brown gas produced is nitrogen dioxide.

experiences with chemical reactions. The chemical reaction that he observed is shown in Figure 1.11 ▲.

> While reading a textbook of chemistry, I came upon the statement "nitric acid acts upon copper," and I determined to see what this meant. Having located some nitric acid, I had only to learn what the words "act upon" meant. In the interest of knowledge I was even willing to sacrifice one of the few copper cents then in my possession. I put one of them on the table, opened a bottle labeled "nitric acid," poured some of the liquid on the copper, and prepared to make an observation. But what was this wonderful thing which I beheld? The cent was already changed, and it was no small change either. A greenish-blue liquid foamed and fumed over the cent and over the table. The air became colored dark red. How could I stop this? I tried by picking the cent up and throwing it out the window. I learned another fact: nitric acid acts upon fingers. The pain led to another unpremeditated experiment. I drew my fingers across my trousers and discovered nitric acid acts upon trousers. That was the most impressive experiment I have ever performed. I tell of it even now with interest. It was a revelation to me. Plainly the only way to learn about such remarkable kinds of action is to see the results, to experiment, to work in the laboratory.

▲ GIVE IT SOME THOUGHT

Which of the following is a physical change, and which is a chemical change? Explain.
(a) Plants use carbon dioxide and water to make sugar. **(b)** Water vapor in the air on a cold day forms frost.

Separation of Mixtures

Because each component of a mixture retains its own properties, we can separate a mixture into its components by taking advantage of the differences in their properties. For example, a heterogeneous mixture of iron filings and gold filings could be sorted individually by color into iron and gold. A less tedious approach would be to use a magnet to attract the iron filings, leaving the gold ones behind. We can also take advantage of an important chemical difference between these two metals: Many acids dissolve iron but not gold. Thus, if we put our mixture into an appropriate acid, the acid would dissolve the iron and the gold would be left behind. The two could then be separated by *filtration*, a

(a)   (b)

 Figure 1.12 **Separation by filtration.** A mixture of a solid and a liquid is poured through a porous medium, in this case filter paper. The liquid passes through the paper while the solid remains on the paper.

procedure illustrated in Figure 1.12 ◄. We would have to use other chemical reactions, which we will learn about later, to transform the dissolved iron back into metal.

An important method of separating the components of a homogeneous mixture is *distillation*, a process that depends on the different abilities of substances to form gases. For example, if we boil a solution of salt and water, the water evaporates, forming a gas, and the salt is left behind. The gaseous water can be converted back to a liquid on the walls of a condenser, as shown in the apparatus depicted in Figure 1.13 ▼.

The differing abilities of substances to adhere to the surfaces of various solids such as paper and starch can also be used to separate mixtures. This ability is the basis of *chromatography* (literally "the writing of colors"), a technique that can give beautiful and dramatic results. An example of the chromatographic separation of ink is shown in Figure 1.14 ▼.

► Figure 1.13 **Distillation.** A simple apparatus for the separation of a sodium chloride solution (salt water) into its components. Boiling the solution vaporizes the water, which is condensed, then collected in the receiving flask. After all the water has boiled away, pure sodium chloride remains in the boiling flask.

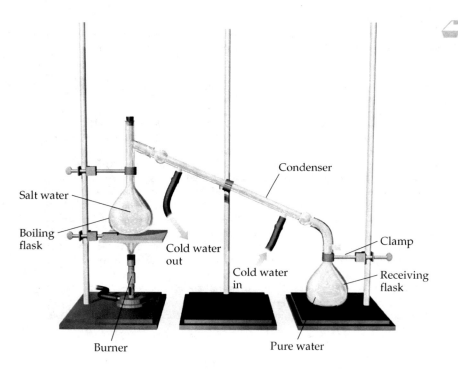

Condenser

Salt water

Boiling flask

Cold water out

Cold water in

Clamp

Receiving flask

Burner

Pure water

► Figure 1.14 **Separation of ink into components by paper chromatography.** (a) Water begins to move up the paper. (b) Water moves past the ink spot, dissolving different components of the ink at different rates. (c) The ink has separated into its several different components.

(a)   (b)   (c)

lthough two scientists rarely approach the same problem in exactly the same way, they use guidelines for the practice of science that are known as the **scientific method**. These guidelines are outlined in Figure 1.15▼. We begin our study by collecting information, or *data*, by observation and experiment. The collection of information, however, is not the ultimate goal. The goal is to find a pattern or sense of order in our observations and to understand the origin of this order.

As we perform our experiments, we may begin to see patterns that lead us to a *tentative explanation*, or **hypothesis**, that guides us in planning further experiments. Eventually, we may be able to tie together a great number of observations in a single statement or equation called a scientific law. A **scientific law** *is a concise verbal statement or a mathematical equation that summarizes a broad variety of observations and experiences.* We tend to think of the laws of nature as the basic rules under which nature operates. However, it is not so much that matter obeys the laws of nature, but rather that the laws of nature describe the behavior of matter.

At many stages of our studies we may propose explanations of why nature behaves in a particular way. If a hypothesis is sufficiently general and is continually effective in predicting facts yet to be observed, it is called a theory. A **theory** *is an explanation of the general causes of certain phenomena, with considerable*

evidence or facts to support it. For example, Einstein's theory of relativity was a revolutionary new way of thinking about space and time. It was more than just a simple hypothesis, however, because it could be used to make predictions that could be tested experimentally. When these experiments were conducted, the results were generally in agreement with the predictions and were not explainable by earlier theories. Thus, the theory of relativity was supported, but not proven. Indeed, theories can never be proven to be absolutely correct.

As we proceed through this text, we will rarely have the opportunity to discuss the doubts, conflicts, clashes of personalities, and revolutions of perception that have led to our present ideas. We need to be aware that just because we can spell out the results of science so concisely and neatly in textbooks, it does not mean that scientific progress is smooth, certain, and predictable. Some of the ideas we present in this text took centuries to develop and involved many scientists. We gain our view of the natural world by standing on the shoulders of the scientists who came before us. Take advantage of this view. As you study, exercise your imagination. Don't be afraid to ask daring questions when they occur to you. You may be fascinated by what you discover!
Related Exercise: 1.57

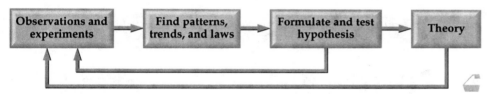

▲ Figure 1.15 **The scientific method.** The scientific method is a general approach to solving problems that involves making observations, seeking patterns in the observations, formulating hypotheses to explain the observations, and testing these hypotheses by further experiments. Those hypotheses that withstand such tests and prove themselves useful in explaining and predicting behavior become known as theories.

1.4 UNITS OF MEASUREMENT

Many properties of matter are *quantitative*; that is, they are associated with numbers. When a number represents a measured quantity, the units of that quantity must always be specified. To say that the length of a pencil is 17.5 is meaningless. Expressing the number with its units, 17.5 centimeters (cm), properly specifies the length. The units used for scientific measurements are those of the **metric system**.

The metric system, which was first developed in France during the late eighteenth century, is used as the system of measurement in most countries throughout the world. The United States has traditionally used the English system, although use of the metric system has become more common. For example, the contents of most canned goods and soft drinks in grocery stores are now given in metric as well as in English units, as shown in Figure 1.16▶.

SI Units

In 1960 an international agreement was reached specifying a particular choice of metric units for use in scientific measurements. These preferred units are

▲ Figure 1.16 **Metric units.** Metric measurements are increasingly common in the United States, as exemplified by the volume printed on this soda can.

TABLE 1.4 ■ SI Base Units		
Physical Quantity	**Name of Unit**	**Abbreviation**
Mass	Kilogram	kg
Length	Meter	m
Time	Second	s[a]
Temperature	Kelvin	K
Amount of substance	Mole	mol
Electric current	Ampere	A
Luminous intensity	Candela	cd

[a]The abbreviation sec is frequently used.

called **SI units**, after the French *Système International d'Unités*. This system has seven *base units* from which all other units are derived. Table 1.4▲ lists these base units and their symbols. In this chapter we will consider the base units for length, mass, and temperature.

In the metric system, prefixes are used to indicate decimal fractions or multiples of various units. For example, the prefix *milli-* represents a 10^{-3} fraction of a unit: A milligram (mg) is 10^{-3} gram (g), a millimeter (mm) is 10^{-3} meter (m), and so forth. Table 1.5▼ presents the prefixes commonly encountered in chemistry. In using SI units and in working problems throughout this text, you must be comfortable using exponential notation. If you are unfamiliar with exponential notation or want to review it, refer to Appendix A.1.

Although non-SI units are being phased out, some are still commonly used by scientists. Whenever we first encounter a non-SI unit in the text, the proper SI unit will also be given.

TABLE 1.5 ■ Selected Prefixes Used in the Metric System			
Prefix	**Abbreviation**	**Meaning**	**Example**
Giga	G	10^{9}	1 gigameter (Gm) = 1×10^{9} m
Mega	M	10^{6}	1 megameter (Mm) = 1×10^{6} m
Kilo	k	10^{3}	1 kilometer (km) = 1×10^{3} m
Deci	d	10^{-1}	1 decimeter (dm) = 0.1 m
Centi	c	10^{-2}	1 centimeter (cm) = 0.01 m
Milli	m	10^{-3}	1 millimeter (mm) = 0.001 m
Micro	μ[a]	10^{-6}	1 micrometer (μm) = 1×10^{-6} m
Nano	n	10^{-9}	1 nanometer (nm) = 1×10^{-9} m
Pico	p	10^{-12}	1 picometer (pm) = 1×10^{-12} m
Femto	f	10^{-15}	1 femtometer (fm) = 1×10^{-15} m

[a]This is the Greek letter mu (pronounced "mew").

GIVE IT SOME THOUGHT

Which of the following quantities is the smallest: 1 mg, 1μg, or 1 pg?

Length and Mass

The SI base unit of *length* is the meter (m), a distance only slightly longer than a yard. The relations between the English and metric system units that we will use most frequently in this text appear on the back inside cover. We will discuss how to convert English units into metric units, and vice versa, in Section 1.6.

Mass* is a measure of the amount of material in an object. The SI base unit of mass is the kilogram (kg), which is equal to about 2.2 pounds (lb). This base unit is unusual because it uses a prefix, *kilo-*, instead of the word *gram* alone. We obtain other units for mass by adding prefixes to the word *gram*.

▬ SAMPLE EXERCISE 1.2 | Using Metric Prefixes

What is the name given to the unit that equals **(a)** 10^{-9} gram, **(b)** 10^{-6} second, **(c)** 10^{-3} meter?

SOLUTION

In each case we can refer to Table 1.5, finding the prefix related to each of the decimal fractions: **(a)** nanogram, ng, **(b)** microsecond, μs, **(c)** millimeter, mm.

▬ PRACTICE EXERCISE

(a) What decimal fraction of a second is a picosecond, ps? **(b)** Express the measurement 6.0×10^3 m using a prefix to replace the power of ten. **(c)** Use exponential notation to express 3.76 mg in grams.
Answers: **(a)** 10^{-12} second, **(b)** 6.0 km, **(c)** 3.76×10^{-3} g

---

Temperature

Temperature is a measure of the hotness or coldness of an object. Indeed, temperature is a physical property that determines the direction of heat flow. Heat always flows spontaneously from a substance at higher temperature to one at lower temperature. Thus, we feel the influx of heat when we touch a hot object, and we know that the object is at a higher temperature than our hand.

The temperature scales commonly employed in scientific studies are the Celsius and Kelvin scales. The **Celsius scale** is also the everyday scale of temperature in most countries (Figure 1.17 ▶). It was originally based on the assignment of 0 °C to the freezing point of water and 100 °C to its boiling point at sea level (Figure 1.18 ▼).

▲ Figure 1.17 **Australian stamp.** Many countries employ the Celsius temperature scale in everyday use, as illustrated by this stamp.

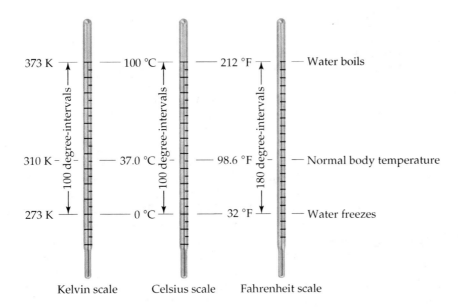

◀ Figure 1.18 **Comparison of the Kelvin, Celsius, and Fahrenheit temperature scales.** The freezing point and boiling point of water as well as normal human body temperature is indicated on each of the scales.

---

*Mass and weight are not interchangeable terms but are often incorrectly thought to be the same. The weight of an object is the force that its mass exerts due to gravity. In space, where gravitational forces are very weak, an astronaut can be weightless, but he or she cannot be massless. In fact, the astronaut's mass in space is the same as it is on Earth.

The **Kelvin scale** is the SI temperature scale, and the SI unit of temperature is the kelvin (K). Historically, the Kelvin scale was based on the properties of gases; its origins will be considered in Chapter 10. Zero on this scale is the lowest attainable temperature, -273.15 °C, a temperature referred to as *absolute zero*. Both the Celsius and Kelvin scales have equal-sized units—that is, a kelvin is the same size as a degree Celsius. Thus, the Kelvin and Celsius scales are related as follows:

$$K = °C + 273.15 \qquad\qquad [1.1]$$

The freezing point of water, 0 °C, is 273.15 K (Figure 1.18). Notice that we do not use a degree sign (°) with temperatures on the Kelvin scale.

The common temperature scale in the United States is the *Fahrenheit scale*, which is not generally used in scientific studies. On the Fahrenheit scale, water freezes at 32 °F and boils at 212 °F. The Fahrenheit and Celsius scales are related as follows:

$$°C = \frac{5}{9}(°F - 32) \quad \text{or} \quad °F = \frac{9}{5}(°C) + 32 \qquad [1.2]$$

■■■ SAMPLE EXERCISE 1.3 | Converting Units of Temperature

If a weather forecaster predicts that the temperature for the day will reach 31 °C, what is the predicted temperature **(a)** in K, **(b)** in °F?

SOLUTION

(a) Using Equation 1.1, we have K = 31 + 273 = 304 K

(b) Using Equation 1.2, we have °F = $\frac{9}{5}$(31) + 32 = 56 + 32 = 88 °F

■■■ PRACTICE EXERCISE

Ethylene glycol, the major ingredient in antifreeze, freezes at -11.5 °C. What is the freezing point in **(a)** K, **(b)** °F?
Answers: **(a)** 261.7 K, **(b)** 11.3 °F

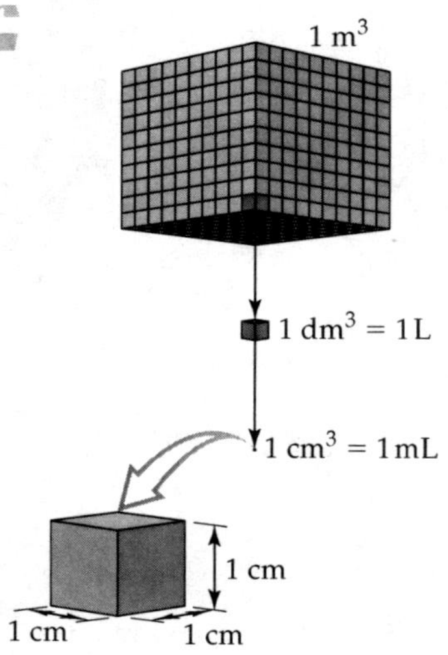

Derived SI Units

The SI base units in Table 1.4 are used to derive the units of other quantities. To do so, we use the defining equation for the quantity, substituting the appropriate base units. For example, speed is defined as the ratio of distance traveled to elapsed time. Thus, the SI unit for speed—m/s, which we read as "meters per second"—is the SI unit for distance (length), m, divided by the SI unit for time, s. We will encounter many derived units, such as those for force, pressure, and energy, later in this text. In this chapter we examine the derived units for volume and density.

Volume

The *volume* of a cube is given by its length cubed, (length)³. Thus, the SI unit of volume is the SI unit of length, m, raised to the third power. The cubic meter, or m³, is the volume of a cube that is 1 m on each edge. Smaller units, such as cubic centimeters, cm³ (sometimes written as cc), are frequently used in chemistry. Another unit of volume commonly used in chemistry is the *liter* (L), which equals a cubic decimeter, dm³, and is slightly larger than a quart. The liter is the first metric unit we have encountered that is *not* an SI unit. There are 1000 milliliters (mL) in a liter (Figure 1.19 ◄), and each milliliter is the same volume as a cubic centimeter: 1 mL = 1 cm³. The terms *milliliter* and *cubic centimeter* are used interchangeably in expressing volume.

The devices used most frequently in chemistry to measure volume are illustrated in Figure 1.20►. Syringes, burets, and pipets deliver liquids with more precision than graduated cylinders. Volumetric flasks are used to contain specific volumes of liquid.

▲ Figure 1.19 **Volume relationships.** The volume occupied by a cube that is 1 m on each edge is a cubic meter, 1 m³ (top). Each cubic meter contains 1000 dm³ (middle). A liter is the same volume as a cubic decimeter, 1 L = 1 dm³. Each cubic decimeter contains 1000 cubic centimeters, 1 dm³ = 1000 cm³. Each cubic centimeter equals 1 milliliter, 1 cm³ = 1 mL (bottom).

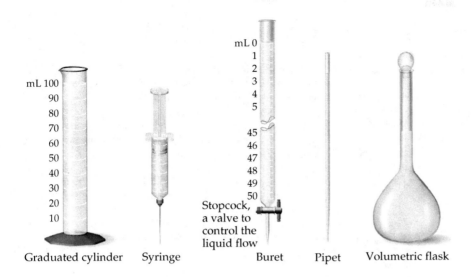

◀ Figure 1.20 **Common volumetric glassware.** The graduated cylinder, syringe, and buret are used in laboratories to deliver variable volumes of liquid. The pipet is used to deliver a specific volume of liquid. The volumetric flask contains a specific volume of liquid when filled to the mark.

GIVE IT SOME THOUGHT

Which of the following quantities represents a volume measurement: 15 m^2; 2.5×10^2 m^3; 5.77 L/s? How do you know?

Density

Density is a property of matter that is widely used to characterize a substance. Density is defined as the amount of mass in a unit volume of the substance:

$$\text{Density} = \frac{\text{mass}}{\text{volume}} \qquad [1.3]$$

The densities of solids and liquids are commonly expressed in units of grams per cubic centimeter (g/cm^3) or grams per milliliter (g/mL). The densities of some common substances are listed in Table 1.6▼. It is no coincidence that the density of water is 1.00 g/mL; the gram was originally defined as the mass of 1 mL of water at a specific temperature. Because most substances change volume when they are heated or cooled, densities are temperature dependent. When reporting densities, the temperature should be specified. If no temperature is reported, we usually assume that the temperature is 25 °C, close to normal room temperature.

The terms *density* and *weight* are sometimes confused. A person who says that iron weighs more than air generally means that iron has a higher density than air—1 kg of air has the same mass as 1 kg of iron, but the iron occupies a smaller volume, thereby giving it a higher density. If we combine two liquids that do not mix, the less dense liquid will float on the denser liquid.

TABLE 1.6 ■ Densities of Some Selected Substances at 25 °C	
Substance	Density (g/cm^3)
Air	0.001
Balsa wood	0.16
Ethanol	0.79
Water	1.00
Ethylene glycol	1.09
Table sugar	1.59
Table salt	2.16
Iron	7.9
Gold	19.32

Chemistry Put to Work   CHEMISTRY IN THE NEWS

Chemistry is a very lively, active field of science. Because chemistry is so central to our lives, reports on matters of chemical significance appear in the news nearly every day. Some reports tell of recent breakthroughs in the development of new pharmaceuticals, materials, and processes. Others deal with environmental and public safety issues. As you study chemistry, we hope you will develop the skills to better understand the importance of chemistry in your life. By way of examples, here are summaries of a few recent stories in which chemistry plays a role.

Biofuels Reality Check

With the Energy Policy Act of 2005, the United States Congress has given a big push to fuels derived from biomass as a renewable, homegrown alternative to gasoline. The law requires that 4 billion gallons of the so-called renewable fuel be mixed with gasoline in 2007, increasing to 7.5 billion gallons by 2012. The United States currently consumes about 140 billion gallons of gasoline per year.

Although the Act does not dictate which renewable fuels to use, ethanol derived from corn currently dominates the alternatives with 40% of all gasoline now containing some ethanol. A blend of 10% ethanol and 90% gasoline, called E10, is the most common blend because it can be used in virtually all vehicles. Blends of 85% ethanol and 15% gasoline, called E85, are also available but can be used only with specially modified engines in what are called flexible-fuel vehicles (FFVs) (Figure 1.21 ▼).

▲ Figure 1.21 **A gasoline pump that dispenses E85 ethanol.**

When it comes to ethanol's pros and cons, there is no shortage of disagreement. In 2006, researchers at the University of Minnesota calculated that "Even dedicating all U.S. corn and soybean production to biofuels would meet only 12% of gasoline and 6% of diesel demand." The conversion of a much wider range of plant material, making use of a much greater fraction of the available plant matter, into fuels will be necessary to improve these numbers substantially. Because most cellulose of which plants are formed does not readily convert to ethanol, a great deal of research will be needed to solve this challenging problem. Meanwhile, it is worth reflecting that a 3% improvement in vehicle efficiency of fuel use would displace more gasoline use than the entire 2006 US ethanol production.

New Element Created

A new entry has been made to the list of elements. The production of the newest and heaviest element—element 118—was announced in October 2006. The synthesis of element 118 resulted from studies performed from 2002 to 2006 at the Joint Institute for Nuclear Research (JINR) in Dubna, Russia. JINR scientists and their collaborators from Lawrence Livermore National Laboratory in California announced that they had produced three atoms of the new element, one atom in 2002 and two more in 2005.

The new element was formed by striking a target of californium atoms (element 98) with a highly energetic beam consisting of the nuclei of calcium atoms (element 20) in a device called a particle accelerator. Occasionally, the nuclei from the atoms of the two different elements fused to form the new, superheavy element 118. The 2002 experiment took four months and used a beam of 2.5×10^{19} calcium atoms to produce the single atom of element 118.

The three atoms of element 118 created during these experiments came and went in a literal flash. On the average, the atoms survived for just 0.9 milliseconds before decomposing.

These experimental results were met with praise but also caution from other scientists in the field, particularly given the difficult history of element 118. Another California lab, the Lawrence Berkeley National Laboratory, announced that it discovered element 118 in 1999 but retracted the claim two years later after an investigation found that one of the researchers had fabricated data.

This discovery brings the total number of elements created by the Livermore-Dubna collaboration to five: elements 113, 114, 115, 116, and 118. As of this writing, element 118 has not yet been named.

Important Antibiotic Modified to Combat Bacterial Resistance

Vancomycin is an antibiotic of last resort—used only when other antibacterial agents are ineffective. Some bacteria have developed a resistance to vancomycin, causing researchers to modify the molecular structure of the substance to make it

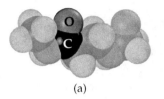
(a)

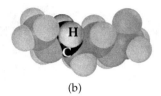
(b)

◀ Figure 1.22 **Comparing CO and CH₂ groups.** Two molecules, one containing the CO group (left) and one containing the CH₂ group (right), are shown. The subtle difference between these two molecules is like that produced when the structure of the much more complex vancomycin molecule was modified.

more effective in killing bacteria. This approach was based on the knowledge that vancomycin works by binding to a particular protein, called a glycoprotein, that is essential to forming the walls of bacterial cells. Researchers have now synthesized an analog of vancomycin in which a CO group in the molecule has been converted to a CH₂ group (Figure 1.22 ▲). This molecular modification increases the compound's binding affinity with the glycoprotein in the cell walls of vancomycin-resistant bacteria. The analog is 100 times more active than vancomycin against vancomycin-resistant bacteria.

The Hole Story

Ozone in the upper atmosphere protects life on Earth by blocking harmful ultraviolet rays coming from the sun. The "ozone hole" is a severe depletion of the ozone layer high above Antarctica. Human-produced compounds that release chlorine and bromine into the stratosphere are the primary cause of the ozone hole.

The production of ozone-depleting chemicals has been banned since 1996, although emissions of previously produced and stored amounts of those chemicals that are not destroyed or recycled will continue. Scientists had predicted that the ozone hole would disappear by 2050 because of the ban. The 2006 World Meteorological Organization/United Nations Environment Programme Scientific Assessment of Ozone De-

pletion, however, recently issued its report changing this estimate. Based on a combination of new ozone measurements, computer models, and revised estimates of the existing stores of ozone-depleting chemicals, scientists now estimate the date for full Antarctic ozone recovery to be 2065.

Replacing the Lightbulb through Chemistry

If you want to save the world from global warming, you can start by replacing incandescent lightbulbs, which waste about 90% of the energy supplied to them by producing heat. A promising place to look for replacement bulbs is in the field of light-emitting diodes (LEDs). Red LEDs and those emitting other colors are found everywhere these days: in flashlights, traffic lights, car taillights, and a host of electronics applications (Figure 1.23 ▼). But to really make it big in the world, LEDs need to be capable of producing white light at a reasonable cost.

Progress is being made in forming high-efficiency LEDs based on organic films that emit white light. In these devices a light-emitting material is sandwiched between two electrical connectors. When electricity passes through the organic film, oppositely charged particles combine and give off light. White organic LEDs have been steadily improving, and are now about as efficient as fluorescent tubes. More work needs to be done before these devices can replace the lightbulb, but progress has been rapid.

▶ Figure 1.23 **Sign made from LEDs.**

SAMPLE EXERCISE 1.4 | Determining Density and Using Density to Determine Volume or Mass

(a) Calculate the density of mercury if 1.00×10^2 g occupies a volume of 7.36 cm^3.
(b) Calculate the volume of 65.0 g of the liquid methanol (wood alcohol) if its density is 0.791 g/mL.
(c) What is the mass in grams of a cube of gold (density = 19.32 g/cm^3) if the length of the cube is 2.00 cm?

SOLUTION

(a) We are given mass and volume, so Equation 1.3 yields

$$\text{Density} = \frac{\text{mass}}{\text{volume}} = \frac{1.00 \times 10^2 \text{ g}}{7.36 \text{ cm}^3} = 13.6 \text{ g/cm}^3$$

(b) Solving Equation 1.3 for volume and then using the given mass and density gives

$$\text{Volume} = \frac{\text{mass}}{\text{density}} = \frac{65.0 \text{ g}}{0.791 \text{ g/mL}} = 82.2 \text{ mL}$$

(c) We can calculate the mass from the volume of the cube and its density. The volume of a cube is given by its length cubed:

$$\text{Volume} = (2.00 \text{ cm})^3 = (2.00)^3 \text{ cm}^3 = 8.00 \text{ cm}^3$$

Solving Equation 1.3 for mass and substituting the volume and density of the cube, we have

$$\text{Mass} = \text{volume} \times \text{density} = (8.00 \text{ cm}^3)(19.32 \text{ g/cm}^3) = 155 \text{ g}$$

PRACTICE EXERCISE

(a) Calculate the density of a 374.5-g sample of copper if it has a volume of 41.8 cm^3. **(b)** A student needs 15.0 g of ethanol for an experiment. If the density of ethanol is 0.789 g/mL, how many milliliters of ethanol are needed? **(c)** What is the mass, in grams, of 25.0 mL of mercury (density = 13.6 g/mL)?
Answers: **(a)** 8.96 g/cm^3, **(b)** 19.0 mL, **(c)** 340 g

1.5 UNCERTAINTY IN MEASUREMENT

Two kinds of numbers are encountered in scientific work: *exact numbers* (those whose values are known exactly) and *inexact numbers* (those whose values have some uncertainty). Most of the exact numbers that we will encounter in this course have defined values. For example, there are exactly 12 eggs in a dozen, exactly 1000 g in a kilogram, and exactly 2.54 cm in an inch. The number 1 in any conversion factor between units, as in 1 m = 100 cm or 1 kg = 2.2046 lb, is also an exact number. Exact numbers can also result from counting numbers of objects. For example, we can count the exact number of marbles in a jar or the exact number of people in a classroom.

Numbers obtained by measurement are always *inexact*. The equipment used to measure quantities always has inherent limitations (equipment errors), and there are differences in how different people make the same measurement (human errors). Suppose that ten students with ten balances are given the same dime and told to determine its mass. The ten measurements will probably vary slightly from one another for various reasons. The balances might be calibrated slightly differently, and there might be differences in how each student reads the mass from the balance. Remember: *Uncertainties always exist in measured quantities*. Counting very large numbers of objects usually has some associated error as well. Consider, for example, how difficult it is to obtain accurate census information for a city or vote counts for an election.

GIVE IT SOME THOUGHT

Which of the following is an inexact quantity: **(a)** the number of people in your chemistry class, **(b)** the mass of a penny, **(c)** the number of grams in a kilogram?

Precision and Accuracy

The terms precision and accuracy are often used in discussing the uncertainties of measured values. **Precision** is a measure of how closely individual measurements agree with one another. **Accuracy** refers to how closely individual measurements agree with the correct, or "true," value. The analogy of darts stuck in a dartboard pictured in Figure 1.24▶ illustrates the difference between these two concepts.

In the laboratory we often perform several different "trials" of the same experiment and average the results. The precision of the measurements is often expressed in terms of what is called the *standard deviation*, which reflects how much the individual measurements differ from the average, as described in Appendix A. We gain confidence in our measurements if we obtain nearly the same value each time—that is, the standard deviation is small. Figure 1.24 should remind us, however, that precise measurements could be inaccurate. For example, if a very sensitive balance is poorly calibrated, the masses we measure will be consistently either high or low. They will be inaccurate even if they are precise.

Significant Figures

Suppose you determine the mass of a dime on a balance capable of measuring to the nearest 0.0001 g. You could report the mass as 2.2405 ± 0.0001 g. The ± notation (read "plus or minus") expresses the magnitude of the uncertainty of your measurement. In much scientific work we drop the ± notation with the understanding that there is always some uncertainty in the last digit of the measured quantity. That is, *measured quantities are generally reported in such a way that only the last digit is uncertain.*

Figure 1.25▼ shows a thermometer with its liquid column between the scale marks. We can read the certain digits from the scale and estimate the uncertain one. From the scale marks on the thermometer, we see that the liquid is between the 25 °C and 30 °C marks. We might estimate the temperature to be 27 °C, being somewhat uncertain of the second digit of our measurement.

All digits of a measured quantity, including the uncertain one, are called **significant figures.** A measured mass reported as 2.2 g has two significant figures, whereas one reported as 2.2405 g has five significant figures. The greater the number of significant figures, the greater is the certainty implied for the measurement. When multiple measurements are made of a quantity, the results can be averaged, and the number of significant figures estimated by using statistical methods.

Good accuracy
Good precision

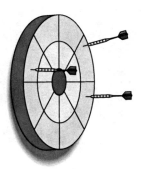

Poor accuracy
Good precision

Poor accuracy
Poor precision

▲ Figure 1.24 **Precision and accuracy.** The distribution of darts on a target illustrates the difference between accuracy and precision.

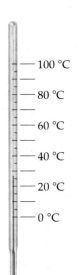

— 100 °C

— 80 °C

— 60 °C

— 40 °C

— 20 °C

— 0 °C

◀ Figure 1.25 **Significant figures in measurements.** The thermometer has markings every 5 °C. The temperature is between 25 °C and 30 °C and is approximately 27 °C. The two significant figures in the measurement include the second digit, which is estimated by reading between the scale marks.

SAMPLE EXERCISE 1.5 | Relating Significant Figures to the Uncertainty of a Measurement

What difference exists between the measured values 4.0 g and 4.00 g?

SOLUTION

Many people would say there is no difference, but a scientist would note the difference in the number of significant figures in the two measurements. The value 4.0 has two significant figures, while 4.00 has three. This difference implies that the first measurement has more uncertainty. A mass of 4.0 g indicates that the uncertainty is in the first decimal place of the measurement. Thus, the mass might be anything between 3.9 and 4.1 g, which we can represent as 4.0 ± 0.1 g. A measurement of 4.00 g implies that the uncertainty is in the second decimal place. Thus, the mass might be anything between 3.99 and 4.01 g, which we can represent as 4.00 ± 0.01 g. Without further information, we cannot be sure whether the difference in uncertainties of the two measurements reflects the precision or accuracy of the measurement.

PRACTICE EXERCISE

A balance has a precision of ±0.001 g. A sample that has a mass of about 25 g is placed on this balance. How many significant figures should be reported for this measurement?
Answer: five, as in the measurement 24.995 g, the uncertainty being in the third decimal place

"MY GOODNESS, IT'S 12:15:0936420175! TIME FOR LUNCH."

To determine the number of significant figures in a reported measurement, read the number from left to right, counting the digits starting with the first digit that is not zero. *In any measurement that is properly reported, all nonzero digits are significant.* Zeros, however, can be used either as part of the measured value or merely to locate the decimal point. Thus, zeros may or may not be significant, depending on how they appear in the number. The following guidelines describe the different situations involving zeros:

1. Zeros *between* nonzero digits are always significant—1005 kg (four significant figures); 1.03 cm (three significant figures).
2. Zeros *at the beginning* of a number are never significant; they merely indicate the position of the decimal point—0.02 g (one significant figure); 0.0026 cm (two significant figures).
3. Zeros *at the end* of a number are significant if the number contains a decimal point—0.0200 g (three significant figures); 3.0 cm (two significant figures).

A problem arises when a number ends with zeros but contains no decimal point. In such cases, it is normally assumed that the zeros are not significant. Exponential notation (Appendix A) can be used to clearly indicate whether zeros at the end of a number are significant. For example, a mass of 10,300 g can be written in exponential notation showing three, four, or five significant figures depending on how the measurement is obtained:

$$1.03 \times 10^4 \text{ g} \qquad \text{(three significant figures)}$$
$$1.030 \times 10^4 \text{ g} \qquad \text{(four significant figures)}$$
$$1.0300 \times 10^4 \text{ g} \qquad \text{(five significant figures)}$$

In these numbers all the zeros to the right of the decimal point are significant (rules 1 and 3). (The exponential term does not add to the number of significant figures.)

SAMPLE EXERCISE 1.6 | Determining the Number of Significant Figures in a Measurement

How many significant figures are in each of the following numbers (assume that each number is a measured quantity): **(a)** 4.003, **(b)** 6.023×10^{23}, **(c)** 5000?

SOLUTION

(a) Four; the zeros are significant figures. **(b)** Four; the exponential term does not add to the number of significant figures. **(c)** One. We assume that the zeros are not significant when there is no decimal point shown. If the number has more significant figures, a decimal point should be employed or the number written in exponential notation. Thus, 5000. has four significant figures, whereas 5.00×10^3 has three.

Science Fundamentals

■ PRACTICE EXERCISE

How many significant figures are in each of the following measurements: **(a)** 3.549 g, **(b)** 2.3×10^4 cm, **(c)** 0.00134 m³?
Answers: **(a)** four, **(b)** two, **(c)** three

Significant Figures in Calculations

When carrying measured quantities through calculations, *the least certain measurement limits the certainty of the calculated quantity and thereby determines the number of significant figures in the final answer.* The final answer should be reported with only one uncertain digit. To keep track of significant figures in calculations, we will make frequent use of two rules, one for addition and subtraction, and another for multiplication and division.

1. *For addition and subtraction*, the result has the same number of decimal places as the measurement with the fewest decimal places. When the result contains more than the correct number of significant figures, it must be rounded off. Consider the following example in which the uncertain digits appear in color:

This number limits	20.42	← two decimal places
the number of significant	1.322	← three decimal places
figures in the result →	83.1	← one decimal place
	104.842	← round off to one decimal place (104.8)

   We report the result as 104.8 because 83.1 has only one decimal place.

2. *For multiplication and division*, the result contains the same number of significant figures as the measurement with the fewest significant figures. When the result contains more than the correct number of significant figures, it must be rounded off. For example, the area of a rectangle whose measured edge lengths are 6.221 cm and 5.2 cm should be reported as 32 cm² even though a calculator shows the product of 6.221 and 5.2 to have more digits:

   $$\text{Area} = (6.221 \text{ cm})(5.2 \text{ cm}) = 32.3492 \text{ cm}^2 \Rightarrow \text{round off to } 32 \text{ cm}^2$$

   We round off to two significant figures because the least precise number—5.2 cm—has only two significant figures.

Notice that for addition and subtraction, decimal places are counted; whereas for multiplication and division, significant figures are counted.

In determining the final answer for a calculated quantity, *exact numbers* can be treated as if they have an infinite number of significant figures. This rule applies to many definitions between units. Thus, when we say, "There are 12 inches in 1 foot," the number 12 is exact, and we need not worry about the number of significant figures in it.

In *rounding off numbers*, look at the leftmost digit to be removed:

- If the leftmost digit removed is less than 5, the preceding number is left unchanged. Thus, rounding 7.248 to two significant figures gives 7.2.
- If the leftmost digit removed is 5 or greater, the preceding number is increased by 1. Rounding 4.735 to three significant figures gives 4.74, and rounding 2.376 to two significant figures gives 2.4.*

■ SAMPLE EXERCISE 1.7 | Determining the Number of Significant Figures in a Calculated Quantity

The width, length, and height of a small box are 15.5 cm, 27.3 cm, and 5.4 cm, respectively. Calculate the volume of the box, using the correct number of significant figures in your answer.

---

*Your instructor may want you to use a slight variation on the rule when the leftmost digit to be removed is exactly 5, with no following digits or only zeros. One common practice is to round up to the next higher number if that number will be even, and down to the next lower number otherwise. Thus, 4.7350 would be rounded to 4.74, and 4.7450 would also be rounded to 4.74.

SOLUTION

The product of the width, length, and height determines the volume of a box. In reporting the product, we can show only as many significant figures as given in the dimension with the fewest significant figures, that for the height (two significant figures):

$$\text{Volume} = \text{width} \times \text{length} \times \text{height}$$

$$= (15.5 \text{ cm})(27.3 \text{ cm})(5.4 \text{ cm}) = 2285.01 \text{ cm}^3 \Rightarrow 2.3 \times 10^3 \text{ cm}^3$$

When we use a calculator to do this calculation, the display shows 2285.01, which we must round off to two significant figures. Because the resulting number is 2300, it is best reported in exponential notation, 2.3×10^3, to clearly indicate two significant figures.

■■■ PRACTICE EXERCISE

It takes 10.5 s for a sprinter to run 100.00 m. Calculate the average speed of the sprinter in meters per second, and express the result to the correct number of significant figures.
Answer: 9.52 m/s (three significant figures)

■■■ SAMPLE EXERCISE 1.8 | Determining the Number of Significant Figures in a Calculated Quantity

A gas at 25 °C fills a container whose volume is $1.05 \times 10^3 \text{ cm}^3$. The container plus gas have a mass of 837.6 g. The container, when emptied of all gas, has a mass of 836.2 g. What is the density of the gas at 25 °C?

SOLUTION

To calculate the density, we must know both the mass and the volume of the gas. The mass of the gas is just the difference in the masses of the full and empty container:

$$(837.6 - 836.2) \text{ g} = 1.4 \text{ g}$$

In subtracting numbers, we determine the number of significant figures in our result by counting decimal places in each quantity. In this case each quantity has one decimal place. Thus, the mass of the gas, 1.4 g, has one decimal place.

Using the volume given in the question, $1.05 \times 10^3 \text{ cm}^3$, and the definition of density, we have

$$\text{Density} = \frac{\text{mass}}{\text{volume}} = \frac{1.4 \text{ g}}{1.05 \times 10^3 \text{ cm}^3}$$

$$= 1.3 \times 10^{-3} \text{ g/cm}^3 = 0.0013 \text{ g/cm}^3$$

In dividing numbers, we determine the number of significant figures in our result by counting the number of significant figures in each quantity. There are two significant figures in our answer, corresponding to the smaller number of significant figures in the two numbers that form the ratio. Notice that in this example, following the rules for determining significant figures gives an answer containing only two significant figures, even though each of the measured quantities contained at least three significant figures.

■■■ PRACTICE EXERCISE

To how many significant figures should the mass of the container be measured (with and without the gas) in Sample Exercise 1.8 for the density to be calculated to three significant figures?
Answer: five (For the difference in the two masses to have three significant figures, there must be two decimal places in the masses of the filled and empty containers. Therefore, each mass must be measured to five significant figures.)

When a calculation involves two or more steps and you write down answers for intermediate steps, retain at least one additional digit—past the number of significant figures—for the intermediate answers. This procedure ensures that small errors from rounding at each step do not combine to affect the final result. When using a calculator, you may enter the numbers one after another, rounding only the final answer. Accumulated rounding-off errors may account for small differences among results you obtain and answers given in the text for numerical problems.

1.6 DIMENSIONAL ANALYSIS

Throughout the text we use an approach called **dimensional analysis** as an aid in problem solving. In dimensional analysis we carry units through all calculations. Units are multiplied together, divided into each other, or "canceled."

Using dimensional analysis helps ensure that the solutions to problems yield the proper units. Moreover, it provides a systematic way of solving many numerical problems and of checking our solutions for possible errors.

The key to using dimensional analysis is the correct use of conversion factors to change one unit into another. A **conversion factor** is a fraction whose numerator and denominator are the same quantity expressed in different units. For example, 2.54 cm and 1 in. are the same length, 2.54 cm = 1 in. This relationship allows us to write two conversion factors:

$$\frac{2.54 \text{ cm}}{1 \text{ in.}} \quad \text{and} \quad \frac{1 \text{ in.}}{2.54 \text{ cm}}$$

We use the first of these factors to convert inches to centimeters. For example, the length in centimeters of an object that is 8.50 in. long is given by

$$\text{Number of centimeters} = (8.50 \text{ in.}) \overbrace{\frac{2.54 \text{ cm}}{1 \text{ in.}}}^{\text{Desired unit}} = 21.6 \text{ cm}$$
Given unit

The unit inches in the denominator of the conversion factor cancels the unit inches in the given data (8.50 *inches*). The unit centimeters in the numerator of the conversion factor becomes the unit of the final answer. Because the numerator and denominator of a conversion factor are equal, multiplying any quantity by a conversion factor is equivalent to multiplying by the number 1 and so does not change the intrinsic value of the quantity. The length 8.50 in. is the same as the length 21.6 cm.

In general, we begin any conversion by examining the units of the given data and the units we desire. We then ask ourselves what conversion factors we have available to take us from the units of the given quantity to those of the desired one. When we multiply a quantity by a conversion factor, the units multiply and divide as follows:

$$\text{Given unit} \times \frac{\text{desired unit}}{\text{given unit}} = \text{desired unit}$$

If the desired units are not obtained in a calculation, then an error must have been made somewhere. Careful inspection of units often reveals the source of the error.

■■■ **SAMPLE EXERCISE 1.9** | Converting Units

If a woman has a mass of 115 lb, what is her mass in grams? (Use the relationships between units given on the back inside cover of the text.)

SOLUTION

Because we want to change from lb to g, we look for a relationship between these units of mass. From the back inside cover we have 1 lb = 453.6 g. To cancel pounds and leave grams, we write the conversion factor with grams in the numerator and pounds in the denominator:

$$\text{Mass in grams} = (115 \text{ lb})\left(\frac{453.6 \text{ g}}{1 \text{ lb}}\right) = 5.22 \times 10^4 \text{ g}$$

The answer can be given to only three significant figures, the number of significant figures in 115 lb. The process we have used is diagrammed in the margin.

■■■ **PRACTICE EXERCISE**

By using a conversion factor from the back inside cover, determine the length in kilometers of a 500.0-mi automobile race.
Answer: 804.7 km

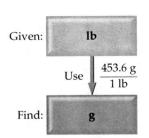

Given: lb

Use $\dfrac{453.6 \text{ g}}{1 \text{ lb}}$

Find: g

Strategies in Chemistry   ESTIMATING ANSWERS

A friend once remarked cynically that calculators let you get the wrong answer more quickly. What he was implying by that remark was that unless you have the correct strategy for solving a problem and have punched in the correct numbers, the answer will be incorrect. If you learn to *estimate* answers, however, you will be able to check whether the answers to your calculations are reasonable.

The idea is to make a rough calculation using numbers that are rounded off in such a way that the arithmetic can be easily performed without a calculator. This approach is often referred to as making a "ballpark" estimate, meaning that while it does not give an exact answer, it gives one that is roughly the right size. By working with units using dimensional analysis and by estimating answers, we can readily check the reasonableness of our answers to calculations.

GIVE IT SOME THOUGHT

How do we determine how many digits to use in conversion factors, such as the one between pounds and grams in Sample Exercise 1.9?

Using Two or More Conversion Factors

It is often necessary to use several conversion factors in solving a problem. As an example, let's convert the length of an 8.00-m rod to inches. The table on the back inside cover does not give the relationship between meters and inches. It *does*, however, give the relationship between centimeters and inches. (1 in. = 2.54 cm). From our knowledge of metric prefixes, we know that 1 cm = 10^{-2} m. Thus, we can convert step by step, first from meters to centimeters, and then from centimeters to inches as diagrammed in the margin.

Combining the given quantity (8.00 m) and the two conversion factors, we have

$$\text{Number of inches} = (8.00 \text{ m})\left(\frac{1 \text{ cm}}{10^{-2} \text{ m}}\right)\left(\frac{1 \text{ in.}}{2.54 \text{ cm}}\right) = 315 \text{ in.}$$

The first conversion factor is applied to cancel meters and convert the length to centimeters. Thus, meters are written in the denominator and centimeters in the numerator. The second conversion factor is written to cancel centimeters, so it has centimeters in the denominator and inches, the desired unit, in the numerator.

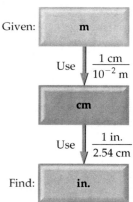

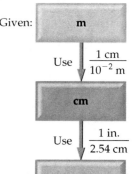

■■■ **SAMPLE EXERCISE 1.10** | Converting Units Using Two or More Conversion Factors

The average speed of a nitrogen molecule in air at 25 °C is 515 m/s. Convert this speed to miles per hour.

SOLUTION

To go from the given units, m/s, to the desired units, mi/hr, we must convert meters to miles and seconds to hours. From our knowledge of metric prefixes we know that 1 km = 10^{3} m. From the relationships given on the back inside cover of the book, we find that 1 mi = 1.6093 km. Thus, we can convert m to km and then convert km to mi. From our knowledge of time we know that 60 s = 1 min and 60 min = 1 hr. Thus, we can convert s to min and then convert min to hr. The overall process is diagrammed in the margin.

Applying first the conversions for distance and then those for time, we can set up one long equation in which unwanted units are canceled:

$$\text{Speed in mi/hr} = \left(515\frac{\text{m}}{\text{s}}\right)\left(\frac{1 \text{ km}}{10^{3} \text{ m}}\right)\left(\frac{1 \text{ mi}}{1.6093 \text{ km}}\right)\left(\frac{60 \text{ s}}{1 \text{ min}}\right)\left(\frac{60 \text{ min}}{1 \text{ hr}}\right)$$

$$= 1.15 \times 10^{3} \text{ mi/hr}$$

Our answer has the desired units. We can check our calculation, using the estimating procedure described in the previous "Strategies" box. The given speed is about

500 m/s. Dividing by 1000 converts m to km, giving 0.5 km/s. Because 1 mi is about 1.6 km, this speed corresponds to 0.5/1.6 = 0.3 mi/s. Multiplying by 60 gives about 0.3 × 60 = 20 mi/min. Multiplying again by 60 gives 20 × 60 = 1200 mi/hr. The approximate solution (about 1200 mi/hr) and the detailed solution (1150 mi/hr) are reasonably close. The answer to the detailed solution has three significant figures, corresponding to the number of significant figures in the given speed in m/s.

▪ PRACTICE EXERCISE

A car travels 28 mi per gallon of gasoline. How many kilometers per liter will it go?
Answer: 12 km/L

Conversions Involving Volume

The conversion factors previously noted convert from one unit of a given measure to another unit of the same measure, such as from length to length. We also have conversion factors that convert from one measure to a different one. The density of a substance, for example, can be treated as a conversion factor between mass and volume. Suppose that we want to know the mass in grams of two cubic inches (2.00 in.^{3}) of gold, which has a density of 19.3 g/cm^3. The density gives us the following factors:

$$\frac{19.3\ \text{g}}{1\ \text{cm}^3} \quad \text{and} \quad \frac{1\ \text{cm}^3}{19.3\ \text{g}}$$

Because the answer we want is a mass in grams, we can see that we will use the first of these factors, which has mass in grams in the numerator. To use this factor, however, we must first convert cubic inches to cubic centimeters. The relationship between in.^{3} and cm^3 is not given on the back inside cover, but the relationship between inches and centimeters is given: 1 in. = 2.54 cm (exactly). Cubing both sides of this equation gives (1 in.)^3 = (2.54 cm)^3, from which we write the desired conversion factor:

$$\frac{(2.54\ \text{cm})^3}{(1\ \text{in.})^3} = \frac{(2.54)^3\ \text{cm}^3}{(1)^3\ \text{in.}^3} = \frac{16.39\ \text{cm}^3}{1\ \text{in.}^3}$$

Notice that both the numbers and the units are cubed. Also, because 2.54 is an exact number, we can retain as many digits of (2.54)^3 as we need. We have used four, one more than the number of digits in the density (19.3 g/cm^3). Applying our conversion factors, we can now solve the problem:

$$\text{Mass in grams} = (2.00\ \text{in.}^3)\left(\frac{16.39\ \text{cm}^3}{1\ \text{in.}^3}\right)\left(\frac{19.3\ \text{g}}{1\ \text{cm}^3}\right) = 633\ \text{g}$$

The procedure is diagrammed below. The final answer is reported to three significant figures, the same number of significant figures as in 2.00 in.^{3} and 19.3 g.

▪ SAMPLE EXERCISE 1.11 │ Converting Volume Units

Earth's oceans contain approximately 1.36 × 10^9 km^3 of water. Calculate the volume in liters.

SOLUTION

This problem involves conversion of km^3 to L. From the back inside cover of the text we find 1 L = 10^{-3} m^3, but there is no relationship listed involving km^3. From our knowledge of metric prefixes, however, we have 1 km = 10^3 m and we can use this relationship between lengths to write the desired conversion factor between volumes:

$$\left(\frac{10^3 \text{ m}}{1 \text{ km}}\right)^3 = \frac{10^9 \text{ m}^3}{1 \text{ km}^3}$$

Thus, converting from km^3 to m^3 to L, we have

$$\text{Volume in liters} = (1.36 \times 10^9 \text{ km}^3)\left(\frac{10^9 \text{ m}^3}{1 \text{ km}^3}\right)\left(\frac{1 \text{ L}}{10^{-3} \text{ m}^3}\right) = 1.36 \times 10^{21} \text{ L}$$

■ PRACTICE EXERCISE

If the volume of an object is reported as 5.0 ft^3, what is the volume in cubic meters?
Answer: 0.14 m^3

Strategies in Chemistry   THE IMPORTANCE OF PRACTICE

If you have ever played a musical instrument or participated in athletics, you know that the keys to success are practice and discipline. You cannot learn to play a piano merely by listening to music, and you cannot learn how to play basketball merely by watching games on television. Likewise, you cannot learn chemistry by merely watching your instructor do it. Simply reading this book, listening to lectures, or reviewing notes will not usually be sufficient when exam time comes around. Your task is not merely to understand how someone else uses chemistry, but to be able to do it yourself. That takes practice on a regular basis, and anything that you have to do on a regular basis requires self-discipline until it becomes a habit.

Throughout the book, we have provided sample exercises in which the solutions are shown in detail. A practice exercise, for which only the answer is given, accompanies each sample exercise. It is important that you use these exercises as learn-

ing aids. End-of-chapter exercises provide additional questions to help you understand the material in the chapter. Red numbers indicate exercises for which answers are given at the back of the book. A review of basic mathematics is given in Appendix A.

The practice exercises in this text and the homework assignments given by your instructor provide the minimal practice that you will need to succeed in your chemistry course. Only by working all the assigned problems will you face the full range of difficulty and coverage that your instructor expects you to master for exams. There is no substitute for a determined and perhaps lengthy effort to work problems on your own. If you are stuck on a problem, however, ask for help from your instructor, a teaching assistant, a tutor, or a fellow student. Spending an inordinate amount of time on a single exercise is rarely effective unless you know that it is particularly challenging and requires extensive thought and effort.

■ SAMPLE EXERCISE 1.12 | Conversions Involving Density

What is the mass in grams of 1.00 gal of water? The density of water is 1.00 g/mL.

SOLUTION

Before we begin solving this exercise, we note the following:

1. We are given 1.00 gal of water (the known, or given, quantity) and asked to calculate its mass in grams (the unknown).
2. We have the following conversion factors either given, commonly known, or available on the back inside cover of the text:

$$\frac{1.00 \text{ g water}}{1 \text{ mL water}} \quad \frac{1 \text{ L}}{1000 \text{ mL}} \quad \frac{1 \text{ L}}{1.057 \text{ qt}} \quad \frac{1 \text{ gal}}{4 \text{ qt}}$$

The first of these conversion factors must be used as written (with grams in the numerator) to give the desired result, whereas the last conversion factor must be inverted in order to cancel gallons:

$$\text{Mass in grams} = (1.00 \text{ gal})\left(\frac{4 \text{ qt}}{1 \text{ gal}}\right)\left(\frac{1 \text{ L}}{1.057 \text{ qt}}\right)\left(\frac{1000 \text{ mL}}{1 \text{ L}}\right)\left(\frac{1.00 \text{ g}}{1 \text{ mL}}\right)$$

$$= 3.78 \times 10^3 \text{ g water}$$

The units of our final answer are appropriate, and we've also taken care of our significant figures. We can further check our calculation by the estimation procedure. We can round 1.057 off to 1. Focusing on the numbers that do not equal 1 then gives merely 4 × 1000 = 4000 g, in agreement with the detailed calculation.

In cases such as this you may also be able to use common sense to assess the reasonableness of your answer. In this case we know that most people can lift a gallon of milk with one hand, although it would be tiring to carry it around all day. Milk is mostly water and will have a density that is not too different than water. Therefore, we might estimate that in familiar units a gallon of water would have mass that was more than 5 lbs but less than 50 lbs. The mass we have calculated is 3.78 kg $\times$ 2.2 lb/kg = 8.3 lbs—an answer that is reasonable at least as an order of magnitude estimate.

■ PRACTICE EXERCISE

The density of benzene is 0.879 g/mL. Calculate the mass in grams of 1.00 qt of benzene.
Answer: 832 g

CHAPTER REVIEW

Following each chapter you will find a summary that highlights important content of the chapter. The summary contains all the key terms from the chapter in their contexts. A list of key skills and key equations follows the summary. These review materials are important tools to help you prepare for exams.

SUMMARY AND KEY TERMS

Introduction and Section 1.1 **Chemistry** is the study of the composition, structure, properties, and changes of **matter**. The composition of matter relates to the kinds of **elements** it contains. The structure of matter relates to the ways the **atoms** of these elements are arranged. A **property** is any characteristic that gives a sample of matter its unique identity. A **molecule** is an entity composed of two or more atoms with the atoms attached to one another in a specific way.

Section 1.2 Matter exists in three physical states, **gas, liquid,** and **solid,** which are known as the **states of matter.** There are two kinds of **pure substances: elements** and **compounds.** Each element has a single kind of atom and is represented by a chemical symbol consisting of one or two letters, with the first letter capitalized. Compounds are composed of two or more elements joined chemically. The **law of constant composition,** also called the **law of definite proportions,** states that the elemental composition of a pure compound is always the same. Most matter consists of a mixture of substances. **Mixtures** have variable compositions and can be either homogeneous or heterogeneous; homogeneous mixtures are called **solutions.**

Section 1.3 Each substance has a unique set of **physical properties** and **chemical properties** that can be used to identify it. During a **physical change,** matter does not change its composition. **Changes of state** are physical changes. In a **chemical change (chemical reaction)** a substance is transformed into a chemically different substance. **Intensive properties** are independent of the amount of matter examined and are used to identify substances. **Extensive properties** relate to the amount of substance present. Differences in physical and chemical properties are used to separate substances.

The **scientific method** is a dynamic process used to answer questions about our physical world. Observations and experiments lead to **scientific laws,** general rules that summarize how nature behaves. Observations also lead to tentative explanations or **hypotheses.** As a hypothesis is tested and refined, a **theory** may be developed.

Section 1.4 Measurements in chemistry are made using the **metric system.** Special emphasis is placed on a particular set of metric units called **SI units,** which are based on the meter, the kilogram, and the second as the basic units of length, **mass,** and time, respectively. The metric system employs a set of prefixes to indicate decimal fractions or multiples of the base units. The SI temperature scale is the **Kelvin scale,** although the **Celsius scale** is frequently used as well. **Density** is an important property that equals mass divided by volume.

Section 1.5 All measured quantities are inexact to some extent. The **precision** of a measurement indicates how closely different measurements of a quantity agree with one another. The **accuracy** of a measurement indicates how well a measurement agrees with the accepted or "true" value. The **significant figures** in a measured quantity include one estimated digit, the last digit of the measurement. The significant figures indicate the extent of the uncertainty of the measurement. Certain rules must be followed so that a calculation involving measured quantities is reported with the appropriate number of significant figures.

Section 1.6 In the **dimensional analysis** approach to problem solving, we keep track of units as we carry measurements through calculations. The units are multiplied together, divided into each other, or canceled like algebraic quantities. Obtaining the proper units for the final result is an important means of checking the method of calculation. When converting units and when carrying out several other types of problems, **conversion factors** can be used. These factors are ratios constructed from valid relations between equivalent quantities.

KEY SKILLS

- Distinguish among elements, compounds, and mixtures.
- Memorize symbols of common elements and common metric prefixes.
- Use significant figures, scientific notation, metric units, and dimensional analysis in calculations.

KEY EQUATIONS

- $K = {}^{\circ}C + 273.15$ [1.1]   Interconverting between Celsius (°C) and Kelvin (K) temperatures scales

- ${}^{\circ}C = \dfrac{5}{9}({}^{\circ}F - 32)$ or ${}^{\circ}F = \dfrac{9}{5}({}^{\circ}C) + 32$ [1.2]   Interconverting between Celsius (°C) and Fahrenheit (°F) temperature scales

- $\text{Density} = \dfrac{\text{mass}}{\text{volume}}$ [1.3]   Definition of density

VISUALIZING CONCEPTS

The exercises in this section are intended to probe your understanding of key concepts rather than your ability to utilize formulas and perform calculations. Those exercises with red exercise numbers have answers in the back of the book.

1.1 Which of the following figures represents (a) a pure ele-
CQ ment, (b) a mixture of two elements, (c) a pure compound, (d) a mixture of an element and a compound? (More than one picture might fit each description.) [Section 1.2]

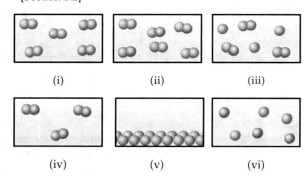

(i)   (ii)   (iii)

(iv)   (v)   (vi)

1.2 Does the following diagram represent a chemical or
CQ physical change? How do you know? [Section 1.3]

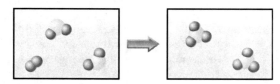

1.3 Identify each of the following as measurements of
CQ length, area, volume, mass, density, time, or temperature: (a) 5 ns, (b) 5.5 kg/m³, (c) 0.88 pm, (d) 540 km²,
(e) 173 K, (f) 2 mm³, (g) 23 °C. [Section 1.4]

1.4 Three spheres of equal size are composed of aluminum
(density = 2.70 g/cm³), silver (density = 10.49 g/cm³),
and nickel (density = 8.90 g/cm³). List the spheres from
lightest to heaviest.

1.5 The following dartboards illustrate the types of errors
CQ often seen when one measurement is repeated several

times. The bull's-eye represents the "true value," and the darts represent the experimental measurements. Which board best represents each of the following scenarios: (a) measurements both accurate and precise, (b) measurements precise but inaccurate, (c) measurements imprecise but yield an accurate average? [Section 1.5]

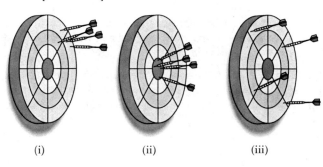

(i)   (ii)   (iii)

1.6 (a) What is the length of the pencil in the following fig-
CQ ure if the scale reads in centimeters? How many signifi-
cant figures are there in this measurement? (b) An oven thermometer with a circular scale reading degrees Fahrenheit is shown. What temperature does the scale indicate? How many significant figures are in the measurement? [Section 1.5]

1.7 What is wrong with the following statement? Twenty
CQ years ago an ancient artifact was determined to be 1900
years old. It must now be 1920 years old. [Section 1.5]

1.8 **(a)** How many significant figures should be reported for
CQ the volume of the metal bar shown below? **(b)** If the
mass of the bar is 104.7 g, how many significant figures
should be reported when its density is calculated using
the calculated volume? [Section 1.5]

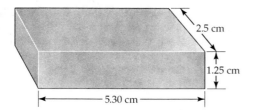

2.5 cm

1.25 cm

5.30 cm

1.9 When you convert units, how do you decide which part
CQ of the conversion factor is in the numerator and which is
in the denominator? [Section 1.6]

1.10 Draw a logic map indicating the steps you would take
CQ to convert miles per hour to kilometers per second.
Write down the conversion factor for each step, as done
in the diagram on page 26. [Section 1.6]

EXERCISES

Classification and Properties of Matter

The following exercises are divided into sections that deal with
specific topics in the chapter. These exercises are grouped in
pairs, with the answer given in the back of the book to the odd-
numbered exercise, as indicated by the red exercise number.
Those exercises whose number appears in brackets are more
challenging than the nonbracketed exercises.

1.11 Classify each of the following as a pure substance or a
mixture. If a mixture, indicate whether it is homogeneous or heterogeneous: **(a)** rice pudding, **(b)** seawater,
(c) magnesium, **(d)** gasoline.

1.12 Classify each of the following as a pure substance or a
mixture. If a mixture, indicate whether it is homogeneous or heterogeneous: **(a)** air, **(b)** tomato juice, **(c)** iodine crystals, **(d)** sand.

1.13 Give the chemical symbol or name for the following
elements, as appropriate: **(a)** sulfur, **(b)** magnesium,
(c) potassium, **(d)** chlorine, **(e)** copper, **(f)** F, **(g)** Ni,
(h) Na, **(i)** Al, **(j)** Si.

1.14 Give the chemical symbol or name for each of the following elements, as appropriate: **(a)** carbon, **(b)** nitro-
gen, **(c)** bromine, **(d)** zinc, **(e)** iron, **(f)** P, **(g)** Ca, **(h)** He,
(i) Pb, **(j)** Ag.

1.15 A solid white substance A is heated strongly in the ab-
CQ sence of air. It decomposes to form a new white substance B and a gas C. The gas has exactly the same
properties as the product obtained when carbon is
burned in an excess of oxygen. Based on these observations, can we determine whether solids A and B and the
gas C are elements or compounds? Explain your conclusions for each substance.

1.16 In 1807 the English chemist Humphry Davy passed an
CQ electric current through molten potassium hydroxide
and isolated a bright, shiny reactive substance. He
claimed the discovery of a new element, which he
named potassium. In those days, before the advent of
modern instruments, what was the basis on which one
could claim that a substance was an element?

1.17 In the process of attempting to characterize a substance,
CQ a chemist makes the following observations: The substance is a silvery white, lustrous metal. It melts at 649
°C and boils at 1105 °C. Its density at 20 °C is
1.738 g/cm^3. The substance burns in air, producing an
intense white light. It reacts with chlorine to give a brittle white solid. The substance can be pounded into thin
sheets or drawn into wires. It is a good conductor of
electricity. Which of these characteristics are physical
properties, and which are chemical properties?

1.18 Read the following description of the element zinc, and
CQ indicate which are physical properties and which are
chemical properties. Zinc is a silver–gray-colored metal
that melts at 420 °C. When zinc granules are added to
dilute sulfuric acid, hydrogen is given off and the metal
dissolves. Zinc has a hardness on the Mohs scale of 2.5
and a density of 7.13 g/cm^3 at 25 °C. It reacts slowly
with oxygen gas at elevated temperatures to form zinc
oxide, ZnO.

1.19 Label each of the following as either a physical process
CQ or a chemical process: **(a)** corrosion of aluminum metal,
(b) melting of ice, **(c)** pulverizing an aspirin, **(d)** digest-
ing a candy bar, **(e)** explosion of nitroglycerin.

1.20 A match is lit and held under a cold piece of metal. The
CQ following observations are made: **(a)** The match burns.
(b) The metal gets warmer. **(c)** Water condenses on the
metal. **(d)** Soot (carbon) is deposited on the metal.
Which of these occurrences are due to physical changes,
and which are due to chemical changes?

1.21 Suggest a method of separating each of the following
CQ mixtures into two components: **(a)** sugar and sand,
(b) iron and sulfur.

1.22 A beaker contains a clear, colorless liquid. If it is water,
CQ how could you determine whether it contained dissolved table salt? Do *not* taste it!

Units and Measurement

1.23 What exponential notation do the following abbreviations represent: (a) d, (b) c, (c) f, (d) μ, (e) M, (f) k, (g) n, (h) m, (i) p?

1.24 Use appropriate metric prefixes to write the following measurements without use of exponents: (a) 6.35×10^{-2} L, (b) 6.5×10^{-6} s, (c) 9.5×10^{-4} m, (d) 4.23×10^{-9} m^3, (e) 12.5×10^{-8} kg, (f) 3.5×10^{-10} g, (g) 6.54×10^{9} fs.

1.25 Make the following conversions: (a) 62 °F to °C, (b) 216.7 °C to °F, (c) 233 °C to K, (d) 315 K to °F, (e) 2500 °F to K.

1.26 (a) The temperature on a warm summer day is 87 °F. What is the temperature in °C? (b) Many scientific data are reported at 25 °C. What is this temperature in kelvins and in degrees Fahrenheit? (c) Suppose that a recipe calls for an oven temperature of 175 °F. Convert this temperature to degrees Celsius and to kelvins. (d) The melting point of sodium bromide (a salt) is 755 °C. Calculate this temperature in °F and in kelvins. (e) Neon, a gaseous element at room temperature, is used to make electronic signs. Neon has a melting point of −248.6 °C and a boiling point of −246.1 °C. Convert these temperatures to kelvins.

1.27 (a) A sample of carbon tetrachloride, a liquid once used in dry cleaning, has a mass of 39.73 g and a volume of 25.0 mL at 25 °C. What is its density at this temperature? Will carbon tetrachloride float on water? (Materials that are less dense than water will float.) (b) The density of platinum is 21.45 g/cm^3 at 20 °C. Calculate the mass of 75.00 cm^3 of platinum at this temperature. (c) The density of magnesium is 1.738 g/cm^3 at 20 °C. What is the volume of 87.50 g of this metal at this temperature?

1.28 (a) A cube of osmium metal 1.500 cm on a side has a mass of 76.31 g at 25 °C. What is its density in g/cm^3 at this temperature? (b) The density of titanium metal is 4.51 g/cm^3 at 25 °C. What mass of titanium displaces 125.0 mL of water at 25 °C? (c) The density of benzene at 15 °C is 0.8787 g/mL. Calculate the mass of 0.1500 L of benzene at this temperature.

1.29 (a) To identify a liquid substance, a student determined its density. Using a graduated cylinder, she measured out a 45-mL sample of the substance. She then measured the mass of the sample, finding that it weighed 38.5 g. She knew that the substance had to be either isopropyl alcohol (density 0.785 g/mL) or toluene (density 0.866 /mL). What are the calculated density and the probable identity of the substance? (b) An experiment requires 45.0 g of ethylene glycol, a liquid whose density is 1.114 g/mL. Rather than weigh the sample on a balance, a chemist chooses to dispense the liquid using a graduated cylinder. What volume of the liquid should he use? (c) A cubic piece of metal measures 5.00 cm on each edge. If the metal is nickel, whose density is 8.90 g/cm^3, what is the mass of the cube?

1.30 (a) After the label fell off a bottle containing a clear liquid believed to be benzene, a chemist measured the density of the liquid to verify its identity. A 25.0-mL portion of the liquid had a mass of 21.95 g. A chemistry handbook lists the density of benzene at 15 °C as 0.8787 g/mL. Is the calculated density in agreement with the tabulated value? (b) An experiment requires 15.0 g of cyclohexane, whose density at 25 °C is 0.7781 g/mL. What volume of cyclohexane should be used? (c) A spherical ball of lead has a diameter of 5.0 cm. What is the mass of the sphere if lead has a density of 11.34 g/cm^3? (The volume of a sphere is $(\frac{4}{3})\pi r^3$ where r is the radius.)

1.31 Gold can be hammered into extremely thin sheets called gold leaf. If a 200-mg piece of gold (density = 19.32 g/cm^3) is hammered into a sheet measuring 2.4×1.0 ft, what is the average thickness of the sheet in meters? How might the thickness be expressed without exponential notation, using an appropriate metric prefix?

1.32 A cylindrical rod formed from silicon is 16.8 cm long and has a mass of 2.17 kg. The density of silicon is 2.33 g/cm^3. What is the diameter of the cylinder? (The volume of a cylinder is given by $\pi r^2 h$, where r is the radius, and h is its length.)

Uncertainty in Measurement

1.33 Indicate which of the following are exact numbers: (a) the mass of a paper clip, (b) the surface area of a dime, (c) the number of inches in a mile, (d) the number of ounces in a pound, (e) the number of microseconds in a week, (f) the number of pages in this book.

1.34 Indicate which of the following are exact numbers: (a) the mass of a 32-oz can of coffee, (b) the number of students in your chemistry class, (c) the temperature of the surface of the sun, (d) the mass of a postage stamp, (e) the number of milliliters in a cubic meter of water, (f) the average height of students in your school.

1.35 What is the number of significant figures in each of the following measured quantities? (a) 358 kg, (b) 0.054 s, (c) 6.3050 cm, (d) 0.0105 L, (e) 7.0500×10^{-3} m^3.

1.36 Indicate the number of significant figures in each of the following measured quantities: (a) 3.774 km, (b) 205 m^2, (c) 1.700 cm, (d) 350.00 K, (e) 307.080 g.

1.37 Round each of the following numbers to four significant figures, and express the result in standard exponential notation: (a) 102.53070, (b) 656,980, (c) 0.008543210, (d) 0.000257870, (e) −0.0357202.

1.38 (a) The diameter of Earth at the equator is 7926.381 mi. Round this number to three significant figures, and express it in standard exponential notation. (b) The circumference of Earth through the poles is 40,008 km. Round this number to four significant figures, and express it in standard exponential notation.

1.39 Carry out the following operations, and express the answers with the appropriate number of significant figures.
 (a) 12.0550 + 9.05
 (b) 257.2 − 19.789
 (c) (6.21×10^3) (0.1050)
 (d) 0.0577/0.753

Dimensional Analysis

1.41 Using your knowledge of metric units, English units, and the information on the back inside cover, write down the conversion factors needed to convert (a) mm to nm, (b) mg to kg, (c) km to ft, (d) in.^{3} to cm^3.

1.42 Using your knowledge of metric units, English units, and the information on the back inside cover, write down the conversion factors needed to convert (a) μm to mm, (b) ms to ns, (c) mi to km, (d) ft^3 to L.

1.43 Perform the following conversions: (a) 0.076 L to mL, (b) 5.0×10^{-8} m to nm, (c) 6.88×10^5 ns to s, (d) 0.50 lb to g, (e) 1.55 kg/m^3 to g/L, (f) 5.850 gal/hr to L/s.

1.44 (a) The speed of light in a vacuum is 2.998×10^8 m/s. Calculate its speed in km/hr. (b) The Sears Tower in Chicago is 1454 ft tall. Calculate its height in meters. (c) The Vehicle Assembly Building at the Kennedy Space Center in Florida has a volume of 3,666,500 m^3. Convert this volume to liters, and express the result in standard exponential notation. (d) An individual suffering from a high cholesterol level in her blood has 232 mg of cholesterol per 100 mL of blood. If the total blood volume of the individual is 5.2 L, how many grams of total blood cholesterol does the individual's body contain?

1.45 Perform the following conversions: (a) 5.00 days to s, (b) 0.0550 mi to m, (c) \$1.89/gal to dollars per liter, (d) 0.510 in./ms to km/hr, (e) 22.50 gal/min to L/s, (f) 0.02500 ft^3 to cm^3.

1.46 Carry out the following conversions: (a) 0.105 in. to mm, (b) 0.650 qt to mL, (c) 8.75 μm/s to km/hr, (d) 1.955 m^3 to yd^3, (e) \$3.99/lb to dollars per kg, (f) 8.75 lb/ft^3 to g/mL.

1.47 (a) How many liters of wine can be held in a wine barrel whose capacity is 31 gal? (b) The recommended adult dose of Elixophyllin®, a drug used to treat asthma, is 6 mg/kg of body mass. Calculate the dose in milligrams for a 150-lb person. (c) If an automobile is able to travel 254 mi on 11.2 gal of gasoline, what is the gas mileage in km/L? (d) A pound of coffee beans yields 50 cups of coffee (4 cups = 1 qt). How many milliliters of coffee can be obtained from 1 g of coffee beans?

1.40 Carry out the following operations, and express the answer with the appropriate number of significant figures.
 (a) 320.5 − (6104.5/2.3)
 (b) $[(285.3 \times 10^5) - (1.200 \times 10^3)] \times 2.8954$
 (c) $(0.0045 \times 20,000.0) + (2813 \times 12)$
 (d) $863 \times [1255 - (3.45 \times 108)]$

1.48 (a) If an electric car is capable of going 225 km on a single charge, how many charges will it need to travel from Boston, Massachusetts, to Miami, Florida, a distance of 1486 mi, assuming that the trip begins with a full charge? (b) If a migrating loon flies at an average speed of 14 m/s, what is its average speed in mi/hr? (c) What is the engine piston displacement in liters of an engine whose displacement is listed as 450 in.^{3}? (d) In March 1989 the *Exxon Valdez* ran aground and spilled 240,000 barrels of crude petroleum off the coast of Alaska. One barrel of petroleum is equal to 42 gal. How many liters of petroleum were spilled?

1.49 The density of air at ordinary atmospheric pressure and 25 °C is 1.19 g/L. What is the mass, in kilograms, of the air in a room that measures $12.5 \times 15.5 \times 8.0$ ft?

1.50 The concentration of carbon monoxide in an urban apartment is 48 μg/m^3. What mass of carbon monoxide in grams is present in a room measuring $9.0 \times 14.5 \times 18.8$ ft?

1.51 By using estimation techniques, arrange these items in order from shortest to longest: a 57-cm length of string, a 14-in. long shoe, and a 1.1-m length of pipe.

1.52 By using estimation techniques, determine which of the following is the heaviest and which is the lightest: a 5-lb bag of potatoes, a 5-kg bag of sugar, or 1 gal of water (density = 1.0 g/mL).

1.53 The Morgan silver dollar has a mass of 26.73 g. By law, it was required to contain 90% silver, with the remainder being copper. (a) When the coin was minted in the late 1800s, silver was worth \$1.18 per troy ounce (31.1 g). At this price, what is the value of the silver in the silver dollar? (b) Today, silver sells for about \$13.25 per troy ounce. How many Morgan silver dollars are required to obtain \$25.00 worth of pure silver?

1.54 A copper refinery produces a copper ingot weighing 150 lb. If the copper is drawn into wire whose diameter is 8.25 mm, how many feet of copper can be obtained from the ingot? The density of copper is 8.94 g/cm^3 (Assume that the wire is a cylinder whose volume is $V = \pi r^2 h$, where r is its radius and h is its height or length.)

ADDITIONAL EXERCISES

The exercises in this section are not divided by category, although they are roughly in the order of the topics in the chapter. They are not paired.

1.55 What is meant by the terms composition and structure when referring to matter?

1.56 (a) Classify each of the following as a pure substance, a
CQ solution, or a heterogeneous mixture: a gold coin, a cup

of coffee, a wood plank. (b) What ambiguities are there in answering part (a) from the descriptions given?

1.57 (a) What is the difference between a hypothesis and a theory? (b) Explain the difference between a theory and a scientific law. Which addresses how matter behaves, and which addresses why it behaves that way?

1.58 A sample of ascorbic acid (vitamin C) is synthesized in
CQ the laboratory. It contains 1.50 g of carbon and 2.00 g of

oxygen. Another sample of ascorbic acid isolated from citrus fruits contains 6.35 g of carbon. How many grams of oxygen does it contain? Which law are you assuming in answering this question?

1.59 Two students determine the percentage of lead in a sample as a laboratory exercise. The true percentage is 22.52%. The students' results for three determinations are as follows:
 1. 22.52, 22.48, 22.54
 2. 22.64, 22.58, 22.62

 (a) Calculate the average percentage for each set of data, and tell which set is the more accurate based on the average. **(b)** Precision can be judged by examining the average of the deviations from the average value for that data set. (Calculate the average value for each data set, then calculate the average value of the absolute deviations of each measurement from the average.) Which set is more precise?

1.60 Is the use of significant figures in each of the following statements appropriate? Why or why not? **(a)** The 2005 circulation of *National Geographic* was 7,812,564. **(b)** On July 1, 2005, the population of Cook County, Illinois, was 5,303,683. **(c)** In the United States, 0.621% of the population has the surname Brown.

1.61 What type of quantity (for example, length, volume, density) do the following units indicate: **(a)** mL, **(b)** cm^2, **(c)** mm^3, **(d)** mg/L, **(e)** ps, **(f)** nm, **(g)** K?

1.62 Give the derived SI units for each of the following quantities in base SI units: **(a)** acceleration = distance/time^2; **(b)** force = mass × acceleration; **(c)** work = force × distance; **(d)** pressure = force/area; **(e)** power = work/time.

1.63 The distance from Earth to the Moon is approximately 240,000 mi. **(a)** What is this distance in meters? **(b)** The peregrine falcon has been measured as traveling up to 350 km/hr in a dive. If this falcon could fly to the Moon at this speed, how many seconds would it take?

1.64 The US quarter has a mass of 5.67 g and is approximately 1.55 mm thick. **(a)** How many quarters would have to be stacked to reach 575 ft, the height of the Washington Monument? **(b)** How much would this stack weigh? **(c)** How much money would this stack contain? **(d)** At the beginning of 2007, the national debt was $8.7 trillion. How many stacks like the one described would be necessary to pay off this debt?

1.65 In the United States, water used for irrigation is measured in acre-feet. An acre-foot of water covers an acre to a depth of exactly 1 ft. An acre is 4840 yd^2. An acre-foot is enough water to supply two typical households for 1.00 yr. **(a)** If desalinated water costs $1950 per acre-foot, how much does desalinated water cost per liter? **(b)** How much would it cost one household per day if it were the only source of water?

1.66 Suppose you decide to define your own temperature scale using the freezing point (−11.5 °C) and boiling point (197.6 °C) of ethylene glycol. If you set the freezing point as 0 °G and the boiling point as 100 °G, what is the freezing point of water on this new scale?

1.67 The liquid substances mercury (density = 13.5 g/mL), water (1.00 g/mL), and cyclohexane (0.778 g/mL) do not form a solution when mixed, but separate in distinct layers. Sketch how the liquids would position themselves in a test tube.

1.68 Small spheres of equal mass are made of lead (density = 11.3 g/cm^3), silver (10.5 g/cm^3), and aluminum (2.70 g/cm^3). Without doing a calculation, list the spheres in order from the smallest to the largest.

1.69 Water has a density of 0.997 g/cm^3 at 25 °C; ice has a density of 0.917 g/cm^3 at −10 °C. **(a)** If a soft-drink bottle whose volume is 1.50 L is completely filled with water and then frozen to −10 °C, what volume does the ice occupy? **(b)** Can the ice be contained within the bottle?

1.70 A 32.65-g sample of a solid is placed in a flask. Toluene, in which the solid is insoluble, is added to the flask so that the total volume of solid and liquid together is 50.00 mL. The solid and toluene together weigh 58.58 g. The density of toluene at the temperature of the experiment is 0.864 g/mL. What is the density of the solid?

1.71 **(a)** You are given a bottle that contains 4.59 cm^3 of a metallic solid. The total mass of the bottle and solid is 35.66 g. The empty bottle weighs 14.23 g. What is the density of the solid? **(b)** Mercury is traded by the "flask," a unit that has a mass of 34.5 kg. What is the volume of a flask of mercury if the density of mercury is 13.5 g/mL? **(c)** A thief plans to steal a gold sphere with a radius of 28.9 cm from a museum. If the gold has a density of 19.3 g/cm^3 what is the mass of the sphere? [The volume of a sphere is $V = (4/3)\pi r^3$.] Is he likely to be able to walk off with it unassisted?

1.72 Automobile batteries contain sulfuric acid, which is commonly referred to as "battery acid." Calculate the number of grams of sulfuric acid in 0.500 L of battery acid if the solution has a density of 1.28 g/mL and is 38.1% sulfuric acid by mass.

1.73 A 40-lb container of peat moss measures 14 × 20 × 30 in. A 40-lb container of topsoil has a volume of 1.9 gal. **(a)** Calculate the average densities of peat moss and topsoil in units of g/cm^3. Would it be correct to say that peat moss is "lighter" than topsoil? Explain. **(b)** How many bags of the peat moss are needed to cover an area measuring 10. ft by 20. ft to a depth of 2.0 in.?

1.74 A coin dealer offers to sell you an ancient gold coin that is 2.2 cm in diameter and 3.0 mm in thickness. **(a)** The density of gold is 19.3 g/cm^3. How much should the coin weigh if it is pure gold? **(b)** If gold sells for $640 per troy ounce, how much is the gold content worth? (1 troy ounce = 31.1 g).

1.75 A package of aluminum foil contains 50 ft^2 of foil, which weighs approximately 8.0 oz. Aluminum has a density of 2.70 g/cm^3. What is the approximate thickness of the foil in millimeters?

1.76 A 15.0-cm long cylindrical glass tube, sealed at one end, is filled with ethanol. The mass of ethanol needed to fill the tube is found to be 11.86 g. The density of ethanol is 0.789 g/mL. Calculate the inner diameter of the tube in centimeters.

1.77 Gold is alloyed (mixed) with other metals to increase its hardness in making jewelry. **(a)** Consider a piece of gold jewelry that weighs 9.85 g and has a volume of

0.675 cm^3. The jewelry contains only gold and silver, which have densities of 19.3 g/cm^3 and 10.5 g/cm^3, respectively. If the total volume of the jewelry is the sum of the volumes of the gold and silver that it contains, calculate the percentage of gold (by mass) in the jewelry. **(b)** The relative amount of gold in an alloy is commonly expressed in units of karats. Pure gold is 24-karat, and the percentage of gold in an alloy is given as a percentage of this value. For example, an alloy that is 50% gold is 12-karat. State the purity of the gold jewelry in karats.

1.78 Suppose you are given a sample of a homogeneous liquid. What would you do to determine whether it is a solution or a pure substance?

1.79 Chromatography (Figure 1.14) is a simple, but reliable, method for separating a mixture into its constituent substances. Suppose you are using chromatography to separate a mixture of two substances. How would you know whether the separation is successful? Can you propose a means of quantifying how good or how poor the separation is?

1.80 You are assigned the task of separating a desired granular material, with a density of 3.62 g/cm^3, from an undesired granular material that has a density of 2.04 g/cm^3. You want to do this by shaking the mixture in a liquid in which the heavier material will fall to the bottom and the lighter material will float. A solid will float on any liquid that is more dense. Using the internet or a handbook of chemistry, find the densities of the following substances: carbon tetrachloride, hexane, benzene, and methylene iodide. Which of these liquids will serve your purpose, assuming no chemical interaction between the liquid and the solids?

1.81 In 2006, Professor Galen Suppes, from the University of Missouri-Columbia, was awarded a Presidential Green Challenge Award for his system of converting glycerin, $C_3H_5(OH)_3$, a by-product of biodiesel production, to propylene glycol, $C_3H_6(OH)_2$. Propylene glycol pro-

duced in this way will be cheap enough to replace the more toxic ethylene glycol that is the primary ingredient in automobile antifreeze. **(a)** If 50.0 mL of propylene glycol has a mass of 51.80 g, what is its density? **(b)** To obtain the same antifreeze protection requires 76 g of propylene glycol to replace each 62 g of ethylene glycol. Calculate the mass of propylene glycol required to replace 1.00 gal of ethylene glycol. The density of ethylene glycol is 1.12 g/mL. **(c)** Calculate the volume of propylene glycol, in gallons, needed to produce the same antifreeze protection as 1.00 gallon of ethylene glycol.

1.82 The concepts of accuracy and precision are not always easy to grasp. Here are two sets of studies: **(a)** The mass of a secondary weight standard is determined by weighing it on a very precise balance under carefully controlled laboratory conditions. The average of 18 different weight measurements is taken as the weight of the standard. **(b)** A group of 10,000 males between the ages of 50 and 55 is surveyed to ascertain a relationship between calorie intake and blood cholesterol level. The survey questionnaire is quite detailed, asking the respondents about what they eat, smoking and drinking habits, and so on. The results are reported as showing that for men of comparable lifestyles, there is a 40% chance of the blood cholesterol level being above 230 for those who consume more than 40 calories per gram of body weight per day, as compared with those who consume fewer than 30 calories per gram of body weight per day.

Discuss and compare these two studies in terms of the precision and accuracy of the result in each case. How do the two studies differ in nature in ways that affect the accuracy and precision of the results? What makes for high precision and accuracy in any given study? In each of these studies, what factors might not be controlled that could affect the accuracy and precision? What steps can be taken generally to attain higher precision and accuracy?

2 ATOMS, MOLECULES, AND IONS

A CIRCLE OF INIDIVUAL IRON ATOMS on a copper surface, as viewed by a technique known as scanning tunneling microscopy (STM). The image is artificially colored to enhance it. The shapes of the iron atoms in the STM image are distorted, and the atoms of the copper surface are not revealed.

WHAT'S AHEAD

LOOK AROUND YOU. Notice the great variety of colors, textures, and other properties in the materials that surround you— the colors in a garden scene, the texture of the fabric in your clothes, the solubility of sugar in a cup of coffee, the

transparency of a window. The materials in our world exhibit a striking and seemingly infinite variety.

We can classify properties in different ways, but how do we understand and explain them? What makes diamonds transparent and hard, while table salt is brittle and dissolves in water? Why does paper burn, and why does water quench fires? The structure and behavior of atoms are key to understanding both the physical and chemical properties of matter.

Remarkably, the diversity of these properties we see around us results from only about 100 different elements and therefore about 100 chemically different kinds of atoms. In a sense, the atoms are like the 26 letters of the English alphabet that join in different combinations to form the immense number of words in our language. But how do atoms combine with one another? What rules govern the ways in which atoms can combine? How do the properties of a substance relate to the kinds of atoms it contains? Indeed, what is an atom like, and what makes the atoms of one element different from those of another?

The chapter-opening photograph is an image of a circle of 48 iron atoms arranged on a copper metal surface. The diameter of the circle is about 1/20,000 the diameter of a human hair. Atoms are indeed very tiny entities.

This very striking image reveals the power of modern experimental methods to identify individual atoms, but it does not reveal the structures of the atoms themselves. Fortunately, we can use a variety of experimental techniques to probe the atom to gain a clearer understanding of what it is like. In this chapter we begin to explore the fascinating world of atoms that we discover by such experiments. We will examine the basic structure of the atom and briefly discuss the formation of molecules and ions, thereby providing a foundation for exploring chemistry more deeply in later chapters.

2.1 THE ATOMIC THEORY OF MATTER

Philosophers from the earliest times have speculated about the nature of the fundamental "stuff" from which the world is made. Democritus (460–370 BC) and other early Greek philosophers thought that the material world must be made up of tiny indivisible particles that they called *atomos*, meaning "indivisible or uncuttable." Later, Plato and Aristotle formulated the notion that there can be no ultimately indivisible particles. The "atomic" view of matter faded for many centuries during which Aristotelean philosophy dominated Western culture.

The notion of atoms reemerged in Europe during the seventeenth century, when scientists tried to explain the properties of gases. Air is composed of something invisible and in constant motion; we can feel the motion of the wind against us, for example. It is natural to think of tiny invisible particles as giving rise to these familiar effects. Isaac Newton (1642–1727), the most famous scientist of his time, favored the idea of atoms. But thinking of atoms as invisible particles in air is very different from thinking of atoms as the fundamental building blocks of elements.

As chemists learned to measure the amounts of elements that reacted with one another to form new substances, the ground was laid for an atomic theory that linked the idea of elements with the idea of atoms. That theory came from the work of an English schoolteacher, John Dalton (Figure 2.1 ◀), during the period from 1803–1807. Dalton's atomic theory involved the following postulates:

1. Each element is composed of extremely small particles called atoms.

2. All atoms of a given element are identical to one another in mass and other properties, but the atoms of one element are different from the atoms of all other elements.

3. The atoms of one element cannot be changed into atoms of a different element by chemical reactions; atoms are neither created nor destroyed in chemical reactions.

4. Compounds are formed when atoms of more than one element combine; a given compound always has the same relative number and kind of atoms.

According to Dalton's atomic theory, **atoms** are the smallest particles of an element that retain the chemical identity of the element.   (Section 1.1) As noted in the postulates of Dalton's theory, an element is composed of only one kind of atom. A compound, in contrast, contains atoms of two or more elements.

Dalton's theory explains several simple laws of chemical combination that were known during his time. One of these laws was the *law of constant composition*: In a given compound, the relative numbers and kinds of atoms are constant.   (Section 1.2) This law is the basis of Dalton's Postulate 4. Another fundamental chemical law was the *law of conservation of mass* (also known as the *law of conservation of matter*): The total mass of materials present after a chemical reaction is the same as the total mass present before the reaction. This law is the basis for Postulate 3. Dalton proposed that atoms always retain their identities and that atoms taking part in a chemical reaction rearrange to give new chemical combinations.

▲ Figure 2.1 **John Dalton (1766–1844).** Dalton was the son of a poor English weaver. He began teaching at the age of 12. He spent most of his years in Manchester, where he taught both grammar school and college. His lifelong interest in meteorology led him to study gases, then chemistry, and eventually atomic theory.

A good theory should explain the known facts and predict new ones. Dalton used his theory to deduce the *law of multiple proportions*: If two elements A and B combine to form more than one compound, the masses of B that can combine with a given mass of A are in the ratio of small whole numbers. We can illustrate this law by considering the substances water and hydrogen peroxide, both of which consist of the elements hydrogen and oxygen. In forming water, 8.0 g of oxygen combine with 1.0 g of hydrogen. In forming hydrogen peroxide, 16.0 g of oxygen combine with 1.0 g of hydrogen. In other words, the ratio of the mass of oxygen per gram of hydrogen in the two compounds is 2 : 1. Using the atomic theory, we can conclude that hydrogen peroxide contains twice as many atoms of oxygen per hydrogen atom as does water.

GIVE IT SOME THOUGHT

One compound of carbon and oxygen contains 1.333 g of oxygen per gram of carbon, whereas a second compound contains 2.666 g of oxygen per gram of carbon. **(a)** What chemical law do these data illustrate? **(b)** If the first compound has an equal number of oxygen and carbon atoms, what can we conclude about the composition of the second compound?

2.2 THE DISCOVERY OF ATOMIC STRUCTURE

Dalton reached his conclusion about atoms based on chemical observations in the macroscopic world of the laboratory. Neither he nor those who followed him during the century after his work was published had direct evidence for the existence of atoms. Today, however, we can use powerful instruments to measure the properties of individual atoms and even provide images of them (Figure 2.2▶).

As scientists began to develop methods for more detailed probing of the nature of matter, the atom, which was supposed to be indivisible, began to show signs of a more complex structure: We now know that the atom is composed of still smaller **subatomic particles**. Before we summarize the current model of atomic structure, we will briefly consider a few of the landmark discoveries that led to that model. We will see that the atom is composed in part of electrically charged particles, some with a positive (+) charge and some with a negative (−) charge. As we discuss the development of our current model of the atom, keep in mind a simple statement of the behavior of charged particles: *Particles with the same charge repel one another, whereas particles with unlike charges attract one another.*

Cathode Rays and Electrons

During the mid-1800s, scientists began to study electrical discharge through partially evacuated tubes (tubes that had been pumped almost empty of air), such as those shown in Figure 2.3▼. When a high voltage was applied to the

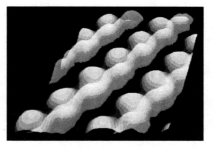

▲ Figure 2.2 **An image of the surface of the semiconductor GaAs (gallium arsenide).** This image was obtained by a technique called scanning tunneling microscopy. The color was added to the image by computer to distinguish the gallium atoms (blue spheres) from the arsenic atoms (red spheres).

▼ Figure 2.3 **Cathode-ray tube.** (a) In a cathode-ray tube, electrons move from the negative electrode (cathode) to the positive electrode (anode). (b) A photo of a cathode-ray tube containing a fluorescent screen to show the path of the cathode rays. (c) The path of the cathode rays is deflected by the presence of a magnet.

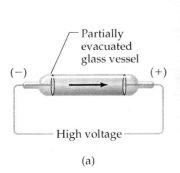

Partially evacuated glass vessel

(−)   (+)

High voltage

(a)

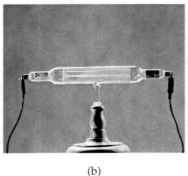

(b)

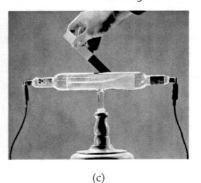

(c)

▶ Figure 2.4 **Cathode-ray tube with perpendicular magnetic and electric fields.** The cathode rays (electrons) originate from the negative plate on the left and are accelerated toward the positive plate on the right, which has a hole in its center. A narrow beam of electrons passes through the hole and is then deflected by the magnetic and electric fields. The three paths result from different strengths of the magnetic and electric fields. The charge-to-mass ratio of the electron can be determined by measuring the effects that the magnetic and electric fields have on the direction of the beam.

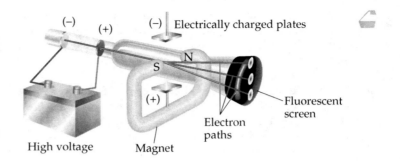

electrodes in the tube, radiation was produced. This radiation, called **cathode rays**, originated from the negative electrode, or cathode. Although the rays themselves could not be seen, their movement was detected because the rays cause certain materials, including glass, to *fluoresce*, or to give off light.

Scientists held conflicting views about the nature of the cathode rays. It was not initially clear whether the rays were an invisible stream of particles or a new form of radiation. Experiments showed that cathode rays are deflected by electric or magnetic fields in a way consistent with their being a stream of negative electrical charge [Figure 2.3(c)]. The British scientist J. J. Thomson observed many properties of the cathode rays, including the fact that they are the same regardless of the identity of the cathode material. In a paper published in 1897, Thomson summarized his observations and concluded that cathode rays are streams of negatively charged particles. Thomson's paper is generally accepted as the "discovery" of what later became known as the *electron*.

Thomson constructed a cathode-ray tube having a fluorescent screen at one end, such as that shown in Figure 2.4 ▲, so that he could quantitatively measure the effects of electric and magnetic fields on the thin stream of electrons passing through a hole in the positively charged electrode. These measurements made it possible to calculate a value of 1.76×10^8 coulombs per gram for the ratio of the electron's electrical charge to its mass.*

Once the charge-to-mass ratio of the electron was known, measuring either the charge or the mass of an electron would yield the value of the other quantity. In 1909, Robert Millikan (1868–1953) of the University of Chicago succeeded in measuring the charge of an electron by performing a series of experiments described in Figure 2.5 ▼. He then calculated the mass of the electron by using

▶ Figure 2.5 **Millikan's oil-drop experiment.** A representation of the apparatus Millikan used to measure the charge of the electron. Small drops of oil, which had picked up extra electrons, were allowed to fall between two electrically charged plates. Millikan monitored the drops, measuring how the voltage on the plates affected their rate of fall. From these data he calculated the charges on the drops. His experiment showed that the charges were always integral multiples of 1.602×10^{-19} C, which he deduced was the charge of a single electron.

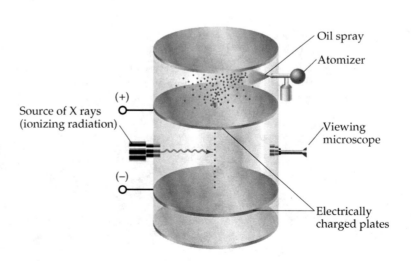

The coulomb (C) is the SI unit for electrical charge.

his experimental value for the charge, 1.602×10^{-19} C, and Thomson's charge-to-mass ratio, 1.76×10^8 C/g:

$$\text{Electron mass} = \frac{1.602 \times 10^{-19}\,\text{C}}{1.76 \times 10^8\,\text{C/g}} = 9.10 \times 10^{-28}\,\text{g}$$

This result agrees well with the presently accepted value for the mass of the electron, 9.10938×10^{-28} g. This mass is about 2000 times smaller than that of hydrogen, the lightest atom.

Radioactivity

In 1896 the French scientist Henri Becquerel (1852–1908) was studying a uranium compound when he discovered that it spontaneously emits high-energy radiation. This spontaneous emission of radiation is called **radioactivity**. At Becquerel's suggestion Marie Curie (Figure 2.6▶) and her husband, Pierre, began experiments to isolate the radioactive components of the compound.

Further study of the nature of radioactivity, principally by the British scientist Ernest Rutherford (Figure 2.7▶), revealed three types of radiation: alpha (α), beta (β), and gamma (γ) radiation. Each type differs in its response to an electric field, as shown in Figure 2.8▼. The paths of both α and β radiation are bent by the electric field, although in opposite directions; γ radiation is unaffected.

Rutherford showed that both α and β rays consist of fast-moving particles, which were called α and β particles. In fact, β particles are high-speed electrons and can be considered the radioactive equivalent of cathode rays. They are attracted to a positively charged plate. The α particles have a positive charge and are attracted toward a negative plate. In units of the charge of the electron, β particles have a charge of $1-$ and α particles a charge of $2+$. Each α particle has a mass about 7400 times that of an electron. Gamma radiation is high-energy radiation similar to X-rays; it does not consist of particles and carries no charge. We will discuss radioactivity in greater detail in Chapter 21.

The Nuclear Atom

With the growing evidence that the atom is composed of smaller particles, attention was given to how the particles fit together. During the early 1900s Thomson reasoned that because electrons contribute only a very small fraction of the mass of an atom, they probably were responsible for an equally small fraction of the atom's size. He proposed that the atom consisted of a uniform positive sphere of matter in which the electrons were embedded, as shown in

▲ Figure 2.6 **Marie Sklodowska Curie (1867–1934).** When M. Curie presented her doctoral thesis, it was described as the greatest single contribution of any doctoral thesis in the history of science. Among other things, Curie discovered two new elements, polonium and radium. In 1903 Henri Becquerel, M. Curie, and her husband, Pierre, were jointly awarded the Nobel Prize in physics. In 1911 M. Curie won a second Nobel Prize, this time in chemistry.

▲ Figure 2.7 **Ernest Rutherford (1871–1937).** Rutherford, whom Einstein called "the second Newton," was born and educated in New Zealand. In 1895 he was the first overseas student ever to be awarded a position at the Cavendish Laboratory at Cambridge University in England, where he worked with J. J. Thomson. In 1898 he joined the faculty of McGill University in Montreal. While at McGill, Rutherford did his research on radioactivity that led to his being awarded the 1908 Nobel Prize in chemistry. In 1907 Rutherford moved back to England to be a faculty member at Manchester University, where in 1910 he performed his famous α-particle scattering experiments that led to the nuclear model of the atom. In 1992 his native New Zealand honored Rutherford by putting his likeness, along with his Nobel Prize medal, on their $100 currency note.

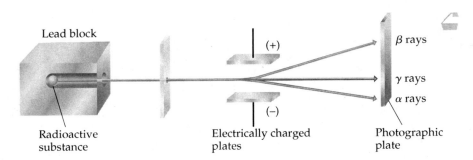

▲ Figure 2.8 **Behavior of alpha (α), beta (β), and gamma (γ) rays in an electric field.** The α rays consist of positively charged particles and are therefore attracted to the negatively charged plate. The β rays consist of negatively charged particles and are attracted to the positively charged plate. The γ rays, which carry no charge, are unaffected by the electric field.

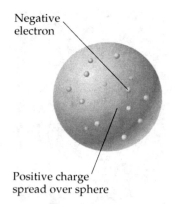

Negative
electron

Positive charge
spread over sphere

▲ Figure 2.9 **J. J. Thomson's "plum-pudding" model of the atom.** Thomson pictured the small electrons to be embedded in the atom much like raisins in a pudding or seeds in a watermelon. Ernest Rutherford proved this model wrong.

Figure 2.9 ◄. This so-called "plum-pudding" model, named after a traditional English dessert, was very short lived.

In 1910, Rutherford and his coworkers performed an experiment that disproved Thomson's model. Rutherford was studying the angles at which α particles were deflected, or *scattered*, as they passed through a thin gold foil only a few thousand atoms thick (Figure 2.10 ▼). Rutherford and his coworkers discovered that almost all the α particles passed directly through the foil without deflection. A few particles were found to be deflected by approximately 1 degree, consistent with Thomson's plum-pudding model. Just for the sake of completeness, Rutherford suggested that Ernest Marsden, an undergraduate student working in the laboratory, look for evidence of scattering at large angles. To everyone's surprise, a small amount of scattering was observed at large angles. Some particles were even scattered back in the direction from which they had come. The explanation for these results was not immediately obvious, but they were clearly inconsistent with Thomson's plum-pudding model.

By 1911, Rutherford was able to explain these observations. He postulated that most of the mass of each gold atom in his foil and all of its positive charge reside in a very small, extremely dense region, which he called the **nucleus**. He postulated further that most of the total volume of an atom is empty space in which electrons move around the nucleus. In the α-scattering experiment, most α particles passed directly through the foil because they did not encounter the minute nucleus of any gold atom; they merely passed through the empty space making up the greatest part of all the atoms in the foil. Occasionally, however, an α particle came close to a gold nucleus. The repulsion between the highly charged gold nucleus and the α particle was strong enough to deflect the less massive α particle, as shown in Figure 2.11 ▶.

Subsequent experimental studies led to the discovery of both positive particles (*protons*) and neutral particles (*neutrons*) in the nucleus. Protons were discovered in 1919 by Rutherford. In 1932 British scientist James Chadwick (1891–1972) discovered neutrons. We examine these particles more closely in Section 2.3.

▶ Figure 2.10 **Rutherford's experiment on the scattering of α particles.** The red lines represent the paths of the α particles. When the incoming beam strikes the gold foil, most particles pass straight through the foil, but some are scattered.

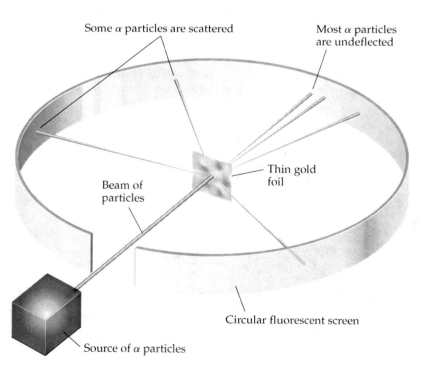

Some α particles are scattered

Most α particles are undeflected

Thin gold foil

Beam of particles

Circular fluorescent screen

Source of α particles

Science Fundamentals

⌂

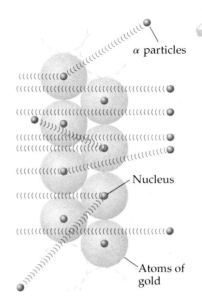

▲ Figure 2.11 **Rutherford's model explaining the scattering of** α **particles.** The gold foil is several thousand atoms thick. Because most of the volume of each atom is empty space, most α particles pass through the foil without deflection. When an α particle passes very close to a gold nucleus, however, it is repelled, causing its path to be altered.

△ GIVE IT SOME THOUGHT

What happens to most of the α particles that strike the gold foil in Rutherford's experiment? Why do they behave that way?

2.3 THE MODERN VIEW OF ATOMIC STRUCTURE

Since the time of Rutherford, physicists have learned much about the detailed composition of atomic nuclei. In the course of these discoveries, the list of particles that make up nuclei has grown long and continues to increase. As chemists, however, we can take a very simple view of the atom because only three subatomic particles—the **proton, neutron,** and **electron**—have a bearing on chemical behavior.

The charge of an electron is -1.602×10^{-19} C, and that of a proton is $+1.602 \times 10^{-19}$ C. The quantity 1.602×10^{-19} C is called the **electronic charge**. For convenience, the charges of atomic and subatomic particles are usually expressed as multiples of this charge rather than in coulombs. Thus, the charge of the electron is $1-$, and that of the proton is $1+$. Neutrons are uncharged and are therefore electrically neutral (which is how they received their name). *Every atom has an equal number of electrons and protons, so atoms have no net electrical charge.*

Protons and neutrons reside together in the nucleus of the atom, which, as Rutherford proposed, is extremely small. The vast majority of an atom's volume is the space in which the electrons reside. The electrons are attracted to the protons in the nucleus by the electrostatic force that exists between particles of opposite electrical charge. In later chapters we will see that the strength of the attractive forces between electrons and nuclei can be used to explain many of the differences between different elements.

△ GIVE IT SOME THOUGHT

(a) If an atom has 15 protons, how many electrons does it have? **(b)** Where do the protons reside in an atom?

Atoms have extremely small masses. The mass of the heaviest known atom, for example, is approximately 4×10^{-22} g. Because it would be cumbersome to express such small masses in grams, we use instead the **atomic mass unit,** or amu.* One amu equals 1.66054×10^{-24} g. The masses of the proton and neutron are very nearly equal, and both are much greater than that of the electron: A proton has a mass of 1.0073 amu, a neutron 1.0087 amu, and an electron 5.486×10^{-4} amu. Because it would take 1836 electrons to equal the mass of 1 proton, the nucleus contains most of the mass of an atom. Table 2.1 ▼ summarizes the charges and masses of the subatomic particles. We will have more to say about atomic masses in Section 2.4.

Atoms are also extremely small. Most atoms have diameters between 1×10^{-10} m and 5×10^{-10} m, or 100–500 pm. A convenient, although non-SI, unit of length used to express atomic dimensions is the **angstrom** (Å). One

TABLE 2.1 ■ Comparison of the Proton, Neutron, and Electron		
Particle	**Charge**	**Mass (amu)**
Proton	Positive (1+)	1.0073
Neutron	None (neutral)	1.0087
Electron	Negative (1−)	5.486×10^{-4}

*The SI abbreviation for the atomic mass unit is u. We will use the more common abbreviation amu.

angstrom equals 10^{-10} m. Thus, atoms have diameters of approximately 1–5 Å. The diameter of a chlorine atom, for example, is 200 pm, or 2.0 Å. Both picometers and angstroms are commonly used to express the dimensions of atoms and molecules.

■ SAMPLE EXERCISE 2.1 | Illustrating the Size of an Atom

The diameter of a US penny is 19 mm. The diameter of a silver atom, by comparison, is only 2.88 Å. How many silver atoms could be arranged side by side in a straight line across the diameter of a penny?

SOLUTION

The unknown is the number of silver (Ag) atoms. We use the relationship 1 Ag atom = 2.88 Å as a conversion factor relating the number of atoms and distance. Thus, we can start with the diameter of the penny, first converting this distance into angstroms and then using the diameter of the Ag atom to convert distance to the number of Ag atoms:

$$\text{Ag atoms} = (19 \text{ mm})\left(\frac{10^{-3} \text{ m}}{1 \text{ mm}}\right)\left(\frac{1 \text{ Å}}{10^{-10} \text{ m}}\right)\left(\frac{1 \text{ Ag atom}}{2.88 \text{ Å}}\right) = 6.6 \times 10^7 \text{ Ag atoms}$$

That is, 66 million silver atoms could sit side by side across a penny!

■ PRACTICE EXERCISE

The diameter of a carbon atom is 1.54 Å. **(a)** Express this diameter in picometers. **(b)** How many carbon atoms could be aligned side by side in a straight line across the width of a pencil line that is 0.20 mm wide?
Answers: **(a)** 154 pm, **(b)** 1.3×10^6 C atoms

The diameters of atomic nuclei are approximately 10^{-4} Å, only a small fraction of the diameter of the atom as a whole. You can appreciate the relative sizes of the atom and its nucleus by imagining that if the hydrogen atom were as large as a football stadium, the nucleus would be the size of a small marble. Because the tiny nucleus carries most of the mass of the atom in such a small volume, it has an incredible density—on the order of 10^{13}–10^{14} g/cm^3. A matchbox full of material of such density would weigh over 2.5 billion tons! Astrophysicists have suggested that the interior of a collapsed star may approach this density.

An illustration of the atom that incorporates the features we have just discussed is shown in Figure 2.12▼. The electrons, which take up most of the volume of the atom, play the major role in chemical reactions. The significance of representing the region containing the electrons as an indistinct cloud will become clear in later chapters when we consider the energies and spatial arrangements of the electrons.

Atomic Numbers, Mass Numbers, and Isotopes

What makes an atom of one element different from an atom of another element? For example, how does an atom of carbon differ from an atom of oxygen? The significant difference is in their subatomic compositions. The atoms of each element have a characteristic number of protons. Indeed, the number

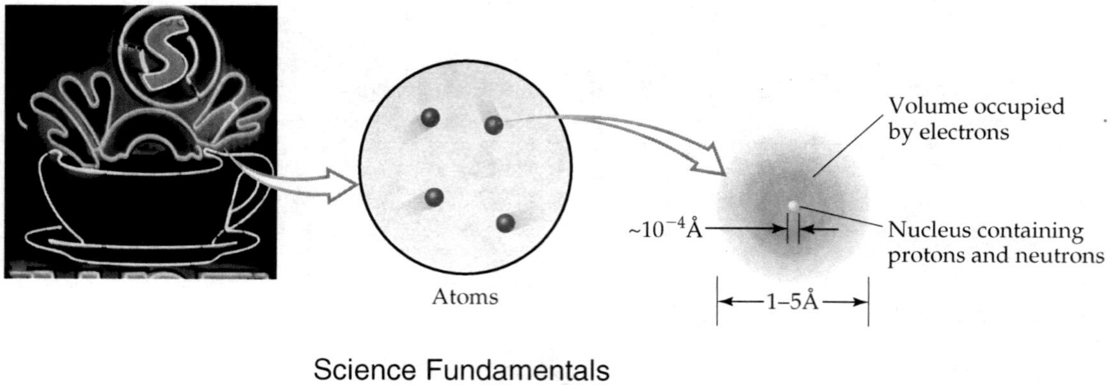

▼ Figure 2.12 **The structure of the atom.** Neon gas is composed of atoms. The nucleus, which contains protons and neutrons, is the location of virtually all the mass of the atom. The rest of the atom is the space in which the light, negatively charged electrons reside.

Atoms

Volume occupied by electrons

~10^{-4}Å

Nucleus containing protons and neutrons

1–5Å

There are four basic forces known in nature: (1) gravitational, (2) electromagnetic, (3) strong nuclear, and (4) weak nuclear. *Gravitational forces* are attractive forces that act between all objects in proportion to their masses. Gravitational forces between atoms or between subatomic particles are so small that they are of no chemical significance.

Electromagnetic forces are attractive or repulsive forces that act between either electrically charged or magnetic objects. Electric and magnetic forces are intimately related. Electric forces are of fundamental importance in understanding the chemical behavior of atoms. The magnitude of the electric force between two charged particles is given by *Coulomb's law*: $F = kQ_1Q_2/d^2$, where Q_1 and Q_2 are the magnitudes of the charges on the two particles, d is the distance between their centers, and k is a constant determined by the units for Q and d. A negative value for the force indicates attraction, whereas a positive value indicates repulsion.

All nuclei except those of hydrogen atoms contain two or more protons. Because like charges repel, electrical repulsion would cause the protons to fly apart if a stronger attractive force, called the *strong nuclear force*, did not keep them together. This force acts between subatomic particles, as in the nucleus. At this distance, the strong nuclear force is stronger than the electric force and holds the nucleus together.

The *weak nuclear force* is weaker than the electric force but stronger than the gravitational force. We are aware of its existence only because it shows itself in certain types of radioactivity.
Related Exercises: 2.83(b) and 2.89

of protons in the nucleus of an atom of any particular element is called that element's **atomic number**. Because an atom has no net electrical charge, the number of electrons it contains must equal the number of protons. All atoms of carbon, for example, have six protons and six electrons, whereas all atoms of oxygen have eight protons and eight electrons. Thus, carbon has atomic number 6, whereas oxygen has atomic number 8. The atomic number of each element is listed with the name and symbol of the element on the inside front cover of the text.

Atoms of a given element can differ in the number of neutrons they contain and consequently in mass. For example, most atoms of carbon have six neutrons, although some have more and some have less. The symbol $^{12}_{6}C$ (read "carbon twelve," carbon-12) represents the carbon atom containing six protons and six neutrons. The atomic number is shown by the subscript, and the superscript, called the **mass number**, is the total number of protons plus neutrons in the atom:

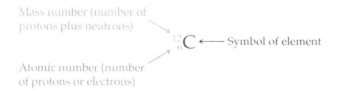

Because all atoms of a given element have the same atomic number, the subscript is redundant and is often omitted. Thus, the symbol for carbon-12 can be represented simply as ^{12}C. As one more example of this notation, atoms that contain six protons and eight neutrons have a mass number of 14 and are represented as $^{14}_{6}C$ or ^{14}C and referred to as carbon-14.

Atoms with identical atomic numbers but different mass numbers (that is, same number of protons but different numbers of neutrons) are called **isotopes** of one another. Several isotopes of carbon are listed in Table 2.2▼. We will

TABLE 2.2 ■ Some Isotopes of Carbon*

Symbol	Number of Protons	Number of Electrons	Number of Neutrons
^{11}C	6	6	5
^{12}C	6	6	6
^{13}C	6	6	7
^{14}C	6	6	8

*Almost 99% of the carbon found in nature is ^{12}C.

generally use the notation with superscripts only when referring to a particular isotope of an element.

■ SAMPLE EXERCISE 2.2 | Determining the Number of Subatomic Particles in Atoms

How many protons, neutrons, and electrons are in (a) an atom of ^{197}Au; (b) an atom of strontium-90?

SOLUTION

(a) The superscript 197 is the mass number, the sum of the number of protons plus the number of neutrons. According to the list of elements given inside the front cover, gold has an atomic number of 79. Consequently, an atom of ^{197}Au has 79 protons, 79 electrons, and $197 - 79 = 118$ neutrons. (b) The atomic number of strontium (listed inside the front cover) is 38. Thus, all atoms of this element have 38 protons and 38 electrons. The strontium-90 isotope has $90 - 38 = 52$ neutrons.

■ PRACTICE EXERCISE

How many protons, neutrons, and electrons are in (a) a ^{138}Ba atom, (b) an atom of phosphorus-31?
Answer: (a) 56 protons, 56 electrons, and 82 neutrons; (b) 15 protons, 15 electrons, and 16 neutrons.

■ SAMPLE EXERCISE 2.3 | Writing Symbols for Atoms

Magnesium has three isotopes, with mass numbers 24, 25, and 26. (a) Write the complete chemical symbol (superscript and subscript) for each of them. (b) How many neutrons are in an atom of each isotope?

SOLUTION

(a) Magnesium has atomic number 12, so all atoms of magnesium contain 12 protons and 12 electrons. The three isotopes are therefore represented by $^{24}_{12}Mg$, $^{25}_{12}Mg$, and $^{26}_{12}Mg$. (b) The number of neutrons in each isotope is the mass number minus the number of protons. The numbers of neutrons in an atom of each isotope are therefore 12, 13, and 14, respectively.

■ PRACTICE EXERCISE

Give the complete chemical symbol for the atom that contains 82 protons, 82 electrons, and 126 neutrons.
Answer: $^{208}_{82}Pb$

2.4 ATOMIC WEIGHTS

Atoms are small pieces of matter, so they have mass. In this section we will discuss the mass scale used for atoms and introduce the concept of *atomic weights*. In Section 3.3 we will extend these concepts to show how atomic masses are used to determine the masses of compounds and *molecular weights*.

The Atomic Mass Scale

Although scientists of the nineteenth century knew nothing about subatomic particles, they were aware that atoms of different elements have different masses. They found, for example, that each 100.0 g of water contains 11.1 g of hydrogen and 88.9 g of oxygen. Thus, water contains $88.9/11.1 = 8$ times as much oxygen, by mass, as hydrogen. Once scientists understood that water contains two hydrogen atoms for each oxygen atom, they concluded that an oxygen atom must have $2 \times 8 = 16$ times as much mass as a hydrogen atom. Hydrogen, the lightest atom, was arbitrarily assigned a relative mass of 1 (no units). Atomic masses of other elements were at first determined relative to this value. Thus, oxygen was assigned an atomic mass of 16.

Today we can determine the masses of individual atoms with a high degree of accuracy. For example, we know that the ^{1}H atom has a mass of 1.6735×10^{-24} g and the ^{16}O atom has a mass of 2.6560×10^{-23} g. As we noted in Section 2.3, it is convenient to use the *atomic mass unit* (amu) when dealing with these extremely small masses:

$$1 \text{ amu} = 1.66054 \times 10^{-24} \text{ g and } 1 \text{ g} = 6.02214 \times 10^{23} \text{ amu}$$

The atomic mass unit is presently defined by assigning a mass of exactly 12 amu to an atom of the ^{12}C isotope of carbon. In these units, an ^{1}H atom has a mass of 1.0078 amu and an ^{16}O atom has a mass of 15.9949 amu.

Average Atomic Masses

Most elements occur in nature as mixtures of isotopes. We can determine the *average atomic mass* of an element by using the masses of its various isotopes and their relative abundances. Naturally occurring carbon, for example, is composed of 98.93% ^{12}C and 1.07% ^{13}C. The masses of these isotopes are 12 amu (exactly) and 13.00335 amu, respectively. We calculate the average atomic mass of carbon from the fractional abundance of each isotope and the mass of that isotope:

$$(0.9893)(12 \text{ amu}) + (0.0107)(13.00335 \text{ amu}) = 12.01 \text{ amu}$$

The average atomic mass of each element (expressed in atomic mass units) is also known as its **atomic weight**. Although the term *average atomic mass* is more proper, the term *atomic weight* is more common. The atomic weights of the elements are listed in both the periodic table and the table of elements inside the front cover of this text.

 GIVE IT SOME THOUGHT

A particular atom of chromium has a mass of 52.94 amu, whereas the atomic weight of chromium is 51.99 amu. Explain the difference in the two masses.

■■ **SAMPLE EXERCISE 2.4** | **Calculating the Atomic Weight of an Element from Isotopic Abundances**

Naturally occurring chlorine is 75.78% ^{35}Cl, which has an atomic mass of 34.969 amu, and 24.22% ^{37}Cl, which has an atomic mass of 36.966 amu. Calculate the average atomic mass (that is, the atomic weight) of chlorine.

SOLUTION

We can calculate the average atomic mass by multiplying the abundance of each isotope by its atomic mass and summing these products. Because 75.78% = 0.7578 and 24.22% = 0.2422, we have

$$\text{Average atomic mass} = (0.7578)(34.969 \text{ amu}) + (0.2422)(36.966 \text{ amu})$$
$$= 26.50 \text{ amu} + 8.953 \text{ amu}$$
$$= 35.45 \text{ amu}$$

This answer makes sense: The average atomic mass of Cl is between the masses of the two isotopes and is closer to the value of ^{35}Cl, which is the more abundant isotope.

■■ **PRACTICE EXERCISE**

Three isotopes of silicon occur in nature: ^{28}Si (92.23%), which has an atomic mass of 27.97693 amu; ^{29}Si (4.68%), which has an atomic mass of 28.97649 amu; and ^{30}Si (3.09%), which has an atomic mass of 29.97377 amu. Calculate the atomic weight of silicon.
Answer: 28.09 amu

A Closer Look   THE MASS SPECTROMETER

The most direct and accurate means for determining atomic and molecular weights is provided by the **mass spectrometer** (Figure 2.13 ▼). A gaseous sample is introduced at *A* and bombarded by a stream of high-energy electrons at *B*. Collisions between the electrons and the atoms or molecules of the gas produce positively charged particles, mostly with a 1+ charge. These charged particles are accelerated toward a negatively charged wire grid (*C*). After the particles pass through the grid, they encounter two slits that allow only a narrow beam of particles to pass. This beam then passes between the poles of a magnet, which deflects the particles into a curved path, much as electrons are deflected by a magnetic field (Figure 2.4). For charged particles with the same charge, the extent of deflection depends on mass—the more massive the particle, the less the deflection. The particles are thereby separated according to their masses. By changing the strength of the magnetic field or the accelerating voltage on the negatively charged grid, charged particles of various masses can be selected to enter the detector at the end of the instrument.

A graph of the intensity of the detector signal versus particle atomic mass is called a *mass spectrum*. The mass spectrum of chlorine atoms, shown in Figure 2.14 ▼, reveals the presence of two isotopes. Analysis of a mass spectrum gives both the masses of the charged particles reaching the detector and their relative abundances. The abundances are obtained from the signal intensities. Knowing the atomic mass and the abundance of each isotope allows us to calculate the atomic weight of an element, as shown in Sample Exercise 2.4.

Mass spectrometers are used extensively today to identify chemical compounds and analyze mixtures of substances. Any molecule that loses electrons can fall apart, forming an array of positively charged fragments. The mass spectrometer measures the masses of these fragments, producing a chemical "fingerprint" of the molecule and providing clues about how the atoms were connected in the original molecule. Thus, a chemist might use this technique to determine the molecular structure of a newly synthesized compound or to identify a pollutant in the environment.

Related Exercises: 2.33, 2.34, 2.35(b), 2.36, 2.93, and 2.94

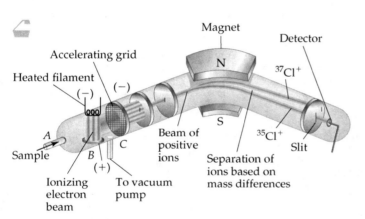

▲ Figure 2.13 **A mass spectrometer.** Cl atoms are introduced on the left side of the spectrometer and are ionized to form Cl$^+$ ions, which are then directed through a magnetic field. The paths of the ions of the two isotopes of Cl diverge as they pass through the magnetic field. As drawn, the spectrometer is tuned to detect ^{35}Cl$^+$ ions. The heavier ^{37}Cl$^+$ ions are not deflected enough for them to reach the detector.

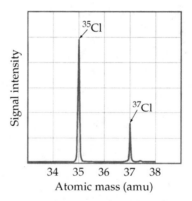

▲ Figure 2.14 **Mass spectrum of atomic chlorine.** The fractional abundances of the ^{35}Cl and ^{37}Cl isotopes of chlorine are indicated by the relative signal intensities of the beams reaching the detector of the mass spectrometer.

2.5 THE PERIODIC TABLE

Dalton's atomic theory set the stage for a vigorous growth in chemical experimentation during the early 1800s. As the body of chemical observations grew and the list of known elements expanded, attempts were made to find regular patterns in chemical behavior. These efforts culminated in the development of the periodic table in 1869. We will have much to say about the periodic table in later chapters, but it is so important and useful that you should become acquainted with it now. You will quickly learn that *the periodic table is the most significant tool that chemists use for organizing and remembering chemical facts.*

Many elements show very strong similarities to one another. The elements lithium (Li), sodium (Na), and potassium (K) are all soft, very reactive metals,

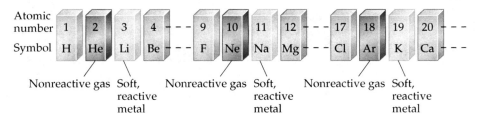

Atomic number
Symbol

| 1 | 2 | 3 | 4 | | 9 | 10 | 11 | 12 | | 17 | 18 | 19 | 20 |
| H | He | Li | Be | | F | Ne | Na | Mg | | Cl | Ar | K | Ca |

Nonreactive gas   Soft, reactive metal   Nonreactive gas   Soft, reactive metal   Nonreactive gas   Soft, reactive metal

◄ Figure 2.15 **Arranging the elements by atomic number reveals a periodic pattern of properties.** This periodic pattern is the basis of the periodic table.

for example. The elements helium (He), neon (Ne), and argon (Ar) are all very nonreactive gases. If the elements are arranged in order of increasing atomic number, their chemical and physical properties show a repeating, or periodic, pattern. For example, each of the soft, reactive metals—lithium, sodium, and potassium—comes immediately after one of the nonreactive gases—helium, neon, and argon—as shown in Figure 2.15▲.

The arrangement of elements in order of increasing atomic number, with elements having similar properties placed in vertical columns, is known as the **periodic table**. The periodic table is shown in Figure 2.16▼ and is also given on the front inside cover of the text. For each element in the table, the atomic number and atomic symbol are given. The atomic weight is often given as well, as in the following typical entry for potassium:

19	← atomic number
K	← atomic symbol
39.0983	← atomic weight

You may notice slight variations in periodic tables from one book to another or between those in the lecture hall and in the text. These are simply matters of style, or they might concern the particular information included. There are no fundamental differences.

1A 1																	8A 18
1 **H**	2A 2											3A 13	4A 14	5A 15	6A 16	7A 17	2 **He**
3 **Li**	4 **Be**											5 **B**	6 **C**	7 **N**	8 **O**	9 **F**	10 **Ne**
11 **Na**	12 **Mg**	3B 3	4B 4	5B 5	6B 6	7B 7	8B 8	9	10	1B 11	2B 12	13 **Al**	14 **Si**	15 **P**	16 **S**	17 **Cl**	18 **Ar**
19 **K**	20 **Ca**	21 **Sc**	22 **Ti**	23 **V**	24 **Cr**	25 **Mn**	26 **Fe**	27 **Co**	28 **Ni**	29 **Cu**	30 **Zn**	31 **Ga**	32 **Ge**	33 **As**	34 **Se**	35 **Br**	36 **Kr**
37 **Rb**	38 **Sr**	39 **Y**	40 **Zr**	41 **Nb**	42 **Mo**	43 **Tc**	44 **Ru**	45 **Rh**	46 **Pd**	47 **Ag**	48 **Cd**	49 **In**	50 **Sn**	51 **Sb**	52 **Te**	53 **I**	54 **Xe**
55 **Cs**	56 **Ba**	71 **Lu**	72 **Hf**	73 **Ta**	74 **W**	75 **Re**	76 **Os**	77 **Ir**	78 **Pt**	79 **Au**	80 **Hg**	81 **Tl**	82 **Pb**	83 **Bi**	84 **Po**	85 **At**	86 **Rn**
87 **Fr**	88 **Ra**	103 **Lr**	104 **Rf**	105 **Db**	106 **Sg**	107 **Bh**	108 **Hs**	109 **Mt**	110 **Ds**	111 **Rg**	112	113	114	115	116		118

| Metals | | 57 **La** | 58 **Ce** | 59 **Pr** | 60 **Nd** | 61 **Pm** | 62 **Sm** | 63 **Eu** | 64 **Gd** | 65 **Tb** | 66 **Dy** | 67 **Ho** | 68 **Er** | 69 **Tm** | 70 **Yb** |
| Metalloids | | 89 **Ac** | 90 **Th** | 91 **Pa** | 92 **U** | 93 **Np** | 94 **Pu** | 95 **Am** | 96 **Cm** | 97 **Bk** | 98 **Cf** | 99 **Es** | 100 **Fm** | 101 **Md** | 102 **No** |

Nonmetals

▲ Figure 2.16 **Periodic table of the elements.** Different colors are used to show the division of the elements into metals, metalloids, and nonmetals.

The horizontal rows of the periodic table are called **periods**. The first period consists of only two elements, hydrogen (H) and helium (He). The second and third periods, which begin with lithium (Li) and sodium (Na), respectively, consist of eight elements each. The fourth and fifth periods contain 18 elements. The sixth period has 32 elements, but for it to fit on a page, 14 of these elements (those with atomic numbers 57–70) appear at the bottom of the table. The seventh and last period is incomplete, but it also has 14 of its members placed in a row at the bottom of the table.

The vertical columns of the periodic table are called **groups**. The way in which the groups are labeled is somewhat arbitrary. Three labeling schemes are in common use, two of which are shown in Figure 2.16. The top set of labels, which have A and B designations, is widely used in North America. Roman numerals, rather than Arabic ones, are often employed in this scheme. Group 7A, for example, is often labeled VIIA. Europeans use a similar convention that numbers the columns from 1A through 8A and then from 1B through 8B, thereby giving the label 7B (or VIIB) instead of 7A to the group headed by fluorine (F). In an effort to eliminate this confusion, the International Union of Pure and Applied Chemistry (IUPAC) has proposed a convention that numbers the groups from 1 through 18 with no A or B designations, as shown in the lower set of labels at the top of the table in Figure 2.16. We will use the traditional North American convention with Arabic numerals.

Elements that belong to the same group often exhibit similarities in physical and chemical properties. For example, the "coinage metals"—copper (Cu), silver (Ag), and gold (Au)— belong to group 1B. As their name suggests, the coinage metals are used throughout the world to make coins. Many other groups in the periodic table also have names, as listed in Table 2.3 ▼.

We will learn in Chapters 6 and 7 that the elements in a group of the periodic table have similar properties because they have the same arrangement of electrons at the periphery of their atoms. However, we need not wait until then to make good use of the periodic table; after all, chemists who knew nothing about electrons developed the table! We can use the table, as they intended, to correlate the behaviors of elements and to aid in remembering many facts. You will find it helpful to refer to the periodic table frequently when studying the remainder of this chapter.

Except for hydrogen, all the elements on the left side and in the middle of the periodic table are **metallic elements**, or **metals**. The majority of elements are metallic; they all share characteristic properties, such as luster and high electrical and heat conductivity. All metals, with the exception of mercury (Hg), are solids at room temperature. The metals are separated from the **nonmetallic elements**, or **nonmetals**, by a diagonal steplike line that runs from boron (B) to astatine (At), as shown in Figure 2.16. Hydrogen, although on the left side of the periodic table, is a nonmetal. At room temperature some of the nonmetals are gaseous, some are solid, and one is liquid. Nonmetals generally differ from the metals in appearance (Figure 2.17 ◄) and in other physical properties. Many of the elements that lie along the line that separates metals from nonmetals, such as antimony (Sb), have properties that fall between those of metals and those of nonmetals. These elements are often referred to as **metalloids**.

▲ Figure 2.17 **Some familiar examples of metals and nonmetals.** The nonmetals (from bottom left) are sulfur (yellow powder), iodine (dark, shiny crystals), bromine (reddish brown liquid and vapor in glass vial), and three samples of carbon (black charcoal powder, diamond, and graphite in the pencil lead). The metals are in the form of an aluminum wrench, copper pipe, lead shot, silver coins, and gold nuggets.

TABLE 2.3 ■ Names of Some Groups in the Periodic Table		
Group	Name	Elements
1A	Alkali metals	Li, Na, K, Rb, Cs, Fr
2A	Alkaline earth metals	Be, Mg, Ca, Sr, Ba, Ra
6A	Chalcogens	O, S, Se, Te, Po
7A	Halogens	F, Cl, Br, I, At
8A	Noble gases (or rare gases)	He, Ne, Ar, Kr, Xe, Rn

GLENN SEABORG AND SEABORGIUM

Prior to 1940 the periodic table ended at uranium, element number 92. Since that time, no scientist has had a greater effect on the periodic table than Glenn Seaborg. Seaborg (Figure 2.18 ▶) became a faculty member in the chemistry department at the University of California, Berkeley in 1937. In 1940 he and his colleagues Edwin McMillan, Arthur Wahl, and Joseph Kennedy succeeded in isolating plutonium (Pu) as a product of the reaction between uranium and neutrons. We will talk about reactions of this type, called *nuclear reactions*, in Chapter 21.

During the period 1944 through 1958, Seaborg and his coworkers also identified various products of nuclear reactions as being the elements having atomic numbers 95 through 102. All these elements are radioactive and are not found in nature; they can be synthesized only via nuclear reactions. For their efforts in identifying the elements beyond uranium (the *transuranium* elements), McMillan and Seaborg shared the 1951 Nobel Prize in chemistry.

From 1961 to 1971, Seaborg served as the chairman of the U.S. Atomic Energy Commission (now the Department of Energy). In this position he had an important role in establishing international treaties to limit the testing of nuclear weapons. Upon his return to Berkeley, he was part of the team that in 1974 first identified element number 106. Another team at Berkeley corroborated that discovery in 1993. In 1994, to honor Seaborg's many contributions to the discovery of new elements, the American Chemical Society proposed that element

◀ Figure 2.18 **Glenn Seaborg (1912–1999).** The photograph shows Seaborg at Berkeley in 1941 using a Geiger counter to try to detect radiation produced by plutonium. Geiger counters will be discussed in Section 21.5.

number 106 be named "seaborgium," with a proposed symbol of Sg. After several years of controversy about whether an element should be named after a living person, the IUPAC officially adopted the name seaborgium in 1997. Seaborg became the first person to have an element named after him while he was still alive.
Related Exercise: 2.96

 GIVE IT SOME THOUGHT

Chlorine is a halogen. Locate this element in the periodic table. **(a)** What is its symbol? **(b)** In what period and in what group is the element located? **(c)** What is its atomic number? **(d)** Is chlorine a metal or nonmetal?

■ **SAMPLE EXERCISE 2.5** | **Using the Periodic Table**

Which two of the following elements would you expect to show the greatest similarity in chemical and physical properties: B, Ca, F, He, Mg, P?

SOLUTION

Elements that are in the same group of the periodic table are most likely to exhibit similar chemical and physical properties. We therefore expect that Ca and Mg should be most alike because they are in the same group (2A, the alkaline earth metals).

■ **PRACTICE EXERCISE**

Locate Na (sodium) and Br (bromine) on the periodic table. Give the atomic number of each, and label each a metal, metalloid, or nonmetal.
Answer: Na, atomic number 11, is a metal; Br, atomic number 35, is a nonmetal.

2.6 MOLECULES AND MOLECULAR COMPOUNDS

Even though the atom is the smallest representative sample of an element, only the noble-gas elements are normally found in nature as isolated atoms. Most matter is composed of molecules or ions, both of which are formed from atoms. We examine molecules here and ions in Section 2.7.

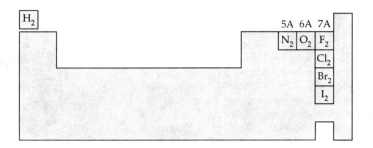

▶ Figure 2.19 **Diatomic molecules.** Seven common elements exist as diatomic molecules at room temperature.

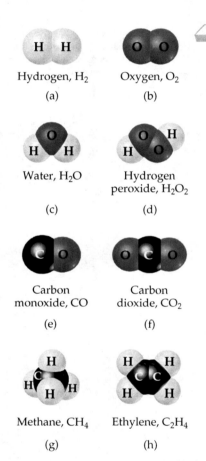

Hydrogen, H_2 | Oxygen, O_2

(a) | (b)

Water, H_2O | Hydrogen peroxide, H_2O_2

(c) | (d)

Carbon monoxide, CO | Carbon dioxide, CO_2

(e) | (f)

Methane, CH_4 | Ethylene, C_2H_4

(g) | (h)

▲ Figure 2.20 **Molecular models of some simple molecules.** Notice how the chemical formulas of these substances correspond to their compositions.

A **molecule** is an assembly of two or more atoms tightly bound together. The resultant "package" of atoms behaves in many ways as a single, distinct object, just as a cell phone composed of many parts can be recognized as a single object. We will discuss the forces that hold the atoms together (the chemical bonds) in Chapters 8 and 9.

Molecules and Chemical Formulas

Many elements are found in nature in molecular form; that is, two or more of the same type of atom are bound together. For example, the oxygen normally found in air consists of molecules that contain two oxygen atoms. We represent this molecular form of oxygen by the **chemical formula** O_2 (read "oh two"). The subscript in the formula tells us that two oxygen atoms are present in each molecule. A molecule that is made up of two atoms is called a **diatomic molecule**. Oxygen also exists in another molecular form known as *ozone*. Molecules of ozone consist of three oxygen atoms, making the chemical formula for this substance O_3. Even though "normal" oxygen (O_2) and ozone (O_3) are both composed only of oxygen atoms, they exhibit very different chemical and physical properties. For example, O_2 is essential for life, but O_3 is toxic; O_2 is odorless, whereas O_3 has a sharp, pungent smell.

The elements that normally occur as diatomic molecules are hydrogen, oxygen, nitrogen, and the halogens. Their locations in the periodic table are shown in Figure 2.19 ▲. When we speak of the substance hydrogen, we mean H_2 unless we explicitly indicate otherwise. Likewise, when we speak of oxygen, nitrogen, or any of the halogens, we are referring to O_2, N_2, F_2, Cl_2, Br_2, or I_2. Thus, the properties of oxygen and hydrogen listed in Table 1.3 are those of O_2 and H_2. Other, less common forms of these elements behave much differently.

Compounds that are composed of molecules contain more than one type of atom and are called **molecular compounds**. A molecule of water, for example, consists of two hydrogen atoms and one oxygen atom and is therefore represented by the chemical formula H_2O. Lack of a subscript on the O indicates one atom of O per water molecule. Another compound composed of these same elements (in different relative proportions) is hydrogen peroxide, H_2O_2. The properties of hydrogen peroxide are very different from the properties of water.

Several common molecules are shown in Figure 2.20 ◀. Notice how the composition of each compound is given by its chemical formula. Notice also that these substances are composed only of nonmetallic elements. *Most molecular substances that we will encounter contain only nonmetals.*

Molecular and Empirical Formulas

Chemical formulas that indicate the actual numbers and types of atoms in a molecule are called **molecular formulas**. (The formulas in Figure 2.20 are molecular formulas.) Chemical formulas that give only the relative number of atoms of each type in a molecule are called **empirical formulas**. The subscripts in an empirical formula are always the smallest possible whole-number ratios. The molecular formula for hydrogen peroxide is H_2O_2, for example, whereas its empirical formula is HO. The molecular formula for ethylene is C_2H_4, and its empirical formula is CH_2. For many substances, the molecular formula and the empirical formula are identical, as in the case of water, H_2O.

Molecular formulas provide more information about molecules than do empirical formulas. Whenever we know the molecular formula of a compound, we can determine its empirical formula. The converse is not true, however. If we know the empirical formula of a substance, we cannot determine its molecular formula unless we have more information. So why do chemists bother with empirical formulas? As we will see in Chapter 3, certain common methods of analyzing substances lead to the empirical formula only. Once the empirical formula is known, additional experiments can give the information needed to convert the empirical formula to the molecular one. In addition, there are substances, such as the most common forms of elemental carbon, that do not exist as isolated molecules. For these substances, we must rely on empirical formulas. Thus, all the common forms of elemental carbon are represented by the element's chemical symbol, C, which is the empirical formula for all the forms.

■ SAMPLE EXERCISE 2.6 | Relating Empirical and Molecular Formulas

Write the empirical formulas for the following molecules: **(a)** glucose, a substance also known as either blood sugar or dextrose, whose molecular formula is $C_6H_{12}O_6$; **(b)** nitrous oxide, a substance used as an anesthetic and commonly called laughing gas, whose molecular formula is N_2O.

SOLUTION

(a) The subscripts of an empirical formula are the smallest whole-number ratios. The smallest ratios are obtained by dividing each subscript by the largest common factor, in this case 6. The resultant empirical formula for glucose is CH_2O.
(b) Because the subscripts in N_2O are already the lowest integral numbers, the empirical formula for nitrous oxide is the same as its molecular formula, N_2O.

■ PRACTICE EXERCISE

Give the empirical formula for the substance called *diborane*, whose molecular formula is B_2H_6.
Answer: BH_3

Picturing Molecules

The molecular formula of a substance summarizes the composition of the substance but does not show how the atoms come together to form the molecule. The **structural formula** of a substance shows which atoms are attached to which within the molecule. For example, the structural formulas for water, hydrogen peroxide, and methane (CH_4) can be written as follows:

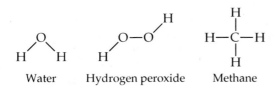

Water   Hydrogen peroxide   Methane

The atoms are represented by their chemical symbols, and lines are used to represent the bonds that hold the atoms together.

A structural formula usually does not depict the actual geometry of the molecule, that is, the actual angles at which atoms are joined together. A structural formula can be written as a *perspective drawing*, however, to give some sense of three-dimensional shape, as shown in Figure 2.21 ▶.

Scientists also rely on various models to help visualize molecules. *Ball-and-stick models* show atoms as spheres and bonds as sticks. This type of model has the advantage of accurately representing the angles at which the atoms are attached to one another within the molecule (Figure 2.21). In a ball-and-stick

Structural formula

Perspective drawing

Ball-and-stick model

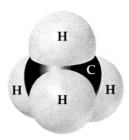

Space-filling model

▲ Figure 2.21 **Different representations of the methane (CH_4) molecule.** Structural formulas, perspective drawings, ball-and-stick models, and space-filling models each help us visualize the ways atoms are attached to each other in molecules. In the perspective drawing, solid lines represent bonds in the plane of the paper, the solid wedge represents a bond that extends out from the plane of the paper, and dashed lines represent bonds behind the paper.

model, balls of the same size may represent all atoms, or the relative sizes of the balls may reflect the relative sizes of the atoms. Sometimes the chemical symbols of the elements are superimposed on the balls, but often the atoms are identified simply by color.

A *space-filling model* depicts what the molecule would look like if the atoms were scaled up in size (Figure 2.21). These models show the relative sizes of the atoms, but the angles between atoms, which help define their molecular geometry, are often more difficult to see than in ball-and-stick models. As in ball-and-stick models, the identities of the atoms are indicated by their colors, but they may also be labeled with the element's symbol.

GIVE IT SOME THOUGHT

The structural formula for the substance ethane is shown here:

$$\begin{array}{ccc} H & H \\ | & | \\ H-C-C-H \\ | & | \\ H & H \end{array}$$

(a) What is the molecular formula for ethane? **(b)** What is its empirical formula? **(c)** Which kind of molecular model would most clearly show the angles between atoms?

2.7 IONS AND IONIC COMPOUNDS

The nucleus of an atom is unchanged by chemical processes, but some atoms can readily gain or lose electrons. If electrons are removed from or added to a neutral atom, a charged particle called an **ion** is formed. An ion with a positive charge is called a **cation** (pronounced CAT-ion); a negatively charged ion is called an **anion** (AN-ion).

To see how ions form, consider the sodium atom, which has 11 protons and 11 electrons. This atom easily loses one electron. The resulting cation has 11 protons and 10 electrons, which means it has a net charge of 1+.

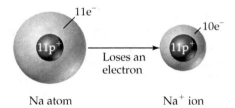

The net charge on an ion is represented by a superscript. The superscripts $+$, $2+$, and $3+$, for instance, mean a net charge resulting from the *loss* of one, two, and three electrons, respectively. The superscripts $-$, $2-$, and $3-$ represent net charges resulting from the *gain* of one, two, and three electrons, respectively. Chlorine, with 17 protons and 17 electrons, for example, can gain an electron in chemical reactions, producing the Cl^- ion:

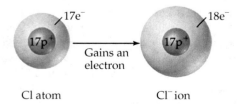

In general, metal atoms tend to lose electrons to form cations, whereas nonmetal atoms tend to gain electrons to form anions.

Science Fundamentals

■ SAMPLE EXERCISE 2.7 | Writing Chemical Symbols for Ions

Give the chemical symbol, including mass number, for each of the following ions:
(a) The ion with 22 protons, 26 neutrons, and 19 electrons; (b) the ion of sulfur that has 16 neutrons and 18 electrons.

SOLUTION

(a) The number of protons (22) is the atomic number of the element. By referring to a periodic table or list of elements, we see that the element with atomic number 22 is titanium (Ti). The mass number of this isotope of titanium is $22 + 26 = 48$ (the sum of the protons and neutrons). Because the ion has three more protons than electrons, it has a net charge of 3+. Thus, the symbol for the ion is $^{48}Ti^{3+}$.

(b) By referring to a periodic table or a table of elements, we see that sulfur (S) has an atomic number of 16. Thus, each atom or ion of sulfur must contain 16 protons. We are told that the ion also has 16 neutrons, meaning the mass number of the ion is $16 + 16 = 32$. Because the ion has 16 protons and 18 electrons, its net charge is 2−. Thus, the symbol for the ion is $^{32}S^{2-}$.

    In general, we will focus on the net charges of ions and ignore their mass numbers unless the circumstances dictate that we specify a certain isotope.

■ PRACTICE EXERCISE

How many protons, neutrons, and electrons does the $^{79}Se^{2-}$ ion possess?
Answer: 34 protons, 45 neutrons, and 36 electrons

    In addition to simple ions, such as Na^+ and Cl^-, there are **polyatomic ions**, such as NH_4^+ (ammonium ion) and SO_4^{2-} (sulfate ion). These latter ions consist of atoms joined as in a molecule, but they have a net positive or negative charge. We will consider further examples of polyatomic ions in Section 2.8.

    It is important to realize that the chemical properties of ions are very different from the chemical properties of the atoms from which the ions are derived. The difference is like the change from Dr. Jekyll to Mr. Hyde: Although a given atom and its ion may be essentially the same (plus or minus a few electrons), the behavior of the ion is very different from that of the atom.

Predicting Ionic Charges

Many atoms gain or lose electrons to end up with the same number of electrons as the noble gas closest to them in the periodic table. The members of the noble-gas family are chemically very nonreactive and form very few compounds. We might deduce that this is because their electron arrangements are very stable. Nearby elements can obtain these same stable arrangements by losing or gaining electrons. For example, the loss of one electron from an atom of sodium leaves it with the same number of electrons as the neutral neon atom (atomic number 10). Similarly, when chlorine gains an electron, it ends up with 18, the same number of electrons as in argon (atomic number 18). We will use this simple observation to explain the formation of ions until Chapter 8, where we discuss chemical bonding.

■ SAMPLE EXERCISE 2.8 | Predicting the Charges of Ions

Predict the charge expected for the most stable ion of barium and for the most stable ion of oxygen.

SOLUTION

We will assume that these elements form ions that have the same number of electrons as the nearest noble-gas atom. From the periodic table, we see that barium has atomic number 56. The nearest noble gas is xenon, atomic number 54. Barium can attain a stable arrangement of 54 electrons by losing two of its electrons, forming the Ba^{2+} cation.

    Oxygen has atomic number 8. The nearest noble gas is neon, atomic number 10. Oxygen can attain this stable electron arrangement by gaining two electrons, thereby forming the O^{2-} anion.

■ PRACTICE EXERCISE

Predict the charge expected for the most stable ion of (a) aluminum and (b) fluorine.
Answer: (a) 3+; (b) 1−

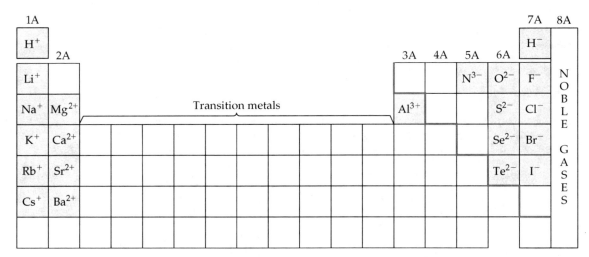

▲ Figure 2.22 **Charges of some common ions.** Notice that the steplike line that divides metals from nonmetals also separates cations from anions. Hydrogen forms both 1+ and 1− ions.

The periodic table is very useful for remembering the charges of ions, especially those of the elements on the left and right sides of the table. As Figure 2.22▲ shows, the charges of these ions relate in a simple way to their positions in the table. On the left side of the table, for example, the group 1A elements (the alkali metals) form 1+ ions, and the group 2A elements (the alkaline earths) form 2+ ions. On the other side of the table the group 7A elements (the halogens) form 1− ions, and the group 6A elements form 2− ions. As we will see later in the text, many of the other groups do not lend themselves to such simple rules.

Ionic Compounds

A great deal of chemical activity involves the transfer of electrons from one substance to another. As we just saw, ions form when one or more electrons transfer from one neutral atom to another. Figure 2.23▼ shows that when elemental sodium is allowed to react with elemental chlorine, an electron transfers from a neutral sodium atom to a neutral chlorine atom. We are left with a Na^+ ion and a Cl^- ion. Because objects of opposite charge attract, the Na^+ and the Cl^- ions bind together to form the compound sodium chloride (NaCl). Sodium chloride, which we know better as common table salt, is an example of an **ionic compound**, a compound that contains both positively and negatively charged ions.

We can often tell whether a compound is ionic (consisting of ions) or molecular (consisting of molecules) from its composition. In general, cations are metal ions, whereas anions are nonmetal ions. Consequently, *ionic compounds*

▼ Figure 2.23 **The formation of an ionic compound.** (a) The transfer of an electron from a neutral Na atom to a neutral Cl atom leads to the formation of a Na^+ ion and a Cl^- ion. (b) Arrangement of these ions in solid sodium chloride (NaCl). (c) A sample of sodium chloride crystals.

are generally combinations of metals and nonmetals, as in NaCl. In contrast, molecular compounds are generally composed of nonmetals only, as in H₂O.

■ SAMPLE EXERCISE 2.9 | Identifying Ionic and Molecular Compounds

Which of the following compounds would you expect to be ionic: N_2O, Na_2O, $CaCl_2$, SF_4?

SOLUTION

We would predict that Na_2O and $CaCl_2$ are ionic compounds because they are composed of a metal combined with a nonmetal. The other two compounds, composed entirely of nonmetals, are predicted (correctly) to be molecular compounds.

■ PRACTICE EXERCISE

Which of the following compounds are molecular: CBr_4, FeS, P_4O_6, PbF_2?
Answer: CBr_4 and P_4O_6

The ions in ionic compounds are arranged in three-dimensional structures. The arrangement of Na^+ and Cl^- ions in NaCl is shown in Figure 2.23. Because there is no discrete molecule of NaCl, we are able to write only an empirical formula for this substance. In fact, only empirical formulas can be written for most ionic compounds.

Chemistry and Life ELEMENTS REQUIRED BY LIVING ORGANISMS

Figure 2.24 ▼ shows the elements that are essential for life. More than 97% of the mass of most organisms comprises just six elements—oxygen, carbon, hydrogen, nitrogen, phosphorus, and sulfur. Water (H_2O) is the most common compound in living organisms, accounting for at least 70% of the mass of most cells. Carbon is the most prevalent element (by mass) in the solid components of cells. Carbon atoms are found in a vast variety of organic molecules, in which the carbon atoms are bonded to other carbon atoms or to atoms of other elements, principally H, O, N, P, and S. All proteins, for example, contain the following group of atoms that occurs repeatedly within the molecules:

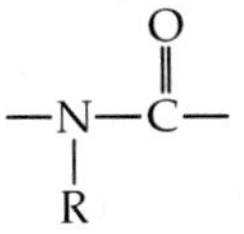

$$
\begin{array}{c}
\quad\quad O \\
\quad\quad \| \\
-N-C- \\
\ \ | \\
\ \ R
\end{array}
$$

(R is either an H atom or a combination of atoms such as CH_3.)

In addition, 23 more elements have been found in various living organisms. Five are ions that are required by all organisms: Ca^{2+}, Cl^-, Mg^{2+}, K^+, and Na^+. Calcium ions, for example, are necessary for the formation of bone and for the transmission of signals in the nervous system, such as those that trigger the contraction of cardiac muscles, causing the heart to beat. Many other elements are needed in only very small quantities and consequently are called *trace* elements. For example, trace quantities of copper are required in the diet of humans to aid in the synthesis of hemoglobin.

▼ Figure 2.24 **Biologically essential elements.** The elements that are essential for life are indicated by colors. Red denotes the six most abundant elements in living systems (hydrogen, carbon, nitrogen, oxygen, phosphorus, and sulfur). Blue indicates the five next most abundant elements. Green indicates the elements needed in only trace amounts.

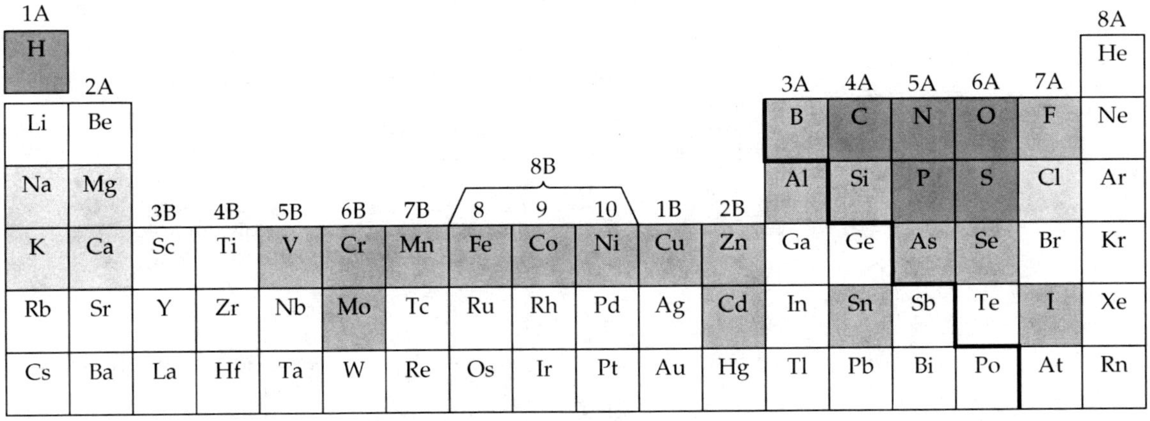

Someone once said that drinking at the fountain of knowledge in a chemistry course is like drinking from a fire hydrant. Indeed, the pace can sometimes seem brisk. More to the point, however, we can drown in the facts if we do not see the general patterns. The value of recognizing patterns and learning rules and generalizations is that the patterns, rules, and generalizations free us from learning (or trying to memorize) many individual facts. The patterns, rules, and generalizations tie ideas together so that we do not get lost in the details.

Many students struggle with chemistry because they do not see how the topics relate to one another, how ideas connect together. They therefore treat every idea and problem as being unique instead of as an example or application of a general rule, procedure, or relationship. You can avoid this pitfall by remembering the following: Begin to notice the structure of the topic you are studying. Pay attention to the trends and rules given to summarize a large body of information. Notice, for example, how atomic structure helps us understand the existence of isotopes (as seen in Table 2.2) and how the periodic table aids us in remembering the charges of ions (as seen in Figure 2.22). You may surprise yourself by observing patterns that are not even explicitly spelled out yet. Perhaps you have even noticed certain trends in chemical formulas. Moving across the periodic table from element 11 (Na), we find that the elements form compounds with F having the following compositions: NaF, MgF_2, and AlF_3. Does this trend continue? Do SiF_4, PF_5, and SF_6 exist? Indeed they do. If you have noticed trends like this from the scraps of information you have seen so far, then you are ahead of the game and you have already prepared yourself for some topics we will address in later chapters.

We can readily write the empirical formula for an ionic compound if we know the charges of the ions of which the compound is composed. Chemical compounds are always electrically neutral. Consequently, the ions in an ionic compound always occur in such a ratio that the total positive charge equals the total negative charge. Thus, there is one Na^+ to one Cl^- (giving $NaCl$), one Ba^{2+} to two Cl^- (giving $BaCl_2$), and so forth.

As you consider these and other examples, you will see that if the charges on the cation and anion are equal, the subscript on each ion will be 1. If the charges are not equal, the charge on one ion (without its sign) will become the subscript on the other ion. For example, the ionic compound formed from Mg (which forms Mg^{2+} ions) and N (which forms N^{3-} ions) is Mg_3N_2:

$$Mg^{2+} \quad N^{3-} \longrightarrow Mg_3N_2$$

GIVE IT SOME THOUGHT

Why don't we write the formula for the compound formed by Ca^{2+} and O^{2-} as Ca_2O_2?

SAMPLE EXERCISE 2.10 | Using Ionic Charge to Write Empirical Formulas for Ionic Compounds

What are the empirical formulas of the compounds formed by (a) Al^{3+} and Cl^- ions, (b) Al^{3+} and O^{2-} ions, (c) Mg^{2+} and NO_3^- ions?

SOLUTION

(a) Three Cl^- ions are required to balance the charge of one Al^{3+} ion. Thus, the formula is $AlCl_3$.

(b) Two Al^{3+} ions are required to balance the charge of three O^{2-} ions (that is, the total positive charge is 6+, and the total negative charge is 6−). Thus, the formula is Al_2O_3.

(c) Two NO_3^- ions are needed to balance the charge of one Mg^{2+}. Thus, the formula is $Mg(NO_3)_2$. In this case the formula for the entire polyatomic ion NO_3^- must be enclosed in parentheses so that it is clear that the subscript 2 applies to all the atoms of that ion.

PRACTICE EXERCISE

Write the empirical formulas for the compounds formed by the following ions:
(a) Na^+ and PO_4^{3-}, (b) Zn^{2+} and SO_4^{2-}, (c) Fe^{3+} and CO_3^{2-}.
Answers: (a) Na_3PO_4, (b) $ZnSO_4$, (c) $Fe_2(CO_3)_3$

2.8 NAMING INORGANIC COMPOUNDS

To obtain information about a particular substance, you must know its chemical formula and name. The names and formulas of compounds are essential vocabulary in chemistry. The system used in naming substances is called **chemical nomenclature** from the Latin words *nomen* (name) and *calare* (to call).

There are now more than 19 million known chemical substances. Naming them all would be a hopelessly complicated task if each had a special name independent of all others. Many important substances that have been known for a long time, such as water (H_2O) and ammonia (NH_3), do have individual, traditional names (so-called "common" names). For most substances, however, we rely on a systematic set of rules that leads to an informative and unique name for each substance, a name based on the composition of the substance.

The rules for chemical nomenclature are based on the division of substances into categories. The major division is between organic and inorganic compounds. *Organic compounds* contain carbon, usually in combination with hydrogen, oxygen, nitrogen, or sulfur. All others are *inorganic compounds*. Early chemists associated organic compounds with plants and animals, and they associated inorganic compounds with the nonliving portion of our world. Although this distinction between living and nonliving matter is no longer pertinent, the classification between organic and inorganic compounds continues to be useful. In this section we consider the basic rules for naming inorganic compounds, and in Section 2.9 we will introduce the names of some simple organic compounds. Among inorganic compounds, we will consider three categories: ionic compounds, molecular compounds, and acids.

Names and Formulas of Ionic Compounds

Recall from Section 2.7 that ionic compounds usually consist of metal ions combined with nonmetal ions. The metals form the positive ions, and the nonmetals form the negative ions. Let's examine the naming of positive ions, then the naming of negative ones. After that, we will consider how to put the names of the ions together to identify the complete ionic compound.

1. Positive Ions (Cations)

   (a) *Cations formed from metal atoms have the same name as the metal:*

   Na^+ sodium ion Zn^{2+} zinc ion Al^{3+} aluminum ion

   Ions formed from a single atom are called *monatomic ions.*

   (b) *If a metal can form different cations, the positive charge is indicated by a Roman numeral in parentheses following the name of the metal:*

Fe^{2+}	iron(II) ion	Cu^+	copper(I) ion
Fe^{3+}	iron(III) ion	Cu^{2+}	copper(II) ion

   Ions of the same element that have different charges exhibit different properties, such as different colors (Figure 2.25 ▶).

   Most of the metals that can form more than one cation are *transition metals*, elements that occur in the middle block of elements, from group 3B to group 2B in the periodic table. The charges of these ions are indicated by Roman numerals. The metals that form only one cation are those of group 1A (Na^+, K^+, and Rb^+) and group 2A (Mg^{2+}, Ca^{2+}, Sr^{2+}, and Ba^{2+}), as well as Al^{3+} (group 3A) and two transition-metal ions: Ag^+ (group 1B) and Zn^{2+} (group 2B). Charges are not expressed explicitly when naming these ions. However, if there is any doubt in your mind whether a metal forms more than one cation, use a Roman numeral to indicate the charge. It is never wrong to do so, even though it may be unnecessary.

   An older method still widely used for distinguishing between two differently charged ions of a metal is to apply the ending *-ous* or *-ic.*

▲ Figure 2.25 **Ions of the same element with different charges exhibit different properties.** Compounds containing ions of the same element but with different charge can be very different in appearance and properties. Both substances shown are complex compounds of iron that also contain K^+ and CN^- ions. The substance on the left is potassium ferrocyanide, which contains Fe(II) bound to CN^- ions. The substance on the right is potassium ferricyanide, which contains Fe(III) bound to CN^- ions. Both substances are used extensively in blueprinting and other dyeing processes.

These endings represent the lower and higher charged ions, respectively. They are added to the root of the element's Latin name:

Fe^{2+} ferrous ion Cu^+ cuprous ion
Fe^{3+} ferric ion Cu^{2+} cupric ion

Although we will only rarely use these older names in this text, you might encounter them elsewhere.

(c) *Cations formed from nonmetal atoms have names that end in* -ium:

NH_4^+ ammonium ion H_3O^+ hydronium ion

These two ions are the only ions of this kind that we will encounter frequently in the text. They are both polyatomic. The vast majority of cations are monatomic metal ions.

The names and formulas of some common cations are shown in Table 2.4 ▼; they are also included in a table of common ions in the back inside cover of the text. The ions listed on the left side in Table 2.4 are the monatomic ions that do not have variable charges. Those listed on the right side are either polyatomic cations or cations with variable charges. The Hg_2^{2+} ion is unusual because this metal ion is not monatomic. It is called the mercury(I) ion because it can be thought of as two Hg^+ ions bound together. The cations that you will encounter most frequently are shown in boldface. You should learn these cations first.

GIVE IT SOME THOUGHT

Why is CrO named using a Roman numeral, chromium(II) oxide, whereas CaO is named without a Roman numeral in the name, calcium oxide?

2. Negative Ions (Anions)

   (a) *The names of monatomic anions are formed by replacing the ending of the name of the element with* -ide:

   H^- hydride ion O^{2-} oxide ion N^{3-} nitride ion

TABLE 2.4 ■ Common Cations*

Charge	Formula	Name	Formula	Name
1+	**H⁺**	**Hydrogen ion**	**NH₄⁺**	**Ammonium ion**
	Li⁺	Lithium ion	Cu⁺	Copper(I) or cuprous ion
	Na⁺	**Sodium ion**		
	K⁺	**Potassium ion**		
	Cs⁺	Cesium ion		
	Ag⁺	**Silver ion**		
2+	**Mg²⁺**	**Magnesium ion**	Co²⁺	Cobalt(II) or cobaltous ion
	Ca²⁺	**Calcium ion**	**Cu²⁺**	**Copper(II)** or cupric ion
	Sr²⁺	Strontium ion	**Fe²⁺**	**Iron(II)** or ferrous ion
	Ba²⁺	Barium ion	Mn²⁺	Manganese(II) or manganous ion
	Zn²⁺	**Zinc ion**	Hg₂²⁺	Mercury(I) or mercurous ion
	Cd²⁺	Cadmium ion	**Hg²⁺**	**Mercury(II)** or mercuric ion
			Ni²⁺	Nickel(II) or nickelous ion
			Pb²⁺	**Lead(II)** or plumbous ion
			Sn²⁺	Tin(II) or stannous ion
3+	**Al³⁺**	**Aluminum ion**	Cr³⁺	Chromium(III) or chromic ion
			Fe³⁺	**Iron(III)** or ferric ion

*The most common ions are in boldface.

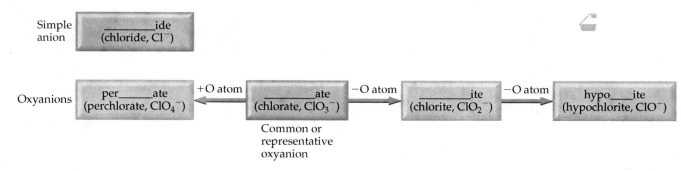

▲ Figure 2.26 **Summary of the procedure for naming anions.** The root of the name (such as "chlor" for chlorine) goes in the blank.

A few simple polyatomic anions also have names ending in *-ide*:

OH^- hydroxide ion CN^- cyanide ion O_2^{2-} peroxide ion

(b) *Polyatomic anions containing oxygen have names ending in* -ate *or* -ite. These anions are called **oxyanions**. The ending *-ate* is used for the most common oxyanion of an element. The ending *-ite* is used for an oxyanion that has the same charge but one O atom fewer:

NO_3^- nitrate ion SO_4^{2-} sulfate ion
NO_2^- nitrite ion SO_3^{2-} sulfite ion

Prefixes are used when the series of oxyanions of an element extends to four members, as with the halogens. The prefix *per-* indicates one more O atom than the oxyanion ending in *-ate*; the prefix *hypo-* indicates one O atom fewer than the oxyanion ending in *-ite*:

ClO_4^- perchlorate ion (one more O atom than chlorate)
ClO_3^- **chlorate ion**
ClO_2^- chlorite ion (one O atom fewer than chlorate)
ClO^- hypochlorite ion (one O atom fewer than chlorite)

These rules are summarized in Figure 2.26 ▲.

△ GIVE IT SOME THOUGHT

What information is conveyed by the endings *-ide*, *-ate*, and *-ite* in the name of an anion?

Students often have a hard time remembering the number of oxygen atoms in the various oxyanions and the charges of these ions. Figure 2.27 ▼ lists the oxyanions of C, N, P, S, and Cl that contain the maximum number of O atoms. The periodic pattern seen in these formulas can help you remember them. Notice that C and N, which are in the second period of the periodic table, have only three O atoms each, whereas P, S, and Cl, which are in the third period, have four O atoms each. If we begin at the lower right side of the figure, with Cl, we see that the charges increase from right to left, from 1− for Cl (ClO_4^-) to 3− for P (PO_4^{3-}). In the second period the charges also increase from right to left, from 1− for N (NO_3^-) to 2− for C (CO_3^{2-}). Each anion

	4A	5A	6A	7A
2	CO_3^{2-} **Carbonate ion**	NO_3^- **Nitrate ion**		
3		PO_4^{3-} **Phosphate ion**	SO_4^{2-} **Sulfate ion**	ClO_4^- **Perchlorate ion**

◀ Figure 2.27 **Common oxyanions.** The composition and charges of common oxyanions are related to their location in the periodic table.

shown in Figure 2.27 has a name ending in *-ate*. The ClO_4^- ion also has a *per-* prefix. If you know the rules summarized in Figure 2.26 and the names and formulas of the five oxyanions in Figure 2.27, you can deduce the names for the other oxyanions of these elements.

 GIVE IT SOME THOUGHT

Predict the formulas for the borate ion and silicate ion, assuming that they contain a single B and Si atom, respectively, and follow the trends shown in Figure 2.27 ▲.

SAMPLE EXERCISE 2.11 | **Determining the Formula of an Oxyanion from Its Name**

Based on the formula for the sulfate ion, predict the formula for **(a)** the selenate ion and **(b)** the selenite ion. (Sulfur and selenium are both members of group 6A and form analogous oxyanions.)

SOLUTION
(a) The sulfate ion is SO_4^{2-} The analogous selenate ion is therefore SeO_4^{2-}.
(b) The ending *-ite* indicates an oxyanion with the same charge but one O atom fewer than the corresponding oxyanion that ends in *-ate*. Thus, the formula for the selenite ion is SeO_3^{2-}.

PRACTICE EXERCISE
The formula for the bromate ion is analogous to that for the chlorate ion. Write the formula for the hypobromite and perbromate ions.
Answer: BrO^- and BrO_4^-

(c) *Anions derived by adding H^+ to an oxyanion are named by adding as a prefix the word* hydrogen *or* dihydrogen, *as appropriate*:

CO_3^{2-}	carbonate ion	PO_4^{3-}	phosphate ion
HCO_3^-	hydrogen carbonate ion	$H_2PO_4^-$	dihydrogen phosphate ion

Notice that each H^+ reduces the negative charge of the parent anion by one. An older method for naming some of these ions is to use the prefix *bi-*. Thus, the HCO_3^- ion is commonly called the bicarbonate ion, and HSO_4^- is sometimes called the bisulfate ion.

The names and formulas of the common anions are listed in Table 2.5 ▼ and on the back inside cover of the text. Those anions whose names end in *-ide* are listed on the left portion of Table 2.5, and those

---

TABLE 2.5 ■ Common Anions*

Charge	Formula	Name	Formula	Name
1−	H^-	Hydride ion	CH_3COO^- (or $C_2H_3O_2^-$)	**Acetate ion**
	F^-	**Fluoride ion**	ClO_3^-	Chlorate ion
	Cl^-	**Chloride ion**	ClO_4^-	**Perchlorate ion**
	Br^-	**Bromide ion**	NO_3^-	**Nitrate ion**
	I^-	**Iodide ion**	MnO_4^-	Permanganate ion
	CN^-	Cyanide ion		
	OH^-	**Hydroxide ion**		
2−	O^{2-}	**Oxide ion**	CO_3^{2-}	**Carbonate ion**
	O_2^{2-}	Peroxide ion	CrO_4^{2-}	Chromate ion
	S^{2-}	**Sulfide ion**	$Cr_2O_7^{2-}$	Dichromate ion
			SO_4^{2-}	**Sulfate ion**
3−	N^{3-}	Nitride ion	PO_4^{3-}	**Phosphate ion**

* The most common ions are in boldface.

whose names end in -ate are listed on the right. The most common of these ions are shown in boldface. You should learn names and formulas of these anions first. The formulas of the ions whose names end with -ite can be derived from those ending in -ate by removing an O atom. Notice the location of the monatomic ions in the periodic table. Those of group 7A always have a 1− charge ($F^−$, $Cl^−$, $Br^−$, and $I^−$), and those of group 6A have a 2− charge ($O^{2−}$ and $S^{2−}$).

3. **Ionic Compounds**

Names of ionic compounds consist of the cation name followed by the anion name:

$CaCl_2$	calcium chloride
$Al(NO_3)_3$	aluminum nitrate
$Cu(ClO_4)_2$	copper(II) perchlorate (or cupric perchlorate)

In the chemical formulas for aluminum nitrate and copper(II) perchlorate, parentheses followed by the appropriate subscript are used because the compounds contain two or more polyatomic ions.

SAMPLE EXERCISE 2.12 | Determining the Names of Ionic Compounds from Their Formulas

Name the following compounds: **(a)** K_2SO_4, **(b)** $Ba(OH)_2$, **(c)** $FeCl_3$.

SOLUTION

Each compound is ionic and is named using the guidelines we have already discussed. In naming ionic compounds, it is important to recognize polyatomic ions and to determine the charge of cations with variable charge.

(a) The cation in this compound is K^+, and the anion is $SO_4^{2−}$. (If you thought the compound contained $S^{2−}$ and $O^{2−}$ ions, you failed to recognize the polyatomic sulfate ion.) Putting together the names of the ions, we have the name of the compound, potassium sulfate.

(b) In this case the compound is composed of Ba^{2+} and $OH^−$ ions. Ba^{2+} is the barium ion and $OH^−$ is the hydroxide ion. Thus, the compound is called barium hydroxide.

(c) You must determine the charge of Fe in this compound because an iron atom can form more than one cation. Because the compound contains three $Cl^−$ ions, the cation must be Fe^{3+} which is the iron(III), or ferric, ion. The $Cl^−$ ion is the chloride ion. Thus, the compound is iron(III) chloride or ferric chloride.

PRACTICE EXERCISE

Name the following compounds: **(a)** NH_4Br, **(b)** Cr_2O_3, **(c)** $Co(NO_3)_2$.
Answers: **(a)** ammonium bromide, **(b)** chromium(III) oxide, **(c)** cobalt(II) nitrate

---

SAMPLE EXERCISE 2.13 | Determining the Formulas of Ionic Compounds from Their Names

Write the chemical formulas for the following compounds: **(a)** potassium sulfide, **(b)** calcium hydrogen carbonate, **(c)** nickel(II) perchlorate.

SOLUTION

In going from the name of an ionic compound to its chemical formula, you must know the charges of the ions to determine the subscripts.

(a) The potassium ion is K^+, and the sulfide ion is $S^{2−}$. Because ionic compounds are electrically neutral, two K^+ ions are required to balance the charge of one $S^{2−}$ ion, giving the empirical formula of the compound, K_2S.

(b) The calcium ion is Ca^{2+}. The carbonate ion is $CO_3^{2−}$, so the hydrogen carbonate ion is $HCO_3^−$. Two $HCO_3^−$ ions are needed to balance the positive charge of Ca^{2+}, giving $Ca(HCO_3)_2$.

(c) The nickel(II) ion is Ni^{2+}. The perchlorate ion is $ClO_4^−$. Two $ClO_4^−$ ions are required to balance the charge on one Ni^{2+} ion, giving $Ni(ClO_4)_2$.

PRACTICE EXERCISE

Give the chemical formula for **(a)** magnesium sulfate, **(b)** silver sulfide, **(c)** lead(II) nitrate.
Answers: **(a)** $MgSO_4$, **(b)** Ag_2S, **(c)** $Pb(NO_3)_2$

► Figure 2.28 **Relating names of anions and acids.** Summary of the way in which anion names and acid names are related. The prefixes *per-* and *hypo-* are retained in going from the anion to the acid.

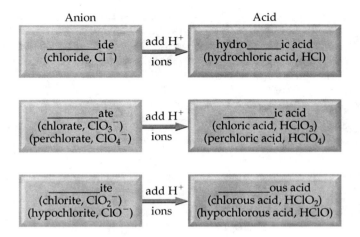

Names and Formulas of Acids

Acids are an important class of hydrogen-containing compounds, and they are named in a special way. For our present purposes, an *acid* is a substance whose molecules yield hydrogen ions (H^+) when dissolved in water. When we encounter the chemical formula for an acid at this stage of the course, it will be written with H as the first element, as in HCl and H_2SO_4.

An acid is composed of an anion connected to enough H^+ ions to neutralize, or balance, the anion's charge. Thus, the SO_4^{2-} ion requires two H^+ ions, forming H_2SO_4. The name of an acid is related to the name of its anion, as summarized in Figure 2.28 ▲.

1. *Acids containing anions whose names end in* -ide *are named by changing the* -ide *ending to* -ic, *adding the prefix* hydro- *to this anion name, and then following with the word* acid, *as in the following examples:*

Anion	Corresponding Acid
Cl^- (chloride)	HCl (hydrochloric acid)
S^{2-} (sulfide)	H_2S (hydrosulfuric acid)

2. *Acids containing anions whose names end in* -ate *or* -ite *are named by changing* -ate *to* -ic *and* -ite *to* -ous, *and then adding the word* acid. Prefixes in the anion name are retained in the name of the acid. These rules are illustrated by the oxyacids of chlorine:

Anion	Corresponding Acid
ClO_4^- (perchloric)	$HClO_4$ (perchloric acid)
ClO_3^- (chlorate)	$HClO_3$ (chloric acid)
ClO_2^- (chlorite)	$HClO_2$ (chlorous acid)
ClO^- (hypochlorite)	HClO (hypochlorous acid)

■■■ **SAMPLE EXERCISE 2.14** | **Relating the Names and Formulas of Acids**

Name the following acids: **(a)** HCN, **(b)** HNO_3, **(c)** H_2SO_4, **(d)** H_2SO_3.

SOLUTION

(a) The anion from which this acid is derived is CN^-, the cyanide ion. Because this ion has an *-ide* ending, the acid is given a *hydro-* prefix and an *-ic* ending: hydrocyanic acid. Only water solutions of HCN are referred to as hydrocyanic acid: The pure compound, which is a gas under normal conditions, is called hydrogen cyanide. Both hydrocyanic acid and hydrogen cyanide are *extremely* toxic.

(b) Because NO_3^- is the nitrate ion, HNO_3 is called nitric acid (the *-ate* ending of the anion is replaced with an *-ic* ending in naming the acid).
(c) Because SO_4^{2-} is the sulfate ion, H_2SO_4 is called sulfuric acid.
(d) Because SO_3^{2-} is the sulfite ion, H_2SO_3 is sulfurous acid (the *-ite* ending of the anion is replaced with an *-ous* ending).

■ PRACTICE EXERCISE

Give the chemical formulas for **(a)** hydrobromic acid, **(b)** carbonic acid.
Answers: **(a)** HBr, **(b)** H_2CO_3

Names and Formulas of Binary Molecular Compounds

The procedures used for naming *binary* (two-element) molecular compounds are similar to those used for naming ionic compounds:

1. *The name of the element farther to the left in the periodic table is usually written first.* An exception to this rule occurs in the case of compounds that contain oxygen. Oxygen is always written last except when combined with fluorine.

2. *If both elements are in the same group in the periodic table, the one having the higher atomic number is named first.*

3. *The name of the second element is given an* -ide *ending.*

4. *Greek prefixes (Table 2.6 ▶) are used to indicate the number of atoms of each element.* The prefix *mono-* is never used with the first element. When the prefix ends in *a* or *o* and the name of the second element begins with a vowel (such as *oxide*), the *a* or *o* of the prefix is often dropped.

The following examples illustrate these rules:

Cl_2O	dichlorine monoxide	NF_3	nitrogen trifluoride
N_2O_4	dinitrogen tetroxide	P_4S_{10}	tetraphosphorus decasulfide

It is important to realize that you cannot predict the formulas of most molecular substances in the same way that you predict the formulas of ionic compounds. For this reason, we name molecular compounds using prefixes that explicitly indicate their composition. Molecular compounds that contain hydrogen and one other element are an important exception, however. These compounds can be treated as if they were neutral substances containing H^+ ions and anions. Thus, you can predict that the substance named hydrogen chloride has the formula HCl, containing one H^+ to balance the charge of one Cl^-. (The name hydrogen chloride is used only for the pure compound; water solutions of HCl are called hydrochloric acid.) Similarly, the formula for hydrogen sulfide is H_2S because two H^+ are needed to balance the charge on S^{2-}.

TABLE 2.6 ■ Prefixes Used in Naming Binary Compounds Formed between Nonmetals

Prefix	Meaning
Mono-	1
Di-	2
Tri-	3
Tetra-	4
Penta-	5
Hexa-	6
Hepta-	7
Octa-	8
Nona-	9
Deca-	10

■ SAMPLE EXERCISE 2.15 | Relating the Names and Formulas of Binary Molecular Compounds

Name the following compounds: **(a)** SO_2, **(b)** PCl_5, **(c)** N_2O_3.

SOLUTION

The compounds consist entirely of nonmetals, so they are molecular rather than ionic. Using the prefixes in Table 2.6, we have **(a)** sulfur dioxide, **(b)** phosphorus pentachloride, and **(c)** dinitrogen trioxide.

■ PRACTICE EXERCISE

Give the chemical formula for **(a)** silicon tetrabromide, **(b)** disulfur dichloride.
Answers: **(a)** $SiBr_4$, **(b)** S_2Cl_2

2.9 SOME SIMPLE ORGANIC COMPOUNDS

The study of compounds of carbon is called **organic chemistry**, and as noted earlier in the chapter, compounds that contain carbon and hydrogen, often in combination with oxygen, nitrogen, or other elements, are called *organic compounds*. We will examine organic compounds and organic chemistry in some detail in Chapter 25. You will see a number of organic compounds throughout this text; many of them have practical applications or are relevant to the chemistry of biological systems. Here we present a very brief introduction to some of the simplest organic compounds to provide you with a sense of what these molecules look like and how they are named.

Alkanes

Compounds that contain only carbon and hydrogen are called **hydrocarbons**. In the most basic class of hydrocarbons, each carbon atom is bonded to four other atoms. These compounds are called **alkanes**. The three simplest alkanes, which contain one, two, and three carbon atoms, respectively, are methane (CH_4), ethane (C_2H_6), and propane (C_3H_8). The structural formulas of these three alkanes are as follows:

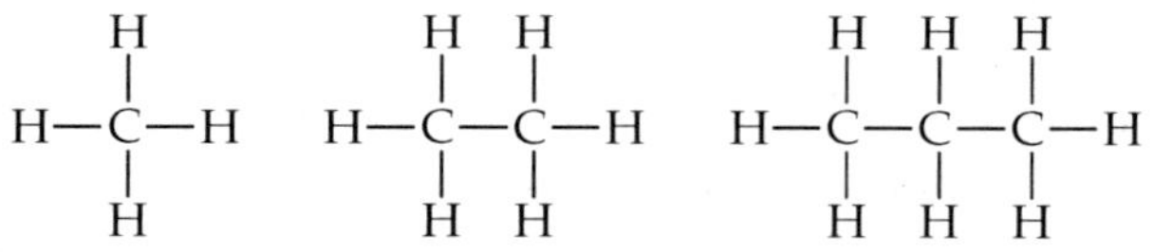

We can make longer alkanes by adding additional carbon atoms to the "skeleton" of the molecule.

Although the hydrocarbons are binary molecular compounds, they are not named like the binary inorganic compounds discussed in Section 2.8. Instead, each alkane has a name that ends in *-ane*. The alkane with four carbon atoms is called butane. For alkanes with five or more carbon atoms, the names are derived from prefixes such as those in Table 2.6. An alkane with eight carbon atoms, for example, is called *octane* (C_8H_{18}), where the *octa-* prefix for eight is combined with the *-ane* ending for an alkane. Gasoline consists primarily of octanes, as will be discussed in Chapter 25.

Some Derivatives of Alkanes

Other classes of organic compounds are obtained when hydrogen atoms of alkanes are replaced with *functional groups*, which are specific groups of atoms. An **alcohol**, for example, is obtained by replacing an H atom of an alkane with an —OH group. The name of the alcohol is derived from that of the alkane by adding an *-ol* ending:

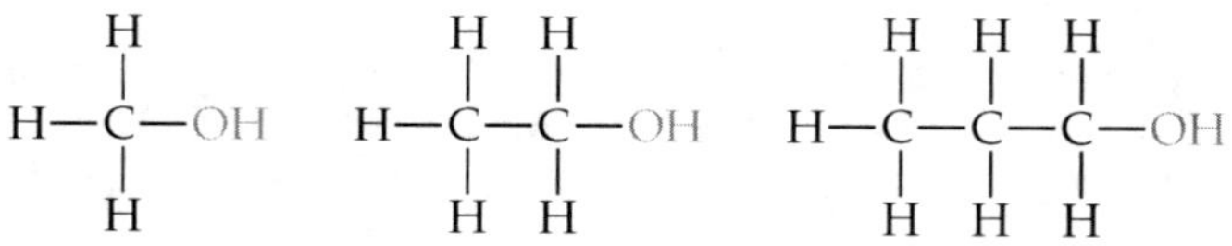

Alcohols have properties that are very different from the properties of the alkanes from which the alcohols are obtained. For example, methane, ethane, and propane are all colorless gases under normal conditions, whereas methanol, ethanol, and propanol are colorless liquids. We will discuss the reasons for these differences in properties in Chapter 11.

The prefix "1" in the name 1-propanol indicates that the replacement of H with OH has occurred at one of the "outer" carbon atoms rather than the "middle" carbon atom. A different compound called 2-propanol (also known as isopropyl alcohol) is obtained if the OH functional group is attached to the middle carbon atom:

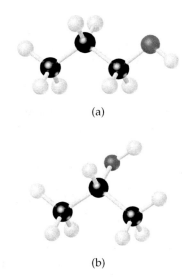

(a)

(b)

▲ Figure 2.29 **The two forms of propanol (C$_3$H$_7$OH).** (a) 1-Propanol, in which the OH group is attached to one of the end carbon atoms, and (b) 2-propanol, in which the OH group is attached to the middle carbon atom.

$$
\begin{array}{ccc}
\text{H} & \text{H} & \text{H} \\
| & | & | \\
\text{H--C--C--C--OH} \\
| & | & | \\
\text{H} & \text{H} & \text{H}
\end{array}
\qquad
\begin{array}{ccc}
\text{H} & \text{H} & \text{H} \\
| & | & | \\
\text{H--C--C--C--H} \\
| & | & | \\
\text{H} & \text{O} & \text{H} \\
& | & \\
& \text{H} &
\end{array}
$$

1-Propanol   2-Propanol

Ball-and-stick models of these two molecules are presented in Figure 2.29 ▶.

Much of the richness of organic chemistry is possible because organic compounds can form long chains of carbon–carbon bonds. The series of alkanes that begins with methane, ethane, and propane and the series of alcohols that begins with methanol, ethanol, and propanol can both be extended for as long as we desire, in principle. The properties of alkanes and alcohols change as the chains get longer. Octanes, which are alkanes with eight carbon atoms, are liquids under normal conditions. If the alkane series is extended to tens of thousands of carbon atoms, we obtain *polyethylene*, a solid substance that is used to make thousands of plastic products, such as plastic bags, food containers, and laboratory equipment.

■ **SAMPLE EXERCISE 2.16** | **Writing Structural and Molecular Formulas for Hydrocarbons**

Consider the alkane called *pentane*. **(a)** Assuming that the carbon atoms are in a straight line, write a structural formula for pentane. **(b)** What is the molecular formula for pentane?

SOLUTION

(a) Alkanes contain only carbon and hydrogen, and each carbon atom is attached to four other atoms. Because the name pentane contains the prefix *penta-* for five (Table 2.6), we can assume that pentane contains five carbon atoms bonded in a chain. If we then add enough hydrogen atoms to make four bonds to each carbon atom, we obtain the following structural formula:

$$
\begin{array}{ccccc}
\text{H} & \text{H} & \text{H} & \text{H} & \text{H} \\
| & | & | & | & | \\
\text{H--C--C--C--C--C--H} \\
| & | & | & | & | \\
\text{H} & \text{H} & \text{H} & \text{H} & \text{H}
\end{array}
$$

This form of pentane is often called *n*-pentane, where the *n*- stands for "normal" because all five carbon atoms are in one line in the structural formula.
(b) Once the structural formula is written, we can determine the molecular formula by counting the atoms present. Thus, *n*-pentane has the formula C$_5$H$_{12}$.

■ **PRACTICE EXERCISE**

Butane is the alkane with four carbon atoms. **(a)** What is the molecular formula of butane? **(b)** What are the name and molecular formula of an alcohol derived from butane?
Answers: **(a)** C$_4$H$_{10}$, **(b)** butanol, C$_4$H$_{10}$O or C$_4$H$_9$OH

CHAPTER REVIEW

SUMMARY AND KEY TERMS

Sections 2.1 and 2.2 **Atoms** are the basic building blocks of matter. They are the smallest units of an element that can combine with other elements. Atoms are composed of even smaller particles, called **subatomic particles**. Some of these subatomic particles are charged and follow the usual behavior of charged particles: Particles with the same charge repel one another, whereas particles with unlike charges are attracted to one another. We considered some of the important experiments that led to the discovery and characterization of subatomic particles. Thomson's experiments on the behavior of **cathode rays** in magnetic and electric fields led to the discovery of the electron and allowed its charge-to-mass ratio to be measured. Millikan's oil-drop experiment determined the charge of the electron. Becquerel's discovery of **radioactivity**, the spontaneous emission of radiation by atoms, gave further evidence that the atom has a substructure. Rutherford's studies of how thin metal foils scatter α particles showed that the atom has a dense, positively charged **nucleus**.

Section 2.3 Atoms have a nucleus that contains **protons** and **neutrons**; **electrons** move in the space around the nucleus. The magnitude of the charge of the electron, 1.602×10^{-19} C, is called the **electronic charge**. The charges of particles are usually represented as multiples of this charge—an electron has a $1-$ charge, and a proton has a $1+$ charge. The masses of atoms are usually expressed in terms of **atomic mass units** (1 amu $= 1.66054 \times 10^{-24}$ g). The dimensions of atoms are often expressed in units of **angstroms** (1 Å $= 10^{-10}$ m).

Elements can be classified by **atomic number**, the number of protons in the nucleus of an atom. All atoms of a given element have the same atomic number. The **mass number** of an atom is the sum of the numbers of protons and neutrons. Atoms of the same element that differ in mass number are known as **isotopes**.

Section 2.4 The atomic mass scale is defined by assigning a mass of exactly 12 amu to a ^{12}C atom. The **atomic weight** (average atomic mass) of an element can be calculated from the relative abundances and masses of that element's isotopes. The **mass spectrometer** provides the most direct and accurate means of experimentally measuring atomic (and molecular) weights.

Section 2.5 The **periodic table** is an arrangement of the elements in order of increasing atomic number. Elements with similar properties are placed in vertical columns. The elements in a column are known as a periodic **group**. The elements in a horizontal row are known as a **period**. The **metallic elements (metals)**, which comprise the majority of the elements, dominate the left side and the middle of the table; the **nonmetallic elements (nonmetals)**

are located on the upper right side. Many of the elements that lie along the line that separates metals from nonmetals are **metalloids**.

Section 2.6 Atoms can combine to form **molecules**. Compounds composed of molecules (**molecular compounds**) usually contain only nonmetallic elements. A molecule that contains two atoms is called a **diatomic molecule**. The composition of a substance is given by its **chemical formula**. A molecular substance can be represented by its **empirical formula**, which gives the relative numbers of atoms of each kind. It is usually represented by its **molecular formula**, however, which gives the actual numbers of each type of atom in a molecule. **Structural formulas** show the order in which the atoms in a molecule are connected. Ball-and-stick models and space-filling models are often used to represent molecules.

Section 2.7 Atoms can either gain or lose electrons, forming charged particles called **ions**. Metals tend to lose electrons, becoming positively charged ions (**cations**). Nonmetals tend to gain electrons, forming negatively charged ions (**anions**). Because **ionic compounds** are electrically neutral, containing both cations and anions, they usually contain both metallic and nonmetallic elements. Atoms that are joined together, as in a molecule, but carry a net charge are called **polyatomic ions**. The chemical formulas used for ionic compounds are empirical formulas, which can be written readily if the charges of the ions are known. The total positive charge of the cations in an ionic compound equals the total negative charge of the anions.

Section 2.8 The set of rules for naming chemical compounds is called **chemical nomenclature**. We studied the systematic rules used for naming three classes of inorganic substances: ionic compounds, acids, and binary molecular compounds. In naming an ionic compound, the cation is named first and then the anion. Cations formed from metal atoms have the same name as the metal. If the metal can form cations of differing charges, the charge is given using Roman numerals. Monatomic anions have names ending in *-ide*. Polyatomic anions containing oxygen and another element (**oxyanions**) have names ending in *-ate* or *-ite*.

Section 2.9 **Organic chemistry** is the study of compounds that contain carbon. The simplest class of organic molecules is the **hydrocarbons**, which contain only carbon and hydrogen. Hydrocarbons in which each carbon atom is attached to four other atoms are called **alkanes**. Alkanes have names that end in *-ane*, such as methane and ethane. Other organic compounds are formed when an H atom of a hydrocarbon is replaced with a functional group. An **alcohol**, for example, is a compound in which an H atom of a hydrocarbon is replaced by an OH functional group. Alcohols have names that end in *-ol*, such as methanol and ethanol.

KEY SKILLS

- Describe the basic postulates of Dalton's atomic theory.
- Describe the key experiments that led to the discovery of electrons and to the nuclear model of the atom.
- Describe the structure of the atom in terms of protons, neutrons, and electrons.
- Describe the electric charge and relative masses of protons, neutrons, and electrons.
- Use chemical symbols together with atomic number and mass number to express the subatomic composition of isotopes.
- Understand atomic weights and how they relate to the masses of individual atoms and to their natural abundances.
- Describe how elements are organized in the periodic table by atomic number and by similarities in chemical behavior, giving rise to periods and groups.
- Describe the locations of metals and nonmetals in the periodic table.
- Distinguish between molecular substances and ionic substances in terms of their composition.
- Distinguish between empirical formulas and molecular formulas.
- Describe how molecular formulas and structural formulas are used to represent the compositions of molecules.
- Explain how ions are formed by the gain or loss of electrons and be able to use the periodic table to predict the charges of ions.
- Write the empirical formulas of ionic compounds, given their charges.
- Write the name of an ionic compound given its chemical formula, or write the chemical formula given its name.
- Name or write chemical formulas for binary inorganic compounds and for acids.
- Identify organic compounds and name simple alkanes and alcohols.

VISUALIZING CONCEPTS

2.1 A charged particle is caused to move between two electrically charged plates, as shown below.

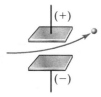

(a) Why does the path of the charged particle bend? **(b)** What is the sign of the electrical charge on the particle? **(c)** As the charge on the plates is increased, would you expect the bending to increase, decrease, or stay the same? **(d)** As the mass of the particle is increased while the speed of the particles remains the same, would you expect the bending to increase, decrease, or stay the same? [Section 2.2]

2.2 The following diagram is a representation of 20 atoms of a fictitious element, which we will call nevadium (Nv). The red spheres are ^{293}Nv, and the blue spheres are ^{295}Nv. **(a)** Assuming that this sample is a statistically representative sample of the element, calculate the percent abundance of each element. **(b)** If the mass of ^{293}Nv is 293.15 amu and that of ^{295}Nv is 295.15 amu, what is the atomic weight of Nv? [Section 2.4]

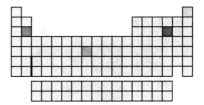

2.3 Four of the boxes in the following periodic table are colored. Which of these are metals and which are nonmetals? Which one is an alkaline earth metal? Which one is a noble gas? [Section 2.5]

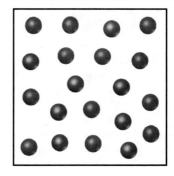

2.4 Does the following drawing represent a neutral atom or
CQ an ion? Write its complete chemical symbol including
mass number, atomic number, and net charge (if any).
[Sections 2.3 and 2.7]

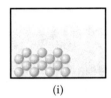

— 16 protons + 16 neutrons

— 18 electrons

2.5 Which of the following diagrams most likely represents
CQ an ionic compound, and which represents a molecular
one? Explain your choice. [Sections 2.6 and 2.7]

(i)   (ii)

2.6 Write the chemical formula for the following com-
CQ pound. Is the compound ionic or molecular? Name the
compound. [Sections 2.6 and 2.8]

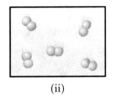

2.7 Five of the boxes in the following periodic table are col-
CQ ored. Predict the charge on the ion associated with each
of these elements. [Section 2.7]

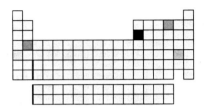

2.8 The following diagram represents an ionic compound in
CQ which the red spheres represent cations and blue
spheres represent anions. Which of the following formulas is consistent with the drawing: KBr, K_2SO_4,
$Ca(NO_3)_2$, $Fe_2(SO_4)_3$? Name the compound. [Sections
2.7 and 2.8]

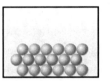

EXERCISES

Atomic Theory and the Discovery of Atomic Structure

2.9 How does Dalton's atomic theory account for the fact
CQ that when 1.000 g of water is decomposed into its elements, 0.111 g of hydrogen and 0.889 g of oxygen are obtained regardless of the source of the water?

2.10 Hydrogen sulfide is composed of two elements: hydro-
CQ gen and sulfur. In an experiment, 6.500 g of hydrogen
sulfide is fully decomposed into its elements. (a) If
0.384 g of hydrogen is obtained in this experiment, how
many grams of sulfur must be obtained? (b) What fundamental law does this experiment demonstrate?
(c) How is this law explained by Dalton's atomic
theory?

2.11 A chemist finds that 30.82 g of nitrogen will react with
17.60 g, 35.20 g, 70.40 g, or 88.00 g of oxygen to form
four different compounds. (a) Calculate the mass of oxygen per gram of nitrogen in each compound. (b) How
do the numbers in part (a) support Dalton's atomic
theory?

2.12 In a series of experiments, a chemist prepared three different compounds that contain only iodine and fluorine

and determined the mass of each element in each
compound:

Compound	Mass of Iodine (g)	Mass of Fluorine (g)
1	4.75	3.56
2	7.64	3.43
3	9.41	9.86

(a) Calculate the mass of fluorine per gram of iodine in
each compound. (b) How do the numbers in part (a)
support the atomic theory?

2.13 Summarize the evidence used by J. J. Thomson to argue
CQ that cathode rays consist of negatively charged
particles.

2.14 An unknown particle is caused to move between two
CQ electrically charged plates, as illustrated in Figure 2.8.
Its path is deflected by a smaller magnitude in the

opposite direction from that of a beta particle. What can you conclude about the charge and mass of this unknown particle?

2.15 (a) Figure 2.5 shows the apparatus used in the Millikan
CQ oil-drop experiment with the positively charged plate above the negatively charged plate. What do you think would be the effect on the rate of oil drops descending if the charges on the plates were reversed (negative above positive)? (b) In his original series of experiments, Millikan measured the charge on 58 separate oil drops. Why do you suppose he chose so many drops before reaching his final conclusions?

2.16 Millikan determined the charge on the electron by
CQ studying the static charges on oil drops falling in an electric field. A student carried out this experiment using several oil drops for her measurements and calcu-lated the charges on the drops. She obtained the follow-ing data:

Droplet	Calculated Charge (C)
A	1.60×10^{-19}
B	3.15×10^{-19}
C	4.81×10^{-19}
D	6.31×10^{-19}

(a) What is the significance of the fact that the droplets carried different charges? (b) What conclusion can the student draw from these data regarding the charge of the electron? (c) What value (and to how many signifi-cant figures) should she report for the electronic charge?

Modern View of Atomic Structure; Atomic Weights

2.17 The radius of an atom of krypton (Kr) is about 1.9 Å. (a) Express this distance in nanometers (nm) and in pi-cometers (pm). (b) How many krypton atoms would have to be lined up to span 1.0 mm? (c) If the atom is as-sumed to be a sphere, what is the volume in cm^3 of a sin-gle Kr atom?

2.18 An atom of tin (Sn) has a diameter of about 2.8×10^{-8} cm. (a) What is the radius of a tin atom in angstroms (Å) and in meters (m)? (b) How many Sn atoms would have to be placed side by side to span a distance of 6.0 μm? (c) If you assume that the tin atom is a sphere, what is the volume in m^3 of a single atom?

2.19 Answer the following questions without referring to Table 2.1: (a) What are the main subatomic particles that make up the atom? (b) What is the relative charge (in multiples of the electronic charge) of each of the par-ticles? (c) Which of the particles is the most massive? (d) Which is the least massive?

2.20 Determine whether each of the following statements is
CQ true or false. If false, correct the statement to make it true: (a) The nucleus has most of the mass and compris-es most of the volume of an atom; (b) every atom of a given element has the same number of protons; (c) the number of electrons in an atom equals the number of neutrons in the atom; (d) the protons in the nucleus of the helium atom are held together by a force called the strong nuclear force.

2.21 (a) Define atomic number and mass number. (b) Which of these can vary without changing the identity of the element?

2.22 (a) Which two of the following are isotopes of the same element: $^{31}_{16}X$, $^{31}_{15}X$, $^{32}_{16}X$? (b) What is the identity of the ele-ment whose isotopes you have selected?

2.23 How many protons, neutrons, and electrons are in the following atoms: (a) ^{40}Ar, (b) ^{65}Zn, (c) ^{70}Ga, (d) ^{80}Br, (e) ^{184}W, (f) ^{243}Am?

2.24 Each of the following isotopes is used in medicine. Indi-cate the number of protons and neutrons in each iso-tope: (a) phosphorus-32, (b) chromium-51, (c) cobalt-60, (d) technetium-99, (e) iodine-131; (f) thallium-201.

2.25 Fill in the gaps in the following table, assuming each column represents a neutral atom:

Symbol	^{52}Cr				
Protons		25			82
Neutrons		30	64		
Electrons			48	86	
Mass no.				222	207

2.26 Fill in the gaps in the following table, assuming each column represents a neutral atom:

Symbol	^{65}Zn				
Protons		44			92
Neutrons		57	49		
Electrons			38	47	
Mass no.				108	235

2.27 Write the correct symbol, with both superscript and sub-script, for each of the following. Use the list of elements inside the front cover as needed: (a) the isotope of plat-inum that contains 118 neutrons, (b) the isotope of kryp-ton with mass number 84, (c) the isotope of arsenic with mass number 75, **(d)** the isotope of magnesium that has an equal number of protons and neutrons.

2.28 One way in which Earth's evolution as a planet can be understood is by measuring the amounts of certain isotopes in rocks. One quantity recently measured is the ratio of ^{129}Xe to ^{130}Xe in some minerals. In what way do these two isotopes differ from one another? In what respects are they the same?

2.29 **(a)** What isotope is used as the standard in establishing
CQ   the atomic mass scale? **(b)** The atomic weight of boron is reported as 10.81, yet no atom of boron has the mass of 10.81 amu. Explain.

2.30 **(a)** What is the mass in amu of a carbon-12 atom?
CQ   **(b)** Why is the atomic weight of carbon reported as 12.011 in the table of elements and the periodic table in the front inside cover of this text?

2.31 Only two isotopes of copper occur naturally, ^{63}Cu (atomic mass = 62.9296 amu; abundance 69.17%) and ^{65}Cu (atomic mass = 64.9278 amu; abundance 30.83%). Calculate the atomic weight (average atomic mass) of copper.

2.32 Rubidium has two naturally occurring isotopes, rubidium-85 (atomic mass = 84.9118 amu; abundance = 72.15%) and rubidium-87 (atomic mass = 86.9092 amu; abundance 27.85%). Calculate the atomic weight of rubidium.

2.33 **(a)** In what fundamental way is mass spectrometry related to Thomson's cathode-ray experiments (Figure 2.4)?
CQ   **(b)** What are the labels on the axes of a mass spectrum? **(c)** To measure the mass spectrum of an atom, the atom must first lose one or more electrons. Why is this so?

2.34 **(a)** The mass spectrometer in Figure 2.13 has a magnet
CQ   as one of its components. What is the purpose of the magnet? **(b)** The atomic weight of Cl is 35.5 amu. However, the mass spectrum of Cl (Figure 2.14) does not show a peak at this mass. Explain. **(c)** A mass spectrum of phosphorus (P) atoms shows only a single peak at a mass of 31. What can you conclude from this observation?

2.35 Naturally occurring magnesium has the following isotopic abundances:

Isotope	Abundance	Atomic mass (amu)
^{24}Mg	78.99%	23.98504
^{25}Mg	10.00%	24.98584
^{26}Mg	11.01%	25.98259

(a) What is the average atomic mass of Mg? **(b)** Sketch the mass spectrum of Mg.

2.36 Mass spectrometry is more often applied to molecules than to atoms. We will see in Chapter 3 that the *molecular weight* of a molecule is the sum of the atomic weights of the atoms in the molecule. The mass spectrum of H_2 is taken under conditions that prevent decomposition into H atoms. The two naturally occurring isotopes of hydrogen are ^{1}H (atomic mass = 1.00783 amu; abundance 99.9885%) and ^{2}H (atomic mass = 2.01410 amu; abundance 0.0115%). **(a)** How many peaks will the mass spectrum have? **(b)** Give the relative atomic masses of each of these peaks. **(c)** Which peak will be the largest, and which the smallest?

The Periodic Table; Molecules and Ions

2.37 For each of the following elements, write its chemical symbol, locate it in the periodic table, and indicate whether it is a metal, metalloid, or nonmetal: **(a)** chromium, **(b)** helium, **(c)** phosphorus, **(d)** zinc, **(e)** magnesium, **(f)** bromine, **(g)** arsenic.

2.38 Locate each of the following elements in the periodic table; indicate whether it is a metal, metalloid, or nonmetal; and give the name of the element: **(a)** Ca, **(b)** Ti, **(c)** Ga, **(d)** Th, **(e)** Pt, **(f)** Se, **(g)** Kr.

2.39 For each of the following elements, write its chemical symbol, determine the name of the group to which it belongs (Table 2.3), and indicate whether it is a metal, metalloid, or nonmetal: **(a)** potassium, **(b)** iodine, **(c)** magnesium, **(d)** argon, **(e)** sulfur.

2.40 The elements of group 4A show an interesting change in properties moving down the group. Give the name and chemical symbol of each element in the group, and label it as a nonmetal, metalloid, or metal.

2.41 What can we tell about a compound when we know the
CQ   empirical formula? What additional information is conveyed by the molecular formula? By the structural formula? Explain in each case.

2.42 Two compounds have the same empirical formula. One
CQ   substance is a gas, the other is a viscous liquid. How is it possible for two substances with the same empirical formula to have markedly different properties?

2.43 Write the empirical formula corresponding to each of the following molecular formulas: **(a)** Al_2Br_6, **(b)** C_8H_{10}, **(c)** $C_4H_8O_2$, **(d)** P_4O_{10}, **(e)** $C_6H_4Cl_2$, **(f)** $B_3N_3H_6$.

2.44 Determine the molecular and empirical formulas of the following: **(a)** The organic solvent *benzene*, which has six carbon atoms and six hydrogen atoms; **(b)** the compound *silicon tetrachloride*, which has a silicon atom and four chlorine atoms and is used in the manufacture of computer chips; **(c)** the reactive substance *diborane*, which has two boron atoms and six hydrogen atoms; **(d)** the sugar called *glucose*, which has six carbon atoms, twelve hydrogen atoms, and six oxygen atoms.

2.45 How many hydrogen atoms are in each of the following: **(a)** C_2H_5OH, **(b)** $Ca(CH_3COO)_2$, **(c)** $(NH_4)_3PO_4$?

2.46 How many of the indicated atoms are represented by each chemical formula: **(a)** carbon atoms in $C_2H_5COOCH_3$, **(b)** oxygen atoms in $Ca(ClO_4)_2$, **(c)** hydrogen atoms in $(NH_4)_2HPO_4$?

2.47 Write the molecular and structural formulas for the
CQ   compounds represented by the following molecular
      models:

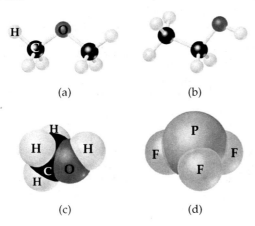

(a)   (b)

(c)   (d)

2.48 Write the molecular and structural formulas for the
CQ   compounds represented by the following models:

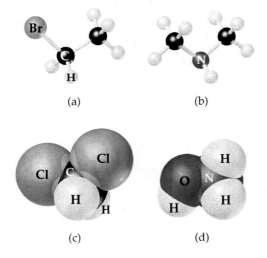

(a)   (b)

(c)   (d)

2.49 Fill in the gaps in the following table:

Symbol	$^{59}Co^{3+}$			
Protons		34	76	80
Neutrons		46	116	120
Electrons		36		78
Net charge			2+	

2.50 Fill in the gaps in the following table:

Symbol	$^{31}P^{3-}$			
Protons		35	49	
Neutrons		45	66	118
Electrons			46	76
Net charge		1−		3+

2.51 Each of the following elements is capable of forming an
      ion in chemical reactions. By referring to the periodic
      table, predict the charge of the most stable ion of each:
      (a) Mg, **(b)** Al, **(c)** K, **(d)** S, **(e)** F.

2.52 Using the periodic table, predict the charges of the ions
      of the following elements: **(a)** Ga, **(b)** Sr, **(c)** As, **(d)** Br,
      (e) Se.

2.53 Using the periodic table to guide you, predict the chem-
      ical formula and name of the compound formed by the
      following elements: **(a)** Ga and F, **(b)** Li and H, **(c)** Al
      and I, **(d)** K and S.

2.54 The most common charge associated with silver in its
      compounds is 1+. Indicate the chemical formulas you
      would expect for compounds formed between Ag and
      (a) iodine, **(b)** sulfur, **(c)** fluorine.

2.55 Predict the chemical formula for the ionic compound
      formed by **(a)** Ca^{2+} and Br^-, **(b)** K^+ and CO_3^{2-}, **(c)** Al^{3+}
      and CH_3COO^-, **(d)** NH_4^+ and SO_4^{2-}, **(e)** Mg^{2+} and
      PO_4^{3-}.

2.56 Predict the chemical formulas of the compounds formed
      by the following pairs of ions: **(a)** Cu^{2+} and Br^-, **(b)** Fe^{3+}
      and O^{2-}, **(c)** Hg_2^{2+} and CO_3^{2-}, **(d)** Ca^{2+} and AsO_4^{3-},
      (e) NH_4^+ and CO_3^{2-}.

2.57 Complete the table by filling in the formula for the ionic
      compound formed by each pair of cations and anions, as
      shown for the first pair.

Ion	K^+	NH_4^+	Mg^{2+}	Fe^{3+}
Cl^-	KCl			
OH^-				
CO_3^{2-}				
PO_4^{3-}				

2.58 Complete the table by filling in the formula for the ionic
      compound formed by each pair of cations and anions, as
      shown for the first pair.

Ion	Na^+	Ca^{2+}	Fe^{2+}	Al^{3+}
O^{2-}	Na_2O			
NO_3^-				
SO_4^{2-}				
AsO_4^{3-}				

2.59 Predict whether each of the following compounds is
      molecular or ionic: **(a)** B_2H_6, **(b)** CH_3OH, **(c)** $LiNO_3$,
      (d) Sc_2O_3, **(e)** CsBr, **(f)** NOCl, **(g)** NF_3, **(h)** Ag_2SO_4.

2.60 Which of the following are ionic, and which are molecu-
      lar? **(a)** PF_5, **(b)** NaI, **(c)** SCl_2, **(d)** $Ca(NO_3)_2$, **(e)** $FeCl_3$,
      (f) LaP, **(g)** $CoCO_3$, **(h)** N_2O_4.

Naming Inorganic Compounds; Organic Molecules

2.61 Give the chemical formula for (a) chlorite ion, (b) chloride ion, (c) chlorate ion, (d) perchlorate ion, (e) hypochlorite ion.

2.62 Selenium, an element required nutritionally in trace quantities, forms compounds analogous to sulfur. Name the following ions: (a) SeO_4^{2-}, (b) Se^{2-}, (c) HSe^-, (d) $HSeO_3^-$.

2.63 Give the names and charges of the cation and anion in each of the following compounds: (a) CaO, (b) Na_2SO_4, (c) $KClO_4$, (d) $Fe(NO_3)_2$, (e) $Cr(OH)_3$.

2.64 Give the names and charges of the cation and anion in each of the following compounds: (a) CuS, (b) Ag_2SO_4, (c) $Al(ClO_3)_3$, (d) $Co(OH)_2$, (e) $PbCO_3$.

2.65 Name the following ionic compounds: (a) MgO, (b) $AlCl_3$, (c) Li_3PO_4, (d) $Ba(ClO_4)_2$, (e) $Cu(NO_3)_2$, (f) $Fe(OH)_2$, (g) $Ca(C_2H_3O_2)_2$, (h) $Cr_2(CO_3)_3$, (i) K_2CrO_4, (j) $(NH_4)_2SO_4$.

2.66 Name the following ionic compounds: (a) K_2O, (b) $NaClO_2$, (c) $Sr(CN)_2$, (d) $Co(OH)_2$, (e) $Fe_2(CO_3)_3$, (f) $Cr(NO_3)_3$, (g) $(NH_4)_2SO_3$, (h) NaH_2PO_4, (i) $KMnO_4$, (j) $Ag_2Cr_2O_7$.

2.67 Write the chemical formulas for the following compounds: (a) aluminum hydroxide, (b) potassium sulfate, (c) copper(I) oxide, (d) zinc nitrate, (e) mercury(II) bromide, (f) iron(III) carbonate, (g) sodium hypobromite.

2.68 Give the chemical formula for each of the following ionic compounds: (a) sodium phosphate, (b) zinc nitrate, (c) barium bromate, (d) iron(II) perchlorate, (e) cobalt(II) hydrogen carbonate, (f) chromium(III) acetate, (g) potassium dichromate.

2.69 Give the name or chemical formula, as appropriate, for each of the following acids: (a) $HBrO_3$, (b) HBr, (c) H_3PO_4, (d) hypochlorous acid, (e) iodic acid, (f) sulfurous acid.

2.70 Provide the name or chemical formula, as appropriate, for each of the following acids: (a) hydrobromic acid, (b) hydrosulfuric acid, (c) nitrous acid, (d) H_2CO_3, (e) $HClO_3$, (f) $HC_2H_3O_2$.

2.71 Give the name or chemical formula, as appropriate, for each of the following binary molecular substances: (a) SF_6, (b) IF_5, (c) XeO_3, (d) dinitrogen tetroxide, (e) hydrogen cyanide, (f) tetraphosphorus hexasulfide.

2.72 The oxides of nitrogen are very important components in urban air pollution. Name each of the following compounds: (a) N_2O, (b) NO, (c) NO_2, (d) N_2O_5, (e) N_2O_4.

2.73 Write the chemical formula for each substance mentioned in the following word descriptions (use the front inside cover to find the symbols for the elements you don't know). (a) Zinc carbonate can be heated to form zinc oxide and carbon dioxide. (b) On treatment with hydrofluoric acid, silicon dioxide forms silicon tetrafluoride and water. (c) Sulfur dioxide reacts with water to form sulfurous acid. (d) The substance phosphorus trihydride, commonly called phosphine, is a toxic gas. (e) Perchloric acid reacts with cadmium to form cadmium(II) perchlorate. (f) Vanadium(III) bromide is a colored solid.

2.74 Assume that you encounter the following sentences in your reading. What is the chemical formula for each substance mentioned? (a) Sodium hydrogen carbonate is used as a deodorant. (b) Calcium hypochlorite is used in some bleaching solutions. (c) Hydrogen cyanide is a very poisonous gas. (d) Magnesium hydroxide is used as a cathartic. (e) Tin(II) fluoride has been used as a fluoride additive in toothpastes. (f) When cadmium sulfide is treated with sulfuric acid, fumes of hydrogen sulfide are given off.

2.75 (a) What is a hydrocarbon? (b) Butane is the alkane with a chain of four carbon atoms. Write a structural formula for this compound, and determine its molecular and empirical formulas.

2.76 (a) What ending is used for the names of alkanes? (b) Hexane is an alkane whose structural formula has all its carbon atoms in a straight chain. Draw the structural formula for this compound, and determine its molecular and empirical formulas. (*Hint:* You might need to refer to Table 2.6.)

2.77 (a) What is a functional group? (b) What functional group characterizes an alcohol? (c) With reference to Exercise 2.75, write a structural formula for 1-butanol, the alcohol derived from butane, by making a substitution on one of the end carbon atoms.

2.78 (a) What do ethane and ethanol have in common? (b) How does 1-propanol differ from propane?

ADDITIONAL EXERCISES

2.79 Describe a major contribution to science made by each of the following scientists: **(a)** Dalton, **(b)** Thomson, **(c)** Millikan, **(d)** Rutherford.

2.80 How did Rutherford interpret the following observations made during his α-particle scattering experiments? **(a)** Most α particles were not appreciably deflected as they passed through the gold foil. **(b)** A few α particles were deflected at very large angles. **(c)** What differences would you expect if beryllium foil were used instead of gold foil in the α-particle scattering experiment?

2.81 Suppose a scientist repeats the Millikan oil-drop experiment, but reports the charges on the drops using an unusual (and imaginary) unit called the *warmomb* (wa). He obtains the following data for four of the drops:

Droplet	Calculated Charge (wa)
A	3.84×10^{-8}
B	4.80×10^{-8}
C	2.88×10^{-8}
D	8.64×10^{-8}

(a) If all the droplets were the same size, which would fall most slowly through the apparatus? **(b)** From these data, what is the best choice for the charge of the electron in warmombs? **(c)** Based on your answer to part (b), how many electrons are there on each of the droplets? **(d)** What is the conversion factor between warmombs and coulombs?

2.82 The natural abundance of ^{3}He is 0.000137%. **(a)** How many protons, neutrons, and electrons are in an atom of ^{3}He? **(b)** Based on the sum of the masses of their subatomic particles, which is expected to be more massive, an atom of ^{3}He or an atom of ^{3}H (which is also called *tritium*)? **(c)** Based on your answer for part (b), what would need to be the precision of a mass spectrometer that is able to differentiate between peaks that are due to ^{3}He$^+$ and ^{3}H$^+$?

2.83 An α particle is the nucleus of an ^{4}He atom. **(a)** How many protons and neutrons are in an α particle? **(b)** What force holds the protons and neutrons together in the α particle? **(c)** What is the charge on an α particle in units of electronic charge? **(d)** The charge-to-mass ratio of an α particle is 4.8224×10^4 C/g. Based on the charge on the particle, calculate its mass in grams and in amu. **(e)** By using the data in Table 2.1, compare your answer for part (d) with the sum of the masses of the individual subatomic particles. Can you explain the difference in mass? (If not, we will discuss such mass differences further in Chapter 21.)

2.84 A cube of gold that is 1.00 cm on a side has a mass of 19.3 g. A single gold atom has a mass of 197.0 amu. **(a)** How many gold atoms are in the cube? **(b)** From the information given, estimate the diameter in Å of a single gold atom. **(c)** What assumptions did you make in arriving at your answer for part (b)?

2.85 The diameter of a rubidium atom is 4.95 Å. We will consider two different ways of placing the atoms on a surface. In arrangement A, all the atoms are lined up with one another. Arrangement B is called a *close-packed* arrangement because the atoms sit in the "depressions" formed by the previous row of atoms:

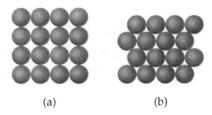

(a)   (b)

(a) Using arrangement A, how many Rb atoms could be placed on a square surface that is 1.0 cm on a side? **(b)** How many Rb atoms could be placed on a square surface that is 1.0 cm on a side, using arrangement B? **(c)** By what factor has the number of atoms on the surface increased in going to arrangement B from arrangement A? If extended to three dimensions, which arrangement would lead to a greater density for Rb metal?

2.86 **(a)** Assuming the dimensions of the nucleus and atom shown in Figure 2.12, what fraction of the *volume* of the atom is taken up by the nucleus? **(b)** Using the mass of the proton from Table 2.1 and assuming its diameter is 1.0×10^{-15} m, calculate the density of a proton in g/cm^3.

2.87 Identify the element represented by each of the following symbols and give the number of protons and neutrons in each: **(a)** $^{74}_{33}$X, **(b)** $^{127}_{53}$X, **(c)** $^{152}_{63}$X, **(d)** $^{209}_{83}$X.

2.88 The element oxygen has three naturally occurring isotopes, with 8, 9, and 10 neutrons in the nucleus, respectively. **(a)** Write the full chemical symbols for these three isotopes. **(b)** Describe the similarities and differences between the three kinds of atoms of oxygen.

2.89 Use Coulomb's law, $F = kQ_1Q_2/d^2$, to calculate the electric force on an electron ($Q = -1.6 \times 10^{-19}$ C) exerted by a single proton if the particles are 0.53×10^{-10} m apart. The constant k in Coulomb's law is 9.0×10^9 N·m^2/C^2. (The unit abbreviated N is the Newton, the SI unit of force.)

2.90 The element lead (Pb) consists of four naturally occurring isotopes with atomic masses 203.97302, 205.97444, 206.97587, and 207.97663 amu. The relative abundances of these four isotopes are 1.4, 24.1, 22.1, and 52.4%, respectively. From these data, calculate the atomic weight of lead.

2.91 Gallium (Ga) consists of two naturally occurring isotopes with masses of 68.926 and 70.925 amu. **(a)** How many protons and neutrons are in the nucleus of each isotope? Write the complete atomic symbol for each, showing the atomic number and mass number. **(b)** The average atomic mass of Ga is 69.72 amu. Calculate the abundance of each isotope.

2.92 Using a suitable reference such as the *CRC Handbook of Chemistry and Physics* or http://www.webelements.com, look up the following information for nickel: **(a)** the number of known isotopes, **(b)** the atomic masses (in amu) and the natural abundance of the five most abundant isotopes.

2.93 There are two different isotopes of bromine atoms. Under normal conditions, elemental bromine consists of Br_2 molecules (Figure 2.19), and the mass of a Br_2 molecule is the sum of the masses of the two atoms in the molecule. The mass spectrum of Br_2 consists of three peaks:

Mass (amu)	Relative Size
157.836	0.2569
159.834	0.4999
161.832	0.2431

(a) What is the origin of each peak (of what isotopes does each consist)? **(b)** What is the mass of each isotope? **(c)** Determine the average molecular mass of a Br_2 molecule. **(d)** Determine the average atomic mass of a bromine atom. **(e)** Calculate the abundances of the two isotopes.

2.94 It is common in mass spectrometry to assume that the mass of a cation is the same as that of its parent atom. **(a)** Using data in Table 2.1, determine the number of significant figures that must be reported before the difference in mass of ^1H and $^1H^+$ is significant. **(b)** What percentage of the mass of an ^1H atom does the electron represent?

2.95 From the following list of elements—Ar, H, Ga, Al, Ca, Br, Ge, K, O—pick the one that best fits each description. Use each element only once: **(a)** an alkali metal, **(b)** an alkaline earth metal, **(c)** a noble gas, **(d)** a halogen, **(e)** a metalloid, **(f)** a nonmetal listed in group 1A, **(g)** a metal that forms a 3+ ion, **(h)** a nonmetal that forms a 2− ion, **(i)** an element that resembles aluminum.

2.96 The first atoms of seaborgium (Sg) were identified in 1974. The longest-lived isotope of Sg has a mass number of 266. **(a)** How many protons, electrons, and neutrons are in an ^{266}Sg atom? **(b)** Atoms of Sg are very unstable, and it is therefore difficult to study this element's properties. Based on the position of Sg in the periodic table, what element should it most closely resemble in its chemical properties?

2.97 From the molecular structures shown here, identify the one that corresponds to each of the following species:

(a) chlorine gas; **(b)** propane, **(c)** nitrate ion; **(d)** sulfur trioxide; **(e)** methyl chloride, CH_3Cl.

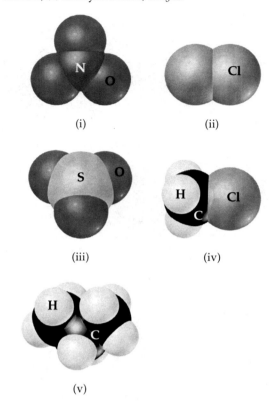

2.98 Name each of the following oxides. Assuming that the compounds are ionic, what charge is associated with the metallic element in each case? **(a)** NiO, **(b)** MnO_2, **(c)** Cr_2O_3, **(d)** MoO_3.

2.99 Iodic acid has the molecular formula HIO_3. Write the formulas for the following: **(a)** the iodate anion, **(b)** the periodate anion, **(c)** the hypoiodite anion, **(d)** hypoiodous acid, **(e)** periodic acid.

2.100 Elements in the same group of the periodic table often form oxyanions with the same general formula. The anions are also named in a similar fashion. Based on these observations, suggest a chemical formula or name, as appropriate, for each of the following ions: **(a)** BrO_4^-, **(b)** SeO_3^{2-}, **(c)** arsenate ion, **(d)** hydrogen tellurate ion.

2.101 Carbonic acid occurs in carbonated beverages. When allowed to react with lithium hydroxide it produces lithium carbonate. Lithium carbonate is used to treat depression and bipolar disorder. Write chemical formulas for carbonic acid, lithium hydroxide, and lithium carbonate.

2.102 Give the chemical names of each of the following familiar compounds: **(a)** NaCl (table salt), **(b)** $NaHCO_3$ (baking soda), **(c)** NaOCl (in many bleaches), **(d)** NaOH (caustic soda), **(e)** $(NH_4)_2CO_3$ (smelling salts), **(f)** $CaSO_4$ (plaster of Paris).

2.103 Many familiar substances have common, unsystematic names. For each of the following, give the correct systematic name: **(a)** saltpeter, KNO_3; **(b)** soda ash, Na_2CO_3; **(c)** lime, CaO; **(d)** muriatic acid, HCl; **(e)** Epsom salts, $MgSO_4$; **(f)** milk of magnesia, $Mg(OH)_2$.

2.104 Many ions and compounds have very similar names, and there is great potential for confusing them. Write the correct chemical formulas to distinguish between **(a)** calcium sulfide and calcium hydrogen sulfide, **(b)** hydrobromic acid and bromic acid, **(c)** aluminum nitride and aluminum nitrite, **(d)** iron(II) oxide and iron(III) oxide, **(e)** ammonia and ammonium ion, **(f)** potassium sulfite and potassium bisulfite, **(g)** mercurous chloride and mercuric chloride, **(h)** chloric acid and perchloric acid.

2.105 The compound *cyclohexane* is an alkane in which six carbon atoms form a ring. The partial structural formula of the compound is as follows:

(a) Complete the structural formula for cyclohexane. **(b)** Is the molecular formula for cyclohexane the same as that for *n*-hexane, in which the carbon atoms are in a straight line? If possible, comment on the source of any differences. **(c)** Propose a structural formula for *cyclohexanol*, the alcohol derived from cyclohexane.

2.106 The periodic table helps organize the chemical behaviors of the elements. As a class discussion or as a short essay, describe how the table is organized, and mention as many ways as you can think of in which the position of an element in the table relates to the chemical and physical properties of the element.

STOICHIOMETRY: CALCULATIONS WITH CHEMICAL FORMULAS AND EQUATIONS

CHAPTER 3

SUGAR CARAMELIZING. Major changes in the appearance of compounds are indications of chemical reactions. Here, prolonged heating of sucrose, common table sugar, produces caramel.

78

3.1 Chemical Equations
We begin by considering how we can use chemical formulas to write equations that represent chemical reactions.

3.2 Some Simple Patterns of Chemical Reactivity
We then examine some simple chemical reactions: *combination reactions, decomposition reactions,* and *combustion reactions.*

3.3 Formula Weights
We can obtain quantitative information from chemical formulas by using their *formula weights.*

3.4 Avogadro's Number and the Mole
We use chemical formulas to relate the masses of substances to the numbers of atoms, molecules, or ions contained in the substances, a relationship that leads to the crucially important concept of a *mole*. A *mole* is 6.022×10^{23} objects (atoms, molecules, ions, etc.).

3.5 Empirical Formulas from Analyses
We apply the mole concept to determine chemical formulas from the masses of each element in a given quantity of a compound.

3.6 Quantitative Information from Balanced Equations
We use the quantitative information inherent in chemical formulas and equations together with the mole concept to predict the amounts of substances consumed or produced in chemical reactions.

3.7 Limiting Reactants
We recognize that one of the reactants may be used up before the others in a chemical reaction. This is the *limiting reactant*. The reaction therefore stops, leaving some of the excess starting material unreacted.

YOU POUR VINEGAR INTO A glass of water containing baking soda, and bubbles form. You strike a match and use the flame to light a candle. You heat sugar in a pan, and it turns brown (caramelizes). The bubbles, the flame, and the color change are visual evidence that something is happening.

To an experienced eye, these visual changes indicate a chemical change, or chemical reaction. The study of chemical changes is at the heart of chemistry. Some chemical changes are simple; others are complex. Some are dramatic; some are very subtle. Even as you sit reading this chapter, chemical changes are occurring within your body. Chemical changes that occur in your eyes and brain, for example, allow you to see these words and think about them. Although such chemical changes are not as obvious as some, they are nevertheless remarkable for how they allow us to function.

In this chapter we begin to explore some important aspects of chemical change. Our focus will be both on the use of chemical formulas to represent re-actions and on the quantitative information we can obtain about the amounts of substances involved in reactions. **Stoichiometry** (pronounced stoy-key-OM-uh-tree) is the area of study that examines the quantities of substances consumed and produced in chemical reactions. The name is derived from the Greek *stoicheion* ("element") and *metron* ("measure"). This study of stoichiome-try provides an essential set of tools that is widely used in chemistry. Aspects of stoichiometry include such diverse problems as measuring the concentra-tion of ozone in the atmosphere, determining the potential yield of gold from an ore, and assessing different processes for converting coal into gaseous fuels.

Stoichiometry is built on an understanding of atomic masses (Section 2.4), chemical formulas, and the law of conservation of mass. (Section 2.1)

79

The French nobleman and scientist Antoine Lavoisier (Figure 3.1 ◄) discovered this important chemical law during the late 1700s. In a chemistry text published in 1789, Lavoisier stated the law in this eloquent way: "We may lay it down as an incontestable axiom that, in all the operations of art and nature, nothing is created; an equal quantity of matter exists both before and after the experiment. Upon this principle, the whole art of performing chemical experiments depends." With the advent of Dalton's atomic theory, chemists understood the basis for this law: *Atoms are neither created nor destroyed during any chemical reaction.* The changes that occur during any reaction merely rearrange the atoms. The same collection of atoms is present both before and after the reaction.

3.1 CHEMICAL EQUATIONS

Chemical reactions are represented in a concise way by **chemical equations**. When the gas hydrogen (H_2) burns, for example, it reacts with oxygen (O_2) in the air to form water (H_2O). We write the chemical equation for this reaction as follows:

$$2\,H_2 + O_2 \longrightarrow 2\,H_2O \tag{3.1}$$

We read the + sign as "reacts with" and the arrow as "produces." The chemical formulas to the left of the arrow represent the starting substances, called **reactants**. The chemical formulas to the right of the arrow represent substances produced in the reaction, called **products**. The numbers in front of the formulas are *coefficients*. (As in algebraic equations, the numeral 1 is usually not written.) The coefficients indicate the relative numbers of molecules of each kind involved in the reaction.

Because atoms are neither created nor destroyed in any reaction, a chemical equation must have an equal number of atoms of each element on each side of the arrow. When this condition is met, the equation is said to be *balanced*. On the right side of Equation 3.1, for example, there are two molecules of H_2O, each composed of two atoms of hydrogen and one atom of oxygen. Thus, $2\,H_2O$ (read "two molecules of water") contains $2 \times 2 = 4$ H atoms and $2 \times 1 = 2$ O atoms. Notice that the number of atoms is obtained by multiplying the coefficient and the subscripts in the chemical formula. Because there are four H atoms and two O atoms on each side of the equation, the equation is balanced. We can represent the balanced equation by the following molecular models, which illustrate that the number of atoms of each kind is the same on both sides of the arrow:

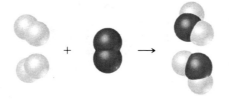

GIVE IT SOME THOUGHT

How many atoms of Mg, O, and H are represented by 3 $Mg(OH)_2$?

Balancing Equations

Once we know the formulas of the reactants and products in a reaction, we can write an unbalanced equation. We then balance the equation by determining the coefficients that provide equal numbers of each type of atom on each side of the equation. For most purposes, a balanced equation should contain the smallest possible whole-number coefficients.

In balancing an equation, you need to understand the difference between a coefficient in front of a formula and a subscript within a formula. Refer to Figure 3.2 ►. Notice that changing a subscript in a formula—from H_2O to H_2O_2,

Chemical symbol	Meaning		Composition
H_2O	One molecule of water:		Two H atoms and one O atom
$2 H_2O$	Two molecules of water:		Four H atoms and two O atoms
H_2O_2	One molecule of hydrogen peroxide:		Two H atoms and two O atoms

◀ Figure 3.2 **The difference between a subscript and a coefficient.** Notice how adding the coefficient 2 in front of the formula (line 2) has a different effect on the implied composition than adding the subscript 2 to the formula (in line 3). The number of atoms of each type (listed under composition) is obtained by multiplying the coefficient and the subscript associated with each element in the formula.

for example—changes the identity of the chemical. The substance H_2O_2, hydrogen peroxide, is quite different from the substance H_2O, water. *You should never change subscripts when balancing an equation.* In contrast, placing a coefficient in front of a formula changes only the *amount* of the substance and not its *identity*. Thus, $2 H_2O$ means two molecules of water, $3 H_2O$ means three molecules of water, and so forth.

To illustrate the process of balancing an equation, consider the reaction that occurs when methane (CH_4), the principal component of natural gas, burns in air to produce carbon dioxide gas (CO_2) and water vapor (H_2O) (Figure 3.3▼). Both of these products contain oxygen atoms that come from O_2 in the air. Thus, O_2 is a reactant, and the unbalanced equation is

$$CH_4 + O_2 \longrightarrow CO_2 + H_2O \quad \text{(unbalanced)} \qquad [3.2]$$

It is usually best to balance first those elements that occur in the fewest chemical formulas on each side of the equation. In our example both C and H appear in only one reactant and, separately, in one product each. So we begin by focusing on CH_4. Let's consider first carbon and then hydrogen.

One molecule of the reactant CH_4 contains the same number of C atoms (one) as one molecule of the product CO_2. The coefficients for these substances *must* be the same, therefore, we start the balancing process by choosing the coefficient one for each. However, one molecule of CH_4 contains more H atoms (four) than one molecule of the product H_2O (two). If we place a coefficient 2 in front of H_2O, there will be four H atoms on each side of the equation:

$$CH_4 + O_2 \longrightarrow CO_2 + 2 H_2O \quad \text{(unbalanced)} \qquad [3.3]$$

Products

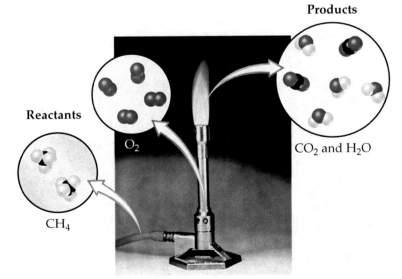

Reactants

O_2

CH_4

CO_2 and H_2O

◀ Figure 3.3 **Methane reacts with oxygen to produce the flame in a Bunsen burner.** The methane (CH_4) in natural gas and oxygen (O_2) from the air are the reactants in the reaction, while carbon dioxide (CO_2) and water vapor (H_2O) are the products.

Science Fundamentals

At this stage the products have more O atoms (four—two from CO_2 and two from $2 H_2O$) than the reactants (two). If we place the coefficient 2 in front of the reactant O_2, we balance the equation by making the number of O atoms equal on both sides of the equation:

$$CH_4 + 2 O_2 \longrightarrow CO_2 + 2 H_2O \quad \text{(balanced)} \qquad [3.4]$$

The molecular view of the balanced equation is shown in Figure 3.4 ◄. We see one C, four H, and four O atoms on each side of the arrow, indicating that the equation is balanced.

The approach we have taken in arriving at balanced Equation 3.4 is largely trial and error. We balance each kind of atom in succession, adjusting coefficients as necessary. This approach works for most chemical equations.

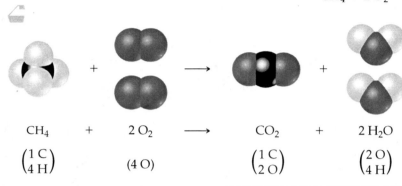

$$CH_4 \quad + \quad 2 O_2 \quad \longrightarrow \quad CO_2 \quad + \quad 2 H_2O$$

$$\begin{pmatrix} 1\,C \\ 4\,H \end{pmatrix} \qquad (4\,O) \qquad \begin{pmatrix} 1\,C \\ 2\,O \end{pmatrix} \quad \begin{pmatrix} 2\,O \\ 4\,H \end{pmatrix}$$

▲ Figure 3.4 **Balanced chemical equation for the combustion of CH_4.** The drawings of the molecules involved call attention to the conservation of atoms through the reaction.

■■ **SAMPLE EXERCISE 3.1** | Interpreting and Balancing Chemical Equations

The following diagram represents a chemical reaction in which the red spheres are oxygen atoms and the blue spheres are nitrogen atoms. (a) Write the chemical formulas for the reactants and products. (b) Write a balanced equation for the reaction. (c) Is the diagram consistent with the law of conservation of mass?

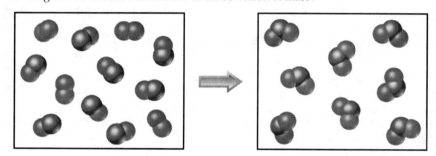

SOLUTION

(a) The left box, which represents the reactants, contains two kinds of molecules, those composed of two oxygen atoms (O_2) and those composed of one nitrogen atom and one oxygen atom (NO). The right box, which represents the products, contains only molecules composed of one nitrogen atom and two oxygen atoms (NO_2).
(b) The unbalanced chemical equation is

$$O_2 + NO \longrightarrow NO_2 \quad \text{(unbalanced)}$$

This equation has three O atoms on the left side of the arrow and two O atoms on the right side. We can increase the number of O atoms by placing a coefficient 2 on the product side:

$$O_2 + NO \longrightarrow 2 NO_2 \quad \text{(unbalanced)}$$

Now there are two N atoms and four O atoms on the right. Placing the coefficient 2 in front of NO balances both the number of N atoms and O atoms:

$$O_2 + 2 NO \longrightarrow 2 NO_2 \quad \text{(balanced)}$$

(c) The left box (reactants) contains four O_2 molecules and eight NO molecules. Thus, the molecular ratio is one O_2 for each two NO as required by the balanced equation. The right box (products) contains eight NO_2 molecules. The number of NO_2 molecules on the right equals the number of NO molecules on the left as the balanced equation requires. Counting the atoms, we find eight N atoms in the eight NO molecules in the box on the left. There are also $4 \times 2 = 8$ O atoms in the O_2 molecules and eight O atoms in the NO molecules, giving a total of 16 O atoms. In the box on the right, we find eight N atoms and $8 \times 2 = 16$ O atoms in the eight NO_2 molecules. Because there are equal numbers of both N and O atoms in the two boxes, the drawing is consistent with the law of conservation of mass.

■ PRACTICE EXERCISE

In the following diagram, the white spheres represent hydrogen atoms, and the blue spheres represent nitrogen atoms. To be consistent with the law of conservation of mass, how many NH_3 molecules should be shown in the right box?

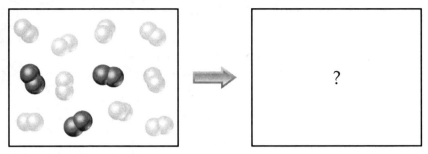

Answer: Six NH_3 molecules

Indicating the States of Reactants and Products

Additional information is often added to the formulas in balanced equations to indicate the physical state of each reactant and product. We use the symbols (*g*), (*l*), (*s*), and (*aq*) for gas, liquid, solid, and aqueous (water) solution, respectively. Thus, Equation 3.4 can be written

$$CH_4(g) + 2\,O_2(g) \longrightarrow CO_2(g) + 2\,H_2O(g) \qquad [3.5]$$

Sometimes the conditions (such as temperature or pressure) under which the reaction proceeds appear above or below the reaction arrow. The symbol Δ (the Greek uppercase letter delta) is often placed above the arrow to indicate the addition of heat.

■ SAMPLE EXERCISE 3.2 | Balancing Chemical Equations

Balance this equation:

$$Na(s) + H_2O(l) \longrightarrow NaOH(aq) + H_2(g)$$

SOLUTION

Begin by counting each kind of atom on both sides of the arrow. The Na and O atoms are balanced—one Na and one O on each side—but there are two H atoms on the left and three H atoms on the right. Thus, we need to increase the number of H atoms on the left. To begin balancing H, let's try placing the coefficient 2 in front of H_2O:

$$Na(s) + 2\,H_2O(l) \longrightarrow NaOH(aq) + H_2(g)$$

Beginning this way does not balance H but does increase the number of H atoms among the reactants, which we need to do. Adding the coefficient 2 causes O to be unbalanced; we will take care of that after we balance H. Now that we have 2 H_2O on the left, we can balance H by putting the coefficient 2 in front of NaOH on the right:

$$Na(s) + 2\,H_2O(l) \longrightarrow 2\,NaOH(aq) + H_2(g)$$

Balancing H in this way fortuitously brings O into balance. But notice that Na is now unbalanced, with one Na on the left and two on the right. To rebalance Na, we put the coefficient 2 in front of the reactant:

$$2\,Na(s) + 2\,H_2O(l) \longrightarrow 2\,NaOH(aq) + H_2(g)$$

Finally, we check the number of atoms of each element and find that we have two Na atoms, four H atoms, and two O atoms on each side of the equation. The equation is balanced.

Comment Notice that in balancing this equation, we moved back and forth placing a coefficient in front of H_2O, then NaOH, and finally Na. In balancing equations, we often find ourselves following this pattern of moving back and forth from one side of the arrow to the other, placing coefficients first in front of a formula on one side and then in front of a formula on the other side until the equation is balanced. You can always tell if you have balanced your equation correctly, no matter how you did it, by checking that the number of atoms of each element is the same on both sides of the arrow.

■ PRACTICE EXERCISE

Balance the following equations by providing the missing coefficients:
(a) __Fe(s) + __$O_2(g) \longrightarrow$ __$Fe_2O_3(s)$
(b) __$C_2H_4(g)$ + __$O_2(g) \longrightarrow$ __$CO_2(g)$ + __$H_2O(g)$
(c) __Al(s) + __HCl(aq) $\longrightarrow$ __$AlCl_3(aq)$ + __$H_2(g)$
Answers: **(a)** 4, 3, 2; **(b)** 1, 3, 2, 2; **(c)** 2, 6, 2, 3

3.2 SOME SIMPLE PATTERNS OF CHEMICAL REACTIVITY

In this section we examine three simple kinds of reactions that we will see frequently throughout this chapter. Our first reason for examining these reactions is merely to become better acquainted with chemical reactions and their balanced equations. Our second reason is to consider how we might predict the products of some of these reactions knowing only their reactants. The key to predicting the products formed by a given combination of reactants is recognizing general patterns of chemical reactivity. Recognizing a pattern of reactivity for a class of substances gives you a broader understanding than merely memorizing a large number of unrelated reactions.

Combination and Decomposition Reactions

Table 3.1 ▼ summarizes two simple types of reactions: combination and decomposition reactions. In **combination reactions** two or more substances react to form one product. There are many examples of combination reactions, especially those in which elements combine to form compounds. For example, magnesium metal burns in air with a dazzling brilliance to produce magnesium oxide, as shown in Figure 3.5 ▶:

$$2\,Mg(s) + O_2(g) \longrightarrow 2\,MgO(s) \qquad [3.6]$$

This reaction is used to produce the bright flame generated by flares and some fireworks.

When a combination reaction occurs between a metal and a nonmetal, as in Equation 3.6, the product is an ionic solid. Recall that the formula of an ionic compound can be determined from the charges of the ions involved. (Section 2.7) When magnesium reacts with oxygen, for example, the magnesium loses electrons and forms the magnesium ion, Mg^{2+}. The oxygen gains electrons and forms the oxide ion, O^{2-}. Thus, the reaction product is MgO. You should be able to recognize when a reaction is a combination reaction and to predict the products of a combination reaction in which the reactants are a metal and a nonmetal.

△ GIVE IT SOME THOUGHT

When Na and S undergo a combination reaction, what is the chemical formula of the product?

In a **decomposition reaction** one substance undergoes a reaction to produce two or more other substances. Many compounds undergo decomposition reactions when heated. For example, many metal carbonates decompose to form metal oxides and carbon dioxide when heated:

$$CaCO_3(s) \xrightarrow{\Delta} CaO(s) + CO_2(g) \qquad [3.7]$$

TABLE 3.1 ■ Combination and Decomposition Reactions

Combination Reactions

A + B $\longrightarrow$ C C(s) + O_2(g) $\longrightarrow$ CO_2(g) N_2(g) + 3 H_2(g) $\longrightarrow$ 2 NH_3(g) CaO(s) + H_2O(l) $\longrightarrow$ Ca(OH)_2(s)	Two reactants combine to form a single product. Many elements react with one another in this fashion to form compounds.

Decomposition Reactions

C $\longrightarrow$ A + B 2 KClO_3(s) $\longrightarrow$ 2 KCl(s) + 3 O_2(g) PbCO_3(s) $\longrightarrow$ PbO(s) + CO_2(g) Cu(OH)_2(s) $\longrightarrow$ CuO(s) + H_2O(l)	A single reactant breaks apart to form two or more substances. Many compounds react this way when heated.

COMBINATION REACTION

In combination reactions, two or more substances react to form one product.

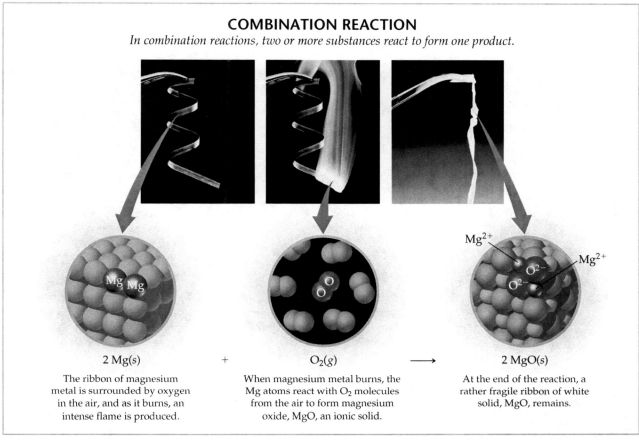

$2 \, Mg(s)$ + $O_2(g)$ $\longrightarrow$ $2 \, MgO(s)$

| The ribbon of magnesium metal is surrounded by oxygen in the air, and as it burns, an intense flame is produced. | When magnesium metal burns, the Mg atoms react with O_2 molecules from the air to form magnesium oxide, MgO, an ionic solid. | At the end of the reaction, a rather fragile ribbon of white solid, MgO, remains. |

▲ Figure 3.5 **Combustion of magnesium metal in air.**

The decomposition of $CaCO_3$ is an important commercial process. Limestone or seashells, which are both primarily $CaCO_3$, are heated to prepare CaO, which is known as lime or quicklime. About 2×10^{10} kg (20 million tons) of CaO is used in the United States each year, principally in making glass, in obtaining iron from its ores, and in making mortar to bind bricks.

The decomposition of sodium azide (NaN_3) rapidly releases $N_2(g)$, so this reaction is used to inflate safety air bags in automobiles (Figure 3.6 ▶):

$$2 \, NaN_3(s) \longrightarrow 2 \, Na(s) + 3 \, N_2(g) \qquad [3.8]$$

The system is designed so that an impact ignites a detonator cap, which in turn causes NaN_3 to decompose explosively. A small quantity of NaN_3 (about 100 g) forms a large quantity of gas (about 50 L). We will consider the volumes of gases produced in chemical reactions in Section 10.5.

▲ Figure 3.6 **An automobile air bag.** The decomposition of sodium azide, $NaN_3(s)$, is used to inflate automobile air bags. When properly ignited, the NaN_3 decomposes rapidly, forming nitrogen gas, $N_2(g)$, which expands the air bag.

■■■ **SAMPLE EXERCISE 3.3** | **Writing Balanced Equations for Combination and Decomposition Reactions**

Write balanced equations for the following reactions: **(a)** The combination reaction that occurs when lithium metal and fluorine gas react. **(b)** The decomposition reaction that occurs when solid barium carbonate is heated. (Two products form: a solid and a gas.)

SOLUTION

(a) The symbol for lithium is Li. With the exception of mercury, all metals are solids at room temperature. Fluorine occurs as a diatomic molecule (see Figure 2.19). Thus, the reactants are Li(s) and $F_2(g)$. The product will be composed of a metal and a nonmetal, so we expect it to be an ionic solid. Lithium ions have a 1+ charge, Li^+, whereas fluoride ions have a 1– charge, F⁻. Thus, the chemical formula for the product is LiF. The balanced chemical equation is

$$2 \, Li(s) + F_2(g) \longrightarrow 2 \, LiF(s)$$

(b) The chemical formula for barium carbonate is $BaCO_3$. As noted in the text, many metal carbonates decompose to form metal oxides and carbon dioxide when heated. In Equation 3.7, for example, $CaCO_3$ decomposes to form CaO and CO_2. Thus, we would expect that $BaCO_3$ decomposes to form BaO and CO_2. Barium and calcium are both in group 2A in the periodic table, which further suggests they would react in the same way:

$$BaCO_3(s) \longrightarrow BaO(s) + CO_2(g)$$

▉ PRACTICE EXERCISE

Write balanced chemical equations for the following reactions: **(a)** Solid mercury(II) sulfide decomposes into its component elements when heated. **(b)** The surface of aluminum metal undergoes a combination reaction with oxygen in the air.
Answers: **(a)** $HgS(s) \longrightarrow Hg(l) + S(s)$; **(b)** $4 \, Al(s) + 3 \, O_2(g) \longrightarrow 2 \, Al_2O_3(s)$

Combustion in Air

Combustion reactions are rapid reactions that produce a flame. Most of the combustion reactions we observe involve O_2 from air as a reactant. Equation 3.5 illustrates a general class of reactions that involve the burning, or combustion, of hydrocarbon compounds (compounds that contain only carbon and hydrogen, such as CH_4 and C_2H_4). (Section 2.9)

When hydrocarbons are combusted in air, they react with O_2 to form CO_2 and H_2O.* The number of molecules of O_2 required in the reaction and the number of molecules of CO_2 and H_2O formed depend on the composition of the hydrocarbon, which acts as the fuel in the reaction. For example, the combustion of propane (C_3H_8), a gas used for cooking and home heating, is described by the following equation:

$$C_3H_8(g) + 5 \, O_2(g) \longrightarrow 3 \, CO_2(g) + 4 \, H_2O(g) \qquad [3.9]$$

The state of the water, $H_2O(g)$ or $H_2O(l)$, depends on the conditions of the reaction. Water vapor, $H_2O(g)$, is formed at high temperature in an open container. The blue flame produced when propane burns is shown in Figure 3.7 ◄.

Combustion of oxygen-containing derivatives of hydrocarbons, such as CH_3OH, also produces CO_2 and H_2O. The simple rule that hydrocarbons and related oxygen-containing derivatives of hydrocarbons form CO_2 and H_2O when they burn in air summarizes the behavior of about 3 million compounds. Many substances that our bodies use as energy sources, such as the sugar glucose ($C_6H_{12}O_6$), similarly react in our bodies with O_2 to form CO_2 and H_2O. In our bodies, however, the reactions take place in a series of intermediate steps that occur at body temperature. These reactions that involve intermediate steps are described as *oxidation reactions* instead of combustion reactions.

▲ Figure 3.7 **Propane burning in air.** The liquid propane, C_3H_8, vaporizes and mixes with air as it escapes through the nozzle. The combustion reaction of C_3H_8 and O_2 produces a blue flame.

▉ SAMPLE EXERCISE 3.4 | Writing Balanced Equations for Combustion Reactions

Write the balanced equation for the reaction that occurs when methanol, $CH_3OH(l)$, is burned in air.

SOLUTION

When any compound containing C, H, and O is combusted, it reacts with the $O_2(g)$ in air to produce $CO_2(g)$ and $H_2O(g)$. Thus, the unbalanced equation is

$$CH_3OH(l) + O_2(g) \longrightarrow CO_2(g) + H_2O(g)$$

When there is an insufficient quantity of O_2 present, carbon monoxide (CO) will be produced along with the CO_2; this is called incomplete combustion. If the amount of O_2 is severely restricted, fine particles of carbon that we call soot will be produced. Complete combustion produces only CO_2 and H_2O. Unless specifically stated to the contrary, we will always take combustion to mean complete combustion.

In this equation the C atoms are balanced with one carbon on each side of the arrow. Because CH_3OH has four H atoms, we place the coefficient 2 in front of H_2O to balance the H atoms:

$$CH_3OH(l) + O_2(g) \longrightarrow CO_2(g) + 2\,H_2O(g)$$

Adding the coefficient balances H but gives four O atoms in the products. Because there are only three O atoms in the reactants (one in CH_3OH and two in O_2), we are not finished yet. We can place the fractional coefficient $\frac{3}{2}$ in front of O_2 to give a total of four O atoms in the reactants (there are $\frac{3}{2} \times 2 = 3$ O atoms in $\frac{3}{2}\,O_2$):

$$CH_3OH(l) + \tfrac{3}{2}\,O_2(g) \longrightarrow CO_2(g) + 2\,H_2O(g)$$

Although the equation is now balanced, it is not in its most conventional form because it contains a fractional coefficient. If we multiply each side of the equation by 2, we will remove the fraction and achieve the following balanced equation:

$$2\,CH_3OH(l) + 3\,O_2(g) \longrightarrow 2\,CO_2(g) + 4\,H_2O(g)$$

■■■ PRACTICE EXERCISE

Write the balanced equation for the reaction that occurs when ethanol, $C_2H_5OH(l)$, is burned in air.

Answer: $C_2H_5OH(l) + 3\,O_2(g) \longrightarrow 2\,CO_2(g) + 3\,H_2O(g)$

3.3 FORMULA WEIGHTS

Chemical formulas and chemical equations both have a *quantitative* significance; the subscripts in formulas and the coefficients in equations represent precise quantities. The formula H_2O indicates that a molecule of this substance (water) contains exactly two atoms of hydrogen and one atom of oxygen. Similarly, the coefficients in a balanced chemical equation indicate the relative quantities of reactants and products. But how do we relate the numbers of atoms or molecules to the amounts we measure in the laboratory? Although we cannot directly count atoms or molecules, we can indirectly determine their numbers if we know their masses. Therefore, before we can pursue the quantitative aspects of chemical formulas or equations, we must examine the masses of atoms and molecules, which we do in this section and the next.

Formula and Molecular Weights

The **formula weight** of a substance is the sum of the atomic weights of each atom in its chemical formula. Using atomic masses from a periodic table, we find, for example, that the formula weight of sulfuric acid (H_2SO_4) is 98.1 amu:*

$$\begin{aligned}
\text{FW of } H_2SO_4 &= 2(\text{AW of H}) + (\text{AW of S}) + 4(\text{AW of O}) \\
&= 2(1.0 \text{ amu}) + 32.1 \text{ amu} + 4(16.0 \text{ amu}) \\
&= 98.1 \text{ amu}
\end{aligned}$$

For convenience, we have rounded off all the atomic weights to one place beyond the decimal point. We will round off the atomic weights in this way for most problems.

If the chemical formula is merely the chemical symbol of an element, such as Na, then the formula weight equals the atomic weight of the element, in this case 23.0 amu. If the chemical formula is that of a molecule, then the formula weight is also called the **molecular weight**. The molecular weight of glucose ($C_6H_{12}O_6$), for example, is

$$\text{MW of } C_6H_{12}O_6 = 6(12.0 \text{ amu}) + 12(1.0 \text{ amu}) + 6(16.0 \text{ amu}) = 180.0 \text{ amu}$$

Because ionic substances, such as NaCl, exist as three-dimensional arrays of ions (Figure 2.23), it is inappropriate to speak of molecules of NaCl. Instead,

---

*The abbreviation AW is used for atomic weight, FW for formula weight, and MW for molecular weight.

we speak of *formula units*, represented by the chemical formula of the sub-stance. The formula unit of NaCl consists of one Na^+ ion and one Cl^- ion. Thus, the formula weight of NaCl is the mass of one formula unit:

$$FW \text{ of } NaCl = 23.0 \text{ amu} + 35.5 \text{ amu} = 58.5 \text{ amu}$$

■ SAMPLE EXERCISE 3.5 | Calculating Formula Weights

Calculate the formula weight of **(a)** sucrose, $C_{12}H_{22}O_{11}$ (table sugar), and **(b)** calcium nitrate, $Ca(NO_3)_2$.

SOLUTION

(a) By adding the atomic weights of the atoms in sucrose, we find the formula weight to be 342.0 amu:

$$
\begin{aligned}
12 \text{ C atoms} &= 12(12.0 \text{ amu}) = 144.0 \text{ amu} \\
22 \text{ H atoms} &= 22(1.0 \text{ amu}) = 22.0 \text{ amu} \\
11 \text{ O atoms} &= 11(16.0 \text{ amu}) = \underline{176.0 \text{ amu}} \\
&\phantom{= 11(16.0 \text{ amu}) =} 342.0 \text{ amu}
\end{aligned}
$$

(b) If a chemical formula has parentheses, the subscript out-side the parentheses is a multiplier for all atoms inside. Thus, for $Ca(NO_3)_2$, we have

$$
\begin{aligned}
1 \text{ Ca atom} &= 1(40.1 \text{ amu}) = 40.1 \text{ amu} \\
2 \text{ N atoms} &= 2(14.0 \text{ amu}) = 28.0 \text{ amu} \\
6 \text{ O atoms} &= 6(16.0 \text{ amu}) = \underline{96.0 \text{ amu}} \\
&\phantom{= 6(16.0 \text{ amu}) =} 164.1 \text{ amu}
\end{aligned}
$$

■ PRACTICE EXERCISE

Calculate the formula weight of **(a)** $Al(OH)_3$ and **(b)** CH_3OH.
Answers: **(a)** 78.0 amu, **(b)** 32.0 amu

Percentage Composition from Formulas

Occasionally we must calculate the *percentage composition* of a compound—that is, the percentage by mass contributed by each element in the substance. For ex-ample, to verify the purity of a compound, we can compare the calculated per-centage composition of the substance with that found experimentally. Forensic chemists, for example, will measure the percentage composition of an un-known white powder and compare it to the percentage compositions for sugar, salt, or cocaine to identify the powder. Calculating percentage composition is a straightforward matter if the chemical formula is known. The calculation de-pends on the formula weight of the substance, the atomic weight of the element of interest, and the number of atoms of that element in the chemical formula:

$$\% \text{ element} = \frac{\left(\begin{array}{c}\text{number of atoms} \\ \text{of that element}\end{array}\right)\left(\begin{array}{c}\text{atomic weight} \\ \text{of element}\end{array}\right)}{\text{formula weight of compound}} \times 100\% \quad [3.10]$$

■ SAMPLE EXERCISE 3.6 | Calculating Percentage Composition

Calculate the percentage of carbon, hydrogen, and oxygen (by mass) in $C_{12}H_{22}O_{11}$.

SOLUTION

Let's examine this question using the problem-solving steps in the "Strategies in Chemistry: Problem Solving" essay that appears on the next page.

Analyze We are given a chemical formula, $C_{12}H_{22}O_{11}$, and asked to calculate the per-centage by mass of its component elements (C, H, and O).

Plan We can use Equation 3.10, relying on a periodic table to obtain the atomic weight of each component element. The atomic weights are first used to determine the formula weight of the compound. (The formula weight of $C_{12}H_{22}O_{11}$, 342.0 amu, was calculated in Sample Exercise 3.5.) We must then do three calculations, one for each element.

Solve Using Equation 3.10, we have

$$\%C = \frac{(12)(12.0 \text{ amu})}{342.0 \text{ amu}} \times 100\% = 42.1\%$$

$$\%H = \frac{(22)(1.0 \text{ amu})}{342.0 \text{ amu}} \times 100\% = 6.4\%$$

$$\%O = \frac{(11)(16.0 \text{ amu})}{342.0 \text{ amu}} \times 100\% = 51.5\%$$

Check The percentages of the individual elements must add up to 100%, which they do in this case. We could have used more significant figures for our atomic weights, giving more significant figures for our percentage composition, but we have adhered to our suggested guideline of rounding atomic weights to one digit beyond the decimal point.

■ **PRACTICE EXERCISE**

Calculate the percentage of nitrogen, by mass, in $Ca(NO_3)_2$.
Answer: 17.1%

3.4 AVOGADRO'S NUMBER AND THE MOLE

Even the smallest samples that we deal with in the laboratory contain enormous numbers of atoms, ions, or molecules. For example, a teaspoon of water (about 5 mL) contains 2×10^{23} water molecules, a number so large that it almost defies comprehension. Chemists, therefore, have devised a special counting unit for describing such large numbers of atoms or molecules.

In everyday life we use counting units such as a dozen (12 objects) and a gross (144 objects) to deal with modestly large quantities. In chemistry the unit for dealing with the number of atoms, ions, or molecules in a common-sized sample is the **mole**, abbreviated mol.* A mole is the amount of matter that contains as many objects (atoms, molecules, or whatever objects we are considering) as the number of atoms in exactly 12 g of isotopically pure ^{12}C. From experiments, scientists have determined this number to be 6.0221421×10^{23}. Scientists call this number **Avogadro's number**, in honor of the Italian scientist Amedeo Avogadro (1776–1856). Avogadro's number has the symbol N_A, which we will usually round to 6.02×10^{23} mol^{-1}. The unit mol^{-1} ("inverse mole" or "per mole") reminds us that there are 6.02×10^{23} objects per one mole. A mole of atoms, a mole of molecules, or a mole of anything else all contain Avogadro's number of these objects:

$$1 \text{ mol } ^{12}C \text{ atoms} = 6.02 \times 10^{23} \ ^{12}C \text{ atoms}$$

$$1 \text{ mol } H_2O \text{ molecules} = 6.02 \times 10^{23} H_2O \text{ molecules}$$

$$1 \text{ mol } NO_3^- \text{ ions} = 6.02 \times 10^{23} NO_3^- \text{ ions}$$

Strategies in Chemistry   PROBLEM SOLVING

Practice is the key to success in problem solving. As you practice, you can improve your skills by following these steps:

Step 1: Analyze the problem. Read the problem carefully for understanding. What does it say? Draw any picture or diagram that will help you to visualize the problem. Write down both the data you are given and the quantity that you need to obtain (the unknown).

Step 2: Develop a plan for solving the problem. Consider the possible paths between the given information and the unknown. What principles or equations relate the known data to the unknown? Recognize that some data may not be given explicitly in the problem; you may be expected to know certain quantities (such as Avogadro's number) or look them up in tables (such as

atomic weights). Recognize also that your plan may involve either a single step or a series of steps with intermediate answers.

Step 3: Solve the problem. Use the known information and suitable equations or relationships to solve for the unknown. Dimensional analysis (Section 1.6) is a very useful tool for solving a great number of problems. Be careful with significant figures, signs, and units.

Step 4: Check the solution. Read the problem again to make sure you have found all the solutions asked for in the problem. Does your answer make sense? That is, is the answer outrageously large or small, or is it in the ballpark? Finally, are the units and significant figures correct?

The term mole *comes from the Latin word* moles, *meaning "a mass." The term* molecule *is the diminutive form of this word and means "a small mass."*

Avogadro's number is so large that it is difficult to imagine. Spreading 6.02×10^{23} marbles over the entire surface of Earth would produce a continuous layer about 3 miles thick. If Avogadro's number of pennies were placed side by side in a straight line, they would encircle Earth 300 trillion (3×10^{14}) times.

■■ SAMPLE EXERCISE 3.7 | Estimating Numbers of Atoms

Without using a calculator, arrange the following samples in order of increasing numbers of carbon atoms: 12 g ^{12}C, 1 mol C_2H_2, 9×10^{23} molecules of CO_2.

SOLUTION

Analyze We are given amounts of different substances expressed in grams, moles, and number of molecules and asked to arrange the samples in order of increasing numbers of C atoms.

Plan To determine the number of C atoms in each sample, we must convert g ^{12}C, 1 mol C_2H_2, and 9×10^{23} molecules CO_2 all to numbers of C atoms. To make these conversions, we use the definition of mole and Avogadro's number.

Solve A mole is defined as the amount of matter that contains as many units of the matter as there are C atoms in exactly 12 g of ^{12}C. Thus, 12 g of ^{12}C contains 1 mol of C atoms (that is, 6.02×10^{23} C atoms). One mol of C_2H_2 contains 6×10^{23} C_2H_2 molecules. Because there are two C atoms in each C_2H_2 molecule, this sample contains 12×10^{23} C atoms. Because each CO_2 molecule contains one C atom, the sample of CO_2 contains 9×10^{23} C atoms. Hence, the order is 12 g ^{12}C (6×10^{23} C atoms) < 9×10^{23} CO_2 molecules (9×10^{23} C atoms) < 1 mol C_2H_2 (12×10^{23} C atoms).

Check We can check our results by comparing the number of moles of C atoms in each sample because the number of moles is proportional to the number of atoms. Thus, 12 g of ^{12}C is 1 mol C; 1 mol of C_2H_2 contains 2 mol C, and 9×10^{23} molecules of CO_2 contain 1.5 mol C, giving the same order as above: 12 g ^{12}C (1 mol C) < 9×10^{23} CO_2 molecules (1.5 mol C) < 1 mol C_2H_2 (2 mol C).

■■ PRACTICE EXERCISE

Without using a calculator, arrange the following samples in order of increasing number of O atoms: 1 mol H_2O, 1 mol CO_2, 3×10^{23} molecules O_3.
Answer: 1 mol H_2O (6×10^{23} O atoms) < 3×10^{23} molecules O_3 (9×10^{23} O atoms) < 1 mol CO_2 (12×10^{23} O atoms)

■■ SAMPLE EXERCISE 3.8 | Converting Moles to Number of Atoms

Calculate the number of H atoms in 0.350 mol of $C_6H_{12}O_6$.

SOLUTION

Analyze We are given both the amount of a substance (0.350 mol) and its chemical formula ($C_6H_{12}O_6$). The unknown is the number of H atoms in the sample.

Plan Avogadro's number provides the conversion factor between the number of moles of $C_6H_{12}O_6$ and the number of molecules of $C_6H_{12}O_6$. Once we know the number of molecules of $C_6H_{12}O_6$, we can use the chemical formula, which tells us that each molecule of $C_6H_{12}O_6$ contains 12 H atoms. Thus, we convert moles of $C_6H_{12}O_6$ to molecules of $C_6H_{12}O_6$ and then determine the number of atoms of H from the number of molecules of $C_6H_{12}O_6$:

$$\text{Moles } C_6H_{12}O_6 \longrightarrow \text{molecules } C_6H_{12}O_6 \longrightarrow \text{atoms H}$$

Solve

$$\text{H atoms} = (0.350 \text{ mol } C_6H_{12}O_6)\left(\frac{6.02 \times 10^{23} \text{ molecules } C_6H_{12}O_6}{1 \text{ mol } C_6H_{12}O_6}\right)\left(\frac{12 \text{ H atoms}}{1 \text{ molecule } C_6H_{12}O_6}\right)$$

$$= 2.53 \times 10^{24} \text{ H atoms}$$

Check The magnitude of our answer is reasonable. It is a large number about the magnitude of Avogadro's number. We can also make the following ballpark calculation: Multiplying $0.35 \times 6 \times 10^{23}$ gives about 2×10^{23} molecules. Multiplying this result by 12 gives $24 \times 10^{23} = 2.4 \times 10^{24}$ H atoms, which agrees with the previous, more detailed calculation. Because we were asked for the number of H atoms, the units of our answer are correct. The given data had three significant figures, so our answer has three significant figures.

PRACTICE EXERCISE

How many oxygen atoms are in **(a)** 0.25 mol $Ca(NO_3)_2$ and **(b)** 1.50 mol of sodium carbonate?
Answers: **(a)** 9.0×10^{23}, **(b)** 2.71×10^{24}

Molar Mass

A dozen (12) is the same number whether we have a dozen eggs or a dozen elephants. Clearly, however, a dozen eggs does not have the same mass as a dozen elephants. Similarly, a mole is always the *same number* (6.02×10^{23}), but 1-mole samples of different substances will have *different masses*. Compare, for example, 1 mol of ^{12}C and 1 mol of ^{24}Mg. A single ^{12}C atom has a mass of 12 amu, whereas a single ^{24}Mg atom is twice as massive, 24 amu (to two significant figures). Because a mole always has the same number of particles, a mole of ^{24}Mg must be twice as massive as a mole of ^{12}C. Because a mole of ^{12}C has a mass of 12 g (by definition), then a mole of ^{24}Mg must have a mass of 24 g. This example illustrates a general rule relating the mass of an atom to the mass of Avogadro's number (1 mol) of these atoms: *The mass of a single atom of an element (in amu) is numerically equal to the mass (in grams) of 1 mol of that element.* This statement is true regardless of the element:

1 atom of ^{12}C has a mass of 12 amu $\Rightarrow$ 1 mol ^{12}C has a mass of 12 g

1 atom of Cl has an atomic weight of 35.5 amu $\Rightarrow$ 1 mol Cl has a mass of 35.5 g

1 atom of Au has an atomic weight of 197 amu $\Rightarrow$ 1 mol Au has a mass of 197 g

Notice that when we are dealing with a particular isotope of an element, we use the mass of that isotope; otherwise we use the atomic weight (the average atomic mass) of the element. (Section 2.4)

For other kinds of substances, the same numerical relationship exists between the formula weight (in amu) and the mass (in grams) of one mole of that substance:

1 H_2O molecule has a mass of 18.0 amu $\Rightarrow$ 1 mol H_2O has a mass of 18.0 g

1 NO_3^- ion has a mass of 62.0 amu $\Rightarrow$ 1 mol NO_3^- has a mass of 62.0 g

1 NaCl unit has a mass of 58.5 amu $\Rightarrow$ 1 mol NaCl has a mass of 58.5 g

Figure 3.8 ▼ illustrates the relationship between the mass of a single molecule of H_2O and that of a mole of H_2O.

GIVE IT SOME THOUGHT

(a) Which has more mass, a mole of water (H_2O) or a mole of glucose ($C_6H_{12}O_6$)?
(b) Which contains more molecules, a mole of water or a mole of glucose?

The mass in grams of one mole of a substance (that is, the mass in grams per mol) is called the **molar mass** of the substance. *The molar mass (in g/mol) of any substance is always numerically equal to its formula weight (in amu).* The substance NaCl, for example, has a formula weight of 58.5 amu and a molar mass

Laboratory-size
sample

Single molecule

▶ Figure 3.8 **Comparing the mass of 1 molecule H_2O and 1 mol H_2O.** Notice that both masses have the same number but have different units (18.0 amu compared to 18.0 g) representing the huge difference in mass.

Avogadro's
number of
molecules
(6.02×10^{23})

1 molecule H_2O
(18.0 amu)

1 mol H_2O
(18.0 g)

TABLE 3.2 ■ Mole Relationships

Name of Substance	Formula	Formula Weight (amu)	Molar Mass (g/mol)	Number and Kind of Particles in One Mole
Atomic nitrogen	N	14.0	14.0	6.02×10^{23} N atoms
Molecular nitrogen	N_2	28.0	28.0	$\begin{cases} 6.02 \times 10^{23} \text{ N}_2 \text{ molecules} \\ 2(6.02 \times 10^{23}) \text{ N atoms} \end{cases}$
Silver	Ag	107.9	107.9	6.02×10^{23} Ag atoms
Silver ions	Ag^+	107.9[a]	107.9	6.02×10^{23} Ag$^+$ ions
Barium chloride	$BaCl_2$	208.2	208.2	$\begin{cases} 6.02 \times 10^{23} \text{ BaCl}_2 \text{ units} \\ 6.02 \times 10^{23} \text{ Ba}^{2+} \text{ ions} \\ 2(6.02 \times 10^{23}) \text{ Cl}^- \text{ ions} \end{cases}$

[a] Recall that the electron has negligible mass; thus, ions and atoms have essentially the same mass.

▲ Figure 3.9 **One mole each of a solid, a liquid, and a gas.** One mole of NaCl, the solid, has a mass of 58.45 g. One mole of H_2O, the liquid, has a mass of 18.0 g and occupies a volume of 18.0 mL. One mole of O_2, the gas, has a mass of 32.0 g and occupies a balloon whose diameter is 35 cm.

of 58.5 g/mol. Further examples of mole relationships are shown in Table 3.2 ▲. Figure 3.9 ◄ shows 1-mole quantities of several common substances.

The entries in Table 3.2 for N and N_2 point out the importance of stating the exact chemical form of a substance when we use the mole concept. Suppose you read that 1 mol of nitrogen is produced in a particular reaction. You might interpret this statement to mean 1 mol of nitrogen atoms (14.0 g). Unless otherwise stated, however, what is probably meant is 1 mol of nitrogen molecules, N_2 (28.0 g), because N_2 is the most common chemical form of the element. To avoid ambiguity, it is important to state explicitly the chemical form being discussed. Using the chemical formula N_2 avoids ambiguity.

■■ **SAMPLE EXERCISE 3.9** | **Calculating Molar Mass**

What is the mass in grams of 1.000 mol of glucose, $C_6H_{12}O_6$?

SOLUTION

Analyze We are given a chemical formula and asked to determine its molar mass.

Plan The molar mass of a substance is found by adding the atomic weights of its component atoms.

Solve

$$\begin{aligned} 6 \text{ C atoms} &= 6(12.0 \text{ amu}) = 72.0 \text{ amu} \\ 12 \text{ H atoms} &= 12(1.0 \text{ amu}) = 12.0 \text{ amu} \\ 6 \text{ O atoms} &= 6(16.0 \text{ amu}) = \underline{96.0 \text{ amu}} \\ & \qquad\qquad\qquad\qquad\quad 180.0 \text{ amu} \end{aligned}$$

Because glucose has a formula weight of 180.0 amu, one mole of this substance has a mass of 180.0 g. In other words, $C_6H_{12}O_6$ has a molar mass of 180.0 g/mol.

Check The magnitude of our answer seems reasonable, and g/mol is the appropriate unit for the molar mass.

Comment Glucose is sometimes called dextrose. Also known as blood sugar, glucose is found widely in nature, occurring in honey and fruits. Other types of sugars used as food are converted into glucose in the stomach or liver before the body uses them as energy sources. Because glucose requires no conversion, it is often given intravenously to patients who need immediate nourishment. People who have diabetes must carefully monitor the amount of glucose in their blood (See "Chemistry and Life" box in Section 3.6).

■■ **PRACTICE EXERCISE**

Calculate the molar mass of $Ca(NO_3)_2$.
Answer: 164.1 g/mol

Interconverting Masses and Moles

Conversions of mass to moles and of moles to mass are frequently encountered in calculations using the mole concept. These calculations are simplified using dimensional analysis, as shown in Sample Exercises 3.10 and 3.11.

▓ SAMPLE EXERCISE 3.10 | Converting Grams to Moles

Calculate the number of moles of glucose ($C_6H_{12}O_6$) in 5.380 g of $C_6H_{12}O_6$.

SOLUTION

Analyze We are given the number of grams of a substance and its chemical formula and asked to calculate the number of moles.

Plan The molar mass of a substance provides the factor for converting grams to moles. The molar mass of $C_6H_{12}O_6$ is 180.0 g/mol (Sample Exercise 3.9).

Solve Using 1 mol $C_6H_{12}O_6$ = 180.0 g $C_6H_{12}O_6$ to write the appropriate conversion factor, we have

$$\text{Moles } C_6H_{12}O_6 = (5.380 \text{ g } C_6H_{12}O_6)\left(\frac{1 \text{ mol } C_6H_{12}O_6}{180.0 \text{ g } C_6H_{12}O_6}\right) = 0.02989 \text{ mol } C_6H_{12}O_6$$

Check Because 5.380 g is less than the molar mass, a reasonable answer is less than one mole. The units of our answer (mol) are appropriate. The original data had four significant figures, so our answer has four significant figures.

▓ PRACTICE EXERCISE

How many moles of sodium bicarbonate ($NaHCO_3$) are in 508 g of $NaHCO_3$?
Answer: 6.05 mol $NaHCO_3$

▓ SAMPLE EXERCISE 3.11 | Converting Moles to Grams

Calculate the mass, in grams, of 0.433 mol of calcium nitrate.

SOLUTION

Analyze We are given the number of moles and the name of a substance and asked to calculate the number of grams in the sample.

Plan To convert moles to grams, we need the molar mass, which we can calculate using the chemical formula and atomic weights.

Solve Because the calcium ion is Ca^{2+} and the nitrate ion is NO_3^-, calcium nitrate is $Ca(NO_3)_2$. Adding the atomic weights of the elements in the compound gives a formula weight of 164.1 amu. Using 1 mol $Ca(NO_3)_2$ = 164.1 g $Ca(NO_3)_2$ to write the appropriate conversion factor, we have

$$\text{Grams } Ca(NO_3)_2 = (0.433 \text{ mol } Ca(NO_3)_2)\left(\frac{164.1 \text{ g } Ca(NO_3)_2}{1 \text{ mol } Ca(NO_3)_2}\right) = 71.1 \text{ g } Ca(NO_3)_2$$

Check The number of moles is less than 1, so the number of grams must be less than the molar mass, 164.1 g. Using rounded numbers to estimate, we have 0.5 × 150 = 75 g. The magnitude of our answer is reasonable. Both the units (g) and the number of significant figures (3) are correct.

▓ PRACTICE EXERCISE

What is the mass, in grams, of **(a)** 6.33 mol of $NaHCO_3$ and **(b)** 3.0×10^{-5} mol of sulfuric acid?
Answers: **(a)** 532 g, **(b)** 2.9×10^{-3} g

▶ Figure 3.10 **Procedure for interconverting the mass and the number of formula units of a substance.** The number of moles of the substance is central to the calculation; thus, the mole concept can be thought of as the bridge between the mass of a substance in grams and the number of formula units.

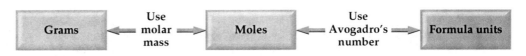

Interconverting Masses and Numbers of Particles

The mole concept provides the bridge between mass and the number of particles. To illustrate how we can interconvert mass and numbers of particles, let's calculate the number of copper atoms in an old copper penny. Such a penny weighs about 3 g, and we will assume that it is 100% copper:

$$Cu \text{ atoms} = (3 \text{ g Cu})\left(\frac{1 \text{ mol Cu}}{63.5 \text{ g Cu}}\right)\left(\frac{6.02 \times 10^{23} \text{ Cu atoms}}{1 \text{ mol Cu}}\right)$$

$$= 3 \times 10^{22} \text{ Cu atoms}$$

We have rounded our answer to one significant figure, since we used only one significant figure for the mass of the penny. Notice how dimensional analysis (Section 1.6) provides a straightforward route from grams to numbers of atoms. The molar mass and Avogadro's number are used as conversion factors to convert grams → moles → atoms. Notice also that our answer is a very large number. Any time you calculate the number of atoms, molecules, or ions in an ordinary sample of matter, you can expect the answer to be very large. In contrast, the number of moles in a sample will usually be much smaller, often less than 1. The general procedure for interconverting mass and number of formula units (atoms, molecules, ions, or whatever is represented by the chemical formula) of a substance is summarized in Figure 3.10 ▲.

■■■ **SAMPLE EXERCISE 3.12** | Calculating the Number of Molecules and Number of Atoms from Mass

(a) How many glucose molecules are in 5.23 g of $C_6H_{12}O_6$? **(b)** How many oxygen atoms are in this sample?

SOLUTION

Analyze We are given the number of grams and the chemical formula and asked to calculate (a) the number of molecules and (b) the number of O atoms in the sample.

(a) Plan The strategy for determining the number of molecules in a given quantity of a substance is summarized in Figure 3.10. We must convert 5.23 g $C_6H_{12}O_6$ to moles $C_6H_{12}O_6$, which can then be converted to molecules $C_6H_{12}O_6$. The first conversion uses the molar mass of $C_6H_{12}O_6$: 1 mol $C_6H_{12}O_6$ = 180.0 g $C_6H_{12}O_6$. The second conversion uses Avogadro's number.

Solve
Molecules $C_6H_{12}O_6$

$$= (5.23 \text{ g } C_6H_{12}O_6)\left(\frac{1 \text{ mol } C_6H_{12}O_6}{180.0 \text{ g } C_6H_{12}O_6}\right)\left(\frac{6.02 \times 10^{23} \text{ molecules } C_6H_{12}O_6}{1 \text{ mol } C_6H_{12}O_6}\right)$$

$$= 1.75 \times 10^{22} \text{ molecules } C_6H_{12}O_6$$

Check The magnitude of the answer is reasonable. Because the mass we began with is less than a mole, there should be fewer than 6.02×10^{23} molecules. We can make a ballpark estimate of the answer: $5/200 = 2.5 \times 10^{-2}$ mol; $2.5 \times 10^{-2} \times 6 \times 10^{23} = 15 \times 10^{21} = 1.5 \times 10^{22}$ molecules. The units (molecules) and significant figures (three) are appropriate.

(b) Plan To determine the number of O atoms, we use the fact that there are six O atoms in each molecule of $C_6H_{12}O_6$. Thus, multiplying the number of molecules $C_6H_{12}O_6$ by the factor (6 atoms O/1 molecule $C_6H_{12}O_6$) gives the number of O atoms.

Solve

$$Atoms \text{ O} = (1.75 \times 10^{22} \text{ molecules } C_6H_{12}O_6)\left(\frac{6 \text{ atoms O}}{1 \text{ molecule } C_6H_{12}O_6}\right)$$

$$= 1.05 \times 10^{23} \text{ atoms O}$$

Check The answer is simply 6 times as large as the answer to part (a). The number of significant figures (three) and the units (atoms O) are correct.

(a) How many nitric acid molecules are in 4.20 g of HNO_3? (b) How many O atoms are in this sample?
Answers: (a) 4.01×10^{22} molecules HNO_3, (b) 1.20×10^{23} atoms O

3.5 EMPIRICAL FORMULAS FROM ANALYSES

As we learned in Section 2.6, the empirical formula for a substance tells us the relative number of atoms of each element it contains. The empirical formula H_2O shows that water contains two H atoms for each O atom. This ratio also applies on the molar level: 1 mol of H_2O contains 2 mol of H atoms and 1 mol of O atoms. Conversely, *the ratio of the number of moles of each element in a compound gives the subscripts in a compound's empirical formula.* In this way, the mole concept provides a way of calculating the empirical formulas of chemical substances, as shown in the following examples.

Mercury and chlorine combine to form a compound that is 73.9% mercury and 26.1% chlorine by mass. This means that if we had a 100.0-g sample of the solid, it would contain 73.9 g of mercury (Hg) and 26.1 g of chlorine (Cl). (Any size sample can be used in problems of this type, but we will generally use 100.0 g to simplify the calculation of mass from percentage.) Using the atomic weights of the elements to give us molar masses, we can calculate the number of moles of each element in the sample:

$$(73.9 \text{ g Hg})\left(\frac{1 \text{ mol Hg}}{200.6 \text{ g Hg}}\right) = 0.368 \text{ mol Hg}$$

$$(26.1 \text{ g Cl})\left(\frac{1 \text{ mol Cl}}{35.5 \text{ g Cl}}\right) = 0.735 \text{ mol Cl}$$

We then divide the larger number of moles (0.735) by the smaller (0.368) to obtain a Cl: Hg mole ratio of 1.99:1:

$$\frac{\text{moles of Cl}}{\text{moles of Hg}} = \frac{0.735 \text{ mol Cl}}{0.368 \text{ mol Hg}} = \frac{1.99 \text{ mol Cl}}{1 \text{ mol Hg}}$$

Because of experimental errors, the results may not lead to exact integers for the ratios of moles. The number 1.99 is very close to 2, so we can confidently conclude that the empirical formula for the compound is $HgCl_2$. The empirical formula is correct because its subscripts are the smallest integers that express the *ratios* of atoms present in the compound. (Section 2.6) The general procedure for determining empirical formulas is outlined in Figure 3.11 ▼.

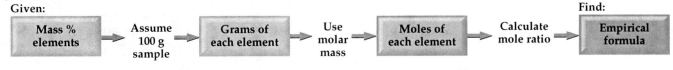

▲ Figure 3.11 **Procedure for calculating an empirical formula from percentage composition.** The central part of the calculation is determining the number of moles of each element in the compound. The procedure is also summarized as "percent to mass, mass to mole, divide by small, multiply 'til whole."

■■ SAMPLE EXERCISE 3.13 | Calculating an Empirical Formula
Ascorbic acid (vitamin C) contains 40.92% C, 4.58% H, and 54.50% O by mass. What is the empirical formula of ascorbic acid?

SOLUTION

Analyze We are to determine an empirical formula of a compound from the mass percentages of its elements.

Plan The strategy for determining the empirical formula involves the three steps given in Figure 3.11.

Solve We *first* assume, for simplicity, that we have exactly 100 g of material (although any mass can be used). In 100 g of ascorbic acid, therefore, we have

40.92 g C, 4.58 g H, and 54.50 g O.

Second, we calculate the number of moles of each element:

$$\text{Moles C} = (40.92 \text{ g C})\left(\frac{1 \text{ mol C}}{12.01 \text{ g C}}\right) = 3.407 \text{ mol C}$$

$$\text{Moles H} = (4.58 \text{ g H})\left(\frac{1 \text{ mol H}}{1.008 \text{ g H}}\right) = 4.54 \text{ mol H}$$

$$\text{Moles O} = (54.50 \text{ g O})\left(\frac{1 \text{ mol O}}{16.00 \text{ g O}}\right) = 3.406 \text{ mol O}$$

Third, we determine the simplest whole-number ratio of moles by dividing each number of moles by the smallest number of moles, 3.406:

$$\text{C:} \frac{3.407}{3.406} = 1.000 \qquad \text{H:} \frac{4.54}{3.406} = 1.33 \qquad \text{O:} \frac{3.406}{3.406} = 1.000$$

The ratio for H is too far from 1 to attribute the difference to experimental error; in fact, it is quite close to $1\frac{1}{3}$. This suggests that if we multiply the ratio by 3, we will obtain whole numbers:

$$\text{C:H:O} = 3(1{:}1.33{:}1) = 3{:}4{:}3$$

The whole-number mole ratio gives us the subscripts for the empirical formula:

$$C_3H_4O_3$$

Check It is reassuring that the subscripts are moderately sized whole numbers. Otherwise, we have little by which to judge the reasonableness of our answer.

■ PRACTICE EXERCISE

A 5.325-g sample of methyl benzoate, a compound used in the manufacture of perfumes, contains 3.758 g of carbon, 0.316 g of hydrogen, and 1.251 g of oxygen. What is the empirical formula of this substance?
Answer: C_4H_4O

Molecular Formula from Empirical Formula

For any compound, the formula obtained from percentage compositions is always the empirical formula. We can obtain the molecular formula from the empirical formula if we are given the molecular weight or molar mass of the compound. *The subscripts in the molecular formula of a substance are always a whole-number multiple of the corresponding subscripts in its empirical formula.* (Section 2.6) This multiple can be found by comparing the empirical formula weight with the molecular weight:

$$\text{Whole-number multiple} = \frac{\text{molecular weight}}{\text{empirical formula weight}} \qquad [3.11]$$

In Sample Exercise 3.13, for example, the empirical formula of ascorbic acid was determined to be $C_3H_4O_3$, giving an empirical formula weight of 3(12.0 amu) + 4(1.0 amu) + 3(16.0 amu) = 88.0 amu. The experimentally determined molecular weight is 176 amu. Thus, the molecular weight is 2 times the empirical formula weight (176/88.0 = 2.00), and the molecular formula must therefore have twice as many of each kind of atom as the empirical formula. Consequently, we multiply the subscripts in the empirical formula by 2 to obtain the molecular formula: $C_6H_8O_6$.

■ SAMPLE EXERCISE 3.14 | Determining a Molecular Formula

Mesitylene, a hydrocarbon that occurs in small amounts in crude oil, has an empirical formula of C_3H_4. The experimentally determined molecular weight of this substance is 121 amu. What is the molecular formula of mesitylene?

SOLUTION

Analyze We are given an empirical formula and a molecular weight and asked to determine a molecular formula.

Plan The subscripts in the molecular formula of a compound are whole-number multiples of the subscripts in its empirical formula. To find the appropriate multiple, we must compare the molecular weight with the formula weight of the empirical formula.

Solve First, we calculate the formula weight of the empirical formula, C_3H_4:

$$3(12.0 \text{ amu}) + 4(1.0 \text{ amu}) = 40.0 \text{ amu}$$

Next, we divide the molecular weight by the empirical formula weight to obtain the multiple used to multiply the subscripts in C_3H_4:

$$\frac{\text{Molecular weight}}{\text{Empirical formula weight}} = \frac{121}{40.0} = 3.02$$

Only whole-number ratios make physical sense because we must be dealing with whole atoms. The 3.02 in this case could result from a small experimental error in the molecular weight. We therefore multiply each subscript in the empirical formula by 3 to give the molecular formula: C_9H_{12}.

Check We can have confidence in the result because dividing the molecular weight by the formula weight yields nearly a whole number.

■ **PRACTICE EXERCISE**

Ethylene glycol, the substance used in automobile antifreeze, is composed of 38.7% C, 9.7% H, and 51.6% O by mass. Its molar mass is 62.1 g/mol. **(a)** What is the empirical formula of ethylene glycol? **(b)** What is its molecular formula?
Answers: **(a)** CH_3O, **(b)** $C_2H_6O_2$

Combustion Analysis

The empirical formula of a compound is based on experiments that give the number of moles of each element in a sample of the compound. The word "empirical" means "based on observation and experiment." Chemists have devised a number of experimental techniques to determine empirical formulas. One technique is combustion analysis, which is commonly used for compounds containing principally carbon and hydrogen as their component elements.

When a compound containing carbon and hydrogen is completely combusted in an apparatus such as that shown in Figure 3.12▶, the carbon in the compound is converted to CO_2, and the hydrogen is converted to H_2O. ⇽⇽ (Section 3.2) The amounts of CO_2 and H_2O produced are determined by measuring the mass increase in the CO_2 and H_2O absorbers. From the masses of CO_2 and H_2O we can calculate the number of moles of C and H in the original compound and thereby the empirical formula. If a third element is present in the compound, its mass can be determined by subtracting the masses of C and H from the compound's original mass. Sample Exercise 3.15 shows how to determine the empirical formula of a compound containing C, H, and O.

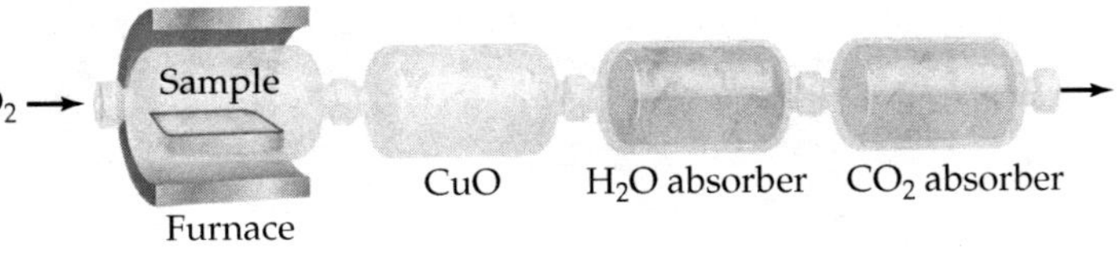

▲ Figure 3.12 **Apparatus to determine percentages of carbon and hydrogen in a compound.** The compound is combusted to form CO_2 and H_2O. Copper oxide helps to oxidize traces of carbon and carbon monoxide to carbon dioxide and to oxidize hydrogen to water.

■ **SAMPLE EXERCISE 3.15 | Determining Empirical Formula by Combustion Analysis**

Isopropyl alcohol, a substance sold as rubbing alcohol, is composed of C, H, and O. Combustion of 0.255 g of isopropyl alcohol produces 0.561 g of CO_2 and 0.306 g of H_2O. Determine the empirical formula of isopropyl alcohol.

SOLUTION

Analyze We are told that isopropyl alcohol contains C, H, and O atoms and given the quantities of CO_2 and H_2O produced when a given quantity of the alcohol is combusted. We must use this information to determine the empirical formula for isopropyl alcohol, a task that requires us to calculate the number of moles of C, H, and O in the sample.

Plan We can use the mole concept to calculate the number of grams of C present in the CO_2 and the number of grams of H present in the H_2O. These amounts are the quantities of C and H present in the isopropyl alcohol before combustion. The number of grams of O in the compound equals the mass of the isopropyl alcohol minus the sum of the C and H masses. Once we have the number of grams of C, H, and O in the sample, we can then proceed as in Sample Exercise 3.13. We can calculate the number of moles of each element, and determine the mole ratio, which gives the subscripts in the empirical formula.

Solve To calculate the number of grams of C, we first use the molar mass of CO_2, 1 mol CO_2 = 44.0 g CO_2, to convert grams of CO_2 to moles of CO_2. Because each CO_2 molecule has only 1 C atom, there is 1 mol of C atoms per mole of CO_2 molecules. This fact allows us to convert the moles of CO_2 to moles of C. Finally, we use the molar mass of C, 1 mol C = 12.0 g C, to convert moles of C to grams of C. Combining the three conversion factors, we have

$$\text{Grams C} = (0.561 \text{ g } CO_2)\left(\frac{1 \text{ mol } CO_2}{44.0 \text{ g } CO_2}\right)\left(\frac{1 \text{ mol C}}{1 \text{ mol } CO_2}\right)\left(\frac{12.0 \text{ g C}}{1 \text{ mol C}}\right) = 0.153 \text{ g C}$$

The calculation of the number of grams of H from the grams of H_2O is similar, although we must remember that there are 2 mol of H atoms per 1 mol of H_2O molecules:

$$\text{Grams H} = (0.306 \text{ g } H_2O)\left(\frac{1 \text{ mol } H_2O}{18.0 \text{ g } H_2O}\right)\left(\frac{2 \text{ mol H}}{1 \text{ mol } H_2O}\right)\left(\frac{1.01 \text{ g H}}{1 \text{ mol H}}\right) = 0.0343 \text{ g H}$$

The total mass of the sample, 0.255 g, is the sum of the masses of the C, H, and O. Thus, we can calculate the mass of O as follows:

$$\begin{aligned}\text{Mass of O} &= \text{mass of sample} - (\text{mass of C} + \text{mass of H}) \\ &= 0.255 \text{ g} - (0.153 \text{ g} + 0.0343 \text{ g}) = 0.068 \text{ g O}\end{aligned}$$

We then calculate the number of moles of C, H, and O in the sample:

$$\text{Moles C} = (0.153 \text{ g C})\left(\frac{1 \text{ mol C}}{12.0 \text{ g C}}\right) = 0.0128 \text{ mol C}$$

$$\text{Moles H} = (0.0343 \text{ g H})\left(\frac{1 \text{ mol H}}{1.01 \text{ g H}}\right) = 0.0340 \text{ mol H}$$

$$\text{Moles O} = (0.068 \text{ g O})\left(\frac{1 \text{ mol O}}{16.0 \text{ g O}}\right) = 0.0043 \text{ mol O}$$

To find the empirical formula, we must compare the relative number of moles of each element in the sample. The relative number of moles of each element is found by dividing each number by the smallest number, 0.0043. The mole ratio of C:H:O so obtained is 2.98:7.91:1.00. The first two numbers are very close to the whole numbers 3 and 8, giving the empirical formula C_3H_8O.

Check The subscripts work out to be moderately sized whole numbers, as expected.

■■■ **PRACTICE EXERCISE**

(a) Caproic acid, which is responsible for the foul odor of dirty socks, is composed of C, H, and O atoms. Combustion of a 0.225-g sample of this compound produces 0.512 g CO_2 and 0.209 g H_2O. What is the empirical formula of caproic acid? **(b)** Caproic acid has a molar mass of 116 g/mol. What is its molecular formula?
Answers: **(a)** C_3H_6O, **(b)** $C_6H_{12}O_2$

        GIVE IT SOME THOUGHT

In Sample Exercise 3.15, how do you explain the fact that the ratios C:H:O are 2.98:7.91:1.00, rather than exact integers 3:8:1?

3.6 QUANTITATIVE INFORMATION FROM BALANCED EQUATIONS

The coefficients in a chemical equation represent the relative numbers of molecules in a reaction. The mole concept allows us to convert this information to the masses of the substances. Consider the following balanced equation:

$$2 H_2(g) + O_2(g) \longrightarrow 2 H_2O(l) \qquad [3.12]$$

The coefficients indicate that two molecules of H_2 react with each molecule of O_2 to form two molecules of H_2O. It follows that the relative numbers of moles are identical to the relative numbers of molecules:

$2 H_2(g)$	+	$O_2(g)$	$\longrightarrow$	$2 H_2O(l)$
2 molecules		1 molecule		2 molecules
$2(6.02 \times 10^{23}$ molecules)		$1(6.02 \times 10^{23}$ molecules)		$2(6.02 \times 10^{23}$ molecules)
2 mol		1 mol		2 mol

Science Fundamentals

We can generalize this observation for all balanced chemical equations: *The coefficients in a balanced chemical equation indicate both the relative numbers of molecules (or formula units) in the reaction and the relative numbers of moles.* Table 3.3 ▼ further summarizes this result and shows how it corresponds to the law of conservation of mass. Notice that the total mass of the reactants (4.0 g + 32.0 g) equals the total mass of the products (36.0 g).

TABLE 3.3 ■ Information from a Balanced Equation

Equation:	$2\ H_2(g)$	+	$O_2(g)$	$\longrightarrow$	$2\ H_2O(l)$
Molecules:	2 molecules H_2	+	1 molecule O_2	$\longrightarrow$	2 molecules H_2O
Mass (amu):	4.0 amu H_2	+	32.0 amu O_2	$\longrightarrow$	36.0 amu H_2O
Amount (mol):	2 mol H_2	+	1 mol O_2	$\longrightarrow$	2 mol H_2O
Mass (g):	4.0 g H_2	+	32.0 g O_2	$\longrightarrow$	36.0 g H_2O

The quantities 2 mol H_2, 1 mol O_2, and 2 mol H_2O, which are given by the coefficients in Equation 3.12, are called *stoichiometrically equivalent quantities.* The relationship between these quantities can be represented as

$$2\ \text{mol } H_2 \mathrel{\hat=} 1\ \text{mol } O_2 \mathrel{\hat=} 2\ \text{mol } H_2O$$

where the $\hat=$ symbol means "is stoichiometrically equivalent to." In other words, Equation 3.12 shows 2 mol of H_2 and 1 mol of O_2 forming 2 mol of H_2O. These stoichiometric relations can be used to convert between quantities of reactants and products in a chemical reaction. For example, the number of moles of H_2O produced from 1.57 mol of O_2 can be calculated as follows:

$$\text{Moles } H_2O = (1.57\ \text{mol } O_2)\left(\frac{2\ \text{mol } H_2O}{1\ \text{mol } O_2}\right) = 3.14\ \text{mol } H_2O$$

GIVE IT SOME THOUGHT

When 1.57 mol O_2 reacts with H_2 to form H_2O, how many moles of H_2 are consumed in the process?

As an additional example, consider the combustion of butane (C_4H_{10}), the fuel in disposable cigarette lighters:

$$2\ C_4H_{10}(l) + 13\ O_2(g) \longrightarrow 8\ CO_2(g) + 10\ H_2O(g) \qquad [3.13]$$

Let's calculate the mass of CO_2 produced when 1.00 g of C_4H_{10} is burned. The coefficients in Equation 3.13 tell how the amount of C_4H_{10} consumed is related to the amount of CO_2 produced: 2 mol $C_4H_{10} \mathrel{\hat=} 8$ mol CO_2. To use this relationship we must use the molar mass of C_4H_{10} to convert grams of C_4H_{10} to moles of C_4H_{10}. Because 1 mol $C_4H_{10} = 58.0$ g C_4H_{10}, we have

$$\text{Moles } C_4H_{10} = (1.00\ \text{g } C_4H_{10})\left(\frac{1\ \text{mol } C_4H_{10}}{58.0\ \text{g } C_4H_{10}}\right)$$
$$= 1.72 \times 10^{-2}\ \text{mol } C_4H_{10}$$

We can then use the stoichiometric factor from the balanced equation, 2 mol $C_4H_{10} \mathrel{\hat=} 8$ mol CO_2, to calculate moles of CO_2:

$$\text{Moles } CO_2 = (1.72 \times 10^{-2}\ \text{mol } C_4H_{10})\left(\frac{8\ \text{mol } CO_2}{2\ \text{mol } C_4H_{10}}\right)$$
$$= 6.88 \times 10^{-2}\ \text{mol } CO_2$$

Finally, we can calculate the mass of the CO_2, in grams, using the molar mass of CO_2 (1 mol CO_2 = 44.0 g CO_2):

$$\text{Grams } CO_2 = (6.88 \times 10^{-2} \text{ mol } CO_2)\left(\frac{44.0 \text{ g } CO_2}{1 \text{ mol } CO_2}\right)$$

$$= 3.03 \text{ g } CO_2$$

Thus, the conversion sequence is

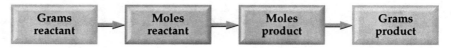

These steps can be combined in a single sequence of factors:

$$\text{Grams } CO_2 = (1.00 \text{ g } C_4H_{10})\left(\frac{1 \text{ mol } C_4H_{10}}{58.0 \text{ g } C_4H_{10}}\right)\left(\frac{8 \text{ mol } CO_2}{2 \text{ mol } C_4H_{10}}\right)\left(\frac{44.0 \text{ g } CO_2}{1 \text{ mol } CO_2}\right)$$

$$= 3.03 \text{ g } CO_2$$

Similarly, we can calculate the amount of O_2 consumed or H_2O produced in this reaction. For example, to calculate the amount of O_2 consumed, we again rely on the coefficients in the balanced equation to give us the appropriate stoichiometric factor: 2 mol $C_4H_{10} \rightleftharpoons$ 13 mol O_2:

$$\text{Grams } O_2 = (1.00 \text{ g } C_4H_{10})\left(\frac{1 \text{ mol } C_4H_{10}}{58.0 \text{ g } C_4H_{10}}\right)\left(\frac{13 \text{ mol } O_2}{2 \text{ mol } C_4H_{10}}\right)\left(\frac{32.0 \text{ g } O_2}{1 \text{ mol } O_2}\right)$$

$$= 3.59 \text{ g } O_2$$

Figure 3.13 ▼ summarizes the general approach used to calculate the quantities of substances consumed or produced in chemical reactions. The balanced chemical equation provides the relative numbers of moles of reactants and products in the reaction.

▶ Figure 3.13 **The procedure for calculating amounts of reactants or products in a reaction.** The number of grams of a reactant consumed or of a product formed in a reaction can be calculated, starting with the number of grams of one of the other reactants or products. Notice how molar masses and the coefficients in the balanced equation are used.

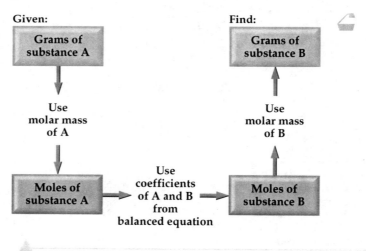

GIVE IT SOME THOUGHT

If 20.00 g of a compound reacts completely with 30.00 g of another compound in a combination reaction, how many grams of product were formed?

■ **SAMPLE EXERCISE 3.16** │ **Calculating Amounts of Reactants and Products**

How many grams of water are produced in the oxidation of 1.00 g of glucose, $C_6H_{12}O_6$?

$$C_6H_{12}O_6(s) + 6 O_2(g) \longrightarrow 6 CO_2(g) + 6 H_2O(l)$$

SOLUTION

Analyze We are given the mass of a reactant and are asked to determine the mass of a product in the given equation.

Plan The general strategy, as outlined in Figure 3.13, requires three steps. First, the amount of $C_6H_{12}O_6$ must be converted from grams to moles. Second, we can use the balanced equation, which relates the moles of $C_6H_{12}O_6$ to the moles of H_2O: 1 mol $C_6H_{12}O_6 \simeq 6$ mol H_2O. Third, we must convert the moles of H_2O to grams.

Solve First, use the molar mass of $C_6H_{12}O_6$ to convert from grams $C_6H_{12}O_6$ to moles $C_6H_{12}O_6$:

$$\text{Moles } C_6H_{12}O_6 = (1.00 \text{ g } C_6H_{12}O_6)\left(\frac{1 \text{ mol } C_6H_{12}O_6}{180.0 \text{ g } C_6H_{12}O_6}\right)$$

Second, use the balanced equation to convert moles of $C_6H_{12}O_6$ to moles of H_2O:

$$\text{Moles } H_2O = (1.00 \text{ g } C_6H_{12}O_6)\left(\frac{1 \text{ mol } C_6H_{12}O_6}{180.0 \text{ g } C_6H_{12}O_6}\right)\left(\frac{6 \text{ mol } H_2O}{1 \text{ mol } C_6H_{12}O_6}\right)$$

Third, use the molar mass of H_2O to convert from moles of H_2O to grams of H_2O:

$$\text{Grams } H_2O = (1.00 \text{ g } C_6H_{12}O_6)\left(\frac{1 \text{ mol } C_6H_{12}O_6}{180.0 \text{ g } C_6H_{12}O_6}\right)\left(\frac{6 \text{ mol } H_2O}{1 \text{ mol } C_6H_{12}O_6}\right)\left(\frac{18.0 \text{ g } H_2O}{1 \text{ mol } H_2O}\right)$$
$$= 0.600 \text{ g } H_2O$$

The steps can be summarized in a diagram like that in Figure 3.13:

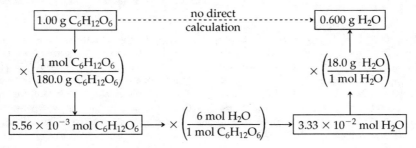

Check An estimate of the magnitude of our answer, 18/180 = 0.1 and 0.1 × 6 = 0.6, agrees with the exact calculation. The units, grams H_2O, are correct. The initial data had three significant figures, so three significant figures for the answer is correct.

Comment An average person ingests 2 L of water daily and eliminates 2.4 L. The difference between 2 L and 2.4 L is produced in the metabolism of foodstuffs, such as in the oxidation of glucose. (*Metabolism* is a general term used to describe all the chemical processes of a living animal or plant.) The desert rat (kangaroo rat), on the other hand, apparently never drinks water. It survives on its metabolic water.

▬▬ PRACTICE EXERCISE

The decomposition of $KClO_3$ is commonly used to prepare small amounts of O_2 in the laboratory: $2 \text{ KClO}_3(s) \longrightarrow 2 \text{ KCl}(s) + 3 \text{ O}_2(g)$. How many grams of O_2 can be prepared from 4.50 g of $KClO_3$?
Answer: 1.77 g

▬▬ SAMPLE EXERCISE 3.17 | Calculating Amounts of Reactants and Products

Solid lithium hydroxide is used in space vehicles to remove the carbon dioxide exhaled by astronauts. The lithium hydroxide reacts with gaseous carbon dioxide to form solid lithium carbonate and liquid water. How many grams of carbon dioxide can be absorbed by 1.00 g of lithium hydroxide?

SOLUTION

Analyze We are given a verbal description of a reaction and asked to calculate the number of grams of one reactant that reacts with 1.00 g of another.

Plan The verbal description of the reaction can be used to write a balanced equation:

$$2 \text{ LiOH}(s) + CO_2(g) \longrightarrow Li_2CO_3(s) + H_2O(l)$$

We are given the grams of LiOH and asked to calculate grams of CO_2. We can accomplish this task by using the following sequence of conversions:

$$\text{Grams LiOH} \longrightarrow \text{moles LiOH} \longrightarrow \text{moles } CO_2 \longrightarrow \text{grams } CO_2$$

The conversion from grams of LiOH to moles of LiOH requires the molar mass of LiOH (6.94 + 16.00 + 1.01 = 23.95 g/mol). The conversion of moles of LiOH to moles of CO_2 is based on the balanced chemical equation: 2 mol LiOH $\simeq$ 1 mol CO_2. To convert the number of moles of CO_2 to grams, we must use the molar mass of CO_2: 12.01 + 2(16.00) = 44.01 g/mol.

Solve

$$(1.00 \text{ g LiOH})\left(\frac{1 \text{ mol LiOH}}{23.95 \text{ g LiOH}}\right)\left(\frac{1 \text{ mol CO}_2}{2 \text{ mol LiOH}}\right)\left(\frac{44.01 \text{ g CO}_2}{1 \text{ mol CO}_2}\right) = 0.919 \text{ g CO}_2$$

Check Notice that $23.95 \approx 24$, $24 \times 2 = 48$, and $44/48$ is slightly less than 1. The magnitude of the answer is reasonable based on the amount of starting LiOH; the significant figures and units are appropriate, too.

■ **PRACTICE EXERCISE**

Propane, C_3H_8, is a common fuel used for cooking and home heating. What mass of O_2 is consumed in the combustion of 1.00 g of propane?
Answer: 3.64 g

Chemistry and Life   GLUCOSE MONITORING

Over 20 million Americans have diabetes. In the world, the number approaches 172 million. Diabetes is a disorder of metabolism in which the body cannot produce or properly use the hormone insulin. One signal that a person is diabetic is that the concentration of glucose in her or his blood is higher than normal. Therefore, people who are diabetic need to measure their blood glucose concentrations regularly. Untreated diabetes can cause severe complications such as blindness and loss of limbs.

How does insulin relate to glucose? The body converts most of the food we eat into glucose. After digestion, glucose is delivered to cells via the bloodstream; cells need glucose to live. Insulin must be present for glucose to enter the cells. Normally, the body adjusts the concentration of insulin automatically, in concert with the glucose concentration after eating. However, in a diabetic person, little or no insulin is produced (Type 1 diabetes), or the cells cannot take up insulin properly (Type 2 diabetes). The result is that the blood glucose concentration is too high. People normally have a range of 70–120 mg glucose per deciliter of blood (about 4–6 mmol glucose per liter of blood). If a person has not eaten for 8 hours or more, he or she would be diagnosed as diabetic if the glucose levels were 126 mg/dL or higher. In the United States, diabetics monitor their blood glucose concentrations in mg/dL; in Europe, they use different units—millimoles glucose per liter of blood.

Glucose monitors work by the introduction of blood from a person, usually by a prick of the finger, onto a small strip of paper that contains numerous chemicals that react specifically with glucose. Insertion of the strip into a small battery-operated reader gives the glucose concentration (Figure 3.14 ▼). The actual mechanism of the readout varies for different devices—it may be a small electrical current or a measure of light produced in a chemical reaction. Depending on the result, a diabetic person may need to receive an injection of insulin or simply stop eating sweets for a while.

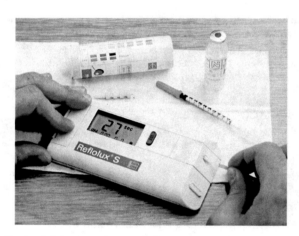

▲ Figure 3.14 **Glucose meter.** This is an example of a commercial glucose meter and its readout.

3.7 LIMITING REACTANTS

Suppose you wish to make several sandwiches using one slice of cheese and two slices of bread for each sandwich. Using Bd = bread, Ch = cheese, and Bd$_2$Ch = sandwich, the recipe for making a sandwich can be represented like a chemical equation:

$$2 \text{ Bd} + \text{Ch} \longrightarrow \text{Bd}_2\text{Ch}$$

If you have 10 slices of bread and 7 slices of cheese, you will be able to make only five sandwiches before you run out of bread. You will have 2 slices of cheese left over. The amount of available bread limits the number of sandwiches.

An analogous situation occurs in chemical reactions when one of the reactants is used up before the others. The reaction stops as soon as any one of the reactants is totally consumed, leaving the excess reactants as leftovers.

Suppose, for example, that we have a mixture of 10 mol H_2 and 7 mol O_2, which react to form water:

$$2\,H_2(g) + O_2(g) \longrightarrow 2\,H_2O(g)$$

Because 2 mol $H_2 \simeq 1$ mol O_2, the number of moles of O_2 needed to react with all the H_2 is

$$\text{Moles } O_2 = (10\ \cancel{\text{mol } H_2})\left(\frac{1\ \text{mol } O_2}{2\ \cancel{\text{mol } H_2}}\right) = 5\ \text{mol } O_2$$

 Students often combine the amounts of product calculated from each reactant when working with limiting reagents. The reagent that leads to the smallest amount of product is the limiting reagent. The amount of product formed in the reaction is the *smallest calculated amount*, *not the sum*.

Because 7 mol O_2 was available at the start of the reaction, 7 mol O_2 − 5 mol O_2 = 2 mol O_2 will still be present when all the H_2 is consumed. The example we have considered is depicted on a molecular level in Figure 3.15 ▶.

The reactant that is completely consumed in a reaction is called either the **limiting reactant** or *limiting reagent* because it determines, or limits, the amount of product formed. The other reactants are sometimes called either *excess reactants* or *excess reagents*. In our example, H_2 is the limiting reactant, which means that once all the H_2 has been consumed, the reaction stops. O_2 is the excess reactant, and some is left over when the reaction stops.

There are no restrictions on the starting amounts of the reactants in any reaction. Indeed, many reactions are carried out using an excess of one reagent. The quantities of reactants consumed and the quantities of products formed, however, are restricted by the quantity of the limiting reactant. When a combustion reaction takes place in the open air, oxygen is plentiful and is therefore the excess reactant. You may have had the unfortunate experience of running out of gasoline while driving. The car stops because you have run out of the limiting reactant in the combustion reaction, the fuel.

Before we leave our present example, let's summarize the data in a tabular form:

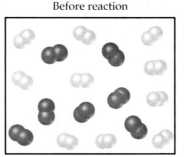

Before reaction

10 H_2 and 7 O_2

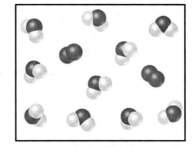

After reaction

10 H_2O and 2 O_2

▲ Figure 3.15 **Example illustrating a limiting reactant.** Because the H_2 is completely consumed, it is the limiting reagent in this case. Because there is a stoichiometric excess of O_2, some is left over at the end of the reaction. The amount of H_2O formed is related directly to the amount of H_2 consumed.

	2 $H_2(g)$	+ $O_2(g)$	⟶	2 $H_2O(g)$
Initial quantities:	10 mol	7 mol		0 mol
Change (reaction):	−10 mol	−5 mol		+10 mol
Final quantities:	0 mol	2 mol		10 mol

The initial amounts of the reactants are what we started with (10 mol H_2 and 7 mol O_2). The second line in the table (change) summarizes the amounts of the reactants consumed and the amount of the product formed in the reaction. These quantities are restricted by the quantity of the limiting reactant and depend on the coefficients in the balanced equation. The mole ratio $H_2 : O_2 : H_2O$ = 10:5:10 conforms to the ratio of the coefficients in the balanced equation, 2:1:2. The changes are negative for the reactants because they are consumed during the reaction and positive for the product because it is formed during the reaction. Finally, the quantities in the third line of the table (final quantities) depend on the initial quantities and their changes, and these entries are found by adding the entries for the initial quantity and change for each column. No amount of the limiting reactant (H_2) remains at the end of the reaction. All that remains is 2 mol O_2 and 10 mol H_2O.

■■ SAMPLE EXERCISE 3.18 | Calculating the Amount of Product Formed from a Limiting Reactant

The most important commercial process for converting N_2 from the air into nitrogen-containing compounds is based on the reaction of N_2 and H_2 to form ammonia (NH_3):

$$N_2(g) + 3\,H_2(g) \longrightarrow 2\,NH_3(g)$$

How many moles of NH_3 can be formed from 3.0 mol of N_2 and 6.0 mol of H_2?

SOLUTION

Analyze We are asked to calculate the number of moles of product, NH_3, given the quantities of each reactant, N_2 and H_2, available in a reaction. Thus, this is a limiting reactant problem.

Plan If we assume that one reactant is completely consumed, we can calculate how much of the second reactant is needed in the reaction. By comparing the calculated quantity with the available amount, we can determine which reactant is limiting. We then proceed with the calculation, using the quantity of the limiting reactant.

Solve The number of moles of H_2 needed for complete consumption of 3.0 mol of N_2 is:

$$\text{Moles } H_2 = (3.0 \text{ mol } N_2)\left(\frac{3 \text{ mol } H_2}{1 \text{ mol } N_2}\right) = 9.0 \text{ mol } H_2$$

Because only 6.0 mol H_2 is available, we will run out of H_2 before the N_2 is gone, and H_2 will be the limiting reactant. We use the quantity of the limiting reactant, H_2, to calculate the quantity of NH_3 produced:

$$\text{Moles } NH_3 = (6.0 \text{ mol } H_2)\left(\frac{2 \text{ mol } NH_3}{3 \text{ mol } H_2}\right) = 4.0 \text{ mol } NH_3$$

Comment The table on the right summarizes this example:

	$N_2(g)$	+	$3\,H_2(g)$	$\longrightarrow$	$2\,NH_3(g)$
Initial quantities:	3.0 mol		6.0 mol		0 mol
Change (reaction):	−2.0 mol		−6.0 mol		+4.0 mol
Final quantities:	1.0 mol		0 mol		4.0 mol

Notice that we can calculate not only the number of moles of NH_3 formed but also the number of moles of each of the reactants remaining after the reaction. Notice also that although the number of moles of H_2 present at the beginning of the reaction is greater than the number of moles of N_2 present, the H_2 is nevertheless the limiting reactant because of its larger coefficient in the balanced equation.

Check The summarizing table shows that the mole ratio of reactants used and product formed conforms to the coefficients in the balanced equation, 1:3:2. Also, because H_2 is the limiting reactant, it is completely consumed in the reaction, leaving 0 mol at the end. Because 6.0 mol H_2 has two significant figures, our answer has two significant figures.

■■ PRACTICE EXERCISE

Consider the reaction $2\,Al(s) + 3\,Cl_2(g) \longrightarrow 2\,AlCl_3(s)$. A mixture of 1.50 mol of Al and 3.00 mol of Cl_2 is allowed to react. **(a)** Which is the limiting reactant? **(b)** How many moles of $AlCl_3$ are formed? **(c)** How many moles of the excess reactant remain at the end of the reaction?
Answers: **(a)** Al, **(b)** 1.50 mol, **(c)** 0.75 mol Cl_2

■■ SAMPLE EXERCISE 3.19 | Calculating the Amount of Product Formed from a Limiting Reactant

Consider the following reaction that occurs in a fuel cell:

$$2\,H_2(g) + O_2(g) \longrightarrow 2\,H_2O(g)$$

This reaction, properly done, produces energy in the form of electricity and water. Suppose a fuel cell is set up with 150 g of hydrogen gas and 1500 grams of oxygen gas (each measurement is given with two significant figures). How many grams of water can be formed?

SOLUTION

Analyze We are asked to calculate the amount of a product, given the amounts of two reactants, so this is a limiting reactant problem.

Plan We must first identify the limiting reagent. To do so, we can calculate the number of moles of each reactant and compare their ratio with that required by the balanced equation. We then use the quantity of the limiting reagent to calculate the mass of water that forms.

Solve From the balanced equation, we have the following stoichiometric relations:

$$2 \text{ mol } H_2 \triangleq 1 \text{ mol } O_2 \triangleq 2 \text{ mol } H_2O$$

Using the molar mass of each substance, we can calculate the number of moles of each reactant:

$$\text{Moles } H_2 = (150 \text{ g } H_2)\left(\frac{1 \text{ mol } H_2}{2.00 \text{ g } H_2}\right) = 75 \text{ mol } H_2$$

$$\text{Moles } O_2 = (1500 \text{ g } O_2)\left(\frac{1 \text{ mol } O_2}{32.0 \text{ g } O_2}\right) = 47 \text{ mol } O_2$$

Thus, there are more moles of H_2 than O_2. The coefficients in the balanced equation indicate, however, that the reaction requires 2 moles of H_2 for every 1 mole of O_2. Therefore, to completely react all the O_2, we would need $2 \times 47 = 94$ moles of H_2. Since there are only 75 moles of H_2, H_2 is the limiting reagent. We therefore use the quantity of H_2 to calculate the quantity of product formed. We can begin this calculation with the grams of H_2, but we can save a step by starting with the moles of H_2 that were calculated previously in the exercise:

$$\text{Grams } H_2O = (75 \text{ moles } H_2)\left(\frac{2 \text{ mol } H_2O}{2 \text{ mol } H_2}\right)\left(\frac{18.0 \text{ g } H_2O}{1 \text{ mol } H_2O}\right)$$
$$= 1400 \text{ g } H_2O \text{ (to two significant figures)}$$

Check The magnitude of the answer seems reasonable. The units are correct, and the number of significant figures (two) corresponds to those in the numbers of grams of the starting materials.

Comment The quantity of the limiting reagent, H_2, can also be used to determine the quantity of O_2 used (37.5 mol = 1200 g). The number of grams of the excess oxygen remaining at the end of the reaction equals the starting amount minus the amount consumed in the reaction, 1500 g − 1200 g = 300 g.

▬▬ PRACTICE EXERCISE
A strip of zinc metal with a mass of 2.00 g is placed in an aqueous solution containing 2.50 g of silver nitrate, causing the following reaction to occur:

$$Zn(s) + 2 \text{ AgNO}_3(aq) \longrightarrow 2 \text{ Ag}(s) + Zn(NO_3)_2(aq)$$

(a) Which reactant is limiting? **(b)** How many grams of Ag will form? **(c)** How many grams of $Zn(NO_3)_2$ will form? **(d)** How many grams of the excess reactant will be left at the end of the reaction?
Answers: **(a)** $AgNO_3$, **(b)** 1.59 g, **(c)** 1.39 g, **(d)** 1.52 g Zn

Theoretical Yields

The quantity of product that is calculated to form when all of the limiting reactant reacts is called the **theoretical yield**. The amount of product actually obtained in a reaction is called the *actual yield*. The actual yield is almost always less than (and can never be greater than) the theoretical yield. There are many reasons for this difference. Part of the reactants may not react, for example, or they may react in a way different from that desired (side reactions). In addition, it is not always possible to recover all of the product from the reaction mixture. The **percent yield** of a reaction relates the actual yield to the theoretical (calculated) yield:

$$\text{Percent yield} = \frac{\text{actual yield}}{\text{theoretical yield}} \times 100\% \qquad [3.14]$$

Strategies in Chemistry   HOW TO TAKE A TEST

At about this time in your study of chemistry, you are likely to face your first hour-long examination. The best way to prepare for the exam is to study and do homework diligently and to make sure you get help from the instructor on any material that is unclear or confusing. (See the advice for learning and studying chemistry presented in the preface of the book.) We present here some general guidelines for taking tests.

Depending on the nature of your course, the exam could consist of a variety of different types of questions. Let's consider some of the more common types and how they can best be addressed.

1. *Multiple-choice questions* In large-enrollment courses, the most common kind of testing device is the multiple-choice question. You are given the problem and usually presented with four or five possible answers from which you must select the correct one. The first thing to realize is that the instructor has written the question so that all of the answer choices appear at first glance to be correct. (There would be little point in offering choices you could

tell were wrong even without knowing much about the concept being tested.) Thus, you should not jump to the conclusion that because one of the choices looks correct, it must be so.

If a multiple-choice question involves a calculation, perform the calculation, quickly double-check your work, and *only then* compare your answer with the choices. If you find a match, you have probably found the correct answer. Keep in mind, though, that your instructor has anticipated the most common errors one can make in solving a given problem and has probably listed the incorrect answers resulting from those errors. Always double-check your reasoning and make sure to use dimensional analysis to arrive at the correct answer, with the correct units.

In multiple-choice questions that do not involve calculations, if you are not sure of the correct choice, eliminate all the choices you know for sure to be incorrect. Additionally, the reasoning you used in eliminating incorrect choices will help you in reasoning about which choice is correct.

■■■ SAMPLE EXERCISE 3.20 | **Calculating the Theoretical Yield and Percent Yield for a Reaction**

Adipic acid, $H_2C_6H_8O_4$, is used to produce nylon. The acid is made commercially by a controlled reaction between cyclohexane (C_6H_{12}) and O_2:

$$2\,C_6H_{12}(l) + 5\,O_2(g) \longrightarrow 2\,H_2C_6H_8O_4(l) + 2\,H_2O(g)$$

(a) Assume that you carry out this reaction starting with 25.0 g of cyclohexane and that cyclohexane is the limiting reactant. What is the theoretical yield of adipic acid?
(b) If you obtain 33.5 g of adipic acid from your reaction, what is the percent yield of adipic acid?

SOLUTION

Analyze We are given a chemical equation and the quantity of the limiting reactant (25.0 g of C_6H_{12}). We are asked first to calculate the theoretical yield of a product ($H_2C_6H_8O_4$) and then to calculate its percent yield if only 33.5 g of the substance is actually obtained.

Plan (a) The theoretical yield, which is the calculated quantity of adipic acid formed in the reaction, can be calculated using the following sequence of conversions:

$$g\,C_6H_{12} \longrightarrow mol\,C_6H_{12} \longrightarrow mol\,H_2C_6H_8O_4 \longrightarrow g\,H_2C_6H_8O_4$$

(b) The percent yield is calculated by comparing the actual yield (33.5 g) to the theoretical yield using Equation 3.14.

Solve

(a) Grams $H_2C_6H_8O_4 = (25.0\text{ g }C_6H_{12})\left(\dfrac{1\text{ mol }C_6H_{12}}{84.0\text{ g }C_6H_{12}}\right)\left(\dfrac{2\text{ mol }H_2C_6H_8O_4}{2\text{ mol }C_6H_{12}}\right)\left(\dfrac{146.0\text{ g }H_2C_6H_8O_4}{1\text{ mol }H_2C_6H_8O_4}\right)$

$= 43.5\text{ g }H_2C_6H_8O_4$

(b) Percent yield $= \dfrac{\text{actual yield}}{\text{theoretical yield}} \times 100\% = \dfrac{33.5\text{ g}}{43.5\text{ g}} \times 100\% = 77.0\%$

Check Our answer in (a) has the appropriate magnitude, units, and significant figures. In (b) the answer is less than 100% as necessary.

2. *Calculations in which you must show your work* Your instructor may present you with a numerical problem in which you are to show your work in arriving at a solution. In questions of this kind, you may receive partial credit even if you do not arrive at the correct answer, depending on whether the instructor can follow your line of reasoning. It is important, therefore, to be as neat and organized as you can be, given the pressures of exam taking. It is helpful in approaching such questions to take a few moments to think about the direction you are going to take in solving the problem. You may even want to write a few words or a diagram on the test paper to indicate your approach. Then write out your calculations as neatly as you can. Show the units for every number you write down, and use dimensional analysis as much as you can, showing how units cancel.

3. *Questions requiring drawings* Sometimes a test question will require you to draw a chemical structure, a diagram related to chemical bonding, or a figure showing some kind of chemical process. Questions of this kind will come later in the course, but it is useful to talk about them here. (You should review this box before each exam you take, to remind yourself of good exam-taking practices.) Be sure to label your drawing as completely as possible.

4. *Other types of questions* Other exam questions you might encounter include true-false questions and ones in which you are given a list and asked to indicate which members of the list match some criterion given in the question. Often students answer such questions incorrectly because, in their haste, they misunderstand the nature of the question. Whatever the form of the question, ask yourself this: What is the instructor testing here? What material am I supposed to know that this question covers?

Finally, if you find that you simply do not understand how to arrive at a reasoned response to a question, do not linger over the question. Put a check next to it and go on to the next one. If time permits, you can come back to the unanswered questions, but lingering over a question when nothing is coming to mind is wasting time you may need to finish the exam.

■■ **PRACTICE EXERCISE**

Imagine that you are working on ways to improve the process by which iron ore containing Fe_2O_3 is converted into iron. In your tests you carry out the following reaction on a small scale:

$$Fe_2O_3(s) + 3\ CO(g) \longrightarrow 2\ Fe(s) + 3\ CO_2(g)$$

(a) If you start with 150 g of Fe_2O_3 as the limiting reagent, what is the theoretical yield of Fe? **(b)** If the actual yield of Fe in your test was 87.9 g, what was the percent yield? *Answers:* **(a)** 105 g Fe, **(b)** 83.7%

C H A P T E R   R E V I E W

SUMMARY AND KEY TERMS

Introduction and Section 3.1 The study of the quantitative relationships between chemical formulas and chemical equations is known as **stoichiometry**. One of the important concepts of stoichiometry is the law of conservation of mass, which states that the total mass of the products of a chemical reaction is the same as the total mass of the reactants. The same numbers of atoms of each type are present before and after a chemical reaction. A balanced **chemical equation** shows equal numbers of atoms of each element on each side of the equation. Equations are balanced by placing coefficients in front of the chemical formulas for the **reactants** and **products** of a reaction, *not* by changing the subscripts in chemical formulas.

Section 3.2 Among the reaction types described in this chapter are (1) **combination reactions**, in which two reactants combine to form one product; (2) **decomposition reactions**, in which a single reactant forms two or more products; and (3) **combustion reactions** in oxygen, in which a hydrocarbon or related compound reacts with O_2 to form CO_2 and H_2O.

Section 3.3 Much quantitative information can be determined from chemical formulas and balanced chemical equations by using atomic weights. The **formula weight** of a compound equals the sum of the atomic weights of the atoms in its formula. If the formula is a molecular formula, the formula weight is also called the **molecular weight**. Atomic weights and formula weights can be used to determine the elemental composition of a compound.

Section 3.4 A mole of any substance is **Avogadro's number** (6.02×10^{23}) of formula units of that substance. The mass of a mole of atoms, molecules, or ions (the **molar mass**) equals the formula weight of that material expressed in grams. The mass of one molecule of H_2O, for example, is 18 amu, so the mass of 1 mol of H_2O is 18 g. That is, the molar mass of H_2O is 18 g/mol.

Section 3.5 The empirical formula of any substance can be determined from its percent composition by calculating the relative number of moles of each atom in 100 g of the substance. If the substance is molecular in nature, its molecular formula can be determined from the empirical formula if the molecular weight is also known.

Sections 3.6 and 3.7 The mole concept can be used to calculate the relative quantities of reactants and products in chemical reactions. The coefficients in a balanced equation give the relative numbers of moles of the reactants and products. To calculate the number of grams of a product from the number of grams of a reactant, first convert grams of reactant to moles of reactant. Then use the coefficients in the balanced equation to convert the number of moles of reactant to moles of product. Finally, convert moles of product to grams of product.

A **limiting reactant** is completely consumed in a reaction. When it is used up, the reaction stops, thus limiting the quantities of products formed. The **theoretical yield** of a reaction is the quantity of product calculated to form when all of the limiting reagent reacts. The actual yield of a reaction is always less than the theoretical yield. The **percent yield** compares the actual and theoretical yields.

KEY SKILLS

- Balance chemical equations.
- Calculate molecular weights.
- Convert grams to moles and moles to grams using molar masses.
- Convert number of molecules to moles and moles to number of molecules using Avogadro's number.
- Calculate the empirical and molecular formula of a compound from percentage composition and molecular weight.
- Calculate amounts, in grams or moles, of reactants and products for a reaction.
- Calculate the percent yield of a reaction.

KEY EQUATIONS

- $\% \text{ element} = \dfrac{\left(\begin{array}{c}\text{number of atoms}\\\text{of that element}\end{array}\right)\left(\begin{array}{c}\text{atomic weight}\\\text{of element}\end{array}\right)}{\text{formula weight of compound}} \times 100\%$ [3.10]

This is the formula to calculate the mass percentage of each element in a compound. The sum of all the percentages of all the elements in a compound should add up to 100%.

- $\% \text{ yield} = \dfrac{(\text{actual yield})}{(\text{theoretical yield})} \times 100\%$ [3.14]

This is the formula to calculate the percent yield of a reaction. The percent yield can never be more than 100%.

VISUALIZING CONCEPTS

3.1 The reaction between reactant A (blue spheres) and reactant B (red spheres) is shown in the following diagram:
CQ

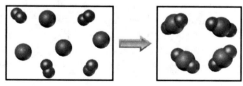

Based on this diagram, which equation best describes the reaction? [Section 3.1]

(a) $A_2 + B \longrightarrow A_2B$

(b) $A_2 + 4B \longrightarrow 2AB_2$

(c) $2A + B_4 \longrightarrow 2AB_2$

(d) $A + B_2 \longrightarrow AB_2$

3.2 Under appropriate experimental conditions, H_2 and CO
CQ undergo a combination reaction to form CH_3OH. The drawing below represents a sample of H_2. Make a corresponding drawing of the CO needed to react completely with the H_2. How did you arrive at the number of CO molecules in your drawing? [Section 3.2]

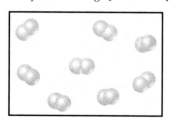

3.3 The following diagram represents the collection of elements formed by a decomposition reaction. (a) If the blue spheres represent N atoms and the red ones represent O atoms, what was the empirical formula of the original compound? (b) Could you draw a diagram representing the molecules of the compound that had been decomposed? Why or why not? [Section 3.2]

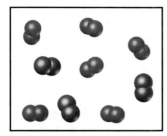

3.4 The following diagram represents the collection of CO_2
CQ and H_2O molecules formed by complete combustion of a hydrocarbon. What is the empirical formula of the hydrocarbon? [Section 3.2]

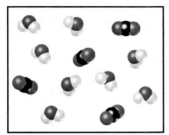

3.5 Glycine, an amino acid used by organisms to make pro-
CQ teins, is represented by the molecular model below.
   (a) Write its molecular formula.
   (b) Determine its molar mass.
   (c) Calculate the mass of 3 moles of glycine.
   (d) Calculate the percent nitrogen by mass in glycine. [Sections 3.3 and 3.5]

3.6 The following diagram represents a high-temperature
CQ reaction between CH_4 and H_2O. Based on this reaction,

how many moles of each product can be obtained starting with 4.0 mol CH_4? [Section 3.6]

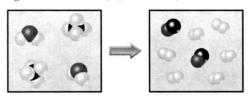

3.7 Nitrogen (N_2) and hydrogen (H_2) react to form ammo-
CQ nia (NH_3). Consider the mixture of N_2 and H_2 shown in the accompanying diagram. The blue spheres represent N, and the white ones represent H. Draw a representation of the product mixture, assuming that the reaction goes to completion. How did you arrive at your representation? What is the limiting reactant in this case? [Section 3.7]

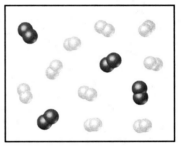

3.8 Nitrogen monoxide and oxygen react to form nitrogen
CQ dioxide. Consider the mixture of NO and O_2 shown in the accompanying diagram. The blue spheres represent N, and the red ones represent O. **(a)** Draw a representation of the product mixture, assuming that the reaction goes to completion. What is the limiting reactant in this case? **(b)** How many NO_2 molecules would you draw as products if the reaction had a percent yield of 75%? [Section 3.7]

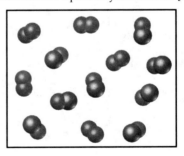

EXERCISES

Balancing Chemical Equations

3.9 **(a)** What scientific principle or law is used in the process
CQ of balancing chemical equations? **(b)** In balancing equations, why should you not change subscripts in chemical formulas? **(c)** How would one write out liquid water, water vapor, aqueous sodium chloride, and solid sodium chloride in chemical equations?

3.10 **(a)** What is the difference between adding a subscript 2
CQ to the end of the formula for CO to give CO_2 and adding a coefficient in front of the formula to give 2 CO?

   (b) Is the following chemical equation, as written, consistent with the law of conservation of mass?

$$3\,Mg(OH)_2\,(s) + 2\,H_3PO_4(aq) \longrightarrow Mg_3(PO_4)_2(s) + 6\,H_2O(l)$$

   Why or why not?

3.11 Balance the following equations:
   (a) $CO(g) + O_2(g) \longrightarrow CO_2(g)$
   (b) $N_2O_5(g) + H_2O(l) \longrightarrow HNO_3(aq)$
   (c) $CH_4(g) + Cl_2(g) \longrightarrow CCl_4(l) + HCl(g)$

(d) $Al_4C_3(s) + H_2O(l) \longrightarrow Al(OH)_3(s) + CH_4(g)$

(e) $C_5H_{10}O_2(l) + O_2(g) \longrightarrow CO_2(g) + H_2O(g)$

(f) $Fe(OH)_3(s) + H_2SO_4(aq) \longrightarrow$
$$Fe_2(SO_4)_3(aq) + H_2O(l)$$

(g) $Mg_3N_2(s) + H_2SO_4(aq) \longrightarrow$
$$MgSO_4(aq) + (NH_4)_2SO_4(aq)$$

3.12 Balance the following equations:

(a) $Li(s) + N_2(g) \longrightarrow Li_3N(s)$

(b) $La_2O_3(s) + H_2O(l) \longrightarrow La(OH)_3(aq)$

(c) $NH_4NO_3(s) \longrightarrow N_2(g) + O_2(g) + H_2O(g)$

(d) $Ca_3P_2(s) + H_2O(l) \longrightarrow Ca(OH)_2(aq) + PH_3(g)$

(e) $Ca(OH)_2(aq) + H_3PO_4(aq) \longrightarrow$
$$Ca_3(PO_4)_2(s) + H_2O(l)$$

(f) $AgNO_3(aq) + Na_2SO_4(aq) \longrightarrow$
$$Ag_2SO_4(s) + NaNO_3(aq)$$

(g) $CH_3NH_2(g) + O_2(g) \longrightarrow$
$$CO_2(g) + H_2O(g) + N_2(g)$$

3.13 Write balanced chemical equations to correspond to each of the following descriptions: (a) Solid calcium carbide, CaC_2, reacts with water to form an aqueous solution of calcium hydroxide and acetylene gas, C_2H_2. (b) When solid potassium chlorate is heated, it decom-

poses to form solid potassium chloride and oxygen gas. (c) Solid zinc metal reacts with sulfuric acid to form hydrogen gas and an aqueous solution of zinc sulfate. (d) When liquid phosphorus trichloride is added to water, it reacts to form aqueous phosphorous acid, $H_3PO_3(aq)$, and aqueous hydrochloric acid. (e) When hydrogen sulfide gas is passed over solid hot iron(III) hydroxide, the resultant reaction produces solid iron(III) sulfide and gaseous water.

3.14 Write balanced chemical equations to correspond to each of the following descriptions: (a) When sulfur trioxide gas reacts with water, a solution of sulfuric acid forms. (b) Boron sulfide, $B_2S_3(s)$, reacts violently with water to form dissolved boric acid, H_3BO_3, and hydrogen sulfide gas. (c) When an aqueous solution of lead(II) nitrate is mixed with an aqueous solution of sodium iodide, an aqueous solution of sodium nitrate and a yellow solid, lead iodide, are formed. (d) When solid mercury(II) nitrate is heated, it decomposes to form solid mercury(II) oxide, gaseous nitrogen dioxide, and oxygen. (e) Copper metal reacts with hot concentrated sulfuric acid solution to form aqueous copper(II) sulfate, sulfur dioxide gas, and water.

Patterns of Chemical Reactivity

3.15 (a) When the metallic element sodium combines with
CQ the nonmetallic element bromine, $Br_2(l)$, how can you determine the chemical formula of the product? How do you know whether the product is a solid, liquid, or gas at room temperature? Write the balanced chemical equation for the reaction. (b) When a hydrocarbon burns in air, what reactant besides the hydrocarbon is involved in the reaction? What products are formed? Write a balanced chemical equation for the combustion of benzene, $C_6H_6(l)$, in air.

3.16 (a) Determine the chemical formula of the product formed when the metallic element calcium combines with the nonmetallic element oxygen, O_2. Write the balanced chemical equation for the reaction. (b) What products form when a compound containing C, H, and O is completely combusted in air? Write a balanced chemical equation for the combustion of acetone, $C_3H_6O(l)$, in air.

3.17 Write a balanced chemical equation for the reaction that occurs when (a) $Mg(s)$ reacts with $Cl_2(g)$; (b) barium carbonate decomposes into barium oxide and carbon dioxide gas when heated; (c) the hydrocarbon styrene, $C_8H_8(l)$, is combusted in air; (d) dimethylether, $CH_3OCH_3(g)$, is combusted in air.

3.18 Write a balanced chemical equation for the reaction that occurs when (a) aluminum metal undergoes a combination reaction with $O_2(g)$; (b) copper(II) hydroxide decomposes into copper(II) oxide and water when heated; (c) heptane, $C_7H_{16}(l)$, burns in air; (d) the gasoline additive MTBE (methyl tert-butyl ether), $C_5H_{12}O(l)$, burns in air.

3.19 Balance the following equations, and indicate whether they are combination, decomposition, or combustion reactions:

(a) $Al(s) + Cl_2(g) \longrightarrow AlCl_3(s)$

(b) $C_2H_4(g) + O_2(g) \longrightarrow CO_2(g) + H_2O(g)$

(c) $Li(s) + N_2(g) \longrightarrow Li_3N(s)$

(d) $PbCO_3(s) \longrightarrow PbO(s) + CO_2(g)$

(e) $C_7H_8O_2(l) + O_2(g) \longrightarrow CO_2(g) + H_2O(g)$

3.20 Balance the following equations, and indicate whether they are combination, decomposition, or combustion reactions:

(a) $C_3H_6(g) + O_2(g) \longrightarrow CO_2(g) + H_2O(g)$

(b) $NH_4NO_3(s) \longrightarrow N_2O(g) + H_2O(g)$

(c) $C_5H_6O(l) + O_2(g) \longrightarrow CO_2(g) + H_2O(g)$

(d) $N_2(g) + H_2(g) \longrightarrow NH_3(g)$

(e) $K_2O(s) + H_2O(l) \longrightarrow KOH(aq)$

Formula Weights

3.21 Determine the formula weights of each of the following compounds: (a) nitric acid, HNO_3; (b) $KMnO_4$; (c) $Ca_3(PO_4)_2$; (d) quartz, SiO_2; (e) gallium sulfide, (f) chromium(III) sulfate, (g) phosphorus trichloride.

3.22 Determine the formula weights of each of the following compounds: (a) nitrous oxide, N_2O, known as laughing

gas and used as an anesthetic in dentistry; (b) benzoic acid, $HC_7H_5O_2$, a substance used as a food preservative; (c) $Mg(OH)_2$, the active ingredient in milk of magnesia; (d) urea, $(NH_2)_2CO$, a compound used as a nitrogen fertilizer; (e) isopentyl acetate, $CH_3CO_2C_5H_{11}$, responsible for the odor of bananas.

3.23 Calculate the percentage by mass of oxygen in the following compounds: **(a)** morphine, $C_{17}H_{19}NO_3$; **(b)** codeine, $C_{18}H_{21}NO_3$; **(c)** cocaine, $C_{17}H_{21}NO_4$; **(d)** tetracycline, $C_{22}H_{24}N_2O_8$; **(e)** digitoxin, $C_{41}H_{64}O_{13}$; **(f)** vancomycin, $C_{66}H_{75}Cl_2N_9O_{24}$.

3.24 Calculate the percentage by mass of the indicated element in the following compounds: **(a)** carbon in acetylene, C_2H_2, a gas used in welding; **(b)** hydrogen in ascorbic acid, $HC_6H_7O_6$, also known as vitamin C; **(c)** hydrogen in ammonium sulfate, $(NH_4)_2SO_4$, a substance used as a nitrogen fertilizer; **(d)** platinum in $PtCl_2(NH_3)_2$, a chemotherapy agent called cisplatin; **(e)** oxygen in the female sex hormone estradiol, $C_{18}H_{24}O_2$; **(f)** carbon in capsaicin, $C_{18}H_{27}NO_3$, the compound that gives the hot taste to chili peppers.

3.25 Based on the following structural formulas, calculate the percentage of carbon by mass present in each compound:

(a) Benzaldehyde (almond fragrance)

(b) Vanillin (vanilla flavor)

(c) Isopentyl acetate (banana flavor)

3.26 Calculate the percentage of carbon by mass in each of the compounds represented by the following models:

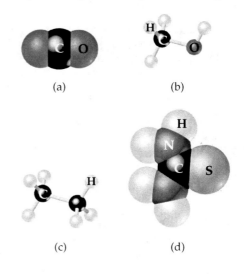

(a)   (b)

(c)   (d)

Avogadro's Number and the Mole

3.27 **(a)** What is Avogadro's number, and how is it related to the mole? **(b)** What is the relationship between the formula weight of a substance and its molar mass?

3.28 (a) What is the mass, in grams, of a mole of ^{12}C? **(b)** How many carbon atoms are present in a mole of ^{12}C?

3.29 Without doing any detailed calculations (but using a periodic table to give atomic weights), rank the following samples in order of increasing number of atoms: 0.50 mol H_2O, 23 g Na, 6.0×10^{23} N_2 molecules.

3.30 Without doing any detailed calculations (but using a periodic table to give atomic weights), rank the following samples in order of increasing number of atoms: 3.0×10^{23} molecules of H_2O_2, 2.0 mol CH_4, 32 g O_2.

3.31 What is the mass, in kilograms, of an Avogadro's number of people, if the average mass of a person is 160 lb? How does this compare with the mass of Earth, 5.98×10^{24} kg?

3.32 If Avogadro's number of pennies is divided equally among the 300 million men, women, and children in the United States, how many dollars would each receive? How does this compare with the gross domestic product of the United States, which was $13.5 trillion in 2006? (The GDP is the total market value of the nation's goods and services.)

3.33 Calculate the following quantities:
(a) mass, in grams, of 0.105 moles sucrose $(C_{12}H_{22}O_{11})$
(b) moles of $Zn(NO_3)_2$ in 143.50 g of this substance
(c) number of molecules in 1.0×10^{-6} mol CH_3CH_2OH
(d) number of N atoms in 0.410 mol NH_3

3.34 Calculate the following quantities
(a) mass, in grams, of 5.76×10^{-3} mol of CdS
(b) number of moles of NH_4Cl in 112.6 g of this substance
(c) number of molecules in 1.305×10^{-2} mol C_6H_6
(d) number of O atoms in 4.88×10^{-3} mol $Al(NO_3)_3$

3.35 **(a)** What is the mass, in grams, of 2.50×10^{-3} mol of ammonium phosphate?
(b) How many moles of chloride ions are in 0.2550 g of aluminum chloride?
(c) What is the mass, in grams, of 7.70×10^{20} molecules of caffeine, $C_8H_{10}N_4O_2$?
(d) What is the molar mass of cholesterol if 0.00105 mol weighs 0.406 g?

3.36 (a) What is the mass, in grams, of 0.0714 mol of iron(III) sulfate?
(b) How many moles of ammonium ions are in 8.776 g of ammonium carbonate?

(c) What is the mass, in grams, of 6.52×10^{21} molecules of aspirin, $C_9H_8O_4$?

(d) What is the molar mass of diazepam (Valium®) if 0.05570 mol weighs 15.86 g?

3.37 The molecular formula of allicin, the compound responsible for the characteristic smell of garlic, is $C_6H_{10}OS_2$. (a) What is the molar mass of allicin? (b) How many moles of allicin are present in 5.00 mg of this substance? (c) How many molecules of allicin are in 5.00 mg of this substance? (d) How many S atoms are present in 5.00 mg of allicin?

3.38 The molecular formula of aspartame, the artificial sweetener marketed as NutraSweet®, is $C_{14}H_{18}N_2O_5$. (a) What is the molar mass of aspartame? (b) How many moles of aspartame are present in 1.00 mg of aspartame? (c) How many molecules of aspartame are present in 1.00 mg of aspartame? (d) How many hydrogen atoms are present in 1.00 mg of aspartame?

3.39 A sample of glucose, $C_6H_{12}O_6$, contains 1.250×10^{21} carbon atoms. (a) How many atoms of hydrogen does it contain? (b) How many molecules of glucose does it contain? (c) How many moles of glucose does it contain? (d) What is the mass of this sample in grams?

3.40 A sample of the male sex hormone testosterone, $C_{19}H_{28}O_2$, contains 7.08×10^{20} hydrogen atoms. (a) How many atoms of carbon does it contain? (b) How many molecules of testosterone does it contain? (c) How many moles of testosterone does it contain? (d) What is the mass of this sample in grams?

3.41 The allowable concentration level of vinyl chloride, C_2H_3Cl, in the atmosphere in a chemical plant is 2.0×10^{-6} g/L. How many moles of vinyl chloride in each liter does this represent? How many molecules per liter?

3.42 At least 25 μg of tetrahydrocannabinol (THC), the active ingredient in marijuana, is required to produce intoxication. The molecular formula of THC is $C_{21}H_{30}O_2$. How many moles of THC does this 25 μg represent? How many molecules?

Empirical Formulas

3.43 Give the empirical formula of each of the following compounds if a sample contains (a) 0.0130 mol C, 0.0390 mol H, and 0.0065 mol O; (b) 11.66 g iron and 5.01 g oxygen; (c) 40.0% C, 6.7% H, and 53.3% O by mass.

3.44 Determine the empirical formula of each of the following compounds if a sample contains (a) 0.104 mol K, 0.052 mol C, and 0.156 mol O; (b) 5.28 g Sn and 3.37 g F; (c) 87.5% N and 12.5% H by mass.

3.45 Determine the empirical formulas of the compounds with the following compositions by mass:
(a) 10.4% C, 27.8% S, and 61.7% Cl
(b) 21.7% C, 9.6% O, and 68.7% F
(c) 32.79% Na, 13.02% Al, and 54.19% F

3.46 Determine the empirical formulas of the compounds with the following compositions by mass:
(a) 55.3% K, 14.6% P, and 30.1% O
(b) 24.5% Na, 14.9% Si, and 60.6% F
(c) 62.1% C, 5.21% H, 12.1% N, and 20.7% O

3.47 What is the molecular formula of each of the following compounds?
(a) empirical formula CH_2, molar mass = 84 g/mol
(b) empirical formula NH_2Cl, molar mass = 51.5 g/mol

3.48 What is the molecular formula of each of the following compounds?
(a) empirical formula HCO_2, molar mass = 90.0 g/mol
(b) empirical formula C_2H_4O, molar mass = 88 g/mol

3.49 Determine the empirical and molecular formulas of each of the following substances:
(a) Styrene, a compound substance used to make Styrofoam® cups and insulation, contains 92.3% C and 7.7% H by mass and has a molar mass of 104 g/mol.
(b) Caffeine, a stimulant found in coffee, contains 49.5% C, 5.15% H, 28.9% N, and 16.5% O by mass and has a molar mass of 195 g/mol.
(c) Monosodium glutamate (MSG), a flavor enhancer in certain foods, contains 35.51% C, 4.77% H, 37.85% O, 8.29% N, and 13.60% Na, and has a molar mass of 169 g/mol.

3.50 Determine the empirical and molecular formulas of each of the following substances:
(a) Ibuprofen, a headache remedy, contains 75.69% C, 8.80% H, and 15.51% O by mass, and has a molar mass of 206 g/mol.
(b) Cadaverine, a foul smelling substance produced by the action of bacteria on meat, contains 58.55% C, 13.81% H, and 27.40% N by mass; its molar mass is 102.2 g/mol.
(c) Epinephrine (adrenaline), a hormone secreted into the bloodstream in times of danger or stress, contains 59.0% C, 7.1% H, 26.2% O, and 7.7% N by mass; its MW is about 180 amu.

3.51 (a) Combustion analysis of toluene, a common organic solvent, gives 5.86 mg of CO_2 and 1.37 mg of H_2O. If the compound contains only carbon and hydrogen, what is its empirical formula? (b) Menthol, the substance we can smell in mentholated cough drops, is composed of C, H, and O. A 0.1005-g sample of menthol is combusted, producing 0.2829 g of CO_2 and 0.1159 g of H_2O. What is the empirical formula for menthol? If menthol has a molar mass of 156 g/mol, what is its molecular formula?

3.52 (a) The characteristic odor of pineapple is due to ethyl butyrate, a compound containing carbon, hydrogen, and oxygen. Combustion of 2.78 mg of ethyl butyrate produces 6.32 mg of CO_2 and 2.58 mg of H_2O. What is the empirical formula of the compound? (b) Nicotine, a component of tobacco, is composed of C, H, and N. A 5.250-mg sample of nicotine was combusted, producing 14.242 mg of CO_2 and 4.083 mg of H_2O. What is the empirical formula for nicotine? If nicotine has a molar mass of 160 ± 5 g/mol, what is its molecular formula?

3.53 Washing soda, a compound used to prepare hard water for washing laundry, is a hydrate, which means that a certain number of water molecules are included in the solid structure. Its formula can be written as $Na_2CO_3 \cdot xH_2O$, where x is the number of moles of H_2O per mole of Na_2CO_3. When a 2.558-g sample of washing soda is heated at 25 °C, all the water of hydration is lost, leaving 0.948 g of Na_2CO_3. What is the value of x?

Calculations Based on Chemical Equations

3.55 Why is it essential to use balanced chemical equations
CQ when determining the quantity of a product formed from a given quantity of a reactant?

3.56 What parts of balanced chemical equations give infor-
CQ mation about the relative numbers of moles of reactants and products involved in a reaction?

3.57 Hydrofluoric acid, HF(aq), cannot be stored in glass bottles because compounds called silicates in the glass are attacked by the HF(aq). Sodium silicate (Na_2SiO_3), for example, reacts as follows:

$$Na_2SiO_3(s) + 8\ HF(aq) \longrightarrow$$
$$H_2SiF_6(aq) + 2\ NaF(aq) + 3\ H_2O(l)$$

(a) How many moles of HF are needed to react with 0.300 mol of Na_2SiO_3?
(b) How many grams of NaF form when 0.500 mol of HF reacts with excess Na_2SiO_3?
(c) How many grams of Na_2SiO_3 can react with 0.800 g of HF?

3.58 The fermentation of glucose ($C_6H_{12}O_6$) produces ethyl alcohol (C_2H_5OH) and CO_2:

$$C_6H_{12}O_6(aq) \longrightarrow 2\ C_2H_5OH(aq) + 2\ CO_2(g)$$

(a) How many moles of CO_2 are produced when 0.400 mol of $C_6H_{12}O_6$ reacts in this fashion?
(b) How many grams of $C_6H_{12}O_6$ are needed to form 7.50 g of C_2H_5OH?
(c) How many grams of CO_2 form when 7.50 g of C_2H_5OH are produced?

3.59 Several brands of antacids use $Al(OH)_3$ to react with stomach acid, which contains primarily HCl:

$$Al(OH)_3(s) + HCl(aq) \longrightarrow AlCl_3(aq) + H_2O(l)$$

(a) Balance this equation.
(b) Calculate the number of grams of HCl that can react with 0.500 g of $Al(OH)_3$.
(c) Calculate the number of grams of $AlCl_3$ and the number of grams of H_2O formed when 0.500 g of $Al(OH)_3$ reacts.
(d) Show that your calculations in parts (b) and (c) are consistent with the law of conservation of mass.

3.60 An iron ore sample contains Fe_2O_3 together with other substances. Reaction of the ore with CO produces iron metal:

$$Fe_2O_3(s) + CO(g) \longrightarrow Fe(s) + CO_2(g)$$

(a) Balance this equation.
(b) Calculate the number of grams of CO that can react with 0.150 kg of Fe_2O_3.
(c) Calculate the number of grams of Fe and the number of grams of CO_2 formed when 0.150 kg of Fe_2O_3 reacts.

3.54 Epsom salts, a strong laxative used in veterinary medicine, is a hydrate, which means that a certain number of water molecules are included in the solid structure. The formula for Epsom salts can be written as $MgSO_4 \cdot xH_2O$, where x indicates the number of moles of H_2O per mole of $MgSO_4$. When 5.061 g of this hydrate is heated to 250 °C, all the water of hydration is lost, leaving 2.472 g of $MgSO_4$. What is the value of x?

(d) Show that your calculations in parts (b) and (c) are consistent with the law of conservation of mass.

3.61 Aluminum sulfide reacts with water to form aluminum hydroxide and hydrogen sulfide. (a) Write the balanced chemical equation for this reaction. (b) How many grams of aluminum hydroxide are obtained from 14.2 g of aluminum sulfide?

3.62 Calcium hydride reacts with water to form calcium hydroxide and hydrogen gas. (a) Write a balanced chemical equation for the reaction. (b) How many grams of calcium hydride are needed to form 8.500 g of hydrogen?

3.63 Automotive air bags inflate when sodium azide, NaN_3, rapidly decomposes to its component elements:

$$2\ NaN_3(s) \longrightarrow 2\ Na(s) + 3\ N_2(g)$$

(a) How many moles of N_2 are produced by the decomposition of 1.50 mol of NaN_3?
(b) How many grams of NaN_3 are required to form 10.0 g of nitrogen gas?
(c) How many grams of NaN_3 are required to produce 10.0 ft^3 of nitrogen gas, about the size of an automotive air bag, if the gas has a density of 1.25 g/L?

3.64 The complete combustion of octane, C_8H_{18}, the main component of gasoline, proceeds as follows:

$$2\ C_8H_{18}(l) + 25\ O_2(g) \longrightarrow 16\ CO_2(g) + 18\ H_2O(g)$$

(a) How many moles of O_2 are needed to burn 1.25 mol of C_8H_{18}?
(b) How many grams of O_2 are needed to burn 10.0 g of C_8H_{18}?
(c) Octane has a density of 0.692 g/mL at 20 °C. How many grams of O_2 are required to burn 1.00 gal of C_8H_{18}?

3.65 A piece of aluminum foil 1.00 cm square and 0.550 mm thick is allowed to react with bromine to form aluminum bromide as shown in the accompanying photo.

(a) How many moles of aluminum were used? (The density of aluminum is 2.699 g/cm^3.) **(b)** How many grams of aluminum bromide form, assuming the aluminum reacts completely?

3.66 Detonation of nitroglycerin proceeds as follows:

$$4\ C_3H_5N_3O_9(l) \longrightarrow$$
$$12\ CO_2(g) + 6\ N_2(g) + O_2(g) + 10\ H_2O(g)$$

Limiting Reactants; Theoretical Yields

3.67 **(a)** Define the terms *limiting reactant* and *excess reactant*.
CQ **(b)** Why are the amounts of products formed in a reaction determined only by the amount of the limiting reactant? **(c)** Why should you base your choice of what compound is the limiting reactant on its number of initial moles, not on its initial mass in grams?

3.68 **(a)** Define the terms *theoretical yield, actual yield*, and
CQ *percent yield*. **(b)** Why is the actual yield in a reaction almost always less than the theoretical yield? **(c)** Can a reaction ever have 110% actual yield?

3.69 A manufacturer of bicycles has 4815 wheels, 2305 frames, and 2255 handlebars. **(a)** How many bicycles can be manufactured using these parts? **(b)** How many parts of each kind are left over? **(c)** Which part limits the production of bicycles?

3.70 A bottling plant has 121,515 bottles with a capacity of 355 mL, 122,500 caps, and 40,875 L of beverage. **(a)** How many bottles can be filled and capped? **(b)** How much of each item is left over? **(c)** Which component limits the production?

3.71 Sodium hydroxide reacts with carbon dioxide as follows:

$$2\ NaOH(s) + CO_2(g) \longrightarrow Na_2CO_3(s) + H_2O(l)$$

Which reagent is the limiting reactant when 1.85 mol NaOH and 1.00 mol CO_2 are allowed to react? How many moles of Na_2CO_3 can be produced? How many moles of the excess reactant remain after the completion of the reaction?

3.72 Aluminum hydroxide reacts with sulfuric acid as follows:

$$2\ Al(OH)_3(s) + 3\ H_2SO_4(aq) \longrightarrow$$
$$Al_2(SO_4)_3(aq) + 6\ H_2O(l)$$

Which reagent is the limiting reactant when 0.500 mol $Al(OH)_3$ and 0.500 mol H_2SO_4 are allowed to react? How many moles of $Al_2(SO_4)_3$ can form under these conditions? How many moles of the excess reactant remain after the completion of the reaction?

3.73 The fizz produced when an Alka-Seltzer® tablet is dissolved in water is due to the reaction between sodium bicarbonate ($NaHCO_3$) and citric acid ($H_3C_6H_5O_7$):

$$3\ NaHCO_3(aq) + H_3C_6H_5O_7(aq) \longrightarrow$$
$$3\ CO_2(g) + 3\ H_2O(l) + Na_3C_6H_5O_7(aq)$$

In a certain experiment 1.00 g of sodium bicarbonate and 1.00 g of citric acid are allowed to react. **(a)** Which is the limiting reactant? **(b)** How many grams of carbon dioxide form? **(c)** How many grams of the excess reac-

(a) If a sample containing 2.00 mL of nitroglycerin (density = 1.592 g/mL) is detonated, how many total moles of gas are produced? **(b)** If each mole of gas occupies 55 L under the conditions of the explosion, how many liters of gas are produced? **(c)** How many grams of N_2 are produced in the detonation?

tant remain after the limiting reactant is completely consumed?

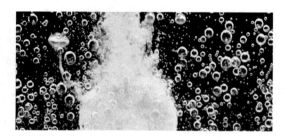

3.74 One of the steps in the commercial process for converting ammonia to nitric acid is the conversion of NH_3 to NO:

$$4\ NH_3(g) + 5\ O_2(g) \longrightarrow 4\ NO(g) + 6\ H_2O(g)$$

In a certain experiment, 1.50 g of NH_3 reacts with 2.75 g of O_2 **(a)** Which is the limiting reactant? **(b)** How many grams of NO and of H_2O form? **(c)** How many grams of the excess reactant remain after the limiting reactant is completely consumed? **(d)** Show that your calculations in parts (b) and (c) are consistent with the law of conservation of mass.

3.75 Solutions of sodium carbonate and silver nitrate react to form solid silver carbonate and a solution of sodium nitrate. A solution containing 3.50 g of sodium carbonate is mixed with one containing 5.00 g of silver nitrate. How many grams of sodium carbonate, silver nitrate, silver carbonate, and sodium nitrate are present after the reaction is complete?

3.76 Solutions of sulfuric acid and lead(II) acetate react to form solid lead(II) sulfate and a solution of acetic acid. If 7.50 g of sulfuric acid and 7.50 g of lead(II) acetate are mixed, calculate the number of grams of sulfuric acid, lead(II) acetate, lead(II) sulfate, and acetic acid present in the mixture after the reaction is complete.

3.77 When benzene (C_6H_6) reacts with bromine (Br_2), bromobenzene (C_6H_5Br) is obtained:

$$C_6H_6 + Br_2 \longrightarrow C_6H_5Br + HBr$$

(a) What is the theoretical yield of bromobenzene in this reaction when 30.0 g of benzene reacts with 65.0 g of bromine? **(b)** If the actual yield of bromobenzene was 42.3 g, what was the percentage yield?

3.78 When ethane (C_2H_6) reacts with chlorine (Cl_2), the main product is C_2H_5Cl; but other products containing Cl, such as $C_2H_4Cl_2$, are also obtained in small quantities. The formation of these other products reduces the yield of C_2H_5Cl. **(a)** Calculate the theoretical yield of C_2H_5Cl when 125 g of C_2H_6 reacts with 255 g of Cl_2, assuming that C_2H_6 and Cl_2 react only to form C_2H_5Cl and HCl. **(b)** Calculate the percent yield of C_2H_5Cl if the reaction produces 206 g of C_2H_5Cl.

3.79 Hydrogen sulfide is an impurity in natural gas that must be removed. One common removal method is called the Claus process, which relies on the reaction:

$$8\,H_2S(g) + 4\,O_2(g) \longrightarrow S_8(l) + 8\,H_2O(g)$$

Under optimal conditions the Claus process gives 98% yield of S_8 from H_2S. If you started with 30.0 grams of H_2S and 50.0 grams of O_2, how many grams of S_8 would be produced, assuming 98% yield?

3.80 When hydrogen sulfide gas is bubbled into a solution of sodium hydroxide, the reaction forms sodium sulfide and water. How many grams of sodium sulfide are formed if 1.50 g of hydrogen sulfide is bubbled into a solution containing 2.00 g of sodium hydroxide, assuming that the sodium sulfide is made in 92.0% yield?

ADDITIONAL EXERCISES

3.81 Write the balanced chemical equations for **(a)** the complete combustion of acetic acid (CH_3COOH), the main active ingredient in vinegar; **(b)** the decomposition of solid calcium hydroxide into solid calcium(II) oxide (lime) and water vapor; **(c)** the combination reaction between nickel metal and chlorine gas.

3.82 The effectiveness of nitrogen fertilizers depends on both their ability to deliver nitrogen to plants and the amount of nitrogen they can deliver. Four common nitrogen-containing fertilizers are ammonia, ammonium nitrate, ammonium sulfate, and urea [$(NH_2)_2CO$]. Rank these fertilizers in terms of the mass percentage nitrogen they contain.

3.83 **(a)** Diamond is a natural form of pure carbon. How many moles of carbon are in a 1.25-carat diamond (1 carat = 0.200 g)? How many atoms are in this diamond? **(b)** The molecular formula of acetylsalicylic acid (aspirin), one of the most common pain relievers, is $C_9H_8O_4$. How many moles of $C_9H_8O_4$ are in a 0.500-g tablet of aspirin? How many molecules of $C_9H_8O_4$ are in this tablet?

3.84 **(a)** One molecule of the antibiotic known as penicillin G has a mass of 5.342×10^{-21} g. What is the molar mass of penicillin G? **(b)** Hemoglobin, the oxygen-carrying protein in red blood cells, has four iron atoms per molecule and contains 0.340% iron by mass. Calculate the molar mass of hemoglobin.

3.85 Very small crystals composed of 1000 to 100,000 atoms, called quantum dots, are being investigated for use in electronic devices.
   (a) A quantum dot was made of solid silicon in the shape of a sphere, with a diameter of 4 nm. Calculate the mass of the quantum dot, using the density of silicon (2.3 g/cm^3).
   (b) How many silicon atoms are in the quantum dot?
   (c) The density of germanium is 5.325 g/cm^3. If you made a 4 nm quantum dot of germanium, how many Ge atoms would it contain? Assume the dot is spherical.

3.86 Serotonin is a compound that conducts nerve impulses in the brain. It contains 68.2 mass percent C, 6.86 mass percent H, 15.9 mass percent N, and 9.08 mass percent O. Its molar mass is 176 g/mol. Determine its molecular formula.

3.87 The koala dines exclusively on eucalyptus leaves. Its digestive system detoxifies the eucalyptus oil, a poison to other animals. The chief constituent in eucalyptus oil is a substance called eucalyptol, which contains 77.87% C,

11.76% H, and the remainder O. **(a)** What is the empirical formula for this substance? **(b)** A mass spectrum of eucalyptol shows a peak at about 154 amu. What is the molecular formula of the substance?

3.88 Vanillin, the dominant flavoring in vanilla, contains C, H, and O. When 1.05 g of this substance is completely combusted, 2.43 g of CO_2 and 0.50 g of H_2O are produced. What is the empirical formula of vanillin?

[3.89] An organic compound was found to contain only C, H, and Cl. When a 1.50-g sample of the compound was completely combusted in air, 3.52 g of CO_2 was formed. In a separate experiment the chlorine in a 1.00-g sample of the compound was converted to 1.27 g of AgCl. Determine the empirical formula of the compound.

[3.90] An oxybromate compound, $KBrO_x$, where x is unknown, is analyzed and found to contain 52.92% Br. What is the value of x?

[3.91] An element X forms an iodide (XI_3) and a chloride (XCl_3). The iodide is quantitatively converted to the chloride when it is heated in a stream of chlorine:

$$2\,XI_3 + 3\,Cl_2 \longrightarrow 2\,XCl_3 + 3\,I_2$$

If 0.5000 g of XI_3 is treated, 0.2360 g of XCl_3 is obtained. **(a)** Calculate the atomic weight of the element X. **(b)** Identify the element X.

3.92 If 1.5 mol of each of the following compounds is completely combusted in oxygen, which one will produce the largest number of moles of H_2O? Which will produce the least? Explain. C_2H_5OH, C_3H_8, $CH_3CH_2COCH_3$.

3.93 A method used by the U.S. Environmental Protection Agency (EPA) for determining the concentration of ozone in air is to pass the air sample through a "bubbler" containing sodium iodide, which removes the ozone according to the following equation:

$$O_3(g) + 2\,NaI(aq) + H_2O(l) \longrightarrow$$
$$O_2(g) + I_2(s) + 2\,NaOH(aq)$$

(a) How many moles of sodium iodide are needed to remove 5.95×10^{-6} mol of O_3? **(b)** How many grams of sodium iodide are needed to remove 1.3 mg of O_3?

3.94 A chemical plant uses electrical energy to decompose aqueous solutions of NaCl to give Cl_2, H_2, and NaOH:

$$2\,NaCl(aq) + 2\,H_2O(l) \longrightarrow$$
$$2\,NaOH(aq) + H_2(g) + Cl_2(g)$$

If the plant produces 1.5×10^6 kg (1500 metric tons) of Cl_2 daily, estimate the quantities of H_2 and NaOH produced.

3.95 The fat stored in the hump of a camel is a source of both energy and water. Calculate the mass of H_2O produced by metabolism of 1.0 kg of fat, assuming the fat consists entirely of tristearin ($C_{57}H_{110}O_6$), a typical animal fat, and assuming that during metabolism, tristearin reacts with O_2 to form only CO_2 and H_2O.

[3.96] When hydrocarbons are burned in a limited amount of air, both CO and CO_2 form. When 0.450 g of a particular hydrocarbon was burned in air, 0.467 g of CO, 0.733 g of CO_2, and 0.450 g of H_2O were formed. **(a)** What is the empirical formula of the compound? **(b)** How many grams of O_2 were used in the reaction? **(c)** How many grams would have been required for complete combustion?

3.97 A mixture of $N_2(g)$ and $H_2(g)$ reacts in a closed container to form ammonia, $NH_3(g)$. The reaction ceases before either reactant has been totally consumed. At this stage 3.0 mol N_2, 3.0 mol H_2, and 3.0 mol NH_3 are present. How many moles of N_2 and H_2 were present originally?

[3.98] A mixture containing $KClO_3$, K_2CO_3, $KHCO_3$, and KCl was heated, producing CO_2, O_2, and H_2O gases according to the following equations:

$$2\ KClO_3(s) \longrightarrow 2\ KCl(s) + 3\ O_2(g)$$
$$2\ KHCO_3(s) \longrightarrow K_2O(s) + H_2O(g) + 2\ CO_2(g)$$
$$K_2CO_3(s) \longrightarrow K_2O(s) + CO_2(g)$$

The KCl does not react under the conditions of the reaction. If 100.0 g of the mixture produces 1.80 g of H_2O, 13.20 g of CO_2, and 4.00 g of O_2, what was the composition of the original mixture? (Assume complete decomposition of the mixture.)

3.99 When a mixture of 10.0 g of acetylene (C_2H_2) and 10.0 g of oxygen (O_2) is ignited, the resultant combustion reaction produces CO_2 and H_2O. **(a)** Write the balanced chemical equation for this reaction. **(b)** Which is the limiting reactant? **(c)** How many grams of C_2H_2, O_2, CO_2, and H_2O are present after the reaction is complete?

3.100 Aspirin ($C_9H_8O_4$) is produced from salicylic acid ($C_7H_6O_3$) and acetic anhydride ($C_4H_6O_3$):

$$C_7H_6O_3 + C_4H_6O_3 \longrightarrow C_9H_8O_4 + HC_2H_3O_2$$

(a) How much salicylic acid is required to produce 1.5×10^2 kg of aspirin, assuming that all of the salicylic acid is converted to aspirin? **(b)** How much salicylic acid would be required if only 80% of the salicylic acid is converted to aspirin? **(c)** What is the theoretical yield of aspirin if 185 kg of salicylic acid is allowed to react with 125 kg of acetic anhydride? **(d)** If the situation described in part (c) produces 182 kg of aspirin, what is the percentage yield?

INTEGRATIVE EXERCISES

(These exercises require skills from earlier chapters as well as skills from the present chapter.)

3.101 Consider a sample of calcium carbonate in the form of a cube measuring 2.005 in. on each edge. If the sample has a density of 2.71 g/cm^3, how many oxygen atoms does it contain?

3.102 **(a)** You are given a cube of silver metal that measures 1.000 cm on each edge. The density of silver is 10.5 g/cm^3. How many atoms are in this cube? **(b)** Because atoms are spherical, they cannot occupy all of the space of the cube. The silver atoms pack in the solid in such a way that 74% of the volume of the solid is actually filled with the silver atoms. Calculate the volume of a single silver atom. **(c)** Using the volume of a silver atom and the formula for the volume of a sphere, calculate the radius in angstroms of a silver atom.

3.103 **(a)** If an automobile travels 225 mi with a gas mileage of 20.5 mi/gal, how many kilograms of CO_2 are produced? Assume that the gasoline is composed of octane, $C_8H_{18}(l)$, whose density is 0.69 g/mL. **(b)** Repeat the calculation for a truck that has a gas mileage of 5 mi/gal.

3.104 In 1865 a chemist reported that he had reacted a weighed amount of pure silver with nitric acid and had recovered all the silver as pure silver nitrate. The mass ratio of silver to silver nitrate was found to be 0.634985. Using only this ratio and the presently accepted values for the atomic weights of silver and oxygen, calculate the atomic weight of nitrogen. Compare this calculated atomic weight with the currently accepted value.

3.105 A particular coal contains 2.5% sulfur by mass. When this coal is burned at a power plant, the sulfur is con-

verted into sulfur dioxide gas, which is a pollutant. To reduce sulfur dioxide emissions, calcium oxide (lime) is used. The sulfur dioxide reacts with calcium oxide to form solid calcium sulfite. **(a)** Write the balanced chemical equation for the reaction. **(b)** If the coal is burned in a power plant that uses 2000 tons of coal per day, what mass of calcium oxide is required daily to eliminate the sulfur dioxide? **(c)** How many grams of calcium sulfite are produced daily by this power plant?

3.106 Copper is an excellent electrical conductor widely used in making electric circuits. In producing a printed circuit board for the electronics industry, a layer of copper is laminated on a plastic board. A circuit pattern is then printed on the board using a chemically resistant polymer. The board is then exposed to a chemical bath that reacts with the exposed copper, leaving the desired copper circuit, which has been protected by the overlaying polymer. Finally, a solvent removes the polymer. One reaction used to remove the exposed copper from the circuit board is

$$Cu(s) + Cu(NH_3)_4Cl_2(aq) + 4\ NH_3(aq) \longrightarrow$$
$$2\ Cu(NH_3)_4Cl(aq)$$

A plant needs to produce 5000 circuit boards, each with a surface area measuring 2.0 in. $\times$ 3.0 in. The boards are covered with a 0.65-mm layer of copper. In subsequent processing, 85% of the copper is removed. Copper has a density of 8.96 g/cm^3. Calculate the masses of $Cu(NH_3)_4Cl_2$ and NH_3 needed to produce the circuit boards, assuming that the reaction used gives a 97% yield.

3.107 Hydrogen cyanide, HCN, is a poisonous gas. The lethal dose is approximately 300 mg HCN per kilogram of air when inhaled. **(a)** Calculate the amount of HCN that gives the lethal dose in a small laboratory room measuring 12 × 15 × 8.0 ft. The density of air at 26 °C is 0.00118 g/cm^3. **(b)** If the HCN is formed by reaction of NaCN with an acid such as H_2SO_4, what mass of NaCN gives the lethal dose in the room?

$$2\,NaCN(s) + H_2SO_4(aq) \longrightarrow Na_2SO_4(aq) + 2\,HCN(g)$$

(c) HCN forms when synthetic fibers containing Orlon® or Acrilan® burn. Acrilan® has an empirical formula of CH_2CHCN, so HCN is 50.9% of the formula by mass. A rug measures 12 × 15 ft and contains 30 oz of Acrilan® fibers per square yard of carpet. If the rug burns, will a lethal dose of HCN be generated in the room? Assume that the yield of HCN from the fibers is 20% and that the carpet is 50% consumed.

3.108 The source of oxygen that drives the internal combustion engine in an automobile is air. Air is a mixture of gases, which are principally N_2 (~79%) and O_2 (~20%). In the cylinder of an automobile engine, nitrogen can react with oxygen to produce nitric oxide gas, NO. As NO is emitted from the tailpipe of the car, it can react with more oxygen to produce nitrogen dioxide gas. **(a)** Write balanced chemical equations for both reactions. **(b)** Both nitric oxide and nitrogen dioxide are pollutants that can lead to acid rain and global warming; collectively, they are called "NO$_x$" gases. In 2004, the United States emitted an estimated 19 million tons of nitrogen dioxide into the atmosphere. How many grams of nitrogen dioxide is this? **(c)** The production of NO$_x$ gases is an unwanted side reaction of the main engine combustion process that turns octane, C_8H_{18}, into CO_2 and water. If 85% of the oxygen in an engine is used to combust octane, and the remainder used to produce nitrogen dioxide, calculate how many grams of nitrogen dioxide would be produced during the combustion of 500 grams of octane.

AQUEOUS REACTIONS AND SOLUTION STOICHIOMETRY

A VIEW OF THE PACIFIC OCEAN along the California coastline.

118

THE WATERS OF THE PACIFIC OCEAN, seen in this chapter-opening photograph of the California coast, are part of the World Ocean that covers almost two-thirds of our planet. Water has been the key to much of Earth's evolutionary history. Life itself almost certainly originated in water, and the

need for water by all forms of life has helped determine diverse biological structures. Your own body is about 60% water by mass. We will see repeatedly throughout this text that water possesses many unusual properties essential to supporting life on Earth.

The waters of the World Ocean may not appear to be any different from those of Lake Tahoe or the water that flows from your kitchen faucet, but a taste of seawater is all it takes to demonstrate that there is an important difference. Water has an exceptional ability to dissolve a wide variety of substances. Water on Earth—whether it is drinking water from the tap, water from a clear mountain stream, or seawater—invariably contains a variety of dissolved substances. A solution in which water is the dissolving medium is called an **aqueous solution**. Seawater is different from what we call "freshwater" because it has a much higher total concentration of dissolved ionic substances.

Water is the medium for most of the chemical reactions that take place within us and around us. Nutrients dissolved in blood are carried to our cells, where they enter into reactions that help keep us alive. Automobile parts rust

119

▲ Figure 4.1 **Limestone cave.** When CO_2 dissolves in water, the resulting solution is slightly acidic. Limestone caves are formed by the dissolving action of this acidic solution acting on $CaCO_3$ in the limestone.

when they come into frequent contact with aqueous solutions that contain various dissolved substances. Spectacular limestone caves (Figure 4.1 ◄) are formed by the dissolving action of underground water containing carbon dioxide, $CO_2(aq)$:

$$CaCO_3(s) + H_2O(l) + CO_2(aq) \longrightarrow Ca(HCO_3)_2(aq) \qquad [4.1]$$

In Chapter 3 we saw a few simple types of chemical reactions and their descriptions. In this chapter we continue to examine chemical reactions by focusing on aqueous solutions. A great deal of important chemistry occurs in aqueous solutions, so we need to learn the vocabulary and concepts used to describe and understand this chemistry. In addition, we will extend the concepts of stoichiometry that we learned in Chapter 3 by considering how solution concentrations are expressed and used.

4.1 GENERAL PROPERTIES OF AQUEOUS SOLUTIONS

Recall that a *solution* is a homogeneous mixture of two or more substances. (Section 1.2) The substance present in the greatest quantity is usually called the **solvent**. The other substances in the solution are called the **solutes**; they are said to be dissolved in the solvent. When a small amount of sodium chloride (NaCl) is dissolved in a large quantity of water, for example, the water is the solvent and the sodium chloride is the solute.

Electrolytic Properties

Imagine preparing two aqueous solutions—one by dissolving a teaspoon of table salt (sodium chloride) in a cup of water and the other by dissolving a teaspoon of table sugar (sucrose) in a cup of water. Both solutions are clear and colorless. How do they differ? One way, which might not be immediately obvious, is in their electrical conductivity: The salt solution is a good conductor of electricity; the sugar solution is not.

Whether a solution conducts electricity can be determined by using a device such as that shown in Figure 4.2 ▶. To light the bulb, an electric current must flow between the two electrodes that are immersed in the solution. Although water itself is a poor conductor of electricity, the presence of ions causes aqueous solutions to become good conductors. Ions carry electrical charge from one electrode to the other, completing the electrical circuit. Thus, the conductivity of NaCl solutions indicates the presence of ions in the solution. The lack of conductivity of sucrose solutions indicates the absence of ions. When NaCl dissolves in water, the solution contains Na^+ and Cl^- ions, each surrounded by water molecules. When sucrose ($C_{12}H_{22}O_{11}$) dissolves in water, the solution contains only neutral sucrose molecules surrounded by water molecules.

A substance (such as NaCl) whose aqueous solutions contain ions is called an **electrolyte**. A substance (such as $C_{12}H_{22}O_{11}$) that does not form ions in solution is called a **nonelectrolyte**. The difference between NaCl and $C_{12}H_{22}O_{11}$ arises largely because NaCl is ionic, whereas $C_{12}H_{22}O_{11}$ is molecular.

Ionic Compounds in Water

Recall from Section 2.7 and especially Figure 2.23 that solid NaCl consists of an orderly arrangement of Na^+ and Cl^- ions. When NaCl dissolves in water, each ion separates from the solid structure and disperses throughout the solution, as shown in Figure 4.3(a) ▶. The ionic solid *dissociates* into its component ions as it dissolves.

ELECTROLYTIC PROPERTIES

One way to differentiate two aqueous solutions is to employ a device that measures their electrical conductivities. The ability of a solution to conduct electricity depends on the number of ions it contains. An electrolyte solution contains ions that serve as charge carriers, causing the bulb to light.

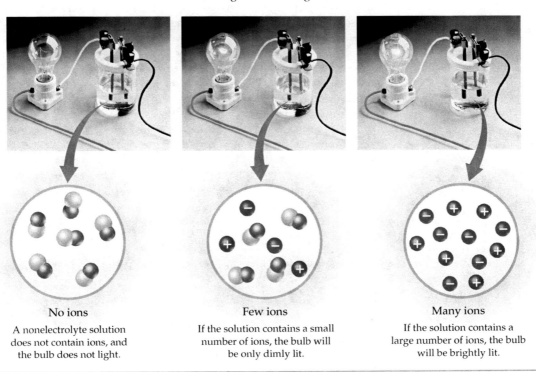

No ions

A nonelectrolyte solution does not contain ions, and the bulb does not light.

Few ions

If the solution contains a small number of ions, the bulb will be only dimly lit.

Many ions

If the solution contains a large number of ions, the bulb will be brightly lit.

▲ Figure 4.2 **Measuring ion concentrations using conductivity.**

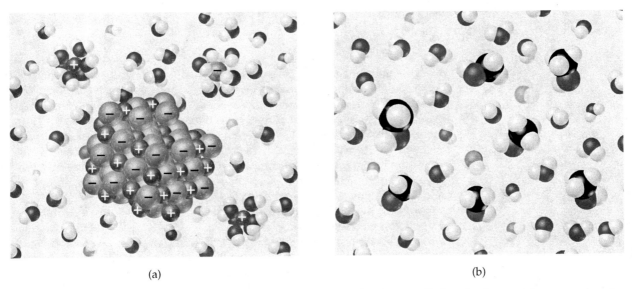

(a)   (b)

▲ Figure 4.3 **Dissolution in water.** (a) When an ionic compound dissolves in water, H_2O molecules separate, surround, and disperse the ions into the liquid. (b) Methanol, CH_3OH, a molecular compound, dissolves without forming ions. The methanol molecules contain black spheres, which represent carbon atoms. In both parts (a) and (b) the water molecules have been moved apart so that the solute particles can be seen more clearly.

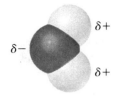

Water is a very effective solvent for ionic compounds. Although water is an electrically neutral molecule, one end of the molecule (the O atom) is rich in electrons and has a partial negative charge, denoted by $\delta-$. The other end (the H atoms) has a partial positive charge, denoted by $\delta+$ as shown in the margin. Positive ions (cations) are attracted by the negative end of H_2O, and negative ions (anions) are attracted by the positive end.

As an ionic compound dissolves, the ions become surrounded by H_2O molecules, as shown in Figure 4.3(a). The ions are said to be solvated. We denote these ions in chemical equations by writing them as $Na^+(aq)$ and $Cl^-(aq)$, where "aq" is an abbreviation for "aqueous." (Section 3.1) The **solvation** process helps stabilize the ions in solution and prevents cations and anions from recombining. Furthermore, because the ions and their shells of surrounding water molecules are free to move about, the ions become dispersed uniformly throughout the solution.

We can usually predict the nature of the ions present in a solution of an ionic compound from the chemical name of the substance. Sodium sulfate (Na_2SO_4), for example, dissociates into sodium ions (Na^+) and sulfate ions (SO_4^{2-}). You must remember the formulas and charges of common ions (Tables 2.4 and 2.5) to understand the forms in which ionic compounds exist in aqueous solution.

GIVE IT SOME THOUGHT

What dissolved species are present in a solution of **(a)** KCN, **(b)** $NaClO_4$?

Molecular Compounds in Water

When a molecular compound dissolves in water, the solution usually consists of intact molecules dispersed throughout the solution. Consequently, most molecular compounds are nonelectrolytes. As we have seen, table sugar (sucrose) is an example of a nonelectrolyte. As another example, a solution of methanol (CH_3OH) in water consists entirely of CH_3OH molecules dispersed throughout the water [Figure 4.3(b)].

A few molecular substances, however, have aqueous solutions that contain ions. Acids are the most important of these solutions. For example, when HCl(g) dissolves in water to form hydrochloric acid, HCl(aq), it *ionizes*; that is, it dissociates into $H^+(aq)$ and $Cl^-(aq)$ ions.

Strong and Weak Electrolytes

Two categories of electrolytes—strong and weak—differ in the extent to which they conduct electricity. **Strong electrolytes** are those solutes that exist in solution completely or nearly completely as ions. Essentially all soluble ionic compounds (such as NaCl) and a few molecular compounds (such as HCl) are strong electrolytes. **Weak electrolytes** are those solutes that exist in solution mostly in the form of molecules with only a small fraction in the form of ions. For example, in a solution of acetic acid (CH_3COOH) most of the solute is present as $CH_3COOH(aq)$ molecules. Only a small fraction (about 1%) of the CH_3COOH is present as $H^+(aq)$ and $CH_3COO^-(aq)$ ions.*

We must be careful not to confuse the extent to which an electrolyte dissolves with whether it is strong or weak. For example, CH_3COOH is extremely soluble in water but is a weak electrolyte. $Ba(OH)_2$, on the other hand, is not very soluble, but the amount of the substance that does dissolve dissociates almost completely. Thus, $Ba(OH)_2$ is a strong electrolyte.

*The chemical formula of acetic acid is sometimes written as $HC_2H_3O_2$ with the acidic H written in front of the chemical formula, so the formula looks like that of other common acids such as HCl. The formula CH_3COOH conforms to the molecular structure of acetic acid, with the acidic H on the O atom at the end of the formula.

When a weak electrolyte such as acetic acid ionizes in solution, we write the reaction in the following manner:

$$CH_3COOH(aq) \rightleftharpoons CH_3COO^-(aq) + H^+(aq) \qquad [4.2]$$

The half-arrows in both directions mean that the reaction is significant in both directions. At any given moment some CH_3COOH molecules are ionizing to form H^+ and CH_3COO^- ions. At the same time, H^+ and CH_3COO^- ions are recombining to form CH_3COOH. The balance between these opposing processes determines the relative numbers of ions and neutral molecules. This balance produces a state of **chemical equilibrium** in which the relative numbers of each type of ion or molecule in the reaction are constant over time. This equilibrium condition varies from one weak electrolyte to another. Chemical equilibria are extremely important. We will devote Chapters 15–17 to examining them in detail.

Chemists use half-arrows in both directions to represent the ionization of weak electrolytes and a single arrow to represent the ionization of strong electrolytes. Because HCl is a strong electrolyte, we write the equation for the ionization of HCl as follows:

$$HCl(aq) \longrightarrow H^+(aq) + Cl^-(aq) \qquad [4.3]$$

The absence of a reverse arrow indicates that the H^+ and Cl^- ions have no tendency to recombine in water to form HCl molecules.

In the following sections we will look more closely at how we can use the composition of a compound to predict whether it is a strong electrolyte, weak electrolyte, or nonelectrolyte. For the moment, you need only to remember that *soluble ionic compounds are strong electrolytes*. We identify ionic compounds as those composed of metals and nonmetals—such as NaCl, $FeSO_4$, and $Al(NO_3)_3$—or compounds containing the ammonium ion, NH_4^+—such as NH_4Br and $(NH_4)_2CO_3$.

GIVE IT SOME THOUGHT

Which solute will cause the lightbulb in the experiment shown in Figure 4.2 to glow more brightly, CH_3OH or $MgBr_2$?

■■ SAMPLE EXERCISE 4.1 | **Relating Relative Numbers of Anions and Cations to Chemical Formulas**

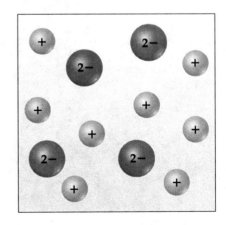

The diagram on the right represents an aqueous solution of one of the following compounds: $MgCl_2$, KCl, or K_2SO_4. Which solution does the drawing best represent?

SOLUTION

Analyze: We are asked to associate the charged spheres in the diagram with ions present in a solution of an ionic substance.

Plan: We examine the ionic substances given in the problem to determine the relative numbers and charges of the ions that each contains. We then correlate these charged ionic species with the ones shown in the diagram.

Solve: The diagram shows twice as many cations as anions, consistent with the formulation K_2SO_4.

Check: Notice that the total net charge in the diagram is zero, as it must be if it is to represent an ionic substance.

■■ PRACTICE EXERCISE

If you were to draw diagrams (such as that shown on the right) representing aqueous solutions of each of the following ionic compounds, how many anions would you show if the diagram contained six cations? **(a)** $NiSO_4$, **(b)** $Ca(NO_3)_2$, **(c)** Na_3PO_4, **(d)** $Al_2(SO_4)_3$
Answers: **(a)** 6, **(b)** 12, **(c)** 2, **(d)** 9

4.2 PRECIPITATION REACTIONS

Figure 4.4 ▼ shows two clear solutions being mixed. One solution contains lead nitrate, $Pb(NO_3)_2$, and the other contains potassium iodide (KI). The reaction between these two solutes produces an insoluble yellow product. Reactions that result in the formation of an insoluble product are called **precipitation reactions**. A **precipitate** is an insoluble solid formed by a reaction in solution. In Figure 4.4 the precipitate is lead iodide (PbI_2), a compound that has a very low solubility in water:

$$Pb(NO_3)_2(aq) + 2\ KI(aq) \longrightarrow PbI_2(s) + 2\ KNO_3(aq) \qquad [4.4]$$

The other product of this reaction, potassium nitrate (KNO_3), remains in solution.

Precipitation reactions occur when certain pairs of oppositely charged ions attract each other so strongly that they form an insoluble ionic solid. To predict whether certain combinations of ions form insoluble compounds, we must consider some guidelines concerning the solubilities of common ionic compounds.

Solubility Guidelines for Ionic Compounds

The **solubility** of a substance at a given temperature is the amount of the substance that can be dissolved in a given quantity of solvent at the given temperature.

▼ Figure 4.4 **A precipitation reaction.**

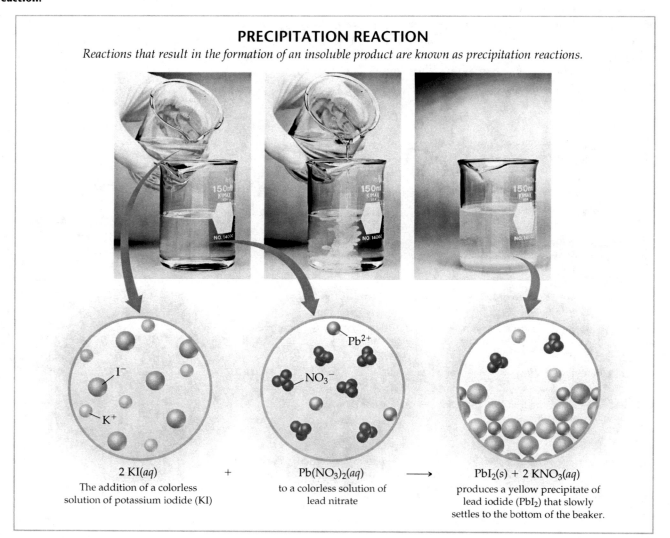

PRECIPITATION REACTION

Reactions that result in the formation of an insoluble product are known as precipitation reactions.

2 KI(aq)   +   Pb(NO₃)₂(aq)   ⟶   PbI₂(s) + 2 KNO₃(aq)

The addition of a colorless   to a colorless solution of   produces a yellow precipitate of
solution of potassium iodide (KI)   lead nitrate   lead iodide (PbI₂) that slowly
                                                                 settles to the bottom of the beaker.

TABLE 4.1 ■ Solubility Guidelines for Common Ionic Compounds in Water		
Soluble Ionic Compounds		**Important Exceptions**
Compounds containing	NO_3^-	None
	CH_3COO^-	None
	Cl^-	Compounds of Ag^+, Hg_2^{2+}, and Pb^{2+}
	Br^-	Compounds of Ag^+, Hg_2^{2+}, and Pb^{2+}
	I^-	Compounds of Ag^+, Hg_2^{2+}, and Pb^{2+}
	SO_4^{2-}	Compounds of Sr^{2+}, Ba^{2+}, Hg_2^{2+}, and Pb^{2+}
Insoluble Ionic Compounds		**Important Exceptions**
Compounds containing	S^{2-}	Compounds of NH_4^+, the alkali metal cations, and Ca^{2+}, Sr^{2+}, and Ba^{2+}
	CO_3^{2-}	Compounds of NH_4^+ and the alkali metal cations
	PO_4^{3-}	Compounds of NH_4^+ and the alkali metal cations
	OH^-	Compounds of the alkali metal cations, and NH_4^+, Ca^{2+}, Sr^{2+}, and Ba^{2+}

For instance, only 1.2×10^{-3} mol of PbI_2 dissolves in a liter of water at 25 °C. In our discussions, any substance with a solubility less than 0.01 mol/L will be referred to as *insoluble*. In those cases the attraction between the oppositely charged ions in the solid is too great for the water molecules to separate the ions to any significant extent; the substance remains largely undissolved.

Unfortunately, there are no rules based on simple physical properties such as ionic charge to guide us in predicting whether a particular ionic compound will be soluble. Experimental observations, however, have led to guidelines for predicting solubility for ionic compounds. For example, experiments show that all common ionic compounds that contain the nitrate anion, NO_3^-, are soluble in water. Table 4.1▲ summarizes the solubility guidelines for common ionic compounds. The table is organized according to the anion in the compound, but it also reveals many important facts about cations. Note that *all common ionic compounds of the alkali metal ions (group 1A of the periodic table) and of the ammonium ion* (NH_4^+) *are soluble in water.*

■■ SAMPLE EXERCISE 4.2 | Using Solubility Rules

Classify the following ionic compounds as soluble or insoluble in water: **(a)** sodium carbonate (Na_2CO_3), **(b)** lead sulfate ($PbSO_4$).

SOLUTION

Analyze: We are given the names and formulas of two ionic compounds and asked to predict whether they are soluble or insoluble in water.

Plan: We can use Table 4.1 to answer the question. Thus, we need to focus on the anion in each compound because the table is organized by anions.

Solve:
(a) According to Table 4.1, most carbonates are insoluble. But carbonates of the alkali metal cations (such as sodium ion) are an exception to this rule and are soluble. Thus, Na_2CO_3 is soluble in water.
(b) Table 4.1 indicates that although most sulfates are water soluble, the sulfate of Pb^{2+} is an exception. Thus, $PbSO_4$ is insoluble in water.

■■ PRACTICE EXERCISE

Classify the following compounds as soluble or insoluble in water: **(a)** cobalt(II) hydroxide, **(b)** barium nitrate, **(c)** ammonium phosphate.
Answers: **(a)** insoluble, **(b)** soluble, **(c)** soluble

To predict whether a precipitate forms when we mix aqueous solutions of two strong electrolytes, we must (1) note the ions present in the reactants, (2) consider the possible combinations of the cations and anions, and (3) use Table 4.1 to determine if any of these combinations is insoluble. For example, will a precipitate form when solutions of $Mg(NO_3)_2$ and NaOH are mixed? Both $Mg(NO_3)_2$ and NaOH are soluble ionic compounds and strong electrolytes. Mixing $Mg(NO_3)_2(aq)$ and NaOH(aq) first produces a solution containing Mg^{2+}, NO_3^-, Na^+, and OH^- ions. Will either of the cations interact with either of the anions to form an insoluble compound? In addition to the reactants, the other possible interactions are Mg^{2+} with OH^- and Na^+ with NO_3^-. From Table 4.1 we see that hydroxides are generally insoluble. Because Mg^{2+} is not an exception, $Mg(OH)_2$ is insoluble and will thus form a precipitate. $NaNO_3$, however, is soluble, so Na^+ and NO_3^- will remain in solution. The balanced equation for the precipitation reaction is

$$Mg(NO_3)_2(aq) + 2\,NaOH(aq) \longrightarrow Mg(OH)_2(s) + 2\,NaNO_3(aq) \quad [4.5]$$

Exchange (Metathesis) Reactions

Notice in Equation 4.5 that the cations in the two reactants exchange anions—Mg^{2+} ends up with OH^-, and Na^+ ends up with NO_3^-. The chemical formulas of the products are based on the charges of the ions—two OH^- ions are needed to give a neutral compound with Mg^{2+}, and one NO_3^- ion is needed to give a neutral compound with Na^+. ⟨⟨ (Section 2.7) The equation can be balanced only after the chemical formulas of the products have been determined.

Reactions in which positive ions and negative ions appear to exchange partners conform to the following general equation:

$$AX + BY \longrightarrow AY + BX \quad [4.6]$$

Example: $AgNO_3(aq) + KCl(aq) \longrightarrow AgCl(s) + KNO_3(aq)$

Such reactions are called **exchange reactions**, or **metathesis reactions** (meh-TATH-eh-sis, which is the Greek word for "to transpose"). Precipitation reactions conform to this pattern, as do many acid–base reactions, as we will see in Section 4.3.

To complete and balance a metathesis equation, we follow these steps:

1. Use the chemical formulas of the reactants to determine the ions that are present.
2. Write the chemical formulas of the products by combining the cation from one reactant with the anion of the other. (Use the charges of the ions to determine the subscripts in the chemical formulas.)
3. Finally, balance the equation.

■ **SAMPLE EXERCISE 4.3** | **Predicting a Metathesis Reaction**

(a) Predict the identity of the precipitate that forms when solutions of $BaCl_2$ and K_2SO_4 are mixed.
(b) Write the balanced chemical equation for the reaction.

SOLUTION

Analyze: We are given two ionic reactants and asked to predict the insoluble product that they form.

Plan: We need to write down the ions present in the reactants and to exchange the anions between the two cations. Once we have written the chemical formulas for these products, we can use Table 4.1 to determine which is insoluble in water. Knowing the products also allows us to write the equation for the reaction.

Solve:
(a) The reactants contain Ba^{2+}, Cl^-, K^+, and SO_4^{2-} ions. If we exchange the anions, we will have $BaSO_4$ and KCl. According to Table 4.1, most compounds of SO_4^{2-} are soluble but those of Ba^{2+} are not. Thus, $BaSO_4$ is insoluble and will precipitate from solution. KCl, on the other hand, is soluble.

(b) From part (a) we know the chemical formulas of the products, $BaSO_4$ and KCl. The balanced equation with phase labels shown is

$$BaCl_2(aq) + K_2SO_4(aq) \longrightarrow BaSO_4(s) + 2\ KCl(aq)$$

■ PRACTICE EXERCISE

(a) What compound precipitates when solutions of $Fe_2(SO_4)_3$ and LiOH are mixed? **(b)** Write a balanced equation for the reaction. **(c)** Will a precipitate form when solutions of $Ba(NO_3)_2$ and KOH are mixed?
Answers: **(a)** $Fe(OH)_3$; **(b)** $Fe_2(SO_4)_3(aq) + 6\ LiOH(aq) \longrightarrow$
$2\ Fe(OH)_3(s) + 3\ Li_2SO_4(aq)$; **(c)** no (both possible products are water soluble)

Ionic Equations

In writing chemical equations for reactions in aqueous solution, it is often useful to indicate explicitly whether the dissolved substances are present predominantly as ions or as molecules. Let's reconsider the precipitation reaction between $Pb(NO_3)_2$ and 2 KI, shown previously in Figure 4.4:

$$Pb(NO_3)_2(aq) + 2\ KI(aq) \longrightarrow PbI_2(s) + 2\ KNO_3(aq)$$

An equation written in this fashion, showing the complete chemical formulas of the reactants and products, is called a **molecular equation** because it shows the chemical formulas of the reactants and products without indicating their ionic character. Because $Pb(NO_3)_2$, KI, and KNO_3 are all soluble ionic compounds and therefore strong electrolytes, we can write the chemical equation to indicate explicitly the ions that are in the solution:

$$Pb^{2+}(aq) + 2\ NO_3^-(aq) + 2\ K^+(aq) + 2\ I^-(aq) \longrightarrow$$
$$PbI_2(s) + 2\ K^+(aq) + 2\ NO_3^-(aq) \quad [4.7]$$

An equation written in this form, with all soluble strong electrolytes shown as ions, is called a **complete ionic equation**.

Notice that $K^+(aq)$ and $NO_3^-(aq)$ appear on both sides of Equation 4.7. Ions that appear in identical forms among both the reactants and products of a complete ionic equation are called **spectator ions**. These ions are present but play no direct role in the reaction. When spectator ions are omitted from the equation (they cancel out like algebraic quantities), we are left with the **net ionic equation**:

$$Pb^{2+}(aq) + 2\ I^-(aq) \longrightarrow PbI_2(s) \quad [4.8]$$

A net ionic equation includes only the ions and molecules directly involved in the reaction. Charge is conserved in reactions, so the sum of the charges of the ions must be the same on both sides of a balanced net ionic equation. In this case the 2+ charge of the cation and the two 1− charges of the anions add to give zero, the charge of the electrically neutral product. *If every ion in a complete ionic equation is a spectator, then no reaction occurs.*

GIVE IT SOME THOUGHT

Are any spectator ions shown in the following chemical equation?

$$Ag^+(aq) + Na^+(aq) + Cl^-(aq) \longrightarrow AgCl(s) + Na^+(aq)$$

Net ionic equations are widely used to illustrate the similarities between large numbers of reactions involving electrolytes. For example, Equation 4.8 expresses the essential feature of the precipitation reaction between any strong electrolyte containing Pb^{2+} and any strong electrolyte containing I^-: The $Pb^{2+}(aq)$ and $I^-(aq)$ ions combine to form a precipitate of PbI_2. Thus, a net ionic equation demonstrates that more than one set of reactants can lead to the same net reaction. For example, aqueous solutions of KI and MgI_2 share many chemical similarities because both contain I^- ions. The complete equation, on the other hand, identifies the actual reactants that participate in a reaction.

The following steps summarize the procedure for writing net ionic equations:

1. Write a balanced molecular equation for the reaction.
2. Rewrite the equation to show the ions that form in solution when each soluble strong electrolyte dissociates into its component ions. *Only strong electrolytes dissolved in aqueous solution are written in ionic form.*
3. Identify and cancel **spectator ions**.

■■■ SAMPLE EXERCISE 4.4 | Writing a Net Ionic Equation

Write the net ionic equation for the precipitation reaction that occurs when solutions of calcium chloride and sodium carbonate are mixed.

SOLUTION

Analyze: Our task is to write a net ionic equation for a precipitation reaction, given the names of the reactants present in solution.

Plan: We first need to write the chemical formulas of the reactants and products and then determine which product is insoluble. We then write and balance the molecular equation. Next, we write each soluble strong electrolyte as separated ions to obtain the complete ionic equation. Finally, we eliminate the spectator ions to obtain the net ionic equation.

Solve: Calcium chloride is composed of calcium ions, Ca^{2+}, and chloride ions, Cl^-; hence an aqueous solution of the substance is $CaCl_2(aq)$. Sodium carbonate is composed of Na^+ ions and CO_3^{2-} ions; hence an aqueous solution of the compound is $Na_2CO_3(aq)$. In the molecular equations for precipitation reactions, the anions and cations appear to exchange partners. Thus, we put Ca^{2+} and CO_3^{2-} together to give $CaCO_3$ and Na^+ and Cl^- together to give $NaCl$. According to the solubility guidelines in Table 4.1, $CaCO_3$ is insoluble and $NaCl$ is soluble. The balanced molecular equation is

$$CaCl_2(aq) + Na_2CO_3(aq) \longrightarrow CaCO_3(s) + 2\,NaCl(aq)$$

In a complete ionic equation, *only* dissolved strong electrolytes (such as soluble ionic compounds) are written as separate ions. As the (aq) designations remind us, $CaCl_2$, Na_2CO_3, and $NaCl$ are all dissolved in the solution. Furthermore, they are all strong electrolytes. $CaCO_3$ is an ionic compound, but it is not soluble. We do not write the formula of any insoluble compound as its component ions. Thus, the complete ionic equation is

$$Ca^{2+}(aq) + 2\,Cl^-(aq) + 2\,Na^+(aq) + CO_3^{2-}(aq) \longrightarrow$$
$$CaCO_3(s) + 2\,Na^+(aq) + 2\,Cl^-(aq)$$

Cl^- and Na^+ are spectator ions. Canceling them gives the following net ionic equation:

$$Ca^{2+}(aq) + CO_3^{2-}(aq) \longrightarrow CaCO_3(s)$$

Check: We can check our result by confirming that both the elements and the electric charge are balanced. Each side has one Ca, one C, and three O, and the net charge on each side equals 0.

Comment: If none of the ions in an ionic equation is removed from solution or changed in some way, then they all are spectator ions and a reaction does not occur.

■■■ PRACTICE EXERCISE

Write the net ionic equation for the precipitation reaction that occurs when aqueous solutions of silver nitrate and potassium phosphate are mixed.

Answers: $3\,Ag^+(aq) + PO_4^{3-}(aq) \longrightarrow Ag_3PO_4(s)$

▲ Figure 4.5 **Some common household acids (left) and bases (right).**

4.3 ACID–BASE REACTIONS

Many acids and bases are industrial and household substances (Figure 4.5 ◄), and some are important components of biological fluids. Hydrochloric acid, for example, is an important industrial chemical and the main constituent of gastric juice in your stomach. Acids and bases are also common electrolytes.

Acids

HCl

Acids are substances that ionize in aqueous solutions to form hydrogen ions, thereby increasing the concentration of $H^+(aq)$ ions. Because a hydrogen atom consists of a proton and an electron, H^+ is simply a proton. Thus, acids are often called proton donors. Molecular models of three common acids, HCl, HNO_3 and CH_3COOH, are shown in the margin.

Just as cations are surrounded and bound by water molecules (see Figure 4.3[a]), the proton is also solvated by water molecules. The nature of the proton in water is discussed in detail in Section 16.2. In writing chemical equations involving the proton in water, we represent it simply as $H^+(aq)$.

HNO_3

Molecules of different acids can ionize to form different numbers of H^+ ions. Both HCl and HNO_3 are *monoprotic* acids, which yield one H^+ per molecule of acid. Sulfuric acid, H_2SO_4, is a *diprotic* acid, one that yields two H^+ per molecule of acid. The ionization of H_2SO_4 and other diprotic acids occurs in two steps:

$$H_2SO_4(aq) \longrightarrow H^+(aq) + HSO_4^-(aq) \qquad [4.9]$$

$$HSO_4^-(aq) \rightleftharpoons H^+(aq) + SO_4^{2-}(aq) \qquad [4.10]$$

Although H_2SO_4 is a strong electrolyte, only the first ionization is complete. Thus, aqueous solutions of sulfuric acid contain a mixture of $H^+(aq)$, $HSO_4^-(aq)$, and $SO_4^{2-}(aq)$.

CH_3COOH

The molecule CH_3COOH (acetic acid) that we have mentioned frequently is the primary component in vinegar. Acetic acid has four hydrogens, but only one of them is capable of being ionized in water. Only the hydrogen that is bound to oxygen in the COOH group will ionize in water; the other hydrogens are bound to carbon and do not break their C—H bonds in water. We will discuss acids much more in Chapter 16.

GIVE IT SOME THOUGHT

The structural formula of citric acid, a main component of citrus fruits, is shown here:

$$
\begin{array}{c}
\text{H} \\
| \\
\text{H}-\text{C}-\text{COOH} \\
| \\
\text{HO}-\text{C}-\text{COOH} \\
| \\
\text{H}-\text{C}-\text{COOH} \\
| \\
\text{H}
\end{array}
$$

How many $H^+(aq)$ can be generated by each citric acid molecule when citric acid is dissolved in water?

Bases

Bases are substances that accept (react with) H^+ ions. Bases produce hydroxide ions (OH^-) when they dissolve in water. Ionic hydroxide compounds such as NaOH, KOH, and $Ca(OH)_2$ are among the most common bases. When dissolved in water, they dissociate into their component ions, introducing OH^- ions into the solution.

Compounds that do not contain OH^- ions can also be bases. For example, ammonia (NH_3) is a common base. When added to water, it accepts an H^+ ion from the water molecule and thereby produces an OH^- ion (Figure 4.6 ▶):

$$NH_3(aq) + H_2O(l) \rightleftharpoons NH_4^+(aq) + OH^-(aq) \qquad [4.11]$$

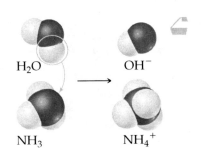

H_2O OH^-

NH_3 NH_4^+

▲ Figure 4.6 **Hydrogen ion transfer.** An H_2O molecule acts as a proton donor (acid), and NH_3 as a proton acceptor (base). Only a fraction of the NH_3 reacts with H_2O; NH_3 is a weak electrolyte.

Ammonia is a weak electrolyte because only a small fraction of the NH_3 (about 1%) forms NH_4^+ and OH^- ions.

TABLE 4.2 ■ Common Strong Acids and Bases	
Strong Acids	**Strong Bases**
Hydrochloric, HCl	Group 1A metal hydroxides (LiOH, NaOH, KOH, RbOH, CsOH)
Hydrobromic, HBr	Heavy group 2A metal hydroxides [Ca(OH)$_2$, Sr(OH)$_2$, Ba(OH)$_2$]
Hydroiodic, HI	
Chloric, HClO$_3$	
Perchloric, HClO$_4$	
Nitric, HNO$_3$	
Sulfuric, H$_2$SO$_4$	

Strong and Weak Acids and Bases

Acids and bases that are strong electrolytes (completely ionized in solution) are called **strong acids** and **strong bases**. Those that are weak electrolytes (partly ionized) are called **weak acids** and **weak bases**. Strong acids are more reactive than weak acids when the reactivity depends only on the concentration of H$^+$(aq). The reactivity of an acid, however, can depend on the anion as well as on H$^+$(aq). For example, hydrofluoric acid (HF) is a weak acid (only partly ionized in aqueous solution), but it is very reactive and vigorously attacks many substances, including glass. This reactivity is due to the combined action of H$^+$(aq) and F$^-$(aq).

Table 4.2 ▲ lists the common strong acids and bases. You should commit these to memory. As you examine this table, notice that some of the most common acids, such as HCl, HNO$_3$, and H$_2$SO$_4$, are strong. (For H$_2$SO$_4$, as we noted earlier, only the first proton completely ionizes.) Three of the strong acids are the hydrogen compounds of the halogen family. (HF, however, is a weak acid.) The list of strong acids is very short. Most acids are weak. The only common strong bases are the hydroxides of Li$^+$, Na$^+$, K$^+$, Rb$^+$, and Cs$^+$ (the alkali metals, group 1A) and the hydroxides of Ca^{2+}, Sr^{2+}, and Ba^{2+} (the heavy alkaline earths, group 2A). These are the common soluble metal hydroxides. Most other metal hydroxides are insoluble in water. The most common weak base is NH$_3$, which reacts with water to form OH$^-$ ions (Equation 4.11).

GIVE IT SOME THOUGHT

Which of the following is a strong acid: H$_2$SO$_3$, HBr, CH$_3$COOH?

SAMPLE EXERCISE 4.5 | Comparing Acid Strengths

The following diagrams represent aqueous solutions of three acids (HX, HY, and HZ) with water molecules omitted for clarity. Rank them from strongest to weakest.

HX   HY   HZ

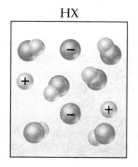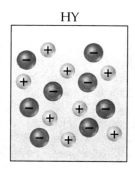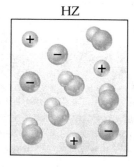

SOLUTION

Analyze: We are asked to rank three acids from strongest to weakest, based on schematic drawings of their solutions.

Plan: We can examine the drawings to determine the relative numbers of uncharged molecular species present. The strongest acid is the one with the most H^+ ions and fewest undissociated acid molecules in solution. The weakest acid is the one with the largest number of undissociated molecules.

Solve: The order is HY > HZ > HX. HY is a strong acid because it is totally ionized (no HY molecules in solution), whereas both HX and HZ are weak acids, whose solutions consist of a mixture of molecules and ions. Because HZ contains more H^+ ions and fewer molecules than HX, it is a stronger acid.

▨ PRACTICE EXERCISE

Imagine a diagram showing 10 Na^+ ions and 10 OH^- ions. If this solution were mixed with the one pictured on the previous page for HY, what would the diagram look like that represents the solution after any possible reaction? (H^+ ions will react with OH^- ions to form H_2O.)
Answer: The final diagram would show 10 Na^+ ions, 2 OH^- ions, 8 Y^- ions, and 8 H_2O molecules.

Identifying Strong and Weak Electrolytes

If we remember the common strong acids and bases (Table 4.2) and also remember that NH_3 is a weak base, we can make reasonable predictions about the electrolytic strength of a great number of water-soluble substances. Table 4.3 ▼ summarizes our observations about electrolytes. To classify a soluble substance as a strong electrolyte, weak electrolyte, or nonelectrolyte, we simply work our way down and across this table. We first ask ourselves whether the substance is ionic or molecular. If it is ionic, it is a strong electrolyte. The second column of Table 4.3 tells us that all ionic compounds are strong electrolytes. If the substance we want to classify is molecular, we ask whether it is an acid or a base. (Does it have H first in the chemical formula or contain a COOH group?) If it is an acid, we rely on the memorized list from Table 4.2 to determine whether it is a strong or weak electrolyte: All strong acids are strong electrolytes, and all weak acids are weak electrolytes. If an acid is not listed in Table 4.2, it is probably a weak acid and therefore a weak electrolyte. For example, H_3PO_4, H_2SO_3, and $HC_7H_5O_2$ are not listed in Table 4.2 and are weak acids. If the substance we want to classify is a base, we again turn to Table 4.2 to determine whether it is one of the listed strong bases. NH_3 is the only molecular base that we consider in this chapter, and Table 4.3 tells us it is a weak electrolyte. (There are compounds called amines that are related to NH_3 and are also molecular bases, but we will not consider them until Chapter 16.) Finally, any molecular substance that we encounter in this chapter that is not an acid or NH_3 is probably a nonelectrolyte.

TABLE 4.3 ▪ Summary of the Electrolytic Behavior of Common Soluble Ionic and Molecular Compounds

	Strong Electrolyte	Weak Electrolyte	Nonelectrolyte
Ionic	All	None	None
Molecular	Strong acids (see Table 4.2)	Weak acids Weak bases	All other compounds

■ SAMPLE EXERCISE 4.6 | Identifying Strong, Weak, and Nonelectrolytes

Classify each of the following dissolved substances as a strong electrolyte, weak electrolyte, or nonelectrolyte: $CaCl_2$, HNO_3, C_2H_5OH (ethanol), HCOOH (formic acid), KOH.

SOLUTION

Analyze: We are given several chemical formulas and asked to classify each substance as a strong electrolyte, weak electrolyte, or nonelectrolyte.

Plan: The approach we take is outlined in Table 4.3. We can predict whether a substance is ionic or molecular based on its composition. As we saw in Section 2.7, most ionic compounds we encounter in this text are composed of a metal and a nonmetal, whereas most molecular compounds are composed only of nonmetals.

Solve: Two compounds fit the criteria for ionic compounds: $CaCl_2$ and KOH. Because Table 4.3 tells us that all ionic compounds are strong electrolytes, that is how we classify these two substances. The three remaining compounds are molecular. Two, HNO_3 and HCOOH, are acids. Nitric acid, HNO_3, is a common strong acid, as shown in Table 4.2, and therefore is a strong electrolyte. Because most acids are weak acids, our best guess would be that HCOOH is a weak acid (weak electrolyte). This is correct. The remaining molecular compound, C_2H_5OH, is neither an acid nor a base, so it is a nonelectrolyte.

Comment: Although C_2H_5OH has an OH group, it is not a metal hydroxide; thus, it is not a base. Rather, it is a member of a class of organic compounds that have C—OH bonds, which are known as alcohols. ⇐⇒ (Section 2.9). The COOH group is called the "carboxylic acid group" (Chapter 16). Molecules that have this group are all weak acids.

■ PRACTICE EXERCISE

Consider solutions in which 0.1 mol of each of the following compounds is dissolved in 1 L of water: $Ca(NO_3)_2$ (calcium nitrate), $C_6H_{12}O_6$ (glucose), CH_3COONa (sodium acetate), and CH_3COOH (acetic acid). Rank the solutions in order of increasing electrical conductivity, based on the fact that the greater the number of ions in solution, the greater the conductivity.

Answers: $C_6H_{12}O_6$ (nonelectrolyte) < CH_3COOH (weak electrolyte, existing mainly in the form of molecules with few ions) < CH_3COONa (strong electrolyte that provides two ions, Na^+ and CH_3COO^-) < $Ca(NO_3)_2$ (strong electrolyte that provides three ions, Ca^{2+} and $2\ NO_3^-$)

Neutralization Reactions and Salts

The properties of acidic solutions are quite different from those of basic solutions. Acids have a sour taste, whereas bases have a bitter taste.* Acids can change the colors of certain dyes in a specific way that differs from the effect of a base (Figure 4.7 ◄). The dye known as litmus, for example, is changed from blue to red by an acid and from red to blue by a base. In addition, acidic and basic solutions differ in chemical properties in several important ways that we will explore in this chapter and in later chapters.

When a solution of an acid and a solution of a base are mixed, a **neutralization reaction** occurs. The products of the reaction have none of the characteristic properties of either the acidic solution or the basic solution. For example, when hydrochloric acid is mixed with a solution of sodium hydroxide, the following reaction occurs:

$$\underset{\text{(acid)}}{HCl(aq)}\ +\ \underset{\text{(base)}}{NaOH(aq)}\ \longrightarrow\ \underset{\text{(water)}}{H_2O(l)}\ +\ \underset{\text{(salt)}}{NaCl(aq)} \qquad [4.12]$$

Water and table salt, NaCl, are the products of the reaction. By analogy to this reaction, the term **salt** has come to mean any ionic compound whose cation comes from a base (for example, Na^+ from NaOH) and whose anion comes from an acid (for example, Cl^- from HCl). In general, *a neutralization reaction between an acid and a metal hydroxide produces water and a salt.*

▲ Figure 4.7 **The acid–base indicator bromthymol blue.** The indicator is blue in basic solution and yellow in acidic solution. The left flask shows the indicator in the presence of a base, aqueous ammonia (labeled as ammonium hydroxide). The right flask shows the indicator in the presence of hydrochloric acid, HCl.

Tasting chemical solutions is not a good practice. However, we have all had acids such as ascorbic acid (vitamin C), acetylsalicylic acid (aspirin), and citric acid (in citrus fruits) in our mouths, and we are familiar with their characteristic sour taste. Soaps, which are basic, have the characteristic bitter taste of bases.

(a)

(b)

(c)

Because HCl, NaOH, and NaCl are all soluble strong electrolytes, the complete ionic equation associated with Equation 4.12 is

$$H^+(aq) + Cl^-(aq) + Na^+(aq) + OH^-(aq) \longrightarrow$$
$$H_2O(l) + Na^+(aq) + Cl^-(aq) \qquad [4.13]$$

Therefore, the net ionic equation is

$$H^+(aq) + OH^-(aq) \longrightarrow H_2O(l) \qquad [4.14]$$

Equation 4.14 summarizes the essential feature of the neutralization reaction between any strong acid and any strong base: $H^+(aq)$ and $OH^-(aq)$ ions combine to form H_2O.

Figure 4.8▲ shows the reaction between hydrochloric acid and the base $Mg(OH)_2$, which is insoluble in water. A milky white suspension of $Mg(OH)_2$ called milk of magnesia is seen dissolving as the neutralization reaction occurs:

Molecular equation:
$$Mg(OH)_2(s) + 2\,HCl(aq) \longrightarrow MgCl_2(aq) + 2\,H_2O(l) \qquad [4.15]$$

Net ionic equation:
$$Mg(OH)_2(s) + 2\,H^+(aq) \longrightarrow Mg^{2+}(aq) + 2\,H_2O(l) \qquad [4.16]$$

Notice that the OH^- ions (this time in a solid reactant) and H^+ ions combine to form H_2O. Because the ions exchange partners, neutralization reactions between acids and metal hydroxides are also metathesis reactions.

▲ Figure 4.8 **Reaction of Mg(OH)₂(s) with acid.** (a) Milk of magnesia is a suspension of magnesium hydroxide, $Mg(OH)_2(s)$, in water. (b) The magnesium hydroxide dissolves upon the addition of hydrochloric acid, HCl(aq). (c) The final clear solution contains soluble $MgCl_2(aq)$, as shown in Equation 4.15.

SAMPLE EXERCISE 4.7 | Writing Chemical Equations for a Neutralization Reaction

(a) Write a balanced molecular equation for the reaction between aqueous solutions of acetic acid (CH_3COOH) and barium hydroxide, $Ba(OH)_2$. **(b)** Write the net ionic equation for this reaction.

SOLUTION

Analyze: We are given the chemical formulas for an acid and a base and asked to write a balanced molecular equation and then a net ionic equation for their neutralization reaction.

Plan: As Equation 4.12 and the italicized statement that follows it indicate, neutralization reactions form two products, H_2O and a salt. We examine the cation of the base and the anion of the acid to determine the composition of the salt.

Solve:

(a) The salt will contain the cation of the base (Ba^{2+}) and the anion of the acid (CH_3COO^-). Thus, the formula of the salt is $Ba(CH_3COO)_2$. According to the solubility guidelines in Table 4.1, this compound is soluble. The unbalanced molecular equation for the neutralization reaction is

$$CH_3COOH(aq) + Ba(OH)_2(aq) \longrightarrow H_2O(l) + Ba(CH_3COO^-)_2(aq)$$

To balance this molecular equation, we must provide two molecules of CH_3COOH to furnish the two CH_3COO^- ions and to supply the two H^+ ions needed to combine with the two OH^- ions of the base. The balanced molecular equation is

$$2\,CH_3COOH(aq) + Ba(OH)_2(aq) \longrightarrow 2\,H_2O(l) + Ba(CH_3COO)_2(aq)$$

(b) To write the net ionic equation, we must determine whether each compound in aqueous solution is a strong electrolyte. CH_3COOH is a weak electrolyte (weak acid), $Ba(OH)_2$ is a strong electrolyte, and $Ba(CH_3COO)_2$ is also a strong electrolyte (ionic compound). Thus, the complete ionic equation is

$$2\,CH_3COOH(aq) + Ba^{2+}(aq) + 2\,OH^-(aq) \longrightarrow$$
$$2\,H_2O(l) + Ba^{2+}(aq) + 2\,CH_3COO^-(aq)$$

Eliminating the spectator ions gives

$$2\,CH_3COOH(aq) + 2\,OH^-(aq) \longrightarrow 2\,H_2O(l) + 2\,CH_3COO^-(aq)$$

Simplifying the coefficients gives the net ionic equation:

$$CH_3COOH(aq) + OH^-(aq) \longrightarrow H_2O(l) + CH_3COO^-(aq)$$

Check: We can determine whether the molecular equation is correctly balanced by counting the number of atoms of each kind on both sides of the arrow. (There are 10 H, 6 O, 4 C, and 1 Ba on each side.) However, it is often easier to check equations by counting groups: There are 2 CH_3COO groups, as well as 1 Ba, and 4 additional H atoms and 2 additional O atoms on each side of the equation. The net ionic equation checks out because the numbers of each kind of element and the net charge are the same on both sides of the equation.

▬ PRACTICE EXERCISE

(a) Write a balanced molecular equation for the reaction of carbonic acid (H_2CO_3) and potassium hydroxide (KOH). **(b)** Write the net ionic equation for this reaction.
Answers: **(a)** $H_2CO_3(aq) + 2\,KOH(aq) \longrightarrow 2\,H_2O(l) + K_2CO_3(aq)$; **(b)** $H_2CO_3(aq) + 2\,OH^-(aq) \longrightarrow 2\,H_2O(l) + CO_3^{2-}(aq)$. ($H_2CO_3$ is a weak acid and therefore a weak electrolyte, whereas KOH, a strong base, and K_2CO_3, an ionic compound, are strong electrolytes.)

Acid–Base Reactions with Gas Formation

Many bases besides OH^- react with H^+ to form molecular compounds. Two of these that you might encounter in the laboratory are the sulfide ion and the carbonate ion. Both of these anions react with acids to form gases that have low solubilities in water. Hydrogen sulfide (H_2S), the substance that gives rotten eggs their foul odor, forms when an acid such as HCl(aq) reacts with a metal sulfide such as Na_2S:

Molecular equation: $2\,HCl(aq) + Na_2S(aq) \longrightarrow H_2S(g) + 2\,NaCl(aq)$ [4.17]

Net ionic equation: $2\,H^+(aq) + S^{2-}(aq) \longrightarrow H_2S(g)$ [4.18]

Carbonates and bicarbonates react with acids to form CO_2 gas. Reaction of CO_3^{2-} or HCO_3^- with an acid first gives carbonic acid (H_2CO_3). For example, when hydrochloric acid is added to sodium bicarbonate, the following reaction occurs:

$$HCl(aq) + NaHCO_3(aq) \longrightarrow NaCl(aq) + H_2CO_3(aq) \qquad [4.19]$$

Carbonic acid is unstable. If carbonic acid is present in solution in sufficient concentrations, it decomposes to form H_2O and CO_2, which escapes from the solution as a gas.

$$H_2CO_3(aq) \longrightarrow H_2O(l) + CO_2(g) \qquad [4.20]$$

The decomposition of H_2CO_3 produces bubbles of CO_2 gas, as shown in Figure 4.9 ◄. The overall reaction is summarized by the following equations:

▲ Figure 4.9 **Carbonates react with acids to form carbon dioxide gas.** Here $NaHCO_3$ (white solid) reacts with hydrochloric acid. The bubbles contain CO_2.

Molecular equation:
$$HCl(aq) + NaHCO_3(aq) \longrightarrow NaCl(aq) + H_2O(l) + CO_2(g) \qquad [4.21]$$

Net ionic equation: $H^+(aq) + HCO_3^-(aq) \longrightarrow H_2O(l) + CO_2(g)$ [4.22]

Your stomach secretes acids to help digest foods. These acids, which include hydrochloric acid, contain about 0.1 mol of H^+ per liter of solution. The stomach and digestive tract are normally protected from the corrosive effects of stomach acid by a mucosal lining. Holes can develop in this lining, however, allowing the acid to attack the underlying tissue, causing painful damage. These holes, known as ulcers, can be caused by the secretion of excess acids or by a weakness in the digestive lining. Studies indicate, however, that many ulcers are caused by bacterial infection. Between 10 and 20% of Americans suffer from ulcers at some point in their lives. Many others experience occasional indigestion or heartburn that is due to digestive acids entering the esophagus.

We can address the problem of excess stomach acid in two simple ways: (1) removing the excess acid, or (2) decreasing the production of acid. Those substances that remove excess acid are called *antacids*, whereas those that decrease the production of acid are called *acid inhibitors*. Figure 4.10 ▼ shows several common, over-the-counter antacids.

Antacids are simple bases that neutralize digestive acids. They are able to neutralize acids because they contain hydroxide, carbonate, or bicarbonate ions. Table 4.4 ◄ lists the active ingredients in some antacids.

The newer generation of antiulcer drugs, such as Tagamet® and Zantac®, are acid inhibitors. They act on acid-producing cells in the lining of the stomach. Formulations that control acid in this way are now available as over-the-counter drugs.

Related Exercise: 4.95

TABLE 4.4 ■ Some Common Antacids

Commercial Name	Acid-Neutralizing Agents
Alka-Seltzer®	$NaHCO_3$
Amphojel®	$Al(OH)_3$
Di-Gel®	$Mg(OH)_2$ and $CaCO_3$
Milk of Magnesia	$Mg(OH)_2$
Maalox®	$Mg(OH)_2$ and $Al(OH)_3$
Mylanta®	$Mg(OH)_2$ and $Al(OH)_3$
Rolaids®	$NaAl(OH)_2CO_3$
Tums®	$CaCO_3$

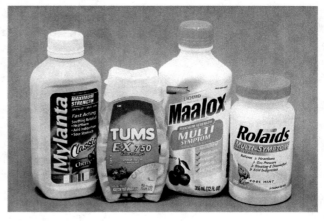

▲ Figure 4.10 **Antacids.** These products all serve as acid-neutralizing agents in the stomach.

Both $NaHCO_3$ and Na_2CO_3 are used as acid neutralizers in acid spills. The bicarbonate or carbonate salt is added until the fizzing due to the formation of $CO_2(g)$ stops. Sometimes sodium bicarbonate is used as an antacid to soothe an upset stomach. In that case the HCO_3^- reacts with stomach acid to form $CO_2(g)$. The fizz when Alka-Seltzer® tablets are added to water arises from the reaction of sodium bicarbonate and citric acid.

▲ GIVE IT SOME THOUGHT

By analogy to examples already given in the text, predict what gas forms when $Na_2SO_3(s)$ is treated with HCl(*aq*).

4.4 OXIDATION-REDUCTION REACTIONS

In precipitation reactions, cations and anions come together to form an insoluble ionic compound. In neutralization reactions H^+ ions and OH^- ions come together to form H_2O molecules. Now let's consider a third important kind of reaction, one in which electrons are transferred between reactants. Such reactions are called **oxidation-reduction**, or *redox*, **reactions**.

▶ Figure 4.11 **Corrosion of iron.**
Corrosion of iron is caused by chemical
attack of oxygen and water on exposed
metal surfaces. Corrosion is even more
rapid in salt water.

Oxidation and Reduction

The corrosion of iron (rusting) and of other metals, such as the corrosion of the terminals of an automobile battery, are familiar processes. What we call *corrosion* is the conversion of a metal into a metal compound by a reaction between the metal and some substance in its environment. Rusting, as shown in Figure 4.11 ▲, involves the reaction of oxygen with iron in the presence of water.

When a metal corrodes, it loses electrons and forms cations. Calcium, for example, is vigorously attacked by acids to form calcium ions:

$$Ca(s) + 2\,H^+(aq) \longrightarrow Ca^{2+}(aq) + H_2(g) \qquad [4.23]$$

When an atom, ion, or molecule has become more positively charged (that is, when it has lost electrons), we say that it has been oxidized. *Loss of electrons by a substance is called* **oxidation.** Thus, Ca, which has no net charge, is *oxidized* (undergoes oxidation) in Equation 4.23, forming Ca^{2+}.

The term oxidation is used because the first reactions of this sort to be studied thoroughly were reactions with oxygen. Many metals react directly with O_2 in air to form metal oxides. In these reactions the metal loses electrons to oxygen, forming an ionic compound of the metal ion and oxide ion. For example, when calcium metal is exposed to air, the bright metallic surface of the metal tarnishes as CaO forms:

$$2\,Ca(s) + O_2(g) \longrightarrow 2\,CaO(s) \qquad [4.24]$$

As Ca is oxidized in Equation 4.24, oxygen is transformed from neutral O_2 to two O^{2-} ions (Figure 4.12 ▼). When an atom, ion, or molecule has become more negatively charged (gained electrons), we say that it is *reduced*.

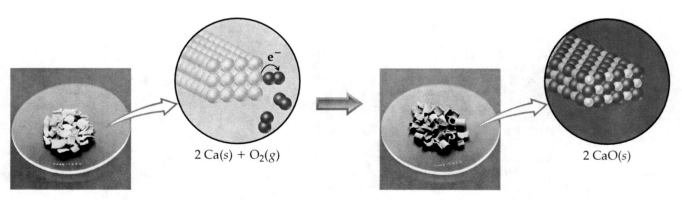

$$2\,Ca(s) + O_2(g) \qquad\qquad 2\,CaO(s)$$

▲ Figure 4.12 **Oxidation of calcium metal by molecular oxygen.** The oxidation involves
transfer of electrons from the metal to O_2, eventually leading to formation of CaO.

The gain of electrons by a substance is called **reduction**. When one reactant loses electrons (that is, when it is *oxidized*), another reactant must gain them. The oxidation of one substance is always accompanied by the reduction of another as electrons are transferred between them.

Substance **oxidized** (loses electron)   Substance **reduced** (gains electron)

Oxidation Numbers

Before we can properly identify an oxidation-reduction reaction, we must have a kind of bookkeeping system—a way of keeping track of the electrons gained by the substance reduced and those lost by the substance oxidized. The concept of oxidation numbers (also called *oxidation states*) was devised as a way of doing this. Each atom in a neutral molecule or charged species is assigned an **oxidation number,** which is the actual charge for a monatomic ion. Otherwise, the oxidation number is the hypothetical charge assigned to the atom, assuming that the electrons are *completely* held by one atom or the other. The oxidation numbers of certain atoms change in an oxidation-reduction reaction. Oxidation occurs when the oxidation number increases, whereas reduction occurs when the oxidation number decreases.

We use the following rules for assigning oxidation numbers:

1. *For an atom in its **elemental form**, the oxidation number is always zero.*
   Thus, each H atom in the H_2 molecule has an oxidation number of 0, and each P atom in the P_4 molecule has an oxidation number of 0.

2. *For any **monatomic ion** the oxidation number equals the charge on the ion.*
   Thus, K^+ has an oxidation number of +1, S^{2-} has an oxidation number of −2, and so forth. The alkali metal ions (group 1A) always have a 1+ charge, and therefore the alkali metals always have an oxidation number of +1 in their compounds. Similarly, the alkaline earth metals (group 2A) are always +2, and aluminum (group 3A) is always +3 in its compounds. (In writing oxidation numbers, we will write the sign before the number to distinguish them from the actual electronic charges, which we write with the number first.)

3. *Nonmetals* usually have negative oxidation numbers, although they can sometimes be positive:
   (a) *The oxidation number of **oxygen** is usually* −2 in both ionic and molecular compounds. The major exception is in compounds called peroxides, which contain the O_2^{2-} ion, giving each oxygen an oxidation number of −1.
   (b) *The oxidation number of **hydrogen** is usually* +1 *when bonded to nonmetals and* −1 *when bonded to metals.*
   (c) *The oxidation number of **fluorine** is* −1 *in all compounds.* The other *halogens* have an oxidation number of −1 in most binary compounds. When combined with oxygen, as in oxyanions, however, they have positive oxidation states.

4. ***The sum of the oxidation numbers*** *of all atoms in a neutral compound is zero. The sum of the oxidation numbers in a polyatomic ion equals the charge of the ion.* For example, in the hydronium ion, H_3O^+, the oxidation number of each hydrogen is +1 and that of oxygen is −2. Thus, the sum of the oxidation numbers is $3(+1) + (-2) = +1$, which equals the net charge of the ion. This rule is very useful in obtaining the oxidation number of one atom in a compound or ion if you know the oxidation numbers of the other atoms, as illustrated in Sample Exercise 4.8.

GIVE IT SOME THOUGHT

(a) What noble gas element has the same number of electrons as the fluoride ion?
(b) What is the oxidation number of that noble gas?

SAMPLE EXERCISE 4.8 | Determining Oxidation Numbers

Determine the oxidation number of sulfur in each of the following: **(a)** H_2S, **(b)** S_8, **(c)** SCl_2, **(d)** Na_2SO_3, **(e)** SO_4^{2-}.

SOLUTION

Analyze: We are asked to determine the oxidation number of sulfur in two molecular species, in the elemental form, and in two ionic substances.

Plan: In each species the sum of oxidation numbers of all the atoms must equal the charge on the species. We will use the rules outlined above to assign oxidation numbers.

Solve:

(a) When bonded to a nonmetal, hydrogen has an oxidation number of +1 (rule 3b). Because the H_2S molecule is neutral, the sum of the oxidation numbers must equal zero (rule 4). Letting x equal the oxidation number of S, we have $2(+1) + x = 0$. Thus, S has an oxidation number of −2.
(b) Because this is an elemental form of sulfur, the oxidation number of S is 0 (rule 1).
(c) Because this is a binary compound, we expect chlorine to have an oxidation number of −1 (rule 3c). The sum of the oxidation numbers must equal zero (rule 4). Letting x equal the oxidation number of S, we have $x + 2(-1) = 0$. Consequently, the oxidation number of S must be +2.
(d) Sodium, an alkali metal, always has an oxidation number of +1 in its compounds (rule 2). Oxygen has a common oxidation state of −2 (rule 3a). Letting x equal the oxidation number of S, we have $2(+1) + x + 3(-2) = 0$. Therefore, the oxidation number of S in this compound is +4.
(e) The oxidation state of O is −2 (rule 3a). The sum of the oxidation numbers equals −2, the net charge of the SO_4^{2-} ion (rule 4). Thus, we have $x + 4(-2) = -2$. From this relation we conclude that the oxidation number of S in this ion is +6.

Comment: These examples illustrate that the oxidation number of a given element depends on the compound in which it occurs. The oxidation numbers of sulfur, as seen in these examples, range from −2 to +6.

PRACTICE EXERCISE

What is the oxidation state of the boldfaced element in each of the following: **(a)** **P**$_2$O$_5$, **(b)** Na**H**, **(c)** **Cr**$_2$O$_7^{2-}$, **(d)** **Sn**Br$_4$, **(e)** Ba**O**$_2$?
Answers: **(a)** +5, **(b)** −1, **(c)** +6, **(d)** +4, **(e)** −1

Oxidation of Metals by Acids and Salts

There are many kinds of redox reactions. For example, combustion reactions are redox reactions because elemental oxygen is converted to compounds of oxygen. (Section 3.2) In this chapter we consider the redox reactions between metals and either acids or salts. In Chapter 20 we will examine more complex kinds of redox reactions.

The reaction of a metal with either an acid or a metal salt conforms to the following general pattern:

$$A + BX \longrightarrow AX + B \qquad [4.25]$$

Examples: $Zn(s) + 2 HBr(aq) \longrightarrow ZnBr_2(aq) + H_2(g)$

$Mn(s) + Pb(NO_3)_2(aq) \longrightarrow Mn(NO_3)_2(aq) + Pb(s)$

These reactions are called **displacement reactions** because the ion in solution is displaced or replaced through oxidation of an element.

Many metals undergo displacement reactions with acids, producing salts and hydrogen gas. For example, magnesium metal reacts with hydrochloric acid to form magnesium chloride and hydrogen gas (Figure 4.13 ▶).

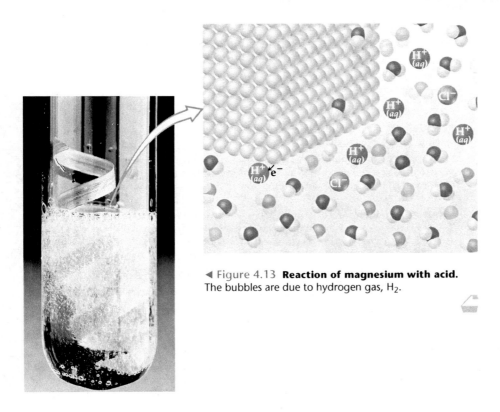

◀ Figure 4.13 **Reaction of magnesium with acid.**
The bubbles are due to hydrogen gas, H_2.

To show that oxidation and reduction have occurred, the oxidation number for each atom is shown below the chemical equation for this reaction:

$$Mg(s) + 2\,HCl(aq) \longrightarrow MgCl_2(aq) + H_2(g) \qquad [4.26]$$

$$0 \qquad +1\ -1 \qquad +2\ -1 \qquad 0$$

Notice that the oxidation number of Mg changes from 0 to +2. The increase in the oxidation number indicates that the atom has lost electrons and has therefore been oxidized. The H^+ ion of the acid decreases in oxidation number from +1 to 0, indicating that this ion has gained electrons and has therefore been reduced. The oxidation number of the Cl^- ion remains −1, and it is a spectator ion in the reaction. The net ionic equation is as follows:

$$Mg(s) + 2\,H^+(aq) \longrightarrow Mg^{2+}(aq) + H_2(g) \qquad [4.27]$$

Metals can also be oxidized by aqueous solutions of various salts. Iron metal, for example, is oxidized to Fe^{2+} by aqueous solutions of Ni^{2+} such as $Ni(NO_3)_2(aq)$:

Molecular equation: $Fe(s) + Ni(NO_3)_2(aq) \longrightarrow Fe(NO_3)_2(aq) + Ni(s)$ [4.28]

Net ionic equation: $Fe(s) + Ni^{2+}(aq) \longrightarrow Fe^{2+}(aq) + Ni(s)$ [4.29]

The oxidation of Fe to form Fe^{2+} in this reaction is accompanied by the reduction of Ni^{2+} to Ni. Remember: *Whenever one substance is oxidized, some other substance must be reduced.*

■■■ **SAMPLE EXERCISE 4.9** | **Writing Molecular and Net Ionic Equations for Oxidation-Reduction Reactions**

Write the balanced molecular and net ionic equations for the reaction of aluminum with hydrobromic acid.

SOLUTION

Analyze: We must write two equations—molecular and net ionic—for the redox reaction between a metal and an acid.

Plan: Metals react with acids to form salts and H_2 gas. To write the balanced equations, we must write the chemical formulas for the two reactants and then determine the formula of the salt. The salt is composed of the cation formed by the metal and the anion of the acid.

Solve: The formulas of the given reactants are Al and HBr. The cation formed by Al is Al^{3+}, and the anion from hydrobromic acid is Br^-. Thus, the salt formed in the reaction is $AlBr_3$. Writing the reactants and products and then balancing the equation gives this molecular equation:

$$2\ Al(s) + 6\ HBr(aq) \longrightarrow 2\ AlBr_3(aq) + 3\ H_2(g)$$

Both HBr and $AlBr_3$ are soluble strong electrolytes. Thus, the complete ionic equation is

$$2\ Al(s) + 6\ H^+(aq) + 6\ Br^-(aq) \longrightarrow 2\ Al^{3+}(aq) + 6\ Br^-(aq) + 3\ H_2(g)$$

Because Br^- is a spectator ion, the net ionic equation is

$$2\ Al(s) + 6\ H^+(aq) \longrightarrow 2\ Al^{3+}(aq) + 3\ H_2(g)$$

Comment: The substance oxidized is the aluminum metal because its oxidation state changes from 0 in the metal to +3 in the cation, thereby increasing in oxidation number. The H^+ is reduced because its oxidation state changes from +1 in the acid to 0 in H_2.

■■■ **PRACTICE EXERCISE**

(a) Write the balanced molecular and net ionic equations for the reaction between magnesium and cobalt(II) sulfate. **(b)** What is oxidized and what is reduced in the reaction?
Answers: **(a)** $Mg(s) + CoSO_4(aq) \longrightarrow MgSO_4(aq) + Co(s)$;
$Mg(s) + Co^{2+}(aq) \longrightarrow Mg^{2+}(aq) + Co(s)$; **(b)** Mg is oxidized and Co^{2+} is reduced.

The Activity Series

Can we predict whether a certain metal will be oxidized either by an acid or by a particular salt? This question is of practical importance as well as chemical interest. According to Equation 4.28, for example, it would be unwise to store a solution of nickel nitrate in an iron container because the solution would dissolve the container. When a metal is oxidized, it reacts to form various compounds. Extensive oxidation can lead to the failure of metal machinery parts or the deterioration of metal structures.

Different metals vary in the ease with which they are oxidized. Zn is oxidized by aqueous solutions of Cu^{2+}, for example, but Ag is not. Zn, therefore, loses electrons more readily than Ag; that is, Zn is easier to oxidize than Ag.

A list of metals arranged in order of decreasing ease of oxidation is called an **activity series**. Table 4.5▶ gives the activity series in aqueous solution for many of the most common metals. Hydrogen is also included in the table. The metals at the top of the table, such as the alkali metals and the alkaline earth metals, are most easily oxidized; that is, they react most readily to form compounds. They are called the *active metals*. The metals at the bottom of the activity series, such as the transition elements from groups 8B and 1B, are very stable and form compounds less readily. These metals, which are used to make coins and jewelry, are called *noble metals* because of their low reactivity.

The activity series can be used to predict the outcome of reactions between metals and either metal salts or acids. *Any metal on the list can be oxidized by the ions of elements below it.* For example, copper is above silver in the series.

Science Fundamentals

Metal	Oxidation Reaction
TABLE 4.5 ■ Activity Series of Metals in Aqueous Solution	
Lithium	$Li(s) \longrightarrow Li^+(aq) + e^-$
Potassium	$K(s) \longrightarrow K^+(aq) + e^-$
Barium	$Ba(s) \longrightarrow Ba^{2+}(aq) + 2e^-$
Calcium	$Ca(s) \longrightarrow Ca^{2+}(aq) + 2e^-$
Sodium	$Na(s) \longrightarrow Na^+(aq) + e^-$
Magnesium	$Mg(s) \longrightarrow Mg^{2+}(aq) + 2e^-$
Aluminum	$Al(s) \longrightarrow Al^{3+}(aq) + 3e^-$
Manganese	$Mn(s) \longrightarrow Mn^{2+}(aq) + 2e^-$
Zinc	$Zn(s) \longrightarrow Zn^{2+}(aq) + 2e^-$
Chromium	$Cr(s) \longrightarrow Cr^{3+}(aq) + 3e^-$
Iron	$Fe(s) \longrightarrow Fe^{2+}(aq) + 2e^-$
Cobalt	$Co(s) \longrightarrow Co^{2+}(aq) + 2e^-$
Nickel	$Ni(s) \longrightarrow Ni^{2+}(aq) + 2e^-$
Tin	$Sn(s) \longrightarrow Sn^{2+}(aq) + 2e^-$
Lead	$Pb(s) \longrightarrow Pb^{2+}(aq) + 2e^-$
Hydrogen	$H_2(g) \longrightarrow 2H^+(aq) + 2e^-$
Copper	$Cu(s) \longrightarrow Cu^{2+}(aq) + 2e^-$
Silver	$Ag(s) \longrightarrow Ag^+(aq) + e^-$
Mercury	$Hg(l) \longrightarrow Hg^{2+}(aq) + 2e^-$
Platinum	$Pt(s) \longrightarrow Pt^{2+}(aq) + 2e^-$
Gold	$Au(s) \longrightarrow Au^{3+}(aq) + 3e^-$

Ease of oxidation increases ↑

Thus, copper metal will be oxidized by silver ions, as pictured in Figure 4.14▼:

$$Cu(s) + 2\,Ag^+(aq) \longrightarrow Cu^{2+}(aq) + 2\,Ag(s) \qquad [4.30]$$

The oxidation of copper to copper ions is accompanied by the reduction of silver ions to silver metal. The silver metal is evident on the surface of the copper wires in Figure 4.14(b) and 4.14(c). The copper(II) nitrate produces a blue color in the solution, which is most evident in part (c).

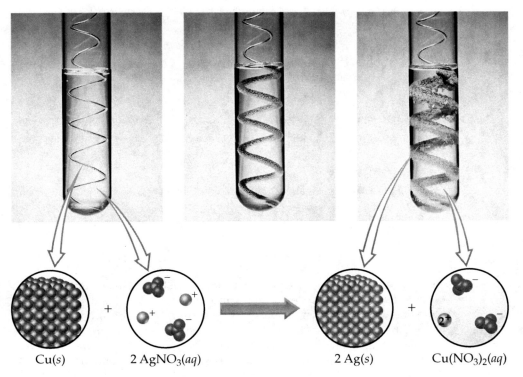

◄ Figure 4.14 **Reaction of copper with silver ion.** When copper metal is placed in a solution of silver nitrate, a redox reaction occurs, forming silver metal and a blue solution of copper(II) nitrate.

Science Fundamentals

Which is the more easily reduced, $Mg^{2+}(aq)$ or $Ni^{2+}(aq)$?

Only those metals above hydrogen in the activity series are able to react with acids to form H_2. For example, Ni reacts with $HCl(aq)$ to form H_2:

$$Ni(s) + 2\,HCl(aq) \longrightarrow NiCl_2(aq) + H_2(g) \qquad [4.31]$$

Because elements below hydrogen in the activity series are not oxidized by H^+, Cu does not react with $HCl(aq)$. Interestingly, copper does react with nitric acid, as shown previously in Figure 1.11. This reaction, however, is not a simple oxidation of Cu by the H^+ ions of the acid. Instead, the metal is oxidized to Cu^{2+} by the nitrate ion of the acid, accompanied by the formation of brown nitrogen dioxide, $NO_2(g)$:

$$Cu(s) + 4\,HNO_3(aq) \longrightarrow Cu(NO_3)_2(aq) + 2\,H_2O(l) + 2\,NO_2(g) \qquad [4.32]$$

What substance is reduced as copper is oxidized in Equation 4.32? In this case the NO_2 results from the reduction of NO_3^-. We will examine reactions of this type in more detail in Chapter 20.

■■■ **SAMPLE EXERCISE 4.10** | **Determining When an Oxidation-Reduction Reaction Can Occur**

Will an aqueous solution of iron(II) chloride oxidize magnesium metal? If so, write the balanced molecular and net ionic equations for the reaction.

SOLUTION

Analyze: We are given two substances—an aqueous salt, $FeCl_2$, and a metal, Mg—and asked if they react with each other.

Plan: A reaction will occur if Mg is above Fe in the activity series, Table 4.5. If the reaction occurs, the Fe^{2+} ion in $FeCl_2$ will be reduced to Fe, and the elemental Mg will be oxidized to Mg^{2+}.

Solve: Because Mg is above Fe in the table, the reaction will occur. To write the formula for the salt that is produced in the reaction, we must remember the charges on common ions. Magnesium is always present in compounds as Mg^{2+}: the chloride ion is Cl^-. The magnesium salt formed in the reaction is $MgCl_2$, meaning the balanced molecular equation is

$$Mg(s) + FeCl_2(aq) \longrightarrow MgCl_2(aq) + Fe(s)$$

Both $FeCl_2$ and $MgCl_2$ are soluble strong electrolytes and can be written in ionic form. Cl^- then, is a spectator ion in the reaction. The net ionic equation is

$$Mg(s) + Fe^{2+}(aq) \longrightarrow Mg^{2+}(aq) + Fe(s)$$

The net ionic equation shows that Mg is oxidized and Fe^{2+} is reduced in this reaction.

Check: Note that the net ionic equation is balanced with respect to both charge and mass.

■■■ **PRACTICE EXERCISE**

Which of the following metals will be oxidized by $Pb(NO_3)_2$: Zn, Cu, Fe?
Answer: Zn and Fe

4.5 CONCENTRATIONS OF SOLUTIONS

The behavior of solutions often depends on the nature of the solutes and their concentrations. Scientists use the term **concentration** to designate the amount of solute dissolved in a given quantity of solvent or quantity of solution. The concept of concentration is intuitive: The greater the amount of solute dissolved in a certain amount of solvent, the more concentrated the resulting solution. In chemistry we often need to express the concentrations of solutions quantitatively.

A Closer Look THE AURA OF GOLD

Gold has been known since the earliest records of human existence. Throughout history people have cherished gold, have fought for it, and have died for it.

The physical and chemical properties of gold serve to make it a special metal. First, its intrinsic beauty and rarity make it precious. Second, gold is soft and can be easily formed into artistic objects, jewelry, and coins (Figure 4.15 ▶). Third, gold is one of the least active metals (Table 4.5). It is not oxidized in air and does not react with water. It is unreactive toward basic solutions and nearly all acidic solutions. As a result, gold can be found in nature as a pure element rather than combined with oxygen or other elements, which accounts for its early discovery.

Many of the early studies of the reactions of gold arose from the practice of alchemy, in which people attempted to turn cheap metals, such as lead, into gold. Alchemists discovered that gold can be dissolved in a 3:1 mixture of concentrated hydrochloric and nitric acids, known as aqua regia ("royal water"). The action of nitric acid on gold is similar to that on copper (Equation 4.32) in that the nitrate ion, rather than H^+, oxidizes the metal to Au^{3+}. The Cl^- ions interact with Au^{3+} to form highly stable $AuCl_4^-$ ions. The net ionic equation for the reaction of gold with aqua regia is

$$Au(s) + NO_3^-(aq) + 4\,H^+(aq) + 4\,Cl^-(aq) \longrightarrow$$
$$AuCl_4^-(aq) + 2\,H_2O(l) + NO(g)$$

All the gold ever mined would easily fit in a cube 19 m on a side and weighing about 1.1×10^8 kg (125,000 tons). More than 90% of this amount has been produced since the beginning of the California gold rush of 1848. Each year, worldwide production of gold amounts to about 1.8×10^6 kg (2000 tons). By contrast, over 1.5×10^{10} kg (16 million tons) of aluminum are produced annually. Gold is used mainly in jewelry (73%), coins (10%), and electronics (9%). Its use in electronics relies on its excellent conductivity and its corrosion resistance. Gold is used, for example, to plate contacts in electrical switches, relays, and connections. A typical touch-tone telephone contains 33 gold-plated contacts. Gold is also used in computers and other microelectronic devices where fine gold wire is used to link components.

Because of its resistance to corrosion by acids and other substances found in saliva, gold is an ideal metal for dental crowns and caps, which accounts for about 3% of the annual use of the element. The pure metal is too soft to use in dentistry, so it is combined with other metals to form alloys.
Related Exercise: 4.97

◀ Figure 4.15 **Portrait of Pharaoh Tutankhamun (1346–1337 BC) made of gold and precious stones.** This highly prized article is from the inner coffin of the tomb of Tutankhamun.

Strategies in Chemistry ANALYZING CHEMICAL REACTIONS

In this chapter you have been introduced to a great number of chemical reactions. A major difficulty that students face in trying to master material of this sort is gaining a "feel" for what happens when chemicals are allowed to react. In fact, you might marvel at the ease with which your professor or teaching assistant can figure out the results of a chemical reaction. One of our goals in this textbook is to help you become more adept at predicting the outcomes of reactions. The key to gaining this "chemical intuition" is understanding how to categorize reactions.

Attempting to memorize the many individual reactions in chemistry would be a futile task. It is far more fruitful to try to recognize patterns to determine the general category of a reaction, such as metathesis or oxidation-reduction. Thus, when you are faced with the challenge of predicting the outcome of a chemical reaction, ask yourself the following pertinent questions:

• What are the reactants in the reaction?
• Are they electrolytes or nonelectrolytes?
• Are they acids and bases?
• If the reactants are electrolytes, will metathesis produce a precipitate? Water? A gas?

• If metathesis cannot occur, can the reactants possibly engage in an oxidation-reduction reaction? This requires that there be both a reactant that can be oxidized and one that can be reduced.

By asking questions such as these, you should be able to predict what might happen during the reaction. You might not always be entirely correct, but if you keep your wits about you, you will not be far off. As you gain experience with chemical reactions, you will begin to look for reactants that might not be immediately obvious, such as water from the solution or oxygen from the atmosphere.

One of the greatest tools available to us in chemistry is experimentation. If you perform an experiment in which two solutions are mixed, you can make observations that help you understand what is happening. For example, using the information in Table 4.1 to predict whether a precipitate will form is not nearly as exciting as actually seeing the precipitate form, as in Figure 4.4. Careful observations in the laboratory portion of the course will make your lecture material easier to master.

(a)

(b)

(c)

(d)

▲ Figure 4.16 **Procedure for preparation of 0.250 L of 1.00 *M* solution of CuSO₄.** (a) Weigh out 0.250 mol (39.9 g) of $CuSO_4$ (formula weight = 159.6 amu). (b) Put the $CuSO_4$ (solute) into a 250-mL volumetric flask, and add a small quantity of water. (c) Dissolve the solute by swirling the flask. (d) Add more water until the solution just reaches the calibration mark etched on the neck of the flask. Shake the stoppered flask to ensure complete mixing.

Molarity

Molarity (symbol *M*) expresses the concentration of a solution as the number of moles of solute in a liter of solution (soln):

$$\text{Molarity} = \frac{\text{moles solute}}{\text{volume of solution in liters}} \qquad [4.33]$$

A 1.00 molar solution (written 1.00 *M*) contains 1.00 mol of solute in every liter of solution. Figure 4.16 ▲ shows the preparation of 250.0 mL of a 1.00 *M* solution of $CuSO_4$ by using a volumetric flask that is calibrated to hold exactly 250.0 mL. First, 0.250 mol of $CuSO_4$ (39.9 g) is weighed out and placed in the volumetric flask. Water is added to dissolve the salt, and the resultant solution is diluted to a total volume of 250.0 mL. The molarity of the solution is (0.250 mol $CuSO_4$)/(0.250 L soln) = 1.00 *M*.

> △ **GIVE IT SOME THOUGHT**
>
> Which is more concentrated, a $1.00 \times 10^{-2}\,M$ solution of sucrose or a $1.00 \times 10^{-4}\,M$ solution of sucrose?

■■■ SAMPLE EXERCISE 4.11 | Calculating Molarity

Calculate the molarity of a solution made by dissolving 23.4 g of sodium sulfate (Na_2SO_4) in enough water to form 125 mL of solution.

SOLUTION

Analyze: We are given the number of grams of solute (23.4 g), its chemical formula (Na_2SO_4), and the volume of the solution (125 ml). We are asked to calculate the molarity of the solution.

Plan: We can calculate molarity using Equation 4.33. To do so, we must convert the number of grams of solute to moles and the volume of the solution from milliliters to liters.

Solve: The number of moles of Na_2SO_4 is obtained by using its molar mass:

$$\text{Moles } Na_2SO_4 = (23.4 \text{ g } Na_2SO_4)\left(\frac{1 \text{ mol } Na_2SO_4}{142 \text{ g } Na_2SO_4}\right) = 0.165 \text{ mol } Na_2SO_4$$

Converting the volume of the solution to liters:

$$\text{Liters soln} = (125 \text{ mL})\left(\frac{1 \text{ L}}{1000 \text{ mL}}\right) = 0.125 \text{ L}$$

Thus, the molarity is

$$\text{Molarity} = \frac{0.165 \text{ mol } Na_2SO_4}{0.125 \text{ L soln}} = 1.32 \frac{\text{mol } Na_2SO_4}{\text{L soln}} = 1.32\,M$$

Check: Because the numerator is only slightly larger than the denominator, it is reasonable for the answer to be a little over 1 *M*. The units (mol/L) are appropriate for molarity, and three significant figures are appropriate for the answer because each of the initial pieces of data had three significant figures.

■ PRACTICE EXERCISE

Calculate the molarity of a solution made by dissolving 5.00 g of glucose ($C_6H_{12}O_6$) in sufficient water to form exactly 100 mL of solution.
Answer: 0.278 *M*

Expressing the Concentration of an Electrolyte

When an ionic compound dissolves, the relative concentrations of the ions introduced into the solution depend on the chemical formula of the compound. For example, a 1.0 *M* solution of NaCl is 1.0 *M* in Na^+ ions and 1.0 *M* in Cl^- ions. Similarly, a 1.0 *M* solution of Na_2SO_4 is 2.0 *M* in Na^+ ions and 1.0 *M* in SO_4^{2-} ions. Thus, the concentration of an electrolyte solution can be specified either in terms of the compound used to make the solution (1.0 *M* Na_2SO_4) or in terms of the ions that the solution contains (2.0 *M* Na^+ and 1.0 *M* SO_4^{2-}).

■ SAMPLE EXERCISE 4.12 | Calculating Molar Concentrations of Ions

What are the molar concentrations of each of the ions present in a 0.025 *M* aqueous solution of calcium nitrate?

SOLUTION

Analyze: We are given the concentration of the ionic compound used to make the solution and asked to determine the concentrations of the ions in the solution.

Plan: We can use the subscripts in the chemical formula of the compound to determine the relative concentrations of the ions.

Solve: Calcium nitrate is composed of calcium ions (Ca^{2+}) and nitrate ions (NO_3^-), so its chemical formula is $Ca(NO_3)_2$. Because there are two NO_3^- ions for each Ca^{2+} ion in the compound, each mole of $Ca(NO_3)_2$ that dissolves dissociates into 1 mol of Ca^{2+} and 2 mol of NO_3^-. Thus, a solution that is 0.025 *M* in $Ca(NO_3)_2$ is 0.025 *M* in Ca^{2+} and $2 \times 0.025 \ M = 0.050 \ M$ in NO_3^-:

$$\frac{\text{mol } NO_3^-}{L} = \left(\frac{0.025 \text{ mol } Ca(NO_3)_2}{L}\right)\left(\frac{2 \text{ mol } NO_3^-}{1 \text{ mol } Ca(NO_3)_2}\right) = 0.050 \ M$$

Check: The concentration of NO_3^- ions is twice that of Ca^{2+} ions, as the subscript 2 after the NO_3^- in the chemical formula $Ca(NO_3)_2$ suggests it should be.

■ PRACTICE EXERCISE

What is the molar concentration of K^+ ions in a 0.015 *M* solution of potassium carbonate?
Answer: 0.030 *M* K^+

Interconverting Molarity, Moles, and Volume

The definition of molarity (Equation 4.33) contains three quantities—molarity, moles solute, and liters of solution. If we know any two of these, we can calculate the third. For example, if we know the molarity of a solution, we can calculate the number of moles of solute in a given volume. Molarity, therefore, is a conversion factor between volume of solution and moles of solute. Calculation of the number of moles of HNO_3 in 2.0 L of 0.200 *M* HNO_3 solution illustrates the conversion of volume to moles:

$$\text{moles } HNO_3 = (2.0 \text{ L soln})\left(\frac{0.200 \text{ mol } HNO_3}{1 \text{ L soln}}\right)$$

$$= 0.40 \text{ mol } HNO_3$$

Dimensional analysis can be used in this conversion if we express molarity as moles/liter soln. To obtain moles, therefore, we multiply liters and molarity:
moles = liters × molarity = liters × moles/liter.

To illustrate the conversion of moles to volume, let's calculate the volume of 0.30 M HNO_3 solution required to supply 2.0 mol of HNO_3:

$$\text{Liters soln} = (2.0 \text{ mol } HNO_3)\left(\frac{1 \text{ L soln}}{0.30 \text{ mol } HNO_3}\right) = 6.7 \text{ L soln}$$

In this case we must use the reciprocal of molarity in the conversion: liters = moles $\times$ $1/M$ = moles $\times$ liters/mole.

■ SAMPLE EXERCISE 4.13 | Using Molarity to Calculate Grams of Solute

How many grams of Na_2SO_4 are required to make 0.350 L of 0.500 M Na_2SO_4?

SOLUTION

Analyze: We are given the volume of the solution (0.350 L), its concentration (0.500 M), and the identity of the solute Na_2SO_4 and asked to calculate the number of grams of the solute in the solution.

Plan: We can use the definition of molarity (Equation 4.33) to determine the number of moles of solute, and then convert moles to grams using the molar mass of the solute.

$$M_{Na_2SO_4} = \frac{\text{moles } Na_2SO_4}{\text{liters soln}}$$

Solve: Calculating the moles of Na_2SO_4 using the molarity and volume of solution gives

$$M_{Na_2SO_4} = \frac{\text{moles } Na_2SO_4}{\text{liters soln}}$$

$$\text{moles } Na_2SO_4 = \text{liters soln} \times M_{Na_2SO_4}$$

$$= (0.350 \text{ L soln})\left(\frac{0.500 \text{ mol } Na_2SO_4}{1 \text{ L soln}}\right)$$

$$= 0.175 \text{ mol } Na_2SO_4$$

Because each mole of Na_2SO_4 weighs 142 g, the required number of grams of Na_2SO_4 is

$$\text{grams } Na_2SO_4 = (0.175 \text{ mol } Na_2SO_4)\left(\frac{142 \text{ g } Na_2SO_4}{1 \text{ mol } Na_2SO_4}\right) = 24.9 \text{ g } Na_2SO_4$$

Check: The magnitude of the answer, the units, and the number of significant figures are all appropriate.

■ PRACTICE EXERCISE

(a) How many grams of Na_2SO_4 are there in 15 mL of 0.50 M Na_2SO_4? **(b)** How many milliliters of 0.50 M Na_2SO_4 solution are needed to provide 0.038 mol of this salt?
Answers: **(a)** 1.1 g, **(b)** 76 mL

Dilution

Solutions that are used routinely in the laboratory are often purchased or prepared in concentrated form (called *stock solutions*). Hydrochloric acid, for example, is purchased as a 12 M solution (concentrated HCl). Solutions of lower concentrations can then be obtained by adding water, a process called **dilution**.*

Let's look at how to prepare a dilute solution from a concentrated one. Suppose we wanted to prepare 250.0 mL (that is, 0.2500 L) of 0.100 M $CuSO_4$ solution by diluting a stock solution containing 1.00 M $CuSO_4$. When solvent is added to dilute a solution, the number of moles of solute remains unchanged.

$$\text{Moles solute before dilution} = \text{moles solute after dilution} \qquad [4.34]$$

*In diluting a concentrated acid or base, the acid or base should be added to water and then further diluted by adding more water. Adding water directly to concentrated acid or base can cause spattering because of the intense heat generated.

For a long time it was thought that dehydration was a potential danger for people engaged in extended vigorous activity. Thus, athletes were encouraged to drink lots of water while engaged in active sport. The trend toward extensive hydration has spread throughout society; many people carry water bottles everywhere and dutifully keep well hydrated.

It turns out, though, that in some circumstances, drinking too much water is a greater danger than not drinking enough. Excess water consumption can lead to *hyponatremia*, a condition in which the concentration of sodium ion in the blood is too low. In the past decade at least four marathon runners have died from hyponatremia-related trauma, and dozens more have become seriously ill. For example, a first-time marathoner named Hillary Bellamy, running in the Marine Corps marathon in 2003, collapsed near mile 22 and died the next day. One physician who treated her said that she died from hyponatremia-induced brain swelling, the result of drinking too much water before and during the race.

The normal blood sodium level is 135 to 145 m*M (millimolar)*. When that level drops to as low as 125 m*M*, dizziness and confusion set in. A concentration below 120 m*M* can be critical. Low sodium level in the blood causes brain tissue to swell. Dangerously low levels can occur in a marathon runner or other active athlete who is sweating out salt at the same time that excessive salt-free water is being drunk to compensate for water loss. The condition affects women more than men because of their generally different body composition and patterns of metabolism. Drinking a sport drink, such as Gatorade, which contains some electrolytes, helps to prevent hyponatremia (Figure 4.17 ▶).

Contrary to popular belief, dehydration is not as likely as overhydration to present a life-threatening situation, though it can contribute to heat stroke when the temperature is high. Athletes frequently lose several pounds in the course of extreme workouts, all in the form of water loss, with no lasting adverse effects. When, for instance, Amby Burfoot ran in the Boston Marathon in 1968, his body weight went from 138 to 129 pounds during the race. He lost 6.5% of his body weight while winning the men's competition that year. Weight losses of this magnitude are typical of elite marathon runners, who produce tremendous amounts of heat and sweat and cannot afford to slow down for much drinking.
Related Exercises: 4.63, 4.64

▲ Figure 4.17 **Water stations.** To help prevent overhydration, the number of water stations such as this one has been reduced in many marathon events.

Because we know both the volume and concentration of the dilute solution, we can calculate the number of moles of $CuSO_4$ it contains.

$$\text{moles } CuSO_4 \text{ in dil soln} = (0.2500 \text{ L soln})\left(0.100 \, \frac{\text{mol } CuSO_4}{\text{L soln}}\right)$$

$$= 0.0250 \text{ mol } CuSO_4$$

Now we can calculate the volume of the concentrated solution needed to provide 0.0250 mol $CuSO_4$:

$$\text{Liters of conc soln} = (0.0250 \text{ mol } CuSO_4)\left(\frac{1 \text{ L soln}}{1.00 \text{ mol } CuSO_4}\right) = 0.0250 \text{ L}$$

Thus, this dilution is achieved by withdrawing 0.0250 L (that is, 25.0 mL) of the 1.00 *M* solution using a pipet, adding it to a 250-mL volumetric flask, and then diluting it to a final volume of 250.0 mL, as shown in Figure 4.18 ▼. Notice that the diluted solution is less intensely colored than the concentrated one.

In laboratory situations, calculations of this sort are often made very quickly with a simple equation that can be derived by remembering that the number of moles of solute is the same in both the concentrated and dilute solutions and that moles = molarity × liters:

$$\text{moles solute in conc soln} = \text{moles solute in dil soln}$$

[4.35]

$$M_{conc} \times V_{conc} = M_{dil} \times V_{dil}$$

◀ Figure 4.18 **Procedure for preparing 250 mL of 0.100 M CuSO₄ by dilution of 1.00 M CuSO₄.** (a) Draw 25.0 mL of the 1.00 M solution into a pipet. (b) Add this to a 250-mL volumetric flask. (c) Add water to dilute the solution to a total volume of 250 mL.

(a)   (b)   (c)

GIVE IT SOME THOUGHT

How is the molarity of a 0.50 M KBr solution changed when water is added to double its volume?

The molarity of the more concentrated stock solution (M_{conc}) is always larger than the molarity of the dilute solution (M_{dil}). Because the volume of the solution increases upon dilution, V_{dil} is always larger than V_{conc}. Although Equation 4.35 is derived in terms of liters, any volume unit can be used as long as that same unit is used on both sides of the equation. For example, in the calculation we did for the CuSO₄ solution, we have

$$(1.00\ M)(V_{conc}) = (0.100\ M)(250.\ \text{mL})$$

Solving for V_{conc} gives $V_{conc} = 25.0$ mL as before.

■ SAMPLE EXERCISE 4.14 | Preparing a Solution by Dilution

How many milliliters of 3.0 M H₂SO₄ are needed to make 450 mL of 0.10 M H₂SO₄?

SOLUTION

Analyze: We need to dilute a concentrated solution. We are given the molarity of a more concentrated solution (3.0 M) and the volume and molarity of a more dilute one containing the same solute (450 mL of 0.10 M solution). We must calculate the volume of the concentrated solution needed to prepare the dilute solution.

Plan: We can calculate the number of moles of solute, H₂SO₄, in the dilute solution and then calculate the volume of the concentrated solution needed to supply this amount of solute. Alternatively, we can directly apply Equation 4.35. Let's compare the two methods.

Solve: Calculating the moles of H₂SO₄ in the dilute solution:

$$\text{moles H}_2\text{SO}_4 \text{ in dilute solution} = (0.450\ \text{L soln})\left(\frac{0.10\ \text{mol H}_2\text{SO}_4}{1\ \text{L soln}}\right)$$

$$= 0.045\ \text{mol H}_2\text{SO}_4$$

Calculating the volume of the concentrated solution that contains 0.045 mol H₂SO₄:

$$\text{L conc soln} = (0.045\ \text{mol H}_2\text{SO}_4)\left(\frac{1\ \text{L soln}}{3.0\ \text{mol H}_2\text{SO}_4}\right) = 0.015\ \text{L soln}$$

Converting liters to milliliters gives 15 mL.

If we apply Equation 4.35, we get the same result:

$$(3.0\ M)(V_{conc}) = (0.10\ M)(450\ mL)$$

$$(V_{conc}) = \frac{(0.10\ M)(450\ mL)}{3.0\ M} = 15\ mL$$

Either way, we see that if we start with 15 mL of 3.0 M H_2SO_4 and dilute it to a total volume of 450 mL, the desired 0.10 M solution will be obtained.

Check: The calculated volume seems reasonable because a small volume of concentrated solution is used to prepare a large volume of dilute solution.

■■ **PRACTICE EXERCISE**

(a) What volume of 2.50 M lead(II) nitrate solution contains 0.0500 mol of Pb^{2+}? **(b)** How many milliliters of 5.0 M $K_2Cr_2O_7$ solution must be diluted to prepare 250 mL of 0.10 M solution? **(c)** If 10.0 mL of a 10.0 M stock solution of NaOH is diluted to 250 mL, what is the concentration of the resulting stock solution?
Answers: **(a)** 0.0200 L = 20.0 mL, **(b)** 5.0 mL, **(c)** 0.40 M

4.6 SOLUTION STOICHIOMETRY
AND CHEMICAL ANALYSIS

Imagine that you have to determine the concentrations of several ions in a sample of lake water. Although many instrumental methods have been developed for such analyses, chemical reactions such as those discussed in this chapter continue to be used. In Chapter 3 we learned that if you know the chemical equation and the amount of one reactant consumed in the reaction, you can calculate the quantities of other reactants and products. In this section we briefly explore such analyses of solutions.

Recall that the coefficients in a balanced equation give the relative number of moles of reactants and products. (Section 3.6) To use this information, we must convert the quantities of substances involved in a reaction into moles. When we are dealing with grams of substances, as we were in Chapter 3, we use the molar mass to achieve this conversion. When we are working with solutions of known molarity, however, we use molarity and volume to determine the number of moles (moles solute = M × L). Figure 4.19▼ summarizes this approach to using stoichiometry.

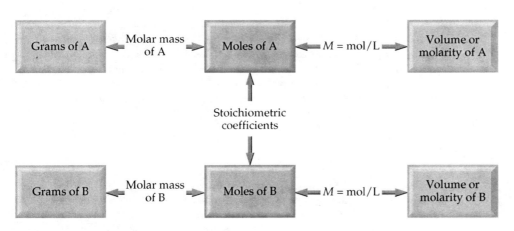

▲ Figure 4.19 **Problem-solving procedure.** Outline of the procedure used to solve stoichiometry problems that involve measured (laboratory) units of mass, solution concentration (molarity), or volume.

■■■ **SAMPLE EXERCISE 4.15** | **Using Mass Relations in a Neutralization Reaction**

How many grams of $Ca(OH)_2$ are needed to neutralize 25.0 mL of 0.100 M HNO_3?

SOLUTION

Analyze: The reactants are an acid, HNO_3, and a base, $Ca(OH)_2$. The volume and molarity of HNO_3 are given, and we are asked how many grams of $Ca(OH)_2$ are needed to neutralize this quantity of HNO_3.

Plan: We can use the molarity and volume of the HNO_3 solution to calculate the number of moles of HNO_3. We then use the balanced equation to relate the moles of HNO_3 to moles of $Ca(OH)_2$. Finally, we can convert moles of $Ca(OH)_2$ to grams. These steps can be summarized as follows:

$$L_{HNO_3} \times M_{HNO_3} \Rightarrow \text{mol } HNO_3 \Rightarrow \text{mol } Ca(OH)_2 \Rightarrow \text{g } Ca(OH)_2$$

Solve: The product of the molar concentration of a solution and its volume in liters gives the number of moles of solute:

$$\text{moles } HNO_3 = L_{HNO_3} \times M_{HNO_3} = (0.0250 \text{ L})\left(0.100 \frac{\text{mol } HNO_3}{L}\right)$$

$$= 2.50 \times 10^{-3} \text{ mol } HNO_3$$

Because this is an acid–base neutralization reaction, HNO_3 and $Ca(OH)_2$ react to form H_2O and the salt containing Ca^{2+} and NO_3^-:

$$2 HNO_3(aq) + Ca(OH)_2(s) \longrightarrow 2 H_2O(l) + Ca(NO_3)_2(aq)$$

Thus, 2 mol $HNO_3 \backsimeq$ 1 mol $Ca(OH)_2$. Therefore,

$$\text{grams } Ca(OH)_2 = (2.50 \times 10^{-3} \text{ mol } HNO_3)\left(\frac{1 \text{ mol } Ca(OH)_2}{2 \text{ mol } HNO_3}\right)\left(\frac{74.1 \text{ g } Ca(OH)_2}{1 \text{ mol } Ca(OH)_2}\right)$$

$$= 0.0926 \text{ g } Ca(OH)_2$$

Check: The size of the answer is reasonable. A small volume of dilute acid will require only a small amount of base to neutralize it.

■■■ **PRACTICE EXERCISE**

(a) How many grams of NaOH are needed to neutralize 20.0 mL of 0.150 M H_2SO_4 solution? **(b)** How many liters of 0.500 M HCl(aq) are needed to react completely with 0.100 mol of $Pb(NO_3)_2(aq)$, forming a precipitate of $PbCl_2(s)$?
Answers: **(a)** 0.240 g, **(b)** 0.400 L

Titrations

To determine the concentration of a particular solute in a solution, chemists often carry out a **titration**, which involves combining a sample of the solution with a reagent solution of known concentration, called a **standard solution**. Titrations can be conducted using acid–base, precipitation, or oxidation-reduction reactions. Suppose we have an HCl solution of unknown concentration and an NaOH solution we know to be 0.100 M. To determine the concentration of the HCl solution, we take a specific volume of that solution, say 20.00 mL. We then slowly add the standard NaOH solution to it until the neutralization reaction between the HCl and NaOH is complete. The point at which stoichiometrically equivalent quantities are brought together is known as the **equivalence point** of the titration.

▲ GIVE IT SOME THOUGHT

25.00 mL of a 0.100 M HBr solution is titrated with a 0.200 M NaOH solution. How many mL of the NaOH solution are required to reach the equivalence point?

To titrate an unknown with a standard solution, there must be some way to determine when the equivalence point of the titration has been reached. In acid–base titrations, dyes known as acid–base **indicators** are used for this purpose.

| (a) | (b) | (c) |

▲ Figure 4.20 **Change in appearance of a solution containing phenolphthalein indicator as base is added.**
Before the end point, the solution is colorless (a). As the end point is approached, a pale pink color forms where the
base is added (b). At the end point, this pale pink color extends throughout the solution after mixing. As even
more base is added, the intensity of the pink color increases (c).

For example, the dye known as phenolphthalein is colorless in acidic solution
but is pink in basic solution. If we add phenolphthalein to an unknown solution
of acid, the solution will be colorless, as seen in Figure 4.20(a) ▲. We can then add
standard base from a buret until the solution barely turns from colorless to pink,
as seen in Figure 4.20(b). This color change indicates that the acid has been neutralized and the drop of base that caused the solution to become colored has no
acid to react with. The solution therefore becomes basic, and the dye turns pink.
The color change signals the *end point* of the titration, which usually coincides
very nearly with the equivalence point. Care must be taken to choose indicators
whose end points correspond to the equivalence point of the titration. We will
consider this matter in Chapter 17. The titration procedure is summarized in
Figure 4.21 ▼.

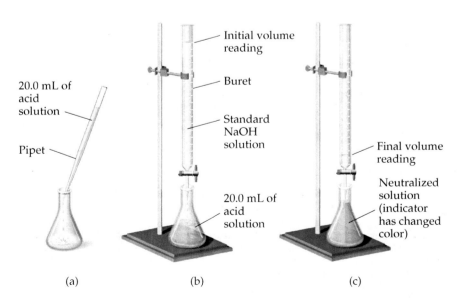

◀ Figure 4.21 **Procedure for
titrating an acid against a
standardized solution of NaOH.**
(a) A known quantity of acid is added
to a flask. (b) An acid–base indicator is
added, and standardized NaOH is
added from a buret. (c) The
equivalence point is signaled by a color
change in the indicator.

| (a) | (b) | (c) |

■■ SAMPLE EXERCISE 4.16 | Determining the Quantity of Solute by Titration

The quantity of Cl^- in a municipal water supply is determined by titrating the sample with Ag^+. The reaction taking place during the titration is

$$Ag^+(aq) + Cl^-(aq) \longrightarrow AgCl(s)$$

The end point in this type of titration is marked by a change in color of a special type of indicator. **(a)** How many grams of chloride ion are in a sample of the water if 20.2 mL of 0.100 M Ag^+ is needed to react with all the chloride in the sample? **(b)** If the sample has a mass of 10.0 g, what percent Cl^- does it contain?

SOLUTION

Analyze: We are given the volume (20.2 mL) and molarity (0.100 M) of a solution of Ag^+ and the chemical equation for reaction of this ion with Cl^-. We are asked first to calculate the number of grams of Cl^- in the sample and, second, to calculate the mass percent of Cl^- in the sample.

(a) Plan: We begin by using the volume and molarity of Ag^+ to calculate the number of moles of Ag^+ used in the titration. We can then use the balanced equation to determine the moles of Cl^- in the sample and from that the grams of Cl^-.

Solve:

$$\text{moles } Ag^+ = (20.2 \text{ mL soln})\left(\frac{1 \text{ L soln}}{1000 \text{ mL soln}}\right)\left(0.100 \frac{\text{mol } Ag^+}{\text{L soln}}\right)$$

$$= 2.02 \times 10^{-3} \text{ mol } Ag^+$$

From the balanced equation we see that 1 mol $Ag^+ \hat{=} 1$ mol Cl^-. Using this information and the molar mass of Cl, we have

$$\text{grams } Cl^- = (2.02 \times 10^{-3} \text{ mol } Ag^+)\left(\frac{1 \text{ mol } Cl^-}{1 \text{ mol } Ag^+}\right)\left(\frac{35.5 \text{ g } Cl^-}{1 \text{ mol } Cl^-}\right)$$

$$= 7.17 \times 10^{-2} \text{ g } Cl^-$$

(b) Plan: To calculate the percentage of Cl^- in the sample, we compare the number of grams of Cl^- in the sample, 7.17×10^{-2} g, with the original mass of the sample, 10.0 g.

Solve: Percent $Cl^- = \dfrac{7.17 \times 10^{-2} \text{ g}}{10.0 \text{ g}} \times 100\% = 0.717\% \text{ } Cl^-$

Comment: Chloride ion is one of the most common ions in water and sewage. Ocean water contains 1.92% Cl^-. Whether water containing Cl^- tastes salty depends on the other ions present. If the only accompanying ions are Na^+, a salty taste may be detected with as little as 0.03% Cl^-.

■■ PRACTICE EXERCISE

A sample of an iron ore is dissolved in acid, and the iron is converted to Fe^{2+}. The sample is then titrated with 47.20 mL of 0.02240 M MnO_4^- solution. The oxidation-reduction reaction that occurs during titration is as follows:

$$MnO_4^-(aq) + 5 Fe^{2+}(aq) + 8 H^+(aq) \longrightarrow Mn^{2+}(aq) + 5 Fe^{3+}(aq) + 4 H_2O(l)$$

(a) How many moles of MnO_4^- were added to the solution? **(b)** How many moles of Fe^{2+} were in the sample? **(c)** How many grams of iron were in the sample? **(d)** If the sample had a mass of 0.8890 g, what is the percentage of iron in the sample?
Answers: **(a)** 1.057×10^{-3} mol MnO_4^- **(b)** 5.286×10^{-3} mol Fe^{2+}, **(c)** 0.2952 g, **(d)** 33.21%

■■ SAMPLE EXERCISE 4.17 | Determining Solution Concentration Via an Acid–Base Titration

One commercial method used to peel potatoes is to soak them in a solution of NaOH for a short time, remove them from the NaOH, and spray off the peel. The concentration of NaOH is normally in the range of 3 to 6 M. The NaOH is analyzed periodically. In one such analysis, 45.7 mL of 0.500 M H_2SO_4 is required to neutralize a 20.0-mL sample of NaOH solution. What is the concentration of the NaOH solution?

SOLUTION

Analyze: We are given the volume (45.7 mL) and molarity (0.500 M) of an H_2SO_4 solution that reacts completely with a 20.0-mL sample of NaOH. We are asked to calculate the molarity of the NaOH solution.

Plan: We can use the volume and molarity of the H_2SO_4 to calculate the number of moles of this substance. Then, we can use this quantity and the balanced equation for the reaction to calculate the number of moles of NaOH. Finally, we can use the moles of NaOH and the volume of this solution to calculate molarity.

Solve: The number of moles of H_2SO_4 is given by the product of the volume and molarity of this solution:

$$\text{moles } H_2SO_4 = (45.7 \text{ mL soln})\left(\frac{1 \text{ L soln}}{1000 \text{ mL soln}}\right)\left(0.500 \frac{\text{mol } H_2SO_4}{\text{L soln}}\right)$$

$$= 2.28 \times 10^{-2} \text{ mol } H_2SO_4$$

Acids react with metal hydroxides to form water and a salt. Thus, the balanced equation for the neutralization reaction is

$$H_2SO_4(aq) + 2\,NaOH(aq) \longrightarrow 2\,H_2O(l) + Na_2SO_4(aq)$$

According to the balanced equation, 1 mol $H_2SO_4 \triangleq 2$ mol NaOH. Therefore,

$$\text{moles NaOH} = (2.28 \times 10^{-2} \text{ mol } H_2SO_4)\left(\frac{2 \text{ mol NaOH}}{1 \text{ mol } H_2SO_4}\right)$$

$$= 4.56 \times 10^{-2} \text{ mol NaOH}$$

Knowing the number of moles of NaOH present in 20.0 mL of solution allows us to calculate the molarity of this solution:

$$\text{Molarity NaOH} = \frac{\text{mol NaOH}}{\text{L soln}} = \left(\frac{4.56 \times 10^{-2} \text{ mol NaOH}}{20.0 \text{ mL soln}}\right)\left(\frac{1000 \text{ mL soln}}{1 \text{ L soln}}\right)$$

$$= 2.28 \frac{\text{mol NaOH}}{\text{L soln}} = 2.28 \, M$$

■■■ PRACTICE EXERCISE

What is the molarity of an NaOH solution if 48.0 mL is needed to neutralize 35.0 mL of 0.144 M H_2SO_4?
Answers: 0.210 M

■■■ SAMPLE INTEGRATIVE EXERCISE | Putting Concepts Together

Note: Integrative exercises require skills from earlier chapters as well as ones from the present chapter.
    A sample of 70.5 mg of potassium phosphate is added to 15.0 mL of 0.050 M silver nitrate, resulting in the formation of a precipitate. **(a)** Write the molecular equation for the reaction. **(b)** What is the limiting reactant in the reaction? **(c)** Calculate the theoretical yield, in grams, of the precipitate that forms.

SOLUTION

(a) Potassium phosphate and silver nitrate are both ionic compounds. Potassium phosphate contains K^+ and PO_4^{3-} ions, so its chemical formula is K_3PO_4. Silver nitrate contains Ag^+ and NO_3^- ions, so its chemical formula is $AgNO_3$. Because both reactants are strong electrolytes, the solution contains K^+, PO_4^{3-}, Ag^+, and NO_3^- ions before the reaction occurs. According to the solubility guidelines in Table 4.1, Ag^+ and PO_4^{3-} form an insoluble compound, so Ag_3PO_4 will precipitate from the solution. In contrast, K^+ and NO_3^- will remain in solution because KNO_3 is water soluble. Thus, the balanced molecular equation for the reaction is

$$K_3PO_4(aq) + 3\,AgNO_3(aq) \longrightarrow Ag_3PO_4(s) + 3\,KNO_3(aq)$$

(b) To determine the limiting reactant, we must examine the number of moles of each reactant. ⟶(Section 3.7) The number of moles of K_3PO_4 is calculated from the mass of the sample using the molar mass as a conversion factor. ⟶(Section 3.4)

The molar mass of K_3PO_4 is $3(39.1) + 31.0 + 4(16.0) = 212.3$ g/mol. Converting milligrams to grams and then to moles, we have

$$(70.5 \text{ mg } K_3PO_4)\left(\frac{10^{-3} \text{ g } K_3PO_4}{1 \text{ mg } K_3PO_4}\right)\left(\frac{1 \text{ mol } K_3PO_4}{212.3 \text{ g } K_3PO_4}\right) = 3.32 \times 10^{-4} \text{ mol } K_3PO_4$$

We determine the number of moles of $AgNO_3$ from the volume and molarity of the solution. ⟵⟶ (Section 4.5) Converting milliliters to liters and then to moles, we have

$$(15.0 \text{ mL})\left(\frac{10^{-3} \text{ L}}{1 \text{ mL}}\right)\left(\frac{0.050 \text{ mol } AgNO_3}{L}\right) = 7.5 \times 10^{-4} \text{ mol } AgNO_3$$

Comparing the amounts of the two reactants, we find that there are $(7.5 \times 10^{-4})/(3.32 \times 10^{-4}) = 2.3$ times as many moles of $AgNO_3$ as there are moles of K_3PO_4. According to the balanced equation, however, 1 mol K_3PO_4 requires 3 mol of $AgNO_3$. Thus, there is insufficient $AgNO_3$ to consume the K_3PO_4, and $AgNO_3$ is the limiting reactant.

(c) The precipitate is Ag_3PO_4, whose molar mass is $3(107.9) + 31.0 + 4(16.0) = 418.7$ g/mol. To calculate the number of grams of Ag_3PO_4 that could be produced in this reaction (the theoretical yield), we use the number of moles of the limiting reactant, converting mol $AgNO_3 \Rightarrow$ mol $Ag_3PO_4 \Rightarrow$ g Ag_3PO_4. We use the coefficients in the balanced equation to convert moles of $AgNO_3$ to moles Ag_3PO_4, and we use the molar mass of Ag_3PO_4 to convert the number of moles of this substance to grams.

$$(7.5 \times 10^{-4} \text{ mol } AgNO_3)\left(\frac{1 \text{ mol } Ag_3PO_4}{3 \text{ mol } AgNO_3}\right)\left(\frac{418.7 \text{ g } Ag_3PO_4}{1 \text{ mol } Ag_3PO_4}\right) = 0.10 \text{ g } Ag_3PO_4$$

The answer has only two significant figures because the quantity of $AgNO_3$ is given to only two significant figures.

CHAPTER REVIEW

SUMMARY AND KEY TERMS

Introduction and Section 4.1 Solutions in which water is the dissolving medium are called **aqueous solutions**. The component of the solution that is in the greater quantity is the **solvent**. The other components are **solutes**.

Any substance whose aqueous solution contains ions is called an **electrolyte**. Any substance that forms a solution containing no ions is a **nonelectrolyte**. Electrolytes that are present in solution entirely as ions are **strong electrolytes**, whereas those that are present partly as ions and partly as molecules are **weak electrolytes**. Ionic compounds dissociate into ions when they dissolve, and they are strong electrolytes. The solubility of ionic substances is made possible by **solvation**, the interaction of ions with polar solvent molecules. Most molecular compounds are nonelectrolytes, although some are weak electrolytes, and a few are strong electrolytes. When representing the ionization of a weak electrolyte in solution, half-arrows in both directions are used, indicating that the forward and reverse reactions can achieve a chemical balance called a **chemical equilibrium**.

Section 4.2 Precipitation reactions are those in which an insoluble product, called a **precipitate**, forms. Solubility guidelines help determine whether or not an ionic compound will be soluble in water. (The **solubility** of a substance is the amount that dissolves in a given quantity of solvent.) Reactions such as precipitation reactions, in which cations and anions appear to exchange partners, are called **exchange reactions**, or **metathesis reactions**.

Chemical equations can be written to show whether dissolved substances are present in solution predominantly as ions or molecules. When the complete chemical formulas of all reactants and products are used, the equation is called a **molecular equation**. A **complete ionic equation** shows all dissolved strong electrolytes as their component ions. In a **net ionic equation**, those ions that go through the reaction unchanged (**spectator ions**) are omitted.

Section 4.3 Acids and bases are important electrolytes. **Acids** are proton donors; they increase the concentration of $H^+(aq)$ in aqueous solutions to which they are added.

Bases are proton acceptors; they increase the concentration of $OH^-(aq)$ in aqueous solutions. Those acids and bases that are strong electrolytes are called **strong acids** and **strong bases**, respectively. Those that are weak electrolytes are **weak acids** and **weak bases**. When solutions of acids and bases are mixed, a **neutralization reaction** results. The neutralization reaction between an acid and a metal hydroxide produces water and a **salt**. Gases can also be formed as a result of acid–base reactions. The reaction of a sulfide with an acid forms $H_2S(g)$; the reaction between a carbonate and an acid forms $CO_2(g)$.

Section 4.4 **Oxidation** is the loss of electrons by a substance, whereas **reduction** is the gain of electrons by a substance. **Oxidation numbers** keep track of electrons during chemical reactions and are assigned to atoms using specific rules. The oxidation of an element results in an increase in its oxidation number, whereas reduction is accompanied by a decrease in oxidation number. Oxidation is always accompanied by reduction, giving **oxidation-reduction**, or redox, **reactions**.

Many metals are oxidized by O_2, acids, and salts. The redox reactions between metals and acids and between metals and salts are called **displacement reactions**. The products of these displacement reactions are always an element (H_2 or a metal) and a salt. Comparing such reactions allows us to rank metals according to their ease of oxidation. A list of metals arranged in order of decreasing ease of oxidation is called an **activity series**. Any metal on the list can be oxidized by ions of metals (or H^+) below it in the series.

Section 4.5 The composition of a solution expresses the relative quantities of solvent and solutes that it contains. One of the common ways to express the **concentration** of a solute in a solution is in terms of molarity. The **molarity** of a solution is the number of moles of solute per liter of solution. Molarity makes it possible to interconvert solution volume and number of moles of solute. Solutions of known molarity can be formed either by weighing out the solute and diluting it to a known volume or by the **dilution** of a more concentrated solution of known concentration (a stock solution). Adding solvent to the solution (the process of dilution) decreases the concentration of the solute without changing the number of moles of solute in the solution ($M_{conc} \times V_{conc} = M_{dil} \times V_{dil}$).

Section 4.6 In the process called **titration**, we combine a solution of known concentration (a **standard solution**) with a solution of unknown concentration to determine the unknown concentration or the quantity of solute in the unknown. The point in the titration at which stoichiometrically equivalent quantities of reactants are brought together is called the **equivalence point**. An **indicator** can be used to show the end point of the titration, which coincides closely with the equivalence point.

KEY SKILLS

- Recognize compounds as acids or bases, and as strong, weak, or nonelectrolytes.

- Recognize reactions as acid–base, precipitation, metathesis, or redox.

- Be able to calculate moles or grams of substances in solution using molarity.

- Understand how to carry out a dilution to achieve a desired solution concentration.

- Understand how to perform and interpret the results of a titration.

KEY EQUATIONS

- $\text{Molarity} = \dfrac{\text{moles solute}}{\text{volume of solution in liters}}$ [4.33]

  Molarity is the most commonly used unit of concentration in chemistry.

- $M_{conc} \times V_{conc} = M_{dil} \times V_{dil}$ [4.35]

  When adding solvent to a concentrated solution to make a dilute solution, molarities and volumes of both concentrated and dilute solutions can be calculated if three of the quantities are known.

VISUALIZING CONCEPTS

4.1 Which of the following schematic drawings best describes a solution of Li_2SO_4 in water (water molecules not shown for simplicity)? [Section 4.1]

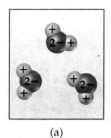

(a)

(b)

(c)

4.2 Methanol, CH_3OH, and hydrogen chloride, HCl, are both molecular substances, yet an aqueous solution of methanol does not conduct an electrical current, whereas a solution of HCl does conduct. Account for this difference. [Section 4.1]

4.3 Aqueous solutions of three different substances, AX, AY, and AZ, are represented by the three diagrams below. Identify each substance as a strong electrolyte, weak electrolyte, or nonelectrolyte. [Section 4.1]

AX

(a)

AY

(b)

AZ

(c)

4.4 A 0.1 M solution of acetic acid, CH_3COOH, causes the lightbulb in the apparatus of Figure 4.2 to glow about as brightly as a 0.001 M solution of HBr. How do you account for this fact? [Section 4.1]

4.5 You are presented with three white solids, A, B, and C, which are glucose (a sugar substance), NaOH, and AgBr. Solid A dissolves in water to form a conducting solution. B is not soluble in water. C dissolves in water to form a nonconducting solution. Identify A, B, and C. [Section 4.2]

4.6 We have seen that ions in aqueous solution are stabilized by the attractions between the ions and the water molecules. Why then do some pairs of ions in solution form precipitates? [Section 4.2]

4.7 Which of the following ions will *always* be a spectator ion in a precipitation reaction? **(a)** Cl^-, **(b)** NO_3^-, **(c)** NH_4^+, **(d)** S^{2-}, **(e)** SO_4^{2-}. Explain briefly. [Section 4.2]

4.8 The labels have fallen off two bottles, one containing $Mg(NO_3)_2$ and the other containing $Pb(NO_3)_2$. You have a bottle of dilute H_2SO_4. How could you use it to test a portion of each solution to identify which solution is which? [Section 4.2]

4.9 Explain how a redox reaction involves electrons in the same way that an acid–base reaction involves protons. [Sections 4.3 and 4.4]

4.10 If you want to double the concentration of a solution, how could you do it? [Section 4.5]

EXERCISES

Electrolytes

4.11 When asked what causes electrolyte solutions to conduct electricity, a student responds that it is due to the movement of electrons through the solution. Is the student correct? If not, what is the correct response?

4.12 When methanol, CH_3OH, is dissolved in water, a nonconducting solution results. When acetic acid, CH_3COOH, dissolves in water, the solution is weakly conducting and acidic in nature. Describe what happens upon dissolution in the two cases, and account for the different results.

4.13 We have learned in this chapter that many ionic solids dissolve in water as strong electrolytes, that is, as separated ions in solution. What properties of water facilitate this process?

4.14 What does it mean to say that ions are hydrated when an ionic substance dissolves in water?

4.15 Specify what ions are present in solution upon dissolving each of the following substances in water: **(a)** $ZnCl_2$, **(b)** HNO_3, **(c)** $(NH_4)_2SO_4$, **(d)** $Ca(OH)_2$.

4.16 Specify what ions are present upon dissolving each of the following substances in water: **(a)** MgI_2, **(b)** $Al(NO_3)_3$, **(c)** $HClO_4$, **(d)** $NaCH_3COO$.

4.17 Formic acid, HCOOH, is a weak electrolyte. What solute particles are present in an aqueous solution of this compound? Write the chemical equation for the ionization of HCOOH.

4.18 Acetone, CH_3COCH_3, is a nonelectrolyte; hypochlorous acid, HClO, is a weak electrolyte; and ammonium chloride, NH_4Cl, is a strong electrolyte. **(a)** What are the solute particles present in aqueous solutions of each compound? **(b)** If 0.1 mol of each compound is dissolved in solution, which one contains 0.2 mol of solute particles, which contains 0.1 mol of solute particles, and which contains somewhere between 0.1 and 0.2 mol of solute particles?

Precipitation Reactions and Net Ionic Equations

4.19 Using solubility guidelines, predict whether each of the following compounds is soluble or insoluble in water: **(a)** $NiCl_2$, **(b)** Ag_2S, **(c)** Cs_3PO_4, **(d)** $SrCO_3$, **(e)** $PbSO_4$.

4.20 Predict whether each of the following compounds is soluble in water: **(a)** $Ni(OH)_2$, **(b)** $PbBr_2$, **(c)** $Ba(NO_3)_2$, **(d)** $AlPO_4$, **(e)** $AgCH_3COO$.

4.21 Will precipitation occur when the following solutions are mixed? If so, write a balanced chemical equation for the reaction. **(a)** Na_2CO_3 and $AgNO_3$, **(b)** $NaNO_3$ and $NiSO_4$, **(c)** $FeSO_4$ and $Pb(NO_3)_2$.

4.22 Identify the precipitate (if any) that forms when the following solutions are mixed, and write a balanced equation for each reaction. **(a)** $Ni(NO_3)_2$ and $NaOH$, **(b)** $NaOH$ and K_2SO_4, **(c)** Na_2S and $Cu(CH_3COO)_2$.

4.23 Name the spectator ions in any reactions that may be involved when each of the following pairs of solutions are mixed.
(a) $Na_2CO_3(aq)$ and $MgSO_4(aq)$
(b) $Pb(NO_3)_2(aq)$ and $Na_2S(aq)$
(c) $(NH_4)_3PO_4(aq)$ and $CaCl_2(aq)$

4.24 Write balanced net ionic equations for the reactions that occur in each of the following cases. Identify the spectator ion or ions in each reaction.

(a) $Cr_2(SO_4)_3(aq) + (NH_4)_2CO_3(aq) \longrightarrow$
(b) $Ba(NO_3)_2(aq) + K_2SO_4(aq) \longrightarrow$
(c) $Fe(NO_3)_2(aq) + KOH(aq) \longrightarrow$

4.25 Separate samples of a solution of an unknown salt are treated with dilute solutions of HBr, H_2SO_4, and $NaOH$. A precipitate forms in all three cases. Which of the following cations could the solution contain: K^+; Pb^{2+}; Ba^{2+}?

4.26 Separate samples of a solution of an unknown ionic compound are treated with dilute $AgNO_3$, $Pb(NO_3)_2$, and $BaCl_2$. Precipitates form in all three cases. Which of the following could be the anion of the unknown salt: Br^-; CO_3^{2-}; NO_3^-?

4.27 You know that an unlabeled bottle contains a solution of one of the following: $AgNO_3$, $CaCl_2$, or $Al_2(SO_4)_3$. A friend suggests that you test a portion of the solution with $Ba(NO_3)_2$ and then with $NaCl$ solutions. Explain how these two tests together would be sufficient to determine which salt is present in the solution.

4.28 Three solutions are mixed together to form a single solution. One contains 0.2 mol $Pb(CH_3COO)_2$, the second contains 0.1 mol Na_2S, and the third contains 0.1 mol $CaCl_2$. **(a)** Write the net ionic equations for the precipitation reaction or reactions that occur. **(b)** What are the spectator ions in the solution?

Acid–Base Reactions

4.29 Which of the following solutions has the largest concentration of solvated protons: **(a)** 0.2 M $LiOH$, **(b)** 0.2 M HI, **(c)** 1.0 M methyl alcohol (CH_3OH)? Explain.

4.30 Which of the following solutions is the most basic? **(a)** 0.6 M NH_3, **(b)** 0.150 M KOH, **(c)** 0.100 M $Ba(OH)_2$. Explain.

4.31 What is the difference between **(a)** a monoprotic acid and a diprotic acid, **(b)** a weak acid and a strong acid, **(c)** an acid and a base?

4.32 Explain the following observations: **(a)** NH_3 contains no OH^- ions, and yet its aqueous solutions are basic; **(b)** HF is called a weak acid, and yet it is very reactive; **(c)** although sulfuric acid is a strong electrolyte, an aqueous solution of H_2SO_4 contains more HSO_4^- ions than SO_4^{2-} ions.

4.33 HCl, HBr, and HI are strong acids, yet HF is a weak acid. What does this mean in terms of the extent to which these substances are ionized in solution?

4.34 What is the relationship between the solubility rules in Table 4.1 and the list of strong bases in Table 4.2? Another way of asking this question is, why is $Cd(OH)_2$, for example, not listed as a strong base in Table 4.2?

4.35 Label each of the following substances as an acid, base, salt, or none of the above. Indicate whether the substance exists in aqueous solution entirely in molecular form, entirely as ions, or as a mixture of molecules and ions. **(a)** HF; **(b)** acetonitrile, CH_3CN; **(c)** $NaClO_4$; **(d)** $Ba(OH)_2$.

4.36 An aqueous solution of an unknown solute is tested with litmus paper and found to be acidic. The solution is weakly conducting compared with a solution of $NaCl$ of the same concentration. Which of the following substances could the unknown be: KOH, NH_3, HNO_3, $KClO_2$, H_3PO_3, CH_3COCH_3 (acetone)?

4.37 Classify each of the following substances as a nonelectrolyte, weak electrolyte, or strong electrolyte in water: **(a)** H_2SO_3, **(b)** C_2H_5OH (ethanol), **(c)** NH_3, **(d)** $KClO_3$, **(e)** $Cu(NO_3)_2$.

4.38 Classify each of the following aqueous solutions as a nonelectrolyte, weak electrolyte, or strong electrolyte: **(a)** $HClO_4$, **(b)** HNO_3, **(c)** NH_4Cl, **(d)** CH_3COCH_3 (acetone), **(e)** $CoSO_4$, **(f)** $C_{12}H_{22}O_{11}$ (sucrose).

4.39 Complete and balance the following molecular equations, and then write the net ionic equation for each:
(a) $HBr(aq) + Ca(OH)_2(aq) \longrightarrow$
(b) $Cu(OH)_2(s) + HClO_4(aq) \longrightarrow$
(c) $Al(OH)_3(s) + HNO_3(aq) \longrightarrow$

4.40 Write the balanced molecular and net ionic equations for each of the following neutralization reactions:
(a) Aqueous acetic acid is neutralized by aqueous potassium hydroxide.
(b) Solid chromium(III) hydroxide reacts with nitric acid.
(c) Aqueous hypochlorous acid and aqueous calcium hydroxide react.

4.41 Write balanced molecular and net ionic equations for the following reactions, and identify the gas formed in each: **(a)** solid cadmium sulfide reacts with an aqueous solution of sulfuric acid; **(b)** solid magnesium carbonate reacts with an aqueous solution of perchloric acid.

4.42 Because the oxide ion is basic, metal oxides react readily with acids. **(a)** Write the net ionic equation for the following reaction:

$$FeO(s) + 2\,HClO_4(aq) \longrightarrow Fe(ClO_4)_2(aq) + H_2O(l)$$

(b) Based on the equation in part (a), write the net ionic equation for the reaction that occurs between $NiO(s)$ and an aqueous solution of nitric acid.

4.43 Write a balanced molecular equation and a net ionic equation for the reaction that occurs when **(a)** solid $CaCO_3$ reacts with an aqueous solution of nitric acid; **(b)** solid iron(II) sulfide reacts with an aqueous solution of hydrobromic acid.

4.44 As K_2O dissolves in water, the oxide ion reacts with water molecules to form hydroxide ions. Write the molecular and net ionic equations for this reaction. Based on the definitions of acid and base, what ion is the base in this reaction? What is the acid? What is the spectator ion in the reaction?

Oxidation-Reduction Reactions

4.45 Define oxidation and reduction in terms of **(a)** electron transfer and **(b)** oxidation numbers.

4.46 Can oxidation occur without accompanying reduction? Explain.

4.47 Which circled region of the periodic table shown here
CQ contains the most readily oxidized elements? Which contains the least readily oxidized?

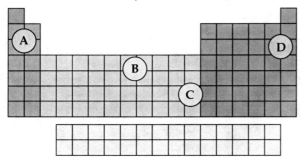

4.48 From the elements listed in Table 4.5, select an element
CQ that lies in region A of the periodic table shown above and an element that lies in region C. Write a balanced oxidation-reduction equation that shows the oxidation of one metal and reduction of an ion of the other. You will need to decide which element is oxidized and which is reduced.

4.49 Determine the oxidation number for the indicated element in each of the following substances: **(a)** S in SO_2, **(b)** C in $COCl_2$, **(c)** Mn in MnO_4^-, **(d)** Br in HBrO, **(e)** As in As_4, **(f)** O in K_2O_2.

4.50 Determine the oxidation number for the indicated element in each of the following compounds: **(a)** Ti in TiO_2, **(b)** Sn in $SnCl_3^-$, **(c)** C in $C_2O_4^{2-}$, **(d)** N in N_2H_4, **(e)** N in HNO_2, **(f)** Cr in $Cr_2O_7^{2-}$.

4.51 Which element is oxidized and which is reduced in the following reactions?
(a) $N_2(g) + 3\,H_2(g) \longrightarrow 2\,NH_3(g)$
(b) $3\,Fe(NO_3)_2(aq) + 2\,Al(s) \longrightarrow$
$$3\,Fe(s) + 2\,Al(NO_3)_3(aq)$$
(c) $Cl_2(aq) + 2\,NaI(aq) \longrightarrow I_2(aq) + 2\,NaCl(aq)$
(d) $PbS(s) + 4\,H_2O_2(aq) \longrightarrow PbSO_4(s) + 4\,H_2O(l)$

4.52 Which of the following are redox reactions? For those that are, indicate which element is oxidized and which is reduced. For those that are not, indicate whether they are precipitation or acid–base reactions.
(a) $Cu(OH)_2(s) + 2\,HNO_3(aq) \longrightarrow$
$$Cu(NO_3)_2(aq) + 2\,H_2O(l)$$
(b) $Fe_2O_3(s) + 3\,CO(g) \longrightarrow 2\,Fe(s) + 3\,CO_2(g)$
(c) $Sr(NO_3)_2(aq) + H_2SO_4(aq) \longrightarrow$
$$SrSO_4(s) + 2\,HNO_3(aq)$$
(d) $4\,Zn(s) + 10\,H^+(aq) + 2\,NO_3^-(aq) \longrightarrow$
$$4\,Zn^{2+}(aq) + N_2O(g) + 5\,H_2O(l)$$

4.53 Write balanced molecular and net ionic equations for the reactions of **(a)** manganese with dilute sulfuric acid; **(b)** chromium with hydrobromic acid; **(c)** tin with hydrochloric acid; **(d)** aluminum with formic acid, HCOOH.

4.54 Write balanced molecular and net ionic equations for the reactions of **(a)** hydrochloric acid with nickel; **(b)** dilute sulfuric acid with iron; **(c)** hydrobromic acid with magnesium; **(d)** acetic acid, CH_3COOH, with zinc.

4.55 Using the activity series (Table 4.5), write balanced chem-
CQ ical equations for the following reactions. If no reaction occurs, simply write NR. **(a)** Iron metal is added to a solution of copper(II) nitrate; **(b)** zinc metal is added to a solution of magnesium sulfate; **(c)** hydrobromic acid is added to tin metal; **(d)** hydrogen gas is bubbled through an aqueous solution of nickel(II) chloride; **(e)** aluminum metal is added to a solution of cobalt(II) sulfate.

4.56 Based on the activity series (Table 4.5), what is the out-
CQ come (if any) of each of the following reactions?
(a) $Mn(s) + NiCl_2(aq) \longrightarrow$
(b) $Cu(s) + Cr(CH_3COO)_3(aq) \longrightarrow$
(c) $Cr(s) + NiSO_4(aq) \longrightarrow$
(d) $Pt(s) + HBr(aq) \longrightarrow$
(e) $H_2(g) + CuCl_2(aq) \longrightarrow$

4.57 The metal cadmium tends to form Cd^{2+} ions. The follow-
CQ ing observations are made: (i) When a strip of zinc metal is placed in $CdCl_2(aq)$, cadmium metal is deposited on

the strip. (ii) When a strip of cadmium metal is placed in $Ni(NO_3)_2(aq)$, nickel metal is deposited on the strip. **(a)** Write net ionic equations to explain each of the observations made above. **(b)** What can you conclude about the position of cadmium in the activity series? **(c)** What experiments would you need to perform to locate more precisely the position of cadmium in the activity series?

4.58 **(a)** Use the following reactions to prepare an activity series for the halogens:

$$Br_2(aq) + 2\ NaI(aq) \longrightarrow 2\ NaBr(aq) + I_2(aq)$$
$$Cl_2(aq) + 2\ NaBr(aq) \longrightarrow 2\ NaCl(aq) + Br_2(aq)$$

(b) Relate the positions of the halogens in the periodic table with their locations in this activity series. **(c)** Predict whether a reaction occurs when the following reagents are mixed: $Cl_2(aq)$ and $KI(aq)$; $Br_2(aq)$ and $LiCl(aq)$.

Solution Composition; Molarity

4.59 **(a)** Is the concentration of a solution an intensive or an extensive property? **(b)** What is the difference between 0.50 mol HCl and 0.50 *M* HCl?

4.60 **(a)** Suppose you prepare 500 mL of a 0.10 *M* solution of some salt and then spill some of it. What happens to the concentration of the solution left in the container? **(b)** Suppose you prepare 500 mL of a 0.10 *M* aqueous solution of some salt and let it sit out, uncovered, for a long time, and some water evaporates. What happens to the concentration of the solution left in the container? **(c)** A certain volume of a 0.50 *M* solution contains 4.5 g of a salt. What mass of the salt is present in the same volume of a 2.50 *M* solution?

4.61 **(a)** Calculate the molarity of a solution that contains 0.0250 mol NH_4Cl in exactly 500 mL of solution. **(b)** How many moles of HNO_3 are present in 50.0 mL of a 2.50 *M* solution of nitric acid? **(c)** How many milliliters of 1.50 *M* KOH solution are needed to provide 0.275 mol of KOH?

4.62 **(a)** Calculate the molarity of a solution made by dissolving 0.750 grams of Na_2SO_4 in enough water to form exactly 850 mL of solution. **(b)** How many moles of $KMnO_4$ are present in 250 mL of a 0.0475 *M* solution? **(c)** How many milliliters of 11.6 *M* HCl solution are needed to obtain 0.250 mol of HCl?

4.63 The average adult human male has a total blood volume of 5.0 L. If the concentration of sodium ion in this average individual is 0.135 *M*, what is the mass of sodium ion circulating in the blood?

4.64 A person suffering from hyponatremia has a sodium ion concentration in the blood of 0.118 *M* and a total blood volume of 4.6 L. What mass of sodium chloride would need to be added to the blood to bring the sodium ion concentration up to 0.138 *M*, assuming no change in blood volume?

4.65 The concentration of alcohol (CH_3CH_2OH) in blood, called the "blood alcohol concentration" or BAC, is given in units of grams of alcohol per 100 mL of blood. The legal definition of intoxication, in many states of the United States, is that the BAC is 0.08 or higher. What is the concentration of alcohol, in terms of molarity, in blood if the BAC is 0.08?

4.66 The average adult male has a total blood volume of 5.0 L. After drinking a few beers, he has a BAC of 0.10 (see Exercise 4.65). What mass of alcohol is circulating in his blood?

4.67 Calculate **(a)** the number of grams of solute in 0.250 L of 0.175 *M* KBr, **(b)** the molar concentration of a solution containing 14.75 g of $Ca(NO_3)_2$ in 1.375 L, **(c)** the volume of 1.50 *M* Na_3PO_4 in milliliters that contains 2.50 g of solute.

4.68 **(a)** How many grams of solute are present in 50.0 mL of 0.488 *M* $K_2Cr_2O_7$? **(b)** If 4.00 g of $(NH_4)_2SO_4$ is dissolved in enough water to form 400 mL of solution, what is the molarity of the solution? **(c)** How many milliliters of 0.0250 *M* $CuSO_4$ contain 1.75 g of solute?

4.69 **(a)** Which will have the highest concentration of potassium ion: 0.20 *M* KCl, 0.15 *M* K_2CrO_4, or 0.080 *M* K_3PO_4? **(b)** Which will contain the greater number of moles of potassium ion: 30.0 mL of 0.15 *M* K_2CrO_4 or 25.0 mL of 0.080 *M* K_3PO_4?

4.70 In each of the following pairs, indicate which has the higher concentration of Cl^- ion: **(a)** 0.10 *M* $CaCl_2$ or 0.15 *M* KCl solution, **(b)** 100 mL of 0.10 *M* KCl solution or 400 mL of 0.080 *M* LiCl solution, **(c)** 0.050 *M* HCl solution or 0.020 *M* $CdCl_2$ solution.

4.71 Indicate the concentration of each ion or molecule present in the following solutions: **(a)** 0.25 *M* $NaNO_3$, **(b)** 1.3×10^{-2} *M* $MgSO_4$, **(c)** 0.0150 *M* $C_6H_{12}O_6$, **(d)** a mixture of 45.0 mL of 0.272 *M* NaCl and 65.0 mL of 0.0247 *M* $(NH_4)_2CO_3$. Assume that the volumes are additive.

4.72 Indicate the concentration of each ion present in the solution formed by mixing **(a)** 42.0 mL of 0.170 *M* NaOH and 37.6 mL of 0.400 *M* NaOH, **(b)** 44.0 mL of 0.100 *M* and Na_2SO_4 and 25.0 mL of 0.150 *M* KCl, **(c)** 3.60 g KCl in 75.0 mL of 0.250 *M* $CaCl_2$ solution. Assume that the volumes are additive.

4.73 **(a)** You have a stock solution of 14.8 *M* NH_3. How many milliliters of this solution should you dilute to make 1000.0 mL of 0.250 *M* NH_3? **(b)** If you take a 10.0-mL portion of the stock solution and dilute it to a total volume of 0.500 L, what will be the concentration of the final solution?

4.74 **(a)** How many milliliters of a stock solution of 10.0 *M* HNO_3 would you have to use to prepare 0.450 L of 0.500 *M* HNO_3? **(b)** If you dilute 25.0 mL of the stock solution to a final volume of 0.500 L, what will be the concentration of the diluted solution?

4.75 **(a)** Starting with solid sucrose, $C_{12}H_{22}O_{11}$, describe how you would prepare 250 mL of a 0.250 *M* sucrose solution. **(b)** Describe how you would prepare 350.0 mL of 0.100 *M* $C_{12}H_{22}O_{11}$ starting with 3.00 L of 1.50 *M* $C_{12}H_{22}O_{11}$.

4.76 **(a)** How would you prepare 175.0 mL of 0.150 M AgNO$_3$ solution starting with pure solute? **(b)** An experiment calls for you to use 100 mL of 0.50 M HNO$_3$ solution. All you have available is a bottle of 3.6 M HNO$_3$. How would you prepare the desired solution?

[4.77] Pure acetic acid, known as glacial acetic acid, is a liquid with a density of 1.049 g/mL at 25 °C. Calculate the molarity of a solution of acetic acid made by dissolving 20.00 mL of glacial acetic acid at 25 °C in enough water to make 250.0 mL of solution.

[4.78] Glycerol, C$_3$H$_8$O$_3$, is a substance used extensively in the manufacture of cosmetics, foodstuffs, antifreeze, and plastics. Glycerol is a water-soluble liquid with a density of 1.2656 g/mL at 15 °C. Calculate the molarity of a solution of glycerol made by dissolving 50.000 mL glycerol at 15 °C in enough water to make 250.00 mL of solution.

Solution Stoichiometry; Titrations

4.79 What mass of KCl is needed to precipitate the silver ions from 15.0 mL of 0.200 M AgNO$_3$ solution?

4.80 What mass of NaOH is needed to precipitate the Cd^{2+} ions from 35.0 mL of 0.500 M Cd(NO$_3$)$_2$ solution?

4.81 **(a)** What volume of 0.115 M HClO$_4$ solution is needed to neutralize 50.00 mL of 0.0875 M NaOH? **(b)** What volume of 0.128 M HCl is needed to neutralize 2.87 g of Mg(OH)$_2$? **(c)** If 25.8 mL of AgNO$_3$ is needed to precipitate all the Cl$^-$ ions in a 785-mg sample of KCl (forming AgCl), what is the molarity of the AgNO$_3$ solution? **(d)** If 45.3 mL of 0.108 M HCl solution is needed to neutralize a solution of KOH, how many grams of KOH must be present in the solution?

4.82 **(a)** How many milliliters of 0.120 M HCl are needed to completely neutralize 50.0 mL of 0.101 M Ba(OH)$_2$ solution? **(b)** How many milliliters of 0.125 M H$_2$SO$_4$ are needed to neutralize 0.200 g of NaOH? **(c)** If 55.8 mL of BaCl$_2$ solution is needed to precipitate all the sulfate ion in a 752-mg sample of Na$_2$SO$_4$, what is the molarity of the solution? **(d)** If 42.7 mL of 0.208 M HCl solution is needed to neutralize a solution of Ca(OH)$_2$, how many grams of Ca(OH)$_2$ must be in the solution?

4.83 Some sulfuric acid is spilled on a lab bench. You can neutralize the acid by sprinkling sodium bicarbonate on it and then mopping up the resultant solution. The sodium bicarbonate reacts with sulfuric acid as follows:

$$2\,NaHCO_3(s) + H_2SO_4(aq) \longrightarrow$$
$$Na_2SO_4(aq) + 2\,H_2O(l) + 2\,CO_2(g)$$

Sodium bicarbonate is added until the fizzing due to the formation of CO$_2$(g) stops. If 27 mL of 6.0 M H$_2$SO$_4$ was spilled, what is the minimum mass of NaHCO$_3$ that must be added to the spill to neutralize the acid?

4.84 The distinctive odor of vinegar is due to acetic acid, CH$_3$COOH, which reacts with sodium hydroxide in the following fashion:

$$CH_3COOH(aq) + NaOH(aq) \longrightarrow$$
$$H_2O(l) + NaC_2H_3O_2(aq)$$

If 3.45 mL of vinegar needs 42.5 mL of 0.115 M NaOH to reach the equivalence point in a titration, how many grams of acetic acid are in a 1.00-qt sample of this vinegar?

4.85 A sample of solid Ca(OH)$_2$ is stirred in water at 30 °C until the solution contains as much dissolved Ca(OH)$_2$ as it can hold. A 100-mL sample of this solution is withdrawn and titrated with 5.00×10^{-2} M HBr. It requires 48.8 mL of the acid solution for neutralization. What is the molarity of the Ca(OH)$_2$ solution? What is the solubility of Ca(OH)$_2$ in water, at 30 °C, in grams of Ca(OH)$_2$ per 100 mL of solution?

4.86 In a laboratory, 6.82 g of Sr(NO$_3$)$_2$ is dissolved in enough water to form 0.500 L of solution. A 0.100-L sample is withdrawn from this stock solution and titrated with a 0.0245 M solution of Na$_2$CrO$_4$. What volume of Na$_2$CrO$_4$ solution is needed to precipitate all the Sr^{2+}(aq) as SrCrO$_4$?

4.87 A solution of 100.0 mL of 0.200 M KOH is mixed with a solution of 200.0 mL of 0.150 M NiSO$_4$. **(a)** Write the balanced chemical equation for the reaction that occurs. **(b)** What precipitate forms? **(c)** What is the limiting reactant? **(d)** How many grams of this precipitate form? **(e)** What is the concentration of each ion that remains in solution?

4.88 A solution is made by mixing 12.0 g of NaOH and 75.0 mL of 0.200 M HNO$_3$. **(a)** Write a balanced equation for the reaction that occurs between the solutes. **(b)** Calculate the concentration of each ion remaining in solution. **(c)** Is the resultant solution acidic or basic?

[4.89] A 0.5895-g sample of impure magnesium hydroxide is dissolved in 100.0 mL of 0.2050 M HCl solution. The excess acid then needs 19.85 mL of 0.1020 M NaOH for neutralization. Calculate the percent by mass of magnesium hydroxide in the sample, assuming that it is the only substance reacting with the HCl solution.

[4.90] A 1.248-g sample of limestone rock is pulverized and then treated with 30.00 mL of 1.035 M HCl solution. The excess acid then requires 11.56 mL of 1.010 M NaOH for neutralization. Calculate the percent by mass of calcium carbonate in the rock, assuming that it is the only substance reacting with the HCl solution.

ADDITIONAL EXERCISES

4.91 Explain why a titration experiment is a good way to
CQ measure the unknown concentration of a compound in solution.

4.92 The accompanying photo shows the reaction between a solution of $Cd(NO_3)_2$ and one of Na_2S. What is the identity of the precipitate? What ions remain in solution? Write the net ionic equation for the reaction.

4.93 Suppose you have a solution that might contain any or
CQ all of the following cations: Ni^{2+}, Ag^+, Sr^{2+}, and Mn^{2+}. Addition of HCl solution causes a precipitate to form. After filtering off the precipitate, H_2SO_4 solution is added to the resultant solution and another precipitate forms. This is filtered off, and a solution of NaOH is added to the resulting solution. No precipitate is observed. Which ions are present in each of the precipitates? Which of the four ions listed above must be absent from the original solution?

4.94 You choose to investigate some of the solubility guide-
CQ lines for two ions not listed in Table 4.1, the chromate ion (CrO_4^{2-}) and the oxalate ion ($C_2O_4^{2-}$). You are given 0.01 M solutions (A, B, C, D) of four water-soluble salts:

Solution	Solute	Color of Solution
A	Na_2CrO_4	Yellow
B	$(NH_4)_2C_2O_4$	Colorless
C	$AgNO_3$	Colorless
D	$CaCl_2$	Colorless

When these solutions are mixed, the following observations are made:

Expt Number	Solutions Mixed	Result
1	A + B	No precipitate, yellow solution
2	A + C	Red precipitate forms
3	A + D	No precipitate, yellow solution
4	B + C	White precipitate forms
5	B + D	White precipitate forms
6	C + D	White precipitate forms

(a) Write a net ionic equation for the reaction that occurs in each of the experiments. **(b)** Identify the precipitate formed, if any, in each of the experiments. **(c)** Based on these limited observations, which ion tends to form the more soluble salts, chromate or oxalate?

4.95 Antacids are often used to relieve pain and promote healing in the treatment of mild ulcers. Write balanced net ionic equations for the reactions between the HCl(aq) in the stomach and each of the following substances used in various antacids: **(a)** $Al(OH)_3(s)$, **(b)** $Mg(OH)_2(s)$, **(c)** $MgCO_3(s)$, **(d)** $NaAl(CO_3)(OH)_2(s)$, **(e)** $CaCO_3(s)$.

[4.96] Salts of the sulfite ion, SO_3^{2-}, react with acids in a way similar to that of carbonates. **(a)** Predict the chemical formula, and name the weak acid that forms when the sulfite ion reacts with acids. **(b)** The acid formed in part (a) decomposes to form water and a gas. Predict the molecular formula, and name the gas formed. **(c)** Use a source book such as the *CRC Handbook of Chemistry and Physics* to confirm that the substance in part (b) is a gas under normal room-temperature conditions. **(d)** Write balanced net ionic equations of the reaction of HCl(aq) with (i) $Na_2SO_3(aq)$, (ii) $Ag_2SO_3(s)$, (iii) $KHSO_3(s)$, and (iv) $ZnSO_3(aq)$.

[4.97] The commercial production of nitric acid involves the following chemical reactions:

$$4\,NH_3(g) + 5\,O_2(g) \longrightarrow 4\,NO(g) + 6\,H_2O(g)$$
$$2\,NO(g) + O_2(g) \longrightarrow 2\,NO_2(g)$$
$$3\,NO_2(g) + H_2O(l) \longrightarrow 2\,HNO_3(aq) + NO(g)$$

(a) Which of these reactions are redox reactions? **(b)** In each redox reaction identify the element undergoing oxidation and the element undergoing reduction.

4.98 Use Table 4.5 to predict which of the following ions can be reduced to their metal forms by reacting with zinc: **(a)** $Na^+(aq)$, **(b)** $Pb^{2+}(aq)$, **(c)** $Mg^{2+}(aq)$, **(d)** $Fe^{2+}(aq)$, **(e)** $Cu^{2+}(aq)$, **(f)** $Al^{3+}(aq)$. Write the balanced net ionic equation for each reaction that occurs.

[4.99] Lanthanum metal forms cations with a charge of 3+.
CQ Consider the following observations about the chemistry of lanthanum: When lanthanum metal is exposed to air, a white solid (compound A) is formed that contains lanthanum and one other element. When lanthanum metal is added to water, gas bubbles are observed and a different white solid (compound B) is formed. Both A and B dissolve in hydrochloric acid to give a clear solution. When either of these solutions is evaporated, a soluble white solid (compound C) remains. If compound C is dissolved in water and sulfuric acid is added, a white precipitate (compound D) forms. **(a)** Propose identities for the substances A, B, C, and D. **(b)** Write net ionic equations for all the reactions described. **(c)** Based on the preceding observations, what can be said about the position of lanthanum in the activity series (Table 4.5)?

4.100 A 35.0-mL sample of 1.00 M KBr and a 60.0-mL sample of 0.600 M KBr are mixed. The solution is then heated to evaporate water until the total volume is 50.0 mL. What is the molarity of the KBr in the final solution?

4.101 Using modern analytical techniques, it is possible to detect sodium ions in concentrations as low as 50 pg/mL. What is this detection limit expressed in **(a)** molarity of Na^+, **(b)** Na^+ ions per cubic centimeter?

4.102 Hard water contains Ca^{2+}, Mg^{2+}, and Fe^{2+}, which interfere with the action of soap and leave an insoluble coating on the insides of containers and pipes when heated. Water softeners replace these ions with Na^+. If 1500 L of hard water contains 0.020 M Ca^{2+} and 0.0040 M Mg^{2+}, how many moles of Na^+ are needed to replace these ions?

4.103 Tartaric acid, $H_2C_4H_4O_6$, has two acidic hydrogens. The acid is often present in wines and precipitates from solution as the wine ages. A solution containing an unknown concentration of the acid is titrated with NaOH. It requires 24.65 mL of 0.2500 M NaOH solution to titrate both acidic protons in 50.00 mL of the tartaric acid solution. Write a balanced net ionic equation for the neutralization reaction, and calculate the molarity of the tartaric acid solution.

4.104 The concentration of hydrogen peroxide in a solution is determined by titrating a 10.0-mL sample of the solution with permanganate ion.
$$2 MnO_4^-(aq) + 5 H_2O_2(aq) + 6 H^+(aq) \longrightarrow$$
$$2 Mn^{2+}(aq) + 5 O_2(g) + 8 H_2O(l)$$
If it takes 14.8 mL of 0.134 M MnO_4^- solution to reach the equivalence point, what is the molarity of the hydrogen peroxide solution?

[4.105] A solid sample of $Zn(OH)_2$ is added to 0.350 L of 0.500 M aqueous HBr. The solution that remains is still acidic. It is then titrated with 0.500 M NaOH solution, and it takes 88.5 mL of the NaOH solution to reach the equivalence point. What mass of $Zn(OH)_2$ was added to the HBr solution?

INTEGRATIVE EXERCISES

4.106 **(a)** By titration, 15.0 mL of 0.1008 M sodium hydroxide is needed to neutralize a 0.2053-g sample of an organic acid. What is the molar mass of the acid if it is monoprotic? **(b)** An elemental analysis of the acid indicates that it is composed of 5.89% H, 70.6% C, and 23.5% O by mass. What is its molecular formula?

4.107 A 3.455-g sample of a mixture was analyzed for barium ion by adding a small excess of sulfuric acid to an aqueous solution of the sample. The resultant reaction produced a precipitate of barium sulfate, which was collected by filtration, washed, dried, and weighed. If 0.2815 g of barium sulfate was obtained, what was the mass percentage of barium in the sample?

[4.108] A tanker truck carrying 5.0×10^3 kg of concentrated sulfuric acid solution tips over and spills its load. If the sulfuric acid is 95.0% H_2SO_4 by mass and has a density of 1.84 g/mL, how many kilograms of sodium carbonate must be added to neutralize the acid?

4.109 A sample of 5.53 g of $Mg(OH)_2$ is added to 25.0 mL of 0.200 M HNO_3. **(a)** Write the chemical equation for the reaction that occurs. **(b)** Which is the limiting reactant in the reaction? **(c)** How many moles of $Mg(OH)_2$, HNO_3, and $Mg(NO_3)_2$ are present after the reaction is complete?

4.110 A sample of 1.50 g of lead(II) nitrate is mixed with 125 mL of 0.100 M sodium sulfate solution. **(a)** Write the chemical equation for the reaction that occurs. **(b)** Which is the limiting reactant in the reaction? **(c)** What are the concentrations of all ions that remain in solution after the reaction is complete?

4.111 A mixture contains 76.5% NaCl, 6.5% $MgCl_2$, and 17.0% Na_2SO_4 by mass. What is the molarity of Cl^- ions in a solution formed by dissolving 7.50 g of the mixture in enough water to form 500.0 mL of solution?

[4.112] The average concentration of bromide ion in seawater is 65 mg of bromide ion per kg of seawater. What is the molarity of the bromide ion if the density of the seawater is 1.025 g/mL?

[4.113] The mass percentage of chloride ion in a 25.00-mL sample of seawater was determined by titrating the sample with silver nitrate, precipitating silver chloride. It took 42.58 mL of 0.2997 M silver nitrate solution to reach the equivalence point in the titration. What is the mass percentage of chloride ion in the seawater if its density is 1.025 g/mL?

4.114 The arsenic in a 1.22-g sample of a pesticide was converted to AsO_4^{3-} by suitable chemical treatment. It was then titrated using Ag^+ to form Ag_3AsO_4 as a precipitate. **(a)** What is the oxidation state of As in AsO_4^{3-}? **(b)** Name Ag_3AsO_4 by analogy to the corresponding compound containing phosphorus in place of arsenic. **(c)** If it took 25.0 mL of 0.102 M Ag^+ to reach the equivalence point in this titration, what is the mass percentage of arsenic in the pesticide?

[4.115] The newest U.S. standard for arsenate in drinking water, mandated by the Safe Drinking Water Act, required that by January 2006, public water supplies must contain no greater than 10 parts per billion (ppb) arsenic. If this arsenic is present as arsenate, AsO_4^{3-}, what mass of sodium arsenate would be present in a 1.00-L sample of drinking water that just meets the standard?

[4.116] The safe drinking water standard for arsenic (which is usually found as arsenate, see 4.115) is 50 parts per billion (ppb) in most developing countries. **(a)** How many grams of sodium arsenate are in 55 gallons of water, if the concentration of arsenate is 50 ppb? **(b)** In 1993, naturally occurring arsenic was discovered as a major contaminant in the drinking water across the country of Bangladesh. Approximately 12 million people in Bangladesh still drink water from wells that have higher concentrations of arsenic than the standard. Recently, a chemistry professor from George Mason University was awarded a $1 million Grainger Challenge Prize for Sustainability for his development of a simple, inexpensive system for filtering naturally occuring arsenic from drinking water. The system uses buckets of sand, cast iron, activated carbon, and wood chips for trapping arsenic-containing minerals. Assuming the efficiency of such a bucket system is 90% (meaning, 90% of the arsenic that comes in is retained in the bucket and 10% passes out of the bucket), how many times should water that is 500 ppb in arsenic be passed through to meet the 50 ppb standard?

[4.117] Federal regulations set an upper limit of 50 parts per million (ppm) of NH_3 in the air in a work environment [that is, 50 molecules of $NH_3(g)$ for every million molecules in the air]. Air from a manufacturing operation was drawn through a solution containing 1.00×10^2 mL of 0.0105 M HCl. The NH_3 reacts with HCl as follows:

$$NH_3(aq) + HCl(aq) \longrightarrow NH_4Cl(aq)$$

After drawing air through the acid solution for 10.0 min at a rate of 10.0 L/min, the acid was titrated. The remaining acid needed 13.1 mL of 0.0588 M NaOH to reach the equivalence point. **(a)** How many grams of NH_3 were drawn into the acid solution? **(b)** How many ppm of NH_3 were in the air? (Air has a density of 1.20 g/L and an average molar mass of 29.0 g/mol under the conditions of the experiment.) **(c)** Is this manufacturer in compliance with regulations?

6

ELECTRONIC STRUCTURE OF ATOMS

THE GLASS TUBES OF NEON LIGHTS contain various gases that can be excited by electricity.
Light is produced when electrically excited atoms return to their lowest-energy states.

210

WHAT HAPPENS WHEN someone switches on a neon light? The electrons in the neon atoms, which are excited to a higher energy by electricity, emit light when they drop back down to a lower energy. The pleasing glow that results is explained by one of the most revolutionary

discoveries of the twentieth century, namely, the *quantum theory*. This theory explains much of the behavior of electrons in atoms. We will see that the behavior of electrons in an atom is quite unlike anything we see in our macroscopic world.

In this chapter we will explore the quantum theory and its importance in chemistry. We will begin by looking more closely at the nature of light and how our description of light was changed by the quantum theory. We will explore some of the tools used in *quantum mechanics*, the "new" physics that had to be developed to describe atoms correctly. We will then use the quantum

211

▲ Figure 6.1 **Water waves.** The movement of the boat through the water forms waves. The regular variation of the peaks and troughs enables us to sense the motion, or *propagation*, of the waves.

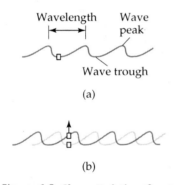

(a)

(b)

▲ Figure 6.2 **Characteristics of water waves.** (a) The distance between corresponding points on each wave is called the *wavelength*. In this drawing, the two corresponding points are two peaks, but they could be any other two corresponding points, such as two adjacent troughs. (b) The number of times per second that the cork bobs up and down is called the *frequency* of the wave.

theory to describe the arrangements of electrons in atoms—what we call the **electronic structure** of atoms. The electronic structure of an atom refers to the number of electrons in an atom as well as the distribution of the electrons around the nucleus and their energies. We will see that the quantum description of the electronic structure of atoms helps us to understand the elegant arrangement of the elements in the periodic table—why, for example, helium and neon are both unreactive gases, whereas sodium and potassium are both soft, reactive metals. In the chapters that follow, we will see how the concepts of quantum theory are used to explain trends in the periodic table and the formation of bonds between atoms.

6.1 THE WAVE NATURE OF LIGHT

Much of our present understanding of the electronic structure of atoms has come from analysis of the light either emitted or absorbed by substances. To understand electronic structure, therefore, we must first learn more about light. The light that we can see with our eyes, *visible light*, is an example of **electromagnetic radiation.** Because electromagnetic radiation carries energy through space, it is also known as *radiant energy*. There are many types of electromagnetic radiation in addition to visible light. These different forms—such as the radio waves that carry music to our radios, the infrared radiation (heat) from a glowing fireplace, and the X-rays used by a dentist—may seem very different from one another, but they all share certain fundamental characteristics.

All types of electromagnetic radiation move through a vacuum at a speed of 3.00×10^8 m/s, the *speed of light*. All have wavelike characteristics similar to those of waves that move through water. Water waves are the result of energy imparted to the water, perhaps by the dropping of a stone or the movement of a boat on the water surface (Figure 6.1 ◄). This energy is expressed as the up-and-down movements of the water.

A cross section of a water wave (Figure 6.2 ◄) shows that it is periodic, which means that the pattern of peaks and troughs repeats itself at regular intervals. The distance between two adjacent peaks (or between two adjacent troughs) is called the **wavelength.** The number of complete wavelengths, or *cycles*, that pass a given point each second is the **frequency** of the wave. We can measure the frequency of a water wave by counting the number of times per second that a cork bobbing on the water moves through a complete cycle of upward and downward motion.

Just as with water waves, we can assign a frequency and wavelength to electromagnetic waves, as illustrated in Figure 6.3 ▼. These and all other wave

▼ Figure 6.3 **Characteristics of electromagnetic waves.** Radiant energy has wave characteristics; it consists of electromagnetic waves. Notice that the shorter the wavelength, λ, the higher the frequency, ν. The wavelength in (b) is half as long as that in (a), and the frequency of the wave in (b) is therefore twice as great as the frequency in (a). The *amplitude* of the wave relates to the intensity of the radiation, which is the maximum extent of the oscillation of the wave. In these diagrams amplitude is measured as the vertical distance from the midline of the wave to its peak. The waves in (a) and (b) have the same amplitude. The wave in (c) has the same frequency as that in (b), but its amplitude is lower.

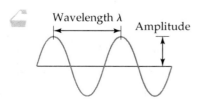

(a) Two complete cycles of wavelength λ

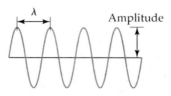

(b) Wavelength half of that in (a); frequency twice as great as in (a)

(c) Same frequency as (b), smaller amplitude

Science Fundamentals

characteristics of electromagnetic radiation are due to the periodic oscillations in the intensities of the electric and magnetic fields associated with the radiation.

The speed of water waves can vary depending on how they are created—for example, the waves produced by a speedboat travel faster than those produced by a rowboat. In contrast, all electromagnetic radiation moves at the same speed, namely the speed of light. As a result, the wavelength and frequency of electromagnetic radiation are always related in a straightforward way. If the wavelength is long, there will be fewer cycles of the wave passing a point per second, and the frequency will be low. Conversely, for a wave to have a high frequency, the wave must have a short wavelength—that is, the distance between the peaks of the waves is small. This inverse relationship between the frequency and the wavelength of electromagnetic radiation can be expressed by the equation

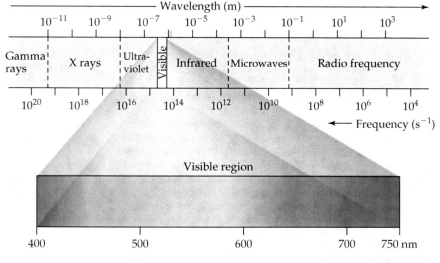

▲ Figure 6.4 **The electromagnetic spectrum.** Wavelengths in the spectrum range from very short gamma rays to very long radio waves. Notice that the color of visible light can be expressed quantitatively by wavelength.

$$c = \lambda\nu \qquad [6.1]$$

where c is the speed of light, λ (lambda) is the wavelength, and ν (nu) is the frequency.

Why do different forms of electromagnetic radiation have different properties? Their differences are due to their different wavelengths, which are expressed in units of length. Figure 6.4 ▲ shows the various types of electromagnetic radiation arranged in order of increasing wavelength, a display called the *electromagnetic spectrum*. Notice that the wavelengths span an enormous range. The wavelengths of gamma rays are similar to the diameters of atomic nuclei, whereas the wavelengths of radio waves can be longer than a football field. Notice also that visible light, which corresponds to wavelengths of about 400 to 700 nm (4×10^{-7} m to 7×10^{-7} m), is an extremely small portion of the electromagnetic spectrum. We can see visible light because of the chemical reactions it triggers in our eyes. The unit of length normally chosen to express wavelength depends on the type of radiation, as shown in Table 6.1 ▼.

Frequency is expressed in cycles per second, a unit also called a *hertz* (Hz). Because it is understood that cycles are involved, the units of frequency are normally given simply as "per second," which is denoted by s^{-1} or /s. For example, a frequency of 820 kilohertz (kHz), a typical frequency for an AM radio station, could be written as 820 kHz, 820,000 Hz, 820,000 s^{-1}, or 820,000/s.

TABLE 6.1 ■ Common Wavelength Units for Electromagnetic Radiation			
Unit	Symbol	Length (m)	Type of Radiation
Angstrom	Å	10^{-10}	X-ray
Nanometer	nm	10^{-9}	Ultraviolet, visible
Micrometer	μm	10^{-6}	Infrared
Millimeter	mm	10^{-3}	Microwave
Centimeter	cm	10^{-2}	Microwave
Meter	m	1	TV, radio
Kilometer	km	1000	Radio

A Closer Look   THE SPEED OF LIGHT

How do we know that light has a speed and does not move infinitely fast?

During the late 1600s, the Danish astonomer Ole Rømer (1644–1710) measured the orbits of several of Jupiter's moons. These moons move much faster than our own—they have orbits of 1–7 days and are eclipsed by Jupiter's shadow at every revolution. Over many months, Rømer measured discrepancies of up to 10 minutes in the times of these orbits. He reasoned that one possible explanation for the discrepancies was that Jupiter was farther from Earth at different times of the year. Thus, the light from the Sun, which reflected off Jupiter and ultimately to his telescope, had farther to travel at different times of the year. Rømer's data led to an estimate of 3.5×10^8 m/s for the speed of light. In 1704, Isaac Newton (1643–1727) used estimates of the distance from the Sun to Earth and the time it takes for the light to travel that distance to calculate the speed of light as $2.4 - 2.7 \times 10^8$ m/s.

In 1927, A. A. Michelson (1852–1931) performed a famous experiment to determine the speed of light. Michelson set up a rotating mirror system at the top of Mount Wilson in southern California (Figure 6.5▶). The mirror system bounced light from the top of Mount Wilson to the top of Mount San Antonio, 22 miles away, where another mirror system bounced the light back to Mount Wilson. If the speed of light was instantaneous, or an exact multiple of the turn speed of the rotating mirror, the reflected spot of light would appear exactly super-

imposed on the original spot. Michelson was able to change the speed of the rotating mirror and measure small displacements in the position of the reflected spot. The value for the speed of light (in air) based on this experiment is $2.9980 \pm 0.0002 \times 10^8$ m/s. The main source of error is the distance between the mirrors at the tops of the two mountains, which was measured within a fifth of an inch in 22 miles.

▲ Figure 6.5 **View of Mount San Antonio from the top of Mount Wilson.** The mountains are 22 miles apart.

■ SAMPLE EXERCISE 6.1 | Concepts of Wavelength and Frequency

Two electromagnetic waves are represented in the margin. **(a)** Which wave has the higher frequency? **(b)** If one wave represents visible light and the other represents infrared radiation, which wave is which?

SOLUTION

(a) The lower wave has a longer wavelength (greater distance between peaks). The longer the wavelength, the lower the frequency ($\nu = c/\lambda$). Thus, the lower wave has the lower frequency, and the upper wave has the higher frequency.
(b) The electromagnetic spectrum (Figure 6.4) indicates that infrared radiation has a longer wavelength than visible light. Thus, the lower wave would be the infrared radiation.

■ PRACTICE EXERCISE

If one of the waves in the margin represents blue light and the other red light, which is which?
Answer: The expanded visible-light portion of Figure 6.4 tells you that red light has a longer wavelength than blue light. The lower wave has the longer wavelength (lower frequency) and would be the red light.

■ SAMPLE EXERCISE 6.2 | Calculating Frequency from Wavelength

The yellow light given off by a sodium vapor lamp used for public lighting has a wavelength of 589 nm. What is the frequency of this radiation?

SOLUTION

Analyze: We are given the wavelength, λ, of the radiation and asked to calculate its frequency, ν.

Plan: The relationship between the wavelength (which is given) and the frequency (which is the unknown) is given by Equation 6.1. We can solve this equation for ν and then use the values of λ and c to obtain a numerical answer. (The speed of light, c, is a fundamental constant whose value is 3.00×10^8 m/s.)

Solve: Solving Equation 6.1 for frequency gives $\nu = c/\lambda$. When we insert the values for c and λ, we note that the units of length in these two quantities are different. We can convert the wavelength from nanometers to meters, so the units cancel:

$$\nu = \frac{c}{\lambda} = \left(\frac{3.00 \times 10^8 \text{ m/s}}{589 \text{ nm}}\right)\left(\frac{1 \text{ nm}}{10^{-9} \text{ m}}\right) = 5.09 \times 10^{14} \text{ s}^{-1}$$

Check: The high frequency is reasonable because of the short wavelength. The units are proper because frequency has units of "per second," or s^{-1}.

■ PRACTICE EXERCISE

(a) A laser used in eye surgery to fuse detached retinas produces radiation with a wavelength of 640.0 nm. Calculate the frequency of this radiation. **(b)** An FM radio station broadcasts electromagnetic radiation at a frequency of 103.4 MHz (megahertz; MHz = 10^6 s^{-1}). Calculate the wavelength of this radiation. The speed of light is 2.998×10^8 m/s to four significant digits.
Answers: **(a)** 4.688×10^{14} s^{-1}, **(b)** 2.901 m

GIVE IT SOME THOUGHT

Our bodies are penetrated by X-rays but not by visible light. Is this because X-rays travel faster than visible light?

6.2 QUANTIZED ENERGY AND PHOTONS

Although the wave model of light explains many aspects of its behavior, this model cannot explain several phenomena. Three of these are particularly pertinent to our understanding of how electromagnetic radiation and atoms interact: (1) the emission of light from hot objects (referred to as *blackbody radiation* because the objects studied appear black before heating), (2) the emission of electrons from metal surfaces on which light shines (the *photoelectric effect*), and (3) the emission of light from electronically excited gas atoms (*emission spectra*). We examine the first two phenomena here and the third in Section 6.3.

Hot Objects and the Quantization of Energy

When solids are heated, they emit radiation, as seen in the red glow of an electric stove burner and the bright white light of a tungsten lightbulb. The wavelength distribution of the radiation depends on temperature; a red-hot object is cooler than a white-hot one (Figure 6.6 ▶). During the late 1800s, a number of physicists were studying this phenomenon, trying to understand the relationship between the temperature and the intensity and wavelengths of the emitted radiation. The prevailing laws of physics could not account for the observations.

In 1900 a German physicist named Max Planck (1858–1947) solved the problem by assuming that energy can be either released or absorbed by atoms only in discrete "chunks" of some minimum size. Planck gave the name **quantum** (meaning "fixed amount") to the smallest quantity of energy that can be emitted or absorbed as electromagnetic radiation. He proposed that the energy, E, of a single quantum equals a constant times the frequency of the radiation:

$$E = h\nu \qquad [6.2]$$

The constant h is called **Planck's constant** and has a value of 6.626×10^{-34} joule-second (J-s). According to Planck's theory, matter is allowed to emit and absorb energy only in whole-number multiples of $h\nu$, such as $h\nu$, $2h\nu$, $3h\nu$, and so forth. If the quantity of energy emitted by an atom is $3h\nu$, for example, we say that three quanta of energy have been emitted (quanta

▲ Figure 6.6 **Color as a function of temperature.** The color and intensity of the light emitted by a hot object depend on the temperature of the object. The temperature is highest at the center of this pour of molten steel. As a result, the light emitted from the center is most intense and of shortest wavelength.

▲ Figure 6.7 **A model for quantized energy.** The potential energy of a person walking up a ramp (a) increases in a uniform, continuous manner, whereas that of a person walking up steps (b) increases in a stepwise, quantized manner.

being the plural of quantum). Because the energy can be released only in specific amounts, we say that the allowed energies are *quantized*—their values are restricted to certain quantities. Planck's revolutionary proposal that energy is quantized was proved correct, and he was awarded the 1918 Nobel Prize in Physics for his work on the quantum theory.

If the notion of quantized energies seems strange, it might be helpful to draw an analogy by comparing a ramp and a staircase (Figure 6.7 ◄). As you walk up a ramp, your potential energy increases in a uniform, continuous manner. When you climb a staircase, you can step only *on* individual stairs, not *between* them, so that your potential energy is restricted to certain values and is therefore quantized.

If Planck's quantum theory is correct, why aren't its effects more obvious in our daily lives? Why do energy changes seem continuous rather than quantized, or "jagged"? Notice that Planck's constant is an extremely small number. Thus, a quantum of energy, $h\nu$, is an extremely small amount. Planck's rules regarding the gain or loss of energy are always the same, whether we are concerned with objects on the size scale of our ordinary experience or with microscopic objects. With everyday macroscopic objects, however, the gain or loss of a single quantum of energy goes completely unnoticed. In contrast, when dealing with matter at the atomic level, the impact of quantized energies is far more significant.

GIVE IT SOME THOUGHT

The temperature of stars is gauged by their colors. For example, red stars have a lower temperature than blue-white stars. How is this temperature scale consistent with Planck's assumption?

The Photoelectric Effect and Photons

▼ Figure 6.8 **The photoelectric effect.** When photons of sufficiently high energy strike a metal surface, electrons are emitted from the metal, as in (a). The photoelectric effect is the basis of the photocell shown in (b). The emitted electrons are drawn toward the positive terminal. As a result, current flows in the circuit. Photocells are used in photographic light meters as well as in numerous other electronic devices.

A few years after Planck presented his theory, scientists began to see its applicability to a great many experimental observations. They recognized that Planck's theory had within it the seeds of a revolution in the way we view the physical world. In 1905, Albert Einstein (1879–1955) used Planck's quantum theory to explain the **photoelectric effect,** which is illustrated in Figure 6.8 ◄. Experiments had shown that light shining on a clean metal surface causes the surface to emit electrons. Each metal has a minimum frequency of light below which no electrons are emitted. For example, light with a frequency of $4.60 \times 10^{14}\ \text{s}^{-1}$ or greater will cause cesium metal to emit electrons, but light of lower frequency has no effect.

To explain the photoelectric effect, Einstein assumed that the radiant energy striking the metal surface does not behave like a wave but rather as if it were a stream of tiny energy packets. Each energy packet, called a **photon,** behaves like a tiny particle. Extending Planck's quantum theory,

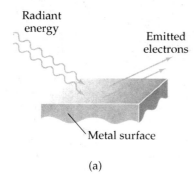

(a)

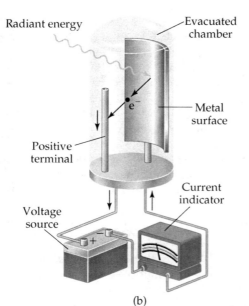

(b)

Einstein deduced that each photon must have an energy equal to Planck's constant times the frequency of the light:

$$\text{Energy of photon} = E = h\nu \qquad [6.3]$$

Thus, radiant energy itself is quantized.

Under the right conditions, a photon can strike a metal surface and be absorbed. When this happens, the photon can transfer its energy to an electron in the metal. A certain amount of energy—called the *work function*—is required for an electron to overcome the attractive forces that hold it in the metal. If the photons of the radiation impinging on the metal have less energy than the work function, electrons do not acquire sufficient energy to escape from the metal surface, even if the light beam is intense. If the photons of radiation have sufficient energy, electrons are emitted from the metal. If the photons have more than the minimum energy required to free electrons, the excess energy appears as the kinetic energy of the emitted electrons. Einstein won the Nobel Prize in Physics in 1921 for his explanation of the photoelectric effect.

To better understand what a photon is, imagine that you have a light source that produces radiation with a single wavelength. Further suppose that you could switch the light on and off faster and faster to provide ever-smaller bursts of energy. Einstein's photon theory tells us that you would eventually come to the smallest energy burst, given by $E = h\nu$. This smallest burst of energy consists of a single photon of light.

■ **SAMPLE EXERCISE 6.3** | **Energy of a Photon**

Calculate the energy of one photon of yellow light with a wavelength of 589 nm.

SOLUTION

Analyze: Our task is to calculate the energy, E, of a photon, given $\lambda = 589$ nm.

Plan: We can use Equation 6.1 to convert the wavelength to frequency:

$$\nu = c/\lambda$$

We can then use Equation 6.3 to calculate energy:

$$E = h\nu$$

Solve: The frequency, ν, is calculated from the given wavelength, as shown in Sample Exercise 6.2:

$$\nu = c/\lambda = 5.09 \times 10^{14}\ \text{s}^{-1}$$

The value of Planck's constant, h, is given both in the text and in the table of physical constants on the inside front cover of the text, and so we can easily calculate E:

$$E = (6.626 \times 10^{-34}\ \text{J-s})(5.09 \times 10^{14}\ \text{s}^{-1}) = 3.37 \times 10^{-19}\ \text{J}$$

Comment: If one photon of radiant energy supplies 3.37×10^{-19} J, then one mole of these photons will supply

$$(6.02 \times 10^{23}\ \text{photons/mol})(3.37 \times 10^{-19}\ \text{J/photon}) = 2.03 \times 10^{5}\ \text{J/mol}$$

This is the magnitude of enthalpies of reactions (Section 5.4), so radiation can break chemical bonds, producing what are called *photochemical reactions*.

■ **PRACTICE EXERCISE**

(a) A laser emits light with a frequency of $4.69 \times 10^{14}\ \text{s}^{-1}$. What is the energy of one photon of the radiation from this laser? **(b)** If the laser emits a pulse of energy containing 5.0×10^{17} photons of this radiation, what is the total energy of that pulse? **(c)** If the laser emits 1.3×10^{-2} J of energy during a pulse, how many photons are emitted during the pulse?
Answers: **(a)** 3.11×10^{-19} J, **(b)** 0.16 J, **(c)** 4.2×10^{16} photons

---

The idea that the energy of light depends on its frequency helps us understand the diverse effects that different kinds of electromagnetic radiation have on matter. For example, the high frequency (short wavelength) of X-rays

▲ Figure 6.9 **Quantum giants.**
Niels Bohr (right) with Albert Einstein.
Bohr (1885–1962) made major
contributions to the quantum theory.
From 1911 to 1913 Bohr studied in
England, working first with J. J. Thomson
at Cambridge University and then with
Ernest Rutherford at the University of
Manchester. He published his quantum
theory of the atom in 1914 and was
awarded the Nobel Prize in Physics
in 1922.

(Figure 6.4) causes X-ray photons to have energy high enough to cause tissue damage and even cancer. Thus, signs are normally posted around X-ray equipment warning us of high-energy radiation.

Although Einstein's theory of light as a stream of particles rather than a wave explains the photoelectric effect and a great many other observations, it also poses a dilemma. Is light a wave, or does it consist of particles? The only way to resolve this dilemma is to adopt what might seem to be a bizarre position: We must consider that light possesses both wavelike and particle-like characteristics and, depending on the situation, will behave more like a wave or more like particles. We will soon see that this dual nature of light is also characteristic of matter.

GIVE IT SOME THOUGHT

What has more energy, a photon of infrared light or a photon of ultraviolet light?

6.3 LINE SPECTRA AND THE BOHR MODEL

The work of Planck and Einstein paved the way for understanding how electrons are arranged in atoms. In 1913, the Danish physicist Niels Bohr (Figure 6.9 ▲) offered a theoretical explanation of *line spectra*, another phenomenon that had puzzled scientists during the nineteenth century. We will examine this phenomenon and then consider how Bohr used the ideas of Planck and Einstein.

Line Spectra

A particular source of radiant energy may emit a single wavelength, as in the light from a laser (Figure 6.10 ◀). Radiation composed of a single wavelength is said to be *monochromatic*. However, most common radiation sources, including lightbulbs and stars, produce radiation containing many different wavelengths. A **spectrum** is produced when radiation from such sources is separated into its different wavelength components. Figure 6.11▼ shows how a prism spreads light from a light source into its component wavelengths. The resulting

▲ Figure 6.10 **Monochromatic radiation.** Lasers produce light of a single wavelength, which we call *monochromatic light*. Different lasers produce light of different wavelengths. The photo shows beams from a variety of lasers that produce visible light of different colors. Other lasers produce light that is not visible, including infrared and ultraviolet light.

▶ Figure 6.11 **Creating a spectrum.** A continuous visible spectrum is produced when a narrow beam of white light is passed through a prism. The white light could be sunlight or light from an incandescent lamp.

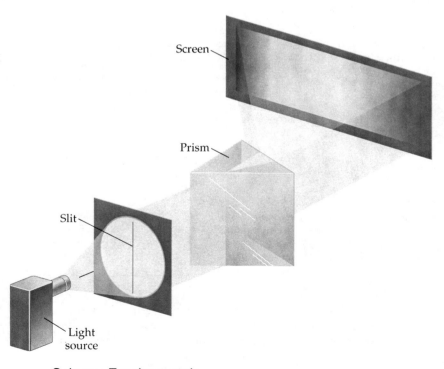

Science Fundamentals

spectrum consists of a continuous range of colors—violet merges into blue, blue into green, and so forth, with no blank spots. This rainbow of colors, containing light of all wavelengths, is called a **continuous spectrum.** The most familiar example of a continuous spectrum is the rainbow produced when raindrops or mist acts as a prism for sunlight.

Not all radiation sources produce a continuous spectrum. When a high voltage is applied to tubes that contain different gases under reduced pressure, the gases emit different colors of light (Figure 6.12▶). The light emitted by neon gas is the familiar red-orange glow of many "neon" lights, whereas sodium vapor emits the yellow light characteristic of some modern streetlights. When light coming from such tubes is passed through a prism, only a few wavelengths are present in the resultant spectra, as shown in Figure 6.13▼. Each wavelength is represented by a colored line in one of these spectra. A spectrum containing radiation of only specific wavelengths is called a **line spectrum.**

When scientists first detected the line spectrum of hydrogen in the mid-1800s, they were fascinated by its simplicity. At that time, only the four lines in the visible portion of the spectrum were observed, as shown in Figure 6.13. These lines correspond to wavelengths of 410 nm (violet), 434 nm (blue), 486 nm (blue-green), and 656 nm (red). In 1885, a Swiss schoolteacher named Johann Balmer showed that the wavelengths of these four visible lines of hydrogen fit an intriguingly simple formula that related the wavelengths of the visible line spectrum to integers. Later, additional lines were found to occur in the ultraviolet and infrared regions of the hydrogen spectrum. Soon Balmer's equation was extended to a more general one, called the *Rydberg equation*, which allowed the calculation of the wavelengths of all the spectral lines of hydrogen:

$$\frac{1}{\lambda} = (R_H)\left(\frac{1}{n_1^2} - \frac{1}{n_2^2}\right) \qquad [6.4]$$

In this formula λ is the wavelength of a spectral line, R_H is the *Rydberg constant* ($1.096776 \times 10^7 \text{ m}^{-1}$), and n_1 and n_2 are positive integers, with n_2 being larger than n_1. How could the remarkable simplicity of this equation be explained? It took nearly 30 more years to answer this question.

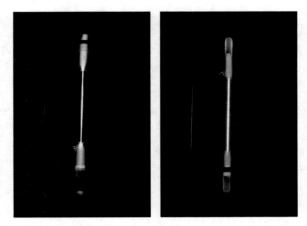

▲ Figure 6.12 **Atomic emission.** Different gases emit light of different characteristic colors upon excitation by an electrical discharge: (a) hydrogen, (b) neon.

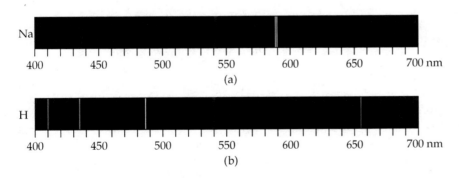

◀ Figure 6.13 **Line spectra.** Spectra obtained from the electrical discharge from (a) Na, (b) H. Light of only a few specific wavelengths is produced, as shown by colored lines in the spectra.

Bohr's Model

Rutherford's discovery of the nuclear nature of the atom ∞ (Section 2.2) suggests that the atom can be thought of as a "microscopic solar system" in which electrons orbit the nucleus. To explain the line spectrum of hydrogen, Bohr assumed that electrons move in circular orbits around the nucleus. According to classical physics, however, an electrically charged particle (such as an electron) that moves in a circular path should continuously lose energy by emitting electromagnetic radiation. As the electron loses energy, it should spiral into the positively charged nucleus. This spiraling obviously does not happen since hydrogen atoms are stable. So how can we explain this apparent violation of the laws of physics? Bohr approached this problem in much the same way that Planck had approached the problem of the nature of the radiation emitted by hot objects: Bohr assumed that the prevailing laws of physics were inadequate to describe all aspects of atoms. Furthermore, Bohr adopted Planck's idea that energies are quantized.

Bohr based his model on three postulates:

1. Only orbits of certain radii, corresponding to certain definite energies, are permitted for the electron in a hydrogen atom.

2. An electron in a permitted orbit has a specific energy and is in an "allowed" energy state. An electron in an allowed energy state will not radiate energy and therefore will not spiral into the nucleus.

3. Energy is emitted or absorbed by the electron only as the electron changes from one allowed energy state to another. This energy is emitted or absorbed as a photon, $E = h\nu$.

▲ GIVE IT SOME THOUGHT

Before reading further about the details of Bohr's model, speculate as to how they explain the fact that hydrogen gas emits a line spectrum (Figure 6.13) rather than a continuous spectrum.

The Energy States of the Hydrogen Atom

Starting with his three postulates and using classical equations for motion and for interacting electrical charges, Bohr calculated the energies corresponding to each allowed orbit for the electron in the hydrogen atom. Ultimately, the energies that Bohr calculated fit the formula

$$E = (-hcR_H)\left(\frac{1}{n^2}\right) = (-2.18 \times 10^{-18} \text{ J})\left(\frac{1}{n^2}\right) \qquad [6.5]$$

In this equation, h, c, and R_H are Planck's constant, the speed of light, and the Rydberg constant, respectively. The product of these three constants equals 2.18×10^{-18} J. The integer n, which can have whole number values of 1, 2, 3, ... to infinity (∞), is called the *principal quantum number*. Each orbit corresponds to a different value of n, and the radius of the orbit gets larger as n increases. Thus, the first allowed orbit (the one closest to the nucleus) has $n = 1$, the next allowed orbit (the one second closest to the nucleus) has $n = 2$, and so forth. The electron in the hydrogen atom can be in any allowed orbit. Equation 6.5 tells us the energy that the electron will have, depending on which orbit it is in.

The energies of the electron of a hydrogen atom given by Equation 6.5 are negative for all values of n. The lower (more negative) the energy is, the more stable the atom will be. The energy is lowest (most negative) for $n = 1$. As n gets larger, the energy becomes successively less negative and therefore increases. We can liken the situation to a ladder in which the rungs are numbered from the bottom rung on up. The higher one climbs the ladder (the greater the value of n), the higher the energy. The lowest energy state ($n = 1$, analogous to the bottom rung) is called the **ground state** of the atom. When the electron is in a higher senergy (less negative) orbit—$n = 2$ or higher—the atom is said to be in an **excited state**. Figure 6.14 ◀ shows the energy of the electron in a hydrogen atom for several values of n.

What happens to the orbit radius and the energy as n becomes infinitely large? The radius increases as n^2, so we reach a point at which the electron is completely separated from the nucleus. When $n = \infty$, the energy is zero:

$$E = (-2.18 \times 10^{-18} \text{ J})\left(\frac{1}{\infty^2}\right) = 0$$

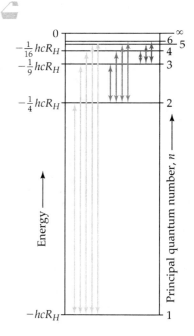

▲ Figure 6.14 **Energy levels in the hydrogen atom from the Bohr model.** The arrows refer to the transitions of the electron from one allowed energy state to another. The states shown are those for which $n = 1$ through $n = 6$ and the state for $n = \infty$ for which the energy, E, equals zero.

Thus, the state in which the electron is removed from the nucleus is the reference, or zero-energy, state of the hydrogen atom. This zero-energy state is *higher* in energy than the states with negative energies.

In his third postulate, Bohr assumed that the electron could "jump" from one allowed energy state to another by either absorbing or emitting photons whose radiant energy corresponds exactly to the energy difference between the two states. Energy must be absorbed for an electron to move to a higher energy state (one with a higher value of n). Conversely, radiant energy is emitted when the electron jumps to a lower energy state (one with a lower value of n). Thus, if the electron jumps from an initial state that has energy E_i to a final state of energy E_f, the change in energy is

$$\Delta E = E_f - E_i = E_{photon} = h\nu \qquad [6.6]$$

Bohr's model of the hydrogen atom states, therefore, that only the specific frequencies of light that satisfy Equation 6.6 can be absorbed or emitted by the atom.

Substituting the energy expression in Equation 6.5 into Equation 6.6 and recalling that $\nu = c/\lambda$, we have

$$\Delta E = h\nu = \frac{hc}{\lambda} = (-2.18 \times 10^{-18} \text{ J})\left(\frac{1}{n_f^2} - \frac{1}{n_i^2}\right) \qquad [6.7]$$

In this equation n_i and n_f are the principal quantum numbers of the initial and final states of the atom, respectively. If n_f is smaller than n_i, the electron moves closer to the nucleus and ΔE is a negative number, indicating that the atom releases energy. For example, if the electron moves from $n_i = 3$ to $n_f = 1$, we have

$$\Delta E = (-2.18 \times 10^{-18} \text{ J})\left(\frac{1}{1^2} - \frac{1}{3^2}\right) = (-2.18 \times 10^{-18} \text{ J})\left(\frac{8}{9}\right) = -1.94 \times 10^{-18} \text{ J}$$

Knowing the energy for the emitted photon, we can calculate either its frequency or its wavelength. For the wavelength, we have

$$\lambda = \frac{c}{\nu} = \frac{hc}{\Delta E} = \frac{(6.626 \times 10^{-34} \text{ J-s})(3.00 \times 10^8 \text{ m/s})}{1.94 \times 10^{-18} \text{ J}} = 1.03 \times 10^{-7} \text{ m}$$

We have not included the negative sign of the energy in this calculation because wavelength and frequency are always reported as positive quantities. The direction of energy flow is indicated by saying that a photon of wavelength 1.03×10^{-7} m has been *emitted*.

If we solve Equation 6.7 for $1/\lambda$, we find that this equation derived from Bohr's theory corresponds to the Rydberg equation, Equation 6.4, which was obtained using experimental data:

$$\frac{1}{\lambda} = \frac{-hcR_H}{hc}\left(\frac{1}{n_f^2} - \frac{1}{n_i^2}\right) = R_H\left(\frac{1}{n_i^2} - \frac{1}{n_f^2}\right)$$

Thus, the existence of discrete spectral lines can be attributed to the quantized jumps of electrons between energy levels.

GIVE IT SOME THOUGHT

As the electron in a hydrogen atom jumps from the $n = 3$ orbit to the $n = 7$ orbit, does it absorb energy or emit energy?

■■■ SAMPLE EXERCISE 6.4 | Electronic Transitions in the Hydrogen Atom

Using Figure 6.14, predict which of the following electronic transitions produces the spectral line having the longest wavelength: $n = 2$ to $n = 1$, $n = 3$ to $n = 2$, or $n = 4$ to $n = 3$.

SOLUTION

The wavelength increases as frequency decreases ($\lambda = c/\nu$). Hence the longest wavelength will be associated with the lowest frequency. According to Planck's equation, $E = h\nu$, the lowest frequency is associated with the lowest energy. In Figure 6.14 the shortest vertical line represents the smallest energy change. Thus, the $n = 4$ to $n = 3$ transition produces the longest wavelength (lowest frequency) line.

■■■ PRACTICE EXERCISE

Indicate whether each of the following electronic transitions emits energy or requires the absorption of energy: (a) $n = 3$ to $n = 1$; (b) $n = 2$ to $n = 4$.
Answers: **(a)** emits energy, **(b)** requires absorption of energy

Limitations of the Bohr Model

While the Bohr model explains the line spectrum of the hydrogen atom, it cannot explain the spectra of other atoms, except in a rather crude way. Bohr also avoided the problem of why the negatively charged electron would not just fall into the positively charged nucleus by simply assuming it would not happen. Therefore, there is a problem with describing an electron merely as a small particle circling about the nucleus. As we will see in Section 6.4, the electron exhibits wavelike properties, a fact that any acceptable model of electronic structure must accommodate. As it turns out, the Bohr model was only an important step along the way toward the development of a more comprehensive model. What is most significant about Bohr's model is that it introduces two important ideas that are also incorporated into our current model: (1) Electrons exist only in certain discrete energy levels, which are described by quantum numbers, and (2) energy is involved in moving an electron from one level to another. We will now start to develop the successor to the Bohr model, which requires that we take a closer look at the behavior of matter.

6.4 THE WAVE BEHAVIOR OF MATTER

In the years following the development of Bohr's model for the hydrogen atom, the dual nature of radiant energy became a familiar concept. Depending on the experimental circumstances, radiation appears to have either a wavelike or a particle-like (photon) character. Louis de Broglie (1892–1987), who was working on his Ph.D. thesis in physics at the Sorbonne in Paris, boldly extended this idea. If radiant energy could, under appropriate conditions, behave as though it were a stream of particles, could matter, under appropriate conditions, possibly show the properties of a wave? Suppose that the electron orbiting the nucleus of a hydrogen atom could be thought of as a wave, with a characteristic wavelength, rather than as a particle. De Broglie suggested that as the electron moves about the nucleus, it is associated with a particular wavelength. He went on to propose that the characteristic wavelength of the electron, or of any other particle, depends on its mass, m, and on its velocity, v, (where h is Planck's constant):

$$\lambda = \frac{h}{mv} \qquad [6.8]$$

The quantity mv for any object is called its **momentum**. De Broglie used the term **matter waves** to describe the wave characteristics of material particles.

Because de Broglie's hypothesis is applicable to all matter, any object of mass m and velocity v would give rise to a characteristic matter wave. However, Equation 6.8 indicates that the wavelength associated with an object of ordinary size, such as a golf ball, is so tiny as to be completely out of the range of any possible observation. This is not so for an electron because its mass is so small, as we see in Sample Exercise 6.5.

■ SAMPLE EXERCISE 6.5 | Matter Waves

What is the wavelength of an electron moving with a speed of 5.97×10^6 m/s? The mass of the electron is 9.11×10^{-31} kg.

SOLUTION

Analyze: We are given the mass, m, and velocity, v, of the electron, and we must calculate its de Broglie wavelength, λ.

Plan: The wavelength of a moving particle is given by Equation 6.8, so λ is calculated by inserting the known quantities h, m, and v. In doing so, however, we must pay attention to units.

Solve: Using the value of Planck's constant, $h = 6.626 \times 10^{-34}$ J-s

and recalling that $1 \text{ J} = 1 \text{ kg-m}^2/\text{s}^2$

we have the following:
$$\lambda = \frac{h}{mv}$$
$$= \frac{(6.626 \times 10^{-34} \text{ J-s})}{(9.11 \times 10^{-31} \text{ kg})(5.97 \times 10^6 \text{ m/s})}\left(\frac{1 \text{ kg-m}^2/\text{s}^2}{1 \text{ J}}\right)$$
$$= 1.22 \times 10^{-10} \text{ m} = 0.122 \text{ nm} = 1.22 \text{ Å}$$

Comment: By comparing this value with the wavelengths of electromagnetic radiation shown in Figure 6.4, we see that the wavelength of this electron is about the same as that of X-rays.

■ PRACTICE EXERCISE

Calculate the velocity of a neutron whose de Broglie wavelength is 500 pm. The mass of a neutron is given in the table inside the back cover of the text.
Answer: 7.92×10^2 m/s

Within a few years after de Broglie published his theory, the wave properties of the electron were demonstrated experimentally. As electrons passed through a crystal, they were diffracted by the crystal, just as X-rays are diffracted. Thus, a stream of moving electrons exhibits the same kinds of wave behavior as electromagnetic radiation.

The technique of electron diffraction has been highly developed. In the electron microscope, for instance, the wave characteristics of electrons are used to obtain images at the atomic scale. This microscope is an important tool for studying surface phenomena at very high magnifications. Electron microscopes can magnify objects by 3,000,000 times (x), far more than can be done with visible light (1000x), because the wavelength of the electrons is so small compared to visible light. Figure 6.15▶ is a photograph of an electron microscope image.

▲ Figure 6.15 **Electrons as waves.** The dots you see in this transmission electron micrograph are columns of atoms. Their regular spacing at the atomic level proves that this material is crystalline. Because this crystal is only about 15 nm in diameter, it is a nanocrystal, which has unusual properties that we will discuss in Chapter 12.

GIVE IT SOME THOUGHT

A baseball pitcher throws a fastball that moves at 95 miles per hour. Does that moving baseball generate matter waves? If so, can we observe them?

The Uncertainty Principle

The discovery of the wave properties of matter raised some new and interesting questions about classical physics. Consider, for example, a ball rolling down a ramp. Using the equations of classical physics, we can calculate the ball's position, direction of motion, and speed at any time, with great accuracy.

▲ Figure 6.16 **Werner Heisenberg (1901–1976).** During his postdoctoral assistantship with Niels Bohr, Heisenberg formulated his famous uncertainty principle. At the age of 25, he became the chair in theoretical physics at the University of Leipzig. At 32 he was one of the youngest scientists to receive the Nobel Prize.

Can we do the same for an electron, which exhibits wave properties? A wave extends in space, and therefore its location is not precisely defined. We might therefore anticipate that it is impossible to determine exactly where an electron is located at a specific time.

The German physicist Werner Heisenberg (Figure 6.16 ◄) proposed that the dual nature of matter places a fundamental limitation on how precisely we can know both the location and the momentum of any object. The limitation becomes important only when we deal with matter at the subatomic level (that is, with masses as small as that of an electron). Heisenberg's principle is called the **uncertainty principle.** When applied to the electrons in an atom, this principle states that it is inherently impossible for us to know simultaneously both the exact momentum of the electron and its exact location in space.

Heisenberg mathematically related the uncertainty of the position (Δx) and the uncertainty in momentum $\Delta(mv)$ to a quantity involving Planck's constant:

$$\Delta x \cdot \Delta(mv) \geq \frac{h}{4\pi} \qquad [6.9]$$

A brief calculation illustrates the dramatic implications of the uncertainty principle. The electron has a mass of 9.11×10^{-31} kg and moves at an average speed of about 5×10^6 m/s in a hydrogen atom. Let's assume that we know the speed to an uncertainty of 1% (that is, an uncertainty of $(0.01)(5 \times 10^6$ m/s$) = 5 \times 10^4$ m/s) and that this is the only important source of uncertainty in the momentum, so that $\Delta(mv) = m\Delta v$. We can then use Equation 6.9 to calculate the uncertainty in the position of the electron:

$$\Delta x \geq \frac{h}{4\pi m \Delta v} = \frac{(6.626 \times 10^{-34} \text{ J-s})}{4\pi (9.11 \times 10^{-31} \text{ kg})(5 \times 10^4 \text{ m/s})} = 1 \times 10^{-9} \text{ m}$$

Because the diameter of a hydrogen atom is only about 1×10^{-10} m, the uncertainty is an order of magnitude greater than the size of the atom. Thus, we have essentially no idea of where the electron is located within the atom. On the other hand, if we were to repeat the calculation with an object of ordinary mass such as a tennis ball, the uncertainty would be so small that it would be inconsequential. In that case, m is large and Δx is out of the realm of measurement and therefore of no practical consequence.

De Broglie's hypothesis and Heisenberg's uncertainty principle set the stage for a new and more broadly applicable theory of atomic structure. In this new approach, any attempt to define precisely the instantaneous location and momentum of the electron is abandoned. The wave nature of the electron is recognized, and its behavior is described in terms appropriate to waves. The result is a model that precisely describes the energy of the electron while describing its location not precisely, but in terms of probabilities.

 GIVE IT SOME THOUGHT

What is the principal reason that the uncertainty principle should be considered when discussing electrons and other subatomic particles, but is not so necessary when discussing our macroscopic world?

6.5 QUANTUM MECHANICS AND ATOMIC ORBITALS

In 1926 the Austrian physicist Erwin Schrödinger (1887–1961) proposed an equation, now known as Schrödinger's wave equation, that incorporates both the wavelike behavior and the particle-like behavior of the electron. His work opened a new way of dealing with subatomic particles, known as either *quantum mechanics* or *wave mechanics.* The application of Schrödinger's equation

MEASUREMENT AND THE UNCERTAINTY PRINCIPLE

Whenever any measurement is made, some uncertainty exists. Our experience with objects of ordinary dimensions, such as balls or trains or laboratory equipment, indicates that using more precise instruments can decrease the uncertainty of a measurement. In fact, we might expect that the uncertainty in a measurement can be made indefinitely small. However, the uncertainty principle states that there is an actual limit to the accuracy of measurements. This limit is not a restriction on how well instruments can be made; rather, it is inherent in nature. This limit has no practical consequences when dealing with ordinary-sized objects, but its implications are enormous when dealing with subatomic particles, such as electrons.

To measure an object, we must disturb it, at least a little, with our measuring device. Imagine using a flashlight to locate a large rubber ball in a dark room. You see the ball when the light from the flashlight bounces off the ball and strikes your eyes. When a beam of photons strikes an object of this size, it does not alter its position or momentum to any practical extent. Imagine, however, that you wish to locate an electron by similarly bouncing light off it into some detector. Objects can be located to an accuracy no greater than the wavelength of the radiation used. Thus, if we want an accurate position measurement for an electron, we must use a short wavelength. This means that photons of high energy must be employed. The more energy the photons have, the more momentum they impart to the electron when they strike it, which changes the electron's motion in an unpredictable way. The attempt to measure accurately the electron's position introduces considerable uncertainty in its momentum; the act of measuring the electron's position at one moment makes our knowledge of its future position inaccurate.

Suppose, then, that we use photons of longer wavelength. Because these photons have lower energy, the momentum of the electron is not so appreciably changed during measurement, but its position will be correspondingly less accurately known. This is the essence of the uncertainty principle: *There is an uncertainty in simultaneously knowing either the position or the momentum of the electron that cannot be reduced beyond a certain minimum level.* The more accurately one is known, the less accurately the other is known. Although we can never know the exact position and momentum of the electron, we can talk about the probability of its being at certain locations in space. In Section 6.5 we introduce a model of the atom that provides the probability of finding electrons of specific energies at certain positions in atoms. *Related Exercises: 6.45 and 6.46*

requires advanced calculus, and we will not be concerned with the details of his approach. We will, however, qualitatively consider the results he obtained, because they give us a powerful new way to view electronic structure. Let's begin by examining the electronic structure of the simplest atom, hydrogen.

In the same way that a plucked guitar string vibrates as a standing wave, Schrödinger treated the electron as a standing circular wave around the nucleus. Just as the plucked guitar string produces a fundamental frequency and higher overtones (harmonics), there is a lowest-energy standing wave, and higher-energy ones, for an electron in an atom. Solving Schrödinger's equation leads to a series of mathematical functions called **wave functions** that describe the electron in an atom. These wave functions are usually represented by the symbol ψ (the lowercase Greek letter *psi*). Although the wave function itself has no direct physical meaning, the square of the wave function, ψ^2, provides information about an electron's location when the electron is in an allowed energy state.

For the hydrogen atom, the allowed energies are the same as those predicted by the Bohr model. However, the Bohr model assumes that the electron is in a circular orbit of some particular radius about the nucleus. In the quantum mechanical model, the electron's location cannot be described so simply. According to the uncertainty principle, if we know the momentum of the electron with high accuracy, our simultaneous knowledge of its location is very uncertain. Thus, we cannot hope to specify the exact location of an individual electron around the nucleus. Rather, we must be content with a kind of statistical knowledge. In the quantum mechanical model, we therefore speak of the *probability* that the electron will be in a certain region of space at a given instant. As it turns out, the square of the wave function, ψ^2, at a given point in space represents the probability that the electron will be found at that location. For this reason, ψ^2 is called either the **probability density** or the **electron density.**

One way of representing the probability of finding the electron in various regions of an atom is shown in Figure 6.17 ▶. In this figure the density of the dots represents the probability of finding the electron. The regions with a high

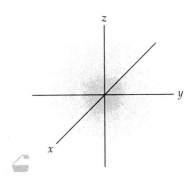

▲ Figure 6.17 **Electron-density distribution.** This rendering represents the probability of where in the space surrounding the nucleus the electron is to be found in a hydrogen atom in its ground state.

density of dots correspond to relatively large values for ψ^2 and are therefore regions where there is a high probability of finding the electron. In Section 6.6 we will say more about the ways in which we can represent electron density.

> ### GIVE IT SOME THOUGHT
>
> Is there a difference between stating, "The electron is located at a particular point in space" and "There is a high probability that the electron is located at a particular point in space"?

Orbitals and Quantum Numbers

The solution to Schrödinger's equation for the hydrogen atom yields a set of wave functions and corresponding energies. These wave functions are called **orbitals**. Each orbital describes a specific distribution of electron density in space, as given by the orbital's probability density. Each orbital, therefore, has a characteristic energy and shape. For example, the lowest-energy orbital in the hydrogen atom has an energy of -2.18×10^{-18} J and the shape illustrated in Figure 6.17. Note that an *orbital* (quantum mechanical model) is not the same as an *orbit* (Bohr model). The quantum mechanical model does not refer to orbits, because the motion of the electron in an atom cannot be precisely measured or tracked (Heisenberg uncertainty principle).

The Bohr model introduced a single quantum number, n, to describe an orbit. The quantum mechanical model uses three quantum numbers, n, l, and m_l, which result naturally from the mathematics used, to describe an orbital. Let's consider what information we obtain from each of these quantum numbers and how they are interrelated.

1. The *principal quantum number, n*, can have positive integral values of 1, 2, 3, and so forth. As n increases, the orbital becomes larger, and the electron spends more time farther from the nucleus. An increase in n also means that the electron has a higher energy and is therefore less tightly bound to the nucleus. For the hydrogen atom, $E_n = -(2.18 \times 10^{-18} \text{ J})(1/n^2)$, as in the Bohr model.

2. The second quantum number—the *angular momentum quantum number, l*—can have integral values from 0 to $(n - 1)$ for each value of n. This quantum number defines the shape of the orbital. (We will consider these shapes in Section 6.6.) The value of l for a particular orbital is generally designated by the letters s, p, d, and f,* corresponding to l values of 0, 1, 2, and 3, respectively, as summarized here:

Value of l	0	1	2	3
Letter used	s	p	d	f

3. The *magnetic quantum number, m_l*, can have integral values between $-l$ and l, including zero. This quantum number describes the orientation of the orbital in space, as we will discuss in Section 6.6.

Notice that because the value of n can be any positive integer, an infinite number of orbitals for the hydrogen atom is possible. The electron in a hydrogen atom is described by only one of these orbitals at any given time—we say that the electron *occupies* a certain orbital. The remaining orbitals are *unoccupied* for that particular state of the hydrogen atom. We will see that we are mainly interested in the orbitals of the hydrogen atom with small values of n.

---

*The letters s, p, d, and f come from the words sharp, principal, diffuse, and fundamental, which were used to describe certain features of spectra before quantum mechanics was developed.

TABLE 6.2 ■ Relationship among Values of n, l, and m_l through $n = 4$					
n	Possible Values of l	Subshell Designation	Possible Values of m_l	Number of Orbitals in Subshell	Total Number of Orbitals in Shell
1	0	1s	0	1	1
2	0	2s	0	1	
	1	2p	1, 0, −1	3	4
3	0	3s	0	1	
	1	3p	1, 0, −1	3	
	2	3d	2, 1, 0, −1, −2	5	9
4	0	4s	0	1	
	1	4p	1, 0, −1	3	
	2	4d	2, 1, 0, −1, −2	5	
	3	4f	3, 2, 1, 0, −1, −2, −3	7	16

GIVE IT SOME THOUGHT

What is the difference between an *orbit* (Bohr model) and an *orbital* (quantum mechanical model)?

The collection of orbitals with the same value of n is called an **electron shell**. All the orbitals that have $n = 3$, for example, are said to be in the third shell. Further, the set of orbitals that have the same n and l values is called a **subshell**. Each subshell is designated by a number (the value of n) and a letter (s, p, d, or f, corresponding to the value of l). For example, the orbitals that have $n = 3$ and $l = 2$ are called 3d orbitals and are in the 3d subshell.

Table 6.2▲ summarizes the possible values of the quantum numbers l and m_l for values of n through $n = 4$. The restrictions on the possible values of the quantum numbers give rise to the following very important observations:

1. The shell with principal quantum number n will consist of exactly n subshells. Each subshell corresponds to a different allowed value of l from 0 to $(n − 1)$. Thus, the first shell ($n = 1$) consists of only one subshell, the 1s ($l = 0$); the second shell ($n = 2$) consists of two subshells, the 2s ($l = 0$) and 2p ($l = 1$); the third shell consists of three subshells, 3s, 3p, and 3d, and so forth.

2. Each subshell consists of a specific number of orbitals. Each orbital corresponds to a different allowed value of m_l. For a given value of l, there are $(2l + 1)$ allowed values of m_l, ranging from $−l$ to $+l$. Thus, each s ($l = 0$) subshell consists of one orbital, each p ($l = 1$) subshell consists of three orbitals, each d ($l = 2$) subshell consists of five orbitals, and so forth.

3. The total number of orbitals in a shell is n^2, where n is the principal quantum number of the shell. The resulting number of orbitals for the shells—1, 4, 9, 16—is related to a pattern seen in the periodic table: We see that the number of elements in the rows of the periodic table—2, 8, 18, and 32—equals twice these numbers. We will discuss this relationship further in Section 6.9.

Figure 6.18▶ shows the relative energies of the hydrogen atom orbitals through $n = 3$. Each box represents an orbital; orbitals of the same subshell, such as the 2p, are grouped together. When the electron occupies the lowest-energy orbital (1s), the hydrogen atom is said to be in its *ground state*. When the

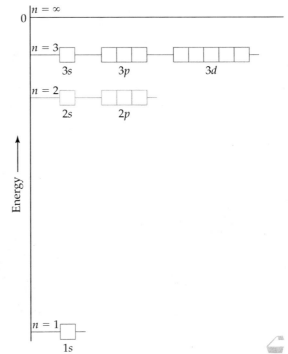

▲ Figure 6.18 **Orbital energy levels in the hydrogen atom.** Each box represents an orbital. Note that all orbitals with the same value for the principal quantum number, n, have the same energy. This is true only in one-electron systems, such as the hydrogen atom.

electron occupies any other orbital, the atom is in an *excited state*. At ordinary temperatures, essentially all hydrogen atoms are in the ground state. The electron can be excited to a higher-energy orbital by absorption of a photon of appropriate energy.

GIVE IT SOME THOUGHT

In Figure 6.18, why is the energy difference between the $n = 1$ and $n = 2$ levels so much greater than the energy difference between the $n = 2$ and $n = 3$ levels?

■■ SAMPLE EXERCISE 6.6 | Subshells of the Hydrogen Atom

(a) Without referring to Table 6.2, predict the number of subshells in the fourth shell, that is, for $n = 4$. **(b)** Give the label for each of these subshells. **(c)** How many orbitals are in each of these subshells?

Analyze and Plan: We are given the value of the principal quantum number, n. We need to determine the allowed values of l and m_l for this given value of n and then count the number of orbitals in each subshell.

SOLUTION

There are four subshells in the fourth shell, corresponding to the four possible values of l (0, 1, 2, and 3).

These subshells are labeled 4s, 4p, 4d, and 4f. The number given in the designation of a subshell is the principal quantum number, n; the letter designates the value of the angular momentum quantum number, l: for $l = 0$, s; for $l = 1$, p; for $l = 2$, d; for $l = 3$, f.

There is one 4s orbital (when $l = 0$, there is only one possible value of m_l: 0). There are three 4p orbitals (when $l = 1$, there are three possible values of m_l: 1, 0, and −1). There are five 4d orbitals (when $l = 2$, there are five allowed values of m_l: 2, 1, 0, −1, −2). There are seven 4f orbitals (when $l = 3$, there are seven permitted values of m_l: 3, 2, 1, 0, −1, −2, −3).

■■ PRACTICE EXERCISE

(a) What is the designation for the subshell with $n = 5$ and $l = 1$? **(b)** How many orbitals are in this subshell? **(c)** Indicate the values of m_l for each of these orbitals.
Answers: **(a)** 5p; **(b)** 3; **(c)** 1, 0, −1

6.6 REPRESENTATIONS OF ORBITALS

In our discussion of orbitals so far, we have emphasized their energies. But the wave function also provides information about the electron's location in space when it occupies an orbital. Let's examine the ways that we can picture the orbitals. In doing so, we will examine some important aspects of the electron-density distributions of the orbitals. First, we will look at the three-dimensional shape of the orbital—is it spherical, for example, or does it have directionality? Second, we will examine how the probability density changes as we move on a straight line farther and farther from the nucleus. Finally, we will look at the typical three-dimensional sketches that chemists use in describing the orbitals.

The *s* Orbitals

One representation of the lowest-energy orbital of the hydrogen atom, the 1s, is shown in Figure 6.17. This type of drawing, which shows the distribution of electron density around the nucleus, is one of the several ways we use to help us visualize orbitals. The first thing that we notice about the electron density for the 1s orbital is that it is *spherically symmetric*—in other words, the electron density at a given distance from the nucleus is the same regardless of the direction in which we proceed from the nucleus. All of the other s orbitals (2s, 3s, 4s, and so forth) are spherically symmetric as well. Recall that the *l* quantum number

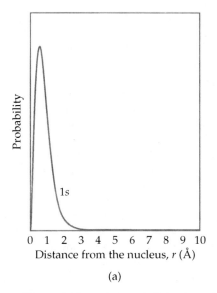

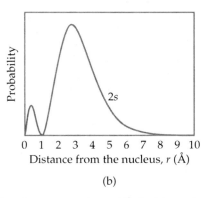

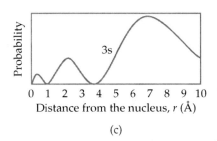

▲ Figure 6.19 **Radial probability functions for the 1s, 2s, and 3s orbitals.** These plots show the probability of finding the electron as a function of distance from the nucleus. As *n* increases, the most likely distance at which to find the electron moves farther from the nucleus, similar to the Bohr model. In the 2s and 3s orbitals the radial probability function drops to zero at certain distances from the nucleus but then rises again. The points at which the probability is zero are called *nodes*.

for the s orbitals is 0; therefore the m_l quantum number must be 0. Therefore, for each value of *n*, there is only one *s* orbital.

So what is different about the *s* orbitals having different *n* quantum numbers? For example, how does the electron-density distribution of the hydrogen atom change when the electron is excited from the 1s orbital to the 2s orbital? To address questions like this, we must look at the *radial probability density*, that is, the probability that we will find the electron at a specific distance from the nucleus. In Figure 6.19 ▲ we have plotted the radial probability density for the 1s orbital as a function of *r*, the distance from the nucleus. The resulting curve is the **radial probability function** for the 1s orbital. (Radial probability functions are described more fully in the "A Closer Look" box in this section.) We see that the probability of finding the electron rises rapidly as we move away from the nucleus, maximizing at a distance of 0.529 Å from the nucleus, and then falls off rapidly. Thus, when the electron occupies the 1s orbital, it is *most likely* to be found 0.529 Å from the nucleus*. We still use the probabilistic description, consistent with the uncertainty principle. Notice also that the probability of finding the electron at a distance greater than 3 Å from the nucleus is essentially zero.

Figure 6.19(b) shows the radial probability function for the 2s orbital of the hydrogen atom. We can see three significant differences between this plot and that for the 1s orbital: (1) There are two separate maxima in the radial probability function for the 2s orbital, namely a small peak at about *r* = 0.5 Å and a much larger peak at about *r* = 3 Å; (2) Between these two peaks is a point at which the function goes to zero (at about *r* = 1 Å). An intermediate point at which a probability function goes to zero is called a **node.** There is a zero probability of finding the electron at a distance corresponding to a node, even though the electron might be found at shorter or longer distances; (3) The radial probability function for the 2s orbital is significantly broader (more spread out) than that for the 1s orbital. Thus, for the 2s orbital, there is a larger range of distances from the

*In the quantum mechanical model, the most probable distance at which to find the electron in the 1s orbital— 0.529 Å—is identical to the radius of the orbit predicted by Bohr for n = 1. The distance 0.529 Å is often called the Bohr radius.

1s

2s

3s

▲ Figure 6.20 **Contour representations of the 1s, 2s, and 3s orbitals.** The relative radii of the spheres correspond to a 90% probability of finding the electron within each sphere.

nucleus at which there is a high probability of finding the electron than for the 1s orbital. This trend continues for the 3s orbital, as shown in Figure 6.19(c). The radial probability function for the 3s orbital has three peaks of increasing size, with the largest peak maximizing even farther from the nucleus (at about $r = 7$ Å) at which it has two nodes and is even more spread out.

The radial probability functions in Figure 6.19 tell us that as n increases, there is also an increase in the most likely distance from the nucleus to find the electron. In other words, the size of the orbital increases with increasing n, just as it did in the Bohr model.

One widely used method of representing orbitals is to display a boundary surface that encloses some substantial portion, say 90%, of the total electron density for the orbital. For the s orbitals, these contour representations are spheres. The contour representations of the 1s, 2s, and 3s orbitals are shown in Figure 6.20 ◀. All the orbitals have the same shape, but they differ in size. Although the details of how the electron density varies within the contour representation are lost in these representations, this is not a serious disadvantage. For more qualitative discussions, the most important features of orbitals are their relative sizes and their shapes, which are adequately displayed by contour representations.

GIVE IT SOME THOUGHT

How many maxima would you expected to find in the radial probability function for the 4s orbital of the hydrogen atom? How many nodes would you expect in the 4s radial probability function?

A Closer Look   PROBABILITY DENSITY AND RADIAL PROBABILITY FUNCTIONS

The quantum mechanical description of the hydrogen atom requires that we talk about the position of the electron in the atom in a somewhat unfamiliar way. In classical physics, we can exactly pinpoint the position and velocity of an orbiting object, such as a planet orbiting a star. Under quantum mechanics, however, we must describe the position of the electron in the hydrogen atom in terms of probabilities rather than an exact location—an exact answer would violate the uncertainty principle, which becomes important when considering subatomic particles. The information we need about the probability of finding the electron is contained in the wave functions, ψ, that are obtained when Schrödinger's equation is solved. Remember that there are an infinite number of wave functions (orbitals) for the hydrogen atom, but the electron can occupy only one of them at any given time. Here we will discuss briefly how we can use the orbitals to obtain radial probability functions, such as those in Figure 6.19.

In Section 6.5 we stated that the square of the wave function, ψ^2, gives the probability that the electron is at any one given point in space. Recall that this quantity is called the *probability density* for the point. For a spherically symmetric s orbital, the value of ψ depends only on the distance from the nucleus, r. Let's consider a straight line outward from the nucleus, as shown in Figure 6.21 ▶. The probability of finding the electron at distance r from the nucleus along that line is $[\psi(r)]^2$, where $\psi(r)$ is the value of ψ at distance r. Figure 6.23 ▶ shows plots of $[\psi(r)]^2$ as a function of r for the 1s, 2s, and 3s orbitals of the hydrogen atom.

You will notice that the plots in Figure 6.23 look distinctly different from the radial probability functions plotted in Figure 6.19. These two types of plots for the s orbitals are very closely related, but they provide somewhat different information. The probability density, $[\psi(r)]^2$, tells us the probability of finding the electron at *a specific* point in space that is at distance r from the nucleus. The radial probability function, which we will denote $P(r)$, tells us the probability of finding the electron at *any* point that is distance r from the nucleus. In other words, to get $P(r)$ we need to "add up" the probabilities of finding the electron over all the points at distance r from the nucleus. The difference between these descriptions may seem rather subtle, but mathematics provides us with a precise way to connect them.

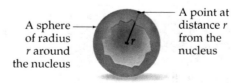

A sphere of radius r around the nucleus ⟶

A point at distance r from the nucleus

▲ Figure 6.21 **Probability at a point.** The probability density, $\psi(r)^2$ gives the probability that the electron will be found at *a specific point* at distance r from the nucleus. The radial probability function, $4\pi r^2\ \psi(r)^2$, gives the probability that the electron will be found at *any* point distance r from the nucleus—in other words, at any point on the sphere of radius r.

The *p* Orbitals

The distribution of electron density for a 2*p* orbital is shown in Figure 6.22(a) ▼. As we can see from this figure, the electron density is not distributed in a spherically symmetric fashion as in an *s* orbital. Instead, the electron density is concentrated in two regions on either side of the nucleus, separated by a node at the nucleus. We say that this dumbbell-shaped orbital has two *lobes*. Recall that we are making no statement of how the electron is moving within the orbital. The only thing Figure 6.22(a) portrays is the *averaged* distribution of the electron density in a 2*p* orbital.

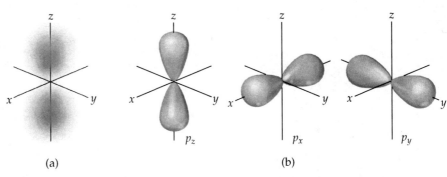

(a)   (b)

▲ Figure 6.22 **The *p* orbitals.** (a) Electron-density distribution of a 2*p* orbital. (b) Contour representations of the three *p* orbitals. Note that the subscript on the orbital label indicates the axis along which the orbital lies.

Beginning with the $n = 2$ shell, each shell has three *p* orbitals. Recall that the *l* quantum number for *p* orbitals is 1. Therefore, the magnetic quantum number m_l can have three possible values: −1, 0, and +1. Thus, there are three 2*p* orbitals, three 3*p* orbitals, and so forth, corresponding to the three possible values of m_l. Each set of *p* orbitals has the dumbbell shapes shown in Figure 6.22(a) for the 2*p* orbitals. For each value of *n*, the three *p* orbitals have the same size and shape but differ from one another in spatial orientation. We usually represent *p* orbitals by drawing the shape and orientation of their wave functions, as shown in Figure 6.22(b). It is convenient to label these as the p_x, p_y and p_z orbitals. The letter subscript indicates the Cartesian axis along which the

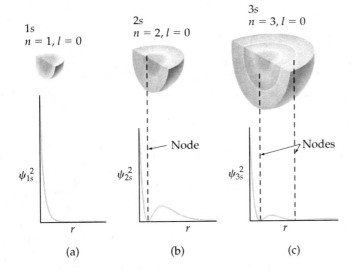

(a)   (b)   (c)

◀ Figure 6.23 **Probability density distribution in 1*s*, 2*s*, and 3*s* orbitals.** The lower part of the figure shows how the probability density, $\psi(r)^2$, varies as a function of distance *r* from the nucleus. The upper part of the figure shows a cutaway of the spherical electron density in each of the *s* orbitals.

to describe, however. The radial probability function at distance *r*, $P(r)$, is simply the probability density at distance *r*, $[\psi(r)]^2$ multiplied by the surface area of the sphere, which is given by the formula $4\pi r^2$:

$$P(r) = 4\pi r^2 [\psi(r)]^2$$

Thus, the plots of $P(r)$ in Figure 6.19 are equal to the plots of $[\psi(r)]^2$ in Figure 6.23 multiplied by $4\pi r^2$. The fact that $4\pi r^2$ increases rapidly as we move away from the nucleus makes the two sets of plots look very different. For example, the plot of $[\psi(r)]^2$ for the 3*s* orbital (Figure 6.23) shows that the function generally gets smaller the farther we go from the nucleus. But when we multiply by $4\pi r^2$, we see peaks that get larger and larger as we move away from the nucleus (Figure 6.19). We will see that the radial probability functions in Figure 6.19 provide us with the more useful information because they tell us the probability for finding the electron at *all* points distance *r* from the nucleus, not just one particular point. *Related Exercises: 6.48, 6.57, 6.58, and 6.91*

As shown in Figure 6.21, the collection of points at distance *r* from the nucleus is simply a sphere of radius *r*. The probability density at every point on that sphere is $[\psi(r)]^2$. To add up all of the individual probability densities requires the use of calculus and is beyond the scope of this text (in the language of calculus "we integrate the probability density over the surface of the sphere"). The result we obtain is easy

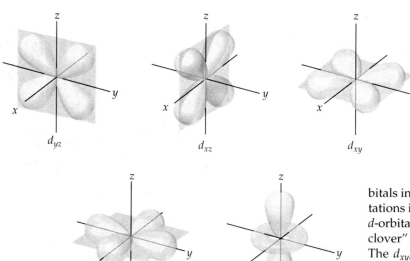

▲ Figure 6.24 **Contour representations of the five *d* orbitals.**

orbital is oriented.* Like *s* orbitals, *p* orbitals increase in size as we move from 2*p* to 3*p* to 4*p*, and so forth.

The *d* and *f* Orbitals

When *n* is 3 or greater, we encounter the *d* orbitals (for which *l* = 2). There are five 3*d* orbitals, five 4*d* orbitals, and so forth because in each shell there are five possible values for the m_l quantum number: −2, −1, 0, 1, and 2. The different *d* orbitals in a given shell have different shapes and orientations in space, as shown in Figure 6.24 ◀. Four of the *d*-orbital contour representations have a "four-leaf clover" shape, and each lies primarily in a plane. The d_{xy}, d_{xz}, and d_{yz} lie in the *xy*, *xz*, and *yz* planes, respectively, with the lobes oriented *between* the axes. The lobes of the $d_{x^2-y^2}$ orbital also lie in the *xy* plane, but the lobes lie *along* the *x* and *y* axes. The d_{z^2} orbital looks very different from the other four: It has two lobes along the *z* axis and a "doughnut" in the *xy* plane. Even though the d_{z^2} orbital looks different from the other *d* orbitals, it has the same energy as the other four *d* orbitals. The representations in Figure 6.24 are commonly used for all *d* orbitals, regardless of principal quantum number.

When *n* is 4 or greater, there are seven equivalent *f* orbitals (for which *l* = 3). The shapes of the *f* orbitals are even more complicated than those of the *d* orbitals and are not presented here. As you will see in the next section, however, you must be aware of *f* orbitals as we consider the electronic structure of atoms in the lower part of the periodic table.

In many instances later in the text you will find that knowing the number and shapes of atomic orbitals will help you understand chemistry at the molecular level. You will therefore find it useful to memorize the shapes of the orbitals shown in Figures 6.20, 6.23, and 6.24.

◢ GIVE IT SOME THOUGHT

Note in Figure 6.22(a) that the color is deep pink in the interior of each lobe but fades to pale pink at the edges. What does this change in color represent?

6.7 MANY-ELECTRON ATOMS

One of our goals in this chapter has been to determine the electronic structures of atoms. So far, we have seen that quantum mechanics leads to a very elegant description of the hydrogen atom. This atom, however, has only one electron. How must our description of the electronic structure of atoms change when we consider atoms with two or more electrons (a *many-electron* atom)? To describe these atoms, we must consider the nature of orbitals and their relative energies as well as how the electrons populate the available orbitals.

Orbitals and Their Energies

The quantum mechanical model would not be very useful if we could not extend what we have learned about hydrogen to other atoms. Fortunately, we can describe the electronic structure of a many-electron atom in terms of orbitals

We cannot make a simple correspondence between the subscripts (x, y, and z) and the allowed m_l values (1, 0, and −1). To explain why this is so is beyond the scope of an introductory text.

like those of the hydrogen atom. Thus, we can continue to designate orbitals as 1s, $2p_x$, and so forth. Further, these orbitals have the same general shapes as the corresponding hydrogen orbitals.

Although the shapes of the orbitals for many-electron atoms are the same as those for hydrogen, the presence of more than one electron greatly changes the energies of the orbitals. In hydrogen the energy of an orbital depends only on its principal quantum number, n (Figure 6.18); the 3s, 3p, and 3d subshells all have the same energy, for instance. In a many-electron atom, however, the electron–electron repulsions cause the different subshells to be at different energies, as shown in Figure 6.25 ▶. To understand why this is so, we must consider the forces between the electrons and how these forces are affected by the shapes of the orbitals. We will, however, forgo this analysis until Chapter 7.

The important idea is this: *In a many-electron atom, for a given value of n, the energy of an orbital increases with increasing value of l.* You can see this illustrated in Figure 6.25. Notice, for example, that the $n = 3$ orbitals (red) increase in energy in the order 3s < 3p < 3d. Figure 6.25 is a *qualitative* energy-level diagram; the exact energies of the orbitals and their spacings differ from one atom to another. Notice that all orbitals of a given subshell (such as the five 3d orbitals) still have the same energy as one another, just as they do in the hydrogen atom. Orbitals with the same energy are said to be **degenerate.**

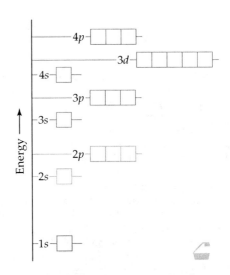

▲ Figure 6.25 **Orbital energy levels in many-electron atoms.** In a many-electron atom, the energies of the subshells in each shell follow the order $ns < np < nd < nf$. As in Figure 6.18, each box represents an orbital.

GIVE IT SOME THOUGHT

For a many-electron atom, can we predict unambiguously whether the 4s orbital is lower in energy or higher in energy than the 3d orbitals?

Electron Spin and the Pauli Exclusion Principle

We have now seen that we can use hydrogen-like orbitals to describe many-electron atoms. What, however, determines which orbitals the electrons reside in? That is, how do the electrons of a many-electron atom populate the available orbitals? To answer this question, we must consider an additional property of the electron.

When scientists studied the line spectra of many-electron atoms in great detail, they noticed a very puzzling feature: Lines that were originally thought to be single were actually closely spaced pairs. This meant, in essence, that there were twice as many energy levels as there were "supposed" to be. In 1925 the Dutch physicists George Uhlenbeck and Samuel Goudsmit proposed a solution to this dilemma. They postulated that electrons have an intrinsic property, called **electron spin,** that causes each electron to behave as if it were a tiny sphere spinning on its own axis.

By now it probably does not surprise you to learn that electron spin is quantized. This observation led to the assignment of a new quantum number for the electron, in addition to n, l, and m_l, which we have already discussed. This new quantum number, the **spin magnetic quantum number,** is denoted m_s (the subscript s stands for *spin*). Two possible values are allowed for m_s, $+\frac{1}{2}$ or $-\frac{1}{2}$, which was first interpreted as indicating the two opposite directions in which the electron can spin. A spinning charge produces a magnetic field. The two opposite directions of spin therefore produce oppositely directed magnetic fields, as shown in Figure 6.26 ▶.* These two opposite magnetic fields lead to the splitting of spectral lines into closely spaced pairs.

Electron spin is crucial for understanding the electronic structures of atoms. In 1925 the Austrian-born physicist Wolfgang Pauli (1900–1958) discovered the principle that governs the arrangements of electrons in many-electron atoms. The **Pauli exclusion principle** states that *no two electrons in an atom can have the same*

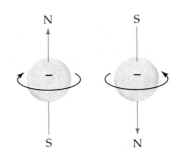

▲ Figure 6.26 **Electron spin.** The electron behaves as if it were spinning about an axis, thereby generating a magnetic field whose direction depends on the direction of spin. The two directions for the magnetic field correspond to the two possible values for the spin quantum number, m_s.

As we discussed earlier, the electron has both particle-like and wavelike properties. Thus, the picture of an electron as a spinning charged sphere is, strictly speaking, just a useful pictorial representation that helps us understand the two directions of magnetic field that an electron can possess.

A Closer Look   EXPERIMENTAL EVIDENCE FOR ELECTRON SPIN

Even before electron spin had been proposed, there was experimental evidence that electrons had an additional property that needed explanation. In 1921, Otto Stern and Walter Gerlach succeeded in separating a beam of neutral atoms into two groups by passing them through a nonhomogeneous magnetic field. Their experiment is diagrammed in Figure 6.27▶. Let's assume that they used a beam of hydrogen atoms (in actuality, they used silver atoms, which contain just one unpaired electron). We would normally expect that neutral atoms would not be affected by a magnetic field. However, the magnetic field arising from the electron's spin interacts with the magnet's field, deflecting the atom from its straight-line path. As shown in Figure 6.27, the magnetic field splits the beam in two, suggesting that there are two (and only two) equivalent values for the electron's own magnetic field. The Stern–Gerlach experiment could be readily interpreted once it was realized that there are exactly two values for the spin of the electron. These values will produce equal magnetic fields that are opposite in direction.

Related Exercise: 6.94

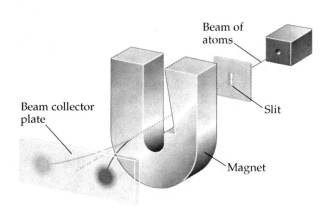

▲ Figure 6.27 **The Stern–Gerlach experiment.** Atoms in which the electron spin quantum number (m_s) of the unpaired electron is $+\frac{1}{2}$ are deflected in one direction, and those in which m_s is $-\frac{1}{2}$ are deflected in the other.

set of four quantum numbers n, l, m_l, and m_s. For a given orbital (ls, $2p_z$, and so forth), the values of n, l, and m_l are fixed. Thus, if we want to put more than one electron in an orbital *and* satisfy the Pauli exclusion principle, our only choice is to assign different m_s values to the electrons. Because there are only two such values, we conclude that *an orbital can hold a maximum of two electrons and they must have opposite spins.* This restriction allows us to index the electrons in an atom, giving their quantum numbers and thereby defining the region in space where each electron is most likely to be found. It also provides the key to one of the great problems in chemistry—understanding the structure of the periodic table of the elements. We will discuss these issues in the next two sections.

6.8 ELECTRON CONFIGURATIONS

Armed with knowledge of the relative energies of orbitals and the Pauli exclusion principle, we are now in a position to consider the arrangements of electrons in atoms. The way in which the electrons are distributed among the various orbitals of an atom is called the **electron configuration** of the atom. The most stable electron configuration of an atom—the ground state—is that in which the electrons are in the lowest possible energy states. If there were no restrictions on the possible values for the quantum numbers of the electrons, all the electrons would crowd into the ls orbital because it is the lowest in energy (Figure 6.25). The Pauli exclusion principle tells us, however, that there can be at most two electrons in any single orbital. Thus, *the orbitals are filled in order of increasing energy, with no more than two electrons per orbital.* For example, consider the lithium atom, which has three electrons. (Recall that the number of electrons in a neutral atom equals its atomic number.) The ls orbital can accommodate two of the electrons. The third one goes into the next lowest energy orbital, the 2s.

We can represent any electron configuration by writing the symbol for the occupied subshell and adding a superscript to indicate the number of electrons in that subshell. For example, for lithium we write $ls^2 2s^1$ (read "ls two, 2s one"). We can also show the arrangement of the electrons as

Li   ⮕⬇   ⬆

  1s   2s

In this kind of representation, which we call an *orbital diagram*, each orbital is denoted by a box and each electron by a half arrow. A half arrow pointing up (↑) represents an electron with a positive spin magnetic quantum number ($m_s = +\frac{1}{2}$) and a half arrow pointing down (↓) represents an electron with a negative spin magnetic quantum number ($m_s = -\frac{1}{2}$). This pictorial representation of electron spin is quite convenient. In fact, chemists and physicists often refer to electrons as "spin-up" and "spin-down" rather than specifying the value for m_s.

Electrons having opposite spins are said to be *paired* when they are in the same orbital (↑↓). An *unpaired electron* is one not accompanied by a partner of opposite spin. In the lithium atom the two electrons in the 1s orbital are paired and the electron in the 2s orbital is unpaired.

Hund's Rule

Consider now how the electron configurations of the elements change as we move from element to element across the periodic table. Hydrogen has one electron, which occupies the 1s orbital in its ground state.

$$\text{H} \quad \boxed{\uparrow} \quad : 1s^1$$
$$\text{1s}$$

The choice of a spin-up electron here is arbitrary; we could equally well show the ground state with one spin-down electron in the 1s orbital. It is customary, however, to show unpaired electrons with their spins up.

The next element, helium, has two electrons. Because two electrons with opposite spins can occupy an orbital, both of helium's electrons are in the 1s orbital.

$$\text{He} \quad \boxed{\uparrow\downarrow} \quad : 1s^2$$
$$\text{1s}$$

The two electrons present in helium complete the filling of the first shell. This arrangement represents a very stable configuration, as is evidenced by the chemical inertness of helium.

The electron configurations of lithium and several elements that follow it in the periodic table are shown in Table 6.3 ▼. For the third electron of lithium, the change in principal quantum number represents a large jump in energy and a corresponding jump in the average distance of the electron from the nucleus.

TABLE 6.3 ■ Electron Configurations of Several Lighter Elements

Element	Total Electrons	Orbital Diagram 1s	2s	2p	3s	Electron Configuration
Li	3	↑↓	↑			$1s^2 2s^1$
Be	4	↑↓	↑↓			$1s^2 2s^2$
B	5	↑↓	↑↓	↑		$1s^2 2s^2 2p^1$
C	6	↑↓	↑↓	↑ ↑		$1s^2 2s^2 2p^2$
N	7	↑↓	↑↓	↑ ↑ ↑		$1s^2 2s^2 2p^3$
Ne	10	↑↓	↑↓	↑↓ ↑↓ ↑↓		$1s^2 2s^2 2p^6$
Na	11	↑↓	↑↓	↑↓ ↑↓ ↑↓	↑	$1s^2 2s^2 2p^6 3s^1$

Chemistry and Life   NUCLEAR SPIN AND MAGNETIC RESONANCE IMAGING

A major challenge facing medical diagnosis is seeing inside the human body from the outside. Until recently, this was accomplished primarily by using X-rays to image human bones, muscles, and organs. However, there are several drawbacks to using X-rays for medical imaging. First, X-rays do not give well-resolved images of overlapping physiological structures. Moreover, because damaged or diseased tissue often yields the same image as healthy tissue, X-rays frequently fail to detect illness or injuries. Finally, X-rays are high-energy radiation that can cause physiological harm, even in low doses.

During the 1980s, a new technique called *magnetic resonance imaging* (MRI) moved to the forefront of medical imaging technology. The foundation of MRI is a phenomenon called nuclear magnetic resonance (NMR), which was discovered in the mid-1940s. Today NMR has become one of the most important spectroscopic methods used in chemistry. It is based on the observation that, like electrons, the nuclei of many elements possess an intrinsic spin. Like electron spin, nuclear spin is quantized. For example, the nucleus of ^1H (a proton) has two possible magnetic nuclear spin quantum numbers, $+\frac{1}{2}$ and $-\frac{1}{2}$. The hydrogen nucleus is the most common one studied by NMR.

A spinning hydrogen nucleus acts like a tiny magnet. In the absence of external effects, the two spin states have the same energy. However, when the nuclei are placed in an external magnetic field, they can align either parallel or opposed (antiparallel) to the field, depending on their spin. The parallel alignment is lower in energy than the antiparallel one by a certain amount, ΔE (Figure 6.28◄). If the nuclei are irradiated with photons with energy equal to ΔE, the spin of the nuclei can be "flipped," that is, excited from the parallel to the antiparallel alignment. Detection of the flipping of nuclei between the two spin states leads to an NMR spectrum. The radiation used in an NMR experiment is in the radiofrequency range, typically 100 to 900 MHz, which is far less energetic per photon than X-rays.

Because hydrogen is a major constituent of aqueous body fluids and fatty tissue, the hydrogen nucleus is the most convenient one for study by MRI. In MRI a person's body is placed in a strong magnetic field. By irradiating the body with pulses of radiofrequency radiation and using sophisticated detection techniques, tissue can be imaged at specific depths within the body, giving pictures with spectacular detail (Figure 6.29▼). The ability to sample at different depths allows medical technicians to construct a three-dimensional picture of the body.

MRI has none of the disadvantages of X-rays. Diseased tissue appears very different from healthy tissue, resolving overlapping structures at different depths in the body is much easier, and the radiofrequency radiation is not harmful to humans in the doses used. The technique has had such a profound influence on the modern practice of medicine that Paul Lauterbur, a chemist, and Peter Mansfield, a physicist, were awarded the 2003 Nobel Prize in Physiology or Medicine for their discoveries concerning MRI. The major drawback of this technique is expense: The current cost of a new MRI instrument for clinical applications is over $1.5 million.
Related Exercises: 6.94 and 6.95

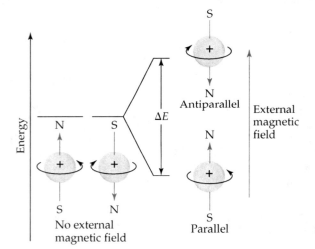

▲ Figure 6.28 **Nuclear spin.** Like electron spin, nuclear spin generates a small magnetic field and has two allowed values. In the absence of an external magnetic field (left), the two spin states have the same energy. If an external magnetic field is applied (right), the parallel alignment of the nuclear magnetic field is lower in energy than the antiparallel alignment. The energy difference, ΔE, is in the radio frequency portion of the electromagnetic spectrum.

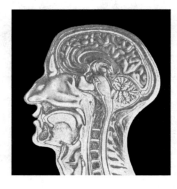

◄ Figure 6.29 **MRI image.** This image of a human head, obtained using MRI, shows the structures of a normal brain, airways, and facial tissues.

It represents the start of a new shell occupied with electrons. As you can see by examining the periodic table, lithium starts a new row of the table. It is the first member of the alkali metals (group 1A).

The element that follows lithium is beryllium; its electron configuration is $1s^2 2s^2$ (Table 6.3). Boron, atomic number 5, has the electron configuration $1s^2 2s^2 2p^1$. The fifth electron must be placed in a $2p$ orbital because the $2s$ orbital is filled. Because all the three $2p$ orbitals are of equal energy, it does not matter which $2p$ orbital is occupied.

With the next element, carbon, we encounter a new situation. We know that the sixth electron must go into a 2p orbital. However, does this new electron go into the 2p orbital that already has one electron, or into one of the other two 2p orbitals? This question is answered by **Hund's rule**, which states that *for degenerate orbitals, the lowest energy is attained when the number of electrons with the same spin is maximized*. This means that electrons will occupy orbitals singly to the maximum extent possible and that these single electrons in a given subshell will all have the same spin magnetic quantum number. Electrons arranged in this way are said to have *parallel spins*. For a carbon atom to achieve its lowest energy, therefore, the two 2p electrons will have the same spin. For this to happen, the electrons must be in different 2p orbitals, as shown in Table 6.3. Thus, a carbon atom in its ground state has two unpaired electrons. Similarly, for nitrogen in its ground state, Hund's rule requires that the three 2p electrons singly occupy each of the three 2p orbitals. This is the only way that all three electrons can have the same spin. For oxygen and fluorine, we place four and five electrons, respectively, in the 2p orbitals. To achieve this, we pair up electrons in the 2p orbitals, as we will see in Sample Exercise 6.7.

Hund's rule is based in part on the fact that electrons repel one another. By occupying different orbitals, the electrons remain as far as possible from one another, thus minimizing electron–electron repulsions.

■■■ **SAMPLE EXERCISE 6.7** | **Orbital Diagrams and Electron Configurations**

Draw the orbital diagram for the electron configuration of oxygen, atomic number 8. How many unpaired electrons does an oxygen atom possess?

SOLUTION

Analyze and Plan: Because oxygen has an atomic number of 8, each oxygen atom has 8 electrons. Figure 6.25 shows the ordering of orbitals. The electrons (represented as arrows) are placed in the orbitals (represented as boxes) beginning with the lowest-energy orbital, the 1s. Each orbital can hold a maximum of two electrons (the Pauli exclusion principle). Because the 2p orbitals are degenerate, we place one electron in each of these orbitals (spin-up) before pairing any electrons (Hund's rule).

Solve: Two electrons each go into the 1s and 2s orbitals with their spins paired. This leaves four electrons for the three degenerate 2p orbitals. Following Hund's rule, we put one electron into each 2p orbital until all three orbitals have one electron each. The fourth electron is then paired up with one of the three electrons already in a 2p orbital, so that the representation is

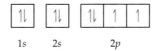

1s   2s   2p

The corresponding electron configuration is written $1s^2 2s^2 2p^4$. The atom has two unpaired electrons.

■■■ **PRACTICE EXERCISE**

(a) Write the electron configuration for phosphorus, element 15. **(b)** How many unpaired electrons does a phosphorus atom possess?
Answers: **(a)** $1s^2 2s^2 2p^6 3s^2 3p^3$, **(b)** three

Condensed Electron Configurations

The filling of the 2p subshell is complete at neon (Table 6.3), which has a stable configuration with eight electrons (an *octet*) in the outermost occupied shell. The next element, sodium, atomic number 11, marks the beginning of a new row of the periodic table. Sodium has a single 3s electron beyond the stable configuration of neon. We can therefore abbreviate the electron configuration of sodium as

$$\text{Na:}\quad [\text{Ne}]3s^1$$

The symbol [Ne] represents the electron configuration of the ten electrons of neon, $1s^2 2s^2 2p^6$. Writing the electron configuration as [Ne]$3s^1$ helps focus attention on the outermost electrons of the atom, which are the ones largely responsible for the chemical behavior of an element.

We can generalize what we have just done for the electron configuration of sodium. In writing the *condensed electron configuration* of an element, the electron configuration of the nearest noble-gas element of lower atomic number is represented by its chemical symbol in brackets. For example, we can write the electron configuration of lithium as

$$\text{Li:} \quad \text{[He]}2s^1$$

We refer to the electrons represented by the symbol for a noble gas as the *noble-gas core* of the atom. More usually, these inner-shell electrons are referred to as the **core electrons.** The electrons given after the noble-gas core are called the *outer-shell electrons*. The outer-shell electrons include the electrons involved in chemical bonding, which are called the **valence electrons.** For lighter elements (those with atomic number of 30 or less), all of the outer-shell electrons are valence electrons. As we will discuss later, many of the heavier elements have completely filled subshells that are not involved in bonding and are therefore not considered valence electrons.

By comparing the condensed electron configuration of lithium with that of sodium, we can appreciate why these two elements are so similar chemically. They have the same type of electron configuration in the outermost occupied shell. Indeed, all the members of the alkali metal group (1A) have a single *s* valence electron beyond a noble-gas configuration.

Transition Metals

The noble-gas element argon marks the end of the row started by sodium. The configuration for argon is $1s^2 2s^2 2p^6 3s^2 3p^6$. The element following argon in the periodic table is potassium (K), atomic number 19. In all its chemical properties, potassium is clearly a member of the alkali metal group. The experimental facts about the properties of potassium leave no doubt that the outermost electron of this element occupies an *s* orbital. But this means that the electron with the highest energy has *not* gone into a 3*d* orbital, which we might have expected it to do. Here the ordering of energy levels is such that the 4*s* orbital is lower in energy than the 3*d* orbital (Figure 6.25). Hence, the condensed electron configuration of potassium is

$$\text{K:} \quad \text{[Ar]}4s^1$$

Following the complete filling of the 4*s* orbital (this occurs in the calcium atom), the next set of orbitals to be filled is the 3*d* (You will find it helpful as we go along to refer often to the periodic table on the front inside cover.) Beginning with scandium and extending through zinc, electrons are added to the five 3*d* orbitals until they are completely filled. Thus, the fourth row of the periodic table is ten elements wider than the two previous rows. These ten elements are known as either **transition elements** or **transition metals.** Note the position of these elements in the periodic table.

In deriving the electron configurations of the transition elements, the orbitals are filled in accordance with Hund's rule—electrons are added to the 3*d* orbitals singly until all five orbitals have one electron each. Additional electrons are then placed in the 3*d* orbitals with spin pairing until the shell is completely filled.

The condensed electron configurations and the corresponding orbital diagram representations of two transition elements are as follows:

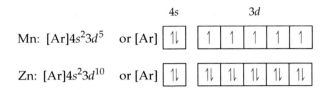

Once all the $3d$ orbitals have been filled with two electrons each, the $4p$ orbitals begin to be occupied until the completed octet of outer electrons $(4s^2 4p^6)$ is reached with krypton (Kr), atomic number 36, another of the noble gases. Rubidium (Rb) marks the beginning of the fifth row. Refer again to the periodic table on the front inside cover. Notice that this row is in every respect like the preceding one, except that the value for n is greater by 1.

GIVE IT SOME THOUGHT

Based on the structure of the periodic table, which becomes occupied first, the $6s$ orbital or the $5d$ orbitals?

The Lanthanides and Actinides

The sixth row of the periodic table begins similarly to the preceding one: one electron in the $6s$ orbital of cesium (Cs) and two electrons in the $6s$ orbital of barium (Ba). Notice, however, that the periodic table then has a break, and the subsequent set of elements (elements 57–70) is placed below the main portion of the table. This place is where we begin to encounter a new set of orbitals, the $4f$.

There are seven degenerate $4f$ orbitals, corresponding to the seven allowed values of m_l, ranging from 3 to -3. Thus, it takes 14 electrons to fill the $4f$ orbitals completely. The 14 elements corresponding to the filling of the $4f$ orbitals are known as either the **lanthanide elements** or the **rare earth elements.** These elements are set below the other elements to avoid making the periodic table unduly wide. The properties of the lanthanide elements are all quite similar, and these elements occur together in nature. For many years it was virtually impossible to separate them from one another.

Because the energies of the $4f$ and $5d$ orbitals are very close to each other, the electron configurations of some of the lanthanides involve $5d$ electrons. For example, the elements lanthanum (La), cerium (Ce), and praseodymium (Pr) have the following electron configurations:

$$[\text{Xe}]6s^2\,5d^1 \qquad [\text{Xe}]6s^2\,5d^1\,4f^1 \qquad [\text{Xe}]6s^2\,4f^3$$
$$\text{Lanthanum} \qquad \text{Cerium} \qquad \text{Praseodymium}$$

Because La has a single $5d$ electron, it is sometimes placed below yttrium (Y) as the first member of the third series of transition elements; Ce is then placed as the first member of the lanthanides. Based on their chemistry, however, La can be considered the first element in the lanthanide series. Arranged this way, there are fewer apparent exceptions to the regular filling of the $4f$ orbitals among the subsequent members of the series.

After the lanthanide series, the third transition element series is completed by the filling of the $5d$ orbitals, followed by the filling of the $6p$ orbitals. This brings us to radon (Rn), heaviest of the known noble-gas elements.

The final row of the periodic table begins by filling the $7s$ orbitals. The **actinide elements,** of which uranium (U, element 92) and plutonium (Pu, element 94) are the best known, are then built up by completing the $5f$ orbitals. The actinide elements are radioactive, and most of them are not found in nature.

6.9 ELECTRON CONFIGURATIONS AND THE PERIODIC TABLE

Our rather brief survey of electron configurations of the elements has taken us through the periodic table. We have seen that the electron configurations of the elements are related to their locations in the periodic table. The periodic table is structured so that elements with the same pattern of outer-shell (valence) electron configuration are arranged in columns. For example, the electron configurations for the elements in groups 2A and 3A are given in Table 6.4 ◄. We see that all the 2A elements have ns^2 outer configurations, while the all the 3A elements have ns^2np^1 configurations.

Earlier, in Table 6.2, we saw that the total number of orbitals in each shell is equal to n^2: 1, 4, 9, or 16. Because each orbital can hold two electrons, each shell can accommodate up to $2n^2$ electrons: 2, 8, 18, or 32. The structure of the periodic table reflects this orbital structure. The first row has two elements, the second and third rows have eight elements, the fourth and fifth rows have 18 elements, and the sixth row has 32 elements (including the lanthanide metals). Some of the numbers repeat because we reach the end of a row of the periodic table before a shell completely fills. For example, the third row has eight elements, which corresponds to filling the $3s$ and $3p$ orbitals. The remaining orbitals of the third shell, the $3d$ orbitals, do not begin to fill until the fourth row of the periodic table (and after the $4s$ orbital is filled). Likewise, the $4d$ orbitals do not begin to fill until the fifth row of the table, and the $4f$ orbitals don't begin filling until the sixth row.

All these observations are evident in the structure of the periodic table. For this reason, we will emphasize that *the periodic table is your best guide to the order in which orbitals are filled.* You can easily write the electron configuration of an element based on its location in the periodic table. The pattern is summarized in Figure 6.30 ◄. Notice that the elements can be grouped by the *type* of orbital into which the electrons are placed. On the left are *two* columns of elements, depicted in blue. These elements, known as the alkali metals (group 1A) and alkaline earth metals (group 2A), are those in which the valence s orbitals are being filled. On the right is a pink block of *six* columns. These are the elements in which the valence p orbitals are being filled. The s block and the p block of the periodic table together are the **representative elements,** which are sometimes called the **main-group elements.**

In the middle of Figure 6.30 is a gold block of *ten* columns containing the transition metals. These are the elements in which the valence d orbitals are being filled. Below the main portion of the table are two tan rows containing 14 columns. These elements are often referred to as the *f*-block metals, because they are the ones in which the valence f orbitals are being filled. Recall that the numbers 2, 6, 10, and 14 are precisely the number of electrons that can fill the s, p, d, and f subshells, respectively. Recall also that the 1s subshell is the first s subshell, the $2p$ is the first p subshell, the $3d$ is the first d subshell, and the $4f$ is the first f subshell.

TABLE 6.4 ■ Electron Configurations of the Group 2A and 3A Elements	
Group 2A	
Be	$[He]2s^2$
Mg	$[Ne]3s^2$
Ca	$[Ar]4s^2$
Sr	$[Kr]5s^2$
Ba	$[Xe]6s^2$
Ra	$[Rn]7s^2$
Group 3A	
B	$[He]2s^22p^1$
Al	$[Ne]3s^23p^1$
Ga	$[Ar]3d^{10}4s^24p^1$
In	$[Kr]4d^{10}5s^25p^1$
Tl	$[Xe]4f^{14}5d^{10}6s^26p^1$

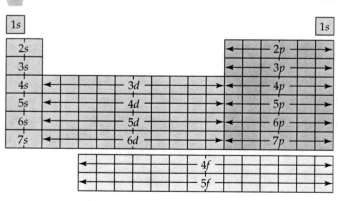

☐ Representative *s*-block elements

☐ *d*-Block metals (transition metals)

☐ Representative *p*-block elements

☐ *f*-Block metals

▲ Figure 6.30 **Regions of the periodic table.** This block diagram of the periodic table shows the order in which electrons are added to orbitals as we move through the table from beginning to end.

▦ SAMPLE EXERCISE 6.8 | Electron Configurations for a Group

What is the characteristic valence electron configuration of the group 7A elements, the halogens?

SOLUTION

Analyze and Plan: We first locate the halogens in the periodic table, write the electron configurations for the first two elements, and then determine the general similarity between them.

Solve: The first member of the halogen group is fluorine, atomic number 9. The condensed electron configuration for fluorine is

$$F: \quad [He]2s^2 2p^5$$

Similarly, that for chlorine, the second halogen, is

$$Cl: \quad [Ne]3s^2 3p^5$$

From these two examples, we see that the characteristic valence electron configuration of a halogen is $ns^2 np^5$, where n ranges from 2 in the case of fluorine to 6 in the case of astatine.

▦ PRACTICE EXERCISE

Which family of elements is characterized by an $ns^2 np^2$ electron configuration in the outermost occupied shell?
Answer: group 4A

▦ SAMPLE EXERCISE 6.9 | Electron Configurations from the Periodic Table

(a) Write the electron configuration for bismuth, element number 83. **(b)** Write the condensed electron configuration for this element. **(c)** How many unpaired electrons does each atom of bismuth possess?

SOLUTION

(a) We write the electron configuration by moving across the periodic table one row at a time and writing the occupancies of the orbital corresponding to each row (refer to Figure 6.29).

First row	$1s^2$
Second row	$2s^2 2p^6$
Third row	$3s^2 3p^6$
Fourth row	$4s^2 3d^{10} 4p^6$
Fifth row	$5s^2 4d^{10} 5p^6$
Sixth row	$6s^2 4f^{14} 5d^{10} 6p^3$
Total:	$1s^2 2s^2 2p^6 3s^2 3p^6 3d^{10} 4s^2 4p^6 4d^{10} 4f^{14} 5s^2 5p^6 5d^{10} 6s^2 6p^3$

Note that 3 is the lowest possible value that n may have for a d orbital and that 4 is the lowest possible value of n for an f orbital.

The total of the superscripted numbers should equal the atomic number of bismuth, 83. The electrons may be listed, as shown above in the "Total" row, in the order of increasing principal quantum number. However, it is equally correct to list the orbitals in the order in which they are read from Figure 6.30: $1s^2 2s^2 2p^6 3s^2 3p^6 4s^2 3d^{10} 4p^6 5s^2 4d^{10} 5p^6 6s^2 4f^{14} 5d^{10} 6p^3$.

(b) We write the condensed electron configuration by locating bismuth on the periodic table and then moving *backward* to the nearest noble gas, which is Xe, element 54. Thus, the noble-gas core is [Xe]. The outer electrons are then read from the periodic table as before. Moving from Xe to Cs, element 55, we find ourselves in the sixth row. Moving across this row to Bi gives us the outer electrons. Thus, the abbreviated electron configuration is $[Xe]6s^2 4f^{14} 5d^{10} 6p^3$ or $[Xe]4f^{14} 5d^{10} 6s^2 6p^3$.

(c) We can see from the abbreviated electron configuration that the only partially occupied subshell is the $6p$. The orbital diagram representation for this subshell is

In accordance with Hund's rule, the three $6p$ electrons occupy the three $6p$ orbitals singly, with their spins parallel. Thus, there are three unpaired electrons in each atom of bismuth.

▦ PRACTICE EXERCISE

Use the periodic table to write the condensed electron configurations for **(a)** Co (atomic number 27), **(b)** Te (atomic number 52).
Answers: **(a)** $[Ar]4s^2 3d^7$ or $[Ar]3d^7 4s^2$, **(b)** $[Kr]5s^2 4d^{10} 5p^4$ or $[Kr]4d^{10} 5s^2 5p^4$

Valence electron configurations of the elements

	1A 1	2A 2	3B 3	4B 4	5B 5	6B 6	7B 7	8	8B 9	10	1B 11	2B 12	3A 13	4A 14	5A 15	6A 16	7A 17	8A 18
Core	1 H $1s^1$																	2 He $1s^2$
[He]	3 Li $2s^1$	4 Be $2s^2$											5 B $2s^2 2p^1$	6 C $2s^2 2p^2$	7 N $2s^2 2p^3$	8 O $2s^2 2p^4$	9 F $2s^2 2p^5$	10 Ne $2s^2 2p^6$
[Ne]	11 Na $3s^1$	12 Mg $3s^2$											13 Al $3s^2 3p^1$	14 Si $3s^2 3p^2$	15 P $3s^2 3p^3$	16 S $3s^2 3p^4$	17 Cl $3s^2 3p^5$	18 Ar $3s^2 3p^6$
[Ar]	19 K $4s^1$	20 Ca $4s^2$	21 Sc $3d^1 4s^2$	22 Ti $3d^2 4s^2$	23 V $3d^3 4s^2$	24 Cr $3d^5 4s^1$	25 Mn $3d^5 4s^2$	26 Fe $3d^6 4s^2$	27 Co $3d^7 4s^2$	28 Ni $3d^8 4s^2$	29 Cu $3d^{10} 4s^1$	30 Zn $3d^{10} 4s^2$	31 Ga $3d^{10} 4s^2 4p^1$	32 Ge $3d^{10} 4s^2 4p^2$	33 As $3d^{10} 4s^2 4p^3$	34 Se $3d^{10} 4s^2 4p^4$	35 Br $3d^{10} 4s^2 4p^5$	36 Kr $3d^{10} 4s^2 4p^6$
[Kr]	37 Rb $5s^1$	38 Sr $5s^2$	39 Y $4d^1 5s^2$	40 Zr $4d^2 5s^2$	41 Nb $4d^3 5s^2$	42 Mo $4d^5 5s^1$	43 Tc $4d^5 5s^2$	44 Ru $4d^7 5s^1$	45 Rh $4d^8 5s^1$	46 Pd $4d^{10}$	47 Ag $4d^{10} 5s^1$	48 Cd $4d^{10} 5s^2$	49 In $4d^{10} 5s^2 5p^1$	50 Sn $4d^{10} 5s^2 5p^2$	51 Sb $4d^{10} 5s^2 5p^3$	52 Te $4d^{10} 5s^2 5p^4$	53 I $4d^{10} 5s^2 5p^5$	54 Xe $4d^{10} 5s^2 5p^6$
[Xe]	55 Cs $6s^1$	56 Ba $6s^2$	71 Lu $4f^{14} 5d^1 6s^2$	72 Hf $4f^{14} 5d^2 6s^2$	73 Ta $4f^{14} 5d^3 6s^2$	74 W $4f^{14} 5d^4 6s^2$	75 Re $4f^{14} 5d^5 6s^2$	76 Os $4f^{14} 5d^6 6s^2$	77 Ir $4f^{14} 5d^7 6s^2$	78 Pt $4f^{14} 5d^9 6s^1$	79 Au $4f^{14} 5d^{10} 6s^1$	80 Hg $4f^{14} 5d^{10} 6s^2$	81 Tl $4f^{14} 5d^{10} 6s^2 6p^1$	82 Pb $4f^{14} 5d^{10} 6s^2 6p^2$	83 Bi $4f^{14} 5d^{10} 6s^2 6p^3$	84 Po $4f^{14} 5d^{10} 6s^2 6p^4$	85 At $4f^{14} 5d^{10} 6s^2 6p^5$	86 Rn $4f^{14} 5d^{10} 6s^2 6p^6$
[Rn]	87 Fr $7s^1$	88 Ra $7s^2$	103 Lr $5f^{14} 6d^1 7s^2$	104 Rf $5f^{14} 6d^2 7s^2$	105 Db $5f^{14} 6d^3 7s^2$	106 Sg $5f^{14} 6d^4 7s^2$	107 Bh $5f^{14} 6d^5 7s^2$	108 Hs $5f^{14} 6d^6 7s^2$	109 Mt $5f^{14} 6d^7 7s^2$	110 Ds	111 Rg	112	113	114	115	116		118

Lanthanide series [Xe]	57 La $5d^1 6s^2$	58 Ce $4f^1 5d^1 6s^2$	59 Pr $4f^3 6s^2$	60 Nd $4f^4 6s^2$	61 Pm $4f^5 6s^2$	62 Sm $4f^6 6s^2$	63 Eu $4f^7 6s^2$	64 Gd $4f^7 5d^1 6s^2$	65 Tb $4f^9 6s^2$	66 Dy $4f^{10} 6s^2$	67 Ho $4f^{11} 6s^2$	68 Er $4f^{12} 6s^2$	69 Tm $4f^{13} 6s^2$	70 Yb $4f^{14} 6s^2$
Actinide series [Rn]	89 Ac $6d^1 7s^2$	90 Th $6d^2 7s^2$	91 Pa $5f^2 6d^1 7s^2$	92 U $5f^3 6d^1 7s^2$	93 Np $5f^4 6d^1 7s^2$	94 Pu $5f^6 7s^2$	95 Am $5f^7 7s^2$	96 Cm $5f^7 6d^1 7s^2$	97 Bk $5f^9 7s^2$	98 Cf $5f^{10} 7s^2$	99 Es $5f^{11} 7s^2$	100 Fm $5f^{12} 7s^2$	101 Md $5f^{13} 7s^2$	102 No $5f^{14} 7s^2$

☐ Metals ☐ Metalloids ☐ Nonmetals

▲ Figure 6.31 **Valence electron configurations of the elements.**

Figure 6.31 ▲ gives the valence ground-state electron configurations for all the elements. You can use this figure to check your answers as you practice writing electron configurations. We have written these configurations with orbitals listed in order of increasing principal quantum number. As we saw in Sample Exercise 6.9, the orbitals can also be listed in order of filling, as they would be read off the periodic table.

The electron configurations in Figure 6.31 allow us to reexamine the concept of *valence electrons*. Notice, for example, that as we proceed from Cl ($[\text{Ne}]3s^2 3p^5$) to Br ($[\text{Ar}]3d^{10} 4s^2 4p^5$) we have added a complete subshell of $3d$ electrons to the outer-shell electrons beyond the noble-gas core of Ar. Although the $3d$ electrons are outer-shell electrons, they are not involved in chemical bonding and are therefore not considered valence electrons. Thus, we consider only the $4s$ and $4p$ electrons of Br to be valence electrons. Similarly, if we compare the electron configuration of Ag and Au, Au has a completely full $4f^{14}$ subshell beyond its noble-gas core, but those $4f$ electrons are not involved in bonding. In general, *for representative elements we do not consider completely full* d *or* f *subshells to be among the valence electrons*, and *for transition elements we likewise do not consider a completely full* f *subshell to be among the valence electrons.*

Anomalous Electron Configurations

If you inspect Figure 6.31 closely, you will see that the electron configurations of certain elements appear to violate the rules we have just discussed. For example, the electron configuration of chromium is $[Ar]3d^54s^1$ rather than the $[Ar]3d^44s^2$ configuration we might have expected. Similarly, the configuration of copper is $[Ar]3d^{10}4s^1$ instead of $[Ar]3d^94s^2$. This anomalous behavior is largely a consequence of the closeness of the $3d$ and $4s$ orbital energies. It frequently occurs when there are enough electrons to lead to precisely half-filled sets of degenerate orbitals (as in chromium) or to completely fill a d subshell (as in copper). There are a few similar cases among the heavier transition metals (those with partially filled $4d$ or $5d$ orbitals) and among the f-block metals. Although these minor departures from the expected are interesting, they are not of great chemical significance.

 GIVE IT SOME THOUGHT

The elements Ni, Pd, and Pt are all in the same group. By examining the electron configurations for these elements in Figure 6.31, what can you conclude about the relative energies of the nd and $(n + 1)s$ orbitals for this group?

■■■ SAMPLE INTEGRATIVE EXERCISE | Putting Concepts Together

Boron, atomic number 5, occurs naturally as two isotopes, ^{10}B and ^{11}B, with natural abundances of 19.9% and 80.1%, respectively. **(a)** In what ways do the two isotopes differ from each other? Does the electronic configuration of ^{10}B differ from that of ^{11}B? **(b)** Draw the orbital diagram for an atom of ^{11}B. Which electrons are the valence electrons? **(c)** Indicate three major ways in which the $1s$ electrons in boron differ from its $2s$ electrons. **(d)** Elemental boron reacts with fluorine to form BF_3, a gas. Write a balanced chemical equation for the reaction of solid boron with fluorine gas. **(e)** ΔH_f° for $BF_3(g)$ is -1135.6 kJ mol^{-1}. Calculate the standard enthalpy change in the reaction of boron with fluorine. **(f)** When BCl_3, also a gas at room temperature, comes into contact with water, the two react to form hydrochloric acid and boric acid, H_3BO_3, a very weak acid in water. Write a balanced net ionic equation for this reaction.

SOLUTION

(a) The two isotopes of boron differ in the number of neutrons in the nucleus. (Sections 2.3 and 2.4) Each of the isotopes contains five protons, but ^{10}B contains five neutrons, whereas ^{11}B contains six neutrons. The two isotopes of boron have identical electron configurations, $1s^22s^22p^1$, because each has five electrons.
(b) The complete orbital diagram is

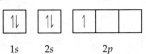

$$1s \qquad 2s \qquad 2p$$

The valence electrons are the ones in the outermost occupied shell, the $2s^2$ and $2p^1$ electrons. The $1s^2$ electrons constitute the core electrons, which we represent as [He] when we write the condensed electron configuration, $[He]2s^22p^1$.
(c) The $1s$ and $2s$ orbitals are both spherical, but they differ in three important respects: First, the $1s$ orbital is lower in energy than the $2s$ orbital. Second, the average distance of the $2s$ electrons from the nucleus is greater than that of the $1s$ electrons, so the $1s$ orbital is smaller than the $2s$. Third, the $2s$ orbital has one node, whereas the $1s$ orbital has no nodes (Figure 6.19).
(d) The balanced chemical equation is

$$2\,B(s) + 3\,F_2(g) \longrightarrow 2\,BF_3(g)$$

(e) $\Delta H^\circ = 2(-1135.6) - [0 + 0] = -2271.2$ kJ. The reaction is strongly exothermic.
(f) $BCl_3(g) + 3\,H_2O(l) \longrightarrow H_3BO_3(aq) + 3\,H^+(aq) + 3\,Cl^-(aq)$. Note that because H_3BO_3 is a very weak acid, its chemical formula is written in molecular form, as discussed in Section 4.3.

CHAPTER REVIEW

SUMMARY AND KEY TERMS

Introduction and Section 6.1 The **electronic structure** of an atom describes the energies and arrangement of electrons around the atom. Much of what is known about the electronic structure of atoms was obtained by observing the interaction of light with matter. Visible light and other forms of **electromagnetic radiation** (also known as radiant energy) move through a vacuum at the speed of light, $c = 3.00 \times 10^8$ m/s. Electromagnetic radiation has both electric and magnetic components that vary periodically in wavelike fashion. The wave characteristics of radiant energy allow it to be described in terms of **wavelength**, λ and **frequency**, ν, which are interrelated: $c = \lambda\nu$.

Section 6.2 Planck proposed that the minimum amount of radiant energy that an object can gain or lose is related to the frequency of the radiation: $E = h\nu$. This smallest quantity is called a **quantum** of energy. The constant h is called **Planck's constant**: $h = 6.626 \times 10^{-34}$ J-s. In the quantum theory, energy is quantized, meaning that it can have only certain allowed values. Einstein used the quantum theory to explain the **photoelectric effect**, the emission of electrons from metal surfaces by light. He proposed that light behaves as if it consists of quantized energy packets called **photons**. Each photon carries energy, $E = h\nu$.

Section 6.3 Dispersion of radiation into its component wavelengths produces a **spectrum.** If the spectrum contains all wavelengths, it is called a **continuous spectrum**; if it contains only certain specific wavelengths, the spectrum is called a **line spectrum.** The radiation emitted by excited hydrogen atoms forms a line spectrum; the frequencies observed in the spectrum follow a simple mathematical relationship that involves small integers.

Bohr proposed a model of the hydrogen atom that explains its line spectrum. In this model the energy of the electron in the hydrogen atom depends on the value of a number n, called the quantum number. The value of n must be a positive integer (1, 2, 3, ...), and each value of n corresponds to a different specific energy, E_n. The energy of the atom increases as n increases. The lowest energy is achieved for $n = 1$; this is called the **ground state** of the hydrogen atom. Other values of n correspond to **excited states** of the atom. Light is emitted when the electron drops from a higher energy state to a lower energy state; light must be absorbed to excite the electron from a lower energy state to a higher one. The frequency of light emitted or absorbed must be such that $h\nu$ equals the difference in energy between two allowed states of the atom.

Section 6.4 De Broglie proposed that matter, such as electrons, should exhibit wavelike properties. This hypothesis of **matter waves** was proved experimentally by observing the diffraction of electrons. An object has a characteristic wavelength that depends on its **momentum**, mv: $\lambda = h/mv$. Discovery of the wave properties of the electron led to Heisenberg's **uncertainty principle,** which states that there is an inherent limit to the accuracy with which the position and momentum of a particle can be measured simultaneously.

Section 6.5 In the quantum mechanical model of the hydrogen atom, the behavior of the electron is described by mathematical functions called **wave functions,** denoted with the Greek letter ψ. Each allowed wave function has a precisely known energy, but the location of the electron cannot be determined exactly; rather, the probability of it being at a particular point in space is given by the **probability density,** ψ^2. The **electron density** distribution is a map of the probability of finding the electron at all points in space.

The allowed wave functions of the hydrogen atom are called **orbitals.** An orbital is described by a combination of an integer and a letter, corresponding to values of three quantum numbers for the orbital. The principal quantum number, n, is indicated by the integers 1,2,3, ... This quantum number relates most directly to the size and energy of the orbital. The angular momentum quantum number, l, is indicated by the letters s, p, d, f, and so on, corresponding to the values of 0, 1,2,3, ... The l quantum number defines the shape of the orbital. For a given value of n, l can have integer values ranging from 0 to $(n - 1)$. The magnetic quantum number, m_l, relates to the orientation of the orbital in space. For a given value of l, m_l can have integral values ranging from $-l$ to l, including 0. Cartesian labels can be used to label the orientations of the orbitals. For example, the three $3p$ orbitals are designated $3p_x$, $3p_y$, and $3p_z$, with the subscripts indicating the axis along which the orbital is oriented.

An **electron shell** is the set of all orbitals with the same value of n, such as $3s$, $3p$, and $3d$. In the hydrogen atom all the orbitals in an electron shell have the same energy. A **subshell** is the set of one or more orbitals with the same n and l values; for example, 3s, 3p, and 3d are each subshells of the $n = 3$ shell. There is one orbital in an s subshell, three in a p subshell, five in a d subshell, and seven in an f subshell.

Section 6.6 Contour representations are useful for visualizing the spatial characteristics (shapes) of the orbitals. Represented this way, s orbitals appear as spheres that increase in size as n increases. The **radial probability function** tells us the probability that the electron will be found at a certain distance from the nucleus. The wave function for each p orbital has two lobes on opposite sides of the nucleus. They are oriented along the x-, y-, and z-axes. Four of the d orbitals appear as shapes with four lobes around the nucleus; the fifth one, the d_{z^2} orbital, is represented as two lobes along the z-axis and a "doughnut" in the xy plane. Regions in which the wave function is zero are called **nodes**. There is zero probability that the electron will be found at a node.

Section 6.7 In many-electron atoms, different subshells of the same electron shell have different energies. For a given value of n, the energy of the subshells increases as the value of l increases: $ns < np < nd < nf$. Orbitals within the same subshell are **degenerate,** meaning they have the same energy.

Electrons have an intrinsic property called **electron spin,** which is quantized. The **spin magnetic quantum number,** m_s, can have two possible values, $+\frac{1}{2}$ and $-\frac{1}{2}$, which can be envisioned as the two directions of an electron spinning about an axis. The **Pauli exclusion principle** states that no two electrons in an atom can have the same values for n, l, m_l, and m_s. This principle places a limit of two on the number of electrons that can occupy any one atomic orbital. These two electrons differ in their value of m_s.

Sections 6.8 and 6.9 The **electron configuration** of an atom describes how the electrons are distributed among the orbitals of the atom. The ground-state electron configurations are generally obtained by placing the electrons in the atomic orbitals of lowest possible energy with the restriction that each orbital can hold no more than two electrons. When electrons occupy a subshell with more than one degenerate orbital, such as the $2p$ subshell, **Hund's rule** states that the lowest energy is attained by maximizing the number of electrons with the same electron spin.

For example, in the ground-state electron configuration of carbon, the two $2p$ electrons have the same spin and must occupy two different $2p$ orbitals.

Elements in any given group in the periodic table have the same type of electron arrangements in their outermost shells. For example, the electron configurations of the halogens fluorine and chlorine are $[He]2s^2 2p^5$ and $[Ne]3s^2 3p^5$, respectively. The outer-shell electrons are those that lie outside the orbitals occupied in the next lowest noble-gas element. The outer-shell electrons that are involved in chemical bonding are the **valence electrons** of an atom; for the elements with atomic number 30 or less, all the outer-shell electrons are valence electrons. The electrons that are not valence electrons are called **core electrons.**

The periodic table is partitioned into different types of elements, based on their electron configurations. Those elements in which the outermost subshell is an s or p subshell are called the **representative** (or **main-group**) **elements.** The alkali metals (group 1A), halogens (group 7A), and noble gases (group 8A) are representative elements. Those elements in which a d subshell is being filled are called the **transition elements** (or **transition metals**). The elements in which the $4f$ subshell is being filled are called the **lanthanide** (or **rare earth**) **elements.** The **actinide elements** are those in which the $5f$ subshell is being filled. The lanthanide and actinide elements are collectively referred to as the f-**block metals.** These elements are shown as two rows of 14 elements below the main part of the periodic table. The structure of the periodic table, summarized in Figure 6.30, allows us to write the electron configuration of an element from its position in the periodic table.

KEY SKILLS

- Be able to calculate the wavelength of electromagnetic radiation given its frequency or its frequency given its wavelength.
- Be able to order the common kinds of radiation in the electromagnetic spectrum according to their wavelengths or energy.
- Understand the concept of photons, and be able to calculate their energies given either their frequency or wavelength.
- Be able to explain how line spectra of the elements relate to the idea of quantized energy states of electrons in atoms.
- Be familiar with the wavelike properties of matter.
- Understand how the uncertainty principle limits how precisely we can specify the position and the momentum of subatomic particles such as electrons.
- Know how the quantum numbers relate to the number and type of orbitals, and recognize the different orbital shapes.
- Interpret radial probability function graphs for the orbitals.
- Be able to draw an energy-level diagram for the orbitals in a many-electron atom, and describe how electrons populate the orbitals in the ground-state of an atom, using the Pauli Exclusion Principle and Hund's rule.
- Be able to use the periodic table to write abbreviated electron configurations and determine the number of unpaired electrons in an atom.

KEY EQUATIONS

- $c = \lambda\nu$ [6.1]

  light as a wave: c = speed of light (3.00×10^8 m/s), λ = wavelength in meters, ν = frequency in s^{-1}

- $E = h\nu$ [6.2]

  light as a particle (photon): E = energy of photon in Joules, h = Planck's constant (6.626×10^{-34} J-s), ν = frequency in s^{-1} (same frequency as previous formula)

- $\lambda = h/mv$ [6.8]

  matter as a wave: λ = wavelength, h = Planck's constant, m = mass of object in kg, v = speed of object in m/s

- $\Delta x \cdot \Delta(mv) \geq \dfrac{h}{4\pi}$ [6.9]

  Heisenberg's uncertainty principle. The uncertainty in position (Δx) and momentum ($\Delta(mv)$) of an object cannot be zero; the smallest value of their product is $h/4\pi$

VISUALIZING CONCEPTS

6.1 Consider the water wave shown here. **(a)** How could
CQ you measure the speed of this wave? **(b)** How would you determine the wavelength of the wave? **(c)** Given the speed and wavelength of the wave, how could you determine the frequency of the wave? **(d)** Suggest an independent experiment to determine the frequency of the wave. [Section 6.1]

6.2 A popular kitchen appliance produces electromagnetic
CQ radiation with a frequency of 2450 MHz. With reference to Figure 6.4, answer the following: **(a)** Estimate the wavelength of this radiation. **(b)** Would the radiation produced by the appliance be visible to the human eye? **(c)** If the radiation is not visible, do photons of this radiation have more or less energy than photons of visible light? **(d)** Propose the identity of the kitchen appliance. [Section 6.1]

6.3 As shown in the accompanying photograph, an electric
CQ stove burner on its highest setting exhibits an orange glow. **(a)** When the burner setting is changed to low, the burner continues to produce heat but the orange glow disappears. How can this observation be explained with reference to one of the fundamental observations that led to the notion of quanta? **(b)** Suppose that the energy provided to the burner could be increased beyond the highest setting of the stove. What would we expect to observe with regard to visible light emitted by the burner? [Section 6.2]

6.4 The familiar phenomenon of a rainbow results from the
CQ diffraction of sunlight through raindrops. **(a)** Does the wavelength of light increase or decrease as we proceed outward from the innermost band of the rainbow? **(b)** Does the frequency of light increase or decrease as we proceed outward? **(c)** Suppose that instead of sunlight, the visible light from a hydrogen discharge tube (Figure 6.12) was used as the light source. What do you think the resulting "hydrogen discharge rainbow" would look like? [Section 6.3]

6.5 A certain quantum mechanical system has the energy
CQ levels shown in the diagram below. The energy levels
are indexed by a single quantum number *n* that is an integer. **(a)** As drawn, which quantum numbers are involved in the transition that requires the most energy?
(b) Which quantum numbers are involved in the transition that requires the least energy? **(c)** Based on the
drawing, put the following in order of increasing wavelength of the light absorbed or emitted during the tran-
sition: (*i*) *n* = 1 to *n* = 2; (*ii*) *n* = 3 to *n* = 2; (*iii*) *n* = 2 to
n = 4; (*iv*) *n* = 3 to *n* = 1. [Section 6.3]

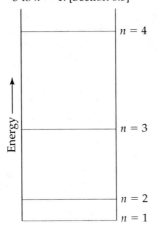

6.6 Consider a fictitious one-dimensional system with one
CQ electron. The wave function for the electron, drawn at the
top of the next column, is $\psi(x) = \sin x$ from $x = 0$ to
$x = 2\pi$. **(a)** Sketch the probability density, $\psi^2(x)$, from
$x = 0$ to $x = 2\pi$ **(b)** At what value or values of x will
there be the greatest probability of finding the electron?
(c) What is the probability that the electron will be found
at $x = \pi$? What is such a point in a wave function called?
[Section 6.5]

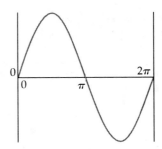

6.7 The contour representation of one of the orbitals for the
CQ *n* = 3 shell of a hydrogen atom is shown below.
(a) What is the quantum number *l* for this orbital?
(b) How do we label this orbital? **(c)** How would you
modify this sketch to show the analogous orbital for the
n = 4 shell? [Section 6.6]

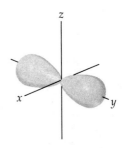

6.8 The drawing below shows part of the orbital diagram
CQ for an element. **(a)** As drawn, the drawing is *incorrect*.
Why? **(b)** How would you correct the drawing without
changing the number of electrons? **(c)** To which group in
the periodic table does the element belong? [Section 6.8]

EXERCISES

The Wave Nature of Light

6.9 What are the basic SI units for **(a)** the wavelength of
light, **(b)** the frequency of light, **(c)** the speed of light?

6.10 **(a)** What is the relationship between the wavelength and
the frequency of radiant energy? **(b)** Ozone in the upper
atmosphere absorbs energy in the 210–230-nm range of
the spectrum. In what region of the electromagnetic
spectrum does this radiation occur?

6.11 Label each of the following statements as true or false.
CQ For those that are false, correct the statement. **(a)** Visible
light is a form of electromagnetic radiation. **(b)** The frequency of radiation increases as the wavelength increases. **(c)** Ultraviolet light has longer wavelengths than
visible light. **(d)** X-rays travel faster than microwaves.
(e) Electromagnetic radiation and sound waves travel at
the same speed.

6.12 Determine which of the following statements are false,
CQ and correct them. **(a)** Electromagnetic radiation is incapable of passing through water. **(b)** Electromagnetic radiation travels through a vacuum at a constant speed,
regardless of wavelength. **(c)** Infrared light has higher

frequencies than visible light. **(d)** The glow from a fireplace, the energy within a microwave oven, and a
foghorn blast are all forms of electromagnetic radiation.

6.13 Arrange the following kinds of electromagnetic radia-
CQ tion in order of increasing wavelength: infrared, green
light, red light, radio waves, X-rays, ultraviolet light.

6.14 List the following types of electromagnetic radiation in
CQ order of increasing wavelength: **(a)** the gamma rays produced by a radioactive nuclide used in medical imaging; **(b)** radiation from an FM radio station at 93.1 MHz
on the dial; **(c)** a radio signal from an AM radio station
at 680 kHz on the dial; **(d)** the yellow light from sodium
vapor streetlights; **(e)** the red light of a light-emitting
diode, such as in a calculator display.

6.15 **(a)** What is the frequency of radiation that has a wavelength of 10 μm, about the size of a bacterium? **(b)** What
is the wavelength of radiation that has a frequency of
5.50×10^{14} s^{-1}? **(c)** Would the radiations in part (a) or
part (b) be visible to the human eye? **(d)** What distance
does electromagnetic radiation travel in 50.0 μs?

6.16 **(a)** What is the frequency of radiation whose wavelength is 10.0 Å? **(b)** What is the wavelength of radiation that has a frequency of 7.6×10^{10} s^{-1}? **(c)** Would the radiations in part (a) or part (b) be detected by an X-ray detector? **(d)** What distance does electromagnetic radiation travel in 25.5 fs?

6.17 An argon ion laser emits light at 532 nm. What is the frequency of this radiation? Using Figure 6.4, predict the color associated with this wavelength.

6.18 It is possible to convert radiant energy into electrical energy using photovoltaic cells. Assuming equal efficiency of conversion, would infrared or ultraviolet radiation yield more electrical energy on a per-photon basis?

Quantized Energy and Photons

6.19 If human height were quantized in one-foot increments,
CQ what would happen to the height of a child as she grows up?

6.20 Einstein's 1905 paper on the photoelectric effect was the
CQ first important application of Planck's quantum hypothesis. Describe Planck's original hypothesis, and explain how Einstein made use of it in his theory of the photoelectric effect.

6.21 **(a)** A red laser pointer emits light with a wavelength of 650 nm. What is the frequency of this light? **(b)** What is the energy of 1 mole of these photons? **(c)** The laser pointer emits light because electrons in the material are excited (by a battery) from their ground state to an upper excited state. When the electrons return to the ground state they lose the excess energy in the form of 650 nm photons. What is the energy gap between the ground state and excited state in the laser material?

6.22 If you put 120 volts of electricity through a pickle, the pickle will smoke and start glowing an orange-yellow color. The light is emitted because the sodium ions in the pickle become excited; their return to the ground state results in light emission (see Figure 6.13b and Sample Exercise 6.3). **(a)** The wavelength of this emitted light is 589 nm. Calculate its frequency. **(b)** What is the energy of 0.10 mole of these photons? **(c)** Calculate the energy gap between the excited and ground states for the sodium ion. **(d)** If you soaked the pickle for a long time in a different salt solution, such as strontium chloride, would you still observe 589 nm light emission? Why or why not?

6.23 **(a)** Calculate and compare the energy of a photon of wavelength 3.3 μm with that of wavelength 0.154 nm. **(b)** Use Figure 6.4 to identify the region of the electromagnetic spectrum to which each belongs.

6.24 An AM radio station broadcasts at 1010 kHz, and its FM partner broadcasts at 98.3 MHz. Calculate and compare the energy of the photons emitted by these two radio stations.

6.25 One type of sunburn occurs on exposure to UV light of wavelength in the vicinity of 325 nm. **(a)** What is the energy of a photon of this wavelength? **(b)** What is the energy of a mole of these photons? **(c)** How many photons are in a 1.00 mJ burst of this radiation? **(d)** These UV photons can break chemical bonds in your skin to cause sunburn—a form of radiation damage. If the 325-nm radiation provides exactly the energy to break an average chemical bond in the skin, estimate the average energy of these bonds in kJ/mol.

6.26 The energy from radiation can be used to cause the rupture of chemical bonds. A minimum energy of 941 kJ/mol is required to break the nitrogen–nitrogen bond in N_2. What is the longest wavelength of radiation that possesses the necessary energy to break the bond? What type of electromagnetic radiation is this?

6.27 A diode laser emits at a wavelength of 987 nm. **(a)** In what portion of the electromagnetic spectrum is this radiation found? **(b)** All of its output energy is absorbed in a detector that measures a total energy of 0.52 J over a period of 32 s. How many photons per second are being emitted by the laser?

6.28 A stellar object is emitting radiation at 3.55 mm. **(a)** What type of electromagnetic spectrum is this radiation? **(b)** If the detector is capturing 3.2×10^8 photons per second at this wavelength, what is the total energy of the photons detected in one hour?

6.29 Molybdenum metal must absorb radiation with a minimum frequency of 1.09×10^{15} s^{-1} before it can eject an electron from its surface via the photoelectric effect. **(a)** What is the minimum energy needed to eject an electron? **(b)** What wavelength of radiation will provide a photon of this energy? **(c)** If molybdenum is irradiated with light of wavelength of 120 nm, what is the maximum possible kinetic energy of the emitted electrons?

6.30 Sodium metal requires a photon with a minimum energy of 4.41×10^{-19} J to emit electrons. **(a)** What is the minimum frequency of light necessary to emit electrons from sodium via the photoelectric effect? **(b)** What is the wavelength of this light? **(c)** If sodium is irradiated with light of 439 nm, what is the maximum possible kinetic energy of the emitted electrons? **(d)** What is the maximum number of electrons that can be freed by a burst of light whose total energy is 1.00 μJ?

Bohr's Model; Matter Waves

6.31 Explain how the existence of line spectra is consistent
CQ with Bohr's theory of quantized energies for the electron in the hydrogen atom.

6.32 **(a)** In terms of the Bohr theory of the hydrogen atom,
CQ what process is occurring when excited hydrogen atoms emit radiant energy of certain wavelengths and only those wavelengths? **(b)** Does a hydrogen atom "expand" or "contract" as it moves from its ground state to an excited state?

6.33 Is energy emitted or absorbed when the following elec-
CQ tronic transitions occur in hydrogen: **(a)** from $n = 4$ to
$n = 2$, **(b)** from an orbit of radius 2.12 Å to one of radius
8.46 Å, **(c)** an electron adds to the H^+ ion and ends up in
the $n = 3$ shell?

6.34 Indicate whether energy is emitted or absorbed when
CQ the following electronic transitions occur in hydrogen:
(a) from $n = 2$ to $n = 6$, **(b)** from an orbit of radius
4.76 Å to one of radius 0.529 Å, **(c)** from the $n = 6$ to the
$n = 9$ state.

6.35 **(a)** Using Equation 6.5, calculate the energy of an electron in the hydrogen atom when $n = 2$ and when
$n = 6$. Calculate the wavelength of the radiation released when an electron moves from $n = 6$ to $n = 2$.
Is this line in the visible region of the electromagnetic
spectrum? If so, what color is it? **(b)** Calculate the energies of an electron in the hydrogen atom for $n = 1$ and
for $n = (\infty)$. How much energy does it require to move
the electron out of the atom completely (from $n = 1$ to
$n = \infty$), according to Bohr? Put your answer in kJ/mol.
(c) The energy for the process $H + energy \rightarrow H^+ + e^-$ is
called the ionization energy of hydrogen. The experimentally determined value for the ionization energy of
hydrogen is 1310 kJ/mol. How does this compare to
your calculation?

6.36 For each of the following electronic transitions in the hydrogen atom, calculate the energy, frequency, and wavelength of the associated radiation, and determine
whether the radiation is emitted or absorbed during the
transition: **(a)** from $n = 4$ to $n = 1$, **(b)** from $n = 5$ to
$n = 2$, **(c)** from $n = 3$ to $n = 6$. Does any of these transitions emit or absorb visible light?

6.37 The visible emission lines observed by Balmer all involved $n_f = 2$. **(a)** Explain why only the lines with
$n_f = 2$ were observed in the visible region of the electromagnetic spectrum. **(b)** Calculate the wavelengths of the
first three lines in the Balmer series—those for which
$n_i = 3, 4,$ and 5—and identify these lines in the emission
spectrum shown in Figure 6.13.

6.38 The Lyman series of emission lines of the hydrogen
atom are those for which $n_f = 1$. **(a)** Determine the region of the electromagnetic spectrum in which the lines
of the Lyman series are observed. **(b)** Calculate the
wavelengths of the first three lines in the Lyman
series—those for which $n_i = 2, 3,$ and 4.

6.39 One of the emission lines of the hydrogen atom has a
wavelength of 93.8 nm. **(a)** In what region of the electromagnetic spectrum is this emission found? **(b)** Determine the initial and final values of n associated with this
emission.

6.40 The hydrogen atom can absorb light of wavelength 2626
nm. **(a)** In what region of the electromagnetic spectrum
is this absorption found? **(b)** Determine the initial and
final values of n associated with this absorption.

6.41 Use the de Broglie relationship to determine the wavelengths of the following objects: **(a)** an 85-kg person skiing
at 50 km/hr, **(b)** a 10.0-g bullet fired at 250 m/s, **(c)** a lithium atom moving at 2.5×10^5 m/s, **(d)** an ozone (O_3) molecule in the upper atmosphere moving at 550 m/s.

6.42 Among the elementary subatomic particles of physics is
the muon, which decays within a few nanoseconds after
formation. The muon has a rest mass 206.8 times that of an
electron. Calculate the de Broglie wavelength associated
with a muon traveling at a velocity of 8.85×10^5 cm/s.

6.43 Neutron diffraction is an important technique for determining the structures of molecules. Calculate the velocity of a neutron needed to achieve a wavelength of
0.955 Å. (Refer to the inside cover for the mass of the
neutron).

6.44 The electron microscope has been widely used to obtain
highly magnified images of biological and other types
of materials. When an electron is accelerated through
a particular potential field, it attains a speed of
9.38×10^6 m/s. What is the characteristic wavelength of
this electron? Is the wavelength comparable to the size
of atoms?

6.45 Using Heisenberg's uncertainty principle, calculate the
uncertainty in the position of **(a)** a 1.50-mg mosquito
moving at a speed of 1.40 m/s if the speed is known to
within ± 0.01 m/s; **(b)** a proton moving at a speed of
$(5.00 \pm 0.01) \times 10^4$ m/s. (The mass of a proton is given
in the table of fundamental constants in the inside cover
of the text.)

6.46 Calculate the uncertainty in the position of **(a)** an electron moving at a speed of $(3.00 \pm 0.01) \times 10^5$ m/s, **(b)** a
neutron moving at this same speed. (The masses of an
electron and a neutron are given in the table of fundamental constants in the inside cover of the text.)
(c) What are the implications of these calculations to our
model of the atom?

Quantum Mechanics and Atomic Orbitals

6.47 **(a)** Why does the Bohr model of the hydrogen atom vio-
CQ late the uncertainty principle? **(b)** In what way is the
description of the electron using a wave function consistent with de Broglie's hypothesis? **(c)** What is meant by
the term *probability density*? Given the wave function,
how do we find the probability density at a certain point
in space?

6.48 **(a)** According to the Bohr model, an electron in the
CQ ground state of a hydrogen atom orbits the nucleus at a
specific radius of 0.53 Å. In the quantum mechanical description of the hydrogen atom, the most probable distance of the electron from the nucleus is 0.53 Å. Why are
these two statements different? **(b)** Why is the use of
Schrödinger's wave equation to describe the location of
a particle very different from the description obtained
from classical physics? **(c)** In the quantum mechanical
description of an electron, what is the physical significance of the square of the wave function, ψ^2?

6.49 (a) For $n = 4$, what are the possible values of l? (b) For $l = 2$, what are the possible values of m_l? (c) If m_l is 2, what are the possible values for l?

6.50 How many possible values for l and m_l are there when (a) $n = 3$; (b) $n = 5$?

6.51 Give the numerical values of n and l corresponding to each of the following orbital designations: (a) $3p$, (b) $2s$, (c) $4f$, (d) $5d$.

6.52 Give the values for n, l, and m_l for (a) each orbital in the $2p$ subshell, (b) each orbital in the $5d$ subshell.

6.53 Which of the following represent impossible combina-
CQ tions of n and l: (a) $1p$, (b) $4s$, (c) $5f$, (d) $2d$?

6.54 For the table below, write which orbital goes with the
CQ quantum numbers. Don't worry about x, y, z subscripts. If the quantum numbers are not allowed, write "not allowed."

n	l	m_l	Orbital
2	1	−1	$2p$ (example)
1	0	0	
3	−3	2	
3	2	−2	
2	0	−1	
0	0	0	
4	2	1	
5	3	0	

6.55 Sketch the shape and orientation of the following types of orbitals: (a) s, (b) p_z, (c) d_{xy}.

6.56 Sketch the shape and orientation of the following types of orbitals: (a) p_x, (b) d_{z^2}, (c) $d_{x^2-y^2}$.

6.57 (a) What are the similarities and differences between the
CQ $1s$ and $2s$ orbitals of the hydrogen atom? (b) In what sense does a $2p$ orbital have directional character? Compare the "directional" characteristics of the p_x and $d_{x^2-y^2}$ orbitals (that is, in what direction or region of space is the electron density concentrated?). (c) What can you say about the average distance from the nucleus of an electron in a $2s$ orbital as compared with a $3s$ orbital? (d) For the hydrogen atom, list the following orbitals in order of increasing energy (that is, most stable ones first): $4f$, $6s$, $3d$, $1s$, $2p$.

6.58 (a) With reference to Figure 6.19, what is the relationship
CQ between the number of nodes in an s orbital and the value of the principal quantum number? (b) Identify the number of nodes; that is, identify places where the electron density is zero, in the $2p_x$ orbital; in the $3s$ orbital. (c) What information is obtained from the radial probability functions in Figure 6.19? (d) For the hydrogen atom, list the following orbitals in order of increasing energy: $3s$, $2s$, $2p$, $5s$, $4d$.

Many-Electron Atoms and Electron Configurations

6.59 For a given value of the principal quantum number, n,
CQ how do the energies of the s, p, d, and f subshells vary for (a) hydrogen, (b) a many-electron atom?

6.60 (a) The average distance from the nucleus of a $3s$ elec-
CQ tron in a chlorine atom is smaller than that for a $3p$ electron. In light of this fact, which orbital is higher in energy? (b) Would you expect it to require more or less energy to remove a $3s$ electron from the chlorine atom, as compared with a $2p$ electron? Explain.

6.61 (a) What experimental evidence is there for the electron
CQ having a "spin"? (b) Draw an energy-level diagram that shows the relative energetic positions of a $1s$ orbital and a $2s$ orbital. Put two electrons in the $1s$ orbital. (c) Draw an arrow showing the excitation of an electron from the $1s$ to the $2s$ orbital.

6.62 (a) State the Pauli exclusion principle in your own
CQ words. (b) The Pauli exclusion principle is, in an important sense, the key to understanding the periodic table. Explain why.

6.63 What is the maximum number of electrons that can occupy each of the following subshells: (a) $3p$, (b) $5d$, (c) $2s$, (d) $4f$?

6.64 What is the maximum number of electrons in an atom that can have the following quantum numbers: (a) $n = 2$, $m_s = -\frac{1}{2}$, (b) $n = 5$, $l = 3$; (c) $n = 4$, $l = 3$, $m_l = -3$; (d) $n = 4$, $l = 1$, $m_l = 1$?

6.65 (a) What are "valence electrons"? (b) What are "core
CQ electrons"? (c) What does each box in an orbital diagram represent? (d) What quantity is represented by the direction (up or down) of the half-arrows in an orbital diagram?

6.66 For each element, count the number of valence electrons, core electrons, and unpaired electrons in the ground state: (a) carbon, (b) phosphorus, (c) neon.

6.67 Write the condensed electron configurations for the following atoms, using the appropriate noble-gas core abbreviations: (a) Cs, (b) Ni, (c) Se, (d) Cd, (e) U, (f) Pb.

6.68 Write the condensed electron configurations for the following atoms, and indicate how many unpaired electrons each has: (a) Ga, (b) Ca, (c) V, (d) I, (e) Y, (f) Pt, (g) Lu.

6.69 Ions also have electron configurations (Section 7.4). Cations have fewer valence electrons, and anions have more valence electrons, respectively, than their parent atoms. For example, chloride, Cl^-, has an electron configuration of $1s^2 2s^2 2p^6 3s^2 3p^6$, for a total of 18 electrons, compared to 17 for neutral chlorine, the element. Na has an electron configuration of $1s^2 2s^2 2p^6 3s^1$, but Na^+ has an electron configuration of $1s^2 2s^2 2p^6$. Write out the electron configurations for (a) F^-, (b) I^-, (c) O^{2-}, (d) K^+, (e) Mg^{2+}, (f) Al^{3+}.

6.70 In the transition metals (the *d*-block), the electron configuration of cations is different than what you might expect. Instead of the d electrons being lost first, *s* electrons are lost first. For example, the electron configuration of iron, Fe, is [Ar]$4s^23d^6$; but the electron configuration of Fe^{2+} is [Ar]$3d^6$; the 4s electrons are eliminated to make the cation. Write out the electron configurations of **(a)** Zn^{2+} **(b)** Pt^{2+} **(c)** Cr^{3+} **(d)** Ti^{4+}.

6.71 Identify the specific element that corresponds to each of the following electron configurations: **(a)** $1s^22s^2$, **(b)** $1s^22s^22p^4$, **(c)** [Ar]$4s^13d^5$, **(d)** [Kr]$5s^24d^{10}5p^4$, **(e)** $1s^1$.

6.72 Identify the group of elements that corresponds to each of the following generalized electron configurations:
(a) [noble gas] ns^2np^5
(b) [noble gas] $ns^2(n-1)d^2$
(c) [noble gas] $ns^2(n-1)d^{10}np^1$
(d) [noble gas] $ns^2(n-2)f^6$

6.73 What is wrong with the following electron configurations for atoms in their ground states? **(a)** $1s^22s^23s^1$, **(b)** [Ne]$2s^22p^3$, **(c)** [Ne]$3s^23d^5$.

6.74 The following electron configurations represent excited states. Identify the element, and write its ground-state condensed electron configuration. **(a)** $1s^22s^23p^24p^1$, **(b)** [Ar]$3d^{10}4s^14p^45s^1$, **(c)** [Kr]$4d^65s^25p^1$.

ADDITIONAL EXERCISES

6.75 Consider the two waves shown here, which we will consider to represent two electromagnetic radiations:
(a) What is the wavelength of wave A? Of wave B?
(b) What is the frequency of wave A? Of wave B?
(c) Identify the regions of the electromagnetic spectrum to which waves A and B belong.

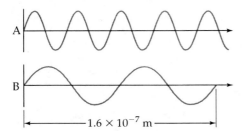

6.76 Certain elements emit light of a specific wavelength when they are burned. Historically, chemists used such emission wavelengths to determine whether specific elements were present in a sample. Some characteristic wavelengths for some of the elements are

Ag	328.1 nm	Fe	372.0 nm
Au	267.6 nm	K	404.7 nm
Ba	455.4 nm	Mg	285.2 nm
Ca	422.7 nm	Na	589.6 nm
Cu	324.8 nm	Ni	341.5 nm

(a) Determine which elements emit radiation in the visible part of the spectrum. **(b)** Which element emits photons of highest energy? Of lowest energy? **(c)** When burned, a sample of an unknown substance is found to emit light of frequency $6.59 \times 10^{14}\ s^{-1}$. Which of these elements is probably in the sample?

6.77 In June 2004, the Cassini–Huygens spacecraft began orbiting Saturn and transmitting images to Earth. The closest distance between Saturn and Earth is 746 million miles. What is the minimum amount of time it takes for the transmitted signals to travel from the spacecraft to Earth?

6.78 The rays of the Sun that cause tanning and burning are in the ultraviolet portion of the electromagnetic spectrum. These rays are categorized by wavelength. So-called UV-A radiation has wavelengths in the range of 320–380 nm, whereas UV-B radiation has wavelengths in the range of 290–320 nm. **(a)** Calculate the frequency of light that has a wavelength of 320 nm. **(b)** Calculate the energy of a mole of 320-nm photons. **(c)** Which are more energetic, photons of UV-A radiation or photons of UV-B radiation? **(d)** The UV-B radiation from the Sun is considered a greater cause of sunburn in humans than is UV-A radiation. Is this observation consistent with your answer to part (c)?

6.79 The watt is the derived SI unit of power, the measure of energy per unit time: 1 W = 1 J/s. A semiconductor laser in a CD player has an output wavelength of 780 nm and a power level of 0.10 mW. How many photons strike the CD surface during the playing of a CD 69 minutes in length?

6.80 The color wheel (Figure 24.24) is a convenient way to relate what colors of light are absorbed by a sample and the visible appearance of the sample. If all visible colors are absorbed by a sample, the sample appears black. If no colors are absorbed by the sample, the sample appears white. If the sample absorbs red, then what we see is green; such *complementary colors* are across the wheel from each other. Carrots appear orange because they contain a compound called carotene. Based on the color wheel, what is the possible wavelength range for the light absorbed by carotene?

6.81 A photocell, such as the one illustrated in Figure 6.8(b), is a device used to measure the intensity of light. In a certain experiment, when light of wavelength 630 nm is directed onto the photocell, electrons are emitted at the rate of 2.6×10^{-12} Coulombs/sec. Assume that each photon that impinges on the photocell emits one electron. How many photons per second are striking the photocell? How much energy per second is the photocell absorbing?

6.82 The light-sensitive substance in black-and-white photographic film is AgBr. Photons provide the energy necessary to transfer an electron from Br^- to Ag^+ to produce elemental Ag and Br and thereby darken the film. **(a)** If a minimum energy of 2.00×10^5 J/mol is needed for this process, what is the minimum energy needed from each photon? **(b)** Calculate the wavelength of the light necessary to provide photons of this energy. **(c)** Explain why this film can be handled in a darkroom under red light.

6.83 In an experiment to study the photoelectric effect, a scientist measures the kinetic energy of ejected electrons as a function of the frequency of radiation hitting a metal surface. She obtains the following plot: The point labeled "ν_0" corresponds to light with a wavelength of 680 nm.

(a) What is the value of ν_0 in s^{-1}? (b) What is the value of the work function of the metal in units of kJ/mol of ejected electrons? (c) What happens when the metal is irradiated with light of frequency less than ν_0? (d) Note that when the frequency of the light is greater than ν_0, the plot shows a straight line with a nonzero slope. Why is this the case? (e) Can you determine the slope of the line segment discussed in part (d)? Explain.

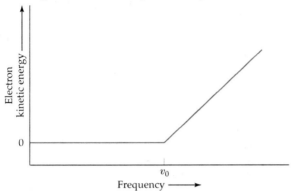

6.84 The series of emission lines of the hydrogen atom for which $n_f = 3$ is called the *Paschen series*. (a) Determine the region of the electromagnetic spectrum in which the lines of the Paschen series are observed. (b) Calculate the wavelengths of the first three lines in the Paschen series—those for which $n_i = 4$, 5, and 6.

6.85 When the spectrum of light from the Sun is examined in
CQ high resolution in an experiment similar to that illustrated in Figure 6.11, dark lines are evident. These are called Fraunhofer lines, after the scientist who studied them extensively in the early nineteenth century. Altogether, about 25,000 lines have been identified in the solar spectrum between 2950 Å and 10,000 Å. The Fraunhofer lines are attributed to absorption of certain wavelengths of the Sun's "white" light by gaseous elements in the Sun's atmosphere. (a) Describe the process that causes absorption of specific wavelengths of light from the solar spectrum. (b) If a scientist wanted to know which Fraunhofer lines belonged to a given element, say neon, what experiments could she conduct here on Earth to provide data?

[6.86] Bohr's model can be used for hydrogen-like ions—ions that have only one electron, such as He^+ and Li^{2+}. (a) Why is the Bohr model applicable to He^+ ions but not to neutral He atoms? (b) The ground-state energies of H, He^+, and Li^{2+} are tabulated as follows:

Atom or ion	H	He^+	Li^{2+}
Ground-state energy	-2.18×10^{-18} J	-8.72×10^{-18} J	-1.96×10^{-17} J

By examining these numbers, propose a relationship between the ground-state energy of hydrogen-like systems and the nuclear charge, Z. (c) Use the relationship you derive in part (b) to predict the ground-state energy of the C^{5+} ion.

6.87 Under appropriate conditions, molybdenum emits X-rays that have a characteristic wavelength of 0.711 Å. These X-rays are used in diffraction experiments to determine the structures of molecules. (a) Why are X-rays,

and not visible light, suitable for the determination of structure at the atomic level? (b) How fast would an electron have to be moving to have the same wavelength as these X-rays?

[6.88] An electron is accelerated through an electric potential to a kinetic energy of 18.6 keV. What is its characteristic wavelength? [*Hint:* Recall that the kinetic energy of a moving object is $E = \frac{1}{2} mv^2$, where m is the mass of the object and v is the speed of the object.]

6.89 In the television series *Star Trek*, the transporter beam is
CQ a device used to "beam down" people from the *Starship Enterprise* to another location, such as the surface of a planet. The writers of the show put a "Heisenberg compensator" into the transporter beam mechanism. Explain why such a compensator would be necessary to get around Heisenberg's uncertainty principle.

6.90 Which of the quantum numbers governs (a) the shape of
CQ an orbital, (b) the energy of an orbital, (c) the spin properties of the electron, (d) the spatial orientation of the orbital?

[6.91] Consider the discussion of radial probability functions in the "A Closer Look" box in Section 6.6. (a) What is the difference between the probability density as a function of r and the radial probability function as a function of r? (b) What is the significance of the term $4\pi r^2$ in the radial probability functions for the s orbitals? (c) Based on Figures 6.19 and 6.23, make sketches of what you think the probability density as a function of r and the radial probability function would look like for the 4s orbital of the hydrogen atom.

6.92 The "magic numbers" in the periodic table are the atomic numbers of elements with high stability (the noble gases): 2, 10, 18, 36, 54, and 86. In terms of allowed values of orbitals and spin quantum numbers, explain why these electron arrangements correspond to special stability.

[6.93] For non-spherically symmetric orbitals, the contour representations (as in Figures 6.23 and 6.24) suggest where nodal planes exist (that is, where the electron density is zero). For example, the p_x orbital has a node wherever $x = 0$. This equation is satisfied by all points on the yz plane, so this plane is called a nodal plane of the p_x orbital. (a) Determine the nodal plane of the p_z orbital. (b) What are the two nodal planes of the d_{xy} orbital? (c) What are the two nodal planes of the $d_{x^2-y^2}$ orbital?

[6.94] As noted in Figure 6.26, the spin of an electron generates a magnetic field, with spin-up and spin-down electrons having opposite fields. In the absence of a magnetic field, a spin-up and a spin-down electron have the same energy. (a) Why do you think that the use of a magnet was important in the discovery of electron spin (see the "A Closer Look" box in Section 6.8)? (b) Imagine that the two spinning electrons in Figure 6.26 were placed between the poles of a horseshoe magnet, with the north pole of the magnet at the top of the figure. Based on what you know about magnets, would you expect the left or right electron in the figure to have the lower energy? (c) A phenomenon called *electron spin resonance* (ESR) is closely related to nuclear magnetic resonance. In ESR a compound with an unpaired electron is placed in a magnetic field, which causes the unpaired electron to have two different energy states analogous to Figure 6.28.

ESR uses microwave radiation to excite the unpaired electron from one state to the other. Based on your reading of the "Chemistry and Life" box in Section 6.8, does an ESR experiment require photons of greater or lesser energy than an NMR experiment?

[6.95] The "Chemistry and Life" box in Section 6.8 described the techniques called NMR and MRI. (a) Instruments for obtaining MRI data are typically labeled with a frequency, such as 600 MHz. Why do you suppose this label is relevant to the experiment? (b) What is the value of ΔE in Figure 6.28 that would correspond to the absorption of a photon of radiation with frequency 450 MHz? (c) In general, the stronger the magnetic field, the greater the

information obtained from an NMR or MRI experiment. Why do you suppose this is the case?

6.96 Suppose that the spin quantum number, m_s, could have *three* allowed values instead of two. How would this affect the number of elements in the first four rows of the periodic table?

6.97 Using only a periodic table as a guide, write the condensed electron configurations for the following atoms: (a) Se, (b) Rh, (c) Si, (d) Hg, (e) Hf.

6.98 Scientists have speculated that element 126 might have a moderate stability, allowing it to be synthesized and characterized. Predict what the condensed electron configuration of this element might be.

INTEGRATIVE EXERCISES

6.99 Microwave ovens use microwave radiation to heat food. The energy of the microwaves is absorbed by water molecules in food, then transferred to other components of the food. (a) Suppose that the microwave radiation has a wavelength of 11.2 cm. How many photons are required to heat 200 mL of coffee from 23 °C to 60 °C? (b) Suppose the microwave's power is 900 W (1 Watt = 1 Joule/sec). How long would you have to heat the coffee in part (a)?

6.100 The stratospheric ozone (O_3) layer helps to protect us from harmful ultraviolet radiation. It does so by absorbing ultraviolet light and falling apart into an O_2 molecule and an oxygen atom, a process known as photodissociation.

$$O_3(g) \longrightarrow O_2(g) + O(g)$$

Use the data in Appendix C to calculate the enthalpy change for this reaction. What is the maximum wavelength a photon can have if it is to possess sufficient energy to cause this dissociation? In what portion of the spectrum does this wavelength occur?

6.101 The discovery of hafnium, element number 72, provided a controversial episode in chemistry. G. Urbain, a French chemist, claimed in 1911 to have isolated an element number 72 from a sample of rare earth (elements 58–71) compounds. However, Niels Bohr believed that hafnium was more likely to be found along with zirconium than with the rare earths. D. Coster and G. von Hevesy, working in Bohr's laboratory in Copenhagen, showed in 1922 that element 72 was present in a sample of Norwegian zircon, an ore of zirconium. (The name hafnium comes from the Latin name for Copenhagen, *Hafnia*). (a) How would you use electron configuration arguments to justify Bohr's prediction? (b) Zirconium, hafnium's neighbor in group 4B, can be produced as a metal by reduction of solid $ZrCl_4$ with molten sodium metal. Write a balanced chemical equation for the reaction. Is this an oxidation-reduction reaction? If yes, what is reduced and what is oxidized? (c) Solid zirconium dioxide, ZrO_2, is reacted with chlorine gas in the presence of carbon. The products of the reaction are $ZrCl_4$ and two gases, CO_2 and CO in the ratio 1 : 2 Write a balanced chemical equation for the reaction. Starting with a 55.4-g sample of ZrO_2, calculate the mass of $ZrCl_4$ formed, assuming that ZrO_2 is the limiting reagent and assuming 100% yield. (d) Using their electron configurations, account for the fact that Zr and Hf form chlorides MCl_4 and oxides MO_2.

6.102 (a) Account for formation of the following series of oxides in terms of the electron configurations of the elements and the discussion of ionic compounds in Section 2.7: K_2O, CaO, Sc_2O_3, TiO_2, V_2O_5, CrO_3. (b) Name these oxides. (c) Consider the metal oxides whose enthalpies of formation (in kJ mol^{-1}) are listed here.

Oxide	$K_2O(s)$	$CaO(s)$	$TiO_2(s)$	$V_2O_5(s)$
ΔH_f°	−363.2	−635.1	−938.7	−1550.6

Calculate the enthalpy changes in the following general reaction for each case:

$$M_nO_m(s) + H_2(g) \longrightarrow nM(s) + mH_2O(g)$$

(You will need to write the balanced equation for each case, then compute ΔH°.) (d) Based on the data given, estimate a value of ΔH_f° for $Sc_2O_3(s)$.

6.103 The first 25 years of the twentieth century were momentous for the rapid pace of change in scientists' understanding of the nature of matter. (a) How did Rutherford's experiments on the scattering of α particles by a gold foil set the stage for Bohr's theory of the hydrogen atom? (b) In what ways is de Broglie's hypothesis, as it applies to electrons, consistent with J. J. Thomson's conclusion that the electron has mass? In what sense is it consistent with proposals that preceded Thomson's work, that the cathode rays are a wave phenomenon?

[6.104] The two most common isotopes of uranium are ^{235}U and ^{238}U. (a) Compare the number of protons, the number of electrons, and the number of neutrons in atoms of these two isotopes. (b) Using the periodic table in the front inside cover, write the electron configuration for a U atom. (c) Compare your answer to part (b) to the electron configuration given in Figure 6.31. How can you explain any differences between these two electron configurations? (d) ^{238}U undergoes radioactive decay to ^{234}Th. How many protons, electrons, and neutrons are gained or lost by the ^{238}U atom during this process? (e) Examine the electron configuration for Th in Figure 6.31. Are you surprised by what you find? Explain.

6.105 Imagine sunlight falling on three square areas. One is an inert black material. The second is a photovoltaic cell surface, which converts radiant energy into electricity. The third is an area on a green tree leaf. Draw diagrams that show the energy conversions in each case, using Figure 5.9 as a model. How are these three examples related to the idea of sustainable energy sources?

7 PERIODIC PROPERTIES OF THE ELEMENTS

OIL PAINTS CONTAIN PIGMENTS, which are usually highly colored salts, suspended in an organic carrier composed of a variety of heavy hydrocarbon molecules. This painting, by the famous French Impressionist Claude Monet (1840–1926), is entitled *La rue Montorgueil, fête du 30 juin 1878*.
Photo credit: Claude Monet (1840–1926) "Rue Montorgueil in Paris, Festival of 30 June 1878," 1878. Herve Lewandowski/Reunion des Muses Nationaux/Art Resource, NY.

254

THE BEAUTY OF AN IMPRESSIONIST OIL PAINTING, such as the Monet masterpiece shown here, begins with chemistry. Colorful inorganic salts are suspended in various organic media that contain hydrocarbons and other molecular substances. Indeed, the great painters had a gift for using compounds of elements that span nearly the entire periodic table.

Today the periodic table is still the most significant tool chemists have for organizing and remembering chemical facts. As we saw in Chapter 6, the periodic nature of the table arises from the repeating patterns in the electron configurations of the elements. Elements in the same column of the table contain the same number of electrons in their **valence orbitals**, the occupied orbitals that hold the electrons involved in bonding. For example, O ([He]$2s^2\,2p^4$) and S ([Ne]$3s^2 3p^4$) are both members of group 6A. The similarity of the electron distribution in their valence s and p orbitals leads to similarities in the properties of these two elements.

When we compare O and S, however, it is apparent that they exhibit differences as well, not the least of which is that oxygen is a colorless gas at room

255

▲ Figure 7.1 **Oxygen and sulfur.** Because they are both group 6A elements, oxygen and sulfur have many chemical similarities. They also have many differences, however, including the forms they take at room temperature. Oxygen consists of O_2 molecules that appear as a colorless gas (shown here enclosed in a glass container on the left). In contrast, sulfur consists of S_8 molecules that form a yellow solid.

temperature, whereas sulfur is a yellow solid (Figure 7.1 ◄)! One of the major differences between atoms of these two elements is their electron configurations: the outermost electrons of O are in the second shell, whereas those of S are in the third shell. We will see that electron configurations can be used to explain differences as well as similarities in the properties of elements.

In this chapter we explore how some of the important properties of elements change as we move across a row or down a column of the periodic table. In many cases the trends within a row or column allow us to make predictions about the physical and chemical properties of the elements.

7.1 DEVELOPMENT OF THE PERIODIC TABLE

The discovery of the chemical elements has been an ongoing process since ancient times (Figure 7.2 ▼). Certain elements, such as gold, appear in nature in elemental form and were thus discovered thousands of years ago. In contrast, some elements, such as technetium, are radioactive and intrinsically unstable. We know about them only because of technology developed during the twentieth century.

The majority of the elements, although stable, readily form compounds. Consequently, they are not found in nature in their elemental form. For centuries, therefore, scientists were unaware of their existence. During the early nineteenth century, advances in chemistry made it easier to isolate elements from their compounds. As a result, the number of known elements more than doubled from 31 in 1800 to 63 by 1865.

As the number of known elements increased, scientists began to investigate the possibilities of classifying them in useful ways. In 1869, Dmitri Mendeleev in Russia and Lothar Meyer in Germany published nearly identical classification schemes. Both scientists noted that similar chemical and physical properties recur periodically when the elements are arranged in order of increasing atomic weight. Scientists at that time had no knowledge of atomic numbers. Atomic weights, however, generally increase with increasing atomic number, so both Mendeleev and Meyer fortuitously arranged the elements in proper sequence. The tables of elements advanced by Mendeleev and Meyer were the forerunners of the modern periodic table.

Although Mendeleev and Meyer came to essentially the same conclusion about the periodicity of elemental properties, Mendeleev is given credit for advancing his ideas more vigorously and stimulating much new work in chemistry.

▶ Figure 7.2 **Discovering the elements.** Periodic table showing the dates of discovery of the elements.

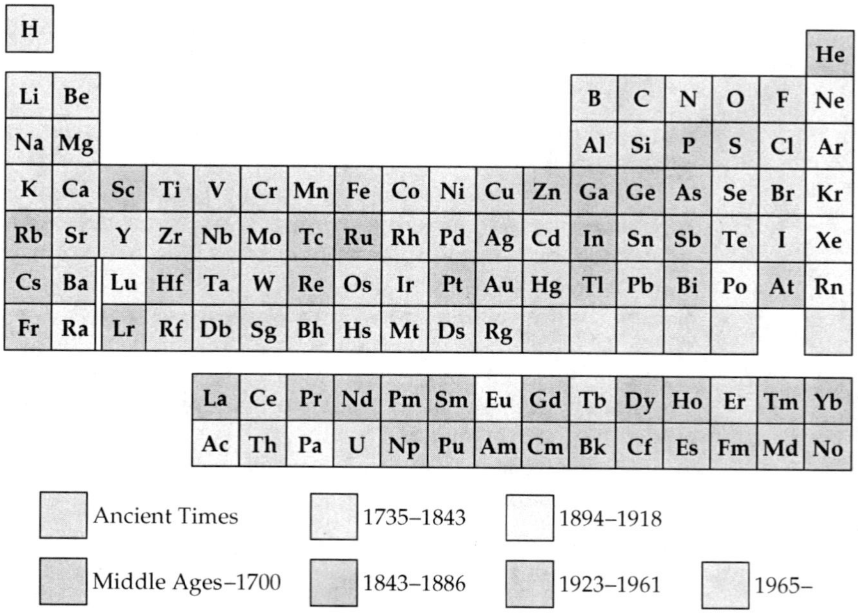

H																	He
Li	Be											B	C	N	O	F	Ne
Na	Mg											Al	Si	P	S	Cl	Ar
K	Ca	Sc	Ti	V	Cr	Mn	Fe	Co	Ni	Cu	Zn	Ga	Ge	As	Se	Br	Kr
Rb	Sr	Y	Zr	Nb	Mo	Tc	Ru	Rh	Pd	Ag	Cd	In	Sn	Sb	Te	I	Xe
Cs	Ba	Lu	Hf	Ta	W	Re	Os	Ir	Pt	Au	Hg	Tl	Pb	Bi	Po	At	Rn
Fr	Ra	Lr	Rf	Db	Sg	Bh	Hs	Mt	Ds	Rg							

La	Ce	Pr	Nd	Pm	Sm	Eu	Gd	Tb	Dy	Ho	Er	Tm	Yb
Ac	Th	Pa	U	Np	Pu	Am	Cm	Bk	Cf	Es	Fm	Md	No

☐ Ancient Times	☐ 1735–1843	☐ 1894–1918
☐ Middle Ages–1700	☐ 1843–1886	☐ 1923–1961	☐ 1965–

TABLE 7.1 ■ Comparison of the Properties of Eka-Silicon Predicted by Mendeleev with the Observed Properties of Germanium

Property	Mendeleev's Predictions for Eka-Silicon (made in 1871)	Observed Properties of Germanium (discovered in 1886)
Atomic weight	72	72.59
Density (g/cm^3)	5.5	5.35
Specific heat (J/g-K)	0.305	0.309
Melting point (°C)	High	947
Color	Dark gray	Grayish white
Formula of oxide	XO_2	GeO_2
Density of oxide (g/cm^3)	4.7	4.70
Formula of chloride	XCl_4	$GeCl_4$
Boiling point of chloride (°C)	A little under 100	84

His insistence that elements with similar characteristics be listed in the same family forced him to leave several blank spaces in his table. For example, both gallium (Ga) and germanium (Ge) were unknown at that time. Mendeleev boldly predicted their existence and properties, referring to them as *eka-aluminum* ("under" aluminum) and *eka-silicon* ("under" silicon), respectively, after the elements under which they appear in the periodic table. When these elements were discovered, their properties closely matched those predicted by Mendeleev, as shown in Table 7.1 ▲.

In 1913, two years after Rutherford proposed the nuclear model of the atom ⇒ (Section 2.2), an English physicist named Henry Moseley (1887–1915) developed the concept of atomic numbers. Moseley determined the frequencies of X-rays emitted as different elements were bombarded with high-energy electrons. He found that each element produces X-rays of a unique frequency; furthermore, he found that the frequency generally increased as the atomic mass increased. He arranged the X-ray frequencies in order by assigning a unique whole number, called an *atomic number*, to each element. Moseley correctly identified the atomic number as the number of protons in the nucleus of the atom. ⇒ (Section 2.3)

The concept of atomic number clarified some problems in the periodic table of Moseley's day, which was based on atomic weights. For example, the atomic weight of Ar (atomic number 18) is greater than that of K (atomic number 19), yet the chemical and physical properties of Ar are much more like that of Ne and Kr than they are like Na and Rb. However, when the elements are arranged in order of increasing atomic number, rather than increasing atomic weight, Ar and K appear in their correct places in the table. Moseley's studies also made it possible to identify "holes" in the periodic table, which led to the discovery of other previously unknown elements.

GIVE IT SOME THOUGHT

Arranging the elements by atomic weight leads to a slightly different order than arranging them by atomic number. Why does this happen? Can you find an example, other than the case of Ar and K discussed above, where the order of the elements would be different if the elements were arranged in order of increasing atomic weight?

7.2 EFFECTIVE NUCLEAR CHARGE

Because electrons are negatively charged, they are attracted to nuclei, which are positively charged. Many of the properties of atoms depend on their electron configurations and on how strongly their outer electrons are attracted to the nucleus. Coulomb's law tells us that the strength of the interaction between two electrical charges depends on the magnitudes of the charges and on the distance between them. (Section 2.3) Thus, the force of attraction between an electron and the nucleus depends on the magnitude of the net nuclear charge acting on the electron and on the average distance between the nucleus and the electron. The force of attraction increases as the nuclear charge increases, and it decreases as the electron moves farther from the nucleus.

In a many-electron atom, each electron is simultaneously attracted to the nucleus and repelled by the other electrons. In general, there are so many electron–electron repulsions that we cannot analyze the situation exactly. We can, however, estimate the net attraction of each electron to the nucleus by considering how it interacts with the *average* environment created by the nucleus and the other electrons in the atom. This approach allows us to treat each electron individually as though it were moving in the net electric field created by the nucleus and the electron density of the other electrons. We can view this net electric field as if it results from a single positive charge located at the nucleus, called the **effective nuclear charge**, Z_{eff}.

It is important to realize that the effective nuclear charge acting on an electron in an atom is smaller than the *actual* nuclear charge because the effective nuclear charge also accounts for the repulsion of the electron by the other electrons in the atom—in other words, $Z_{eff} < Z$. Let's consider how we can get a sense of the magnitude of Z_{eff} for an electron in an atom.

A valence electron in an atom is attracted to the nucleus of the atom and is repelled by the other electrons in the atom. In particular, the electron density that is due to the inner (core) electrons is particularly effective at partially canceling the attraction of the valence electron to the nucleus. We say that the inner electrons partially *shield* or *screen* the outer electrons from the attraction of the nucleus. We can therefore write a simple relationship between the effective nuclear charge, Z_{eff}, and the number of protons in the nucleus, Z:

$$Z_{eff} = Z - S \qquad [7.1]$$

The factor S is a positive number called the *screening constant*. It represents the portion of the nuclear charge that is screened from the valence electron by the other electrons in the atom. Because the core electrons are most effective at screening a valence electron from the nucleus, *the value of S is usually close to the number of core electrons in an atom*. Electrons in the same valence shell do not screen one another very effectively, but they do affect the value of S slightly (see "A Closer Look" on Effective Nuclear Charge). Let's take a look at a Na atom to see what we would expect for the magnitude of Z_{eff}. Sodium (atomic number 11) has a condensed electron configuration of $[Ne]3s^1$. The nuclear charge of the atom is 11+, and the Ne inner core consists of ten electrons ($1s^2 2s^2 2p^6$). Very roughly then, we would expect the 3s valence electron of the Na atom to experience an effective nuclear charge of about $11 - 10 = 1+$, as pictured in a simplified way in Figure 7.3(a) ◄. The situation is a bit more complicated because of the electron distributions of atomic orbitals. (Section 6.6) Recall that a 3s electron has a small probability of being found close to the nucleus and inside the core electrons, as shown in Figure 7.3(b). Thus, there is a probability that the 3s electron will experience a greater attraction than our simple model suggests, which will increase the value of Z_{eff} somewhat. Indeed, the value of Z_{eff} obtained from detailed calculations indicate that the effective nuclear charge acting on the 3s electron in Na is 2.5+.

▼ Figure 7.3 **Effective nuclear charge.** (a) The effective nuclear charge experienced by the valence electron in sodium depends mostly on the 11+ charge of the nucleus and the 10− charge of the neon core. If the neon core were totally effective in shielding the valence electron from the nucleus, then the valence electron would experience an effective nuclear charge of 1+. (b) The 3s electron has some probability of being inside the Ne core. Because of this "penetration," the core is not completely effective in screening the 3s electron from the nucleus. Thus, the effective nuclear charge experienced by the 3s electron is somewhat greater than 1+.

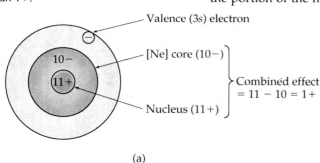

(a)

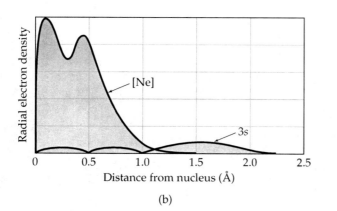

(b)

The notion of effective nuclear charge also explains an important effect we noted in Section 6.7, namely, that for a many-electron atom the energies of orbitals with the same n value increase with increasing l value. For example, consider a carbon atom, for which the electron configuration is $1s^2 2s^2 2p^2$. The energy of the $2p$ orbital ($l = 1$) is somewhat higher than that of the $2s$ orbital ($l = 0$) even though both of these orbitals are in the $n = 2$ shell (Figure 6.25). The reason that these orbitals have different energy in a many-electron atom is due to the radial probability functions for the orbitals, shown in Figure 7.4▶. Notice that the $2s$ probability function has a small peak fairly close to the nucleus, whereas the $2p$ probability function does not. As a result, an electron in the $2s$ orbital is less effectively screened by the core orbitals than is an electron in the $2p$ orbital. In other words, the electron in the $2s$ orbital experiences a higher effective nuclear charge than one in the $2p$ orbital. The greater attraction between the 2s electron and the nucleus leads to a lower energy for the $2s$ orbital than for the $2p$ orbital. The same reasoning explains the general trend in orbital energies ($ns < np < nd$) in many-electron atoms.

Finally, let's examine the trends in Z_{eff} for valence electrons as we move from one element to another in the periodic table. *The effective nuclear charge increases as we move across any row (period) of the table.* Although the number of core electrons stays the same as we move across the row, the actual nuclear charge increases. The valence electrons added to counterbalance the increasing nuclear charge shield one another very ineffectively. Thus, the effective nuclear charge, Z_{eff}, increases steadily. For example, the $1s^2$ core electrons of lithium ($1s^2 2s^1$) shield the $2s$ valence electron from the 3+ nucleus fairly efficiently. Consequently, the outer electron experiences an effective nuclear charge of roughly $3 - 2 = 1+$. For beryllium ($1s^2 2s^2$) the effective nuclear charge experienced by each $2s$ valence electron is larger; in this case, the inner $1s$ electrons are shielding a 4+ nucleus, and each $2s$ electron only partially shields the other from the nucleus. Consequently, the effective nuclear charge experienced by each $2s$ electron is about $4 - 2 = 2+$.

Going down a column, the effective nuclear charge experienced by valence electrons changes far less than it does across a row. For example, we would expect the effective nuclear charge for the outer electrons in lithium and sodium to be about the same, roughly $3 - 2 = 1+$ for lithium and $11 - 10 = 1+$ for sodium. In fact, however, the effective nuclear charge increases slightly as we go down a family because larger electron cores are less able to screen the outer electrons from the nuclear charge. In the case of the alkali metals, the value of Z_{eff} increases from 1.3+ for lithium, to 2.5+ for sodium, to 3.5+ for potassium. Nevertheless, the increase in effective nuclear charge that occurs moving down a column is smaller than the change that occurs when moving horizontally from one side of the periodic table to the other.

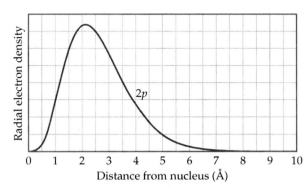

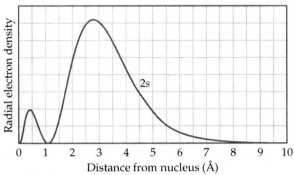

▲ **Figure 7.4 2s and 2p radial functions.** The radial probability function for the 2s orbital of the hydrogen atom (red curve) shows a "bump" of probability close to the nucleus, whereas that for the 2p orbital (blue curve) does not. As a result, an electron in the 2s orbital for a many-electron atom "sees" more of the nuclear charge than does an electron in the 2p orbital. Hence, the effective nuclear charge experienced by the 2s electron is greater than that for the 2p electron.

GIVE IT SOME THOUGHT

Which would you expect to experience a greater effective nuclear charge, a 2p electron of a Ne atom or a 3s electron of a Na atom?

7.3 SIZES OF ATOMS AND IONS

Size is one of the important properties of an atom or an ion. We often think of atoms and ions as hard, spherical objects. According to the quantum mechanical model, however, atoms and ions do not have sharply defined boundaries at which the electron distribution becomes zero. (Section 6.5) Nevertheless,

A Closer Look   EFFECTIVE NUCLEAR CHARGE

To get a better sense of how the effective nuclear charge varies as both the charge of the nucleus and the number of electrons increase, consider Figure 7.5▶. This figure shows the variation in Z_{eff} for elements in the second (Li – Ne) and third (Na – Ar) periods. The effective nuclear charge is plotted for electrons in the 1s subshell (in red) and for the outermost valence electrons (in blue). These values are considered the most accurate estimate of Z_{eff}. Although the details of how they are calculated are beyond the scope of our discussion, the trends are instructive. The effective nuclear charge as felt by electrons in the 1s subshell closely track the increasing charge of the nucleus, Z, (in black) because the other electrons do little to shield these innermost electrons from the charge of the nucleus.

Compare the values of Z_{eff} experienced by the inner core electron (in red) with those experienced by the outermost electrons (in blue). The values of Z_{eff} as felt by the outermost electrons are smaller because of screening by the inner electrons. In addition, the effective nuclear charge felt by the outermost electrons does not increase as steeply with increasing atomic number, because the valence electrons make a small, but non-negligible contribution to the screening constant, S. However, the most striking feature associated with the Z_{eff} for the outermost electrons is the sharp drop between the last element of the second period (Ne) and the first element of the third period (Na). This drop reflects the fact that the core electrons are much more effective than the valence electrons at screening the charge of the nucleus.

Effective nuclear charge is a tool that can be used to understand many physically measurable quantities, such as ionization energy, atomic radii, and electron affinity. Therefore, it is desirable to have a simple method for estimating Z_{eff} without resorting to sophisticated calculations or memorization. The charge of the nucleus, Z, is known exactly, so the challenge boils down to estimating accurately the value of the screening constant, S. The approach outlined in the text was to estimate S by assuming that the core electrons contribute a value of 1.00 to the screening constant, and the outer electrons contribute nothing to S. A more accurate approach is to use an empirical set of rules developed by John Slater. If we limit ourselves to elements that do not have electrons in d or f subshells (the rules become somewhat more complicated for such elements), Slater's rules are straightforward to apply. Electrons with larger values of n, the principal quantum number, than the electron of interest contribute 0 to the value of the screening constant, S. Electrons with the same value of n, as the electron of interest contribute 0.35 to the value of S. Electrons with a

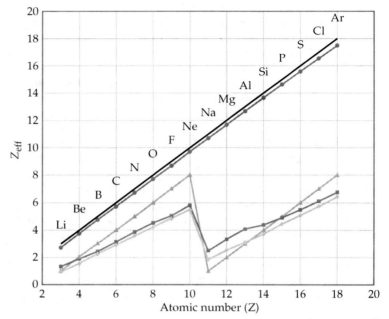

▲ Figure 7.5 **Variations in effective nuclear charge.** This figure shows the variation in effective nuclear charge, Z_{eff}, as felt by the innermost electrons, those in the 1s subshell (red circles), which closely tracks the increase in nuclear charge, Z (black line). The Z_{eff} felt by the outermost valence electrons (blue squares) not only is significantly smaller than Z, it does not evolve linearly with increasing atomic number. It is also possible to estimate Z_{eff} using certain rules. The values shown as green triangles were obtained by assuming the core electrons are completely effective at screening and the valence electrons do not screen the nuclear charge at all. The values shown as gray diamonds were estimated using Slater's rules.

principal quantum number one less than the electron of interest contribute 0.85 to the value of S, while those with even smaller values of n contribute 1.00 to the value of S. Values of Z_{eff} as estimated using the simple method outlined in the text (in green), as well as those estimated with Slater's rules (in grey), are plotted in Figure 7.5. While neither of these methods exactly replicate the values of Z_{eff} obtained from more sophisticated calculations, we see that both methods effectively capture the periodic variation in Z_{eff}. While Slater's approach is more accurate, the method outlined in the text does a reasonably good job of estimating the effective nuclear charge, despite its simplicity. For our purposes, we can assume that the screening constant, S, in Equation 7.1 is roughly equal to the number of core electrons.
Related Exercises: 7.13, 7.14, 7.33, 7.34, 7.85, 7.87

we can define atomic size in several ways, based on the distances between atoms in various situations.

Imagine a collection of argon atoms in the gas phase. When two atoms collide with each other in the course of their motions, they ricochet apart—somewhat like billiard balls. This movement happens because the electron clouds of the colliding atoms cannot penetrate each other to any significant extent. The closest distances separating the nuclei during such collisions determine the *apparent* radii of the argon atoms. We might call this radius the *nonbonding atomic radius* of an atom.

When two atoms are chemically bonded to each other, as in the Cl_2 molecule, an attractive interaction exists between the two atoms leading to a chemical bond. We will discuss the nature of such bonding in Chapter 8. For now, the only thing we need to realize is that this attractive interaction brings the two atoms closer together than they would be in a nonbonding collision. We can define an atomic radius based on the distances separating the nuclei of atoms when they are chemically bonded to each other. This distance, called the **bonding atomic radius**, is shorter than the nonbonding atomic radius, as illustrated in Figure 7.6 ▶. Unless otherwise noted, we will refer to the bonding atomic radius when we speak of the size of an atom.

Scientists have developed a variety of experimental techniques for measuring the distances separating nuclei in molecules. From observations of these distances in many molecules, each element can be assigned a bonding atomic radius. For example, in the I_2 molecule, the distance separating the iodine nuclei is observed to be 2.66 Å.* We can define the bonding atomic radius of iodine on this basis to be one-half of the bond distance, namely 1.33 Å. Similarly, the distance separating two adjacent carbon nuclei in diamond, which is a three-dimensional solid network, is 1.54 Å; thus, the bonding atomic radius of carbon is assigned the value 0.77 Å. The radii of other elements can be similarly defined (Figure 7.7 ▶). (For helium and neon, the bonding radii must be estimated because there are no known compounds of these elements.)

Knowing atomic radii allows us to estimate the bond lengths between different elements in molecules. For example, the Cl—Cl bond length in Cl_2 is 1.99 Å, so a radius of 0.99 Å is assigned to Cl. In the compound CCl_4 the measured length of the C—Cl bond is 1.77 Å, very close to the sum (0.77 + 0.99 Å) of the atomic radii of C and Cl.

If we consider the radius of an atom as one-half the distance between the nuclei of atoms that are held together by a bond, you may wonder why the spheres representing atoms seem to overlap in some drawings, such as those in Figures 1.1 and 2.20. These depictions of molecules are called space-filling models, and they use nonbonding atomic radii (also called *van der Waals radii*) to represent the sizes of different elements. Even in these representations the distance between the centers of two adjacent atoms in the molecule is determined from bonding atomic radii (also called *covalent radii*).

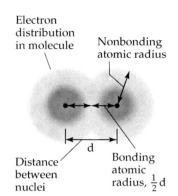

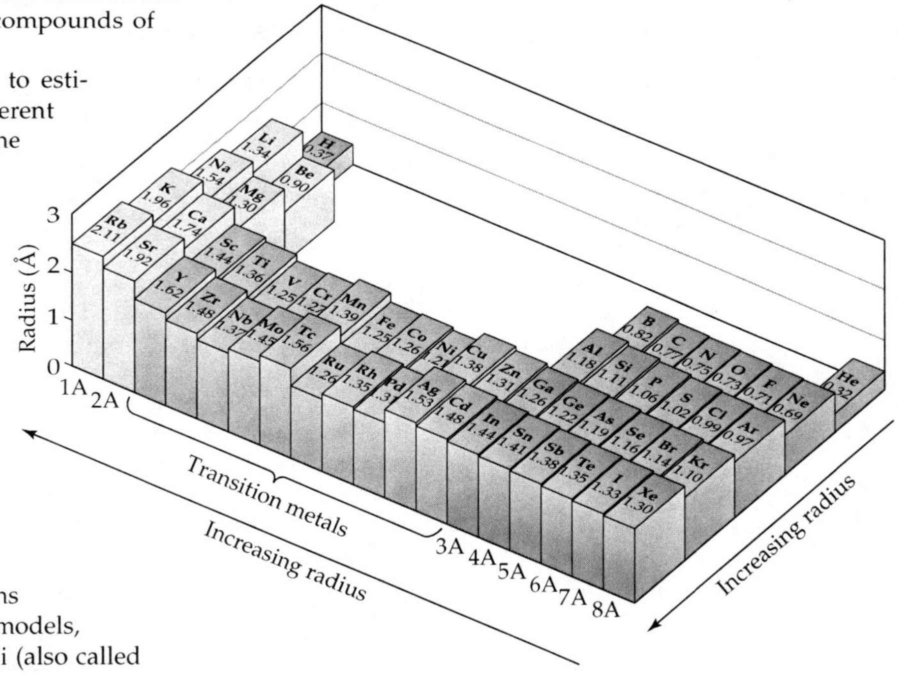

▲ Figure 7.6 **Distinction between nonbonding and bonding atomic radii.** The nonbonding atomic radius is the effective radius of an atom when it is not involved in bonding to another atom. Values of bonding atomic radii are obtained from measurements of interatomic distances in chemical compounds.

▲ Figure 7.7 **Trends in atomic radii.** Bonding atomic radii for the first 54 elements of the periodic table. The height of the bar for each element is proportional to its radius, giving a "relief map" view of the radii.

*Remember: The angstrom (1 Å = 10^{-10} m) is a convenient metric unit for atomic measurements of length. The angstrom is not an SI unit. The most commonly used SI unit for such measurements is the picometer (1 pm = 10^{-12} m; 1 Å = 100 pm).

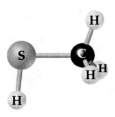

■■ SAMPLE EXERCISE 7.1 | Bond Lengths in a Molecule

Natural gas used in home heating and cooking is odorless. Because natural gas leaks pose the danger of explosion or suffocation, various smelly substances are added to the gas to allow detection of a leak. One such substance is methyl mercaptan, CH_3SH, whose structure is shown in the margin. Use Figure 7.7 to predict the lengths of the C—S, C—H, and S—H bonds in this molecule.

SOLUTION

Analyze and Plan: We are given three bonds and the list of bonding atomic radii. We will assume that each bond length is the sum of the radii of the two atoms involved.

Solve: Using radii for C, S, and H from Figure 7.7, we predict

$$C—S \text{ bond length} = \text{radius of C} + \text{radius of S}$$
$$= 0.77 \text{ Å} + 1.02 \text{ Å} = 1.79 \text{ Å}$$
$$C—H \text{ bond length} = 0.77 \text{ Å} + 0.37 \text{ Å} = 1.14 \text{ Å}$$
$$S—H \text{ bond length} = 1.02 \text{ Å} + 0.37 \text{ Å} = 1.39 \text{ Å}$$

Check: The experimentally determined bond lengths in methyl mercaptan (taken from the chemical literature) are C—S = 1.82 Å, C—H = 1.10 Å, and S—H = 1.33 Å. (In general, the lengths of bonds involving hydrogen show larger deviations from the values predicted by the sum of the atomic radii than do those bonds involving larger atoms.)

Comment: Notice that the estimated bond lengths using bonding atomic radii are close, but not exact matches, to the experimental bond lengths. Atomic radii must be used with some caution in estimating bond lengths. In Chapter 8 we will examine some of the average lengths of common types of bonds.

■■ PRACTICE EXERCISE

Using Figure 7.7, predict which will be greater, the P—Br bond length in PBr_3 or the As—Cl bond length in $AsCl_3$.
Answer: P—Br

Periodic Trends in Atomic Radii

If we examine the "relief map" of atomic radii shown in Figure 7.7, we observe two interesting trends in the data:

1. Within each column (group), atomic radius tends to increase from top to bottom. This trend results primarily from the increase in the principal quantum number (*n*) of the outer electrons. As we go down a column, the outer electrons have a greater probability of being farther from the nucleus, causing the atom to increase in size.

2. Within each row (period), atomic radius tends to decrease from left to right. The major factor influencing this trend is the increase in the effective nuclear charge (Z_{eff}) as we move across a row. The increasing effective nuclear charge steadily draws the valence electrons closer to the nucleus, causing the atomic radius to decrease.

▲ GIVE IT SOME THOUGHT

In section 7.2 we said that the effective nuclear charge generally increases when you move down a column of the periodic table, whereas in Chapter 6 we saw that the "size" of an orbital increases as the principal quantum number increases. With respect to atomic radii, do these trends work together or against each other? Which effect is larger?

Science Fundamentals

■ SAMPLE EXERCISE 7.2 | Atomic Radii

Referring to a periodic table, arrange (as much as possible) the following atoms in order of increasing size: $_{15}P$, $_{16}S$, $_{33}As$, $_{34}Se$. (Atomic numbers are given for the elements to help you locate them quickly in the periodic table.)

SOLUTION

Analyze and Plan: We are given the chemical symbols for four elements. We can use their relative positions in the periodic table and the two periodic trends just described to predict the relative order of their atomic radii.

Solve: Notice that P and S are in the same row of the periodic table, with S to the right of P. Therefore, we expect the radius of S to be smaller than that of P. (Radii decrease as we move from left to right.) Likewise, the radius of Se is expected to be smaller than that of As. We also notice that As is directly below P and that Se is directly below S. We expect, therefore, that the radius of As is greater than that of P and the radius of Se is greater than that of S. From these observations, we predict S < P, P < As, S < Se, and Se < As. We can therefore conclude that S has the smallest radius of the four elements and that As has the largest radius.

Using just the two trends described above, we cannot determine whether P or Se has the larger radius. To go from P to Se in the periodic table, we must move down (radius tends to increase) and to the right (radius tends to decrease). In Figure 7.7 we see that the radius of Se (1.16 Å) is greater than that of P (1.06 Å). If you examine the figure carefully, you will discover that for the s- and p-block elements the increase in radius moving down a column tends to be the greater effect. There are exceptions, however.

Check: From Figure 7.7, we have S (1.02 Å) < P (1.06 Å) < Se (1.16 Å) < As (1.19 Å).

Comment: Note that the trends we have just discussed are for the s- and p-block elements. You will see in Figure 7.7 that the transition elements do not show a regular decrease upon moving from left to right across a row.

■ PRACTICE EXERCISE

Arrange the following atoms in order of increasing atomic radius: $_{11}Na$, $_4Be$, $_{12}Mg$.
Answer: Be < Mg < Na

Periodic Trends in Ionic Radii

Just as bonding atomic radii can be determined from interatomic distances in elements, ionic radii can be determined from interatomic distances in ionic compounds. Like the size of an atom, the size of an ion depends on its nuclear charge, the number of electrons it possesses, and the orbitals in which the valence electrons reside. The formation of a cation vacates the most spatially extended occupied orbitals in an atom and decreases the number of electron–electron repulsions. Therefore, *cations are smaller than their parent atoms*, as illustrated in Figure 7.8 ▶. The opposite is true of anions. When electrons are added

▶ Figure 7.8 **Cation and anion size.** Comparisons of the radii, in Å, of neutral atoms and ions for several of the groups of representative elements. Neutral atoms are shown in gray, cations in red, and anions in blue.

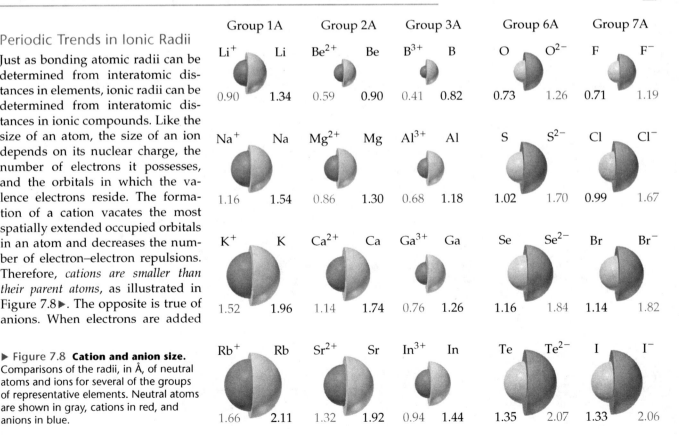

Group 1A		Group 2A		Group 3A		Group 6A		Group 7A	
Li^+	Li	Be^{2+}	Be	B^{3+}	B	O	O^{2-}	F	F^-
0.90	1.34	0.59	0.90	0.41	0.82	0.73	1.26	0.71	1.19
Na^+	Na	Mg^{2+}	Mg	Al^{3+}	Al	S	S^{2-}	Cl	Cl^-
1.16	1.54	0.86	1.30	0.68	1.18	1.02	1.70	0.99	1.67
K^+	K	Ca^{2+}	Ca	Ga^{3+}	Ga	Se	Se^{2-}	Br	Br^-
1.52	1.96	1.14	1.74	0.76	1.26	1.16	1.84	1.14	1.82
Rb^+	Rb	Sr^{2+}	Sr	In^{3+}	In	Te	Te^{2-}	I	I^-
1.66	2.11	1.32	1.92	0.94	1.44	1.35	2.07	1.33	2.06

to an atom to form an anion, the increased electron-electron repulsions cause the electrons to spread out more in space. Thus, *anions are larger than their parent atoms.*

For ions carrying the same charge, size increases as we move down a column in the periodic table. This trend is also seen in Figure 7.8. As the principal quantum number of the outermost occupied orbital of an ion increases, the radius of the ion increases.

■■■ SAMPLE EXERCISE 7.3 | Atomic and Ionic Radii

Arrange these atoms and ions in order of decreasing size: Mg^{2+}, Ca^{2+}, and Ca.

SOLUTION

Cations are smaller than their parent atoms, and so the Ca^{2+} ion is smaller than the Ca atom. Because Ca is below Mg in group 2A of the periodic table, Ca^{2+} is larger than Mg^{2+}. Consequently, Ca > Ca^{2+} > Mg^{2+}.

■■■ PRACTICE EXERCISE

Which of the following atoms and ions is largest: S^{2-}, S, O^{2-}?
Answer: S^{2-}

An **isoelectronic series** is a group of ions all containing the same number of electrons. For example, each ion in the isoelectronic series O^{2-}, F^-, Na^+, Mg^{2+}, Al^{3+} has 10 electrons. In any isoelectronic series we can list the members in order of increasing atomic number; therefore, nuclear charge increases as we move through the series. (Recall that the charge on the nucleus of an atom or monatomic ion is given by the atomic number of the element.) Because the number of electrons remains constant, the radius of the ion decreases with increasing nuclear charge, as the electrons are more strongly attracted to the nucleus:

— Increasing nuclear charge ⟶

| O^{2-} | F^- | Na^+ | Mg^{2+} | Al^{3+} |
| 1.26 Å | 1.19 Å | 1.16 Å | 0.86 Å | 0.68 Å |

— Decreasing ionic radius ⟶

Notice the positions and the atomic numbers of these elements in the periodic table. The nonmetal anions precede the noble gas Ne in the table. The metal cations follow Ne. Oxygen, the largest ion in this isoelectronic series, has the lowest atomic number, 8. Aluminum, the smallest of these ions, has the highest atomic number, 13.

■■■ SAMPLE EXERCISE 7.4 | Ionic Radii in an Isoelectronic Series

Arrange the ions K^+, Cl^-, Ca^{2+}, and S^{2-} in order of decreasing size.

SOLUTION

First, we note that this is an isoelectronic series of ions, with all ions having 18 electrons. In such a series, size decreases as the nuclear charge (atomic number) of the ion increases. The atomic numbers of the ions are S (16), Cl (17), K (19), and Ca (20). Thus, the ions decrease in size in the order S^{2-} > Cl^- > K^+ > Ca^{2+}.

■■■ PRACTICE EXERCISE

Which of the following ions is largest, Rb^+, Sr^{2+}, or Y^{3+}?
Answer: Rb^+

7.4 IONIZATION ENERGY

The ease with which electrons can be removed from an atom or ion has a major impact on chemical behavior. The **ionization energy** of an atom or ion is the minimum energy required to remove an electron from the ground state of the isolated gaseous atom or ion. The *first ionization energy*, I_1, is the energy

Chemistry and Life   IONIC SIZE MAKES A BIG DIFFERENCE

Ionic size plays a major role in determining the properties of ions in solution. For example, a small difference in ionic size is often sufficient for one metal ion to be biologically important and another not to be. To illustrate, let's examine some of the biological chemistry of the zinc ion (Zn^{2+}) and compare it with the cadmium ion (Cd^{2+}).

Recall from the "Chemistry and Life" box in Section 2.7 that zinc is needed in our diets in trace amounts. Zinc is an essential part of several enzymes—the proteins that facilitate or regulate the speeds of key biological reactions. For example, one of the most important zinc-containing enzymes is *carbonic anhydrase*. This enzyme is found in red blood cells. Its job is to facilitate the reaction of carbon dioxide (CO_2) with water to form the bicarbonate ion (HCO_3^-):

$$CO_2(aq) + H_2O(l) \longrightarrow HCO_3^-(aq) + H^+(aq) \qquad [7.2]$$

You might be surprised to know that our bodies need an enzyme for such a simple reaction. In the absence of carbonic anhydrase, however, the CO_2 produced in cells when they are oxidizing glucose or other fuels in vigorous exercise would be cleared out much too slowly. About 20% of the CO_2 produced by cell metabolism binds to hemoglobin and is carried to the lungs, where it is expelled. About 70% of the CO_2 produced is converted to bicarbonate ion through the action of carbonic anhydrase. When the CO_2 has been converted into bicarbonate ion, it diffuses into the blood plasma and eventually is passed into the lungs in the reverse of Equation 7.2. These processes are illustrated in Figure 7.9 ▶. In the absence of zinc, the carbonic anhydrase would be inactive, and serious imbalances would result in the amount of CO_2 present in blood.

Zinc is also found in several other enzymes, including some found in the liver and kidneys. It is obviously essential to life. By contrast, cadmium, zinc's neighbor in group 2B, is extremely toxic to humans. But why are two elements so dif-

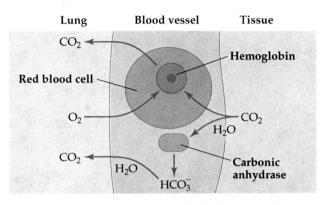

▲ Figure 7.9 **Ridding the body of carbon dioxide.** Illustration of the flow of CO_2 from tissues into blood vessels and eventually into the lungs. About 20% of the CO_2 binds to hemoglobin and is released in the lungs. About 70% is converted by carbonic anhydrase into HCO_3^- ion, which remains in the blood plasma until the reverse reaction releases CO_2 into the lungs. Small amounts of CO_2 simply dissolve in the blood plasma and are released in the lungs.

ferent? Both occur as 2+ ions, but Zn^{2+} is smaller than Cd^{2+}. The radius of Zn^{2+} is 0.88 Å; that of Cd^{2+} is 1.09 Å. Can this difference be the cause of such a dramatic reversal of biological properties? The answer is that while size is not the only factor, it is very important. In the carbonic anhydrase enzyme the Zn^{2+} ion is found electrostatically bonded to atoms on the protein, as shown in Figure 7.10 ▼. It turns out that Cd^{2+} binds in this same place preferentially over Zn^{2+}, thus displacing it. When Cd^{2+} is present instead of Zn^{2+}, however, the reaction of CO_2 with water is not facilitated. More seriously, Cd^{2+} inhibits reactions that are essential to the kidneys' functioning. *Related Exercises: 7.30, 7.91, and 7.92*

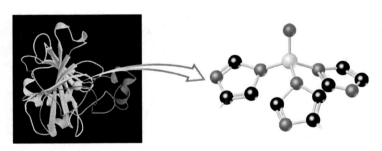

◀ Figure 7.10 **A zinc-containing enzyme.** The enzyme called carbonic anhydrase (left) catalyzes the reaction between CO_2 and water to form HCO_3^-. The ribbon represents the folding of the protein chain. The "active site" of the enzyme (represented by the ball-and-stick model) is where the reaction occurs. (H atoms have been excluded from this model for clarity.) The red sphere represents the oxygen of a water molecule that is bound to the zinc ion (gold sphere) at the center of the active site. The water molecule is replaced by CO_2 in the reaction. The bonds coming off the five-member rings attach the active site to the protein (nitrogen and carbon atoms are represented by blue and black spheres, respectively).

needed to remove the first electron from a neutral atom. For example, the first ionization energy for the sodium atom is the energy required for the process

$$Na(g) \longrightarrow Na^+(g) + e^- \qquad [7.3]$$

The *second ionization energy*, I_2, is the energy needed to remove the second electron, and so forth, for successive removals of additional electrons. Thus, I_2 for the sodium atom is the energy associated with the process

$$Na^+(g) \longrightarrow Na^{2+}(g) + e^- \qquad [7.4]$$

The greater the ionization energy, the more difficult it is to remove an electron.

GIVE IT SOME THOUGHT

Light can be used to ionize atoms and ions, as in Equations 7.3 and 7.4. Which of the two processes, [7.3] or [7.4], would require shorter wavelength radiation?

Variations in Successive Ionization Energies

Ionization energies for the elements sodium through argon are listed in Table 7.2▼. Notice that the values for a given element increase as successive electrons are removed: $I_1 < I_2 < I_3$, and so forth. This trend exists because with each successive removal, an electron is being pulled away from an increasingly more positive ion, requiring increasingly more energy.

TABLE 7.2 ■ Successive Values of Ionization Energies, *I*, for the Elements Sodium through Argon (kJ/mol)

Element	I_1	I_2	I_3	I_4	I_5	I_6	I_7
Na	496	4562	(inner-shell electrons)				
Mg	738	1451	7733				
Al	578	1817	2745	11,577			
Si	786	1577	3232	4356	16,091		
P	1012	1907	2914	4964	6274	21,267	
S	1000	2252	3357	4556	7004	8496	27,107
Cl	1251	2298	3822	5159	6542	9362	11,018
Ar	1521	2666	3931	5771	7238	8781	11,995

A second important feature shown in Table 7.2 is the sharp increase in ionization energy that occurs when an inner-shell electron is removed. For example, consider silicon, whose electron configuration is $1s^2 2s^2 2p^6 3s^2 3p^2$ or $[Ne]3s^2 3p^2$. The ionization energies increase steadily from 786 kJ/mol to 4356 kJ/mol for the loss of the four electrons in the outer 3s and 3p subshells. Removal of the fifth electron, which comes from the 2p subshell, requires a great deal more energy: 16,091 kJ/mol. The large increase occurs because the 2p electron is much more likely to be found close to the nucleus than are the four $n = 3$ electrons, and therefore the 2p electron experiences a much greater effective nuclear charge than do the 3s and 3p electrons.

GIVE IT SOME THOUGHT

Which would you expect to be greater, I_1 for a boron atom or I_2 for a carbon atom?

Every element exhibits a large increase in ionization energy when electrons are removed from its noble-gas core. This observation supports the idea that only the outermost electrons, those beyond the noble-gas core, are involved in the sharing and transfer of electrons that give rise to chemical bonding and reactions. The inner electrons are too tightly bound to the nucleus to be lost from the atom or even shared with another atom.

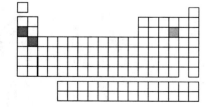

■■ **SAMPLE EXERCISE 7.5** | **Trends in Ionization Energy**

Three elements are indicated in the periodic table in the margin. Based on their locations, predict the one with the largest second ionization energy.

SOLUTION

Analyze and Plan: The locations of the elements in the periodic table allow us to predict the electron configurations. The greatest ionization energies involve removal of core electrons. Thus, we should look first for an element with only one electron in the outermost occupied shell.

Solve: The element in group 1A (Na), indicated by the red box, has only one valence electron. The second ionization energy of this element is associated, therefore, with the removal of a core electron. The other elements indicated, S (green box) and Ca (blue box), have two or more valence electrons. Thus, Na should have the largest second ionization energy.

Check: If we consult a chemistry handbook, we find the following values for the second ionization energies (I_2) of the respective elements: Ca (1,145 kJ/mol) < S (2,252 kJ/mol) < Na (4,562 kJ/mol).

■■■ **PRACTICE EXERCISE**

Which will have the greater third ionization energy, Ca or S?
Answer: Ca

Periodic Trends in First Ionization Energies

We have seen that the ionization energy for a given element increases as we remove successive electrons. What trends do we observe in ionization energy as we move from one element to another in the periodic table? Figure 7.11 ▶ shows a graph of I_1 versus atomic number for the first 54 elements. The important trends are as follows:

1. Within each row (period) of the table, I_1 generally increases with increasing atomic number. The alkali metals show the lowest ionization energy in each row, and the noble gases show the highest. There are slight irregularities in this trend that we will discuss shortly.

2. Within each column (group) of the table, the ionization energy generally decreases with increasing atomic number. For example, the ionization energies of the noble gases follow the order He > Ne > Ar > Kr > Xe.

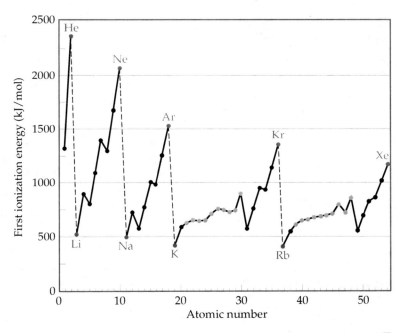

▲ Figure 7.11 **First ionization energy versus atomic number.** The red dots mark the beginning of a period (alkali metals), the blue dots mark the end of a period (noble gases), and the black dots indicate *s*- and *p*-block elements, while green dots are used to represent the transition metals.

3. The *s*- and *p*-block elements show a larger range of values of I_1 than do the transition-metal elements. Generally, the ionization energies of the transition metals increase slowly as we proceed from left to right in a period. The *f*-block metals, which are not shown in Figure 7.11, also show only a small variation in the values of I_1.

The periodic trends in the first ionization energies of the *s*- and *p*-block elements are further illustrated in Figure 7.12 ▼.

In general, smaller atoms have higher ionization energies. The same factors that influence atomic size also influence ionization energies. The energy needed to remove an electron from the outermost occupied shell depends on both the effective nuclear charge and the average distance of the electron from the nucleus. Either increasing the effective nuclear charge or decreasing the distance from the nucleus increases the attraction between the electron and the nucleus.

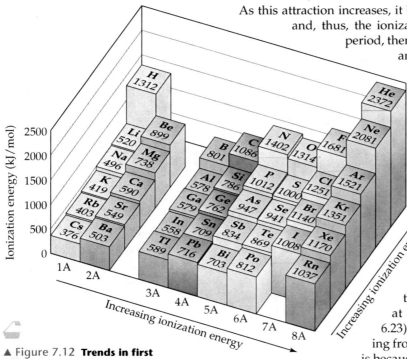

As this attraction increases, it becomes more difficult to remove the electron and, thus, the ionization energy increases. As we move across a period, there is both an increase in effective nuclear charge and a decrease in atomic radius, causing the ionization energy to increase. As we move down a column, however, the atomic radius increases, while the effective nuclear charge increases rather gradually. Thus, the attraction between the nucleus and the electron decreases, causing the ionization energy to decrease.

The irregularities within a given row are somewhat subtler but still readily explained. For example, the decrease in ionization energy from beryllium ($[He]2s^2$) to boron ($[He]2s^22p^1$), shown in Figures 7.11 and 7.12, occurs because the third valence electron of B must occupy the $2p$ subshell, which is empty for Be. Recall that, as we discussed earlier, the $2p$ subshell is at a higher energy than the $2s$ subshell (Figure 6.23). The decrease in ionization energy when moving from nitrogen ($[He]2s^22p^3$) to oxygen ($[He]2s^22p^4$) is because of the repulsion of paired electrons in the p^4 configuration, as shown in Figure 7.13 ◄. Remember that according to Hund's rule, each electron in the p^3 configuration resides in a different p orbital, which minimizes the electron–electron repulsion among the three $2p$ electrons. (Section 6.8)

▲ Figure 7.12 **Trends in first ionization energy.** First ionization energies for the *s*- and *p*-block elements in the first six periods. The ionization energy generally increases from left to right and decreases from top to bottom. The ionization energy of astatine has not been determined.

Oxygen

Nitrogen

▲ Figure 7.13 **2p orbital filling in nitrogen and oxygen.** The presence of a fourth electron in the 2p orbitals of oxygen leads to an extra repulsion associated with putting two electrons in a single orbital. This repulsion is responsible for the lower first ionization energy of oxygen.

■■ SAMPLE EXERCISE 7.6 | Periodic Trends in Ionization Energy

Referring to a periodic table, arrange the following atoms in order of increasing first ionization energy: Ne, Na, P, Ar, K.

SOLUTION

Analyze and Plan: We are given the chemical symbols for five elements. To rank them according to increasing first ionization energy, we need to locate each element in the periodic table. We can then use their relative positions and the trends in first ionization energies to predict their order.

Solve: Ionization energy increases as we move left to right across a row. It decreases as we move from the top of a group to the bottom. Because Na, P, and Ar are in the same row of the periodic table, we expect I_1 to vary in the order Na < P < Ar.

Because Ne is above Ar in group 8A, we expect Ne to have the greater first ionization energy: Ar < Ne. Similarly, K is the alkali metal directly below Na in group 1A, and so we expect I_1 for K to be less than that of Na: K < Na.

From these observations, we conclude that the ionization energies follow the order

K < Na < P < Ar < Ne

Check: The values shown in Figure 7.12 confirm this prediction.

■■ PRACTICE EXERCISE

Which has the lowest first ionization energy, B, Al, C, or Si? Which has the highest first ionization energy?
Answer: Al lowest, C highest

Electron Configurations of Ions

When electrons are removed from an atom to form a cation, they are always removed first from the occupied orbitals having the largest principal quantum number, n. For example, when one electron is removed from a lithium atom $(1s^2 2s^1)$, it is the $2s^1$ electron that is removed:

$$Li\ (1s^2 2s^1) \Rightarrow Li^+\ (1s^2) + e^-$$

Likewise, when two electrons are removed from Fe $([Ar]3d^6 4s^2)$, the $4s^2$ electrons are the ones removed:

$$Fe\ ([Ar]3d^6 4s^2) \Rightarrow Fe^{2+}\ ([Ar]3d^6) + 2e^-$$

If an additional electron is removed, forming Fe^{3+}, it now comes from a $3d$ orbital because all the orbitals with $n = 4$ are empty:

$$Fe^{2+}\ ([Ar]3d^6) \Rightarrow Fe^{3+}\ ([Ar]3d^5) + e^-$$

It may seem odd that the $4s$ electrons are removed before the $3d$ electrons in forming transition-metal cations. After all, in writing electron configurations, we added the $4s$ electrons before the $3d$ ones. In writing electron configurations for atoms, however, we are going through an imaginary process in which we move through the periodic table from one element to another. In doing so, we are adding both an electron to an orbital and a proton to the nucleus to change the identity of the element. In ionization, we do not reverse this process because no protons are being removed.

If there is more than one occupied subshell for a given value of n the electrons are first removed from the orbital with the highest value of l. For example a tin atom loses its $5p$ electrons before it loses its $5s$ electrons:

$$Sn\ ([Kr]4d^{10}5s^2 5p^2) \Rightarrow Sn^{2+}\ ([Kr]4d^{10}5s^2) + 2e^- \Rightarrow Sn^{4+}\ ([Kr]4d^{10}) + 4e^-$$

When electrons are added to an atom to form an anion, they are added to the empty or partially filled orbital having the lowest value of n. For example, when an electron is added to a fluorine atom to form the F^- ion, the electron goes into the one remaining vacancy in the $2p$ subshell:

$$F\ (1s^2 2s^2 2p^5) + e^- \Rightarrow F^-\ (1s^2 2s^2 2p^6)$$

GIVE IT SOME THOUGHT

Would Cr^{3+} and V^{2+} have the same or different electron configurations?

■■ SAMPLE EXERCISE 7.7 | Electron Configurations of Ions

Write the electron configuration for (a) Ca^{2+} (b) Co^{3+}, and (c) S^{2-}.

SOLUTION

Analyze and Plan: We are asked to write electron configurations for three ions. To do so, we first write the electron configuration of the parent atom. We then remove electrons to form cations or add electrons to form anions. Electrons are first removed from the orbitals having the highest value of n. They are added to the empty or partially filled orbitals having the lowest value of n.

Solve:

(a) Calcium (atomic number 20) has the electron configuration

$$Ca:\ [Ar]4s^2$$

To form a 2+ ion, the two outer electrons must be removed, giving an ion that is isoelectronic with Ar:

$$Ca^{2+}:\ [Ar]$$

(b) Cobalt (atomic number 27) has the electron configuration

$$Co:\ [Ar]3d^7 4s^2$$

To form a 3+ ion, three electrons must be removed. As discussed in the text preceding this Sample Exercise, the $4s$ electrons are removed before the $3d$ electrons. Consequently, the electron configuration for Co^{3+} is

$$Co^{3+}:\ [Ar]3d^6$$

(c) Sulfur (atomic number 16) has the electron configuration

$$S: [Ne]3s^2 3p^4$$

To form a 2− ion, two electrons must be added. There is room for two additional electrons in the $3p$ orbitals. Thus, the S^{2-} electron configuration is

$$S^{2-}: [Ne]3s^2 3p^6 = [Ar]$$

Comment: Remember that many of the common ions of the s- and p-block elements, such as Ca^{2+} and S^{2-}, have the same number of electrons as the closest noble gas. (Section 2.7)

■ PRACTICE EXERCISE

Write the electron configuration for **(a)** Ga^{3+}, **(b)** Cr^{3+}, and **(c)** Br^-.
Answers: **(a)** $[Ar]3d^{10}$, **(b)** $[Ar]3d^3$, **(c)** $[Ar]3d^{10}4s^24p^6 = [Kr]$

7.5 ELECTRON AFFINITIES

The first ionization energy of an atom is a measure of the energy change associated with removing an electron from the atom to form a positively charged ion. For example, the first ionization energy of $Cl(g)$, 1251 kJ/mol, is the energy change associated with the process

$$\text{Ionization energy: } Cl(g) \longrightarrow Cl^+(g) + e^- \qquad \Delta E = 1251 \text{ kJ/mol} \qquad [7.5]$$

$$[Ne]3s^23p^5 \qquad [Ne]3s^23p^4$$

The positive value of the ionization energy means that energy must be put into the atom to remove the electron.

In addition, most atoms can gain electrons to form negatively charged ions. The energy change that occurs when an electron is added to a gaseous atom is called the **electron affinity** because it measures the attraction, or *affinity*, of the atom for the added electron. For most atoms, energy is released when an electron is added. For example, the addition of an electron to a chlorine atom is accompanied by an energy change of −349 kJ/mol, the negative sign indicating that energy is released during the process. We therefore say that the electron affinity of Cl is −349 kJ/mol:*

$$\text{Electron affinity: } Cl(g) + e^- \longrightarrow Cl^-(g) \qquad \Delta E = -349 \text{ kJ/mol} \qquad [7.6]$$

$$[Ne]3s^23p^5 \qquad [Ne]3s^23p^6$$

It is important to understand the difference between ionization energy and electron affinity: Ionization energy measures the ease with which an atom *loses* an electron, whereas electron affinity measures the ease with which an atom *gains* an electron.

The greater the attraction between a given atom and an added electron, the more negative the atom's electron affinity will be. For some elements, such as the noble gases, the electron affinity has a positive value, meaning that the anion is higher in energy than are the separated atom and electron:

$$Ar(g) + e^- \longrightarrow Ar^-(g) \qquad \Delta E > 0 \qquad [7.7]$$

$$[Ne]3s^23p^6 \qquad [Ne]3s^23p^64s^1$$

The fact that the electron affinity is a positive number means that an electron will not attach itself to an Ar atom; the Ar^- ion is unstable and does not form.

Two sign conventions are used for electron affinity. In most introductory texts, including this one, the thermodynamic sign convention is used: a negative sign indicates that the addition of an electron is an exothermic process, as in the electron affinity given for chlorine, −349 kJ/mol. Historically, however, electron affinity has been defined as the energy released when an electron is added to a gaseous atom or ion. Because 349 kJ/mol is released when an electron is added to Cl(g), the electron affinity by this convention would be +349 kJ/mol.

Figure 7.14 ▶ shows the electron affinities for the *s*- and *p*-block elements in the first five rows of the periodic table. Notice that the trends in electron affinity as we proceed through the periodic table are not as evident as they were for ionization energy. The halogens, which are one electron shy of a filled *p* subshell, have the most-negative electron affinities. By gaining an electron, a halogen atom forms a stable negative ion that has a noble-gas configuration (Equation 7.6). The addition of an electron to a noble gas, however, requires that the electron reside in a higher-energy subshell that is empty in the neutral atom (Equation 7.7). Because occupying a higher-energy subshell is energetically very unfavorable, the electron affinity is highly positive. The electron affinities of Be and Mg are positive for the same reason; the added electron would reside in a previously empty *p* subshell that is higher in energy.

The electron affinities of the group 5A elements (N, P, As, Sb) are also interesting. Because these elements have half-filled *p* subshells, the added electron must be put in an orbital that is already occupied, resulting in larger electron–electron repulsions. Consequently, these elements have electron affinities that are either positive (N) or less negative than their neighbors to the left (P, As, Sb). Recall that we saw a discontinuity in the regular periodic trends for first ionization energy in Section 7.4 for the same reason.

Electron affinities do not change greatly as we move down a group. For example, consider the electron affinities of the halogens (Figure 7.14). For F, the added electron goes into a 2*p* orbital, for Cl a 3*p* orbital, for Br a 4*p* orbital, and so forth. As we proceed from F to I, therefore, the average distance between the added electron and the nucleus steadily increases, causing the electron-nucleus attraction to decrease. However, the orbital that holds the outermost electron is increasingly spread out, so that as we proceed from F to I, the electron-electron repulsions are also reduced. As a result, the reduction in the electron-nucleus attraction is counterbalanced by the reduction in electron–electron repulsions.

H −73							He >0
Li −60	Be >0	B −27	C −122	N >0	O −141	F −328	Ne >0
Na −53	Mg >0	Al −43	Si −134	P −72	S −200	Cl −349	Ar >0
K −48	Ca −2	Ga −30	Ge −119	As −78	Se −195	Br −325	Kr >0
Rb −47	Sr −5	In −30	Sn −107	Sb −103	Te −190	I −295	Xe >0
1A	2A	3A	4A	5A	6A	7A	8A

▲ Figure 7.14 **Electron affinity.** Electron affinities in kJ/mol for the *s*- and *p*-block elements in the first five rows of the periodic table. The more negative the electron affinity, the greater the attraction of the atom for an electron. An electron affinity > 0 indicates that the negative ion is higher in energy than the separated atom and electron.

GIVE IT SOME THOUGHT

Suppose you were asked for a value for the first ionization energy of a Cl⁻(*g*) ion. What is the relationship between this quantity and the electron affinity of Cl(*g*)?

7.6 METALS, NONMETALS, AND METALLOIDS

Atomic radii, ionization energies, and electron affinities are properties of individual atoms. With the exception of the noble gases, however, none of the elements exists in nature as individual atoms. To get a broader understanding of the properties of elements, we must also examine periodic trends in properties that involve large collections of atoms.

The elements can be broadly grouped into the categories of metals, nonmetals, and metalloids. (Section 2.5) This classification is shown in Figure 7.15 ▶. Roughly three-quarters of the elements are metals, situated in the left and middle portions of the table. The nonmetals are located

▼ Figure 7.15 **Metals, metalloids, and nonmetals.** The majority of elements are metals. Metallic character increases from right to left across a period and also increases from top to bottom in a group.

Increasing metallic character →

Increasing metallic character ↓

1A 1												8A 18
1 H	2A 2							3A 13	4A 14	5A 15	6A 16	7A 17	2 He

(periodic table as shown)

	Metals
	Metalloids
	Nonmetals

| 57 La | 58 Ce | 59 Pr | 60 Nd | 61 Pm | 62 Sm | 63 Eu | 64 Gd | 65 Tb | 66 Dy | 67 Ho | 68 Er | 69 Tm | 70 Yb |
| 89 Ac | 90 Th | 91 Pa | 92 U | 93 Np | 94 Pu | 95 Am | 96 Cm | 97 Bk | 98 Cf | 99 Es | 100 Fm | 101 Md | 102 No |

Metals	Nonmetals
TABLE 7.3 ▪ Characteristic Properties of Metals and Nonmetals	
Have a shiny luster; various colors, although most are silvery	Do not have a luster; various colors
Solids are malleable and ductile	Solids are usually brittle; some are hard, some are soft
Good conductors of heat and electricity	Poor conductors of heat and electricity
Most metal oxides are ionic solids that are basic	Most nonmetal oxides are molecular substances that form acidic solutions
Tend to form cations in aqueous solution	Tend to form anions or oxyanions in aqueous solution

at the top right corner, and the metalloids lie between the metals and nonmetals. Hydrogen, which is located at the top left corner, is a nonmetal. This is why we set off hydrogen from the remaining group 1A elements in Figure 7.15 by inserting a space between the H box and the Li box. Some of the distinguishing properties of metals and nonmetals are summarized in Table 7.3 ▲.

The more an element exhibits the physical and chemical properties of metals, the greater its **metallic character**. As indicated in Figure 7.15, metallic character generally increases as we proceed down a column of the periodic table and increases as we proceed from right to left in a row. Let's now examine the close relationships that exist between electron configurations and the properties of metals, nonmetals, and metalloids.

Metals

▲ Figure 7.16 **The luster of metals.** Metallic objects are readily recognized by their characteristic shiny luster.

Most metallic elements exhibit the shiny luster that we associate with metals (Figure 7.16 ◄). Metals conduct heat and electricity. In general they are malleable (can be pounded into thin sheets) and ductile (can be drawn into wires). All are solids at room temperature except mercury (melting point = −39 °C), which is a liquid. Two metals melt at slightly above room temperature, cesium at 28.4 °C and gallium at 29.8 °C. At the other extreme, many metals melt at very high temperatures. For example, chromium melts at 1900 °C.

Metals tend to have low ionization energies and therefore tend to form positive ions relatively easily. As a result, metals are oxidized (lose electrons) when they undergo chemical reactions. This fact is illustrated in Figure 7.17 ▼, where the first ionization energies of the metals, nonmetals, and metalloids are compared.

Among the fundamental atomic properties (radius, electron configuration, electron affinity, and so forth), the first ionization energy is the best indicator of whether an element will behave as a metal or a nonmetal. The relative ease of oxidation of common metals was discussed earlier, in Section 4.4. As we noted there, many metals are oxidized by a variety of common substances, including O_2 and acids.

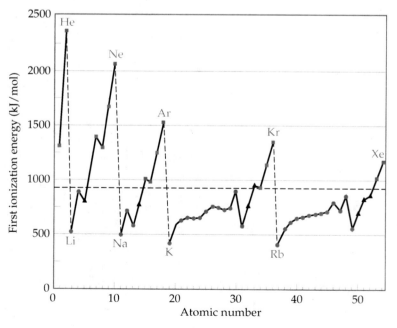

◄ Figure 7.17 **A comparison of the first ionization energies of metals vs. nonmetals.** Values of first ionization energy for metals are markedly lower than those of nonmetals. The red circles correspond to metallic elements, the blue squares to nonmetals, and the black triangles to metalloids. The dashed line at 925 kJ/mol separates the metals from the nonmetals.

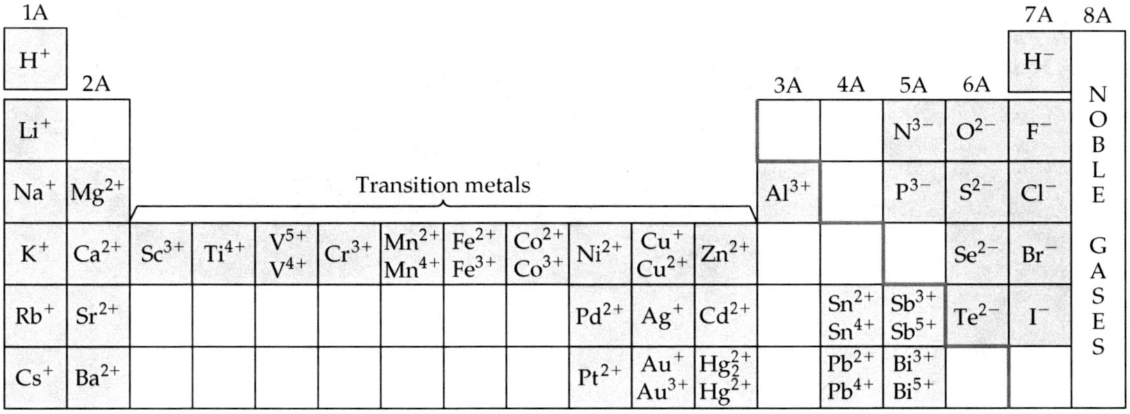

1A	2A											3A	4A	5A	6A	7A	8A
H^+																H^-	N
Li^+														N^{3-}	O^{2-}	F^-	O B
Na^+	Mg^{2+}				Transition metals							Al^{3+}		P^{3-}	S^{2-}	Cl^-	L E
K^+	Ca^{2+}	Sc^{3+}	Ti^{4+}	V^{5+} V^{4+}	Cr^{3+}	Mn^{2+} Mn^{4+}	Fe^{2+} Fe^{3+}	Co^{2+} Co^{3+}	Ni^{2+}	Cu^+ Cu^{2+}	Zn^{2+}				Se^{2-}	Br^-	G A
Rb^+	Sr^{2+}								Pd^{2+}	Ag^+	Cd^{2+}		Sn^{2+} Sn^{4+}	Sb^{3+} Sb^{5+}	Te^{2-}	I^-	S E
Cs^+	Ba^{2+}								Pt^{2+}	Au^+ Au^{3+}	Hg_2^{2+} Hg^{2+}		Pb^{2+} Pb^{4+}	Bi^{3+} Bi^{5+}			S

▲ Figure 7.18 **Representative oxidation states.** Oxidation states found in ionic compounds, including some examples of higher oxidation states adopted by *p*-block metals. Notice that the steplike line that divides metals from nonmetals also separates cations from anions.

Figure 7.18 ▲ shows the oxidation states of some representative ions of both metals and nonmetals. As we noted in Section 2.7, the charge on any alkali metal ion is always 1+, and that on any alkaline earth metal is always 2+ in their compounds. For atoms belonging to either of these groups, the outer *s* electrons are easily lost, yielding a noble-gas electron configuration. For metals belonging to groups with partially occupied *p* orbitals (Groups 3A–7A), the observed cations are formed either by losing only the outer *p* electrons (such as Sn^{2+}) or the outer *s* and *p* electrons (such as Sn^{4+}). The charge on transition-metal ions does not follow an obvious pattern. One of the characteristic features of the transition metals is their ability to form more than one positive ion. For example, iron may be 2+ in some compounds and 3+ in others.

GIVE IT SOME THOUGHT

Based on periodic trends discussed in this chapter, can you see a general relationship between the trends in metallic character and those for ionization energy?

Compounds of metals with nonmetals tend to be ionic substances. For example, most metal oxides and halides are ionic solids. To illustrate, the reaction between nickel metal and oxygen produces nickel oxide, an ionic solid containing Ni^{2+} and O^{2-} ions:

$$2\,Ni(s) + O_2(g) \longrightarrow 2\,NiO(s) \qquad [7.8]$$

The oxides are particularly important because of the great abundance of oxygen in our environment.

Most metal oxides are basic. Those that dissolve in water react to form metal hydroxides, as in the following examples:

$$\text{Metal oxide + water} \longrightarrow \text{metal hydroxide}$$

$$Na_2O(s) + H_2O(l) \longrightarrow 2\,NaOH(aq) \qquad [7.9]$$

$$CaO(s) + H_2O(l) \longrightarrow Ca(OH)_2(aq) \qquad [7.10]$$

The basicity of metal oxides is due to the oxide ion, which reacts with water according to the net ionic equation

$$O^{2-}(aq) + H_2O(l) \longrightarrow 2\,OH^-(aq) \qquad [7.11]$$

▶ Figure 7.19 **Metal oxides react with acids.** (a) Nickel oxide (NiO), nitric acid (HNO_3), and water. (b) NiO is insoluble in water, but reacts with HNO_3 to give a green solution of the salt $Ni(NO_3)_2$.

NiO

(a)   (b)

Metal oxides also demonstrate their basicity by reacting with acids to form a salt plus water, as illustrated in Figure 7.19 ▲:

$$\text{Metal oxide} + \text{acid} \longrightarrow \text{salt} + \text{water}$$

$$NiO(s) + 2\,HNO_3(aq) \longrightarrow Ni(NO_3)_2(aq) + H_2O(l) \qquad [7.12]$$

In contrast, we will soon see that nonmetal oxides are acidic, dissolving in water to form acidic solutions and reacting with bases to form salts.

■ **SAMPLE EXERCISE 7.8** | Metal Oxides

(a) Would you expect scandium oxide to be a solid, liquid, or gas at room temperature? **(b)** Write the balanced chemical equation for the reaction of scandium oxide with nitric acid.

SOLUTION

Analyze and Plan: We are asked about one physical property of scandium oxide—its state at room temperature—and one chemical property—how it reacts with nitric acid.

Solve:

(a) Because scandium oxide is the oxide of a metal, we would expect it to be an ionic solid. Indeed it is, with the very high melting point of 2485 °C.
(b) In its compounds, scandium has a 3+ charge, Sc^{3+}; the oxide ion is O^{2-}. Consequently, the formula of scandium oxide is Sc_2O_3. Metal oxides tend to be basic and therefore to react with acids to form a salt plus water. In this case the salt is scandium nitrate, $Sc(NO_3)_3$. The balanced chemical equation is

$$Sc_2O_3(s) + 6\,HNO_3(aq) \longrightarrow 2\,Sc(NO_3)_3(aq) + 3\,H_2O(l)$$

■ **PRACTICE EXERCISE**

Write the balanced chemical equation for the reaction between copper(II) oxide and sulfuric acid.
Answer: $CuO(s) + H_2SO_4(aq) \longrightarrow CuSO_4(aq) + H_2O(l)$

▼ Figure 7.20 **The diversity of nonmetals.** Nonmetallic elements are diverse in their appearances. Shown here are (clockwise from top left) sulfur, bromine, phosphorus, iodine, and carbon.

Nonmetals

Nonmetals vary greatly in appearance (Figure 7.20 ◀). They are not lustrous and generally are poor conductors of heat and electricity. Their melting points are generally lower than those of metals (although diamond, a form of carbon, melts at 3570 °C). Under ordinary conditions, seven nonmetals exist as diatomic molecules. Five of these are gases (H_2, N_2, O_2, F_2, and Cl_2), one is a liquid (Br_2), and one is a volatile solid (I_2). Excluding the noble gases, the remaining nonmetals are solids that can be either hard, such as diamond, or soft, such as sulfur.

Science Fundamentals

Because of their electron affinities, nonmetals tend to gain electrons when they react with metals. For example, the reaction of aluminum with bromine produces aluminum bromide, an ionic compound containing the aluminum ion, Al^{3+}, and the bromide ion, Br^-:

$$2\ Al(s) + 3\ Br_2(l) \longrightarrow 2\ AlBr_3(s) \qquad\qquad [7.13]$$

A nonmetal typically will gain enough electrons to fill its outermost occupied *p* subshell, giving a noble-gas electron configuration. For example, the bromine atom gains one electron to fill its 4*p* subshell:

$$Br\ ([Ar]4s^23d^{10}4p^5) + e^- \Rightarrow Br^-\ ([Ar]4s^23d^{10}4p^6)$$

Compounds composed entirely of nonmetals are typically molecular substances. For example, the oxides, halides, and hydrides of the nonmetals are molecular substances that tend to be gases, liquids, or low-melting solids at room temperature.

Most nonmetal oxides are acidic; those that dissolve in water react to form acids, as in the following examples:

$$Nonmetal\ oxide + water \longrightarrow acid$$

$$CO_2(g) + H_2O(l) \longrightarrow H_2CO_3(aq) \qquad\qquad [7.14]$$

$$P_4O_{10}(s) + 6\ H_2O(l) \longrightarrow 4\ H_3PO_4(aq) \qquad\qquad [7.15]$$

The reaction of carbon dioxide with water (Figure 7.21 ▼) accounts for the acidity of carbonated water and, to some extent, rainwater. Because sulfur is present in oil and coal, combustion of these common fuels produces sulfur dioxide and sulfur trioxide. These substances dissolve in water to produce *acid rain*, a major pollution problem in many parts of the world. Like acids, most nonmetal oxides dissolve in basic solutions to form a salt plus water:

$$Nonmetal\ oxide + base \longrightarrow salt + water$$

$$CO_2(g) + 2\ NaOH(aq) \longrightarrow Na_2CO_3(aq) + H_2O(l) \qquad\qquad [7.16]$$

GIVE IT SOME THOUGHT

A compound ACl_3 (A is an element) has a melting point of −112 °C. Would you expect the compound to be a molecular or ionic substance? If you were told that element A was either scandium (Sc) or phosphorus (P), which do you think would be a more likely choice?

(a)

(b)

◀ Figure 7.21 **The reaction of CO_2 with water.** (a) The water has been made slightly basic and contains a few drops of bromthymol blue, an acid–base indicator that is blue in basic solution. (b) Upon the addition of a piece of solid carbon dioxide, $CO_2(s)$, the color changes to yellow, indicating an acidic solution. The mist is due to water droplets condensed from the air by the cold CO_2 gas.

SAMPLE EXERCISE 7.9 | Nonmetal Oxides

Write the balanced chemical equations for the reactions of solid selenium dioxide with **(a)** water, **(b)** aqueous sodium hydroxide.

SOLUTION

Analyze and Plan: We first note that selenium (Se) is a nonmetal. We therefore need to write chemical equations for the reaction of a nonmetal oxide, first with water and then with a base, NaOH. Nonmetal oxides are acidic, reacting with water to form an acid and with bases to form a salt and water.

Solve:

(a) Selenium dioxide is SeO_2. Its reaction with water is like that of carbon dioxide (Equation 7.14):

$$SeO_2(s) + H_2O(l) \longrightarrow H_2SeO_3(aq)$$

(It does not matter that SeO_2 is a solid and CO_2 is a gas under ambient conditions; the point is that both are water-soluble nonmetal oxides.)

(b) The reaction with sodium hydroxide is like the reaction summarized by Equation 7.16:

$$SeO_2(s) + 2\,NaOH(aq) \longrightarrow Na_2SeO_3(aq) + H_2O(l)$$

PRACTICE EXERCISE

Write the balanced chemical equation for the reaction of solid tetraphosphorus hexoxide with water.
Answer: $P_4O_6(s) + 6\,H_2O(l) \longrightarrow 4\,H_3PO_3(aq)$

Metalloids

Metalloids have properties intermediate between those of metals and those of nonmetals. They may have *some* characteristic metallic properties but lack others. For example, silicon *looks* like a metal (Figure 7.22 ◄), but it is brittle rather than malleable and is a much poorer conductor of heat and electricity than are metals. Compounds of metalloids can have characteristics of the compounds of metals or nonmetals, depending on the specific compound.

Several of the metalloids, most notably silicon, are electrical semiconductors and are the principal elements used in the manufacture of integrated circuits and computer chips. One of the reasons metalloids such as silicon can be used for integrated circuits is the fact that their electrical conductivity is intermediate between that of metals and nonmetals. Very pure silicon is an electrical insulator, but its conductivity can be dramatically increased with the addition of specific impurities (dopants). This modification provides a mechanism for controlling the electrical conductivity by controlling the chemical composition. We will return to this point in Chapter 12.

7.7 GROUP TRENDS FOR THE ACTIVE METALS

Our discussion of atomic radius, ionization energy, electron affinity, and metallic character gives some idea of the way the periodic table can be used to organize and remember facts. As we have seen, elements in a group possess general similarities. However, trends also exist as we move through a group. In this section we will use the periodic table and our knowledge of electron configurations to examine the chemistry of the **alkali metals** (group 1A) and the **alkaline earth metals** (group 2A).

Group 1A: The Alkali Metals

The alkali metals are soft metallic solids (Figure 7.23 ◄). All have characteristic metallic properties such as a silvery, metallic luster and high thermal and electrical conductivities. The name *alkali* comes from an Arabic word meaning "ashes." Many compounds of sodium and potassium, two alkali metals, were isolated from wood ashes by early chemists.

▲ Figure 7.22 **Elemental silicon.** Silicon is an example of a metalloid. Although it looks metallic, silicon is brittle and is a poor thermal and electrical conductor as compared to metals. Large crystals of silicon are sliced into thin wafers for use in integrated circuits.

▼ Figure 7.23 **Alkali metals.** Sodium and the other alkali metals are soft enough to be cut with a knife. The shiny metallic surface quickly tarnishes as the metal reacts with oxygen in the air.

TABLE 7.4 ■ Some Properties of the Alkali Metals

Element	Electron Configuration	Melting Point (°C)	Density (g/cm³)	Atomic Radius (Å)	I_1 (kJ/mol)
Lithium	$[He]2s^1$	181	0.53	1.34	520
Sodium	$[Ne]3s^1$	98	0.97	1.54	496
Potassium	$[Ar]4s^1$	63	0.86	1.96	419
Rubidium	$[Kr]5s^1$	39	1.53	2.11	403
Cesium	$[Xe]6s^1$	28	1.88	2.25	376

Sodium and potassium are relatively abundant in Earth's crust, in seawater, and in biological systems. We all have sodium ions in our bodies. However, ingesting too much sodium can raise our blood pressure. Potassium is also prevalent in our bodies; a 140-pound person contains about 130 g of potassium, as K^+ ions in intracellular fluids. Plants require potassium for growth and development (Figure 7.24 ▶).

Some of the physical and chemical properties of the alkali metals are given in Table 7.4 ▲. The elements have low densities and melting points, and these properties vary in a fairly regular way with increasing atomic number. We can also see some of the usual trends as we move down the group, such as increasing atomic radius and decreasing first ionization energy. For each row of the periodic table, the alkali metal has the lowest I_1 value (Figure 7.11), which reflects the relative ease with which its outer s electron can be removed. As a result, the alkali metals are all very reactive, readily losing one electron to form ions carrying a 1+ charge. (Section 4.4)

The alkali metals exist in nature only as compounds. The metals combine directly with most nonmetals. For example, they react with hydrogen to form hydrides and with sulfur to form sulfides:

$$2\,M(s) + H_2(g) \longrightarrow 2\,MH(s) \qquad [7.17]$$

$$2\,M(s) + S(s) \longrightarrow M_2S(s) \qquad [7.18]$$

(The symbol M in Equations 7.17 and 7.18 represents any one of the alkali metals.) In hydrides of the alkali metals (LiH, NaH, and so forth), hydrogen is present as H^-, called the **hydride ion**. The hydride ion, which is a hydrogen atom that has *gained* an electron, is distinct from the hydrogen ion, H^+, formed when a hydrogen atom *loses* its electron.

The alkali metals react vigorously with water, producing hydrogen gas and a solution of an alkali metal hydroxide:

$$2\,M(s) + 2\,H_2O(l) \longrightarrow 2\,MOH(aq) + H_2(g) \qquad [7.19]$$

These reactions are very exothermic. In many cases enough heat is generated to ignite the H_2, producing a fire or sometimes even an explosion (Figure 7.25 ▼).

▲ Figure 7.24 **Elements in fertilizers.** Fertilizers contain large quantities of potassium, phosphorus, and nitrogen to meet the needs of growing plants.

(a)   (b)   (c)

◀ Figure 7.25 **The alkali metals react vigorously with water.** (a) The reaction of lithium is evidenced by the bubbling of escaping hydrogen gas. (b) The reaction of sodium is more rapid and is so exothermic that the hydrogen gas produced burns in air. (c) Potassium reacts almost explosively.

▶ Figure 7.26 **Flame tests.** (a) Li (crimson red), (b) Na (yellow), and (c) K (lilac).

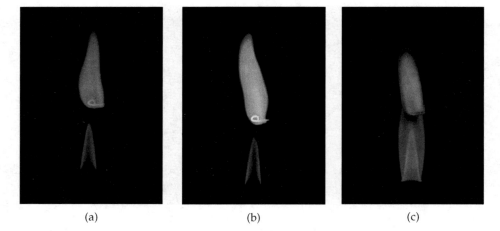

(a)   (b)   (c)

This reaction is most violent for the heavier members of the group, in keeping with their weaker hold on the single valence electron.

The reactions between the alkali metals and oxygen are more complex. When oxygen reacts with metals, metal oxides, which contain the O^{2-} ion, are usually formed. Indeed, lithium shows this reactivity:

$$4\,Li(s) + O_2(g) \longrightarrow \underset{\text{lithium oxide}}{2\,Li_2O(s)} \qquad [7.20]$$

When dissolved in water, Li_2O and other soluble metal oxides react with water to form hydroxide ions from the reaction of O^{2-} ions with H_2O (Equation 7.11).

In contrast, the other alkali metals all react with oxygen to form metal *peroxides*, which contain the O_2^{2-} ion. For example, sodium forms sodium peroxide, Na_2O_2.

$$2\,Na(s) + O_2(g) \longrightarrow \underset{\text{sodium peroxide}}{Na_2O_2(s)} \qquad [7.21]$$

Potassium, rubidium, and cesium also form compounds that contain the O_2^- ion, which we call the *superoxide ion*. For example, potassium forms potassium superoxide, KO_2:

$$K(s) + O_2(g) \longrightarrow \underset{\text{potassium superoxide}}{KO_2(s)} \qquad [7.22]$$

You should be aware that the reactions shown in Equations 7.21 and 7.22 are somewhat surprising; in most cases, the reaction of oxygen with a metal forms the metal oxide.

As is evident from Equations 7.19 through 7.22, the alkali metals are extremely reactive toward water and oxygen. Because of this, the metals are usually stored submerged in a liquid hydrocarbon, such as mineral oil or kerosene.

Although alkali metal ions are colorless, each emits a characteristic color when placed in a flame (Figure 7.26▲). The ions are reduced to gaseous metal atoms in the central region of the flame. The high temperature of the flame then excites the valence electron to a higher-energy orbital, causing the atom to be in an excited state. The atom then emits energy in the form of visible light as the electron falls back into the lower-energy orbital and the atom returns to its ground state. Sodium, for instance, gives a yellow flame because of emission at 589 nm. This wavelength is produced when the excited valence electron drops from the $3p$ subshell to the lower-energy $3s$ subshell. The characteristic yellow emission of sodium is the basis for sodium vapor lamps (Figure 7.27 ◀).

▲ Figure 7.27 **Light from sodium.** Sodium vapor lamps, which are used for commercial and highway lighting, have a yellow glow because of the emission from excited sodium atoms.

GIVE IT SOME THOUGHT

Cesium metal tends to be the most reactive of the stable alkali metals (francium, element number 87, is radioactive and has not been extensively studied). What *atomic* property of Cs is most responsible for its high reactivity?

■ SAMPLE EXERCISE 7.10 | Reactions of an Alkali Metal

Write a balanced equation that predicts the reaction of cesium metal with (a) $Cl_2(g)$, (b) $H_2O(l)$, (c) $H_2(g)$.

SOLUTION

Analyze and Plan: Cesium is an alkali metal (atomic number 55). We therefore expect that its chemistry will be dominated by oxidation of the metal to Cs^+ ions. Further, we recognize that Cs is far down the periodic table, which means it will be among the most active of all metals and will probably react with all three of the substances listed.

Solve: The reaction between Cs and Cl_2 is a simple combination reaction between two elements, one a metal and the other a nonmetal, forming the ionic compound CsCl:

$$2\,Cs(s) + Cl_2(g) \longrightarrow 2\,CsCl(s)$$

By analogy to Equations 7.19 and 7.17, respectively, we predict the reactions of cesium with water and hydrogen to proceed as follows:

$$2\,Cs(s) + 2\,H_2O(l) \longrightarrow 2\,CsOH(aq) + H_2(g)$$
$$2\,Cs(s) + H_2(g) \longrightarrow 2\,CsH(s)$$

All three of these reactions are redox reactions where cesium forms a Cs^+ ion in the product. The chloride (Cl^-), hydroxide (OH^-), and hydride (H^-) ions are all 1− ions, which means the final products have 1:1 stoichiometry with Cs^+.

■ PRACTICE EXERCISE

Write a balanced equation for the reaction between potassium metal and elemental sulfur.
Answer: $2\,K(s) + S(s) \longrightarrow K_2S(s)$

Group 2A: The Alkaline Earth Metals

Like the alkali metals, the group 2A elements are all solids at room temperature and have typical metallic properties, some of which are listed in Table 7.5 ▼. Compared with the alkali metals, the alkaline earth metals are harder and more dense, and they melt at higher temperatures.

The first ionization energies of the alkaline earth elements are low, but they are not as low as those of the alkali metals. Consequently, the alkaline earth metals are less reactive than their alkali metal neighbors. As we noted in Section 7.4, the ease with which the elements lose electrons decreases as we move across the periodic table from left to right and increases as we move down a group. Thus, beryllium and magnesium, the lightest members of the alkaline earth metals, are the least reactive.

The trend of increasing reactivity within the group is shown by the way the alkaline earth metals behave in the presence of water. Beryllium does not react with water or steam, even when heated red-hot. Magnesium reacts slowly with liquid water and more readily with steam to form magnesium oxide and hydrogen:

$$Mg(s) + H_2O(g) \longrightarrow MgO(s) + H_2(g) \qquad [7.23]$$

Calcium and the elements below it react readily with water at room temperature (although more slowly than the alkali metals adjacent to them in the

Element	Electron Configuration	Melting Point (°C)	Density (g/cm³)	Atomic Radius (Å)	I_1 (kJ/mol)
Beryllium	$[He]2s^2$	1287	1.85	0.90	899
Magnesium	$[Ne]3s^2$	650	1.74	1.30	738
Calcium	$[Ar]4s^2$	842	1.55	1.74	590
Strontium	$[Kr]5s^2$	777	2.63	1.92	549
Barium	$[Xe]6s^2$	727	3.51	1.98	503

TABLE 7.5 ■ Some Properties of the Alkaline Earth Metals

Chemistry and Life   THE IMPROBABLE DEVELOPMENT OF LITHIUM DRUGS

The alkali metal ions tend to play a rather unexciting role in most chemical reactions in general chemistry. As noted in Section 4.2, all salts of the alkali metal ions are soluble, and the ions are spectators in most aqueous reactions (except for those involving the alkali metals in their elemental form, such as in Equations 7.17 through 7.22). However, the alkali metal ions play an important role in human physiology. Sodium and potassium ions, for example, are major components of blood plasma and intracellular fluid, respectively, with average concentrations of 0.1 M. These electrolytes serve as vital charge carriers in normal cellular function. We will see in Chapter 20 that these ions are also two of the principal ions involved in regulation of the heart.

In contrast, the lithium ion (Li^+) has no known function in normal human physiology. Since the discovery of lithium in 1817, however, people thought salts of the element possessed almost mystical healing powers. There were even claims that lithium ions were an ingredient in ancient "fountain of youth" formulas. In 1927, Mr. C. L. Grigg began marketing a soft drink that contained lithium. The original unwieldy name of the beverage was "Bib-Label Lithiated Lemon-Lime Soda," which was soon changed to the simpler and more familiar name Seven Up® (Figure 7.28 ▶).

Because of concerns of the Food and Drug Administration, lithium was removed from Seven Up® during the early 1950s. At nearly the same time, psychiatrists discovered that the lithium ion has a remarkable therapeutic effect on the mental disorder called *bipolar affective disorder*, or *manic-depressive illness*. Over 1 million Americans suffer from this psychosis, undergoing severe mood swings from deep depression to a manic euphoria. The lithium ion smooths these mood swings, allowing the bipolar patient to function more effectively in daily life.

The antipsychotic action of Li^+ was discovered by accident during the late 1940s by Australian psychiatrist John Cade as he was researching the use of uric acid—a component of urine—to treat manic-depressive illness. He administered the acid to manic laboratory animals in the form of its most soluble salt, lithium urate, and found that many of the manic symptoms seemed to disappear. Later studies showed that uric acid has no role in the therapeutic effects observed; rather, the seemingly innocuous Li^+ ions were responsible. Because lithium overdose can cause severe side effects in humans, including kidney failure and death, lithium salts were not approved as antipsychotic drugs for humans until 1970. Today Li^+ is usually administered orally in the form of Li_2CO_3, which is the active ingredient in prescription drugs such as Eskalith®. Lithium drugs are effective for about 70% of the bipolar patients who take it.

In this age of sophisticated drug design and biotechnology, the simple lithium ion is still the most effective treatment of this destructive psychological disorder. Remarkably, in spite of intensive research, scientists still do not fully understand the biochemical action of lithium that leads to its therapeutic effects. Because of its similarity to the Na^+ ion, the Li^+ ion is incorporated into blood plasma, where it can affect the behavior of both nerve cells and muscle cells. The Li^+ ion has a smaller radius than the Na^+ ion (Figure 7.8), so its interaction with molecules in cells is somewhat different. Other studies indicate that Li^+ alters the function of certain neurotransmitters, which might lead to its effectiveness as an antipsychotic drug.

▲ Figure 7.28 **Lithium no more.** The soft drink Seven Up® originally contained lithium citrate, the lithium salt of citric acid. The lithium was claimed to give the beverage healthful benefits, including "an abundance of energy, enthusiasm, a clear complexion, lustrous hair, and shining eyes!" The lithium was removed from the beverage in the early 1950s, about the same time that the antipsychotic action of Li^+ was discovered.

▲ Figure 7.29 **Elemental calcium solution.** Calcium metal reacts with water to form hydrogen gas and aqueous calcium hydroxide, $Ca(OH)_2(aq)$.

periodic table), as shown in Figure 7.29 ◀. The reaction between calcium and water, for example, is

$$Ca(s) + 2\,H_2O(l) \longrightarrow Ca(OH)_2(aq) + H_2(g) \qquad [7.24]$$

The reactions represented in Equations 7.23 and 7.24 illustrate the dominant pattern in the reactivity of the alkaline earth elements: they tend to lose their two outer s electrons and form 2+ ions. For example, magnesium reacts with chlorine at room temperature to form $MgCl_2$ and burns with dazzling brilliance in air to give MgO (Figure 3.5):

$$Mg(s) + Cl_2(g) \longrightarrow MgCl_2(s) \qquad [7.25]$$

$$2\,Mg(s) + O_2(g) \longrightarrow 2\,MgO(s) \qquad [7.26]$$

In the presence of O_2, magnesium metal is protected from many chemicals by a thin surface coating of water-insoluble MgO. Thus, even though Mg is high in the activity series ⟶ (Section 4.4), it can be incorporated into lightweight structural alloys used in, for example, automobile wheels. The heavier alkaline earth metals (Ca, Sr, and Ba) are even more reactive toward nonmetals than is magnesium.

The heavier alkaline earth ions give off characteristic colors when strongly heated in a flame. The colored flame produced by calcium is brick red, that of strontium is crimson red, and that of barium is green. Strontium salts produce the brilliant red color in fireworks, and barium salts produce the green color (Figure 7.30 ▶).

Both magnesium and calcium are essential for living organisms (Figure 2.24). Calcium is particularly important for growth and maintenance of bones and teeth (Figure 7.31 ▶). In humans 99% of the calcium is found in the skeletal system.

◀ Figure 7.30 **Fireworks display.** The colors in a fireworks display originate from the characteristic emissions of elements, including the alkaline earths. In this display the crimson color comes from strontium, while the green color comes from barium.

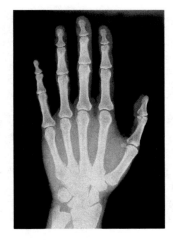

▲ Figure 7.31 **Calcium in the body.** This X-ray photograph shows the bone structure of the human hand. The primary mineral in bone and teeth is hydroxyapatite, $Ca_5(PO_4)_3OH$, in which calcium is present as Ca^{2+}.

GIVE IT SOME THOUGHT

Calcium carbonate, $CaCO_3$, is often used as a dietary calcium supplement for bone health. Although $CaCO_3(s)$ is insoluble in water (Table 4.1), it can be taken orally to allow for the delivery of $Ca^{2+}(aq)$ ions to the musculoskeletal system. Why is this the case? [*Hint:* Recall the reactions of metal carbonates that were discussed in Section 4.3.]

7.8 GROUP TRENDS FOR SELECTED NONMETALS

Hydrogen

Hydrogen, the first element in the periodic table, has a $1s^1$ electron configuration, and for this reason its usual position in the table is above the alkali metals. However, hydrogen does not truly belong to any particular group. Unlike the alkali metals, hydrogen is a nonmetal that occurs as a colorless diatomic gas, $H_2(g)$, under most conditions. Nevertheless, hydrogen can be metallic under tremendous pressures. The interiors of the planets Jupiter and Saturn, for example, are believed to consist of a dense core of rock and ice surrounded by a thick shell of metallic hydrogen. The metallic hydrogen is in turn surrounded by a layer of liquid molecular hydrogen that gradually transforms to a mixture of gaseous hydrogen and helium upon moving closer to the surface. The Cassini–Huygens satellite mission, launched in 1997, has provided a wealth of new information regarding Saturn and its largest moon, Titan, including their chemical compositions. The spacecraft successfully entered orbit around Saturn in June 2004, and in January 2005 the Huygens probe descended through Titan's atmosphere (Figure 7.32 ▶).

Owing to the complete absence of nuclear shielding of its sole electron, the ionization energy of hydrogen, 1312 kJ/mol, is more than double that of any of the alkali metals (Figure 7.11). In fact, hydrogen's ionization energy is comparable to the I_1 values of other nonmetals, such as oxygen and chlorine. As a result, hydrogen does not lose its valence electron as easily as do the alkali metals. Whereas the alkali metals readily lose their valence electron to nonmetals to form ionic compounds, hydrogen shares its electron with nonmetals and thereby forms molecular compounds. The reactions between hydrogen and nonmetals can be quite exothermic, as evidenced by the combustion reaction between hydrogen and oxygen to form water (Figure 5.13):

$$2 H_2(g) + O_2(g) \longrightarrow 2 H_2O(l) \qquad \Delta H° = -571.7 \text{ kJ} \qquad [7.27]$$

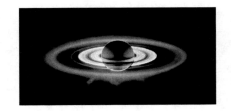

▲ Figure 7.32 **Exploring Saturn.** This panoramic view of Saturn was taken from the Cassini spacecraft. From this perspective Saturn shelters the spacecraft from the Sun's blinding glare.

We have also seen (Equation 7.17) that hydrogen reacts with active metals to form solid metal hydrides that contain the hydride ion, H^-. The fact that hydrogen can gain an electron further illustrates that it is not truly a member of the alkali metal family. In fact, in terms of chemical reactivity, hydrogen has more in common with the halogens (Group 7A) than with the alkali metals.

In addition to its ability to form covalent bonds and metal hydrides, probably the most important characteristic of hydrogen is its ability to lose its electron to form a cation. Indeed, the aqueous chemistry of hydrogen is dominated by the $H^+(aq)$ ion, which we first encountered in Chapter 4. (Section 4.1) We will study this important ion in greater detail in Chapter 16.

Group 6A: The Oxygen Group

As we proceed down group 6A, there is a change from nonmetallic to metallic character (Figure 7.15). Oxygen, sulfur, and selenium are typical nonmetals. Tellurium has some metallic properties and is classified as a metalloid. Polonium, which is radioactive and quite rare, is a metal.

Oxygen is a colorless gas at room temperature; all of the other members of group 6A are solids. Some of the physical properties of the group 6A elements are given in Table 7.6 ▼.

As we saw in Section 2.6, oxygen is encountered in two molecular forms, O_2 and O_3. The O_2 form is the more common one. People generally mean O_2 when they say "oxygen," although the name *dioxygen* is more descriptive. The O_3 form is called **ozone**. The two forms of oxygen are examples of *allotropes*. Allotropes are different forms of the same element in the same state. (In this case both forms are gases.) About 21% of dry air consists of O_2 molecules. Ozone is present in very small amounts in the upper atmosphere and in polluted air. It is also formed from O_2 in electrical discharges, such as in lightning storms:

$$3\,O_2(g) \longrightarrow 2\,O_3(g) \qquad \Delta H^\circ = 284.6\ \text{kJ} \qquad [7.28]$$

This reaction is strongly endothermic, telling us that O_3 is less stable than O_2.

It is interesting to consider the differences in physical and chemical properties of the allotropes of oxygen. Although both O_2 and O_3 are colorless and therefore do not absorb visible light, O_3 absorbs certain wavelengths of ultraviolet light that O_2 does not. Because of this difference, the presence of ozone in the upper atmosphere is beneficial, filtering out harmful UV light (Section 18.3). Ozone and dioxygen also have different chemical properties. Ozone, which has a pungent odor, is a powerful oxidizing agent. Because of this property ozone is sometimes added to water to kill bacteria or used in low levels to help to purify air. However, the reactivity of ozone also makes its presence in polluted air near Earth's surface detrimental to human health.

Oxygen has a great tendency to attract electrons from other elements (to *oxidize* them). Oxygen in combination with a metal is almost always present as the oxide ion, O^{2-}. This ion has a noble-gas configuration and is particularly stable. As shown in Equation 7.27, the formation of nonmetal oxides is also often very exothermic and thus energetically favorable.

TABLE 7.6 ■ Some Properties of the Group 6A Elements

Element	Electron Configuration	Melting Point (°C)	Density	Atomic Radius (Å)	I_1 (kJ/mol)
Oxygen	$[\text{He}]2s^2 2p^4$	−218	1.43 g/L	0.73	1314
Sulfur	$[\text{Ne}]3s^2 3p^4$	115	1.96 g/cm^3	1.02	1000
Selenium	$[\text{Ar}]3d^{10}\,4s^2\,4p^4$	221	4.82 g/cm^3	1.16	941
Tellurium	$[\text{Kr}]4d^{10}\,5s^2\,5p^4$	450	6.24 g/cm^3	1.35	869
Polonium	$[\text{Xe}]4f^{14}\,5d^{10}\,6s^2\,6p^4$	254	9.20 g/cm^3	—	812

In our discussion of the alkali metals, we noted two less common oxygen anions—the peroxide (O_2^{2-}) ion and the superoxide (O_2^-) ion. Compounds of these ions often react with themselves to produce an oxide and O_2. For example, aqueous hydrogen peroxide, H_2O_2, slowly decomposes into water and O_2 at room temperature:

$$2\,H_2O_2(aq) \longrightarrow 2\,H_2O(l) + O_2(g) \qquad \Delta H^\circ = -196.1\ \text{kJ} \qquad [7.29]$$

For this reason, bottles of aqueous hydrogen peroxide are topped with caps that are able to release the $O_2(g)$ produced before the pressure inside becomes too great (Figure 7.33▶).

After oxygen, the most important member of group 6A is sulfur. This element also exists in several allotropic forms, the most common and stable of which is the yellow solid having the molecular formula S_8. This molecule consists of an eight-membered ring of sulfur atoms, as shown in Figure 7.34▼. Even though solid sulfur consists of S_8 rings, we usually write it simply as $S(s)$ in chemical equations to simplify the stoichiometric coefficients.

Like oxygen, sulfur has a tendency to gain electrons from other elements to form sulfides, which contain the S^{2-} ion. In fact, most sulfur in nature is present as metal sulfides. Sulfur is below oxygen in the periodic table, and the tendency of sulfur to form sulfide anions is not as great as that of oxygen to form oxide ions. As a result, the chemistry of sulfur is more complex than that of oxygen. In fact, sulfur and its compounds (including those in coal and petroleum) can be burned in oxygen. The main product is sulfur dioxide, a major pollutant:

$$S(s) + O_2(g) \longrightarrow SO_2(g) \qquad [7.30]$$

We will discuss the environmental aspects of sulfur oxide chemistry in greater depth in Chapter 18.

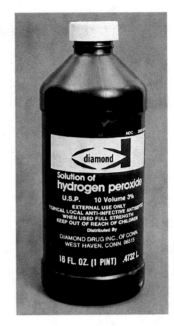

▲ Figure 7.33 **Hydrogen peroxide solution.** Bottles of this common antiseptic are topped with a cap that allows any excess pressure created by $O_2(g)$ to be released from the bottle. Hydrogen peroxide is often stored in dark-colored or opaque bottles to minimize exposure to light, which accelerates its decomposition.

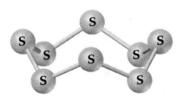

◀ Figure 7.34 **Elemental sulfur.** At room temperature, the most common allotropic form of sulfur is an eight-member ring, S_8.

Group 7A: The Halogens

The group 7A elements are known as the **halogens**, after the Greek words *halos* and *gennao*, meaning "salt formers." Some of the properties of these elements are given in Table 7.7▼. Astatine, which is both extremely rare and radioactive, is omitted because many of its properties are not yet known.

Unlike the group 6A elements, all the halogens are typical nonmetals. Their melting and boiling points increase with increasing atomic number. Fluorine and chlorine are gases at room temperature, bromine is a liquid, and iodine is a solid. Each element consists of diatomic molecules: F_2, Cl_2, Br_2, and I_2. Fluorine gas is pale yellow; chlorine gas is yellow-green; bromine liquid is reddish

TABLE 7.7 ■ Some Properties of the Halogens					
Element	Electron Configuration	Melting Point (°C)	Density	Atomic Radius (Å)	I_1 (kJ/mol)
Fluorine	$[He]2s^2 2p^5$	−220	1.69 g/L	0.71	1681
Chlorine	$[Ne]3s^2 3p^5$	−102	3.12 g/L	0.99	1251
Bromine	$[Ar]3d^{10}4s^2 4p^5$	−7.3	3.12 g/cm³	1.14	1140
Iodine	$[Kr]4d^{10}5s^2 5p^5$	114	4.94 g/cm³	1.33	1008

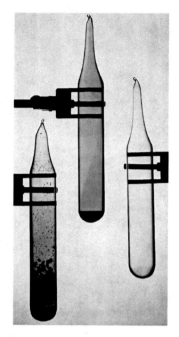

▲ Figure 7.35 **Elemental halogens.**
All three of these elements—from left to
right, iodine (I_2), bromine (Br_2), and
chlorine (Cl_2)—exist as diatomic
molecules.

brown and readily forms a reddish brown vapor; and solid iodine is grayish black and readily forms a violet vapor (Figure 7.35 ◄).

The halogens have highly negative electron affinities (Figure 7.14). Thus, it is not surprising that the chemistry of the halogens is dominated by their tendency to gain electrons from other elements to form halide ions, X^-. (In many equations X is used to indicate any one of the halogen elements.) Fluorine and chlorine are more reactive than bromine and iodine. In fact, fluorine removes electrons from almost any substance with which it comes into contact, including water, and usually does so very exothermically, as in the following examples:

$$2\ H_2O(l) + 2\ F_2(g) \longrightarrow 4\ HF(aq) + O_2(g) \qquad \Delta H = -758.9\ kJ \quad [7.31]$$
$$SiO_2(s) + 2\ F_2(g) \longrightarrow SiF_4(g) + O_2(g) \qquad \Delta H = -704.0\ kJ \quad [7.32]$$

As a result, fluorine gas is difficult and dangerous to use in the laboratory, requiring specialized equipment.

Chlorine is the most industrially useful of the halogens. In 2005, total production was 22 billion pounds, making it the eighth most produced chemical in the United States. Unlike fluorine, chlorine reacts slowly with water to form relatively stable aqueous solutions of HCl and HOCl (hypochlorous acid):

$$Cl_2(g) + H_2O(l) \longrightarrow HCl(aq) + HOCl(aq) \qquad [7.33]$$

Chlorine is often added to drinking water and swimming pools, where the HOCl(aq) that is generated serves as a disinfectant.

The halogens react directly with most metals to form ionic halides. The halogens also react with hydrogen to form gaseous hydrogen halide compounds:

$$H_2(g) + X_2 \longrightarrow 2\ HX(g) \qquad [7.34]$$

These compounds are all very soluble in water and dissolve to form the hydrohalic acids. As we discussed in Section 4.3, HCl(aq), HBr(aq), and HI(aq) are strong acids, whereas HF(aq) is a weak acid.

GIVE IT SOME THOUGHT

Can you use data in Table 7.7 to provide estimates for the atomic radius and first ionization energy of an astatine atom?

Group 8A: The Noble Gases

The group 8A elements, known as the **noble gases**, are all nonmetals that are gases at room temperature. They are all *monatomic* (that is, they consist of single atoms rather than molecules). Some physical properties of the noble-gas elements are listed in Table 7.8 ▼. The high radioactivity of radon (Rn, atomic number 86) has limited the study of its reaction chemistry and some of its properties.

The noble gases have completely filled s and p subshells. All elements of group 8A have large first ionization energies, and we see the expected decrease as we move down the column. Because the noble gases possess such stable electron configurations, they are exceptionally unreactive. In fact, until the early

TABLE 7.8 ■ Some Properties of the Noble Gases

Element	Electron Configuration	Boiling Point (K)	Density (g/L)	Atomic Radius* (Å)	I_1 (kJ/mol)
Helium	$1s^2$	4.2	0.18	0.32	2372
Neon	$[He]2s^22p^6$	27.1	0.90	0.69	2081
Argon	$[Ne]3s^23p^6$	87.3	1.78	0.97	1521
Krypton	$[Ar]3d^{10}4s^24p^6$	120	3.75	1.10	1351
Xenon	$[Kr]4d^{10}5s^25p^6$	165	5.90	1.30	1170
Radon	$[Xe]4f^{14}5d^{10}6s^26p^6$	211	9.73	1.45	1037

*Only the heaviest of the noble-gas elements form chemical compounds. Thus, the atomic radii for the lighter noble-gas elements are estimated values.

1960s the elements were called the *inert gases* because they were thought to be incapable of forming chemical compounds. In 1962, Neil Bartlett at the University of British Columbia reasoned that the ionization energy of Xe might be low enough to allow it to form compounds. In order for this to happen, Xe would have to react with a substance with an extremely high ability to remove electrons from other substances, such as fluorine. Bartlett synthesized the first noble-gas compound by combining Xe with the fluorine-containing compound PtF_6. Xenon also reacts directly with $F_2(g)$ to form the molecular compounds XeF_2, XeF_4, and XeF_6 (Figure 7.36▶). Krypton has a higher I_1 value than xenon and is therefore less reactive. In fact, only a single stable compound of krypton is known, KrF_2. In 2000, Finnish scientists reported the first neutral molecule that contains argon, the HArF molecule, which is stable only at low temperatures.

▲ Figure 7.36 **A compound of xenon.** Crystals of XeF_4, which is one of the very few compounds that contain a group 8A element.

■ SAMPLE INTEGRATIVE EXERCISE | Putting Concepts Together

The element bismuth (Bi, atomic number 83) is the heaviest member of group 5A. A salt of the element, bismuth subsalicylate, is the active ingredient in Pepto-Bismol®, an over-the-counter medication for gastric distress.

(a) The covalent atomic radii of thallium (Tl) and lead (Pb) are 1.48 Å and 1.47 Å, respectively. Using these values and those in Figure 7.7, predict the covalent atomic radius of the element bismuth (Bi). Explain your answer.
(b) What accounts for the general increase in atomic radius going down the group 5A elements?
(c) Another major use of bismuth has been as an ingredient in low-melting metal alloys, such as those used in fire sprinkler systems and in typesetting. The element itself is a brittle white crystalline solid. How do these characteristics fit with the fact that bismuth is in the same periodic group with such nonmetallic elements as nitrogen and phosphorus?
(d) Bi_2O_3 is a basic oxide. Write a balanced chemical equation for its reaction with dilute nitric acid. If 6.77 g of Bi_2O_3 is dissolved in dilute acidic solution to make 0.500 L of solution, what is the molarity of the solution of Bi^{3+} ion?
(e) ^{209}Bi is the heaviest stable isotope of any element. How many protons and neutrons are present in this nucleus?
(f) The density of Bi at 25 °C is 9.808 g/cm^3. How many Bi atoms are present in a cube of the element that is 5.00 cm on each edge? How many moles of the element are present?

SOLUTION

(a) Note that there is a gradual decrease in radius of the elements in Groups 3A–5A as we proceed across the fifth period, that is, in the series In–Sn–Sb. Therefore, it is reasonable to expect a decrease of about 0.02 Å as we move from Pb to Bi, leading to an estimate of 1.45 Å. The tabulated value is 1.46 Å.
(b) The general increase in radius with increasing atomic number in the group 5A elements occurs because additional shells of electrons are being added, with corresponding increases in nuclear charge. The core electrons in each case largely shield the outermost electrons from the nucleus, so the effective nuclear charge does not vary greatly as we go to higher atomic numbers. However, the principal quantum number, n, of the outermost electrons steadily increases, with a corresponding increase in orbital radius.
(c) The contrast between the properties of bismuth and those of nitrogen and phosphorus illustrates the general rule that there is a trend toward increased metallic character as we move down in a given group. Bismuth, in fact, is a metal. The increased metallic character occurs because the outermost electrons are more readily lost in bonding, a trend that is consistent with its lower ionization energy.
(d) Following the procedures described in Section 4.2 for writing molecular and net ionic equations, we have the following:

Molecular equation: $Bi_2O_3(s) + 6\ HNO_3(aq) \longrightarrow 2\ Bi(NO_3)_3(aq) + 3\ H_2O(l)$

Net ionic equation: $Bi_2O_3(s) + 6\ H^+(aq) \longrightarrow 2\ Bi^{3+}(aq) + 3\ H_2O(l)$

In the net ionic equation, nitric acid is a strong acid and $Bi(NO_3)_3$ is a soluble salt, so we need show only the reaction of the solid with the hydrogen ion forming the $Bi^{3+}(aq)$ ion and water.
To calculate the concentration of the solution, we proceed as follows (Section 4.5):

$$\frac{6.77\ g\ Bi_2O_3}{0.500\ L\ soln} \times \frac{1\ mol\ Bi_2O_3}{466.0\ g\ Bi_2O_3} \times \frac{2\ mol\ Bi^{3+}}{1\ mol\ Bi_2O_3} = \frac{0.0581\ mol\ Bi^{3+}}{L\ soln} = 0.0581\ M$$

(e) We can proceed as in Section 2.3. Bismuth is element 83; there are therefore 83 protons in the nucleus. Because the atomic mass number is 209, there are $209 - 83 = 126$ neutrons in the nucleus.

(f) We proceed as in Sections 1.4 and 3.4: the volume of the cube is $(5.00)^3 \text{ cm}^3 = 125 \text{ cm}^3$. Then we have

$$125 \text{ cm}^3 \text{ Bi} \times \frac{9.808 \text{ g Bi}}{1 \text{ cm}^3} \times \frac{1 \text{ mol Bi}}{209.0 \text{ g Bi}} = 5.87 \text{ mol Bi}$$

$$5.87 \text{ mol Bi} \times \frac{6.022 \times 10^{23} \text{ atom Bi}}{1 \text{ mol Bi}} = 3.54 \times 10^{24} \text{ atoms Bi}$$

CHAPTER REVIEW

SUMMARY AND KEY TERMS

Introduction and Section 7.1 The periodic table was first developed by Mendeleev and Meyer on the basis of the similarity in chemical and physical properties exhibited by certain elements. Moseley established that each element has a unique atomic number, which added more order to the periodic table. We now recognize that elements in the same column of the periodic table have the same number of electrons in their **valence orbitals**. This similarity in valence electronic structure leads to the similarities among elements in the same group. The differences among elements in the same group arise because their valence orbitals are in different shells.

Section 7.2 Many properties of atoms are due to the average distance of the outer electrons from the nucleus and to the **effective nuclear charge** experienced by these electrons. The core electrons are very effective in screening the outer electrons from the full charge of the nucleus, whereas electrons in the same shell do not screen each other effectively. As a result, the effective nuclear charge experienced by valence electrons increases as we move left to right across a period.

Section 7.3 The size of an atom can be gauged by its **bonding atomic radius**, based on measurements of the distances separating atoms in their chemical compounds. In general, atomic radii increase as we go down a column in the periodic table and decrease as we proceed left to right across a row.

Cations are smaller than their parent atoms; anions are larger than their parent atoms. For ions of the same charge, size increases going down a column of the periodic table. An **isoelectronic series** is a series of ions that has the same number of electrons. For such a series, size decreases with increasing nuclear charge as the electrons are attracted more strongly to the nucleus.

Section 7.4 The first **ionization energy** of an atom is the minimum energy needed to remove an electron from the atom in the gas phase, forming a cation. The second ionization energy is the energy needed to remove a second electron, and so forth. Ionization energies show a sharp increase after all the valence electrons have been removed, because of the much higher effective nuclear charge experienced by the core electrons. The first ionization energies of the elements show periodic trends that are opposite those seen for atomic radii, with smaller atoms having higher first ionization energies. Thus, first ionization energies decrease as we go down a column and increase as we proceed left to right across a row.

We can write electron configurations for ions by first writing the electron configuration of the neutral atom and then removing or adding the appropriate number of electrons. Electrons are removed first from the orbitals with the largest value of n. If there are two valence orbitals with the same value of n (such as $4s$ and $4p$), then the electrons are lost first from the orbital with a higher value of l (in this case, $4p$). Electrons are added to orbitals in the reverse order.

Section 7.5 The **electron affinity** of an element is the energy change upon adding an electron to an atom in the gas phase, forming an anion. A negative electron affinity means that the anion is stable; a positive electron affinity means that the anion is not stable relative to the separated atom and electron, in which case its exact value cannot be measured. In general, electron affinities become more negative as we proceed from left to right across the periodic table. The halogens have the most-negative electron affinities. The electron affinities of the noble gases are positive because the added electron would have to occupy a new, higher-energy subshell.

Section 7.6 The elements can be categorized as metals, nonmetals, and metalloids. Most elements are metals; they occupy the left side and the middle of the periodic table. Nonmetals appear in the upper-right section of the table. Metalloids occupy a narrow band between the metals and nonmetals. The tendency of an element to exhibit the properties of metals, called the **metallic character**, increases as we proceed down a column and decreases as we proceed from left to right across a row.

Metals have a characteristic luster, and they are good conductors of heat and electricity. When metals react with nonmetals, the metal atoms are oxidized to cations and ionic substances are generally formed. Most metal oxides are basic; they react with acids to form salts and water.

Nonmetals lack metallic luster and are generally poor conductors of heat and electricity. Several are gases at room temperature. Compounds composed entirely of nonmetals are generally molecular. Nonmetals usually form anions in their reactions with metals. Nonmetal oxides are acidic; they react with bases to form salts and water. Metalloids have properties that are intermediate between those of metals and nonmetals.

Section 7.7 The periodic properties of the elements can help us understand the properties of groups of the representative elements. The **alkali metals** (group 1A) are soft metals with low densities and low melting points. They have the lowest ionization energies of the elements. As a result, they are very reactive toward nonmetals, easily losing their outer s electron to form 1+ ions. The **alkaline earth metals** (group 2A) are harder and more dense and have higher melting points than the alkali metals. They are also very reactive toward nonmetals, although not as reactive as the alkali metals. The alkaline earth metals readily lose their two outer s electrons to form 2+ ions. Both alkali and alkaline earth metals react with hydrogen to form ionic substances that contain the **hydride ion**, H^-.

Section 7.8 Hydrogen is a nonmetal with properties that are distinct from any of the groups of the periodic table. It forms molecular compounds with other nonmetals, such as oxygen and the halogens.

Oxygen and sulfur are the most important elements in group 6A. Oxygen is usually found as a diatomic molecule, O_2. **Ozone**, O_3, is an important allotrope of oxygen. Oxygen has a strong tendency to gain electrons from other elements, thus oxidizing them. In combination with metals, oxygen is usually found as the oxide ion, O^{2-}, although salts of the peroxide ion, O_2^{2-}, and superoxide ion, O_2^-, are sometimes formed. Elemental sulfur is most commonly found as S_8 molecules. In combination with metals, it is most often found as the sulfide ion, S^{2-}.

The **halogens** (group 7A) are nonmetals that exist as diatomic molecules. The halogens have the most negative electron affinities of the elements. Thus their chemistry is dominated by a tendency to form 1– ions, especially in reactions with metals.

The **noble gases** (group 8A) are nonmetals that exist as monatomic gases. They are very unreactive because they have completely filled s and p subshells. Only the heaviest noble gases are known to form compounds, and they do so only with very active nonmetals, such as fluorine.

KEY SKILLS

- Understand the meaning of effective nuclear charge, Z_{eff}, and how Z_{eff} depends upon nuclear charge and electron configuration.
- Use the periodic table to predict the trends in atomic radii, ionic radii, ionization energy, and electron affinity.
- Understand how the radius of an atom changes upon losing electrons to form a cation or gaining electrons to form an anion.
- Understand how the ionization energy changes as we remove successive electrons. Recognize the jump in ionization energy that occurs when the ionization corresponds to removing a core electron.
- Be able to write the electron configurations of ions.
- Understand how irregularities in the periodic trends for electron affinity can be related to electron configuration.
- Recognize the differences in chemical and physical properties of metals and nonmetals, including the basicity of metal oxides and the acidity of nonmetal oxides.
- Understand how the atomic properties, such as ionization energy and electron configuration, are related to the chemical reactivity and physical properties of the alkali and alkaline earth metals (groups 1A and 2A).
- Be able to write balanced equations for the reactions of the group 1A and 2A metals with water, oxygen, hydrogen, and the halogens.
- Understand and recognize the unique characteristics of hydrogen.
- Understand how the atomic properties (such as ionization energy, electron configuration, and electron affinity) of group 6A, 7A, and 8A elements are related to their chemical reactivity and physical properties.

KEY EQUATIONS

- $Z_{eff} = Z - S$ [7.1]   Estimating effective nuclear charge

VISUALIZING CONCEPTS

7.1 We can draw an analogy between the attraction of an
CQ electron to a nucleus and seeing a lightbulb—in essence,
the more nuclear charge the electron "sees," the greater
the attraction. **(a)** Within this analogy, discuss how the
shielding by core electrons is analogous to putting a
frosted-glass lampshade between the lightbulb and
your eyes, as shown in the illustration. **(b)** Explain how
we could mimic moving to the right in a row of the periodic table by changing the wattage of the lightbulb.
(c) How would you change the wattage of the bulb
and/or the frosted glass to mimic the effect of moving
down a column of the periodic table? [Section 7.2]

Light bulb   Frosted
glass

Observer

7.2 Fluorine has atomic number 9. If we represent the ra-
CQ dius of a fluorine atom with the billiard ball illustrated
here, would the analogy be more appropriate for the
bonding or nonbonding atomic radius? If we used the
same billiard ball to illustrate the concept of fluorine's
bonding atomic radius, would we overestimate or
underestimate the bonding atomic radius? Explain.
[Section 7.3]

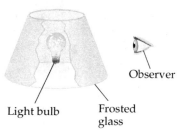

7.3 Consider the A_2X_4 molecule depicted below, where A
CQ and X are elements. The A—A bond length in this molecule is d_1, and the four A—X bond lengths are each d_2.
(a) In terms of d_1 and d_2, how could you define the
bonding atomic radii of atoms A and X? **(b)** In terms of
d_1 and d_2, what would you predict for the X—X bond
length of an X_2 molecule? [Section 7.3]

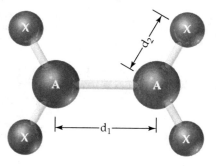

7.4 Make a simple sketch of the shape of the main part of
CQ the periodic table, as shown. **(a)** Ignoring H and He,
write a single straight arrow from the element with the
smallest bonding atomic radius to the element with the
largest. **(b)** Ignoring H and He, write a single straight
arrow from the element with the smallest first ionization
energy to the element with the largest. **(c)** What significant observation can you make from the arrows you
drew in parts (a) and (b)? [Sections 7.3 and 7.4]

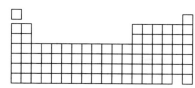

7.5 In the chemical process called *electron transfer*, an elec-
CQ tron is transferred from one atom or molecule to another
(We will talk about electron transfer extensively in
Chapter 20.) A simple electron transfer reaction is

$$A(g) + A(g) \longrightarrow A^+(g) + A^-(g)$$

In terms of the ionization energy and electron affinity of
atom A, what is the energy change for this reaction? For
a representative nonmetal such as chlorine, is this
process exothermic? For a representative metal such
as sodium, is this process exothermic? [Sections 7.4
and 7.5]

7.6 An element X reacts with $F_2(g)$ to form the molecular
CQ product shown below. **(a)** Write a balanced equation for
this reaction (do not worry about the phases for X and
the product). **(b)** Do you think that X is a metal or nonmetal? Explain. [Section 7.6]

EXERCISES

Periodic Table; Effective Nuclear Charge

7.7 Why did Mendeleev leave blanks in his early version of the periodic table? How did he predict the properties of the elements that belonged in those blanks?

7.8 The prefix *eka-* comes from the Sanskrit word for one. Mendeleev used this prefix to indicate that the unknown element was one place away from the known element that followed the prefix. For example, *eka-silicon*, which we now call germanium, is one element below silicon. Mendeleev also predicted the existence of *eka-manganese*, which was not experimentally confirmed until 1937 because this element is radioactive and does not occur in nature. Based on the periodic table shown in Figure 7.2, what do we now call the element Mendeleev called *eka-manganese*?

7.9 In Chapter 1 we learned that silicon is the second most abundant element in Earth's crust, accounting for more than one-fourth of the mass of the crust (Figure 1.6). Yet we see that silicon is not among the elements that have been known since ancient times (Figure 7.2), whereas iron, which accounts for less than 5% of Earth's crust, has been known since prehistoric times. Given silicon's abundance how do you account for its relatively late discovery?

7.10 **(a)** During the period from about 1800 to about 1865, the atomic weights of many elements were accurately measured. Why was this important to Mendeleev's formulation of the periodic table? **(b)** What property of the atom did Moseley associate with the wavelength of X-rays emitted from an element in his experiments? **(c)** Why are chemical and physical properties of the elements more closely related to atomic number than they are to atomic weight?

7.11 **(a)** What is meant by the term *effective nuclear charge*? **(b)** How does the effective nuclear charge experienced by the valence electrons of an atom vary going from left to right across a period of the periodic table?

7.12 **(a)** How is the concept of effective nuclear charge used to simplify the numerous electron-electron repulsions in a many-electron atom? **(b)** Which experiences a greater effective nuclear charge in a Be atom, the $1s$ electrons or the $2s$ electrons? Explain.

7.13 Detailed calculations show that the value of Z_{eff} for Na and K atoms is 2.51+ and 3.49+, respectively. **(a)** What value do you estimate for Z_{eff} experienced by the outermost electron in both Na and K by assuming core electrons contribute 1.00 and valence electrons contribute 0.00 to the screening constant? **(b)** What values do you estimate for Z_{eff} using Slater's rules? **(c)** Which approach gives a more accurate estimate of Z_{eff}? **(d)** Does either method of approximation account for the gradual increase in Z_{eff} that occurs upon moving down a group?

7.14 Detailed calculations show that the value of Z_{eff} for Si and Cl atoms is 4.29+ and 6.12+, respectively. **(a)** What value do you estimate for Z_{eff} experienced by the outermost electron in both Si and Cl by assuming core electrons contribute 1.00 and valence electrons contribute 0.00 to the screening constant? **(b)** What values do you estimate for Z_{eff} using Slater's rules? **(c)** Which approach gives a more accurate estimate of Z_{eff}? **(d)** Which method of approximation more accurately accounts for the steady increase in Z_{eff} that occurs upon moving left to right across a period?

7.15 Which will experience the greater effective nuclear charge, the electrons in the $n = 3$ shell in Ar or the $n = 3$ shell in Kr? Which will be closer to the nucleus? Explain.

7.16 Arrange the following atoms in order of increasing effective nuclear charge experienced by the electrons in the $n = 3$ electron shell: K, Mg, P, Rh, and Ti. Explain the basis for your order.

Atomic and Ionic Radii

7.17 **(a)** Because an exact outer boundary cannot be measured or even calculated for an atom, how are atomic radii determined? **(b)** What is the difference between a bonding radius and a nonbonding radius? **(c)** For a given element, which one is larger?

7.18 **(a)** Why does the quantum mechanical description of many-electron atoms make it difficult to define a precise atomic radius? **(b)** When nonbonded atoms come up against one another, what determines how closely the nuclear centers can approach?

7.19 The distance between W atoms in tungsten metal is 2.74 Å. What is the atomic radius of a tungsten atom in this environment? (This radius is called the *metallic radius*.)

7.20 Based on the radii presented in Figure 7.7, predict the distance between Si atoms in solid silicon.

7.21 Estimate the As—I bond length from the data in Figure 7.7, and compare your value to the experimental As—I bond length in arsenic triiodide, AsI_3, 2.55 Å.

7.22 The experimental Bi—I bond length in bismuth triiodide, BiI_3, is 2.81 Å. Based on this value and data in Figure 7.7, predict the atomic radius of Bi.

7.23 How do the sizes of atoms change as we move **(a)** from left to right across a row in the periodic table, **(b)** from top to bottom in a group in the periodic table? **(c)** Arrange the following atoms in order of increasing atomic radius: F, P, S, As.

7.24 **(a)** Among the nonmetallic elements, the change in
CQ   atomic radius in moving one place left or right in a row
is smaller than the change in moving one row up or
down. Explain these observations. **(b)** Arrange the following atoms in order of increasing atomic radius: Si,
Al, Ge, Ga.

7.25 Using only the periodic table, arrange each set of atoms
CQ   in order of increasing radius: **(a)** Ca, Mg, Be; **(b)** Ga, Br,
Ge; **(c)** Al, Tl, Si.

7.26 Using only the periodic table, arrange each set of atoms
CQ   in order of increasing radius: **(a)** Ba, Ca, Na; **(b)** Sn, Sb,
As; **(c)** Al, Be, Si.

7.27 **(a)** Why are monatomic cations smaller than their corre-
CQ   sponding neutral atoms? **(b)** Why are monatomic anions larger than their corresponding neutral atoms?
(c) Why does the size of ions increase as one proceeds
down a column in the periodic table?

7.28 Explain the following variations in atomic or ionic radii:
CQ   **(a)** $I^- > I > I^+$, **(b)** $Ca^{2+} > Mg^{2+} > Be^{2+}$,
(c) $Fe > Fe^{2+} > Fe^{3+}$.

7.29 Consider a reaction represented by the following spheres:
CQ

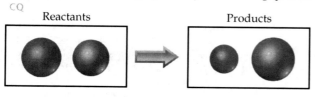

Reactants   Products

Which sphere represents a metal and which a nonmetal?
Explain.

7.30 Consider the following spheres:
CQ

Which one represents Ca, which Ca^{2+}, and which Mg^{2+}?

7.31 **(a)** What is an isoelectronic series? **(b)** Which neutral
atom is isoelectronic with each of the following ions:
Al^{3+}, Ti^{4+}, Br^-, Sn^{2+}.

7.32 Some ions do not have a corresponding neutral atom
that has the same electron configuration. For each of
the following ions identify the neutral atom that has the
same number of electrons and determine if this atom
has the same electron configuration. If such an atom
does not exist explain why: **(a)** Cl^-, **(b)** Sc^{3+}, **(c)** Fe^{2+},
(d) Zn^{2+}, **(e)** Sn^{4+}.

7.33 Consider the isoelectronic ions F^- and Na^+. **(a)** Which
CQ   ion is smaller? **(b)** Using Equation 7.1 and assuming that
core electrons contribute 1.00 and valence electrons contribute 0.00 to the screening constant, S, calculate Z_{eff} for
the 2p electrons in both ions. **(c)** Repeat this calculation
using Slater's rules to estimate the screening constant, S.
(d) For isoelectronic ions, how are effective nuclear
charge and ionic radius related?

7.34 Consider the isoelectronic ions Cl^- and K^+. **(a)** Which ion is
smaller? **(b)** Use Equation 7.1 and assuming that core electrons contribute 1.00 and valence electrons contribute nothing to the screening constant, S, calculate Z_{eff} for these two
ions. **(c)** Repeat this calculation using Slater's rules to estimate the screening constant, S. **(d)** For isoelectronic ions
how are effective nuclear charge and ionic radius related?

7.35 Consider S, Cl, and K and their most common ions.
CQ   **(a)** List the atoms in order of increasing size. **(b)** List the
ions in order of increasing size. **(c)** Explain any differences in the orders of the atomic and ionic sizes.

7.36 For each of the following sets of atoms and ions, arrange
the members in order of increasing size: **(a)** Se^{2-}, Te^{2-}, Se;
(b) Co^{3+}, Fe^{2+}, Fe^{3+}; **(c)** Ca, Ti^{4+}, Sc^{3+}; **(d)** Be^{2+}, Na^+, Ne.

7.37 For each of the following statements, provide an explanation: **(a)** O^{2-} is larger than O; **(b)** S^{2-} is larger than O^{2-};
(c) S^{2-} is larger than K^+; **(d)** K^+ is larger than Ca^{2+}.

7.38 In the ionic compounds LiF, NaCl, KBr, and RbI, the
measured cation–anion distances are 2.01 Å (Li–F), 2.82 Å
(Na–Cl), 3.30 Å (K–Br), and 3.67 Å (Rb–I), respectively.
(a) Predict the cation–anion distance using the values of
ionic radii given in Figure 7.8. **(b)** Is the agreement between the prediction and the experiment perfect? If not,
why not? **(c)** What estimates of the cation–anion distance
would you obtain for these four compounds using
bonding atomic radii? Are these estimates as accurate as the
estimates using ionic radii?

Ionization Energies; Electron Affinities

7.39 Write equations that show the processes that describe the
CQ   first, second, and third ionization energies of a boron atom.

7.40 Write equations that show the process for **(a)** the first
CQ   two ionization energies of tin and **(b)** the fourth ionization energy of titanium.

7.41 **(a)** Why are ionization energies always positive quanti-
CQ   ties? **(b)** Why does F have a larger first ionization energy
than O? **(c)** Why is the second ionization energy of an
atom always greater than its first ionization energy?

7.42 **(a)** Why does Li have a larger first ionization energy
CQ   than Na? **(b)** The difference between the third and
fourth ionization energies of scandium is much larger
than the difference between the third and fourth ionization energies of titanium. Why? **(c)** Why does Li have a
much larger second ionization energy than Be?

7.43 **(a)** What is the general relationship between the size of
CQ   an atom and its first ionization energy? **(b)** Which element in the periodic table has the largest ionization energy? Which has the smallest?

7.44 **(a)** What is the trend in first ionization energies as one
CQ   proceeds down the group 7A elements? Explain how
this trend relates to the variation in atomic radii.
(b) What is the trend in first ionization energies as one
moves across the fourth period from K to Kr? How does
this trend compare with the trend in atomic radii?

7.45 Based on their positions in the periodic table, predict
CQ   which atom of the following pairs will have the larger
first ionization energy: **(a)** Cl, Ar; **(b)** Be, Ca; **(c)** K, Co;
(d) S, Ge; **(e)** Sn, Te.

7.46 For each of the following pairs, indicate which element
CQ has the larger first ionization energy: **(a)** Ti, Ba; **(b)** Ag, Cu; **(c)** Ge, Cl; **(d)** Pb, Sb. (In each case use electron configuration and effective nuclear charge to explain your answer.)

7.47 Write the electron configurations for the following ions: **(a)** In^{3+}, **(b)** Sb^{3+}, **(c)** Te^{2-}, **(d)** Te^{6+}, **(e)** Hg^{2+}, **(f)** Rh^{3+}.

7.48 Write electron configurations for the following ions, and determine which have noble-gas configurations: **(a)** Cr^{3+}, **(b)** N^{3-}, **(c)** Sc^{3+}, **(d)** Cu^{2+}, **(e)** Tl^+, **(f)** Au^+.

7.49 Write the electron configuration for **(a)** the Ni^{2+} ion and **(b)** the Sn^{2+} ion. How many unpaired electrons does each contain?

7.50 Identify the element whose ions have the following electron configurations: **(a)** a 2+ ion with $[Ar]3d^9$, **(b)** a 1+ ion with $[Xe]4f^{14}5d^{10}6s^2$. How many unpaired electrons does each ion contain?

7.51 The first ionization energy of Ar and the electron affini-
CQ ty of Ar are both positive values. What is the significance of the positive value in each case?

7.52 The electron affinity of lithium is a negative value,
CQ whereas the electron affinity of beryllium is a positive value. Use electron configurations to account for this observation.

7.53 While the electron affinity of bromine is a negative
CQ quantity, it is positive for Kr. Use the electron configurations of the two elements to explain the difference.

7.54 What is the relationship between the ionization energy
CQ of an anion with a 1− charge such as F^- and the electron affinity of the neutral atom, F?

7.55 Consider the first ionization energy of neon and the
CQ electron affinity of fluorine. **(a)** Write equations, including electron configurations, for each process. **(b)** These two quantities will have opposite signs. Which will be positive, and which will be negative? **(c)** Would you expect the **magnitudes** of these two quantities to be equal? If not, which one would you expect to be larger? Explain your answer.

7.56 Write an equation for the process that corresponds to
CQ the electron affinity of the Mg^+ ion. Also write the electron configurations of the species involved. What is the magnitude of the energy change in the process? [*Hint:* The answer is in Table 7.2.]

Properties of Metals and Nonmetals

7.57 How are metallic character and first ionization energy
CQ related?

7.58 Arrange the following pure solid elements in order of
CQ increasing electrical conductivity: Ge, Ca, S, and Si. Explain the reasoning you used.

7.59 If we look at groups 3A through 5A, we see two metal-
CQ loids for groups 4A (Si, Ge) and 5A (As, Sb), but only one metalloid in group 3A (B). To maintain a regular geometric pattern one might expect that aluminum would also be a metalloid, giving group 3A two metalloids. What can you say about the metallic character of aluminum with respect to its neighbors based on its first ionization energy?

7.60 For each of the following pairs, which element will have
CQ the greater metallic character: **(a)** Li or Be, **(b)** Li or Na, **(c)** Sn or P, **(d)** Al or B?

7.61 Predict whether each of the following oxides is ionic or
CQ molecular: SO_2, MgO, Li_2O, P_2O_5, Y_2O_3, N_2O, and XeO_3. Explain the reasons for your choices.

7.62 Some metal oxides, such as Sc_2O_3, do not react with pure
CQ water, but they do react when the solution becomes either acidic or basic. Do you expect Sc_2O_3 to react when the solution becomes acidic or when it becomes basic? Write a balanced chemical equation to support your answer.

7.63 **(a)** What is meant by the terms acidic oxide and basic
CQ oxide? **(b)** How can we predict whether an oxide will be acidic or basic, based on its composition?

7.64 Arrange the following oxides in order of increasing
CQ acidity: CO_2, CaO, Al_2O_3, SO_3, SiO_2, and P_2O_5.

7.65 Chlorine reacts with oxygen to form Cl_2O_7. **(a)** What is
the name of this product (see Table 2.6)? **(b)** Write a balanced equation for the formation of $Cl_2O_7(l)$ from the elements. **(c)** Under usual conditions, Cl_2O_7 is a colorless liquid with a boiling point of 81 °C. Is this boiling point expected or surprising? **(d)** Would you expect Cl_2O_7 to be more reactive toward $H^+(aq)$ or $OH^-(aq)$? Explain.

[7.66] An element X reacts with oxygen to form XO_2 and with chlorine to form XCl_4. XO_2 is a white solid that melts at high temperatures (above 1000 °C). Under usual conditions, XCl_4 is a colorless liquid with a boiling point of 58 °C. **(a)** XCl_4 reacts with water to form XO_2 and another product. What is the likely identity of the other product? **(b)** Do you think that element X is a metal, nonmetal, or metalloid? Explain. **(c)** By using a source-book such as the *CRC Handbook of Chemistry and Physics*, try to determine the identity of element X.

7.67 Write balanced equations for the following reactions: **(a)** barium oxide with water, **(b)** iron(II) oxide with perchloric acid, **(c)** sulfur trioxide with water, **(d)** carbon dioxide with aqueous sodium hydroxide.

7.68 Write balanced equations for the following reactions: **(a)** potassium oxide with water, **(b)** diphosphorus trioxide with water, **(c)** chromium(III) oxide with dilute hydrochloric acid, **(d)** selenium dioxide with aqueous potassium hydroxide.

Group Trends in Metals and Nonmetals

7.69 Compare the elements sodium and magnesium with re-
CQ spect to the following properties: (a) electron configuration, (b) most common ionic charge, (c) first ionization
energy, (d) reactivity toward water, (e) atomic radius.
Account for the differences between the two elements.

7.70 (a) Compare the electron configurations and atomic
CQ radii (see Figure 7.7) of rubidium and silver. In what respects are their electronic configurations similar? Account for the difference in radii of the two elements.
(b) As with rubidium, silver is most commonly found as
the 1+ ion, Ag^+. However, silver is far less reactive. Explain these observations.

7.71 (a) Why is calcium generally more reactive than magne-
CQ sium? (b) Why is calcium generally less reactive than
potassium?

7.72 (a) Why is cesium more reactive toward water than is
lithium? (b) One of the alkali metals reacts with oxygen
to form a solid white substance. When this substance is
dissolved in water, the solution gives a positive test for
hydrogen peroxide, H_2O_2. When the solution is tested in
a burner flame, a lilac-purple flame is produced. What is
the likely identity of the metal? (c) Write a balanced
chemical equation for reaction of the white substance
with water.

7.73 Write a balanced equation for the reaction that occurs in
each of the following cases: (a) Potassium metal burns in
an atmosphere of chlorine gas. (b) Strontium oxide is
added to water. (c) A fresh surface of lithium metal is exposed to oxygen gas. (d) Sodium metal is reacted with
molten sulfur.

7.74 Write a balanced equation for the reaction that occurs in
each of the following cases: (a) Cesium is added to
water. (b) Stontium is added to water. (c) Sodium reacts
with oxygen. (d) Calcium reacts with iodine.

7.75 (a) If we arrange the elements of the second period
CQ (Li–Ne) in order of increasing first ionization energy,
where would hydrogen fit into this series? (b) If we now
arrange the elements of the third period (Na–Ar) in
order of increasing first ionization energy, where would
lithium fit into this series? (c) Are these series consistent
with the assignment of hydrogen as a nonmetal and
lithium as a metal?

7.76 (a) As described in Section 7.7, the alkali metals react
with hydrogen to form hydrides and react with
halogens—for example, fluorine—to form halides.
Compare the roles of hydrogen and the halogen in these
reactions. In what sense are the forms of hydrogen and
halogen in the products alike? (b) Write balanced equations for the reaction of fluorine with calcium and for
the reaction of hydrogen with calcium. What are the
similarities among the products of these reactions?

7.77 Compare the elements fluorine and chlorine with respect to the following properties: (a) electron configuration, (b) most common ionic charge, (c) first ionization
energy, (d) reactivity toward water, (e) electron affinity,
(f) atomic radius. Account for the differences between
the two elements.

7.78 Little is known about the properties of astatine, At,
CQ because of its rarity and high radioactivity. Nevertheless, it is possible for us to make many predictions about
its properties. (a) Do you expect the element to be a gas,
liquid, or solid at room temperature? Explain. (b) What
is the chemical formula of the compound it forms
with Na?

7.79 Until the early 1960s the group 8A elements were called
CQ the inert gases; before that they were called the rare
gases. The term rare gases was dropped after it was discovered that argon accounts for roughly 1% of Earth's
atmosphere. (a) Why was the term inert gases dropped?
(b) What discovery triggered this change in name?
(c) What name is applied to the group now?

7.80 Why does xenon react with fluorine, whereas neon
does not?

7.81 Write a balanced equation for the reaction that occurs in
each of the following cases: (a) Ozone decomposes to
dioxygen. (b) Xenon reacts with fluorine. (Write three
different equations.) (c) Sulfur reacts with hydrogen gas.
(d) Fluorine reacts with water.

7.82 Write a balanced equation for the reaction that occurs in
each of the following cases: (a) Chlorine reacts with
water. (b) Barium metal is heated in an atmosphere of
hydrogen gas. (c) Lithium reacts with sulfur. (d) Fluorine reacts with magnesium metal.

ADDITIONAL EXERCISES

7.83 Consider the stable elements through lead ($Z = 82$). In
how many instances are the atomic weights of the elements in the reverse order relative to the atomic numbers of the elements? What is the explanation for these
cases?

7.84 (a) Which will have the lower energy, a $4s$ or a $4p$ elec-
CQ tron in an As atom? (b) How can we use the concept of
effective nuclear charge to explain your answer to
part (a)?

7.85 (a) If the core electrons were totally effective at shielding
the valence electrons and the valence electrons provided
no shielding for each other, what would be the effective
nuclear charge acting on the $3s$ and $3p$ valence electrons
in P? (b) Repeat these calculations using Slater's rules.
(c) Detailed calculations indicate that the effective nuclear charge is 5.6+ for the $3s$ electrons and 4.9+ for the
$3p$ electrons. Why are the values for the $3s$ and $3p$ electrons different? (d) If you remove a single electron from
a P atom, which orbital will it come from? Explain.

7.86 Nearly all the mass of an atom is in the nucleus, which
CQ has a very small radius. When atoms bond together (for example, two fluorine atoms in F_2), why is the distance separating the nuclei so much larger than the radii of the nuclei?

[7.87] Consider the change in effective nuclear charge experienced by a 2p electron as we proceed from C to N. **(a)** Based on a simple model in which core electrons screen the valence electrons completely and valence electrons do not screen other valence electrons, what do you predict for the change in Z_{eff} from C to N? **(b)** What change do you predict using Slater's rules? **(c)** The actual change in Z_{eff} from C to N is 0.70+. Which approach to estimating Z_{eff} is more accurate? **(d)** The change in Z_{eff} from N to O is smaller than that from C to N. Can you provide an explanation for this observation?

7.88 As we move across a period of the periodic table, why
CQ do the sizes of the transition elements change more gradually than those of the representative elements?

7.89 In the series of group 5A hydrides, of general formula MH_3, the measured bond distances are P—H, 1.419 Å; As—H, 1.519 Å; Sb—H, 1.707 Å. **(a)** Compare these values with those estimated by use of the atomic radii in Figure 7.7. **(b)** Explain the steady increase in M—H bond distance in this series in terms of the electronic configurations of the M atoms.

7.90 It is possible to produce compounds of the form $GeClH_3$, $GeCl_2H_2$, and $GeCl_3H$. What values do you predict for the Ge—H and Ge—Cl bond lengths in these compounds?

7.91 Note from the following table that the increase in atomic radius in moving from Zr to Hf is smaller than in moving from Y to La. Suggest an explanation for this effect.

Atomic Radii (Å)

Sc	1.44	Ti	1.36
Y	1.62	Zr	1.48
La	1.69	Hf	1.50

7.92 The "Chemistry and Life" box on ionic size in Section 7.3 compares the ionic radii of Zn^{2+} and Cd^{2+} **(a)** The 2+ ion of which other element seems the most obvious one to compare to Zn^{2+} and Cd^{2+}? **(b)** With reference to Figure 2.24, is the element in part (a) essential for life? **(c)** Estimate the ionic radius of the 2+ ion of the element in part (a). Explain any assumptions you have made. **(d)** Would you expect the 2+ ion of the element in part (a) to be physiologically more similar to Zn^{2+} or to Cd^{2+}? **(e)** Use a sourcebook or a Web search to determine whether the element in part (a) is toxic to humans.

[7.93] The ionic substance strontium oxide, SrO, forms from the direct reaction of strontium metal with molecular oxygen. The arrangement of the ions in solid SrO is analogous to that in solid NaCl (see Figure 2.23) and is shown here. **(a)** Write a balanced equation for the formation of SrO(s) from the elements. **(b)** Based on the ionic radii in Figure 7.8, predict the length of the side of the cube in the figure (the distance from the center of an atom at one corner to the center of an atom at a neighboring corner). **(c)** The experimental density of SrO is 5.10 g/cm^3. Given your answer to part (b), what is the number of formula units of SrO that are contained in the cube in the figure? (We will examine structures like those in the figure more closely in Chapter 11.)

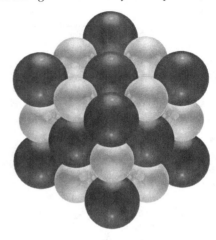

7.94 Explain the variation in ionization energies of carbon, as
CQ displayed in the following graph:

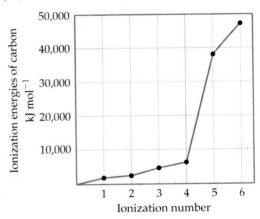

7.95 Do you agree with the following statement? "A negative
CQ value for the electron affinity of an atom occurs when the outermost electrons incompletely shield one another from the nucleus." If not, change it to make it more nearly correct in your view. Apply either the statement as given or your revised statement to explain why the electron affinity of bromine is −325 kJ/mol and that for its neighbor Kr is > 0.

7.96 Use orbital diagrams to illustrate what happens when
CQ an oxygen atom gains two electrons. Why is it extremely difficult to add a third electron to the atom?

[7.97] Use electron configurations to explain the following observations: **(a)** The first ionization energy of phosphorus is greater than that of sulfur. **(b)** The electron affinity of nitrogen is lower (less negative) than those of both carbon and oxygen. **(c)** The second ionization energy of oxygen is greater than the first ionization energy of fluorine. **(d)** The third ionization energy of manganese is greater than those of both chromium and iron.

7.98 The following table gives the electron affinities, in kJ/mol, for the group 1B and group 2B metals: **(a)** Why are the electron affinities of the group 2B elements greater than zero? **(b)** Why do the electron affinities of the group 1B elements become more negative as we move down the group? [*Hint:* Examine the trends in the electron affinity of other groups as we proceed down the periodic table.]

Cu	Zn
−119	> 0
Ag	Cd
−126	> 0
Au	Hg
−223	> 0

7.99 Hydrogen is an unusual element because it behaves in some ways like the alkali metal elements and in other ways like a nonmetal. Its properties can be explained in part by its electron configuration and by the values for its ionization energy and electron affinity. **(a)** Explain why the electron affinity of hydrogen is much closer to the values for the alkali elements than for the halogens. **(b)** Is the following statement true? "Hydrogen has the smallest bonding atomic radius of any element that forms chemical compounds." If not, correct it. If it is, explain in terms of electron configurations. **(c)** Explain why the ionization energy of hydrogen is closer to the values for the halogens than for the alkali metals.

[**7.100**] The first ionization energy of the oxygen molecule is the energy required for the following process:

$$O_2(g) \longrightarrow O_2^+(g) + e^-$$

The energy needed for this process is 1175 kJ/mol, very similar to the first ionization energy of Xe. Would you expect O_2 to react with F_2? If so, suggest a product or products of this reaction.

7.101 Based on your reading of this chapter, arrange the following in order of increasing melting point: K, Br_2, Mg, and O_2. Explain the factors that determine the order.

7.102 The element strontium is used in a variety of industrial processes. It is not an extremely hazardous substance, but low levels of strontium ingestion could affect the health of children. Radioactive strontium is very hazardous; it was a by-product of nuclear weapons testing and was found widely distributed following nuclear tests. Calcium is quite common in the environment, including food products, and is frequently present in drinking water. Discuss the similarities and differences between calcium and strontium, and indicate how and why strontium might be expected to accompany calcium in water supplies, uptake by plants, and so on.

[**7.103**] There are certain similarities in properties that exist between the first member of any periodic family and the element located below it and to the right in the periodic table. For example, in some ways Li resembles Mg, Be resembles Al, and so forth. This observation is called the diagonal relationship. Using what we have learned in this chapter, offer a possible explanation for this relationship.

[**7.104**] A historian discovers a nineteenth-century notebook in which some observations, dated 1822, on a substance thought to be a new element, were recorded. Here are some of the data recorded in the notebook: Ductile, silver-white, metallic looking. Softer than lead. Unaffected by water. Stable in air. Melting point: 153 °C Density: 7.3 g/cm³. Electrical conductivity: 20% that of copper. Hardness: About 1% as hard as iron. When 4.20 g of the unknown is heated in an excess of oxygen, 5.08 g of a white solid is formed. The solid could be sublimed by heating to over 800 °C. **(a)** Using information in the text and a handbook of chemistry, and making allowances for possible variations in numbers from current values, identify the element reported. **(b)** Write a balanced chemical equation for the reaction with oxygen. **(c)** Judging from Figure 7.2, might this nineteenth-century investigator have been the first to discover a new element?

INTEGRATIVE EXERCISES

[**7.105**] Moseley established the concept of atomic number by studying X-rays emitted by the elements. The X-rays emitted by some of the elements have the following wavelengths:

Element	Wavelength (Å)
Ne	14.610
Ca	3.358
Zn	1.435
Zr	0.786
Sn	0.491

(a) Calculate the frequency, ν, of the X-rays emitted by each of the elements, in Hz. **(b)** Using graph paper (or suitable computer software), plot the square root of ν versus the atomic number of the element. What do you observe about the plot? **(c)** Explain how the plot in part **(b)** allowed Moseley to predict the existence of undiscovered elements. **(d)** Use the result from part **(b)** to predict the X-ray wavelength emitted by iron. **(e)** A particular element emits X-rays with a wavelength of 0.980 Å. What element do you think it is?

[**7.106**] **(a)** Write the electron configuration for Li, and estimate the effective nuclear charge experienced by the valence electron. **(b)** The energy of an electron in a one-electron atom or ion equals $(-2.18 \times 10^{-18}\,\text{J})\left(\dfrac{Z^2}{n^2}\right)$ where Z is the nuclear charge and n is the principal quantum number of the electron. Estimate the first ionization energy of Li. **(c)** Compare the result of your calculation with the value reported in table 7.4, and explain the difference. **(d)** What value of the effective nuclear charge gives the proper value for the ionization energy? Does this agree with your explanation in (c)?

[7.107] One way to measure ionization energies is photoelectron spectroscopy (PES), a technique based on the photoelectric effect. ~~(Section 6.2)~~ In PES, monochromatic light is directed onto a sample, causing electrons to be emitted. The kinetic energy of the emitted electrons is measured. The difference between the energy of the photons and the kinetic energy of the electrons corresponds to the energy needed to remove the electrons (that is, the ionization energy). Suppose that a PES experiment is performed in which mercury vapor is irradiated with ultraviolet light of wavelength 58.4 nm. **(a)** What is the energy of a photon of this light, in eV? **(b)** Write an equation that shows the process corresponding to the first ionization energy of Hg. **(c)** The kinetic energy of the emitted electrons is measured to be 10.75 eV. What is the first ionization energy of Hg, in kJ/mol? **(d)** With reference to Figure 7.11, determine which of the halogen elements has a first ionization energy closest to that of mercury.

7.108 Consider the gas-phase transfer of an electron from a sodium atom to a chlorine atom:

$$Na(g) + Cl(g) \longrightarrow Na^+(g) + Cl^-(g)$$

(a) Write this reaction as the sum of two reactions, one that relates to an ionization energy and one that relates to an electron affinity. **(b)** Use the result from part (a), data in this chapter, and Hess's law to calculate the enthalpy of the above reaction. Is the reaction exothermic or endothermic? **(c)** The reaction between sodium metal and chlorine gas is highly exothermic and produces $NaCl(s)$, whose structure was discussed in Section 2.7. Comment on this observation relative to the calculated enthalpy for the aforementioned gas-phase reaction.

[7.109] When magnesium metal is burned in air (Figure 3.5), two products are produced. One is magnesium oxide, MgO. The other is the product of the reaction of Mg with molecular nitrogen, magnesium nitride. When water is added to magnesium nitride, it reacts to form magnesium oxide and ammonia gas. **(a)** Based on the charge of the nitride ion (Table 2.5), predict the formula of magnesium nitride. **(b)** Write a balanced equation for the reaction of magnesium nitride with water. What is the driving force for this reaction? **(c)** In an experiment a piece of magnesium ribbon is burned in air in a crucible.

The mass of the mixture of MgO and magnesium nitride after burning is 0.470 g. Water is added to the crucible, further reaction occurs, and the crucible is heated to dryness until the final product is 0.486 g of MgO. What was the mass percentage of magnesium nitride in the mixture obtained after the initial burning? **(d)** Magnesium nitride can also be formed by reaction of the metal with ammonia at high temperature. Write a balanced equation for this reaction. If a 6.3-g Mg ribbon reacts with 2.57 g $NH_3(g)$ and the reaction goes to completion, which component is the limiting reactant? What mass of $H_2(g)$ is formed in the reaction? **(e)** The standard enthalpy of formation of solid magnesium nitride is −461.08 kJ/mol. Calculate the standard enthalpy change for the reaction between magnesium metal and ammonia gas.

7.110 **(a)** The experimental Bi—Br bond length in bismuth tribromide, $BiBr_3$, is 2.63 Å. Based on this value and the data in Figure 7.7, predict the atomic radius of Bi. **(b)** Bismuth tribromide is soluble in acidic solution. It is formed by treating solid bismuth(III) oxide with aqueous hydrobromic acid. Write a balanced chemical equation for this reaction. **(c)** While bismuth(III) oxide is soluble in acidic solutions, it is insoluble in basic solutions such as NaOH(aq). Based on these properties, is bismuth characterized as a metallic, metalloid, or nonmetallic element? **(d)** Treating bismuth with fluorine gas forms BiF_5. Use the electron configuration of Bi to explain the formation of a compound with this formulation. **(e)** While it is possible to form BiF_5 in the manner just described, pentahalides of bismuth are not known for the other halogens. Explain why the pentahalide might form with fluorine, but not with the other halogens. How does the behavior of bismuth relate to the fact that xenon reacts with fluorine to form compounds, but not with the other halogens?

7.111 Potassium superoxide, KO_2, is often used in oxygen masks (such as those used by firefighters) because KO_2 reacts with CO_2 to release molecular oxygen. Experiments indicate that 2 mol of $KO_2(s)$ react with each mole of $CO_2(g)$. **(a)** The products of the reaction are $K_2CO_3(s)$ and $O_2(g)$. Write a balanced equation for the reaction between $KO_2(s)$ and $CO_2(g)$. **(b)** Indicate the oxidation number for each atom involved in the reaction in part (a). What elements are being oxidized and reduced? **(c)** What mass of $KO_2(s)$ is needed to consume 18.0 g $CO_2(g)$? What mass of $O_2(g)$ is produced during this reaction?

CHAPTER 8

BASIC CONCEPTS OF CHEMICAL BONDING

THE WHITE CLIFFS OF DOVER in southeastern England are made up largely of chalk, a porous form of limestone. The mineral calcite, with a composition of $CaCO_3$, is the predominant chemical substance in both chalk and limestone. Much of Earth's calcite is produced by marine organisms, which combine Ca^{2+} and CO_3^{2-} ions to form shells of $CaCO_3$. The presence of CO_3^{2-} ions in oceans can be traced to dissolved CO_2 from the atmosphere.

296

8.1 Chemical Bonds, Lewis Symbols, and the Octet Rule
We can broadly characterize chemical bonds into three types: *ionic*, *covalent*, and *metallic*. In evaluating bonding, *Lewis symbols* provide a useful shorthand notation for keeping track of the valence electrons in atoms and ions.

8.2 Ionic Bonding
We will observe that in ionic substances the atoms are held together by the electrostatic attractions between ions of opposite charge. We will study the energetics of formation of ionic substances and describe the *lattice energy* of these substances.

8.3 Covalent Bonding
We also recognize that the atoms in molecular substances are held together by the sharing of one or more electron pairs between atoms. In general the electrons are shared in such a way that each atom attains an *octet* of electrons.

8.4 Bond Polarity and Electronegativity
We define *electronegativity* as the ability of an atom in a compound to attract electrons to itself. In general, electron pairs will be shared unequally between atoms of differing electronegativity, leading to *polar covalent bonds*.

8.5 Drawing Lewis Structures
We will see that *Lewis structures* are a simple yet powerful way of predicting the covalent bonding patterns within molecules. In addition to the octet rule, we will see that the concept of *formal charge* can be used to identify the most favorable Lewis structure.

8.6 Resonance Structures
We observe that in some cases more than one equivalent Lewis structure can be drawn for a molecule or polyatomic ion. The actual structure in such cases is a blend of two or more contributing Lewis structures, called *resonance structures*.

8.7 Exceptions to the Octet Rule
We recognize that the octet rule is more of a guideline than an inviolate rule. Exceptions to the octet rule include molecules with an odd number of electrons; molecules where large differences in electronegativity prevent an atom from completing its octet; and, most commonly, molecules where an element from the third period or lower attains more than an octet of electrons.

8.8 Strengths of Covalent Bonds
We observe that bond strengths vary with the number of shared electron pairs as well as other factors. We can use *average bond enthalpy* values to estimate the enthalpies of reactions in cases where thermodynamic data such as heats of formation are unavailable.

CALCIUM CARBONATE, $CaCO_3$, IS ONE OF THE MOST INTERESTING AND VERSATILE COMPOUNDS on the planet. It accounts for roughly 4% of Earth's crust and is the major component of rocks such as limestone and marble. The white cliffs of Dover in southeastern England are one of the most

famous natural formations of $CaCO_3$. The cliffs consist almost entirely of a porous form of limestone called chalk.

Unlike most inorganic substances, $CaCO_3$ is widely used by living organisms and is found in objects such as seashells, coral, eggshells, and pearls. Calcium carbonate plays a role in the complex chemistry associated with the greenhouse effect because it is formed in the oceans through the reaction between calcium ions and dissolved carbon dioxide. When limestone is heated to elevated temperatures, $CaCO_3$ decomposes into solid CaO (the important industrial chemical called quicklime) and gaseous CO_2. Calcium carbonate undergoes the reactions that it does because the atoms in $CaCO_3$ are held

297

together by a combination of two different types of bonds. The carbon and oxygen atoms that make up the carbonate ion share valence electrons, resulting in the formation of *covalent bonds*. The oppositely charged Ca^{2+} and CO_3^{2-} ions are held together by electrostatic attractions, which are called *ionic bonds*.

The properties of substances are determined in large part by the *chemical bonds* that hold their atoms together. What determines the type of bonding in each substance? How do the characteristics of these bonds give rise to different physical and chemical properties? The keys to answering the first question are found in the electronic structures of the atoms involved, which we discussed in Chapters 6 and 7. In this chapter and the next, we will examine the relationship between the electronic structures of atoms and the chemical bonds they form. We will also see how the properties of ionic and covalent substances arise from the distributions of electronic charge within atoms, ions, and molecules.

8.1 CHEMICAL BONDS, LEWIS SYMBOLS, AND THE OCTET RULE

Whenever two atoms or ions are strongly attached to each other, we say there is a **chemical bond** between them. There are three general types of chemical bonds: ionic, covalent, and metallic. Figure 8.1 ◄ shows examples of substances in which we find each of these types of attractive forces.

The term **ionic bond** refers to electrostatic forces that exist between ions of opposite charge. Ions may be formed from atoms by the transfer of one or more electrons from one atom to another. Ionic substances generally result from the interaction of metals on the left side of the periodic table with nonmetals on the right side (excluding the noble gases, group 8A). Ionic bonding will be discussed in Section 8.2.

A **covalent bond** results from the sharing of electrons between two atoms. The most familiar examples of covalent bonding are seen in the interactions of nonmetallic elements with one another. We devote much of this chapter and the next to describing and understanding covalent bonds.

Metallic bonds are found in metals, such as copper, iron, and aluminum. Each atom in a metal is bonded to several neighboring atoms. The bonding electrons are relatively free to move throughout the three-dimensional structure of the metal. Metallic bonds give rise to such typical metallic properties as high electrical conductivity and luster. We will examine these bonds in Chapter 23.

Lewis Symbols

The electrons involved in chemical bonding are the *valence electrons*, which, for most atoms, are those residing in the outermost occupied shell of an atom. ⇐⇒ (Section 6.8) The American chemist G. N. Lewis (1875–1946) suggested a simple way of showing the valence electrons in an atom and tracking them in the course of bond formation, using what are now known as *Lewis electron-dot symbols*, or merely Lewis symbols.

The **Lewis symbol** for an element consists of the chemical symbol for the element plus a dot for each valence electron. Sulfur, for example, has the electron configuration $[Ne]3s^2 3p^4$; its Lewis symbol therefore shows six valence electrons:

The dots are placed on the four sides of the atomic symbol: the top, the bottom, and the left and right sides. Each side can accommodate up to two electrons. All four sides of the symbol are equivalent, which means that the choice of which sides accommodate the fifth and sixth electrons is arbitrary.

▼ Figure 8.1 **Chemical bonds.** Examples of substances in which (a) ionic, (b) covalent, and (c) metallic bonds are found.

Magnesium oxide

Potassium dichromate   Nickel(II) oxide

(a)

Sulfur

Bromine   Sucrose

(b)

Magnesium

Gold   Copper

(c)

TABLE 8.1 ■ Lewis Symbols					
Element	**Electron Configuration**	**Lewis Symbol**	**Element**	**Electron Configuration**	**Lewis Symbol**
Li	$[He]2s^1$	Li·	Na	$[Ne]3s^1$	Na·
Be	$[He]2s^2$	·Be·	Mg	$[Ne]3s^2$	·Mg·
B	$[He]2s^22p^1$	·Ḃ·	Al	$[Ne]3s^23p^1$	·Ȧl·
C	$[He]2s^22p^2$	·Ċ·	Si	$[Ne]3s^23p^2$	·Ṡi·
N	$[He]2s^22p^3$	·N̈:	P	$[Ne]3s^23p^3$	·P̈:
O	$[He]2s^22p^4$	:Ö:	S	$[Ne]3s^23p^4$	:S̈:
F	$[He]2s^22p^5$	·F̈:	Cl	$[Ne]3s^23p^5$	·C̈l:
Ne	$[He]2s^22p^6$	:N̈e:	Ar	$[Ne]3s^23p^6$	:Ȧr:

The electron configurations and Lewis symbols for the representative elements of the second and third rows of the periodic table are shown in Table 8.1 ▲. Notice that the number of valence electrons in any representative element is the same as the group number of the element. For example, the Lewis symbols for oxygen and sulfur, members of group 6A, both show six dots.

GIVE IT SOME THOUGHT

Are all three of the following Lewis symbols for Cl correct?

:C̈l·   ·C̈l: :Ċl·

The Octet Rule

Atoms often gain, lose, or share electrons to achieve the same number of electrons as the noble gas closest to them in the periodic table. The noble gases have very stable electron arrangements, as evidenced by their high ionization energies, low affinity for additional electrons, and general lack of chemical reactivity. (Section 7.8) Because all noble gases (except He) have eight valence electrons, many atoms undergoing reactions also end up with eight valence electrons. This observation has led to a guideline known as the **octet rule:** *Atoms tend to gain, lose, or share electrons until they are surrounded by eight valence electrons.*

An octet of electrons consists of full s and p subshells in an atom. In terms of Lewis symbols, an octet can be thought of as four pairs of valence electrons arranged around the atom, as in the Lewis symbol for Ne in Table 8.1. There are many exceptions to the octet rule, but it provides a useful framework for introducing many important concepts of bonding.

8.2 IONIC BONDING

When sodium metal, Na(s), is brought into contact with chlorine gas, $Cl_2(g)$, a violent reaction ensues (Figure 8.2 ▼). The product of this very exothermic reaction is sodium chloride, NaCl(s):

$$Na(s) + \tfrac{1}{2}Cl_2(g) \longrightarrow NaCl(s) \qquad \Delta H_f^\circ = -410.9 \text{ kJ} \qquad [8.1]$$

Sodium chloride is composed of Na^+ and Cl^- ions, which are arranged in a regular three-dimensional array, as shown in Figure 8.3 ▼.

The formation of Na^+ from Na and Cl^- from Cl_2 indicates that an electron has been lost by a sodium atom and gained by a chlorine atom—we can envision an *electron transfer* from the Na atom to the Cl atom. Two of the atomic properties we discussed in Chapter 7 give us an indication of how readily electron transfer

FORMATION OF SODIUM CHLORIDE

When metals and nonmetals react, electrons are transferred from the metal atoms to the nonmetal atoms, forming ions. The principal reason that ionic compounds are stable is the attraction between ions of unlike charge, which draws them together, releasing energy and causing the ions to form a solid array or lattice.

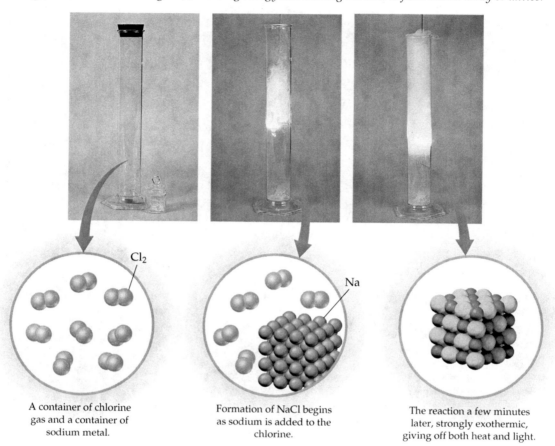

Cl₂

Na

A container of chlorine gas and a container of sodium metal.

Formation of NaCl begins as sodium is added to the chlorine.

The reaction a few minutes later, strongly exothermic, giving off both heat and light.

▲ Figure 8.2 **Formation of sodium chloride.**

▲ Figure 8.3 **The crystal structure of sodium chloride.** In this three-dimensional array of ions, each Na^+ ion is surrounded by six Cl^- ions, and each Cl^- ion is surrounded by six Na^+ ions.

occurs: the ionization energy, which indicates how easily an electron can be removed from an atom, and the electron affinity, which measures how much an atom wants to gain an electron. (Sections 7.4 and 7.5) Electron transfer to form oppositely charged ions occurs when one of the atoms readily gives up an electron (low ionization energy) and the other atom readily gains an electron (high electron affinity). Thus, NaCl is a typical ionic compound because it consists of a metal of low ionization energy and a nonmetal of high electron affinity. Using Lewis electron-dot symbols (and showing a chlorine atom rather than the Cl_2 molecule), we can represent this reaction as follows:

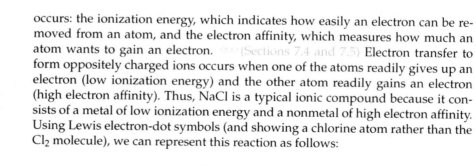

$$Na\cdot + \cdot\ddot{\underset{..}{Cl}}: \longrightarrow Na^+ + [:\ddot{\underset{..}{Cl}}:]^- \qquad [8.2]$$

The arrow indicates the transfer of an electron from the Na atom to the Cl atom. Each ion has an octet of electrons, the octet on Na^+ being the $2s^2 2p^6$ electrons that lie below the single $3s$ valence electron of the Na atom. We have put a bracket around the chloride ion to emphasize that all eight electrons are located on the Cl^- ion.

Science Fundamentals

GIVE IT SOME THOUGHT

Describe the electron transfers that occur in the formation of calcium oxide from elemental calcium and oxygen.

Energetics of Ionic Bond Formation

As seen in Figure 8.2, the reaction of sodium with chlorine is *very* exothermic. In fact, Equation 8.1 is the reaction for the formation of $NaCl(s)$ from its elements, so that the enthalpy change for the reaction is ΔH_f° for $NaCl(s)$. In Appendix C we see that the heat of formation of other ionic substances is also quite negative. What factors make the formation of ionic compounds so exothermic?

In Equation 8.2 we represented the formation of NaCl as the transfer of an electron from Na to Cl. Recall from our discussion of ionization energies, however, that the loss of electrons from an atom is always an endothermic process. (Section 7.4) Removing an electron from $Na(g)$ to form $Na^+(g)$, for instance, requires 496 kJ/mol. Conversely, when a nonmetal gains an electron, the process is generally exothermic, as seen from the negative electron affinities of the elements. (Section 7.5) Adding an electron to $Cl(g)$, for example, releases 349 kJ/mol. If the transfer of an electron from one atom to another were the only factor in forming an ionic bond, the overall process would not be exothermic. For example, removing an electron from $Na(g)$ and adding it to $Cl(g)$ is an endothermic process that requires $496 - 349 = 147$ kJ/mol. This endothermic process corresponds to the formation of sodium and chloride ions that are infinitely far apart—in other words, the positive energy change assumes that the ions are not interacting with one another, which is quite different from the situation in ionic solids.

GIVE IT SOME THOUGHT

Consider the ionization energies of the alkali metals and the electron affinities of the halogens given in Chapter 7. Can you find any pair where the transfer of an electron from the alkali metal to the halogen would be an exothermic process?

The principal reason that ionic compounds are stable is the attraction between ions of unlike charge. This attraction draws the ions together, releasing energy and causing the ions to form a solid array, or lattice, such as that shown for NaCl in Figure 8.3. A measure of just how much stabilization results from arranging oppositely charged ions in an ionic solid is given by the **lattice energy**, which is *the energy required to completely separate a mole of a solid ionic compound into its gaseous ions.*

To get a picture of this process for NaCl, imagine that the structure shown in Figure 8.3 expands from within, so that the distances between the ions increase until the ions are very far apart. This process requires 788 kJ/mol, which is the value of the lattice energy:

$$NaCl(s) \longrightarrow Na^+(g) + Cl^-(g)$$

$$\Delta H_{lattice} = +788 \text{ kJ/mol} \qquad [8.3]$$

Notice that this process is highly endothermic. The reverse process—the coming together of $Na(g)^+$ and $Cl(g)^-$ to form $NaCl(s)$—is therefore highly exothermic $\Delta H = -788$ kJ/mol.

Table 8.2 ▶ lists the lattice energies of NaCl and other ionic compounds. All are large positive values, indicating that the ions are strongly attracted to one another in these solids. The energy released by the

TABLE 8.2 ▪ Lattice Energies for Some Ionic Compounds

Compound	Lattice Energy (kJ/mol)	Compound	Lattice Energy (kJ/mol)
LiF	1030	MgCl$_2$	2326
LiCl	834	SrCl$_2$	2127
LiI	730		
NaF	910	MgO	3795
NaCl	788	CaO	3414
NaBr	732	SrO	3217
NaI	682		
KF	808	ScN	7547
KCl	701		
KBr	671		
CsCl	657		
CsI	600		

attraction between ions of unlike charge more than makes up for the endother-mic nature of ionization energies, making the formation of ionic compounds an exothermic process. The strong attractions also cause most ionic materials to be hard and brittle, with high melting points—for example, NaCl melts at 801 °C.

The magnitude of the lattice energy of a solid depends on the charges of the ions, their sizes, and their arrangement in the solid. We saw in Chapter 5 that the potential energy of two interacting charged particles is given by

$$E_{el} = \frac{\kappa Q_1 Q_2}{d}$$ [8.4]

In this equation Q_1 and Q_2 are the charges on the particles, d is the distance be-tween their centers, and κ is a constant, 8.99×10^9 J-m/C^2. ᴄᴄᴄ (Section 5.1) Equation 8.4 indicates that the attractive interaction between two oppositely charged ions increases as the magnitudes of their charges increase and as the distance between their centers decreases. Thus, *for a given arrangement of ions, the lattice energy increases as the charges on the ions increase and as their radii decrease*. The magnitude of lattice energies depends predominantly on the ionic charges because ionic radii vary over only a limited range.

■■ **SAMPLE EXERCISE 8.1** | **Magnitudes of Lattice Energies**

Without consulting Table 8.2, arrange the following ionic compounds in order of in-creasing lattice energy: NaF, CsI, and CaO.

SOLUTION

Analyze: From the formulas for three ionic compounds, we must determine their relative lattice energies.

Plan: We need to determine the charges and relative sizes of the ions in the com-pounds. We can then use Equation 8.4 qualitatively to determine the relative ener-gies, knowing that the larger the ionic charges, the greater the energy and the farther apart the ions are, the lower the energy.

Solve: NaF consists of Na^+ and F^- ions, CsI of Cs^+ and I^- ions, and CaO of Ca^{2+} and O^{2-} ions. Because the product of the charges, $Q_1 Q_2$, appears in the numerator of Equation 8.4, the lattice energy will increase dramatically when the charges of the ions increase. Thus, we expect the lattice energy of CaO, which has 2+ and 2− ions, to be the greatest of the three.

The ionic charges in NaF and CsI are the same. As a result, the difference in their lattice energies will depend on the difference in the distance between the centers of the ions in their lattice. Because ionic size increases as we go down a group in the period-ic table (Section 7.3), we know that Cs^+ is larger than Na^+ and I^- is larger than F^-. Therefore the distance between the Na^+ and F^- ions in NaF will be less than the dis-tance between the Cs^+ and I^- ions in CsI. As a result, the lattice energy of NaF should be greater than that of CsI. In order of increasing energy, therefore, we have CsI < NaF < CaO.

Check: Table 8.2 confirms our predicted order is correct.

■■ **PRACTICE EXERCISE**

Which substance would you expect to have the greatest lattice energy, MgF_2, CaF_2, or ZrO_2?
Answer: ZrO_2

Electron Configurations of Ions of the *s*- and *p*-Block Elements

We began considering the electron configurations of ions in Section 7.4. In light of our examination of ionic bonding, we will continue with that discussion here. The energetics of ionic bond formation helps explain why many ions tend to have noble-gas electron configurations. For example, sodium readily loses one electron to form Na^+, which has the same electron configuration as Ne:

Na $1s^2 2s^2 2p^6 3s^1$ = [Ne]$3s^1$

Na^+ $1s^2 2s^2 2p^6$ = [Ne]

Even though lattice energy increases with increasing ionic charge, we never find ionic compounds that contain Na^{2+} ions. The second electron removed would have to come from an inner shell of the sodium atom, and removing electrons from an inner shell requires a very large amount of energy. (Section 7.4) The increase in lattice energy is not enough to compensate for the energy needed to remove an inner-shell electron. Thus, sodium and the other group 1A metals are found in ionic substances only as 1+ ions.

Similarly, the addition of electrons to nonmetals is either exothermic or only slightly endothermic as long as the electrons are being added to the valence shell. Thus, a Cl atom easily adds an electron to form Cl^-, which has the same electron configuration as Ar:

$$Cl \qquad 1s^2 2s^2 2p^6 3s^2 3p^5 = [Ne]3s^2 3p^5$$
$$Cl^- \qquad 1s^2 2s^2 2p^6 3s^2 3p^6 = [Ne]3s^2 3p^6 = [Ar]$$

To form a Cl^{2-} ion, the second electron would have to be added to the next higher shell of the Cl atom, which is energetically very unfavorable. Therefore, we never observe Cl^{2-} ions in ionic compounds. Based on these concepts, we expect that ionic compounds of the representative metals from groups 1A, 2A, and 3A will contain cations with charges of 1+, 2+, and 3+, respectively. Likewise, ionic compounds of the representative nonmetals of groups 5A, 6A, and 7A usually contain anions of charge 3−, 2−, and 1−, respectively.

■ SAMPLE EXERCISE 8.2 | Charges on Ions

Predict the ion generally formed by (a) Sr, (b) S, (c) Al.

SOLUTION

Analyze: We must decide how many electrons are most likely to be gained or lost by atoms of Sr, S, and Al.

Plan: In each case we can use the element's position in the periodic table to predict whether it will form a cation or an anion. We can then use its electron configuration to determine the ion that is likely to be formed.

Solve: (a) Strontium is a metal in group 2A and will therefore form a cation. Its electron configuration is $[Kr]5s^2$, and so we expect that the two valence electrons can be lost easily to give an Sr^{2+} ion. (b) Sulfur is a nonmetal in group 6A and will thus tend to be found as an anion. Its electron configuration ($[Ne]3s^2 3p^4$) is two electrons short of a noble-gas configuration. Thus, we expect that sulfur will form S^{2-} ions. (c) Aluminum is a metal in group 3A. We therefore expect it to form Al^{3+} ions.

Check: The ionic charges we predict here are confirmed in Tables 2.4 and 2.5.

■ PRACTICE EXERCISE

Predict the charges on the ions formed when magnesium reacts with nitrogen.
Answer: Mg^{2+} and N^{3-}

Transition-Metal Ions

Because ionization energies increase rapidly for each successive electron removed, the lattice energies of ionic compounds are generally large enough to compensate for the loss of up to only three electrons from atoms. Thus, we find cations with charges of 1+, 2+, or 3+ in ionic compounds. Most transition metals, however, have more than three electrons beyond a noble-gas core. Silver, for example, has a $[Kr]4d^{10}5s^1$ electron configuration. Metals of group 1B (Cu, Ag, Au) often occur as 1+ ions (as in CuBr and AgCl). In forming Ag^+, the 5s electron is lost, leaving a completely filled 4d subshell. As in this example, transition metals generally do not form ions that have a noble-gas configuration. The octet rule, although useful, is clearly limited in scope.

Recall from our discussion in Section 7.4 that when a positive ion is formed from an atom, electrons are always lost first from the subshell having the

A Closer Look CALCULATION OF LATTICE ENERGIES: THE BORN–HABER CYCLE

Lattice energy is a useful concept because it relates directly to the stability of an ionic solid. Unfortunately, the lattice energy cannot be determined directly by experiment. It can, however, be calculated by envisioning the formation of an ionic compound as occurring in a series of well-defined steps. We can then use Hess's law (Section 5.6) to put these steps together in a way that gives us the lattice energy for the compound. By so doing, we construct a **Born–Haber cycle**, a thermochemical cycle named after the German scientists Max Born (1882–1970) and Fritz Haber (1868–1934), who introduced it to analyze the factors contributing to the stability of ionic compounds.

In the Born–Haber cycle for NaCl, we consider the formation of NaCl(s) from the elements Na(s) and $Cl_2(g)$ by two different routes, as shown in Figure 8.4▶. The enthalpy change for the direct route (red arrow) is the heat of formation of NaCl(s):

$$Na(s) + \tfrac{1}{2} Cl_2(g) \longrightarrow NaCl(s)$$

$$\Delta H_f^\circ[NaCl(s)] = -411 \text{ kJ} \quad [8.5]$$

The indirect route consists of five steps, shown by the green arrows in Figure 8.4. First, we generate gaseous atoms of sodium by vaporizing sodium metal. Then we form gaseous atoms of chlorine by breaking the bonds in the Cl_2 molecules. The enthalpy changes for these processes are available to us as enthalpies of formation (Appendix C):

$$Na(s) \longrightarrow Na(g) \quad \Delta H_f^\circ[Na(g)] = 108 \text{ kJ} \quad [8.6]$$

$$\tfrac{1}{2} Cl_2(g) \longrightarrow Cl(g) \quad \Delta H_f^\circ[Cl(g)] = 122 \text{ kJ} \quad [8.7]$$

Both of these processes are endothermic; energy is required to generate gaseous sodium and chlorine atoms.

In the next two steps we remove the electron from Na(g) to form $Na^+(g)$ and then add the electron to Cl(g) to form $Cl^-(g)$. The enthalpy changes for these processes equal the first ionization energy of Na, $I_1(Na)$, and the electron affinity of Cl, denoted E(Cl), respectively: (Sections 7.4, 7.5)

$$Na(g) \longrightarrow Na^+(g) + e^- \quad \Delta H = I_1(Na) = 496 \text{ kJ} \quad [8.8]$$

$$Cl(g) + e^- \longrightarrow Cl^-(g) \quad \Delta H = E(Cl) = -349 \text{ kJ} \quad [8.9]$$

Finally, we combine the gaseous sodium and chloride ions to form solid sodium chloride. Because this process is just the reverse of the lattice energy (breaking a solid into gaseous ions), the enthalpy change is the negative of the lattice energy, the quantity that we want to determine:

$$Na^+(g) + Cl^-(g) \longrightarrow NaCl(s)$$

$$\Delta H = -\Delta H_{lattice} = ? \quad [8.10]$$

The sum of the five steps in the indirect path (green arrows) gives us NaCl(s) from Na(s) and $\tfrac{1}{2} Cl_2(g)$. Thus, from Hess's law we know that the sum of the enthalpy changes for these five steps equals that for the direct path, indicated by the red arrow, Equation 8.5:

$$\Delta H_f^\circ[NaCl(s)] = \Delta H_f^\circ[Na(g)] + \Delta H_f^\circ[Cl(g)]$$
$$+ I_1(Na) + E(Cl) - \Delta H_{lattice}$$

$$-411 \text{ kJ} = 108 \text{ kJ} + 122 \text{ kJ} + 496 \text{ kJ} - 349 \text{ kJ} - \Delta H_{lattice}$$

Solving for $\Delta H_{lattice}$:

$$\Delta H_{lattice} = 108 \text{ kJ} + 122 \text{ kJ} + 496 \text{ kJ} - 349 \text{ kJ} + 411 \text{ kJ}$$
$$= 788 \text{ kJ}$$

Thus, the lattice energy of NaCl is 788 kJ/mol.

Related Exercises: 8.26, 8.27, and 8.28

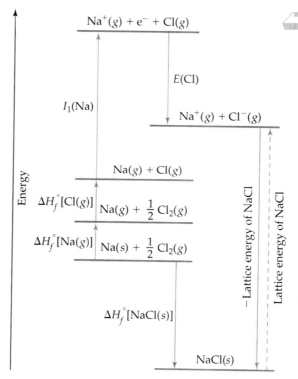

▲ Figure 8.4 **The Born–Haber cycle.** This representation shows the energetic relationships in the formation of ionic solids from the elements. By Hess's law, the enthalpy of formation of NaCl(s) from elemental sodium and chlorine (Equation 8.5) is equal to the sum of the energies of several individual steps (Equations 8.6 through 8.10).

largest value of *n*. Thus, *in forming ions, transition metals lose the valence-shell s electrons first, then as many d electrons as are required to reach the charge of the ion.* Let's consider Fe, which has the electron configuration $[Ar]3d^6 4s^2$. In forming the Fe^{2+} ion, the two 4s electrons are lost, leading to an $[Ar]3d^6$ configuration. Removal of an additional electron gives the Fe^{3+} ion, whose electron configuration is $[Ar]3d^5$.

Which element forms a 2+ ion that has the electron configuration $[Kr]4d^8$?

8.3 COVALENT BONDING

Ionic substances possess several characteristic properties. They are usually brittle substances with high melting points. They are usually crystalline. Furthermore, ionic crystals often can be cleaved; that is, they break apart along smooth, flat surfaces. These characteristics result from electrostatic forces that maintain the ions in a rigid, well-defined, three-dimensional arrangement such as that shown in Figure 8.3.

The vast majority of chemical substances do not have the characteristics of ionic materials. Most of the substances with which we come into daily contact—such as water—tend to be gases, liquids, or solids with low melting points. Many, such as gasoline, vaporize readily. Many are pliable in their solid forms—for example, plastic bags and paraffin.

For the very large class of substances that do not behave like ionic substances, we need a different model for the bonding between atoms. G. N. Lewis reasoned that atoms might acquire a noble-gas electron configuration by sharing electrons with other atoms. As we noted in Section 8.1, a chemical bond formed by sharing a pair of electrons is called a *covalent bond*.

The hydrogen molecule, H_2, provides the simplest example of a covalent bond. When two hydrogen atoms are close to each other, electrostatic interactions occur between them. The two positively charged nuclei repel each other, the two negatively charged electrons repel each other, and the nuclei and electrons attract each other, as shown in Figure 8.5▶. Because the H_2 molecule exists as a stable entity, the attractive forces must exceed the repulsive ones. Let's take a closer look at the attractive forces that hold this molecule together.

By using quantum mechanical methods analogous to those employed for atoms   (Section 6.5), it is possible to calculate the distribution of electron density in molecules. Such a calculation for H_2 shows that the attractions between the nuclei and the electrons cause electron density to concentrate between the nuclei, as shown in Figure 8.5(b). As a result, the overall electrostatic interactions are attractive. Thus, the atoms in H_2 are held together principally because the two nuclei are electrostatically attracted to the concentration of negative charge between them. In essence, the shared pair of electrons in any covalent bond acts as a kind of "glue" to bind atoms together.

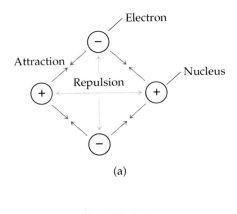

(a)

(b)

▲ Figure 8.5 **The covalent bond in H_2.** (a) The attractions and repulsions among electrons and nuclei in the hydrogen molecule. (b) Electron distribution in the H_2 molecule. The concentration of electron density between the nuclei leads to a net attractive force that constitutes the covalent bond holding the molecule together.

If a H_2 molecule is ionized to form H_2^+, it will change the bond strength. Based on the simple description of covalent bonding given above, would you expect the H—H bond in H_2^+ to be weaker or stronger than the H—H bond in H_2?

Lewis Structures

The formation of covalent bonds can be represented using Lewis symbols for the constituent atoms. The formation of the H_2 molecule from two H atoms, for example, can be represented as

$$H\cdot + \cdot H \longrightarrow H:H$$

In this way, each hydrogen atom acquires a second electron, achieving the stable, two-electron, noble-gas electron configuration of helium.

The formation of a bond between two Cl atoms to give a Cl_2 molecule can be represented in a similar way:

$$:\ddot{C}l\cdot + \cdot\ddot{C}l: \longrightarrow :\ddot{C}l:\ddot{C}l:$$

By sharing the bonding electron pair, each chlorine atom has eight electrons (an octet) in its valence shell. It thus achieves the noble-gas electron configuration of argon.

The structures shown here for H_2 and Cl_2 are called **Lewis structures** (or Lewis electron-dot structures). In writing Lewis structures, we usually show each electron pair shared between atoms as a line and the unshared electron pairs as dots. Written this way, the Lewis structures for H_2 and Cl_2 are

$$H\!-\!H \qquad\qquad :\!\ddot{C}l\!-\!\ddot{C}l\!:$$

For the nonmetals, the number of valence electrons in a neutral atom is the same as the group number. Therefore, one might predict that 7A elements, such as F, would form one covalent bond to achieve an octet; 6A elements, such as O, would form two covalent bonds; 5A elements, such as N, would form three covalent bonds; and 4A elements, such as C, would form four covalent bonds. These predictions are borne out in many compounds. For example, consider the simple hydrogen compounds of the nonmetals of the second row of the periodic table:

$$H\!-\!\ddot{\underset{}{F}}\!: \qquad H\!-\!\underset{\underset{H}{|}}{\ddot{O}}\!: \qquad H\!-\!\underset{\underset{H}{|}}{\ddot{N}}\!-\!H \qquad H\!-\!\underset{\underset{H}{|}}{\overset{\overset{H}{|}}{C}}\!-\!H$$

Thus, the Lewis model succeeds in accounting for the compositions of many compounds of nonmetals, in which covalent bonding predominates.

■ SAMPLE EXERCISE 8.3 | Lewis Structure of a Compound

Given the Lewis symbols for the elements nitrogen and fluorine shown in Table 8.1, predict the formula of the stable binary compound (a compound composed of two elements) formed when nitrogen reacts with fluorine, and draw its Lewis structure.

SOLUTION

Analyze: The Lewis symbols for nitrogen and fluorine reveal that nitrogen has five valence electrons and fluorine has seven.

Plan: We need to find a combination of the two elements that results in an octet of electrons around each atom in the compound. Nitrogen requires three additional electrons to complete its octet, whereas fluorine requires only one. Sharing a pair of electrons between one N atom and one F atom will result in an octet of electrons for fluorine but not for nitrogen. We therefore need to figure out a way to get two more electrons for the N atom.

Solve: Nitrogen must share a pair of electrons with three fluorine atoms to complete its octet. Thus, the Lewis structure for the resulting compound, NF_3, is

$$\cdot\ddot{N}\cdot + 3\cdot\ddot{F}\!: \longrightarrow :\!\ddot{F}\!:\!\underset{\underset{:\ddot{F}:}{}}{\ddot{N}}\!:\!\ddot{F}\!: \longrightarrow :\!\ddot{F}\!-\!\underset{\underset{:\ddot{F}:}{|}}{\ddot{N}}\!-\!\ddot{F}\!:$$

Check: The Lewis structure in the center shows that each atom is surrounded by an octet of electrons. Once you are accustomed to thinking of each line in a Lewis structure as representing *two* electrons, you can just as easily use the structure on the right to check for octets.

■ PRACTICE EXERCISE

Compare the Lewis symbol for neon with the Lewis structure for methane, CH_4. In what important way are the electron arrangements about neon and carbon alike? In what important respect are they different?
Answer: Both atoms have an octet of electrons about them. However, the electrons about neon are unshared electron pairs, whereas those about carbon are shared with four hydrogen atoms.

Multiple Bonds

The sharing of a pair of electrons constitutes a single covalent bond, generally referred to simply as a **single bond**. In many molecules, atoms attain complete octets by sharing more than one pair of electrons. When two electron pairs are shared, two lines are drawn, representing a **double bond**. In carbon dioxide, for example, bonding occurs between carbon, with four valence electrons, and oxygen, with six:

$$:\ddot{O}: + \cdot\dot{C}\cdot + :\ddot{O}: \longrightarrow \ddot{O}::C::\ddot{O} \quad (\text{or } \ddot{O}=C=\ddot{O})$$

As the diagram shows, each oxygen acquires an octet of electrons by sharing two electron pairs with carbon. Carbon, on the other hand, acquires an octet of electrons by sharing two electron pairs in each of the two bonds it forms with oxygen.

A **triple bond** corresponds to the sharing of three pairs of electrons, such as in the N_2 molecule:

$$:\dot{N}\cdot + \cdot\dot{N}: \longrightarrow :N:::N: \quad (\text{or } :N\equiv N:)$$

Because each nitrogen atom possesses five electrons in its valence shell, three electron pairs must be shared to achieve the octet configuration.

The properties of N_2 are in complete accord with its Lewis structure. Nitrogen is a diatomic gas with exceptionally low reactivity that results from the very stable nitrogen–nitrogen bond. Study of the structure of N_2 reveals that the nitrogen atoms are separated by only 1.10 Å. The short N—N bond distance is a result of the triple bond between the atoms. From structure studies of many different substances in which nitrogen atoms share one or two electron pairs, we have learned that the average distance between bonded nitrogen atoms varies with the number of shared electron pairs:

N—N	N=N	N≡N
1.47 Å	1.24 Å	1.10 Å

As a general rule, the distance between bonded atoms decreases as the number of shared electron pairs increases. The distance between the nuclei of the atoms involved in a bond is called the **bond length** for the bond. We first encountered bond lengths in Section 7.3 in our discussion of atomic radii, and we will discuss them further in Section 8.8.

GIVE IT SOME THOUGHT

The C—O bond length in carbon monoxide, CO, is 1.13 Å, whereas the C—O bond length in CO_2 is 1.24 Å. Without drawing a Lewis structure, do you think that carbon monoxide has a single, double, or triple bond between the C and O atoms?

8.4 BOND POLARITY AND ELECTRONEGATIVITY

When two identical atoms bond, as in Cl_2 or H_2, the electron pairs must be shared equally. In highly ionic compounds, on the other hand, such as NaCl, there is relatively little sharing of electrons, which means that NaCl is best described as composed of Na^+ and Cl^- ions. The 3s electron of the Na atom is, in effect, transferred completely to chlorine. The bonds that are found in most substances fall somewhere between these extremes.

The concept of **bond polarity** helps describe the sharing of electrons between atoms. A **nonpolar covalent bond** is one in which the electrons are shared equally between two atoms, as in the Cl_2 and N_2 examples we just cited.

In a **polar covalent bond**, one of the atoms exerts a greater attraction for the bonding electrons than the other. If the difference in relative ability to attract electrons is large enough, an ionic bond is formed.

Electronegativity

We use a quantity called electronegativity to estimate whether a given bond will be nonpolar covalent, polar covalent, or ionic. **Electronegativity** is defined as the ability of an atom *in a molecule* to attract electrons to itself. The greater an atom's electronegativity, the greater is its ability to attract electrons to itself. The electronegativity of an atom in a molecule is related to its ionization energy and electron affinity, which are properties of isolated atoms. The *ionization energy* measures how strongly a gaseous atom holds on to its electrons, (Section 7.4) while the *electron affinity* is a measure of how strongly an atom attracts additional electrons. (Section 7.5) An atom with a very negative electron affinity and high ionization energy will both attract electrons from other atoms and resist having its electrons attracted away; it will be highly electronegative.

Numerical estimates of electronegativity can be based on a variety of properties, not just ionization energy and electron affinity. The American chemist Linus Pauling (1901–1994) developed the first and most widely used electronegativity scale; he based his scale on thermochemical data. Figure 8.6 ◄ shows Pauling's electronegativity values for many of the elements. The values are unitless. Fluorine, the most electronegative element, has an electronegativity of 4.0. The least electronegative element, cesium, has an electronegativity of 0.7. The values for all other elements lie between these two extremes.

Within each period there is generally a steady increase in electronegativity from left to right; that is, from the most metallic to the most nonmetallic elements. With some exceptions (especially within the transition metals), electronegativity decreases with increasing atomic number in any one group. This is what we might expect because we know that ionization energies tend to decrease with increasing atomic number in a group and electron affinities do not change very much. You do not need to memorize numerical values for electronegativity. Instead, you should know the periodic trends so that you can predict which of two elements is more electronegative.

▼ Figure 8.6 **Electronegativities of the elements.** Electronegativity generally increases from left to right across a period and decreases from top to bottom down a group.

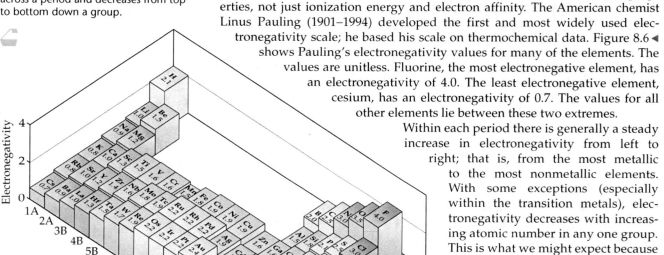

GIVE IT SOME THOUGHT

How does the *electronegativity* of an element differ from its *electron affinity*?

Electronegativity and Bond Polarity

We can use the difference in electronegativity between two atoms to gauge the polarity of the bonding between them. Consider these three fluorine-containing compounds:

Compound	F_2	HF	LiF
Electronegativity difference	$4.0 - 4.0 = 0$	$4.0 - 2.1 = 1.9$	$4.0 - 1.0 = 3.0$
Type of bond	Nonpolar covalent	Polar covalent	Ionic

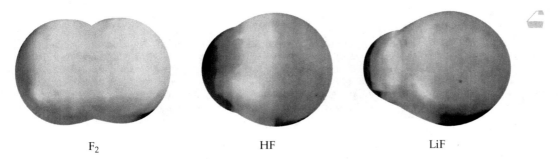

F_2 HF   LiF

▲ Figure 8.7 **Electron density distribution.** This computer-generated rendering shows the calculated electron-density distribution on the surface of the F_2, HF, and LiF molecules. The regions of relatively low electron density (net positive charge) appear blue, those of relatively high electron density (net negative charge) appear red, and regions that are close to electrically neutral appear green.

In F_2 the electrons are shared equally between the fluorine atoms, and thus the covalent bond is *nonpolar*. In general, a nonpolar covalent bond results when the electronegativities of the bonded atoms are equal.

In HF the fluorine atom has a greater electronegativity than the hydrogen atom, with the result that the sharing of electrons is unequal—the bond is polar. In general, a polar covalent bond results when the atoms differ in electronegativity. In HF the more electronegative fluorine atom attracts electron density away from the less electronegative hydrogen atom, leaving a partial positive charge on the hydrogen atom and a partial negative charge on the fluorine atom. We can represent this charge distribution as

$$\overset{\delta+ \quad \delta-}{H - F}$$

The $\delta+$ and $\delta-$ (read "delta plus" and "delta minus") symbolize the partial positive and negative charges, respectively.

In LiF the electronegativity difference is very large, meaning that the electron density is shifted far toward F. The resultant bond is therefore most accurately described as *ionic*. This shift of electron density toward the more electronegative atom can be seen in the results of calculations of electron density distributions. For the three species in our example, the calculated electron density distributions are shown in Figure 8.7 ▲. The regions of space that have relatively higher electron density are shown in red, and those with a relatively lower electron density are shown in blue. You can see that in F_2 the distribution is symmetrical, in HF it is clearly shifted toward fluorine, and in LiF the shift is even greater. These examples illustrate, therefore, that *the greater the difference in electronegativity between two atoms, the more polar their bond.*

GIVE IT SOME THOUGHT

Based on differences in electronegativity, how would you characterize the bonding in silicon nitride, Si_3N_4? Would you expect the bonds between Si and N to be nonpolar, polar covalent, or ionic?

■ **SAMPLE EXERCISE 8.4** | **Bond Polarity**

In each case, which bond is more polar: **(a)** B—Cl or C—Cl, **(b)** P—F or P—Cl? Indicate in each case which atom has the partial negative charge.

SOLUTION

Analyze: We are asked to determine relative bond polarities, given nothing but the atoms involved in the bonds.

Plan: Because we are not asked for quantitative answers, we can use the periodic table and our knowledge of electronegativity trends to answer the question.

Solve:

(a) The chlorine atom is common to both bonds. Therefore, the analysis reduces to a comparison of the electronegativities of B and C. Because boron is to the left of carbon in the periodic table, we predict that boron has the lower electronegativity. Chlorine, being on the right side of the table, has a higher electronegativity. The more polar bond will be the one between the atoms having the lowest electronegativity (boron) and the highest electronegativity (chlorine). Consequently, the B—Cl bond is more polar; the chlorine atom carries the partial negative charge because it has a higher electronegativity.

(b) In this example phosphorus is common to both bonds, and the analysis reduces to a comparison of the electronegativities of F and Cl. Because fluorine is above chlorine in the periodic table, it should be more electronegative and will form the more polar bond with P. The higher electronegativity of fluorine means that it will carry the partial negative charge.

Check:

(a) Using Figure 8.6: The difference in the electronegativities of chlorine and boron is $3.0 - 2.0 = 1.0$; the difference between chlorine and carbon is $3.0 - 2.5 = 0.5$. Hence the B—Cl bond is more polar, as we had predicted.

(b) Using Figure 8.6: The difference in the electronegativities of chlorine and phosphorus is $3.0 - 2.1 = 0.9$; the difference between fluorine and phosphorus is $4.0 - 2.1 = 1.9$. Hence the P—F bond is more polar, as we had predicted.

■ PRACTICE EXERCISE

Which of the following bonds is most polar: S—Cl, S—Br, Se—Cl, or Se—Br?
Answer: Se—Cl

Dipole Moments

The difference in electronegativity between H and F leads to a polar covalent bond in the HF molecule. As a consequence, there is a concentration of negative charge on the more electronegative F atom, leaving the less electronegative H atom at the positive end of the molecule. A molecule such as HF, in which the centers of positive and negative charge do not coincide, is said to be a **polar molecule**. Thus, we describe both bonds and entire molecules as being polar and nonpolar.

We can indicate the polarity of the HF molecule in two ways:

$$\overset{\delta+}{H}-\overset{\delta-}{F} \quad or \quad \overset{\longleftrightarrow}{H-F}$$

Recall from the preceding subsection that "$\delta+$" and "$\delta-$" indicate the partial positive and negative charges on the H and F atoms. In the notation on the right, the arrow denotes the shift in electron density toward the fluorine atom. The crossed end of the arrow can be thought of as a plus sign that designates the positive end of the molecule.

Polarity helps determine many of the properties of substances that we observe at the macroscopic level, in the laboratory and in everyday life. Polar molecules align themselves with respect to one another, with the negative end of one molecule and the positive end of another attracting each other. Polar molecules are likewise attracted to ions. The negative end of a polar molecule is attracted to a positive ion, and the positive end is attracted to a negative ion. These interactions account for many properties of liquids, solids, and solutions, as you will see in Chapters 11, 12, and 13.

How can we quantify the polarity of a molecule? Whenever a distance separates two electrical charges of equal magnitude but opposite sign, a **dipole** is established. The quantitative measure of the magnitude of a dipole is called its **dipole moment**, denoted μ. If a distance r separates two equal and opposite charges $Q+$ and $Q-$, the magnitude of the dipole moment is the product of Q and r (Figure 8.8 ◄):

$$\mu = Qr \tag{8.11}$$

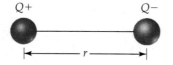

$Q+$ $Q-$

|←———r———→|

▲ Figure 8.8 **Dipole and dipole moment.** When charges of equal magnitude and opposite sign $Q+$ and $Q-$ are separated by a distance r, a dipole is produced. The size of the dipole is given by the dipole moment, μ, which is the product of the charge separated and the distance of separation between the charge centers: $\mu = Qr$.

The dipole moment increases as the magnitude of charge that is separated increases and as the distance between the charges increases. For a nonpolar molecule, such as F_2, the dipole moment is zero because there is no charge separation.

GIVE IT SOME THOUGHT

The molecules chlorine monofluoride, ClF, and iodine monofluoride, IF, are examples of *interhalogen* compounds—compounds that contain bonds between different halogen elements. Which of these molecules will have the larger dipole moment?

Dipole moments are usually reported in *debyes* (D), a unit that equals 3.34×10^{-30} coulomb-meters (C-m). For molecules, we usually measure charge in units of the electronic charge e, 1.60×10^{-19} C, and distance in units of angstroms. Suppose that two charges $1+$ and $1-$ (in units of e) are separated by a distance of 1.00 Å. The dipole moment produced is

$$\mu = Qr = (1.60 \times 10^{-19}\,\text{C})(1.00\,\text{Å})\left(\frac{10^{-10}\,\text{m}}{1\,\text{Å}}\right)\left(\frac{1\,\text{D}}{3.34 \times 10^{-30}\,\text{C-m}}\right) = 4.79\,\text{D}$$

Measurement of the dipole moments can provide us with valuable information about the charge distributions in molecules, as illustrated in Sample Exercise 8.5.

■ SAMPLE EXERCISE 8.5 | Dipole Moments of Diatomic Molecules

The bond length in the HCl molecule is 1.27 Å. **(a)** Calculate the dipole moment, in debyes, that would result if the charges on the H and Cl atoms were $1+$ and $1-$, respectively. **(b)** The experimentally measured dipole moment of $HCl(g)$ is 1.08 D. What magnitude of charge, in units of e, on the H and Cl atoms would lead to this dipole moment?

SOLUTION

Analyze and Plan: We are asked in (a) to calculate the dipole moment of HCl that would result if there were a full charge transferred from H to Cl. We can use Equation 8.11 to obtain this result. In (b), we are given the actual dipole moment for the molecule and will use that value to calculate the actual partial charges on the H and Cl atoms.

Solve:

(a) The charge on each atom is the electronic charge, $e = 1.60 \times 10^{-19}$ C. The separation is 1.27 Å. The dipole moment is therefore

$$\mu = Qr = (1.60 \times 10^{-19}\,\text{C})(1.27\,\text{Å})\left(\frac{10^{-10}\,\text{m}}{1\,\text{Å}}\right)\left(\frac{1\,\text{D}}{3.34 \times 10^{-30}\,\text{C-m}}\right) = 6.08\,\text{D}$$

(b) We know the value of μ, 1.08 D and the value of r, 1.27 Å. We want to calculate the value of Q:

$$Q = \frac{\mu}{r} = \frac{(1.08\,\text{D})\left(\dfrac{3.34 \times 10^{-30}\,\text{C-m}}{1\,\text{D}}\right)}{(1.27\,\text{Å})\left(\dfrac{10^{-10}\,\text{m}}{1\,\text{Å}}\right)} = 2.84 \times 10^{-20}\,\text{C}$$

We can readily convert this charge to units of e:

$$\text{Charge in } e = (2.84 \times 10^{-20}\,\text{C})\left(\frac{1\,e}{1.60 \times 10^{-19}\,\text{C}}\right) = 0.178e$$

Thus, the experimental dipole moment indicates that the charge separation in the HCl molecule is

$$\overset{0.178+}{\text{H}} - \overset{0.178-}{\text{Cl}}$$

Because the experimental dipole moment is less than that calculated in part (a), the charges on the atoms are much less than a full electronic charge. We could have anticipated this because the H—Cl bond is polar covalent rather than ionic.

■ PRACTICE EXERCISE

The dipole moment of chlorine monofluoride, $ClF(g)$, is 0.88 D. The bond length of the molecule is 1.63 Å. **(a)** Which atom is expected to have the partial negative charge? **(b)** What is the charge on that atom, in units of e?
Answers: **(a)** F, **(b)** 0.11−

TABLE 8.3 ▪ Bond Lengths, Electronegativity Differences, and Dipole Moments of the Hydrogen Halides

Compound	Bond Length (Å)	Electronegativity Difference	Dipole Moment (D)
HF	0.92	1.9	1.82
HCl	1.27	0.9	1.08
HBr	1.41	0.7	0.82
HI	1.61	0.4	0.44

Table 8.3 ◀ presents the bond lengths and dipole moments of the hydrogen halides. Notice that as we proceed from HF to HI, the electronegativity difference decreases and the bond length increases. The first effect decreases the amount of charge separated and causes the dipole moment to decrease from HF to HI, even though the bond length is increasing. Calculations identical to those used in Sample Exercise 8.5 show that the actual charges on the atoms decrease from 0.41+/0.41− in HF to 0.057+/0.057− in HI. We can "visualize" the varying degree of electronic charge shift in these substances from computer-generated renderings based on calculations of electron distribution, as shown in Figure 8.9 ▼. For these molecules, the change in the electronegativity difference has a greater effect on the dipole moment than does the change in bond length.

GIVE IT SOME THOUGHT

The bond between carbon and hydrogen is one of the most important types of bonds in chemistry. The length of a H—C bond is approximately 1.1 Å. Based on this distance and differences in electronegativity, would you predict the dipole moment of an individual H—C bond to be larger or smaller than the dipole moment of the H—I bond?

Before leaving this section let's return to the LiF molecule pictured in Figure 8.7. Under standard conditions LiF exists as an extended ionic solid with an arrangement of atoms analogous to the sodium chloride structure shown in Figure 8.3. However, it is possible to generate LiF molecules by vaporizing the solid at high temperature. The molecules have a dipole moment of 6.28 D and a bond distance of 1.53 Å. From these values we can calculate the charge on lithium and fluorine to be 0.857+ and 0.857−, respectively. This bond is extremely polar, and the presence of such large charges strongly favors the formation of an extended ionic lattice whereby each lithium ion is surrounded by fluoride ions and vice versa.

Differentiating Ionic and Covalent Bonding

To understand the interactions responsible for chemical bonding, it is advantageous to treat ionic and covalent bonding separately. That is the approach taken in this chapter, as well as in most undergraduate-level chemistry texts. The partitioning of bonding into ionic and covalent extremes is considered when we name chemical substances. We saw in Section 2.8 that there are two general approaches

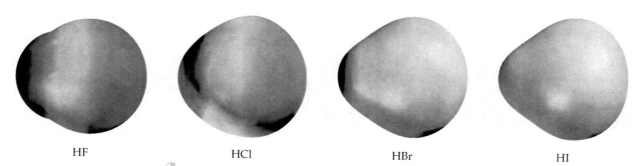

HF   HCl   HBr   HI

▲ Figure 8.9 **Charge separation in the hydrogen halides.** Blue represents regions of lowest electron density, red regions of highest electron density. In HF the strongly electronegative F pulls much of the electron density away from H. In HI the I, being much less electronegative than F, does not attract the shared electrons as strongly, and consequently there is far less polarization of the bond.

to naming binary compounds: one used for ionic compounds and the other for molecular ones. However, in reality there is a continuum between the extremes of ionic and covalent bonding. This lack of a well-defined separation between the two types of bonding may seem unsettling or confusing at first.

Fortunately, the simple models of ionic and covalent bonding presented in this chapter go quite a long way toward understanding and predicting the structures and properties of chemical compounds. When covalent bonding is dominant, more often than not we expect compounds to exist as molecules*, with all of the properties we associate with molecular substances, such as relatively low melting and boiling points and non-electrolyte behavior when dissolved in water. Furthermore, we will see later that the polarity of covalent bonds has important consequence for the properties of substances. On the other hand, when ionic bonding is dominant, we expect the compounds to possess very different properties. Ionic compounds tend to be brittle, high-melting solids with extended lattice structures and they exhibit strong electrolyte behavior when dissolved in water.

There are of course exceptions to these general stereotypes, some of which we will examine later in the book. Nonetheless, the ability to quickly categorize the predominant bonding interactions in a substance as covalent or ionic imparts considerable insight into the properties of that substance. The question then becomes what is the best system for recognizing which type of bonding will be dominant?

The simplest approach one can take is to assume that the interaction between a metal and a nonmetal will be ionic, while the interaction between two nonmetals will be covalent. While this classification scheme is reasonably predictive, there are far too many exceptions to use it blindly. For example, tin is a metal and chlorine is a nonmetal, but $SnCl_4$ is a molecular substance that exists as a colorless liquid at room temperature. It freezes at $-33\ °C$ and boils at $114\ °C$. Clearly the bonding in this substance is better described as polar covalent than ionic. A more sophisticated approach, as outlined in the preceding discussion, is to use the difference in electronegativity as the main criterion for determining whether ionic or covalent bonding will be dominant. This approach correctly predicts the bonding in $SnCl_4$ to be polar covalent based on an electronegativity difference of 1.2 and at the same time correctly predicts the bonding in NaCl to be predominantly ionic based on an electronegativity difference of 2.1.

Evaluating the bonding based on electronegativity difference is a useful system, but it has one shortcoming. Our electronegativity scale does not explicitly take into account changes in bonding that accompany changes in the oxidation state of the metal. For example, the electronegativity difference between manganese and oxygen is $3.5 - 1.5 = 2.0$, which falls in the range where the bonding is normally considered to be ionic (the electronegativity difference for NaCl was 2.1). Therefore, it is not surprising to learn that manganese (II) oxide, MnO, is a green solid that melts at $1842\ °C$ and has the same crystal structure as NaCl.

However, it would be incorrect to assume that the bonding between manganese and oxygen is always ionic. Manganese (VII) oxide, which has the formula Mn_2O_7, is a green liquid that freezes at $5.9\ °C$, signaling that covalent rather than ionic bonding is dominant. The change in the oxidation state of manganese is responsible for the change in bonding type. As a general principle, whenever the oxidation state of the metal increases, it will lead to an increase in the degree of covalent character in the bonding. When the oxidation state of the metal becomes highly positive (roughly speaking $+4$ or larger), we should expect a significant degree of covalency in bonds it forms with nonmetals. In such instances you should not be surprised if a compound or polyatomic ion (such as MnO_4^- or CrO_4^{2-}) exhibits the general properties of molecular, rather than ionic compounds.

*There are some obvious exceptions to this rule, such as the network solids, including diamond, silicon, and germanium, where an extended structure is formed even though the bonding is clearly covalent. These examples are discussed in more detail in Section 11.8.

⚠ GIVE IT SOME THOUGHT

You encounter two substances: one is a yellow solid that melts at 41 °C and boils at 131 °C. The other is a green solid that melts at 2320 °C. If you are told that one of the compounds is Cr_2O_3 and the other is OsO_4, which one would you expect to be the yellow solid?

8.5 DRAWING LEWIS STRUCTURES

Lewis structures can help us understand the bonding in many compounds and are frequently used when discussing the properties of molecules. For this reason, drawing Lewis structures is an important skill that you should practice. To do so, you should follow a regular procedure. First we will outline the procedure, and then we will go through several examples.

1. *Sum the valence electrons from all atoms.* (Use the periodic table as necessary to help you determine the number of valence electrons in each atom.) For an anion, add one electron to the total for each negative charge. For a cation, subtract one electron from the total for each positive charge. Do not worry about keeping track of which electrons come from which atoms. Only the total number is important.

2. *Write the symbols for the atoms to show which atoms are attached to which, and connect them with a single bond* (a dash, representing *two* electrons). Chemical formulas are often written in the order in which the atoms are connected in the molecule or ion. The formula HCN, for example, tells you that the carbon atom is bonded to the H and to the N. In many polyatomic molecules and ions, the central atom is usually written first, as in CO_3^{2-} and SF_4. Remember that the central atom is generally less electronegative than the atoms surrounding it. In other cases, you may need more information before you can draw the Lewis structure.

3. *Complete the octets around all the atoms bonded to the central atom.* Remember, however, that you use only a single pair of electrons around hydrogen.

4. *Place any leftover electrons on the central atom,* even if doing so results in more than an octet of electrons around the atom. In Section 8.7 we will discuss molecules that do not adhere to the octet rule.

5. *If there are not enough electrons to give the central atom an octet, try multiple bonds.* Use one or more of the unshared pairs of electrons on the atoms bonded to the central atom to form double or triple bonds.

■ **SAMPLE EXERCISE 8.6** │ **Drawing Lewis Structures**
Draw the Lewis structure for phosphorus trichloride, PCl_3.

SOLUTION

Analyze and Plan: We are asked to draw a Lewis structure from a molecular formula. Our plan is to follow the five-step procedure just described.

Solve:

First, we sum the valence electrons. Phosphorus (group 5A) has five valence electrons, and each chlorine (group 7A) has seven. The total number of valence electrons is therefore

$$5 + (3 \times 7) = 26$$

Second, we arrange the atoms to show which atom is connected to which, and we draw a single bond between them. There are various ways the atoms might be arranged. In binary (two-element) compounds, however, the first element listed in the chemical formula is generally surrounded by the remaining atoms. Thus, we begin with a skeleton structure that shows a single bond between the phosphorus atom and each chlorine atom:

Cl—P—Cl
        |
        Cl

(It is not crucial to place the atoms in exactly this arrangement.)

Third, we complete the octets on the atoms bonded to the central atom. Placing octets around each Cl atom accounts for 24 electrons (remember, each line in our structure represents *two* electrons):

$$:\ddot{Cl}—P—\ddot{Cl}: \\ | \\ :\ddot{Cl}:$$

Fourth, we place the remaining two electrons on the central atom, completing the octet around it:

$$:\ddot{Cl}—\ddot{P}—\ddot{Cl}: \\ | \\ :\ddot{Cl}:$$

This structure gives each atom an octet, so we stop at this point. (Remember that in achieving an octet, the bonding electrons are counted for both atoms.)

■ **PRACTICE EXERCISE**

(a) How many valence electrons should appear in the Lewis structure for CH_2Cl_2?
(b) Draw the Lewis structure.

Answers: **(a)** 20, **(b)**
$$\begin{array}{c} H \\ | \\ :\ddot{Cl}—C—\ddot{Cl}: \\ | \\ H \end{array}$$

■ **SAMPLE EXERCISE 8.7** │ **Lewis Structures with Multiple Bonds**

Draw the Lewis structure for HCN.

SOLUTION

Hydrogen has one valence electron, carbon (group 4A) has four, and nitrogen (group 5A) has five. The total number of valence electrons is therefore $1 + 4 + 5 = 10$. In principle, there are different ways in which we might choose to arrange the atoms. Because hydrogen can accommodate only one electron pair, it always has only one single bond associated with it in any compound. Therefore, C—H—N is an impossible arrangement. The remaining two possibilities are H—C—N and H—N—C. The first is the arrangement found experimentally. You might have guessed this to be the atomic arrangement because **(a)** the formula is written with the atoms in this order, and **(b)** carbon is less electronegative than nitrogen. Thus, we begin with a skeleton structure that shows single bonds between hydrogen, carbon, and nitrogen:

$$H—C—N$$

These two bonds account for four electrons. If we then place the remaining six electrons around N to give it an octet, we do not achieve an octet on C:

$$H—C—\ddot{N}:$$

We therefore try a double bond between C and N, using one of the unshared pairs of electrons we placed on N. Again, there are fewer than eight electrons on C, and so we next try a triple bond. This structure gives an octet around both C and N:

$$H—C\overset{\frown}{⟵}\ddot{N}: \quad \longrightarrow \quad H—C≡N:$$

We see that the octet rule is satisfied for the C and N atoms, and the H atom has two electrons around it. This appears to be a correct Lewis structure.

■ **PRACTICE EXERCISE**

Draw the Lewis structure for **(a)** NO^+ ion, **(b)** C_2H_4.

Answers: **(a)** $[:N≡O:]^+$, **(b)**
$$\begin{array}{cc} H \diagdown & \diagup H \\ C=C \\ H \diagup & \diagdown H \end{array}$$

■ **SAMPLE EXERCISE 8.8** | **Lewis Structure for a Polyatomic Ion**

Draw the Lewis structure for the BrO_3^- ion.

SOLUTION

Bromine (group 7A) has seven valence electrons, and oxygen (group 6A) has six. We must now add one more electron to our sum to account for the 1− charge of the ion. The total number of valence electrons is therefore $7 + (3 \times 6) + 1 = 26$. For oxyanions—$BrO_3^-$, SO_4^{2-}, NO_3^-, CO_3^{2-}, and so forth—the oxygen atoms surround the central nonmetal atoms. After following this format and then putting in the single bonds and distributing the unshared electron pairs, we have

$$\left[\ddot{\underset{\cdot\cdot}{O}}\!-\!\ddot{Br}\!-\!\ddot{\underset{\cdot\cdot}{O}} \atop {\underset{\cdot\cdot}{\overset{|}{\ddot{O}}}} \right]^-$$

Notice here and elsewhere that the Lewis structure for an ion is written in brackets with the charge shown outside the brackets at the upper right.

■ **PRACTICE EXERCISE**

Draw the Lewis structure for **(a)** ClO_2^- ion, **(b)** PO_4^{3-} ion.

Answers: **(a)** $\left[\ddot{\underset{\cdot\cdot}{O}}\!-\!\ddot{\underset{\cdot\cdot}{Cl}}\!-\!\ddot{\underset{\cdot\cdot}{O}} \right]^-$ **(b)** $\left[\ddot{\underset{\cdot\cdot}{O}}\!-\!\underset{{\underset{\cdot\cdot}{\overset{|}{\ddot{O}}}}}{\overset{{\overset{|}{\ddot{O}}}}{P}}\!-\!\ddot{\underset{\cdot\cdot}{O}} \right]^{3-}$

Formal Charge

When we draw a Lewis structure, we are describing how the electrons are distributed in a molecule (or polyatomic ion). In some instances we can draw several different Lewis structures that all obey the octet rule. How do we decide which one is the most reasonable? One approach is to do some "bookkeeping" of the valence electrons to determine the formal charge of each atom in each Lewis structure. The **formal charge** of any atom in a molecule is the charge the atom would have if all the atoms in the molecule had the same electronegativity (that is, if each bonding electron pair in the molecule were shared equally between its two atoms).

To calculate the formal charge on any atom in a Lewis structure, we assign the electrons to the atom as follows:

1. *All* unshared (nonbonding) electrons are assigned to the atom on which they are found.

2. For any bond—single, double, or triple—*half* of the bonding electrons are assigned to each atom in the bond.

The formal charge of each atom is then calculated *by subtracting the number of electrons assigned to the atom from the number of valence electrons in the isolated atom.*

Let's illustrate this procedure by calculating the formal charges on the C and N atoms in the cyanide ion, CN^-, which has the Lewis structure

$$[:C\!\equiv\!N:]^-$$

For the C atom, there are 2 nonbonding electrons and 3 electrons from the 6 in the triple bond ($\frac{1}{2} \times 6 = 3$) for a total of 5. The number of valence electrons on a neutral C atom is 4. Thus, the formal charge on C is $4 - 5 = -1$. For N, there are 2 nonbonding electrons and 3 electrons from the triple bond. Because the number of valence electrons on a neutral N atom is 5, its formal charge is $5 - 5 = 0$. Thus, the formal charges on the atoms in the Lewis structure of CN^- are

$$[\overset{-1}{:C}\!\equiv\!\overset{0}{N}:]^-$$

Notice that the sum of the formal charges equals the overall charge on the ion, 1−. The formal charges on a neutral molecule must add to zero, whereas those on an ion add to give the overall charge on the ion.

The concept of formal charge can help us choose between alternative Lewis structures. We will consider the CO_2 molecule to see how this is done. As shown in Section 8.3, CO_2 is represented as having two double bonds. However, we can also satisfy the octet rule by drawing a Lewis structure having one single bond and one triple bond. Calculating the formal charge for each atom in these structures, we have

Valence electrons:	6	4	6	6	4	6
−(Electrons assigned to atom):	6	4	6	7	4	5
Formal charge:	0	0	0	−1	0	+1

Note that in both cases the formal charges add up to zero, as they must because CO_2 is a neutral molecule. So, which is the correct structure? As a general rule, when several Lewis structures are possible, we will use the following guidelines to choose the most correct one:

1. We generally choose the Lewis structure in which the atoms bear formal charges closest to zero.

2. We generally choose the Lewis structure in which any negative charges reside on the more electronegative atoms.

Thus, the first Lewis structure of CO_2 is preferred because the atoms carry no formal charges and so satisfy the first guideline.

Although the concept of formal charge helps us choose between alternative Lewis structures, it is very important that you remember that *formal charges do not represent real charges on atoms*. These charges are just a bookkeeping convention. The actual charge distributions in molecules and ions are determined not by formal charges but by a number of factors, including the electronegativity differences between atoms.

GIVE IT SOME THOUGHT

Suppose that a Lewis structure for a neutral fluorine-containing molecule results in a formal charge on the fluorine atom of +1. What conclusion would you draw?

◼ SAMPLE EXERCISE 8.9 | Lewis Structures and Formal Charges

The following are three possible Lewis structures for the thiocyanate ion, NCS^-:

$$[:\ddot{N}-C\equiv S:]^- \qquad [\ddot{N}=C=\ddot{S}]^- \qquad [:N\equiv C-\ddot{S}:]^-$$

(a) Determine the formal charges of the atoms in each structure. **(b)** Which Lewis structure is the preferred one?

SOLUTION

(a) Neutral N, C, and S atoms have five, four, and six valence electrons, respectively. We can determine the following formal charges in the three structures by using the rules we just discussed:

$$\underset{[:\ddot{N}-C\equiv S:]^-}{-2\quad 0\quad +1} \qquad \underset{[\ddot{N}=C=\ddot{S}]^-}{-1\quad 0\quad 0} \qquad \underset{[:N\equiv C-\ddot{S}:]^-}{0\quad 0\quad -1}$$

As they must, the formal charges in all three structures sum to 1−, the overall charge of the ion.

(b) We will use the guidelines for the best Lewis structure to determine which of the three structures is likely the most correct. As discussed in Section 8.4, N is more electronegative than C or S. Therefore, we expect that any negative formal charge will reside on the N atom (guideline 2). Further, we usually choose the Lewis structure that produces the formal charges of smallest magnitude (guideline 1). For these two reasons, the middle structure is the preferred Lewis structure of the NCS⁻ ion.

▨ PRACTICE EXERCISE

The cyanate ion (NCO⁻), like the thiocyanate ion, has three possible Lewis structures. **(a)** Draw these three Lewis structures, and assign formal charges to the atoms in each structure. **(b)** Which Lewis structure is the preferred one?

$$
\begin{array}{ccc}
{\scriptstyle -2\ \ \ 0\ \ +1} & {\scriptstyle -1\ \ \ 0\ \ \ 0} & {\scriptstyle 0\ \ \ \ 0\ \ -1} \\
[:\ddot{N}\!-\!C\!\equiv\!O:]^- & [\ddot{N}\!=\!C\!=\!\ddot{O}:]^- & [:N\!\equiv\!C\!-\!\ddot{O}:]^- \\
\text{(i)} & \text{(ii)} & \text{(iii)}
\end{array}
$$

Answers: **(a)** (as shown above)

(b) Structure (iii), which places a negative charge on oxygen, the most electronegative of the three elements, is the preferred Lewis structure.

A Closer Look   OXIDATION NUMBERS, FORMAL CHARGES, AND ACTUAL PARTIAL CHARGES

In Chapter 4 we introduced the rules for assigning *oxidation numbers* to atoms. The concept of electronegativity is the basis of these numbers. The oxidation number of an atom is the charge it would have if its bonds were completely ionic. That is, in determining the oxidation number, all shared electrons are counted with the more electronegative atom. For example, consider the Lewis structure of HCl shown in Figure 8.10(a)▼. To assign oxidation numbers, the pair of electrons in the covalent bond between the atoms is assigned to the more electronegative Cl atom. This procedure gives Cl eight valence-shell electrons, one more than the neutral atom. Thus, its oxidation number is −1. Hydrogen has no valence electrons when they are counted this way, giving it an oxidation number of +1.

In this section we have just considered another way of counting electrons that gives rise to *formal charges*. The formal charge is assigned by ignoring electronegativity and assigning equally the electrons in bonds between the bonded atoms. Consider again the HCl molecule, but this time divide the bonding pair of electrons equally between H and Cl as shown in Figure 8.10(b). In this case Cl has seven assigned electrons, the same as that of the neutral Cl atom. Thus, the formal charge of Cl in this compound is 0. Likewise, the formal charge of H is also 0.

Neither the oxidation number nor the formal charge gives an accurate depiction of the actual charges on atoms. Oxidation numbers overstate the role of electronegativity, and formal charges ignore it completely. It seems reasonable that electrons in covalent bonds should be apportioned according to the relative electronegativities of the bonded atoms. From Figure 8.6 we see that Cl has an electronegativity of 3.0, while that of H is 2.1. The more electronegative Cl atom might therefore be expected to have roughly $3.0/(3.0 + 2.1) = 0.59$ of the electrical charge in the bonding pair, whereas the H atom has $2.1/(3.0 + 2.1) = 0.41$ of the charge. Because the bond consists of two electrons, the Cl atom's share is $0.59 \times 2e = 1.18e$, or $0.18e$ more than the neutral Cl atom. This gives rise to a partial charge of 0.18− on Cl and 0.18+ on H (notice again that we place the + and − signs before the magnitude when speaking about oxidation numbers and formal charges, but after the magnitude when talking about actual charges).

The dipole moment of HCl gives an experimental measure of the partial charges on each atom. In Sample Exercise 8.5 we saw that the dipole moment of HCl indicates a charge separation with a partial charge of 0.178+ on H and 0.178− on Cl, in remarkably good agreement with our simple approximation based on electronegativities. Although that type of calculation provides "ballpark" numbers for the magnitude of charge on atoms, the relationship between electronegativities and charge separation is generally more complicated. As we have already seen, computer programs employing quantum mechanical principles have been developed to obtain more accurate estimates of the partial charges on atoms, even in complex molecules. Figure 8.10(c) shows a graphical representation of the charge distribution in HCl.

Related Exercises: 8.6, 8.47, 8.48, 8.49, 8.50, 8.88, and 8.89

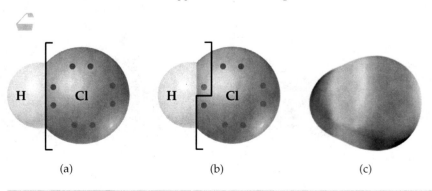

◀ Figure 8.10 **Oxidation number and formal charge.** (a) The oxidation number for any atom in a molecule is determined by assigning all shared electrons to the more electronegative atom (in this case Cl). (b) Formal charges are derived by dividing all shared electron pairs equally between the bonded atoms. (c) The calculated distribution of electron density on an HCl molecule. Regions of relatively more negative charge are red; those of more positive charge are blue. Negative charge is clearly localized on the chlorine atom.

(a)   (b)   (c)

8.6 RESONANCE STRUCTURES

We sometimes encounter molecules and ions in which the experimentally determined arrangement of atoms is not adequately described by a single Lewis structure. Consider a molecule of ozone, O_3, which is a bent molecule with two equal O—O bond lengths (Figure 8.11 ▶). Because each oxygen atom contributes 6 valence electrons, the ozone molecule has 18 valence electrons. In writing the Lewis structure, we find that we must have one O—O single bond and one O—O double bond to attain an octet of electrons about each atom:

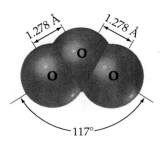

▲ Figure 8.11 **Ozone.** Molecular structure (top) and electron-distribution diagram (bottom) for the ozone molecule, O_3.

However, this structure cannot by itself be correct because it requires that one O—O bond be different from the other, contrary to the observed structure—we would expect the O=O double bond to be shorter than the O—O single bond. ▭▭▭ (Section 8.3) In drawing the Lewis structure, however, we could just as easily have put the O=O bond on the left:

The placement of the atoms in these two alternative but completely equivalent Lewis structures for ozone is the same, but the placement of the electrons is different. Lewis structures of this sort are called **resonance structures.** To describe the structure of ozone properly, we write both Lewis structures and use a double-headed arrow to indicate that the real molecule is described by an average of the two resonance structures:

To understand why certain molecules require more than one resonance structure, we can draw an analogy to the mixing of paint (Figure 8.12 ▶). Blue and yellow are both primary colors of paint pigment. An equal blend of blue and yellow pigments produces green pigment. We cannot describe green paint in terms of a single primary color, yet it still has its own identity. Green paint does not oscillate between its two primary colors: It is not blue part of the time and yellow the rest of the time. Similarly, molecules such as ozone cannot be described as oscillating between the two individual Lewis structures shown above.

The true arrangement of the electrons in molecules such as O_3 must be considered as a blend of two (or more) Lewis structures. By analogy to the green paint, the molecule has its own identity separate from the individual resonance structures. For example, the ozone molecule always has two equivalent O—O bonds whose lengths are intermediate between the lengths of an oxygen–oxygen single bond and an oxygen–oxygen double bond. Another way of looking at it is to say that the rules for drawing Lewis structures do not allow us to have a single structure that adequately represents the ozone molecule. For example, there are no rules for drawing half-bonds. We can get around this limitation by drawing two equivalent Lewis structures that, when averaged, amount to something very much like what is observed experimentally.

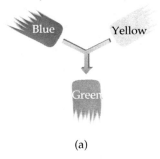

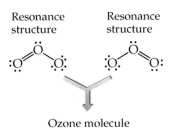

▲ Figure 8.12 **Resonance.** Describing a molecule as a blend of different resonance structures is similar to describing a paint color as a blend of primary colors. (a) Green paint is a blend of blue and yellow. We cannot describe green as a single primary color. (b) The ozone molecule is a blend of two resonance structures. We cannot describe the ozone molecule in terms of a single Lewis structure.

△ **GIVE IT SOME THOUGHT**

The O—O bonds in ozone are often described as "one-and-a-half" bonds. Is this description consistent with the idea of resonance?

As an additional example of resonance structures, consider the nitrate ion, NO_3^-, for which three equivalent Lewis structures can be drawn:

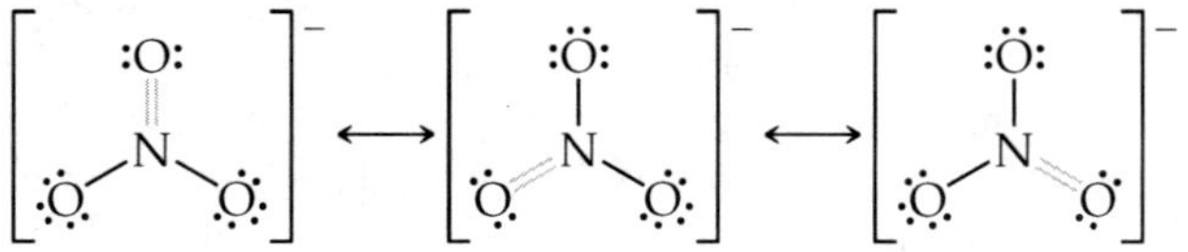

Notice that the arrangement of atoms is the same in each structure—only the placement of electrons differs. In writing resonance structures, the same atoms must be bonded to each other in all structures, so that the only differences are in the arrangements of electrons. All three Lewis structures taken together adequately describe the nitrate ion, in which all three N—O bond lengths are the same.

△ GIVE IT SOME THOUGHT

In the same sense that we describe the O—O bonds in O_3 as "one-and-a-half" bonds, how would you describe the N—O bonds in NO_3^-?

In some instances all the possible Lewis structures for a species may not be equivalent to one another. Instead, one or more may represent a more stable arrangement than other possibilities. We will encounter examples of this as we proceed.

■■■ SAMPLE EXERCISE 8.10 | Resonance Structures

Which is predicted to have the shorter sulfur–oxygen bonds, SO_3 or SO_3^{2-}?

SOLUTION

The sulfur atom has six valence electrons, as does oxygen. Thus, SO_3 contains 24 valence electrons. In writing the Lewis structure, we see that three equivalent resonance structures can be drawn:

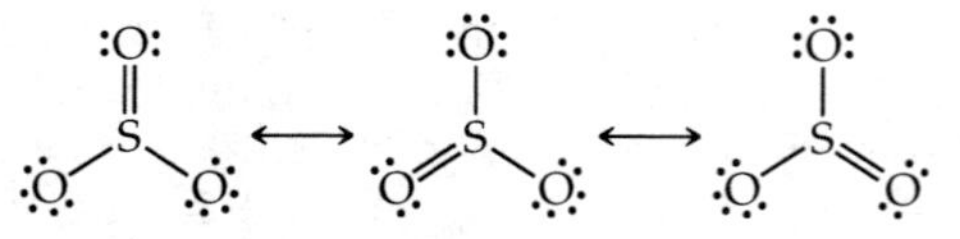

As was the case for NO_3^-, the actual structure of SO_3 is an equal blend of all three. Thus, each S—O bond distance should be about one-third of the way between that of a single and that of a double bond (see the Give It Some Thought exercise above). That is, they should be shorter than single bonds but not as short as double bonds.

The SO_3^{2-} ion has 26 electrons, which leads to a Lewis structure in which all the S—O bonds are single bonds:

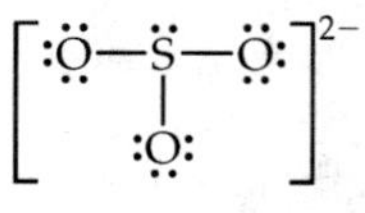

There are no other reasonable Lewis structures for this ion. It can be described quite well by a single Lewis structure rather than by multiple resonance structures.

Our analysis of the Lewis structures leads us to conclude that SO_3 should have the shorter S—O bonds and SO_3^{2-} the longer ones. This conclusion is correct: The experimentally measured S—O bond lengths are 1.42 Å in SO_3 and 1.51 Å in SO_3^{2-}.

■■■ PRACTICE EXERCISE

Draw two equivalent resonance structures for the formate ion, HCO_2^-.

Answer:

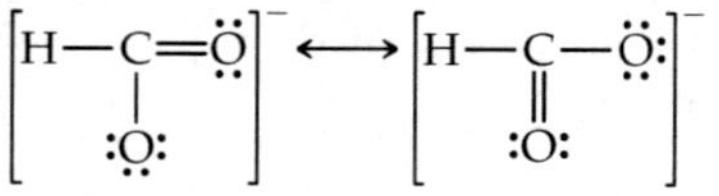

Resonance in Benzene

Resonance is an extremely important concept in describing the bonding in organic molecules, particularly in the ones called *aromatic* molecules. Aromatic organic molecules include the hydrocarbon called *benzene*, which has the molecular formula C_6H_6 (Figure 8.13▶). The six C atoms of benzene are bonded in a hexagonal ring, and one H atom is bonded to each C atom.

We can write two equivalent Lewis structures for benzene, each of which satisfies the octet rule. These two structures are in resonance:

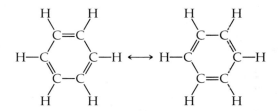

Each resonance structure shows three C—C single bonds and three C=C double bonds, but the double bonds are in different places in the two structures. The experimental structure of benzene shows that all six C—C bonds are of equal length, 1.40 Å, intermediate between the typical bond lengths for a C—C single bond (1.54 Å) and a C=C double bond (1.34 Å).

Benzene is commonly represented by omitting the hydrogen atoms attached to carbon and showing only the carbon-carbon framework with the vertices unlabeled. In this convention, the resonance in the benzene molecule is represented either by two structures separated by a double-headed arrow, as with our other examples, or by a shorthand notation in which we draw a hexagon with a circle in it:

The shorthand notation on the right reminds us that benzene is a blend of two resonance structures—it emphasizes that the C=C double bonds cannot be assigned to specific edges of the hexagon. Chemists use both representations of benzene interchangeably.

The bonding arrangement in benzene confers special stability to the molecule. As a result, literally millions of organic compounds contain the six-membered rings characteristic of benzene. Many of these compounds are important in biochemistry, in pharmaceuticals, and in the production of modern materials. We will say more about the bonding in benzene in Chapter 9 and about its unusual stability in Chapter 25.

(a)

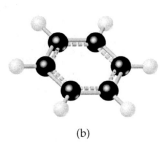

(b)

▲ Figure 8.13 **Benzene, an "aromatic" organic compound.** (a) Benzene is obtained from the distillation of fossil fuels. More than 4 billion pounds of benzene is produced annually in the United States. Because benzene is a carcinogen, its use is closely regulated. (b) The benzene molecule is a regular hexagon of carbon atoms with a hydrogen atom bonded to each one.

GIVE IT SOME THOUGHT

Each Lewis structure of benzene has three C=C double bonds. Another hydrocarbon containing three C=C double bonds is *hexatriene*, C_6H_8. A Lewis structure of hexatriene is

Would you expect hexatriene to have multiple resonance structures like benzene? If not, why is this molecule different from benzene with respect to resonance?

8.7 EXCEPTIONS TO THE OCTET RULE

The octet rule is so simple and useful in introducing the basic concepts of bonding that you might assume it is always obeyed. In Section 8.2, however, we noted its limitation in dealing with ionic compounds of the transition metals. The octet rule also fails in many situations involving covalent bonding. These exceptions to the octet rule are of three main types:

1. Molecules and polyatomic ions containing an odd number of electrons
2. Molecules and polyatomic ions in which an atom has fewer than an octet of valence electrons
3. Molecules and polyatomic ions in which an atom has more than an octet of valence electrons

Odd Number of Electrons

In the vast majority of molecules and polyatomic ions, the total number of valence electrons is even, and complete pairing of electrons occurs. However, in a few molecules and polyatomic ions, such as ClO_2, NO, NO_2, and O_2^-, the number of valence electrons is odd. Complete pairing of these electrons is impossible, and an octet around each atom cannot be achieved. For example, NO contains $5 + 6 = 11$ valence electrons. The two most important Lewis structures for this molecule are

$$\ddot{\ddot{N}}=\ddot{\ddot{O}} \quad \text{and} \quad \dot{\ddot{N}}=\ddot{\ddot{O}}$$

▲ GIVE IT SOME THOUGHT

Which of the Lewis structures shown above for NO would be preferred based on analysis of the formal charges?

Less than an Octet of Valence Electrons

A second type of exception occurs when there are fewer than eight valence electrons around an atom in a molecule or polyatomic ion. This situation is also relatively rare (with the exception of hydrogen and helium as we have already discussed), most often encountered in compounds of boron and beryllium. As an example, let's consider boron trifluoride, BF_3. If we follow the first four steps of the procedure at the beginning of Section 8.5 for drawing Lewis structures, we obtain the structure

There are only six electrons around the boron atom. In this Lewis structure the formal charges on both the B and the F atoms are zero. We could complete the octet around boron by forming a double bond (step 5). In so doing, we see that there are three equivalent resonance structures (the formal charges on each atom are shown in red):

These Lewis structures force a fluorine atom to share additional electrons with the boron atom, which is inconsistent with the high electronegativity of fluorine. In fact, the formal charges tell us that this is an unfavorable situation.

In each of the Lewis structures, the F atom involved in the B=F double bond has a formal charge of +1, while the less electronegative B atom has a formal charge of −1. Thus, the Lewis structures in which there is a B=F double bond are less important than the one in which there are fewer than an octet of valence electrons around boron:

Most important   Less important

We usually represent BF_3 solely by the leftmost resonance structure, in which there are only six valence electrons around boron. The chemical behavior of BF_3 is consistent with this representation. In particular, BF_3 reacts very energetically with molecules having an unshared pair of electrons that can be used to form a bond with boron. For example, BF_3 reacts with ammonia, NH_3, to form the compound NH_3BF_3:

In this stable compound, boron has an octet of valence electrons. We will consider reactions of this type in more detail in Chapter 16 when we study Lewis acids and bases. (Section 16.11)

More than an Octet of Valence Electrons

The third and largest class of exceptions consists of molecules or polyatomic ions in which there are more than eight electrons in the valence shell of an atom. When we draw the Lewis structure for PCl_5, for example, we are forced to "expand" the valence shell and place ten electrons around the central phosphorus atom:

Other examples of molecules and ions with "expanded" valence shells are SF_4, AsF_6^-, and ICl_4^-. The corresponding molecules with a second-period atom as the central atom, such as NCl_5 and OF_4, do *not* exist. Let's take a look at why expanded valence shells are observed only for elements in period 3 and beyond in the periodic table.

Elements of the second period have only the $2s$ and $2p$ valence orbitals available for bonding. Because these orbitals can hold a maximum of eight electrons, we never find more than an octet of electrons around elements from the second period. Elements from the third period and beyond, however, have ns, np, and unfilled nd orbitals that can be used in bonding. For example, the orbital diagram for the valence shell of a phosphorus atom is

Although third-period elements often satisfy the octet rule, as in PCl_3, they also often exceed an octet by seeming to use their empty *d* orbitals to accommodate additional electrons.*

Size also plays an important role in determining whether an atom in a molecule or polyatomic ion can accommodate more than eight electrons in its valence shell. The larger the central atom is, the larger the number of atoms that can surround it. The number of molecules and ions with expanded valence shells therefore increases with increasing size of the central atom. The size of the surrounding atoms is also important. Expanded valence shells occur most often when the central atom is bonded to the smallest and most electronegative atoms, such as F, Cl, and O.

▣ SAMPLE EXERCISE 8.11 | Lewis Structure for an Ion with an Expanded Valence Shell

Draw the Lewis structure for ICl_4^-.

SOLUTION

Iodine (group 7A) has seven valence electrons. Each chlorine (group 7A) also has seven. An extra electron is added to account for the 1− charge of the ion. Therefore, the total number of valence electrons is

$$7 + 4(7) + 1 = 36$$

The I atom is the central atom in the ion. Putting eight electrons around each Cl atom (including a pair of electrons between I and each Cl to represent the single bond between these atoms) requires $8 \times 4 = 32$ electrons.

We are thus left with $36 - 32 = 4$ electrons to be placed on the larger iodine:

$$\left[\begin{array}{c} :\ddot{C}l \diagdown \diagup \ddot{C}l: \\ :\ddot{C}l \diagup I \diagdown \ddot{C}l: \end{array} \right]^-$$

Iodine has 12 valence electrons around it, four more than needed for an octet.

▣ PRACTICE EXERCISE

(a) Which of the following atoms is never found with more than an octet of valence electrons around it: S, C, P, Br? **(b)** Draw the Lewis structure for XeF_2.

Answers: **(a)** C, **(b)** $:\ddot{F}\!-\!\ddot{X}\!e\!-\!\ddot{F}:$

At times you may see Lewis structures written with an expanded valence shell even though structures can be written with an octet. For example, consider the following Lewis structures for the phosphate ion, PO_4^{3-}:

$$\left[\begin{array}{c} :\ddot{O}:^{-1} \\ | \\ :\ddot{O}\!-\!\overset{+1}{P}\!-\!\ddot{O}:^{-1} \\ _{-1}| \\ :\ddot{O}:^{-1} \end{array} \right]^{3-} \qquad \left[\begin{array}{c} :\ddot{O}:^{-1} \\ || \\ ^0\ddot{O}\!=\!\overset{0}{P}\!-\!\ddot{O}:^{-1} \\ | \\ :\ddot{O}:^{-1} \end{array} \right]^{3-}$$

The formal charges on the atoms are shown in red. In the Lewis structure shown on the left, the P atom obeys the octet rule. In the Lewis structure shown on the right, the P atom has an expanded valence shell of five electron pairs[†] leading to smaller formal charges on the atoms. Which Lewis structure is a better representation of the bonding in PO_4^{3-}? Theoretical calculations based on quantum

---

Based on theoretical calculations, some chemists have questioned whether valence d orbitals are actually used in the bonding of molecules and ions with expanded valence shells. Nevertheless, the presence of valence d orbitals in period 3 and beyond provides the simplest explanation of this phenomenon, especially within the scope of a general chemistry textbook.

[†]*The Lewis structure shown on the right has four equivalent resonance forms. Only one is shown for clarity.*

mechanics suggest that the structure on the left is the best single Lewis structure for the phosphate ion. In general, when choosing between alternative Lewis structures, if it is possible to draw a Lewis structure where the octet rule is satisfied without using multiple bonds, that structure will be preferred.

8.8 STRENGTHS OF COVALENT BONDS

The stability of a molecule is related to the strengths of the covalent bonds it contains. The strength of a covalent bond between two atoms is determined by the energy required to break that bond. It is easiest to relate bond strength to the enthalpy change in reactions in which bonds are broken. (Section 5.4) The **bond enthalpy** is the enthalpy change, ΔH, for the breaking of a particular bond in one mole of a gaseous substance. For example, the bond enthalpy for the bond between chlorine atoms in the Cl_2 molecule is the enthalpy change when 1 mol of Cl_2 is dissociated into chlorine atoms:

$$:\ddot{Cl}—\ddot{Cl}:(g) \longrightarrow 2\;:\ddot{Cl}\cdot(g)$$

We use the designation D(bond type) to represent bond enthalpies.

It is relatively simple to assign bond enthalpies to bonds that are found in diatomic molecules, such as the Cl—Cl bond in Cl_2, D(Cl—Cl), or the H—Br bond in HBr, D(H—Br). The bond enthalpy is just the energy required to break the diatomic molecule into its component atoms. Many important bonds, such as the C—H bond, exist only in polyatomic molecules. For these types of bonds, we usually use *average* bond enthalpies. For example, the enthalpy change for the following process in which a methane molecule is decomposed to its five atoms (a process called *atomization*) can be used to define an average bond enthalpy for the C—H bond, D (C—H):

$$
\begin{array}{c}
\text{H} \\
| \\
\text{H}—\text{C}—\text{H}(g) \\
| \\
\text{H}
\end{array}
\longrightarrow \;\cdot\dot{C}\cdot(g) \;+\; 4\,\text{H}\cdot(g) \qquad \Delta H = 1660\ \text{kJ}
$$

Because there are four equivalent C—H bonds in methane, the heat of atomization is equal to the sum of the bond enthalpies of the four C—H bonds. Therefore, the average C—H bond enthalpy for CH_4 is D(C—H) = (1660/4) kJ/mol = 415 kJ/mol.

The bond enthalpy for a given set of atoms, say C—H, depends on the rest of the molecule of which the atom pair is a part. However, the variation from one molecule to another is generally small, which supports the idea that bonding electron pairs are localized between atoms. If we consider C—H bond enthalpies in many different compounds, we find that the average bond enthalpy is 413 kJ/mol, which compares closely with the 415 kJ/mol value calculated from CH_4.

GIVE IT SOME THOUGHT

The hydrocarbon *ethane*, C_2H_6, was first introduced in Section 2.9. How could you use the enthalpy of atomization of $C_2H_6(g)$ along with the value of D(C—H) to provide an estimate for D(C—C)?

Table 8.4 ▼ lists several average bond enthalpies. *The bond enthalpy is always a positive quantity*; energy is always required to break chemical bonds. Conversely, energy is always released when a bond forms between two gaseous atoms or molecular fragments. The greater the bond enthalpy is, the stronger the bond.

TABLE 8.4 ■ Average Bond Enthalpies (kJ/mol)

Single Bonds

C—H	413	N—H	391	O—H	463	F—F	155
C—C	348	N—N	163	O—O	146		
C—N	293	N—O	201	O—F	190	Cl—F	253
C—O	358	N—F	272	O—Cl	203	Cl—Cl	242
C—F	485	N—Cl	200	O—I	234		
C—Cl	328	N—Br	243			Br—F	237
C—Br	276			S—H	339	Br—Cl	218
C—I	240	H—H	436	S—F	327	Br—Br	193
C—S	259	H—F	567	S—Cl	253		
		H—Cl	431	S—Br	218	I—Cl	208
Si—H	323	H—Br	366	S—S	266	I—Br	175
Si—Si	226	H—I	299			I—I	151
Si—C	301						
Si—O	368						
Si—Cl	464						

Multiple Bonds

C=C	614	N=N	418	O$_2$	495
C≡C	839	N≡N	941		
C=N	615	N=O	607	S=O	523
C≡N	891			S=S	418
C=O	799				
C≡O	1072				

A molecule with strong chemical bonds generally has less tendency to undergo chemical change than does one with weak bonds. This relationship between strong bonding and chemical stability helps explain the chemical form in which many elements are found in nature. For example, Si—O bonds are among the strongest ones that silicon forms. It should not be surprising, therefore, that SiO_2 and other substances containing Si—O bonds (silicates) are so common; it is estimated that over 90% of Earth's crust is composed of SiO_2 and silicates.

Bond Enthalpies and the Enthalpies of Reactions

We can use average bond enthalpies to estimate the enthalpies of reactions in which bonds are broken and new bonds are formed. This procedure allows us to estimate quickly whether a given reaction will be endothermic ($\Delta H > 0$) or exothermic ($\Delta H < 0$) even if we do not know ΔH_f° for all the chemical species involved.

Our strategy for estimating reaction enthalpies is a straightforward application of Hess's law.   (Section 5.6) We use the fact that breaking bonds is always an endothermic process, and bond formation is always exothermic. We therefore imagine that the reaction occurs in two steps: (1) We supply enough energy to break those bonds in the reactants that are not present in the products. In this step the enthalpy of the system is increased by the sum of the bond enthalpies of the bonds that are broken. (2) We form the bonds in the products that were not present in the reactants. This step releases energy and therefore lowers the enthalpy of the system by the sum of the bond enthalpies of the bonds that are formed. The enthalpy of the reaction, ΔH_{rxn}, is estimated as the sum of the bond enthalpies of the bonds broken minus the sum of the bond enthalpies of the bonds formed:

$$\Delta H_{rxn} = \Sigma(\text{bond enthalpies of bonds broken}) -$$

$$\Sigma(\text{bond enthalpies of bonds formed}) \quad [8.12]$$

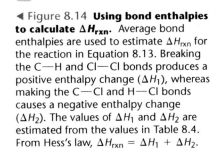

◀ Figure 8.14 **Using bond enthalpies to calculate ΔH_{rxn}.** Average bond enthalpies are used to estimate ΔH_{rxn} for the reaction in Equation 8.13. Breaking the C—H and Cl—Cl bonds produces a positive enthalpy change (ΔH_1), whereas making the C—Cl and H—Cl bonds causes a negative enthalpy change (ΔH_2). The values of ΔH_1 and ΔH_2 are estimated from the values in Table 8.4. From Hess's law, $\Delta H_{rxn} = \Delta H_1 + \Delta H_2$.

Consider, for example, the gas-phase reaction between methane, CH_4, and chlorine to produce methyl chloride, CH_3Cl, and hydrogen chloride, HCl:

$$H—CH_3(g) + Cl—Cl(g) \longrightarrow Cl—CH_3(g) + H—Cl(g) \quad \Delta H_{rxn} = ? \quad [8.13]$$

Our two-step procedure is outlined in Figure 8.14 ▲. We note that in the course of this reaction the following bonds are broken and made:

Bonds broken: 1 mol C—H, 1 mol Cl—Cl

Bonds made: 1 mol C—Cl, 1 mol H—Cl

We first supply enough energy to break the C—H and Cl—Cl bonds, which will raise the enthalpy of the system. We then form the C—Cl and H—Cl bonds, which will release energy and lower the enthalpy of the system. By using Equation 8.12 and the data in Table 8.4, we estimate the enthalpy of the reaction as

$$\Delta H_{rxn} = [D(C—H) + D(Cl—Cl) - [D(C—Cl) + D(H—Cl)]$$
$$= (413 \text{ kJ} + 242 \text{ kJ}) - (328 \text{ kJ} + 431 \text{ kJ}) = -104 \text{ kJ}$$

The reaction is exothermic because the bonds in the products (especially the H—Cl bond) are stronger than the bonds in the reactants (especially the Cl—Cl bond).

We usually use bond enthalpies to estimate ΔH_{rxn} only if we do not have the needed ΔH_f° values readily at hand. For the above reaction, we cannot calculate ΔH_{rxn} from ΔH_f° values and Hess's law because the value of ΔH_f° for $CH_3Cl(g)$ is not given in Appendix C. If we obtain the value of ΔH_f° for $CH_3Cl(g)$ from another source (such as the *CRC Handbook of Chemistry and Physics*) and use Equation 5.31, we find that $\Delta H_{rxn} = -99.8$ kJ for the reaction in Equation 8.13. Thus, the use of average bond enthalpies provides a reasonably accurate estimate of the actual reaction enthalpy change.

It is important to remember that bond enthalpies are derived for *gaseous* molecules and that they are often *averaged* values. Nonetheless, average bond enthalpies are useful for estimating reaction enthalpies quickly, especially for gas-phase reactions.

Chemistry Put to Work EXPLOSIVES AND ALFRED NOBEL

Enormous amounts of energy can be stored in chemical bonds. Perhaps the most graphic illustration of this fact is seen in certain molecular substances that are used as explosives. Our discussion of bond enthalpies allows us to examine more closely some of the properties of such explosive substances.

An explosive must have the following characteristics: (1) It must decompose very exothermically; (2) the products of its decomposition must be gaseous, so that a tremendous gas pressure accompanies the decomposition; (3) its decomposition must occur very rapidly; and (4) it must be stable enough so that it can be detonated predictably. The combination of the first three effects leads to the violent evolution of heat and gases.

To give the most exothermic reaction, an explosive should have weak chemical bonds and should decompose into molecules with very strong bonds. Looking at bond enthalpies (Table 8.4), the $N \equiv N$, $C \equiv O$, and $C = O$ bonds are among the strongest. Not surprisingly, explosives are usually designed to produce the gaseous products $N_2(g)$, $CO(g)$, and $CO_2(g)$. Water vapor is nearly always produced as well.

Many common explosives are organic molecules that contain nitro (NO_2) or nitrate (NO_3) groups attached to a carbon skeleton. The Lewis structures of two of the most familiar explosives, nitroglycerin and trinitrotoluene (TNT), are shown here (resonance structures are not shown for clarity). TNT contains the six-membered ring characteristic of benzene.

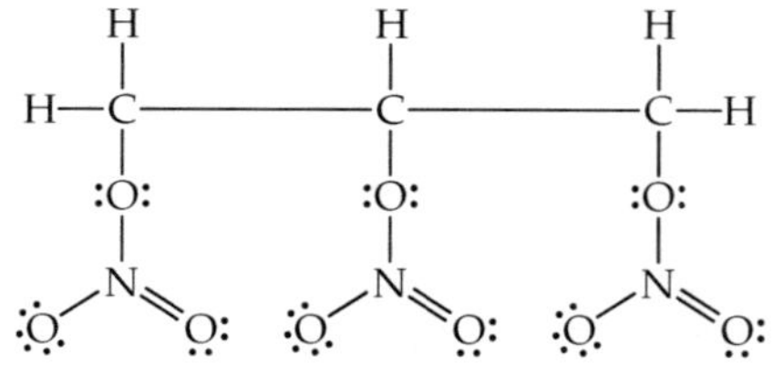

Nitroglycerin

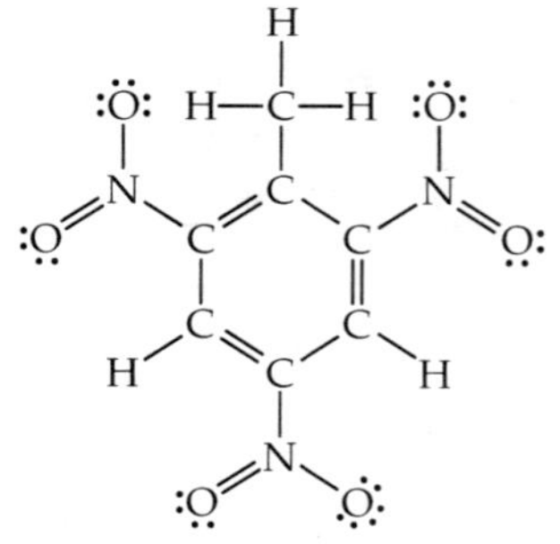

Trinitrotoluene (TNT)

SAMPLE EXERCISE 8.12 | Using Average Bond Enthalpies

Using Table 8.4, estimate ΔH for the following reaction (where we explicitly show the bonds involved in the reactants and products):

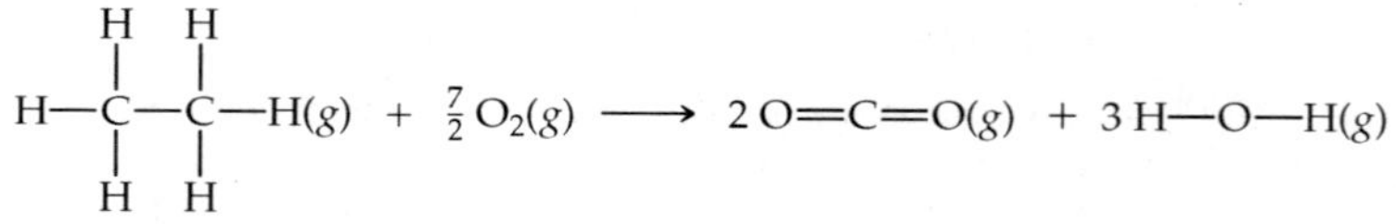

SOLUTION

Analyze: We are asked to estimate the enthalpy change for a chemical process by using average bond enthalpies for the bonds that are broken in the reactants and formed in the products.

Plan: Among the reactants, we must break six C—H bonds and a C—C bond in C_2H_6; we also break $\frac{7}{2} O_2$ bonds. Among the products, we form four C=O bonds (two in each CO_2) and six O—H bonds (two in each H_2O).

Solve: Using Equation 8.12 and data from Table 8.4, we have

$$\Delta H = 6D(C-H) + D(C-C) + \tfrac{7}{2}D(O_2) - 4D(C=O) - 6D(O-H)$$
$$= 6(413 \text{ kJ}) + 348 \text{ kJ} + \tfrac{7}{2}(495 \text{ kJ}) - (4(799 \text{ kJ}) + 6(463 \text{ kJ}))$$
$$= 4558 \text{ kJ} - 5974 \text{ kJ}$$
$$= -1416 \text{ kJ}$$

Check: This estimate can be compared with the value of -1428 kJ calculated from more accurate thermochemical data; the agreement is good.

PRACTICE EXERCISE

Using Table 8.4, estimate ΔH for the reaction

Answer: -86 kJ

Nitroglycerin is a pale yellow, oily liquid. It is highly *shock-sensitive*: Merely shaking the liquid can cause its explosive decomposition into nitrogen, carbon dioxide, water, and oxygen gases:

$$4\,C_3H_5N_3O_9(l) \longrightarrow$$
$$6\,N_2(g) + 12\,CO_2(g) + 10\,H_2O(g) + O_2(g)$$

The large bond enthalpies of the N_2 molecules (941 kJ/mol), CO_2 molecules (2 × 799 kJ/mol), and water molecules (2 × 463 kJ/mol) make this reaction enormously exothermic. Nitroglycerin is an exceptionally unstable explosive because it is in nearly perfect *explosive balance*: With the exception of a small amount of $O_2(g)$ produced, the only products are N_2, CO_2, and H_2O. Note also that, unlike combustion reactions (Section 3.2), explosions are entirely self-contained. No other reagent, such as $O_2(g)$, is needed for the explosive decomposition.

Because nitroglycerin is so unstable, it is difficult to use as a controllable explosive. The Swedish inventor Alfred Nobel (Figure 8.15►) found that mixing nitroglycerin with an absorbent solid material such as diatomaceous earth or cellulose gives a solid explosive (*dynamite*) that is much safer than liquid nitroglycerin.

Related Exercises: 8.93 and 8.94

▲ Figure 8.15 **Alfred Nobel (1833–1896), the Swedish inventor of dynamite.** By many accounts Nobel's discovery that nitroglycerin could be made more stable by absorbing it onto cellulose was an accident. This discovery made Nobel a very wealthy man. He was also a complex and lonely man, however, who never married, was frequently ill, and suffered from chronic depression. He had invented the most powerful military explosive to date, but he strongly supported international peace movements. His will stated that his fortune be used to establish prizes awarding those who "have conferred the greatest benefit on mankind," including the promotion of peace and "fraternity between nations." The Nobel Prize is probably the most coveted award that a scientist, writer, or peace advocate can receive.

Bond Enthalpy and Bond Length

Just as we can define an average bond enthalpy, we can also define an average bond length for a number of common bond types. Some of these are listed in Table 8.5▼. Of particular interest is the relationship among bond enthalpy, bond length, and the number of bonds between the atoms. For example, we can use data in Tables 8.4 and 8.5 to compare the bond lengths and bond enthalpies of carbon–carbon single, double, and triple bonds:

C—C	C=C	C≡C
1.54 Å	1.34 Å	1.20 Å
348 kJ/mol	614 kJ/mol	839 kJ/mol

As the number of bonds between the carbon atoms increases, the bond enthalpy increases and the bond length decreases; that is, the carbon atoms are held more closely and more tightly together. In general, *as the number of bonds between two atoms increases, the bond grows shorter and stronger.*

TABLE 8.5 ■ Average Bond Lengths for Some Single, Double, and Triple Bonds

Bond	Bond Length (Å)	Bond	Bond Length (Å)
C—C	1.54	N—N	1.47
C=C	1.34	N=N	1.24
C≡C	1.20	N≡N	1.10
C—N	1.43	N—O	1.36
C=N	1.38	N=O	1.22
C≡N	1.16		
		O—O	1.48
C—O	1.43	O=O	1.21
C=O	1.23		
C≡O	1.13		

SAMPLE INTEGRATIVE EXERCISE | Putting Concepts Together

Phosgene, a substance used in poisonous gas warfare duirng World War I, is so named because it was first prepared by the action of sunlight on a mixture of carbon monoxide and chlorine gases. Its name comes from the Greek words *phos* (light) and *genes* (born of). Phosgene has the following elemental composition: 12.14% C, 16.17% O, and 71.69% Cl by mass. Its molar mass is 98.9 g/mol. **(a)** Determine the molecular formula of this compound. **(b)** Draw three Lewis structures for the molecule that satisfy the octet rule for each atom. (The Cl and O atoms bond to C.) **(c)** Using formal charges, determine which Lewis structure is the most important one. **(d)** Using average bond enthalpies, estimate ΔH for the formation of gaseous phosgene from $CO(g)$ and $Cl_2(g)$.

SOLUTION

(a) The empirical formula of phosgene can be determined from its elemental composition. (Section 3.5) Assuming 100 g of the compound and calculating the number of moles of C, O, and Cl in this sample, we have

$$(12.14 \text{ g C})\left(\frac{1 \text{ mol C}}{12.01 \text{ g C}}\right) = 1.011 \text{ mol C}$$

$$(16.17 \text{ g O})\left(\frac{1 \text{ mol O}}{16.00 \text{ g O}}\right) = 1.011 \text{ mol O}$$

$$(71.69 \text{ g Cl})\left(\frac{1 \text{ mol Cl}}{35.45 \text{ g Cl}}\right) = 2.022 \text{ mol Cl}$$

The ratio of the number of moles of each element, obtained by dividing each number of moles by the smallest quantity, indicates that there is one C and one O for each two Cl in the empirical formula, $COCl_2$.

The molar mass of the empirical formula is $12.01 + 16.00 + 2(35.45) = 98.91$ g/mol, the same as the molar mass of the molecule. Thus, $COCl_2$ is the molecular formula.

(b) Carbon has four valence electrons, oxygen has six, and chlorine has seven, giving $4 + 6 + 2(7) = 24$ electrons for the Lewis structures. Drawing a Lewis structure with all single bonds does not give the central carbon atom an octet. Using multiple bonds, three structures satisfy the octet rule:

(c) Calculating the formal charges on each atom gives

The first structure is expected to be the most important one because it has the lowest formal charges on each atom. Indeed, the molecule is usually represented by this Lewis structure.

(d) Writing the chemical equation in terms of the Lewis structures of the molecules, we have

Thus, the reaction involves breaking a $C \equiv O$ bond and a $Cl-Cl$ bond and forming a $C=O$ bond and two $C-Cl$ bonds. Using bond enthalpies from Table 8.4, we have

$$\Delta H = D(C \equiv O) + D(Cl-Cl) - (D(C=O) + 2D(C-Cl))$$
$$= 1072 \text{ kJ} + 242 \text{ kJ} - (799 \text{ kJ} + 2(328 \text{ kJ})) = -141 \text{ kJ}$$

CHAPTER REVIEW

SUMMARY AND KEY TERMS

Introduction and Section 8.1 In this chapter we have focused on the interactions that lead to the formation of **chemical bonds**. We classify these bonds into three broad groups: **ionic bonds**, which result from the electrostatic forces that exist between ions of opposite charge; **covalent bonds**, which result from the sharing of electrons by two atoms; and **metallic bonds**, which result from a delocalized sharing of electrons in metals. The formation of bonds involves interactions of the outermost electrons of atoms, their valence electrons. The valence electrons of an atom can be represented by electron-dot symbols, called **Lewis symbols**. The tendencies of atoms to gain, lose, or share their valence electrons often follow the **octet rule**, which can be viewed as an attempt by atoms to achieve a noble-gas electron configuration.

Section 8.2 Ionic bonding results from the transfer of electrons from one atom to another, leading to the formation of a three-dimensional lattice of charged particles. The stabilities of ionic substances result from the strong electrostatic attractions between an ion and the surrounding ions of opposite charge. The magnitude of these interactions is measured by the **lattice energy**, which is the energy needed to separate an ionic lattice into gaseous ions. Lattice energy increases with increasing charge on the ions and with decreasing distance between the ions. The **Born–Haber** cycle is a useful thermochemical cycle in which we use Hess's law to calculate the lattice energy as the sum of several steps in the formation of an ionic compound.

Section 8.3 A covalent bond results from the sharing of electrons. We can represent the electron distribution in molecules by means of **Lewis structures**, which indicate how many valence electrons are involved in forming bonds and how many remain as unshared electron pairs. The octet rule helps determine how many bonds will be formed between two atoms. The sharing of one pair of electrons produces a **single bond**; the sharing of two or three pairs of electrons between two atoms produces **double** or **triple bonds**, respectively. Double and triple bonds are examples of multiple bonding between atoms. The **bond length** between two bonded atoms is the distance between the two nuclei. The bond length decreases as the number of bonds between the atoms increases.

Section 8.4 In covalent bonds, the electrons may not necessarily be shared equally between two atoms. **Bond polarity** helps describe unequal sharing of electrons in a bond. In a **nonpolar covalent bond** the electrons in the bond are shared equally by the two atoms; in a **polar covalent bond** one of the atoms exerts a greater attraction for the electrons than the other.

Electronegativity is a numerical measure of the ability of an atom to compete with other atoms for the electrons shared between them. Fluorine is the most electronegative element, meaning it has the greatest ability to attract electrons from other atoms. Electronegativity values range from 0.7 for Cs to 4.0 for F. Electronegativity generally increases from left to right in a row of the periodic table, and decreases going down a column. The difference in the electronegativities of bonded atoms can be used to determine the polarity of a bond. The greater the electronegativity difference the more polar the bond.

A **polar molecule** is one whose centers of positive and negative charge do not coincide. Thus, a polar molecule has a positive side and a negative side. This separation of charge produces a **dipole**, the magnitude of which is given by the **dipole moment**, which is measured in debyes (D). Dipole moments increase with increasing amount of charge separated and increasing distance of separation. Any diatomic molecule $X-Y$ in which X and Y have different electronegativities is a polar molecule.

Most bonding interactions lie between the extremes of covalent and ionic bonding. While it is generally true that the bonding between a metal and a nonmetal is predominantly ionic, exceptions to this guideline are not uncommon when the difference in electronegativity of the atoms is relatively small or when the oxidation state of the metal becomes large.

Sections 8.5 and 8.6 If we know which atoms are connected to one another, we can draw Lewis structures for molecules and ions by a simple procedure. Once we do so, we can determine the **formal charge** of each atom in a Lewis structure, which is the charge that the atom would have if all atoms had the same electronegativity. Most acceptable Lewis structures will have low formal charges with any negative formal charges residing on more electronegative atoms.

Sometimes a single Lewis structure is inadequate to represent a particular molecule (or ion). In such situations, we describe the molecule by using two or more **resonance structures** for the molecule. The molecule is envisioned as a blend of these multiple resonance structures. Resonance structures are important in describing the bonding in molecules such as ozone, O_3, and the organic molecule benzene, C_6H_6.

Section 8.7 The octet rule is not obeyed in all cases. Exceptions occur when (a) a molecule has an odd number of electrons, (b) it is not possible to complete an octet around an atom without forcing an unfavorable distribution of electrons, or (c) a large atom is surrounded by a sufficiently large number of small electronegative atoms that it has more than an octet of electrons around it. In this last case we envision using the unfilled d orbitals of the large atom to "expand" the valence shell of the atom. Expanded valence shells are observed for atoms in the third row and beyond in the periodic table, for which low-energy d orbitals are available.

Section 8.8 The strength of a covalent bond is measured by its **bond enthalpy**, which is the molar enthalpy change upon breaking a particular bond. Average bond enthalpies can be determined for a wide variety of covalent bonds. The strengths of covalent bonds increase with the number of electron pairs shared between two atoms.

We can use bond enthalpies to estimate the enthalpy change during chemical reactions in which bonds are broken and new bonds formed. The average bond length between two atoms decreases as the number of bonds between the atoms increases, consistent with the bond being stronger as the number of bonds increases.

KEY SKILLS

- Write Lewis symbols for atoms and ions.
- Understand lattice energy and be able to arrange compounds in order of increasing lattice energy based on the charges and sizes of the ions involved.
- Use atomic electron configurations and the octet rule to write Lewis structures for molecules to determine their electron distribution.
- Use electronegativity differences to identify nonpolar covalent, polar covalent, and ionic bonds.
- Calculate charge separation in diatomic molecules based on the experimentally measured dipole moment and bond distance.
- Calculate formal charges from Lewis structures and use those formal charges to identify the most favorable Lewis structures.
- Recognize molecules where resonance structures are needed to describe the bonding.
- Recognize exceptions to the octet rule and draw accurate Lewis structures even when the octet rule is not obeyed.
- Understand the relationship between bond type (single, double, and triple), bond strength (or enthalpy) and bond length.
- Use bond enthalpies to estimate enthalpy changes for reactions involving gas phase reactants and products.

KEY EQUATIONS

- $E_{el} = \dfrac{\kappa Q_1 Q_2}{d}$ [8.4]

  The potential energy of two interacting charges

- $\mu = Qr$ [8.11]

  The dipole moment of two charges of equal magnitude but opposite sign, separated by a distance r

- $\Delta H_{rxn} = \Sigma(\text{bond enthalpies of bonds broken}) - \Sigma(\text{bond enthalpies of bonds formed})$ [8.12]

  The enthalpy change as a function of bond enthalpies for reactions involving gas phase molecules.

VISUALIZING CONCEPTS

8.1 For each of these Lewis symbols, indicate the group in the periodic table in which the element X belongs:
(a) $\cdot \ddot{X} \cdot$ **(b)** $\cdot X \cdot$ **(c)** $: \ddot{X} \cdot$

8.2 Illustrated at right are four ions—A, B, X, and Y— showing their relative ionic radii. The ions shown in red carry positive charges: a 2+ charge for A and a 1+ charge for B. Ions shown in blue carry negative charges: a 1− charge for X and a 2− charge for Y. **(a)** Which combinations of these ions produce ionic compounds where there is a 1:1 ratio of cations and anions? **(b)** Among those compounds, which combination of ions leads to the ionic compound having the largest lattice energy? **(c)** Which combination of ions leads to the ionic compound having the smallest lattice energy? [Section 8.2]

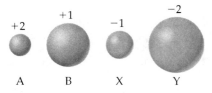

8.3 The orbital diagram below shows the valence electrons for a 2+ ion of an element. **(a)** What is the element? **(b)** What is the electron configuration of an atom of this element? [Section 8.2]

3d

8.4 In the Lewis structure shown below, A, D, E, Q, X, and Z
CQ represent elements in the first two rows of the periodic table (H—Ne). Identify all six elements so that the formal charges of all atoms are zero. [Section 8.3]

$$\overset{\displaystyle :\ddot{E}:}{\underset{\displaystyle }{\overset{\displaystyle \|}{:\ddot{A}-D-\underset{}{Q}-Z}}}\quad\overset{X}{\underset{}{|}}$$

8.5 The partial Lewis structure below is for a hydrocarbon
CQ molecule. In the full Lewis structure, each carbon atom satisfies the octet rule, and there are no unshared electron pairs in the molecule. The carbon–carbon bonds are labeled 1, 2, and 3. **(a)** Determine where the hydrogen atoms are in the molecule. **(b)** Rank the carbon–carbon bonds in order of increasing bond length. **(c)** Rank the carbon–carbon bonds in order of increasing bond enthalpy. [Section 8.3 and 8.8]

$$C\overset{1}{=}C\overset{2}{-}C\overset{3}{\equiv}C$$

8.6 Consider the Lewis structure for the polyatomic oxyan-
CQ ion shown below, where X is an element from the 3rd period (Na—Ar). By changing the overall charge, n, from 1− to 2− to 3− we get three different polyatomic ions. For each of these ions **(a)** Identify the central atom, X. **(b)** Determine the formal charge of the central atom, X. **(c)** Draw a Lewis structure that makes the formal charge on the central atom equal to zero. **(d)** If the Lewis structure you drew in part (c) differs from the Lewis structure shown below, which one do you think is the best one (if you were able to choose only a single Lewis structure)? [Sections 8.5, 8.6, and 8.7]

$$\left[\ :\ddot{O}-X-\ddot{O}:\ \right]^{n-}$$
with $:\ddot{O}:$ above and $:\ddot{O}:$ below

EXERCISES

Lewis Symbols

8.7 **(a)** What are valence electrons? **(b)** How many valence
CQ electrons does a nitrogen atom possess? **(c)** An atom has the electron configuration $1s^2 2s^2 2p^6 3s^2 3p^2$. How many valence electrons does the atom have?

8.8 **(a)** What is the octet rule? **(b)** How many electrons must
CQ a sulfur atom gain to achieve an octet in its valence shell? **(c)** If an atom has the electron configuration $1s^2 2s^2 2p^3$, how many electrons must it gain to achieve an octet?

8.9 Write the electron configuration for phosphorus. Identi-
CQ fy the valence electrons in this configuration and the nonvalence electrons. From the standpoint of chemical reactivity, what is the important difference between them?

8.10 **(a)** Write the electron configuration for the element tita-
CQ nium, Ti. How many valence electrons does this atom possess? **(b)** Hafnium, Hf, is also found in group 4B. Write the electron configuration for Hf. **(c)** Both Ti and Hf behave as though they possess the same number of valence electrons. Which of the subshells in the electron configuration of Hf behave as valence orbitals? Which behave as core orbitals?

8.11 Write the Lewis symbol for atoms of each of the follow-ing elements: **(a)** Al, **(b)** Br, **(c)** Ar, **(d)** Sr.

8.12 What is the Lewis symbol for each of the following atoms or ions: **(a)** Ca, **(b)** P, **(c)** Mg^{2+}, **(d)** S^{2-}?

Ionic Bonding

8.13 Using Lewis symbols, diagram the reaction between
CQ magnesium and oxygen atoms to give the ionic sub-stance MgO.

8.14 Use Lewis symbols to represent the reaction that occurs
CQ between Ca and F atoms.

8.15 Predict the chemical formula of the ionic compound formed between the following pairs of elements: **(a)** Al and F, **(b)** K and S, **(c)** Y and O, **(d)** Mg and N.

8.16 Which ionic compound is expected to form from com-bining the following pairs of elements: **(a)** barium and fluorine, **(b)** cesium and chlorine, **(c)** lithium and nitro-gen, **(d)** aluminum and oxygen?

8.17 Write the electron configuration for each of the follow-ing ions, and determine which ones possess noble-gas configurations: **(a)** Sr^{2+}, **(b)** Ti^{2+}, **(c)** Se^{2-}, **(d)** Ni^{2+}, **(e)** Br^-, **(f)** Mn^{3+}.

8.18 Write electron configurations for the following ions, and determine which have noble-gas configurations: **(a)** Zn^{2+}, **(b)** Te^{2-}, **(c)** Sc^{3+}, **(d)** Rh^{3+}, **(e)** Tl^+, **(f)** Bi^{3+}.

8.19 **(a)** Define the term *lattice energy*. **(b)** Which factors gov-
CQ ern the magnitude of the lattice energy of an ionic compound?

8.20 NaCl and KF have the same crystal structure. The only
CQ difference between the two is the distance that separates cations and anions. **(a)** The lattice energies of NaCl and KF are given in Table 8.2. Based on the lattice energies, would you expect the Na–Cl or the K–F distance to be longer? **(b)** Use the ionic radii given in Figure 7.8 to esti-mate the Na–Cl and K–F distances. Does this estimate agree with the prediction you made based upon the lat-tice energies?

8.21 The ionic substances KF, CaO, and ScN are isoelectronic
CQ (they have the same number of electrons). Examine the lattice energies for these substances in Table 8.2, and ac-count for the trends you observe.

8.22 **(a)** Does the lattice energy of an ionic solid increase or
CQ decrease **(i)** as the charges of the ions increase, **(ii)** as the sizes of the ions increase? **(b)** Using a periodic table,

arrange the following substances according to their expected lattice energies, listing them from lowest lattice energy to the highest: ScN, KBr, MgO, NaF. Compare your list with the data in Table 8.2.

8.23 The lattice energies of KBr and CsCl are nearly equal
CQ (Table 8.2). What can you conclude from this observation?

8.24 Explain the following trends in lattice energy: (a)
CQ $CaF_2 > BaF_2$; (b) NaCl > RbBr > CsBr; (c) BaO > KF.

8.25 Energy is required to remove two electrons from Ca to
CQ form Ca^{2+} and is required to add two electrons to O to form O^{2-}. Why, then, is CaO stable relative to the free elements?

8.26 Construct a Born–Haber cycle for the formation of the
CQ hypothetical compound $NaCl_2$, where the sodium ion

has a 2+ charge (the 2nd ionization energy for sodium is given in Table 7.2). (a) How large would the lattice energy need to be for the formation of $NaCl_2$ to be exothermic? (b) If we were to estimate the lattice energy of $NaCl_2$ to be roughly equal to that of $MgCl_2$ (2326 kJ/mol from Table 8.2), what value would you obtain for the standard enthalpy of formation, ΔH°_f, of $NaCl_2$?

8.27 Use data from Appendix C, Figure 7.12, and Figure 7.14 to calculate the lattice energy of RbCl. Is this value greater than or less than the lattice energy of NaCl? Explain.

8.28 (a) Based on the lattice energies of $MgCl_2$ and $SrCl_2$ given in Table 8.2, what is the range of values that you would expect for the lattice energy of $CaCl_2$? (b) Using data from Appendix C, Figure 7.12, and Figure 7.14 and the value of the second ionization energy for Ca, 1145 kJ/mol, calculate the lattice energy of $CaCl_2$.

Covalent Bonding, Electronegativity, and Bond Polarity

8.29 (a) What is meant by the term *covalent bond*? (b) Give
CQ three examples of covalent bonding. (c) A substance XY, formed from two different elements, boils at −33 °C. Is XY likely to be a covalent or an ionic substance? Explain.

8.30 Which of these elements is unlikely to form covalent
CQ bonds: S, H, K, Ar, Si? Explain your choices.

8.31 Using Lewis symbols and Lewis structures, diagram the formation of $SiCl_4$ from Si and Cl atoms.

8.32 Use Lewis symbols and Lewis structures to diagram the formation of PF_3 from P and F atoms.

8.33 (a) Construct a Lewis structure for O_2 in which each
CQ atom achieves an octet of electrons. (b) Explain why it is necessary to form a double bond in the Lewis structure. (c) The bond in O_2 is shorter than the O—O bond in compounds that contain an O—O single bond. Explain this observation.

8.34 (a) Construct a Lewis structure for hydrogen peroxide,
CQ H_2O_2, in which each atom achieves an octet of electrons. (b) Do you expect the O—O bond in H_2O_2 to be longer or shorter than the O—O bond in O_2?

8.35 (a) What is meant by the term electronegativity? (b) On
CQ the Pauling scale what is the range of electronegativity values for the elements? (c) Which element has the greatest electronegativity? (d) Which element has the smallest electronegativity?

8.36 (a) What is the trend in electronegativity going from left
CQ to right in a row of the periodic table? (b) How do electronegativity values generally vary going down a column in the periodic table? (c) How do periodic trends in electronegativity relate to those for ionization energy and electron affinity?

8.37 Using only the periodic table as your guide, select the
CQ most electronegative atom in each of the following sets: (a) Se, Rb, O, In; (b) Al, Ca, C, Si; (c) Ge, As, P, Sn; (d) Li, Rb, Be, Sr.

8.38 By referring only to the periodic table, select (a) the most
CQ electronegative element in group 6A; (b) the least elec-

tronegative element in the group Al, Si, P; (c) the most electronegative element in the group Ga, P, Cl, Na; (d) the element in the group K, C, Zn, F, that is most likely to form an ionic compound with Ba.

8.39 Which of the following bonds are polar: (a) B—F, (b) Cl—Cl, (c) Se—O, (d) H—I? Which is the more electronegative atom in each polar bond?

8.40 Arrange the bonds in each of the following sets in order of increasing polarity: (a) C—F, O—F, Be—F; (b) O—Cl, S—Br, C—P; (c) C—S, B—F, N—O.

8.41 The dipole moment and bond distance measured for the highly reactive gas phase OH molecule are 1.78 D and 0.98 Å, respectively. (a) Given these values calculate the effective charges on the H and O atoms of the OH molecule in units of the electronic charges e. (b) Is this bond more or less polar than the H—Cl bond in an HCl molecule? (c) Is that what you would have expected based on electronegativities?

8.42 The iodine monobromide molecule, IBr, has a bond length of 2.49 Å and a dipole moment of 1.21 D. (a) Which atom of the molecule is expected to have a negative charge? Explain. (b) Calculate the effective charges on the I and Br atoms in IBr, in units of the electronic charge e.

8.43 In the following pairs of binary compounds determine which one is a molecular substance and which one is an ionic substance. Use the appropriate naming convention (for ionic or molecular substances) to assign a name to each compound: (a) SiF_4 and LaF_3, (b) $FeCl_2$ and $ReCl_6$, (c) $PbCl_4$ and RbCl.

8.44 In the following pairs of binary compounds determine which one is a molecular substance and which one is an ionic substance. Use the appropriate naming convention (for ionic or molecular substances) to assign a name to each compound: (a) $TiCl_4$ and CaF_2, (b) ClF_3 and VF_3, (c) $SbCl_5$ and AlF_3.

Lewis Structures; Resonance Structures

8.45 Draw Lewis structures for the following: **(a)** SiH_4, **(b)** CO, **(c)** SF_2, **(d)** H_2SO_4 (H is bonded to O), **(e)** ClO_2^- **(f)** NH_2OH.

8.46 Write Lewis structures for the following: **(a)** H_2CO (both H atoms are bonded to C), **(b)** H_2O_2, **(c)** C_2F_6 (contains a C—C bond), **(d)** AsO_3^{3-}, **(e)** H_2SO_3 (H is bonded to O), **(f)** C_2H_2.

8.47 **(a)** When talking about atoms in a Lewis structure, what CQ is meant by the term *formal charge*? **(b)** Does the formal charge of an atom represent the actual charge on that atom? Explain. **(c)** How does the formal charge of an atom in a Lewis structure differ from the oxidation number of the atom?

8.48 **(a)** Write a Lewis structure for the phosphorus trifluoride molecule, PF_3. Is the octet rule satisfied for all the atoms in your structure? **(b)** Determine the oxidation numbers of the P and F atoms. **(c)** Determine the formal charges of the P and F atoms. **(d)** Is the oxidation number for the P atom the same as its formal charge? Explain why or why not.

8.49 Write Lewis structures that obey the octet rule for each of the following, and assign oxidation numbers and formal charges to each atom: **(a)** NO^+, **(b)** $POCl_3$ (P is bonded to the three Cl atoms and to the O), **(c)** ClO_4^-, **(d)** $HClO_3$ (H is bonded to O).

8.50 For each of the following molecules or ions of sulfur and oxygen, write a single Lewis structure that obeys the octet rule, and calculate the oxidation numbers and formal charges on all the atoms: **(a)** SO_2, **(b)** SO_3, **(c)** SO_3^{2-}. **(d)** Arrange these molecules/ions in order of increasing S—O bond distance.

8.51 **(a)** Write one or more appropriate Lewis structures for the nitrite ion, NO_2^-. **(b)** With what allotrope of oxygen is it isoelectronic? **(c)** What would you predict for the lengths of the bonds in NO_2^- relative to N—O single bonds?

8.52 Consider the nitryl cation, NO_2^+. **(a)** Write one or more appropriate Lewis structures for this ion. **(b)** Are resonance structures needed to describe the structure? **(c)** With what familiar molecule is it isoelectronic?

8.53 Predict the ordering of the C—O bond lengths in CO, CO_2, and CO_3^{2-}.

8.54 Based on Lewis structures, predict the ordering of N—O bond lengths in NO^+, NO_2^-, and NO_3^-.

8.55 **(a)** Use the concept of resonance to explain why all six C—C bonds in benzene are equal in length. **(b)** Are the C—C bond lengths in benzene shorter than C—C single bonds? Are they shorter than C=C double bonds?

8.56 Mothballs are composed of naphthalene, $C_{10}H_8$, a molecule of which consists of two six-membered rings of carbon fused along an edge, as shown in this incomplete Lewis structure:

(a) Write two complete Lewis structures for naphthalene. **(b)** The observed C—C bond lengths in the molecule are intermediate between C—C single and C=C double bonds. Explain. **(c)** Represent the resonance in naphthalene in a way analogous to that used to represent it in benzene.

Exceptions to the Octet Rule

8.57 **(a)** State the octet rule. **(b)** Does the octet rule apply to CQ ionic as well as to covalent compounds? Explain, using examples as appropriate.

8.58 Considering the nonmetals, what is the relationship CQ between the group number for an element (carbon, for example, belongs to group 4A; see the periodic table on the inside front cover) and the number of single covalent bonds that element needs to form to conform to the octet rule?

8.59 What is the most common exception to the octet rule? CQ Give two examples.

8.60 For elements in the third row of the periodic table and CQ beyond, the octet rule is often not obeyed. What factors are usually cited to explain this fact?

8.61 Draw the Lewis structures for each of the following ions or molecules. Identify those that do not obey the octet rule, and explain why they do not. **(a)** SO_3^{2-}, **(b)** AlH_3, **(c)** N_3^-, **(d)** CH_2Cl_2, **(e)** SbF_5.

8.62 Draw the Lewis structures for each of the following molecules or ions. Which do not obey the octet rule? **(a)** NH_4^+, **(b)** SCN^-, **(c)** PCl_3, **(d)** TeF_4, **(e)** XeF_2.

8.63 In the vapor phase, $BeCl_2$ exists as a discrete molecule. **(a)** Draw the Lewis structure of this molecule, using only single bonds. Does this Lewis structure satisfy the octet rule? **(b)** What other resonance forms are possible that satisfy the octet rule? **(c)** Using formal charges, select the resonance form from among all the Lewis structures that is most important in describing $BeCl_2$.

8.64 **(a)** Describe the molecule chlorine dioxide, ClO_2, using three possible resonance structures. **(b)** Do any of these resonance structures satisfy the octet rule for every atom in the molecule? Why or why not? **(c)** Using formal charges, select the resonance structure(s) that is (are) most important.

Bond Enthalpies

8.65 Using the bond enthalpies tabulated in Table 8.4, estimate ΔH for each of the following gas-phase reactions:

(a)

$$+ \; H-O-O-H \longrightarrow$$

(b)

$$+ \; H-C{\equiv}N \longrightarrow$$

(c)

8.66 Using bond enthalpies (Table 8.4), estimate ΔH for the following gas-phase reactions:

(a)

(b)

(c)

8.67 Using bond enthalpies (Table 8.4), estimate ΔH for each of the following reactions:

(a) $2\,CH_4(g) + O_2(g) \longrightarrow 2\,CH_3OH(g)$
(b) $H_2(g) + Br_2(g) \longrightarrow 2\,HBr(g)$
(c) $2\,H_2O_2(g) \longrightarrow 2\,H_2O(g) + O_2(g)$

[8.68] Use bond enthalpies (Table 8.4) to estimate the enthalpy change for each of the following reactions:
(a) $C_3H_8(g) + 5\,O_2(g) \longrightarrow 3\,CO_2(g) + 4\,H_2O(g)$
(b) $C_2H_5OH(g) + 3\,O_2(g) \longrightarrow 2\,CO_2(g) + 3\,H_2O(g)$
(c) $8\,H_2S(g) \longrightarrow 8\,H_2(g) + S_8(s)$

8.69 Ammonia is produced directly from nitrogen and hydrogen by using the Haber process. The chemical reaction is

$$N_2(g) + 3\,H_2(g) \longrightarrow 2\,NH_3(g)$$

(a) Use bond enthalpies (Table 8.4) to estimate the enthalpy change for the reaction, and tell whether this reaction is exothermic or endothermic. **(b)** Compare the enthalpy change you calculate in (a) to the true enthalpy change as obtained using ΔH_f° values.

8.70 **(a)** Use bond enthalpies to estimate the enthalpy change for the reaction of hydrogen with ethene:

$$H_2(g) + C_2H_4(g) \longrightarrow C_2H_6(g)$$

(b) Calculate the standard enthalpy change for this reaction, using heats of formation. Why does this value differ from that calculated in (a)?

8.71 Given the following bond-dissociation energies, calculate the average bond enthalpy for the Ti—Cl bond.

	ΔH (kJ/mol)
$TiCl_4(g) \longrightarrow TiCl_3(g) + Cl(g)$	335
$TiCl_3(g) \longrightarrow TiCl_2(g) + Cl(g)$	423
$TiCl_2(g) \longrightarrow TiCl(g) + Cl(g)$	444
$TiCl(g) \longrightarrow Ti(g) + Cl(g)$	519

[8.72] **(a)** Using average bond enthalpies, predict which of the following reactions will be most exothermic:
(i) $C(g) + 2\,F_2(g) \longrightarrow CF_4(g)$
(ii) $CO(g) + 3\,F_2 \longrightarrow CF_4(g) + OF_2(g)$
(iii) $CO_2(g) + 4\,F_2 \longrightarrow CF_4(g) + 2\,OF_2(g)$
(b) Explain the trend, if any, that exists between reaction exothermicity and the extent to which the carbon atom is bonded to oxygen.

ADDITIONAL EXERCISES

8.73 How many elements in the periodic table are represented by a Lewis symbol with a single dot? Are all these elements in the same group? Explain.

8.74 **(a)** Explain the following trend in lattice energy: BeH_2, 3205 kJ/mol; MgH_2, 2791 kJ/mol; CaH_2, 2410 kJ/mol; SrH_2, 2250 kJ/mol; BaH_2, 2121 kJ/mol. **(b)** The lattice energy of ZnH_2 is 2870 kJ/mol. Based on the data given in part (a), the radius of the Zn^{2+} ion is expected to be closest to that of which group 2A element?

8.75 Based on data in Table 8.2, estimate (within 30 kJ/mol) the lattice energy for **(a)** LiBr, **(b)** CsBr, **(c)** $CaCl_2$.

8.76 Would you expect AlN to have a lattice energy that is larger or smaller than ScN? Explain.

[8.77] From the ionic radii given in Figure 7.8, calculate the potential energy of a Ca^{2+} and O^{2-} ion pair that are just touching (the magnitude of the electronic charge is given on the back inside cover). Calculate the energy of a mole of such pairs. How does this value compare with the lattice energy of CaO (Table 8.2)? Explain the difference.

[8.78] From Equation 8.4 and the ionic radii given in Figure 7.8, calculate the potential energy of the following pairs of ions. Assume that the ions are separated by a distance equal to the sum of their ionic radii: **(a)** Na^+, Br^-; **(b)** Rb^+, Br^-; **(c)** Sr^{2+}, S^{2-}.

8.79 **(a)** How does a polar molecule differ from a nonpolar CQ one? **(b)** Atoms X and Y have different electronegativities. Will the diatomic molecule $X—Y$ necessarily be polar? Explain. **(c)** What factors affect the size of the dipole moment of a diatomic molecule?

8.80 Which of the following molecules or ions contain polar bonds: **(a)** P_4, **(b)** H_2S, **(c)** NO_2^-, **(d)** S_2^{2-}?

8.81 To address energy and environmental issues, there is great interest in powering vehicles with hydrogen rather than gasoline. One of the most attractive aspects of the "hydrogen economy" is the fact that in principle the only emission would be water. However, two daunting obstacles must be overcome before this vision can become a reality. First, an economical method of producing hydrogen must be found. Second, a safe, lightweight, and compact way of storing hydrogen must be found. The hydrides of light metals are attractive for hydrogen storage because they can store a high weight percentage of hydrogen in a small volume. One of the most attractive hydrides is $NaAlH_4$, which can release 5.6% of its mass as H_2 upon decomposing to $NaH(s)$, $Al(s)$, and $H_2(g)$. $NaAlH_4$ possesses both covalent bonds, which hold polyatomic anions together, and ionic bonds. **(a)** Write a balanced equation for the decomposition of $NaAlH_4$. **(b)** Which element in $NaAlH_4$ is the most electronegative? Which one is the least electronegative? **(c)** Based on electronegativity differences, what do you think is the identity of the polyatomic anion? Draw a Lewis structure for this ion.

8.82 For the following collection of nonmetallic elements, O, P, Te, I, B, **(a)** which two would form the most polar single bond? **(b)** Which two would form the longest single bond? **(c)** Which two would be likely to form a compound of formula XY_2? **(d)** Which combinations of elements would likely yield a compound of empirical formula X_2Y_3? In each case explain your answer.

8.83 You and a partner are asked to complete a lab entitled CQ "Oxides of Ruthenium" that is scheduled to extend over two lab periods. The first lab, which is to be completed by your partner, is devoted to carrying out compositional analysis. In the second lab, you are to determine melting points. Upon going to lab you find two unlabeled vials, one containing a soft yellow substance and the other a black powder. You also find the following notes in your partner's notebook—*Compound 1*: 76.0% Ru and 24.0% O (by mass), *Compound 2*: 61.2% Ru and 38.8% O (by mass). **(a)** What is the empirical formula for Compound 1? **(b)** What is the empirical formula for Compound 2? **(c)** Upon determining the melting points of these two compounds, you find that the yellow compound melts at 25 °C, while the black powder does not melt up to the maximum temperature of your apparatus, 1200 °C. What is the identity of the yellow compound? What is the identity of the black compound? Be sure to use the appropriate naming convention depending upon whether the compound is better described as a molecular or ionic compound.

8.84 You and a partner are asked to complete a lab entitled CQ "Fluorides of Group 6B Metals" that is scheduled to extend over two lab periods. The first lab, which is to be completed by your partner, is devoted to carrying out compositional analysis. In the second lab, you are to determine melting points. Upon going to lab you find two unlabeled vials, one containing a colorless liquid and the other a green powder. You also find the following notes in your partner's notebook—*Compound 1*: 47.7% Cr and 52.3% F (by mass), *Compound 2*: 45.7% Mo and 54.3% F (by mass). **(a)** What is the empirical formula for Compound 1? **(b)** What is the empirical formula for Compound 2? **(c)** Upon determining the melting points of these two compounds you find that the colorless liquid solidifies at 18 °C, while the green powder does not melt up to the maximum temperature of your apparatus, 1200 °C. What is the identity of the colorless liquid? What is the identity of the green powder? Be sure to use the appropriate naming convention depending upon whether the compound is better described as a molecular or ionic compound.

[8.85] **(a)** Triazine, $C_3H_3N_3$, is like benzene except that in triazine every other $C—H$ group is replaced by a nitrogen atom. Draw the Lewis structure(s) for the triazine molecule. **(b)** Estimate the carbon–nitrogen bond distances in the ring.

[8.86] Using the electronegativities of Br and Cl, estimate the partial charges on the atoms in the $Br—Cl$ molecule. Using these partial charges and the atomic radii given in Figure 7.7, estimate the dipole moment of the molecule. The measured dipole moment is 0.57 D.

8.87 Although I_3^- is known, F_3^- is not. Using Lewis structures, explain why F_3^- does not form.

8.88 Calculate the formal charge on the indicated atom in each of the following molecules or ions: **(a)** the central oxygen atom in O_3, **(b)** phosphorus in PF_6^-, **(c)** nitrogen in NO_2, **(d)** iodine in ICl_3, **(e)** chlorine in $HClO_4$ (hydrogen is bonded to O).

8.89 **(a)** Determine the formal charge on the chlorine atom in the hypochlorite ion, ClO^-, and the perchlorate ion, ClO_4^-, using resonance structures where the Cl atom has an octet. **(b)** What are the oxidation numbers of chlorine in ClO^- and in ClO_4^-? **(c)** Is it uncommon for the formal charge and the oxidation state to be different? Explain. **(d)** Perchlorate is a much stronger oxidizing agent than hypochlorite. Would you expect there to be any relationship between the oxidizing power of the oxyanion and either the oxidation state or the formal charge of chlorine?

8.90 The following three Lewis structures can be drawn for N_2O:

$$:N{\equiv}N{-}\ddot{\ddot{O}}: \longleftrightarrow :\ddot{N}{-}N{\equiv}O: \longleftrightarrow :\ddot{N}{=}N{=}\ddot{O}:$$

(a) Using formal charges, which of these three resonance forms is likely to be the most important? **(b)** The $N—N$ bond length in N_2O is 1.12 Å, slightly longer than a typical $N{\equiv}N$ bond; and the $N—O$ bond length is 1.19 Å, slightly shorter than a typical $N{=}O$ bond. (See Table 8.5.) Rationalize these observations in terms of the resonance structures shown previously and your conclusion for (a).

8.91 An important reaction for the conversion of natural gas to other useful hydrocarbons is the conversion of methane to ethane.

$$2\,CH_4(g) \longrightarrow C_2H_6(g) + H_2(g)$$

In practice, this reaction is carried out in the presence of oxygen, which converts the hydrogen produced to water.

$$2\,CH_4(g) + \tfrac{1}{2}\,O_2(g) \longrightarrow C_2H_6(g) + H_2O(g)$$

Use bond enthalpies (Table 8.4) to estimate ΔH for these two reactions. Why is the conversion of methane to ethane more favorable when oxygen is used?

8.92 Two compounds are isomers if they have the same chemical formula but a different arrangement of atoms. Use bond enthalpies (Table 8.4) to estimate ΔH for each of the following gas-phase isomerization reactions, and indicate which isomer has the lower enthalpy:

(a)

Ethanol   Dimethyl ether

(b)

Ethylene oxide   Acetaldehyde

(c)

Cyclopentene   Pentadiene

(d)

Methyl isocyanide   Acetonitrile

[8.93] With reference to the "Chemistry Put to Work" box on explosives, **(a)** use bond enthalpies to estimate the enthalpy change for the explosion of 1.00 g of nitroglycerin. **(b)** Write a balanced equation for the decomposition of TNT.

Assume that, upon explosion, TNT decomposes into $N_2(g)$, $CO_2(g)$, $H_2O(g)$, and $C(s)$.

[8.94] The "plastic" explosive C-4, often used in action movies, contains the molecule *cyclotrimethylenetrinitramine*, which is often called RDX (for Royal Demolition eXplosive):

Cyclotrimethylenetrinitramine (RDX)

(a) Complete the Lewis structure for the molecule by adding unshared electron pairs where they are needed. **(b)** Does the Lewis structure you drew in part (a) have any resonance structures? If so, how many? **(c)** The molecule causes an explosion by decomposing into $CO(g)$, $N_2(g)$, and $H_2O(g)$. Write a balanced equation for the decomposition reaction. **(d)** With reference to Table 8.4, which is the weakest type of bond in the molecule? **(e)** Use average bond enthalpies to estimate the enthalpy change when 5.0 g of RDX decomposes.

8.95 The bond lengths of carbon–carbon, carbon–nitrogen, carbon–oxygen, and nitrogen–nitrogen single, double, and triple bonds are listed in Table 8.5. Plot bond enthalpy (Table 8.4) versus bond length for these bonds. What do you conclude about the relationship between bond length and bond enthalpy? What do you conclude about the relative strengths of C—C, C—N, C—O, and N—N bonds?

8.96 Use the data in Table 8.5 and the following data: S—S distance in $S_8 = 2.05$ Å; S—O distance in $SO_2 = 1.43$ Å to answer the following questions: **(a)** Predict the bond length in a S—N single bond. **(b)** Predict the bond length in a S—O single bond. **(c)** Why is the S—O bond length in SO_2 considerably shorter than your predicted value for the S—O single bond? **(d)** When elemental sulfur, S_8, is carefully oxidized, a compound S_8O is formed, in which one of the sulfur atoms in the S_8 ring is bonded to an oxygen atom. The S—O bond length in this compound is 1.48 Å. In light of this information, write Lewis structures that can account for the observed S—O bond length. Does the sulfur bearing the oxygen in this compound obey the octet rule?

INTEGRATIVE EXERCISES

8.97 The Ti^{2+} ion is isoelectronic with the Ca atom. **(a)** Are there any differences in the electron configurations of Ti^{2+} and Ca? **(b)** With reference to Figure 6.25, comment on the changes in the ordering of the 4s and 3d subshells in Ca and Ti^{2+}. **(c)** Will Ca and Ti^{2+} have the same number of unpaired electrons? Explain.

[8.98] **(a)** Write the chemical equations that are used in calculating the lattice energy of $SrCl_2(s)$ via a Born–Haber cycle. **(b)** The second ionization energy of $Sr(g)$ is 1064 kJ/mol. Use this fact along with data in Appendix C, Figure 7.12, Figure 7.14, and Table 8.2 to calculate ΔH_f° for $SrCl_2(s)$.

[8.99] The electron affinity of oxygen is −141 kJ/mol, corresponding to the reaction

$$O(g) + e^- \longrightarrow O^-(g)$$

The lattice energy of $K_2O(s)$ is 2238 kJ/mol. Use these data along with data in Appendix C and Figure 7.12 to calculate the "second electron affinity" of oxygen, corresponding to the reaction

$$O^-(g) + e^- \longrightarrow O^{2-}(g)$$

8.100 The reaction of indium, In, with sulfur leads to three binary compounds, which we will assume to be purely ionic. The three compounds have the following properties:

Compound	Mass % In	Melting Point (°C)
A	87.7	653
B	78.2	692
C	70.5	1050

(a) Determine the empirical formulas of compounds A, B, and C. **(b)** Give the oxidation state of In in each of the three compounds. **(c)** Write the electron configuration for the In ion in each compound. Do any of these configurations correspond to a noble-gas configuration? **(d)** In which compound is the ionic radius of In expected to be smallest? Explain. **(e)** The melting point of ionic compounds often correlates with the lattice energy. Explain the trends in the melting points of compounds A, B, and C in these terms.

[8.101] One scale for electronegativity is based on the concept
CQ that the electronegativity of any atom is proportional to the ionization energy of the atom minus its electron affinity: electronegativity $= k(\text{IE} - \text{EA})$, where k is a proportionality constant. **(a)** How does this definition explain why the electronegativity of F is greater than that of Cl even though Cl has the greater electron affinity? **(b)** Why are both ionization energy and electron affinity relevant to the notion of electronegativity? **(c)** By using data in Chapter 7, determine the value of k that would lead to an electronegativity of 4.0 for F under this definition. **(d)** Use your result from part (c) to determine the electronegativities of Cl and O using this scale. Do these values follow the trend shown in Figure 8.6?

8.102 The compound chloral hydrate, known in detective stories as knockout drops, is composed of 14.52% C, 1.83% H, 64.30% Cl, and 19.35% O by mass and has a molar mass of 165.4 g/mol. **(a)** What is the empirical formula of this substance? **(b)** What is the molecular formula of this substance? **(c)** Draw the Lewis structure of the molecule, assuming that the Cl atoms bond to a single C atom and that there are a C—C bond and two C—O bonds in the compound.

8.103 Barium azide is 62.04% Ba and 37.96% N. Each azide ion has a net charge of 1−. **(a)** Determine the chemical formula of the azide ion. **(b)** Write three resonance structures for the azide ion. **(c)** Which structure is most important? **(d)** Predict the bond lengths in the ion.

8.104 Acetylene (C_2H_2) and nitrogen (N_2) both contain a triple bond, but they differ greatly in their chemical properties. **(a)** Write the Lewis structures for the two substances. **(b)** By referring to Appendix C, look up the enthalpies of formation of acetylene and nitrogen and compare their reactivities. **(c)** Write balanced chemical equations for the complete oxidation of N_2 to form $N_2O_5(g)$ and of acetylene to form $CO_2(g)$ and $H_2O(g)$. **(d)** Calculate the enthalpy of oxidation per mole of N_2 and C_2H_2 (the enthalpy of formation of $N_2O_5(g)$ is 11.30 kJ/mol). How do these comparative values relate to your response to part (b)? Both N_2 and C_2H_2 possess triple bonds with quite high bond enthalpies (Table 8.4). What aspect of chemical bonding in these molecules or

in the oxidation products seems to account for the difference in chemical reactivities?

[8.105] Under special conditions, sulfur reacts with anhydrous liquid ammonia to form a binary compound of sulfur and nitrogen. The compound is found to consist of 69.6% S and 30.4% N. Measurements of its molecular mass yield a value of 184.3 g mol^{-1}. The compound occasionally detonates on being struck or when heated rapidly. The sulfur and nitrogen atoms of the molecule are joined in a ring. All the bonds in the ring are of the same length. **(a)** Calculate the empirical and molecular formulas for the substance. **(b)** Write Lewis structures for the molecule, based on the information you are given. (*Hint:* You should find a relatively small number of dominant Lewis structures.) **(c)** Predict the bond distances between the atoms in the ring. (*Note:* The S—S distance in the S_8 ring is 2.05Å.) **(d)** The enthalpy of formation of the compound is estimated to be 480 kJ mol^{-1}. ΔH_f° of S(g) is 222.8 kJ mol^{-1}. Estimate the average bond enthalpy in the compound.

[8.106] A common form of elemental phosphorus is the tetrahedral P_4 molecule, where all four phosphorus atoms are equivalent:

P_4

At room temperature phosphorus is a solid. **(a)** Do you think there are any unshared pairs of electrons in the P_4 molecule? **(b)** How many P—P bonds are there in the molecule? **(c)** Can you draw a Lewis structure for a linear P_4 molecule that satisfies the octet rule? **(d)** Using formal charges, what can you say about the stability of the linear molecule vs. that of the tetrahedral molecule?

[8.107] Consider benzene (C_6H_6) in the gas phase. **(a)** Write the reaction for breaking all the bonds in $C_6H_6(g)$, and use data in Appendix C to determine the enthalpy change for this reaction. **(b)** Write a reaction that corresponds to breaking all the carbon–carbon bonds in $C_6H_6(g)$. **(c)** By combining your answers to parts (a) and (b) and using the average bond enthalpy for C—H from Table 8.4, calculate the average bond enthalpy for the carbon–carbon bonds in $C_6H_6(g)$. **(d)** Comment on your answer from part (c) as compared to the values for C—C single bonds and C=C double bonds in Table 8.4.

8.108 Average bond enthalpies are generally defined for gas-phase molecules. Many substances are liquids in their standard state. (Section 5.7) By using appropriate thermochemical data from Appendix C, calculate average bond enthalpies in the liquid state for the following bonds, and compare these values to the gas-phase values given in Table 8.4: **(a)** Br—Br, from $Br_2(l)$; **(b)** C—Cl, from $CCl_4(l)$; **(c)** O—O, from $H_2O_2(l)$ (assume that the O—H bond enthalpy is the same as in the gas phase). **(d)** What can you conclude about the process of breaking bonds in the liquid as compared to the gas phase? Explain the difference in the ΔH values between the two phases.

16 ACID–BASE EQUILIBRIA

VARIETIES OF CITRUS FRUITS
(oranges, limes, lemons,
grapefruit, and tangerines).

666

WHAT IS THE SOUREST FOOD YOU'VE EVER TASTED? Citrus fruit, such as the lemons shown in the chapter-opening photograph? Sour cherries? Rhubarb? The sour taste of foods is due primarily to the presence of acids. Citric acid ($H_3C_6H_5O_7$), malic acid ($H_2C_4H_4O_5$), oxalic acid ($H_2C_2O_4$), and ascorbic

acid, also known as vitamin C ($HC_6H_7O_6$), are present in many fruits as well as in certain vegetables, such as rhubarb and tomatoes.

Acids and bases are important in numerous chemical processes that occur around us—from industrial processes to biological ones, from reactions in the laboratory to those in our environment. The time required for a metal object immersed in water to corrode, the ability of an aquatic environment to support fish and plant life, the fate of pollutants washed out of the air by rain, and even the rates of reactions that maintain our lives all critically depend upon the acidity or basicity of solutions. Indeed, an enormous amount of chemistry can be understood in terms of acid–base reactions.

667

We have encountered acids and bases many times in earlier discussions. For example, a portion of Chapter 4 focused on their reactions. But what makes a substance behave as an acid or as a base? In this chapter we reexamine acids and bases, taking a closer look at how they are identified and characterized. In doing so, we will consider their behavior both in terms of their structure and bonding and in terms of the chemical equilibria in which they participate.

16.1 ACIDS AND BASES: A BRIEF REVIEW

From the earliest days of experimental chemistry, scientists have recognized acids and bases by their characteristic properties. Acids have a sour taste and cause certain dyes to change color (for example, litmus turns red on contact with acids). Indeed, the word *acid* comes from the Latin word *acidus*, meaning sour or tart. Bases, in contrast, have a bitter taste and feel slippery (soap is a good example). The word *base* comes from an old English meaning of the word, which is "to bring low." (We still use the word *debase* in this sense, meaning to lower the value of something.) When bases are added to acids, they lower the amount of acid. Indeed, when acids and bases are mixed in certain proportions, their characteristic properties disappear altogether. (Section 4.3)

Historically, chemists have sought to relate the properties of acids and bases to their compositions and molecular structures. By 1830 it was evident that all acids contain hydrogen but not all hydrogen-containing substances are acids. During the 1880s, the Swedish chemist Svante Arrhenius (1859–1927) linked acid behavior with the presence of H^+ ions and base behavior with the presence of OH^- ions in aqueous solution.

Arrhenius defined acids as substances that produce H^+ ions in water and bases as substances that produce OH^- ions in water. Indeed, the properties of aqueous solutions of acids, such as sour taste, are due to $H^+(aq)$, whereas the properties of aqueous solutions of bases are due to $OH^-(aq)$. Over time the Arrhenius concept of acids and bases came to be stated in the following way:

- An *acid* is a substance that, when dissolved in water, increases the concentration of H^+ ions.
- A *base* is a substance that, when dissolved in water, increases the concentration of OH^- ions.

Hydrogen chloride is an Arrhenius acid. Hydrogen chloride gas is highly soluble in water because of its chemical reaction with water, which produces hydrated H^+ and Cl^- ions:

$$HCl(g) \xrightarrow{H_2O} H^+(aq) + Cl^-(aq) \qquad [16.1]$$

The aqueous solution of HCl is known as hydrochloric acid. Concentrated hydrochloric acid is about 37% HCl by mass and is 12 M in HCl. Sodium hydroxide, on the other hand, is an Arrhenius base. Because NaOH is an ionic compound, it dissociates into Na^+ and OH^- ions when it dissolves in water, thereby releasing OH^- ions into the solution.

GIVE IT SOME THOUGHT

What two ions are central to the Arrhenius definitions of acids and bases?

16.2 BRØNSTED–LOWRY ACIDS AND BASES

The Arrhenius concept of acids and bases, while useful, has limitations. For one thing, it is restricted to aqueous solutions. In 1923 the Danish chemist Johannes Brønsted (1879–1947) and the English chemist Thomas Lowry (1874–1936) independently proposed a more general definition of acids and bases. Their concept is based on the fact that *acid–base reactions involve the transfer of* H^+ *ions from one substance to another.*

The H⁺ Ion in Water

In Equation 16.1 hydrogen chloride is shown ionizing in water to form $H^+(aq)$. *An H^+ ion is simply a proton with no surrounding valence electron.* This small, positively charged particle interacts strongly with the nonbonding electron pairs of water molecules to form hydrated hydrogen ions. For example, the interaction of a proton with one water molecule forms the **hydronium ion**, $H_3O^+(aq)$:

$$H^+ + :\overset{..}{\underset{H}{O}}-H \longrightarrow \left[H-\overset{..}{\underset{H}{O}}-H \right]^+ \qquad [16.2]$$

The formation of hydronium ions is one of the complex features of the interaction of the H^+ ion with liquid water. In fact, the H_3O^+ ion can form hydrogen bonds to additional H_2O molecules to generate larger clusters of hydrated hydrogen ions, such as $H_5O_2^+$ and $H_9O_4^+$ (Figure 16.1▶).

Chemists use $H^+(aq)$ and $H_3O^+(aq)$ interchangeably to represent the same thing—namely the hydrated proton that is responsible for the characteristic properties of aqueous solutions of acids. We often use the $H^+(aq)$ ion for simplicity and convenience, as we did in Equation 16.1. The $H_3O^+(aq)$ ion, however, more closely represents reality.

Proton-Transfer Reactions

When we closely examine the reaction that occurs when HCl dissolves in water, we find that the HCl molecule actually transfers an H^+ ion (a proton) to a water molecule as depicted in Figure 16.2▶. Thus, we can represent the reaction as occurring between an HCl molecule and a water molecule to form hydronium and chloride ions:

$$HCl(g) + H_2O(l) \longrightarrow H_3O^+(aq) + Cl^-(aq) \qquad [16.3]$$

The polar H_2O molecule promotes the ionization of acids in water solution by accepting a proton to form H_3O^+.

Brønsted and Lowry proposed definitions of acids and bases in terms of their ability to transfer protons:

- An *acid* is a substance (molecule or ion) that donates a proton to another substance.

- A *base* is a substance that accepts a proton.

Thus, when HCl dissolves in water (Equation 16.3), HCl acts as a **Brønsted–Lowry acid** (it donates a proton to H_2O), and H_2O acts as a **Brønsted–Lowry base** (it accepts a proton from HCl).

Because the emphasis in the Brønsted–Lowry concept is on proton transfer, the concept also applies to reactions that do not occur in aqueous solution. In the reaction between HCl and NH_3, for example, a proton is transferred from the acid HCl to the base NH_3:

$$:\overset{..}{\underset{..}{Cl}}-H + :\overset{H}{\underset{H}{N}}-H \longrightarrow :\overset{..}{\underset{..}{Cl}}:^- + \left[H-\overset{H}{\underset{H}{N}}-H \right]^+ \qquad [16.4]$$

This reaction can occur in the gas phase. The hazy film that forms on the windows of general chemistry laboratories and on glassware in the lab is largely solid NH_4Cl formed by the gas-phase reaction of HCl and NH_3 (Figure 16.3▼).

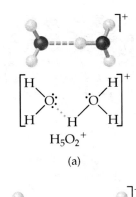

$H_5O_2^+$

(a)

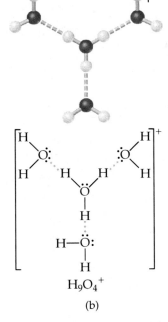

$H_9O_4^+$

(b)

▲ Figure 16.1 **Hydrated hydronium ions.** Lewis structures and molecular models for $H_5O_2^+$ and $H_9O_4^+$. There is good experimental evidence for the existence of both these species.

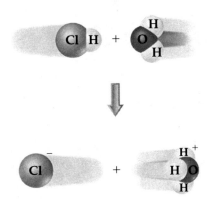

▲ Figure 16.2 **A proton-transfer reaction.** When a proton is transferred from HCl to H_2O, HCl acts as the Brønsted–Lowry acid and H_2O acts as the Brønsted–Lowry base.

▲ Figure 16.3 **A gas-phase acid–base reaction.** The HCl(*g*) escaping from concentrated hydrochloric acid and the NH₃(*g*) escaping from aqueous ammonia (here labeled ammonium hydroxide) combine to form a white fog of NH₄Cl(*s*).

Let's consider another example that compares the relationship between the Arrhenius definitions and the Brønsted–Lowry definitions of acids and bases—an aqueous solution of ammonia, in which the following equilibrium occurs:

$$NH_3(aq) + H_2O(l) \rightleftharpoons NH_4^+(aq) + OH^-(aq) \qquad [16.5]$$

Ammonia is an Arrhenius base because adding it to water leads to an increase in the concentration of OH⁻(*aq*). It is a Brønsted–Lowry base because it accepts a proton from H₂O. The H₂O molecule in Equation 16.5 acts as a Brønsted–Lowry acid because it donates a proton to the NH₃ molecule.

An acid and a base always work together to transfer a proton. In other words, a substance can function as an acid only if another substance simultaneously behaves as a base. To be a Brønsted–Lowry acid, a molecule or ion must have a hydrogen atom that it can lose as an H⁺ ion. To be a Brønsted–Lowry base, a molecule or ion must have a nonbonding pair of electrons that it can use to bind the H⁺ ion.

Some substances can act as an acid in one reaction and as a base in another. For example, H₂O is a Brønsted–Lowry base in its reaction with HCl (Equation 16.3) and a Brønsted–Lowry acid in its reaction with NH₃ (Equation 16.5). A substance that is capable of acting as either an acid or a base is called **amphiprotic**. An amphiprotic substance acts as a base when combined with something more strongly acidic than itself and as an acid when combined with something more strongly basic than itself.

GIVE IT SOME THOUGHT

In the forward reaction, which substance acts as the Brønsted–Lowry base:
$HSO_4^-(aq) + NH_3(aq) \rightleftharpoons SO_4^{2-}(aq) + NH_4^+(aq)$?

Conjugate Acid–Base Pairs

In any acid–base equilibrium both the forward reaction (to the right) and the reverse reaction (to the left) involve proton transfers. For example, consider the reaction of an acid, which we will denote HX, with water:

$$HX(aq) + H_2O(l) \rightleftharpoons X^-(aq) + H_3O^+(aq) \qquad [16.6]$$

In the forward reaction HX donates a proton to H₂O. Therefore, HX is the Brønsted–Lowry acid, and H₂O is the Brønsted–Lowry base. In the reverse reaction the H₃O⁺ ion donates a proton to the X⁻ ion, so H₃O⁺ is the acid and X⁻ is the base. When the acid HX donates a proton, it leaves behind a substance, X⁻, which can act as a base. Likewise, when H₂O acts as a base, it generates H₃O⁺, which can act as an acid.

An acid and a base such as HX and X⁻ that differ only in the presence or absence of a proton are called a **conjugate acid–base pair.*** Every acid has a **conjugate base**, formed by removing a proton from the acid. For example, OH⁻ is the conjugate base of H₂O, and X⁻ is the conjugate base of HX. Similarly, every base has associated with it a **conjugate acid**, formed by adding a proton to the base. Thus, H₃O⁺ is the conjugate acid of H₂O, and HX is the conjugate acid of X⁻.

In any acid–base (proton-transfer) reaction we can identify two sets of conjugate acid–base pairs. For example, consider the reaction between nitrous acid (HNO₂) and water:

remove H⁺

$$HNO_2(aq) + H_2O(l) \rightleftharpoons NO_2^-(aq) + H_3O^+(aq) \qquad [16.7]$$

Acid   Base   Conjugate   Conjugate
                            base   acid

add H⁺

*The word conjugate *means "joined together as a pair."*

Likewise, for the reaction between NH_3 and H_2O (Equation 16.5), we have

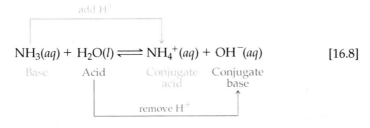

$$NH_3(aq) + H_2O(l) \rightleftharpoons NH_4^+(aq) + OH^-(aq) \qquad [16.8]$$

■ SAMPLE EXERCISE 16.1 | Identifying Conjugate Acids and Bases

(a) What is the conjugate base of each of the following acids: $HClO_4$, H_2S, PH_4^+, HCO_3^-? **(b)** What is the conjugate acid of each of the following bases: CN^-, SO_4^{2-}, H_2O, HCO_3^-?

SOLUTION

Analyze: We are asked to give the conjugate base for each of a series of species and to give the conjugate acid for each of another series of species.

Plan: The conjugate base of a substance is simply the parent substance minus one proton, and the conjugate acid of a substance is the parent substance plus one proton.

Solve: (a) $HClO_4$ less one proton (H^+) is ClO_4^-. The other conjugate bases are HS^-, PH_3, and CO_3^{2-}. **(b)** CN^- plus one proton (H^+) is HCN. The other conjugate acids are HSO_4^-, H_3O^+, and H_2CO_3.
 Notice that the hydrogen carbonate ion (HCO_3^-) is amphiprotic. It can act as either an acid or a base.

■ PRACTICE EXERCISE

Write the formula for the conjugate acid of each of the following: HSO_3^-, F^-, PO_4^{3-}, CO.
Answers: H_2SO_3, HF, HPO_4^{2-}, HCO^+

■ SAMPLE EXERCISE 16.2 | Writing Equations for Proton-Transfer Reactions

The hydrogen sulfite ion (HSO_3^-) is amphiprotic. **(a)** Write an equation for the reaction of HSO_3^- with water, in which the ion acts as an acid. **(b)** Write an equation for the reaction of HSO_3^- with water, in which the ion acts as a base. In both cases identify the conjugate acid–base pairs.

SOLUTION

Analyze and Plan: We are asked to write two equations representing reactions between HSO_3^- and water, one in which HSO_3^- should donate a proton to water, thereby acting as a Brønsted–Lowry acid, and one in which HSO_3^- should accept a proton from water, thereby acting as a base. We are also asked to identify the conjugate pairs in each equation.

Solve:

(a)
$$HSO_3^-(aq) + H_2O(l) \rightleftharpoons SO_3^{2-}(aq) + H_3O^+(aq)$$

The conjugate pairs in this equation are HSO_3^- (acid) and SO_3^{2-} (conjugate base); and H_2O (base) and H_3O^+ (conjugate acid).

(b)
$$HSO_3^-(aq) + H_2O(l) \rightleftharpoons H_2SO_3(aq) + OH^-(aq)$$

The conjugate pairs in this equation are H_2O (acid) and OH^- (conjugate base), and HSO_3^- (base) and H_2SO_3 (conjugate acid).

■ PRACTICE EXERCISE

When lithium oxide (Li_2O) is dissolved in water, the solution turns basic from the reaction of the oxide ion (O^{2-}) with water. Write the reaction that occurs, and identify the conjugate acid–base pairs.
Answer: $O^{2-}(aq) + H_2O(l) \longrightarrow OH^-(aq) + OH^-(aq)$. OH^- is the conjugate acid of the base O^{2-}. OH^- is also the conjugate base of the acid H_2O.

Relative Strengths of Acids and Bases

Some acids are better proton donors than others; likewise, some bases are better proton acceptors than others. If we arrange acids in order of their ability to donate a proton, we find that the more easily a substance gives up a proton, the less easily its conjugate base accepts a proton. Similarly, the more easily a base accepts a proton, the less easily its conjugate acid gives up a proton. In other words, *the stronger an acid, the weaker is its conjugate base; the stronger a base, the weaker is its conjugate acid.* Thus, if we know something about the strength of an acid (its ability to donate protons), we also know something about the strength of its conjugate base (its ability to accept protons).

The inverse relationship between the strengths of acids and the strengths of their conjugate bases is illustrated in Figure 16.4 ◀. Here we have grouped acids and bases into three broad categories based on their behavior in water.

		ACID	BASE	
100% ionized in H_2O	Strong	HCl	Cl^-	Negligible
	Strong	H_2SO_4	HSO_4^-	Negligible
	Strong	HNO_3	NO_3^-	Negligible
		$H_3O^+(aq)$	H_2O	
	Weak	HSO_4^-	SO_4^{2-}	Weak
	Weak	H_3PO_4	$H_2PO_4^-$	Weak
	Weak	HF	F^-	Weak
	Weak	CH_3COOH	CH_3COO^-	Weak
	Weak	H_2CO_3	HCO_3^-	Weak
	Weak	H_2S	HS^-	Weak
	Weak	$H_2PO_4^-$	HPO_4^{2-}	Weak
	Weak	NH_4^+	NH_3	Weak
	Weak	HCO_3^-	CO_3^{2-}	Weak
	Weak	HPO_4^{2-}	PO_4^{3-}	Weak
		H_2O	OH^-	
	Negligible	OH^-	O^{2-}	Strong (100% protonated in H_2O)
	Negligible	H_2	H^-	Strong (100% protonated in H_2O)
	Negligible	CH_4	CH_3^-	Strong (100% protonated in H_2O)

Acid strength increases ↑ Base strength increases ↓

▲ Figure 16.4 **Relative strengths of some conjugate acid–base pairs.** The two members of each pair are listed opposite each other in the two columns. The acids decrease in strength from top to bottom, whereas their conjugate bases increase in strength from top to bottom.

1. A *strong acid* completely transfers its protons to water, leaving no undissociated molecules in solution. (Section 4.3) Its conjugate base has a negligible tendency to be protonated (to abstract protons) in aqueous solution.
2. A *weak acid* only partially dissociates in aqueous solution and therefore exists in the solution as a mixture of acid molecules and their constituent ions. The conjugate base of a weak acid shows a slight ability to remove protons from water. (*The conjugate base of a weak acid is a weak base.*)
3. A substance with *negligible acidity,* such as CH_4, contains hydrogen but does not demonstrate any acidic behavior in water. Its conjugate base is a strong base, reacting completely with water, abstracting protons to form OH^- ions.

GIVE IT SOME THOUGHT

Using the three categories above, specify the strength of HNO_3 and the strength of its conjugate base, NO_3^-.

We can think of proton-transfer reactions as being governed by the relative abilities of two bases to abstract protons. For example, consider the proton transfer that occurs when an acid HX dissolves in water:

$$HX(aq) + H_2O(l) \rightleftharpoons H_3O^+(aq) + X^-(aq) \qquad [16.9]$$

If H_2O (the base in the forward reaction) is a stronger base than X^- (the conjugate base of HX), then H_2O will abstract the proton from HX to produce H_3O^+ and X^-. As a result, the equilibrium will lie to the right. This describes the behavior of a strong acid in water. For example, when HCl dissolves in water, the solution consists almost entirely of H_3O^+ and Cl^- ions with a negligible concentration of HCl molecules.

$$HCl(g) + H_2O(l) \longrightarrow H_3O^+(aq) + Cl^-(aq) \qquad [16.10]$$

H_2O is a stronger base than Cl^- (Figure 16.4), so H_2O acquires the proton to become the hydronium ion.

When X^- is a stronger base than H_2O, the equilibrium will lie to the left. This situation occurs when HX is a weak acid. For example, an aqueous solution of acetic acid (CH_3COOH) consists mainly of CH_3COOH molecules with only a relatively few H_3O^+ and CH_3COO^- ions.

$$CH_3COOH(aq) + H_2O(l) \rightleftharpoons H_3O^+(aq) + CH_3COO^-(aq) \qquad [16.11]$$

CH_3COO^- is a stronger base than H_2O (Figure 16.4) and therefore abstracts the proton from H_3O^+.

From these examples, we conclude that *in every acid–base reaction the position of the equilibrium favors transfer of the proton from the stronger acid to the stronger base to form the weaker acid and the weaker base.* As a result, the equilibrium mixture contains more of the weaker acid and weaker base and less of the stronger acid and stronger base.

■■ **SAMPLE EXERCISE 16.3** | **Predicting the Position of a Proton-Transfer Equilibrium**

For the following proton-transfer reaction, use Figure 16.4 to predict whether the equilibrium lies predominantly to the left (that is, $K_c < 1$) or to the right ($K_c > 1$):

$$HSO_4^-(aq) + CO_3^{2-}(aq) \rightleftharpoons SO_4^{2-}(aq) + HCO_3^-(aq)$$

SOLUTION

Analyze: We are asked to predict whether the equilibrium shown lies to the right, favoring products, or to the left, favoring reactants.

Plan: This is a proton-transfer reaction, and the position of the equilibrium will favor the proton going to the stronger of two bases. The two bases in the equation are CO_3^{2-}, the base in the forward reaction as written, and SO_4^{2-}, the conjugate base of HSO_4^-. We can find the relative positions of these two bases in Figure 16.4 to determine which is the stronger base.

Solve: CO_3^{2-} appears lower in the right-hand column in Figure 16.4 and is therefore a stronger base than SO_4^{2-}. CO_3^{2-}, therefore, will get the proton preferentially to become HCO_3^-, while SO_4^{2-} will remain mostly unprotonated. The resulting equilibrium will lie to the right, favoring products (that is, $K_c > 1$).

$$\underset{\text{Acid}}{HSO_4^-(aq)} + \underset{\text{Base}}{CO_3^{2-}(aq)} \rightleftharpoons \underset{\text{Conjugate base}}{SO_4^{2-}(aq)} + \underset{\text{Conjugate acid}}{HCO_3^-(aq)} \qquad K_c > 1$$

Comment: Of the two acids in the equation, HSO_4^- and HCO_3^-, the stronger one gives up a proton more readily while the weaker one tends to retain its proton. Thus, the equilibrium favors the direction in which the proton moves from the stronger acid and becomes bonded to the stronger base.

■■ **PRACTICE EXERCISE**

For each of the following reactions, use Figure 16.4 to predict whether the equilibrium lies predominantly to the left or to the right:
(a) $HPO_4^{2-}(aq) + H_2O(l) \rightleftharpoons H_2PO_4^-(aq) + OH^-(aq)$
(b) $NH_4^+(aq) + OH^-(aq) \rightleftharpoons NH_3(aq) + H_2O(l)$
Answers: **(a)** left, **(b)** right

16.3 THE AUTOIONIZATION OF WATER

One of the most important chemical properties of water is its ability to act as either a Brønsted acid or a Brønsted base, depending on the circumstances. In the presence of an acid, water acts as a proton acceptor; in the presence of a base, water acts as a proton donor. In fact, one water molecule can donate a proton to another water molecule:

$$H{-}\overset{\cdot\cdot}{\underset{|}{O}}{:} + H{-}\overset{\cdot\cdot}{\underset{|}{O}}{:} \rightleftharpoons \left[H{-}\overset{\cdot\cdot}{\underset{|}{O}}{-}H\right]^+ + {:}\overset{\cdot\cdot}{\underset{\cdot\cdot}{O}}{-}H^- \qquad [16.12]$$

We call this process the **autoionization** of water. No individual molecule remains ionized for long; the reactions are extremely rapid in both directions.

At room temperature only about two out of every 10^9 molecules are ionized at any given instant. Thus, pure water consists almost entirely of H_2O molecules and is an extremely poor conductor of electricity. Nevertheless, the autoionization of water is very important, as we will soon see.

The Ion Product of Water

Because the autoionization of water (Equation 16.12) is an equilibrium process, we can write the following equilibrium-constant expression for it:

$$K_c = [H_3O^+][OH^-] \qquad [16.13]$$

The term $[H_2O]$ is excluded from the equilibrium-constant expression because we exclude the concentrations of pure solids and liquids. (Section 15.4) Because this equilibrium-constant expression refers specifically to the autoionization of water, we use the symbol K_w to denote the equilibrium constant, which we call the **ion-product constant** for water. At 25 °C, K_w equals 1.0×10^{-14}. Thus, we have

$$K_w = [H_3O^+][OH^-] = 1.0 \times 10^{-14} \quad (\text{at } 25 \text{ °C}) \qquad [16.14]$$

Because we use $H^+(aq)$ and $H_3O^+(aq)$ interchangeably to represent the hydrated proton, the autoionization reaction for water can also be written as

$$H_2O(l) \rightleftharpoons H^+(aq) + OH^-(aq) \qquad [16.15]$$

Likewise, the expression for K_w can be written in terms of either H_3O^- or H^+, and K_w has the same value in either case:

$$K_w = [H_3O^+][OH^-] = [H^+][OH^-] = 1.0 \times 10^{-14} \quad (\text{at } 25 \text{ °C}) \qquad [16.16]$$

This equilibrium-constant expression and the value of K_w at 25 °C are extremely important, and you should commit them to memory.

What makes Equation 16.16 particularly useful is that it is applicable to pure water and to any aqueous solution. Although the equilibrium between $H^+(aq)$ and $OH^-(aq)$ as well as other ionic equilibria are affected somewhat by the presence of additional ions in solution, it is customary to ignore these ionic effects except in work requiring exceptional accuracy. Thus, Equation 16.16 is taken to be valid for any dilute aqueous solution, and it can be used to calculate either $[H^+]$ (if $[OH^-]$ is known) or $[OH^-]$ (if $[H^+]$ is known).

A solution in which $[H^+] = [OH^-]$ is said to be *neutral*. In most solutions H^+ and OH^- concentrations are not equal. As the concentration of one of these ions increases, the concentration of the other must decrease, so that the product of their concentrations equals 1.0×10^{-14}. In acidic solutions $[H^+]$ exceeds $[OH^-]$. In basic solutions $[OH^-]$ exceeds $[H^+]$.

■■■ **SAMPLE EXERCISE 16.4** | **Calculating [H⁺] for Pure Water**

Calculate the values of $[H^+]$ and $[OH^-]$ in a neutral solution at 25 °C.

SOLUTION

Analyze: We are asked to determine the concentrations of H^+ and OH^- ions in a neutral solution at 25 °C.

Plan: We will use Equation 16.16 and the fact that, by definition, $[H^+] = [OH^-]$ in a neutral solution.

Solve: We will represent the concentration of $[H^+]$ and $[OH^-]$ in neutral solution with x. This gives

$$[H^+][OH^-] = (x)(x) = 1.0 \times 10^{-14}$$
$$x^2 = 1.0 \times 10^{-14}$$
$$x = 1.0 \times 10^{-7} \, M = [H^+] = [OH^-]$$

In an acid solution $[H^+]$ is greater than $1.0 \times 10^{-7} \, M$; in a basic solution $[H^+]$ is less than $1.0 \times 10^{-7} \, M$.

▩ PRACTICE EXERCISE

Indicate whether solutions with each of the following ion concentrations are neutral, acidic, or basic: **(a)** $[H^+] = 4 \times 10^{-9}\ M$; **(b)** $[OH^-] = 1 \times 10^{-7}\ M$; **(c)** $[OH^-] = 7 \times 10^{-13}\ M$.
Answers: **(a)** basic, **(b)** neutral, **(c)** acidic

▩ SAMPLE EXERCISE 16.5 │ Calculating [H⁺] from [OH⁻]

Calculate the concentration of $H^+(aq)$ in **(a)** a solution in which $[OH^-]$ is $0.010\ M$, **(b)** a solution in which $[OH^-]$ is $1.8 \times 10^{-9}\ M$. *Note:* In this problem and all that follow, we assume, unless stated otherwise, that the temperature is 25 °C.

SOLUTION

Analyze: We are asked to calculate the hydronium ion concentration in an aqueous solution where the hydroxide concentration is known.

Plan: We can use the equilibrium-constant expression for the autoionization of water and the value of K_w to solve for each unknown concentration.

Solve:

(a) Using Equation 16.16, we have: $[H^+][OH^-] = 1.0 \times 10^{-14}$

$$[H^+] = \frac{(1.0 \times 10^{-14})}{[OH^-]} = \frac{1.0 \times 10^{-14}}{0.010} = 1.0 \times 10^{-12}\ M$$

This solution is basic because $[OH^-] > [H^+]$

(b) In this instance $[H^+] = \frac{(1.0 \times 10^{-14})}{[OH^-]} = \frac{1.0 \times 10^{-14}}{1.8 \times 10^{-9}} = 5.6 \times 10^{-6}\ M$

This solution is acidic because $[H^+] > [OH^-]$

▩ PRACTICE EXERCISE

Calculate the concentration of $OH^-(aq)$ in a solution in which **(a)** $[H^+] = 2 \times 10^{-6}\ M$; **(b)** $[H^+] = [OH^-]$; **(c)** $[H^+] = 100 \times [OH^-]$.
Answers: **(a)** $5 \times 10^{-9}\ M$, **(b)** $1.0 \times 10^{-7}\ M$, **(c)** $1.0 \times 10^{-8}\ M$

16.4 THE pH SCALE

The molar concentration of $H^+(aq)$ in an aqueous solution is usually very small. For convenience, we therefore usually express $[H^+]$ in terms of **pH**, which is the negative logarithm in base 10 of $[H^+]$.*

$$pH = -\log[H^+] \qquad [16.17]$$

If you need to review the use of logs, see Appendix A.

We can use Equation 16.17 to calculate the pH of a neutral solution at 25 °C (that is, one in which $[H^+] = 1.0 \times 10^{-7}\ M$):

$$pH = -\log(1.0 \times 10^{-7}) = -(-7.00) = 7.00$$

The pH of a neutral solution is 7.00 at 25 °C. Notice that the pH is reported with two decimal places. We do so because only the numbers to the right of the decimal point are the significant figures in a logarithm. Because our original value for the concentration ($1.0 \times 10^{-7}\ M$) has two significant figures, the corresponding pH has two decimal places (7.00).

What happens to the pH of a solution as we make the solution acidic? An acidic solution is one in which $[H^+] > 1.0 \times 10^{-7}\ M$. Because of the negative sign in Equation 16.17, *the pH decreases as $[H^+]$ increases.* For example, the pH of an acidic solution in which $[H^+] = 1.0 \times 10^{-3}\ M$ is

$$pH = -\log(1.0 \times 10^{-3}) = -(-3.00) = 3.00$$

At 25 °C the pH of an acidic solution is less than 7.00.

*Because $[H^+]$ and $[H_3O^+]$ are used interchangeably, you might see pH defined as $-\log[H_3O^+]$.

TABLE 16.1 ■ Relationships among [H⁺], [OH⁻], and pH at 25 °C

Solution Type	$[H^+]$ (M)	$[OH^-]$ (M)	pH Value
Acidic	$>1.0 \times 10^{-7}$	$<1.0 \times 10^{-7}$	<7.00
Neutral	$=1.0 \times 10^{-7}$	$=1.0 \times 10^{-7}$	$=7.00$
Basic	$<1.0 \times 10^{-7}$	$>1.0 \times 10^{-7}$	>7.00

We can also calculate the pH of a basic solution, one in which $[OH^-] > 1.0 \times 10^{-7}$ M. Suppose $[OH^-] = 2.0 \times 10^{-3}$ M. We can use Equation 16.16 to calculate $[H^+]$ for this solution, and Equation 16.17 to calculate the pH:

$$[H^+] = \frac{K_w}{[OH^-]} = \frac{1.0 \times 10^{-14}}{2.0 \times 10^{-3}} = 5.0 \times 10^{-12} \, M$$

$$pH = -\log(5.0 \times 10^{-12}) = 11.30$$

At 25 °C the pH of a basic solution is greater than 7.00. The relationships among $[H^+]$, $[OH^-]$, and pH are summarized in Table 16.1 ▲ and in Figure 16.5 ▼.

The pH values characteristic of several familiar solutions are shown in Figure 16.5. Notice that a change in $[H^+]$ by a factor of 10 causes the pH to change by 1. Thus, a solution of pH 6 has 10 times the concentration of $H^+(aq)$ as a solution of pH 7.

GIVE IT SOME THOUGHT

(a) What is the significance of pH = 7? **(b)** How does the pH change as OH^- is added to the solution?

You might think that when $[H^+]$ is very small, as it is for some of the examples shown in Figure 16.5, it would be unimportant. Nothing is further from the truth. If $[H^+]$ is part of a kinetic rate law, then changing its concentration will

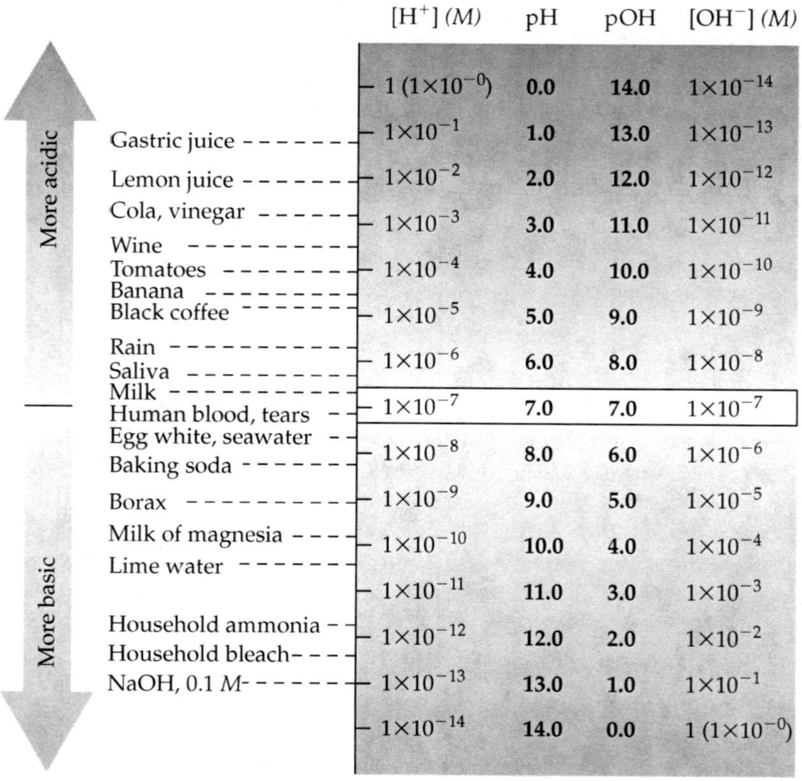

▶ Figure 16.5 **H⁺ concentrations and pH values of some common substances at 25 °C.** The pH of a solution can be estimated using the benchmark concentrations of H^+ and OH^- corresponding to whole-number pH values.

	$[H^+]$ (M)	pH	pOH	$[OH^-]$ (M)
	$1\,(1\times10^{-0})$	0.0	14.0	1×10^{-14}
Gastric juice	1×10^{-1}	1.0	13.0	1×10^{-13}
Lemon juice	1×10^{-2}	2.0	12.0	1×10^{-12}
Cola, vinegar	1×10^{-3}	3.0	11.0	1×10^{-11}
Wine / Tomatoes	1×10^{-4}	4.0	10.0	1×10^{-10}
Banana / Black coffee	1×10^{-5}	5.0	9.0	1×10^{-9}
Rain / Saliva / Milk	1×10^{-6}	6.0	8.0	1×10^{-8}
Human blood, tears	1×10^{-7}	7.0	7.0	1×10^{-7}
Egg white, seawater / Baking soda	1×10^{-8}	8.0	6.0	1×10^{-6}
Borax	1×10^{-9}	9.0	5.0	1×10^{-5}
Milk of magnesia	1×10^{-10}	10.0	4.0	1×10^{-4}
Lime water	1×10^{-11}	11.0	3.0	1×10^{-3}
Household ammonia	1×10^{-12}	12.0	2.0	1×10^{-2}
Household bleach / NaOH, 0.1 M	1×10^{-13}	13.0	1.0	1×10^{-1}
	1×10^{-14}	14.0	0.0	$1\,(1\times10^{-0})$

More acidic ↑   More basic ↓

change the rate. ⟲⟲ (Section 14.3) Thus, if the rate law is first order in $[H^+]$ doubling its concentration will double the rate even if the change is merely from 1×10^{-7} M to 2×10^{-7} M. In biological systems many reactions involve proton transfers and have rates that depend on $[H^+]$. Because the speeds of these reactions are crucial, the pH of biological fluids must be maintained within narrow limits. For example, human blood has a normal pH range of 7.35 to 7.45. Illness and even death can result if the pH varies much from this narrow range.

▇ SAMPLE EXERCISE 16.6 | Calculating pH from [H⁺]

Calculate the pH values for the two solutions described in Sample Exercise 16.5.

SOLUTION

Analyze: We are asked to determine the pH of aqueous solutions for which we have already calculated $[H^+]$.

Plan: We can calculate pH using its defining equation, Equation 16.17.

Solve:

(a) In the first instance we found $[H^+]$ to be 1.0×10^{-12} M.

$$pH = -\log(1.0 \times 10^{-12}) = -(-12.00) = 12.00$$

Because **1.0 × 10⁻¹²** has two significant figures, the pH has two decimal places, **12.00**.
(b) For the second solution, $[H^+] = 5.6 \times 10^{-6}$ M. Before performing the calculation, it is helpful to estimate the pH. To do so, we note that $[H^+]$ lies between 1×10^{-6} and 1×10^{-5}.

$$1 \times 10^{-6} < 5.6 \times 10^{-6} < 1 \times 10^{-5}$$

Thus, we expect the pH to lie between 6.0 and 5.0. We use Equation 16.17 to calculate the pH.

$$pH = -\log(5.6 \times 10^{-6}) = 5.25$$

Check: After calculating a pH, it is useful to compare it to your prior estimate. In this case the pH, as we predicted, falls between 6 and 5. Had the calculated pH and the estimate not agreed, we should have reconsidered our calculation or estimate or both.

▇ PRACTICE EXERCISE

(a) In a sample of lemon juice $[H^+]$ is 3.8×10^{-4} M. What is the pH? **(b)** A commonly available window-cleaning solution has $[OH^-] = 1.9 \times 10^{-6}$ M. What is the pH?
Answers: **(a)** 3.42, **(b)** $[H^+] = 5.3 \times 10^{-9}$ M, so pH = 8.28

▇ SAMPLE EXERCISE 16.7 | Calculating [H⁺] from pH

A sample of freshly pressed apple juice has a pH of 3.76. Calculate $[H^+]$.

SOLUTION

Analyze: We need to calculate $[H^+]$ from pH.

Plan: We will use Equation 16.17, $pH = -\log[H^+]$, for the calculation.

Solve: From Equation 16.17, we have

$$pH = -\log[H^+] = 3.76$$

Thus,

$$\log[H^+] = -3.76$$

To find $[H^+]$, we need to determine the *antilog* of −3.76. Scientific calculators have an antilog function (sometimes labeled INV log or 10^x) that allows us to perform the calculation:

$$[H^+] = \text{antilog}(-3.76) = 10^{-3.76} = 1.7 \times 10^{-4} \text{ M}$$

Comment: Consult the user's manual for your calculator to find out how to perform the antilog operation. The number of significant figures in $[H^+]$ is two because the number of decimal places in the pH is two.

Check: Because the pH is between 3.0 and 4.0, we know that $[H^+]$ will be between 1×10^{-3} and 1×10^{-4} M. Our calculated $[H^+]$ falls within this estimated range.

▇ PRACTICE EXERCISE

A solution formed by dissolving an antacid tablet has a pH of 9.18. Calculate $[H^+]$.
Answer: $[H^+] = 6.6 \times 10^{-10}$ M

pOH and Other "p" Scales

The negative log is also a convenient way of expressing the magnitudes of small quantities. We use the convention that the negative log of a quantity is labeled "p" (quantity). Thus, we can express the concentration of OH^- as pOH:

$$pOH = -\log[OH^-] \qquad [16.18]$$

Likewise, pK_w equals $-\log K_w$.

By taking the negative log of both sides of Equation 16.16,

$$-\log[H^+] + (-\log[OH^-]) = -\log K_w \qquad [16.19]$$

we obtain the following useful expression:

$$pH + pOH = 14.00 \quad \text{(at 25 °C)} \qquad [16.20]$$

We will see in Section 16.8 that p scales are also useful when working with other equilibrium constants.

GIVE IT SOME THOUGHT

If the pOH for a solution is 3.00, what is the pH of the solution? Is the solution acidic or basic?

Measuring pH

▲ Figure 16.6 **A digital pH meter.** The device is a millivoltmeter, and the electrodes immersed in the solution being tested produce a voltage that depends on the pH of the solution.

The pH of a solution can be measured quickly and accurately with a *pH meter* (Figure 16.6 ◄). A complete understanding of how this important device works requires a knowledge of electrochemistry, a subject we take up in Chapter 20. In brief, a pH meter consists of a pair of electrodes connected to a meter capable of measuring small voltages, on the order of millivolts. A voltage, which varies with the pH, is generated when the electrodes are placed in a solution. This voltage is read by the meter, which is calibrated to give pH.

The electrodes used with pH meters come in many shapes and sizes, depending on their intended use. Electrodes have even been developed that are so small that they can be inserted into single living cells to monitor the pH of the cell medium. Pocket-size pH meters are also available for use in environmental studies, in monitoring industrial effluents, and in agricultural work.

Although less precise, acid–base indicators can be used to measure pH. An acid–base indicator is a colored substance that itself can exist in either an acid or a base form. The two forms have different colors. Thus, the indicator turns one color in an acid and another color in a base. If you know the pH at which the indicator turns from one form to the other, you can determine whether a solution has a higher or lower pH than this value. Litmus, for example, changes color in the vicinity of pH 7. The color change, however, is not very sharp. Red litmus indicates a pH of about 5 or lower, and blue litmus indicates a pH of about 8 or higher.

Some of the more common indicators are listed in Figure 16.7 ▶. Methyl orange, for example, changes color over the pH interval from 3.1 to 4.4. Below pH 3.1 it is in the acid form, which is red. In the interval between 3.1 and 4.4, it is gradually converted to its basic form, which has a yellow color. By pH 4.4 the conversion is complete, and the solution is yellow. Paper tape that is impregnated with several indicators and comes complete with a comparator color scale is widely used for approximate determinations of pH.

GIVE IT SOME THOUGHT

If phenolphthalein turns pink when added to a solution, what can we conclude about the pH of the solution?

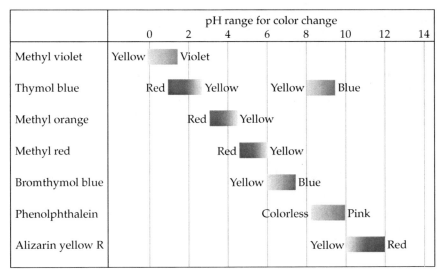

	pH range for color change
	0 2 4 6 8 10 12 14
Methyl violet	Yellow ▨ Violet
Thymol blue	Red ▨ Yellow Yellow ▨ Blue
Methyl orange	Red ▨ Yellow
Methyl red	Red ▨ Yellow
Bromthymol blue	Yellow ▨ Blue
Phenolphthalein	Colorless ▨ Pink
Alizarin yellow R	Yellow ▨ Red

▲ Figure 16.7 **Some common acid–base indicators.** The pH ranges for the color changes of some common acid–base indicators. Most indicators have a useful range of about 2 pH units.

16.5 STRONG ACIDS AND BASES

The chemistry of an aqueous solution often depends critically on the pH of the solution. It is therefore important to examine how the pH of solutions relates to the concentrations of acids and bases. The simplest cases are those involving strong acids and strong bases. Strong acids and bases are *strong electrolytes*, existing in aqueous solution entirely as ions. There are relatively few common strong acids and bases, and we listed these substances in Table 4.2.

Strong Acids

The seven most common strong acids include six monoprotic acids (HCl, HBr, HI, HNO_3, $HClO_3$, and $HClO_4$), and one diprotic acid (H_2SO_4). Nitric acid (HNO_3) exemplifies the behavior of the monoprotic strong acids. For all practical purposes, an aqueous solution of HNO_3 consists entirely of H_3O^+ and NO_3^- ions.

$$HNO_3(aq) + H_2O(l) \longrightarrow H_3O^+(aq) + NO_3^-(aq) \text{ (complete ionization) [16.21]}$$

We have not used equilibrium arrows for Equation 16.21 because the reaction lies entirely to the right, the side with the ions. (Section 4.1) As noted in Section 16.3, we use $H_3O^+(aq)$ and $H^+(aq)$ interchangeably to represent the hydrated proton in water. Thus, we often simplify the equations for the ionization reactions of acids as follows:

$$HNO_3(aq) \longrightarrow H^+(aq) + NO_3^-(aq)$$

In an aqueous solution of a strong acid, the acid is normally the only significant source of H^+ ions.* As a result, calculating the pH of a solution of a strong monoprotic acid is straightforward because $[H^+]$ equals the original concentration of acid. In a 0.20 M solution of $HNO_3(aq)$, for example, $[H^+] = [NO_3^-] = 0.20$ M. The situation with the diprotic acid H_2SO_4 is more complex, as we will see in Section 16.6.

*If the concentration of the acid is 10^{-6} M or less, we also need to consider H^+ ions that result from the autoionization of H_2O. Normally, the concentration of H^+ from H_2O is so small that it can be neglected.

■■ SAMPLE EXERCISE 16.8 | Calculating the pH of a Strong Acid

What is the pH of a 0.040 M solution of $HClO_4$?

SOLUTION

Analyze and Plan: Because $HClO_4$ is a strong acid, it is completely ionized, giving $[H^+] = [ClO_4^-] = 0.040\ M$.

Solve: The pH of the solution is given by

$$pH = -\log(0.040) = 1.40.$$

Check: Because $[H^+]$ lies between 1×10^{-2} and 1×10^{-1}, the pH will be between 2.0 and 1.0. Our calculated pH falls within the estimated range. Furthermore, because the concentration has two significant figures, the pH has two decimal places.

■■ PRACTICE EXERCISE

An aqueous solution of HNO_3 has a pH of 2.34. What is the concentration of the acid?
Answer: 0.0046 M

Strong Bases

There are relatively few common strong bases. The most common soluble strong bases are the ionic hydroxides of the alkali metals (group 1A) and the heavier alkaline earth metals (group 2A), such as NaOH, KOH, and $Ca(OH)_2$. These compounds completely dissociate into ions in aqueous solution. Thus, a solution labeled 0.30 M NaOH consists of 0.30 M $Na^+(aq)$ and 0.30 M $OH^-(aq)$; there is essentially no undissociated NaOH.

■■ SAMPLE EXERCISE 16.9 | Calculating the pH of a Strong Base

What is the pH of **(a)** a 0.028 M solution of NaOH, **(b)** a 0.0011 M solution of $Ca(OH)_2$?

SOLUTION

Analyze: We are asked to calculate the pH of two solutions of strong bases.

Plan: We can calculate each pH by either of two equivalent methods. First, we could use Equation 16.16 to calculate $[H^+]$ and then use Equation 16.17 to calculate the pH. Alternatively, we could use $[OH^-]$ to calculate pOH and then use Equation 16.20 to calculate the pH.

Solve:

(a) NaOH dissociates in water to give one OH^- ion per formula unit. Therefore, the OH^- concentration for the solution in (a) equals the stated concentration of NaOH, namely 0.028 M.

Method 1:

$$[H^+] = \frac{1.0 \times 10^{-14}}{0.028} = 3.57 \times 10^{-13}\ M \qquad pH = -\log(3.57 \times 10^{-13}) = 12.45$$

Method 2:

$$pOH = -\log(0.028) = 1.55 \qquad pH = 14.00 - pOH = 12.45$$

(b) $Ca(OH)_2$ is a strong base that dissociates in water to give two OH^- ions per formula unit. Thus, the concentration of $OH^-(aq)$ for the solution in part (b) is $2 \times (0.0011\ M) = 0.0022\ M$.

Method 1:

$$[H^+] = \frac{1.0 \times 10^{-14}}{0.0022} = 4.55 \times 10^{-12}\ M \qquad pH = -\log(4.55 \times 10^{-12}) = 11.34$$

Method 2:

$$pOH = -\log(0.0022) = 2.66 \qquad pH = 14.00 - pOH = 11.34$$

■■ PRACTICE EXERCISE

What is the concentration of a solution of **(a)** KOH for which the pH is 11.89; **(b)** $Ca(OH)_2$ for which the pH is 11.68?
Answers: **(a)** $7.8 \times 10^{-3}\ M$, **(b)** $2.4 \times 10^{-3}\ M$

Although all the hydroxides of the alkali metals (group 1A) are strong electrolytes, LiOH, RbOH, and CsOH are not commonly encountered in the laboratory. The hydroxides of the heavier alkaline earth metals, $Ca(OH)_2$, $Sr(OH)_2$, and $Ba(OH)_2$, are also strong electrolytes. They have limited solubilities, however, so they are used only when high solubility is not critical.

Strongly basic solutions are also created by certain substances that react with water to form $OH^-(aq)$. The most common of these contain the oxide ion. Ionic metal oxides, especially Na_2O and CaO, are often used in industry when a strong base is needed. The O^{2-} reacts with water to form OH^-, leaving virtually no O^{2-} remaining in the solution:

$$O^{2-}(aq) + H_2O(l) \longrightarrow 2\,OH^-(aq) \qquad [16.22]$$

Thus, a solution formed by dissolving 0.010 mol of $Na_2O(s)$ in enough water to form 1.0 L of solution will have $[OH^-] = 0.020\ M$ and a pH of 12.30.

GIVE IT SOME THOUGHT

The CH_3^- ion is the conjugate base of CH_4, and CH_4 shows no evidence of being an acid in water. What happens when CH_3^- is added to water?

16.6 WEAK ACIDS

Most acidic substances are weak acids and are therefore only partially ionized in aqueous solution. We can use the equilibrium constant for the ionization reaction to express the extent to which a weak acid ionizes. If we represent a general weak acid as HA, we can write the equation for its ionization reaction in either of the following ways, depending on whether the hydrated proton is represented as $H_3O^+(aq)$ or $H^+(aq)$:

$$HA(aq) + H_2O(l) \rightleftharpoons H_3O^+(aq) + A^-(aq) \qquad [16.23]$$

or

$$HA(aq) \rightleftharpoons H^+(aq) + A^-(aq) \qquad [16.24]$$

Because H_2O is the solvent, it is omitted from the equilibrium-constant expression. (Section 15.4) Thus, we can write the equilibrium-constant expression as either

$$K_c = \frac{[H_3O^+][A^-]}{[HA]} \quad \text{or} \quad K_c = \frac{[H^+][A^-]}{[HA]}$$

As we did for the ion-product constant for the autoionization of water, we change the subscript on this equilibrium constant to indicate the type of equation to which it corresponds.

$$K_a = \frac{[H_3O^+][A^-]}{[HA]} \quad \text{or} \quad K_a = \frac{[H^+][A^-]}{[HA]} \qquad [16.25]$$

The subscript a on K_a denotes that it is an equilibrium constant for the ionization of an acid, so K_a is called the **acid-dissociation constant**.

Table 16.2 ▼ shows the names, structures, and K_a values for several weak acids. Appendix D provides a more complete list. Many weak acids are organic compounds composed entirely of carbon, hydrogen, and oxygen. These compounds usually contain some hydrogen atoms bonded to carbon atoms and some bonded to oxygen atoms. In almost all cases the hydrogen atoms bonded to carbon do not ionize in water; instead, the acidic behavior of these compounds is due to the hydrogen atoms attached to oxygen atoms.

The magnitude of K_a indicates the tendency of the acid to ionize in water: *The larger the value of K_a, the stronger the acid.* Hydrofluoric acid (HF), for example, is the strongest acid listed in Table 16.2, and phenol (HOC_6H_5) is the weakest. Notice that K_a is typically less than 10^{-3}.

TABLE 16.2 ■ Some Weak Acids in Water at 25 °C

Acid	Structural Formula*	Conjugate Base	Equilibrium Reaction	K_a
Hydrofluoric (HF)	H—F	F^-	$HF(aq) + H_2O(l) \rightleftharpoons H_3O^+(aq) + F^-(aq)$	6.8×10^{-4}
Nitrous (HNO_2)	H—O—N=O	NO_2^-	$HNO_2(aq) + H_2O(l) \rightleftharpoons H_3O^+(aq) + NO_2^-(aq)$	4.5×10^{-4}
Benzoic (C_6H_5COOH)	H—O—C(=O)—⬡	$C_6H_5COO^-$	$C_6H_5COOH(aq) + H_2O(l) \rightleftharpoons$ $H_3O^+(aq) + C_6H_5COO^-(aq)$	6.3×10^{-5}
Acetic (CH_3COOH)	H—O—C(=O)—C(H)(H)—H	CH_3COO^-	$CH_3COOH(aq) + H_2O(l) \rightleftharpoons$ $H_3O^+(aq) + CH_3COO^-(aq)$	1.8×10^{-5}
Hypochlorous (HClO)	H—O—Cl	ClO^-	$HClO(aq) + H_2O(l) \rightleftharpoons H_3O^+(aq) + ClO^-(aq)$	3.0×10^{-8}
Hydrocyanic (HCN)	H—C≡N	CN^-	$HCN(aq) + H_2O(l) \rightleftharpoons H_3O^+(aq) + CN^-(aq)$	4.9×10^{-10}
Phenol (HOC_6H_5)	H—O—⬡	$C_6H_5O^-$	$HOC_6H_5(aq) + H_2O(l) \rightleftharpoons$ $H_3O^+(aq) + C_6H_5O^-(aq)$	1.3×10^{-10}

* The proton that ionizes is shown in blue.

Calculating K_a from pH

In order to calculate either the K_a value for a weak acid or the pH of its solutions, we will use many of the skills for solving equilibrium problems that we developed in Section 15.5. In many cases the small magnitude of K_a allows us to use approximations to simplify the problem. In doing these calculations, it is important to realize that proton-transfer reactions are generally very rapid. As a result, the measured or calculated pH for a weak acid always represents an equilibrium condition.

■■■ **SAMPLE EXERCISE 16.10** | Calculating K_a from Measured pH

A student prepared a 0.10 M solution of formic acid (HCOOH) and measured its pH. The pH at 25 °C was found to be 2.38. Calculate K_a for formic acid at this temperature.

SOLUTION

Analyze: We are given the molar concentration of an aqueous solution of weak acid and the pH of the solution, and we are asked to determine the value of K_a for the acid.

Plan: Although we are dealing specifically with the ionization of a weak acid, this problem is very similar to the equilibrium problems we encountered in Chapter 15. We can solve this problem using the method first outlined in Sample Exercise 15.9, starting with the chemical reaction and a tabulation of initial and equilibrium concentrations.

Solve: The first step in solving any equilibrium problem is to write the equation for the equilibrium reaction. The ionization of formic acid can be written as follows:

$$HCOOH(aq) \rightleftharpoons H^+(aq) + HCOO^-(aq)$$

The equilibrium-constant expression is

$$K_a = \frac{[H^+][HCOO^-]}{[HCOOH]}$$

From the measured pH, we can calculate $[H^+]$:

$$pH = -\log[H^+] = 2.38$$

$$\log[H^+] = -2.38$$

$$[H^+] = 10^{-2.38} = 4.2 \times 10^{-3}\ M$$

We can do a little accounting to determine the concentrations of the species involved in the equilibrium. We imagine that the solution is initially 0.10 M in HCOOH molecules. We then consider the ionization of the acid into H^+ and $HCOO^-$. For each HCOOH molecule that ionizes, one H^+ ion and one $HCOO^-$ ion are produced in solution. Because the pH measurement indicates that $[H^+] = 4.2 \times 10^{-3}\ M$ at equilibrium, we can construct the following table:

	$HCOOH(aq)$	$\rightleftharpoons$	$H^+(aq)$	$+$	$HCOO^-(aq)$
Initial	0.10 M		0		0
Change	$-4.2 \times 10^{-3}\ M$		$+4.2 \times 10^{-3}\ M$		$+4.2 \times 10^{-3}\ M$
Equilibrium	$(0.10 - 4.2 \times 10^{-3})\ M$		$4.2 \times 10^{-3}\ M$		$4.2 \times 10^{-3}\ M$

Notice that we have neglected the very small concentration of $H^+(aq)$ that is due to the autoionization of H_2O. Notice also that the amount of HCOOH that ionizes is very small compared with the initial concentration of the acid. To the number of significant figures we are using, the subtraction yields 0.10 M:

$$(0.10 - 4.2 \times 10^{-3})\ M \simeq 0.10\ M$$

We can now insert the equilibrium concentrations into the expression for K_a:

$$K_a = \frac{(4.2 \times 10^{-3})(4.2 \times 10^{-3})}{0.10} = 1.8 \times 10^{-4}$$

Check: The magnitude of our answer is reasonable because K_a for a weak acid is usually between 10^{-3} and 10^{-10}.

■ PRACTICE EXERCISE

Niacin, one of the B vitamins, has the following molecular structure:

A 0.020 M solution of niacin has a pH of 3.26. What is the acid-dissociation constant, K_a, for niacin?
Answers: 1.5×10^{-5}

Percent Ionization

We have seen that the magnitude of K_a indicates the strength of a weak acid. Another measure of acid strength is **percent ionization**, which is defined as

$$\text{Percent ionization} = \frac{\text{concentration ionized}}{\text{original concentration}} \times 100\% \qquad [16.26]$$

The stronger the acid, the greater is the percent ionization.

For any acid, the concentration of acid that undergoes ionization equals the concentration of $H^+(aq)$ that forms, assuming that the autoionization of water is negligible. Thus, the percent ionization for an acid HA is also given by

$$\text{Percent ionization} = \frac{[H^+]_{\text{equilibrium}}}{[HA]_{\text{initial}}} \times 100\% \qquad [16.27]$$

For example, a 0.035 M solution of HNO_2 contains $3.7 \times 10^{-3}\ M\ H^+(aq)$. Thus, the percent ionization is

$$\text{Percent ionization} = \frac{[H^+]_{\text{equilibrium}}}{[HNO_2]_{\text{initial}}} \times 100\% = \frac{3.7 \times 10^{-3}\ M}{0.035\ M} \times 100\% = 11\%$$

■ **SAMPLE EXERCISE 16.11** | **Calculating Percent Ionization**

A 0.10 M solution of formic acid (HCOOH) contains 4.2×10^{-3} M H$^+(aq)$. Calculate the percentage of the acid that is ionized.

SOLUTION

Analyze: We are given the molar concentration of an aqueous solution of weak acid and the equilibrium concentration of H$^+(aq)$ and asked to determine the percent ionization of the acid.

Plan: The percent ionization is given by Equation 16.27.

Solve:

$$\text{Percent ionization} = \frac{[\text{H}^+]_{\text{equilibrium}}}{[\text{HCOOH}]_{\text{initial}}} \times 100\% = \frac{4.2 \times 10^{-3} \, M}{0.10 \, M} \times 100\% = 4.2\%$$

■ **PRACTICE EXERCISE**

A 0.020 M solution of niacin has a pH of 3.26. Calculate the percent ionization of the niacin.

Answer: 2.7%

Using K_a to Calculate pH

Knowing the value of K_a and the initial concentration of the weak acid, we can calculate the concentration of H$^+(aq)$ in a solution of a weak acid. Let's calculate the pH of a 0.30 M solution of acetic acid (CH$_3$COOH), the weak acid responsible for the characteristic odor and acidity of vinegar, at 25 °C.

Our *first* step is to write the ionization equilibrium for acetic acid:

$$\text{CH}_3\text{COOH}(aq) \rightleftharpoons \text{H}^+(aq) + \text{CH}_3\text{COO}^-(aq) \qquad [16.28]$$

Notice that the hydrogen that ionizes is the one attached to an oxygen atom.

The *second* step is to write the equilibrium-constant expression and the value for the equilibrium constant. From Table 16.2, we have $K_a = 1.8 \times 10^{-5}$. Thus, we can write the following:

$$K_a = \frac{[\text{H}^+][\text{CH}_3\text{COO}^-]}{[\text{CH}_3\text{COOH}]} = 1.8 \times 10^{-5} \qquad [16.29]$$

As the *third* step, we need to express the concentrations that are involved in the equilibrium reaction. This can be done with a little accounting, as described in Sample Exercise 16.10. Because we want to find the equilibrium value for [H$^+$], let's call this quantity x. The concentration of acetic acid before any of it ionizes is 0.30 M. The chemical equation tells us that for each molecule of CH$_3$COOH that ionizes, one H$^+(aq)$ and one CH$_3$COO$^-(aq)$ are formed. Consequently, if x moles per liter of H$^+(aq)$ form at equilibrium, x moles per liter of CH$_3$COO$^-(aq)$ must also form, and x moles per liter of CH$_3$COOH must be ionized. This gives rise to the following table with the equilibrium concentrations shown on the last line:

	CH$_3$COOH(aq) $\rightleftharpoons$	H$^+$(aq) +	CH$_3$COO$^-$(aq)
Initial	0.30 M	0	0
Change	$-x$ M	$+x$ M	$+x$ M
Equilibrium	$(0.30 - x)$ M	x M	x M

As the *fourth* step of the problem, we need to substitute the equilibrium concentrations into the equilibrium-constant expression. The substitutions give the following equation:

$$K_a = \frac{[\text{H}^+][\text{CH}_3\text{COO}^-]}{[\text{CH}_3\text{COOH}]} = \frac{(x)(x)}{0.30 - x} = 1.8 \times 10^{-5} \qquad [16.30]$$

This expression leads to a quadratic equation in x, which we can solve by using an equation-solving calculator or by using the quadratic formula. We can also simplify the problem, however, by noting that the value of K_a is quite small. As a result, we anticipate that the equilibrium will lie far to the left and that x will be very small compared to the initial concentration of acetic acid. Thus, we will *assume* that x is negligible compared to 0.30, so that $0.30 - x$ is essentially equal to 0.30.

$$0.30 - x \simeq 0.30$$

As we will see, we can (and should!) check the validity of this assumption when we finish the problem. By using this assumption, Equation 16.30 now becomes

$$K_a = \frac{x^2}{0.30} = 1.8 \times 10^{-5}$$

Solving for x, we have

$$x^2 = (0.30)(1.8 \times 10^{-5}) = 5.4 \times 10^{-6}$$

$$x = \sqrt{5.4 \times 10^{-6}} = 2.3 \times 10^{-3}$$

$$[H^+] = x = 2.3 \times 10^{-3}\ M$$

$$pH = -\log(2.3 \times 10^{-3}) = 2.64$$

We should now go back and check the validity of our simplifying assumption that $0.30 - x \simeq 0.30$. The value of x we determined is so small that, for this number of significant figures, the assumption is entirely valid. We are thus satisfied that the assumption was a reasonable one to make. Because x represents the moles per liter of acetic acid that ionize, we see that, in this particular case, less than 1% of the acetic acid molecules ionize:

$$\text{Percent ionization of } CH_3COOH = \frac{0.0023\ M}{0.30\ M} \times 100\% = 0.77\%$$

As a general rule, if the quantity x is more than about 5% of the initial value, it is better to use the quadratic formula. You should always check the validity of any simplifying assumptions after you have finished solving a problem.

GIVE IT SOME THOUGHT

Why can we generally assume that the equilibrium concentration of a weak acid equals its initial concentration?

Finally, we can compare the pH value of this weak acid to a solution of a strong acid of the same concentration. The pH of the 0.30 M solution of acetic acid is 2.64. By comparison, the pH of a 0.30 M solution of a strong acid such as HCl is $-\log(0.30) = 0.52$. As expected, the pH of a solution of a weak acid is higher than that of a solution of a strong acid of the same molarity.

■■■ **SAMPLE EXERCISE 16.12** | Using K_a to Calculate pH

Calculate the pH of a 0.20 M solution of HCN. (Refer to Table 16.2 or Appendix D for the value of K_a.)

SOLUTION

Analyze: We are given the molarity of a weak acid and are asked for the pH. From Table 16.2, K_a for HCN is 4.9×10^{-10}.

Plan: We proceed as in the example just worked in the text, writing the chemical equation and constructing a table of initial and equilibrium concentrations in which the equilibrium concentration of H^+ is our unknown.

Solve: Writing both the chemical equation for the ionization reaction that forms $H^+(aq)$ and the equilibrium-constant (K_a) expression for the reaction:

$$HCN(aq) \rightleftharpoons H^+(aq) + CN^-(aq)$$

$$K_a = \frac{[H^+][CN^-]}{[HCN]} = 4.9 \times 10^{-10}$$

Next, we tabulate the concentration of the species involved in the equilibrium reaction, letting $x = [H^+]$ at equilibrium:

	HCN(aq) $\rightleftharpoons$	H$^+$(aq) $+$	CN$^-$(aq)
Initial	0.20 M	0	0
Change	$-x$ M	$+x$ M	$+x$ M
Equilibrium	$(0.20 - x)$ M	x M	x M

Substituting the equilibrium concentrations from the table into the equilibrium-constant expression yields

$$K_a = \frac{(x)(x)}{0.20 - x} = 4.9 \times 10^{-10}$$

We next make the simplifying approximation that x, the amount of acid that dissociates, is small compared with the initial concentration of acid; that is,

$$0.20 - x \simeq 0.20$$

Thus,

$$\frac{x^2}{0.20} = 4.9 \times 10^{-10}$$

Solving for x, we have

$$x^2 = (0.20)(4.9 \times 10^{-10}) = 0.98 \times 10^{-10}$$

$$x = \sqrt{0.98 \times 10^{-10}} = 9.9 \times 10^{-6} \, M = [H^+]$$

A concentration of $9.9 \times 10^{-6} \, M$ is much smaller than 5% of 0.20, the initial HCN concentration. Our simplifying approximation is therefore appropriate. We now calculate the pH of the solution:

$$pH = -\log[H^+] = -\log(9.9 \times 10^{-6}) = 5.00$$

■ PRACTICE EXERCISE

The K_a for niacin (Practice Exercise 16.10) is 1.5×10^{-5}. What is the pH of a 0.010 M solution of niacin?
Answer: 3.41

The properties of the acid solution that relate directly to the concentration of H$^+$(aq), such as electrical conductivity and rate of reaction with an active metal, are much less evident for a solution of a weak acid than for a solution of a strong acid of the same concentration. Figure 16.8 ▼ presents an experiment that demonstrates this difference by comparing the behavior of 1 M CH$_3$COOH and 1 M HCl. The 1 M CH$_3$COOH contains only 0.004 M H$^+$(aq), whereas the 1 M HCl solution contains 1 M H$^+$(aq). As a result, the rate of reaction with the metal is much faster for the solution of HCl.

As the concentration of a weak acid increases, the equilibrium concentration of H$^+$(aq) increases, as expected. However, as shown in Figure 16.9 ▶, *the percent ionization decreases as the concentration increases.* Thus, the concentration of H$^+$(aq) is not directly proportional to the concentration of the weak acid. For example, doubling the concentration of a weak acid does not double the concentration of H$^+$(aq). This lack of proportionality between the concentration of a weak acid and the concentration of H$^+$(aq) is demonstrated in Sample Exercise 16.13.

▶ Figure 16.8 **Reaction rates for weak and strong acids.** (a) The flask on the left contains 1 M CH$_3$COOH; the one on the right contains 1 M HCl. Each balloon contains the same amount of magnesium metal. (b) When the Mg metal is dropped into the acid, H$_2$ gas is formed. The rate of H$_2$ formation is higher for the 1 M HCl solution on the right as evidenced by more gas in the balloon. Eventually, the same amount of H$_2$ forms in both cases.

(a)

(b)

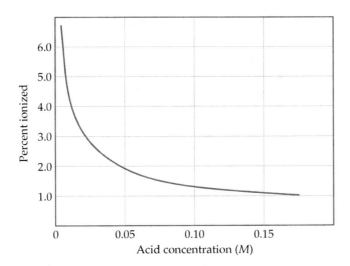

◀ Figure 16.9 **The effect of concentration on ionization of a weak acid.** The percent ionization of a weak acid decreases with increasing concentration. The data shown are for acetic acid.

■ **SAMPLE EXERCISE 16.13** │ Using K_a to Calculate Percent Ionization

Calculate the percentage of HF molecules ionized in **(a)** a 0.10 *M* HF solution, **(b)** a 0.010 *M* HF solution.

SOLUTION

Analyze: We are asked to calculate the percent ionization of two HF solutions of different concentration. From Appendix D, we find $K_a = 6.8 \times 10^{-4}$.

Plan: We approach this problem as we would previous equilibrium problems. We begin by writing the chemical equation for the equilibrium and tabulating the known and unknown concentrations of all species. We then substitute the equilibrium concentrations into the equilibrium-constant expression and solve for the unknown concentration, that of H^+.

Solve:

(a) The equilibrium reaction and equilibrium concentrations are as follows:

	HF(*aq*) ⇌	H^+(*aq*) +	F^-(*aq*)
Initial	0.10 *M*	0	0
Change	−*x* *M*	+*x* *M*	+*x* *M*
Equilibrium	(0.10 − *x*) *M*	*x* *M*	*x* *M*

The equilibrium-constant expression is

$$K_a = \frac{[H^+][F^-]}{[HF]} = \frac{(x)(x)}{0.10 - x} = 6.8 \times 10^{-4}$$

When we try solving this equation using the approximation $0.10 - x = 0.10$ (that is, by neglecting the concentration of acid that ionizes in comparison with the initial concentration), we obtain

$$x = 8.2 \times 10^{-3} \, M$$

Because this value is greater than 5% of 0.10 *M*, we should work the problem without the approximation, using an equation-solving calculator or the quadratic formula. Rearranging our equation and writing it in standard quadratic form, we have

$$x^2 = (0.10 - x)(6.8 \times 10^{-4})$$
$$= 6.8 \times 10^{-5} - (6.8 \times 10^{-4})x$$
$$x^2 + (6.8 \times 10^{-4})x - 6.8 \times 10^{-5} = 0$$

This equation can be solved using the standard quadratic formula.

$$x = \frac{-b \pm \sqrt{b^2 - 4ac}}{2a}$$

Substituting the appropriate numbers gives

$$x = \frac{-6.8 \times 10^{-4} \pm \sqrt{(6.8 \times 10^{-4})^2 + 4(6.8 \times 10^{-5})}}{2}$$
$$= \frac{-6.8 \times 10^{-4} \pm 1.6 \times 10^{-2}}{2}$$

Of the two solutions, only the one that gives a positive value for x is chemically reasonable. Thus,

$$x = [H^+] = [F^-] = 7.9 \times 10^{-3}\ M$$

From our result, we can calculate the percent of molecules ionized:

$$\text{Percent ionization of HF} = \frac{\text{concentration ionized}}{\text{original concentration}} \times 100\%$$

$$= \frac{7.9 \times 10^{-3}\ M}{0.10\ M} \times 100\% = 7.9\%$$

(b) Proceeding similarly for the 0.010 M solution, we have

$$\frac{x^2}{0.010 - x} = 6.8 \times 10^{-4}$$

Solving the resultant quadratic expression, we obtain

$$x = [H^+] = [F^-] = 2.3 \times 10^{-3}\ M$$

The percentage of molecules ionized is

$$\frac{0.0023\ M}{0.010\ M} \times 100\% = 23\%$$

Comment: Notice that if we do not use the quadratic formula to solve the problem properly, we calculate 8.2% ionization for (a) and 26% ionization for (b). Notice also that in diluting the solution by a factor of 10, the percentage of molecules ionized increases by a factor of 3. This result is in accord with what we see in Figure 16.9. It is also what we would expect from Le Châtelier's principle. (Section 15.7) There are more "particles" or reaction components on the right side of the equation than on the left. Dilution causes the reaction to shift in the direction of the larger number of particles because this counters the effect of the decreasing concentration of particles.

■ PRACTICE EXERCISE

In Practice Exercise 16.11, we found that the percent ionization of niacin ($K_a = 1.5 \times 10^{-5}$) in a 0.020 M solution is 2.7%. Calculate the percentage of niacin molecules ionized in a solution that is **(a)** 0.010 M, **(b)** $1.0 \times 10^{-3}\ M$.
Answers: **(a)** 3.9%, **(b)** 12%

Polyprotic Acids

Many acids have more than one ionizable H atom. These acids are known as **polyprotic acids**. For example, each of the H atoms in sulfurous acid (H_2SO_3) can ionize in successive steps:

$$H_2SO_3(aq) \rightleftharpoons H^+(aq) + HSO_3^-(aq) \qquad K_{a1} = 1.7 \times 10^{-2} \qquad [16.31]$$

$$HSO_3^-(aq) \rightleftharpoons H^+(aq) + SO_3^{2-}(aq) \qquad K_{a2} = 6.4 \times 10^{-8} \qquad [16.32]$$

The acid-dissociation constants for these equilibria are labeled K_{a1} and K_{a2}. The numbers on the constants refer to the particular proton of the acid that is ionizing. Thus, K_{a2} always refers to the equilibrium involving removal of the second proton of a polyprotic acid.

In the preceding example K_{a2} is much smaller than K_{a1}. Because of electrostatic attractions, we would expect a positively charged proton to be lost more readily from the neutral H_2SO_3 molecule than from the negatively charged HSO_3^- ion. This observation is general: *It is always easier to remove the first proton from a polyprotic acid than to remove the second.* Similarly, for an acid with three ionizable protons, it is easier to remove the second proton than the third. Thus, the K_a values become successively smaller as successive protons are removed.

▲ GIVE IT SOME THOUGHT

What is meant by the symbol K_{a3} for H_3PO_4?

The acid-dissociation constants for a few common polyprotic acids are listed in Table 16.3▶. Appendix D provides a more complete list. The structures for ascorbic and citric acids are shown in the margin. Notice that the K_a values for successive losses of protons from these acids usually differ by a factor of at least 10^3. Notice also that the value of K_{a1} for sulfuric acid is listed simply as "large."

TABLE 16.3 ■ Acid-Dissociation Constants of Some Common Polyprotic Acids

Name	Formula	K_{a1}	K_{a2}	K_{a3}
Ascorbic	$H_2C_6H_6O_6$	8.0×10^{-5}	1.6×10^{-12}	
Carbonic	H_2CO_3	4.3×10^{-7}	5.6×10^{-11}	
Citric	$H_3C_6H_5O_7$	7.4×10^{-4}	1.7×10^{-5}	4.0×10^{-7}
Oxalic	$H_2C_2O_4$	5.9×10^{-2}	6.4×10^{-5}	
Phosphoric	H_3PO_4	7.5×10^{-3}	6.2×10^{-8}	4.2×10^{-13}
Sulfurous	H_2SO_3	1.7×10^{-2}	6.4×10^{-8}	
Sulfuric	H_2SO_4	Large	1.2×10^{-2}	
Tartaric	$H_2C_4H_4O_6$	1.0×10^{-3}	4.6×10^{-5}	

Ascorbic acid
(vitamin C)

Sulfuric acid is a strong acid with respect to the removal of the first proton. Thus, the reaction for the first ionization step lies completely to the right:

$$H_2SO_4(aq) \longrightarrow H^+(aq) + HSO_4^-(aq) \quad \text{(complete ionization)}$$

HSO_4^-, on the other hand, is a weak acid for which $K_{a2} = 1.2 \times 10^{-2}$.

Because K_{a1} is so much larger than subsequent dissociation constants for these polyprotic acids, most of the $H^+(aq)$ in the solution comes from the first ionization reaction. As long as successive K_a values differ by a factor of 10^3 or more, it is possible to obtain a satisfactory estimate of the pH of polyprotic acid solutions by treating them as if they were monoprotic acids, considering only K_{a1}.

Citric acid

SAMPLE EXERCISE 16.14 | Calculating the pH of a Polyprotic Acid Solution

The solubility of CO_2 in pure water at 25 °C and 0.1 atm pressure is 0.0037 M. The common practice is to assume that all of the dissolved CO_2 is in the form of carbonic acid (H_2CO_3), which is produced by reaction between the CO_2 and H_2O:

$$CO_2(aq) + H_2O(l) \rightleftharpoons H_2CO_3(aq)$$

What is the pH of a 0.0037 M solution of H_2CO_3?

SOLUTION

Analyze: We are asked to determine the pH of a 0.0037 M solution of a polyprotic acid.

Plan: H_2CO_3 is a diprotic acid; the two acid-dissociation constants, K_{a1} and K_{a2} (Table 16.3), differ by more than a factor of 10^3. Consequently, the pH can be determined by considering only K_{a1}, thereby treating the acid as if it were a monoprotic acid.

Solve: Proceeding as in Sample Exercises 16.12 and 16.13, we can write the equilibrium reaction and equilibrium concentrations as follows:

	$H_2CO_3(aq)$	$\rightleftharpoons$	$H^+(aq)$	$+$	$HCO_3^-(aq)$
Initial	0.0037 M		0		0
Change	$-x\ M$		$+x\ M$		$+x\ M$
Equilibrium	$(0.0037 - x)\ M$		$x\ M$		$x\ M$

The equilibrium-constant expression is as follows:

$$K_{a1} = \frac{[H^+][HCO_3^-]}{[H_2CO_3]} = \frac{(x)(x)}{0.0037 - x} = 4.3 \times 10^{-7}$$

Solving this equation using an equation-solving calculator, we get

$$x = 4.0 \times 10^{-5}\ M$$

Alternatively, because K_{a1} is small, we can make the simplifying approximation that x is small, so that

$$0.0037 - x \simeq 0.0037$$

Thus,

$$\frac{(x)(x)}{0.0037} = 4.3 \times 10^{-7}$$

Solving for x, we have

$$x^2 = (0.0037)(4.3 \times 10^{-7}) = 1.6 \times 10^{-9}$$

$$x = [H^+] = [HCO_3^-] = \sqrt{1.6 \times 10^{-9}} = 4.0 \times 10^{-5}\ M$$

The small value of x indicates that our simplifying assumption was justified. The pH is therefore

$$pH = -\log[H^+] = -\log(4.0 \times 10^{-5}) = 4.40$$

Comment: If we were asked to solve for $[CO_3^{2-}]$, we would need to use K_{a2}. Let's illustrate that calculation. Using the values of $[HCO_3^-]$ and $[H^+]$ calculated above, and setting $[CO_3^{2-}] = y$, we have the following initial and equilibrium concentration values:

	$HCO_3^-(aq)$	$\rightleftharpoons$	$H^+(aq)$	$+$	$CO_3^{2-}(aq)$
Initial	$4.0 \times 10^{-5}\ M$		$4.0 \times 10^{-5}\ M$		0
Change	$-y\ M$		$+y\ M$		$+y\ M$
Equilibrium	$(4.0 \times 10^{-5} - y)\ M$		$(4.0 \times 10^{-5} + y)\ M$		$y\ M$

Assuming that y is small compared to 4.0×10^{-5}, we have

$$K_{a2} = \frac{[H^+][CO_3^{2-}]}{[HCO_3^-]} = \frac{(4.0 \times 10^{-5})(y)}{4.0 \times 10^{-5}} = 5.6 \times 10^{-11}$$

$$y = 5.6 \times 10^{-11}\ M = [CO_3^{2-}]$$

The value calculated for y is indeed very small compared to 4.0×10^{-5}, showing that our assumption was justified. It also shows that the ionization of HCO_3^- is negligible compared to that of H_2CO_3, as far as production of H^+ is concerned. However, it is the *only* source of CO_3^{2-}, which has a very low concentration in the solution. Our calculations thus tell us that in a solution of carbon dioxide in water, most of the CO_2 is in the form of CO_2 or H_2CO_3, a small fraction ionizes to form H^+ and HCO_3^-, and an even smaller fraction ionizes to give CO_3^{2-}. Notice also that $[CO_3^{2-}]$ is numerically equal to K_{a2}.

■ PRACTICE EXERCISE
(a) Calculate the pH of a 0.020 M solution of oxalic acid ($H_2C_2O_4$). (See Table 16.3 for K_{a1} and K_{a2}.) **(b)** Calculate the concentration of oxalate ion, $[C_2O_4^{2-}]$, in this solution.
Answers: **(a)** pH = 1.80, **(b)** $[C_2O_4^{2-}] = 6.4 \times 10^{-5}\ M$

16.7 WEAK BASES

Many substances behave as weak bases in water. Weak bases react with water, abstracting protons from H_2O, thereby forming the conjugate acid of the base and OH^- ions.

$$B(aq) + H_2O(l) \rightleftharpoons HB^+(aq) + OH^-(aq) \qquad [16.33]$$

The equilibrium-constant expression for this reaction can be written as

$$K_b = \frac{[BH^+][OH^-]}{[B]} \qquad [16.34]$$

Water is the solvent, so it is omitted from the equilibrium-constant expression. The most commonly encountered weak base is ammonia.

$$NH_3(aq) + H_2O(l) \rightleftharpoons NH_4^+(aq) + OH^-(aq) \quad K_b = \frac{[NH_4^+][OH^-]}{[NH_3]} \quad [16.35]$$

As with K_w and K_a, the subscript "b" denotes that this equilibrium constant refers to a particular type of reaction, namely the ionization of a weak base in water. The constant K_b is called the **base-dissociation constant**. *The constant K_b always refers to the equilibrium in which a base reacts with H_2O to form the corresponding conjugate acid and OH^-.*

Table 16.4 ▶ lists the names, formulas, Lewis structures, equilibrium reactions, and values of K_b for several weak bases in water. Appendix D includes a more extensive list. These bases contain one or more lone pairs of electrons because a lone pair is necessary to form the bond with H^+. Notice that in the neutral molecules in Table 16.4, the lone pairs are on nitrogen atoms. The other bases listed are anions derived from weak acids.

Science Fundamentals

TABLE 16.4 ■ Some Weak Bases and Their Aqueous Solution Equilibria

Base	Lewis Structure	Conjugate Acid	Equilibrium Reaction	K_b
Ammonia (NH_3)	$H-\overset{..}{N}-H$ $\vert$ H	NH_4^+	$NH_3 + H_2O \rightleftharpoons NH_4^+ + OH^-$	1.8×10^{-5}
Pyridine (C_5H_5N)	(ring)$N:$	$C_5H_5NH^+$	$C_5H_5N + H_2O \rightleftharpoons C_5H_5NH^+ + OH^-$	1.7×10^{-9}
Hydroxylamine (H_2NOH)	$H-\overset{..}{N}-\overset{..}{O}H$ $\vert$ H	H_3NOH^+	$H_2NOH + H_2O \rightleftharpoons H_3NOH^+ + OH^-$	1.1×10^{-8}
Methylamine (NH_2CH_3)	$H-\overset{..}{N}-CH_3$ $\vert$ H	$NH_3CH_3^+$	$NH_2CH_3 + H_2O \rightleftharpoons NH_3CH_3^+ + OH^-$	4.4×10^{-4}
Hydrosulfide ion (HS^-)	$\left[H-\overset{..}{\underset{..}{S}}:\right]^-$	H_2S	$HS^- + H_2O \rightleftharpoons H_2S + OH^-$	1.8×10^{-7}
Carbonate ion (CO_3^{2-})	$\left[\overset{:\overset{..}{O}:}{\underset{:\overset{..}{O}.}{\overset{\vert}{C}}\overset{}{\underset{}{}}\overset{..}{O}:\right]^{2-}$	HCO_3^-	$CO_3^{2-} + H_2O \rightleftharpoons HCO_3^- + OH^-$	1.8×10^{-4}
Hypochlorite ion (ClO^-)	$\left[:\overset{..}{\underset{..}{Cl}}-\overset{..}{\underset{..}{O}}:\right]^-$	$HClO$	$ClO^- + H_2O \rightleftharpoons HClO + OH^-$	3.3×10^{-7}

■ **SAMPLE EXERCISE 16.15** │ **Using K_b to Calculate OH^-**

Calculate the concentration of OH^- in a 0.15 M solution of NH_3.

SOLUTION

Analyze: We are given the concentration of a weak base and are asked to determine the concentration of OH^-.

Plan: We will use essentially the same procedure here as used in solving problems involving the ionization of weak acids; that is, we write the chemical equation and tabulate initial and equilibrium concentrations.

Solve: We first write the ionization reaction and the corresponding equilibrium-constant (K_b) expression:

$$NH_3(aq) + H_2O(l) \rightleftharpoons NH_4^+(aq) + OH^-(aq)$$

$$K_b = \frac{[NH_4^+][OH^-]}{[NH_3]} = 1.8 \times 10^{-5}$$

We then tabulate the equilibrium concentrations involved in the equilibrium:

	$NH_3(aq)$	$+$	$H_2O(l)$	$\rightleftharpoons$	$NH_4^+(aq)$	$+$	$OH^-(aq)$
Initial	0.15 M		—		0		0
Change	$-x$ M		—		$+x$ M		$+x$ M
Equilibrium	$(0.15 - x)$ M		—		x M		x M

(We ignore the concentration of H_2O because it is not involved in the equilibrium-constant expression.) Inserting these quantities into the equilibrium-constant expression gives the following:

$$K_b = \frac{[NH_4^+][OH^-]}{[NH_3]} = \frac{(x)(x)}{0.15 - x} = 1.8 \times 10^{-5}$$

Because K_b is small, we can neglect the small amount of NH_3 that reacts with water, as compared to the total NH_3 concentration; that is, we can neglect x relative to 0.15 M. Then we have

$$\frac{x^2}{0.15} = 1.8 \times 10^{-5}$$

$$x^2 = (0.15)(1.8 \times 10^{-5}) = 2.7 \times 10^{-6}$$

$$x = [NH_4^+] = [OH^-] = \sqrt{2.7 \times 10^{-6}} = 1.6 \times 10^{-3} M$$

Check: The value obtained for x is only about 1% of the NH_3 concentration, 0.15 M. Therefore, neglecting x relative to 0.15 was justified.

Comment: You may be asked to find the pH of a solution of a weak base. Once you have found $[OH^-]$, you can proceed as in Sample Exercise 16.9, where we calculated the pH of a strong base. In the present sample exercise, we have seen that the 0.15 M solution of NH_3 contains $[OH^-] = 1.6 \times 10^{-3}$ M. Thus, $pOH = -\log(1.6 \times 10^{-3}) = 2.80$, and $pH = 14.00 - 2.80 = 11.20$. The pH of the solution is above 7 because we are dealing with a solution of a base.

■ PRACTICE EXERCISE

Which of the following compounds should produce the highest pH as a 0.05 M solution: pyridine, methylamine, or nitrous acid?
Answer: methylamine (because it has the largest K_b value of the two amine bases in the list)

Types of Weak Bases

How can we recognize from a chemical formula whether a molecule or ion is able to behave as a weak base? Weak bases fall into two general categories. The first category contains neutral substances that have an atom with a nonbonding pair of electrons that can serve as a proton acceptor. Most of these bases, including all of the uncharged bases listed in Table 16.4, contain a nitrogen atom. These substances include ammonia and a related class of compounds called **amines**. In organic amines, one or more of the N—H bonds in NH_3 is replaced with a bond between N and C. Thus, the replacement of one N—H bond in NH_3 with a N—CH_3 bond gives methylamine, NH_2CH_3 (usually written CH_3NH_2). Like NH_3, amines can abstract a proton from a water molecule by forming an additional N—H bond, as shown here for methylamine:

$$H-\overset{\cdot\cdot}{\underset{|}{N}}-CH_3(aq) + H_2O(l) \rightleftharpoons \left[H-\overset{H}{\underset{|}{N}}-CH_3 \right]^+ (aq) + OH^-(aq) \quad [16.36]$$

The chemical formula for the conjugate acid of methylamine is usually written $CH_3NH_3^+$.

The second general category of weak bases consists of the anions of weak acids. In an aqueous solution of sodium hypochlorite (NaClO), for example, NaClO dissociates to give Na^+ and ClO^- ions. The Na^+ ion is always a spectator ion in acid–base reactions. ∞ (Section 4.3) The ClO^- ion, however, is the conjugate base of a weak acid, hypochlorous acid. Consequently, the ClO^- ion acts as a weak base in water:

$$ClO^-(aq) + H_2O(l) \rightleftharpoons HClO(aq) + OH^-(aq) \quad K_b = 3.3 \times 10^{-7} \quad [16.37]$$

■ SAMPLE EXERCISE 16.16 | Using pH to Determine the Concentration of a Salt

A solution made by adding solid sodium hypochlorite (NaClO) to enough water to make 2.00 L of solution has a pH of 10.50. Using the information in Equation 16.37, calculate the number of moles of NaClO that were added to the water.

SOLUTION

Analyze: We are given the pH of a 2.00-L solution of NaClO and must calculate the number of moles of NaClO needed to raise the pH to 10.50. NaClO is an ionic compound consisting of Na^+ and ClO^- ions. As such, it is a strong electrolyte that completely dissociates in solution into Na^+, which is a spectator ion, and ClO^- ion, which is a weak base with $K_b = 3.3 \times 10^{-7}$ (Equation 16.37).

Plan: From the pH, we can determine the equilibrium concentration of OH^-. We can then construct a table of initial and equilibrium concentrations in which the initial concentration of ClO^- is our unknown. We can calculate $[ClO^-]$ using the equilibrium-constant expression, K_b.

Solve: We can calculate $[OH^-]$ by using either Equation 16.16 or Equation 16.20; we will use the latter method here:

$pOH = 14.00 - pH = 14.00 - 10.50 = 3.50$

$[OH^-] = 10^{-3.50} = 3.2 \times 10^{-4}$ M

This concentration is high enough that we can assume that Equation 16.37 is the only source of OH^-; that is, we can neglect any OH^- produced by the autoionization of H_2O. We now assume a value of x for the initial concentration of ClO^- and solve the equilibrium problem in the usual way.

	$ClO^-(aq)$	$+$ $H_2O(l)$ $\rightleftharpoons$	$HClO(aq)$	$+$ $OH^-(aq)$
Initial	$x\ M$	—	0	0
Change	$-3.2 \times 10^{-4}\ M$	—	$+3.2 \times 10^{-4}\ M$	$+3.2 \times 10^{-4}\ M$
Equilibrium	$(x - 3.2 \times 10^{-4})\ M$	—	$3.2 \times 10^{-4}\ M$	$3.2 \times 10^{-4}\ M$

We now use the expression for the base-dissociation constant to solve for x:

$$K_b = \frac{[HClO][OH^-]}{[ClO^-]} = \frac{(3.2 \times 10^{-4})^2}{x - 3.2 \times 10^{-4}} = 3.3 \times 10^{-7}$$

Thus

$$x = \frac{(3.2 \times 10^{-4})^2}{3.3 \times 10^{-7}} + (3.2 \times 10^{-4}) = 0.31\ M$$

We say that the solution is 0.31 M in NaClO even though some of the ClO^- ions have reacted with water. Because the solution is 0.31 M in NaClO and the total volume of solution is 2.00 L, 0.62 mol of NaClO is the amount of the salt that was added to the water.

■ PRACTICE EXERCISE

A solution of NH_3 in water has a pH of 11.17. What is the molarity of the solution?
Answer: 0.12 M

16.8 RELATIONSHIP BETWEEN K_a AND K_b

We have seen in a qualitative way that the stronger acids have the weaker conjugate bases. To see if we can find a corresponding *quantitative* relationship, let's consider the NH_4^+ and NH_3 conjugate acid–base pair. Each of these species reacts with water:

$$NH_4^+(aq) \rightleftharpoons NH_3(aq) + H^+(aq) \qquad [16.38]$$

$$NH_3(aq) + H_2O(l) \rightleftharpoons NH_4^+(aq) + OH^-(aq) \qquad [16.39]$$

Each of these equilibria is expressed by a characteristic dissociation constant:

$$K_a = \frac{[NH_3][H^+]}{[NH_4^+]}$$

$$K_b = \frac{[NH_4^+][OH^-]}{[NH_3]}$$

When Equations 16.38 and 16.39 are added together, the NH_4^+ and NH_3 species cancel and we are left with just the autoionization of water.

$$NH_4^+(aq) \rightleftharpoons NH_3(aq) + H^+(aq)$$

$$\underline{NH_3(aq) + H_2O(l) \rightleftharpoons NH_4^+(aq) + OH^-(aq)}$$

$$H_2O(l) \rightleftharpoons H^+(aq) + OH^-(aq)$$

Recall that when two equations are added to give a third, the equilibrium constant associated with the third equation equals the product of the equilibrium constants for the two equations added together. (Section 15.3)

Applying this rule to our present example, when we multiply K_a and K_b, we obtain the following:

$$K_a \times K_b = \left(\frac{[NH_3][H^+]}{[NH_4^+]} \right) \left(\frac{[NH_4^+][OH^-]}{[NH_3]} \right)$$

$$= [H^+][OH^-] = K_w$$

TABLE 16.5 ■ Some Conjugate Acid–Base Pairs

Acid	K_a	Base	K_b
HNO_3	(Strong acid)	NO_3^-	(Negligible basicity)
HF	6.8×10^{-4}	F^-	1.5×10^{-11}
$HC_2H_3O_2$	1.8×10^{-5}	$C_2H_3O_2^-$	5.6×10^{-10}
H_2CO_3	4.3×10^{-7}	HCO_3^-	2.3×10^{-8}
NH_4^+	5.6×10^{-10}	NH_3	1.8×10^{-5}
HCO_3^-	5.6×10^{-11}	CO_3^{2-}	1.8×10^{-4}
OH^-	(Negligible acidity)	O^{2-}	(Strong base)

Thus, the result of multiplying K_a times K_b is just the ion-product constant for water, K_w (Equation 16.16). We expect this result because adding Equations 16.38 and 16.39 gave us the autoionization equilibrium for water, for which the equilibrium constant is K_w.

This relationship is so important that it should receive special attention: *The product of the acid-dissociation constant for an acid and the base-dissociation constant for its conjugate base equals the ion-product constant for water.*

$$K_a \times K_b = K_w \qquad [16.40]$$

As the strength of an acid increases (larger K_a), the strength of its conjugate base must decrease (smaller K_b) so that the product $K_a \times K_b$ equals 1.0×10^{-14} at 25 °C. The K_a and K_b data in Table 16.5 ▲ demonstrate this relationship. Remember, this important relationship applies *only* to conjugate acid–base pairs.

Chemistry Put to Work   AMINES AND AMINE HYDROCHLORIDES

Many amines with low molecular weights have unpleasant "fishy" odors. Amines and NH_3 are produced by the anaerobic (absence of O_2) decomposition of dead animal or plant matter. Two such amines with very disagreeable odors are $H_2N(CH_2)_4NH_2$, known as *putrescine*, and $H_2N(CH_2)_5NH_2$, known as *cadaverine*.

Many drugs, including quinine, codeine, caffeine, and amphetamine (Benzedrine®), are amines. Like other amines, these substances are weak bases; the amine nitrogen is readily protonated upon treatment with an acid. The resulting products are called *acid salts*. If we use A as the abbreviation for an amine, the acid salt formed by reaction with hydrochloric acid can be written as AH^+Cl^-. It can also be written as A·HCl and referred to as a hydrochloride. Amphetamine hydrochloride, for example, is the acid salt formed by treating amphetamine with HCl:

Such acid salts are much less volatile, more stable, and generally more water soluble than the corresponding neutral amines. Many drugs that are amines are sold and administered as acid salts. Some examples of over-the-counter medications that contain amine hydrochlorides as active ingredients are shown in Figure 16.10 ▼.

Related Exercises: 16.77, 16.78, 16.108, 16.119, and 16.127

▲ Figure 16.10 Some over-the-counter medications in which an amine hydrochloride is a major active ingredient.

By using Equation 16.40, we can calculate K_b for any weak base if we know K_a for its conjugate acid. Similarly, we can calculate K_a for a weak acid if we know K_b for its conjugate base. As a practical consequence, ionization constants are often listed for only one member of a conjugate acid–base pair. For example, Appendix D does not contain K_b values for the anions of weak acids because they can be readily calculated from the tabulated K_a values for their conjugate acids.

If you look up the values for acid- or base-dissociation constants in a chemistry handbook, you may find them expressed as pK_a or pK_b (that is, as $-\log K_a$ or $-\log K_b$).   (Section 16.4) Equation 16.40 can be written in terms of pK_a and pK_b by taking the negative log of both sides:

$$pK_a + pK_b = pK_w = 14.00 \quad \text{at } 25\,^\circ\text{C} \qquad [16.41]$$

■ SAMPLE EXERCISE 16.17 | Calculating K_a or K_b for a Conjugate
Acid–Base Pair

Calculate **(a)** the base-dissociation constant, K_b, for the fluoride ion (F^-); **(b)** the acid-dissociation constant, K_a, for the ammonium ion (NH_4^+).

SOLUTION

Analyze: We are asked to determine dissociation constants for F^-, the conjugate base of HF, and NH_4^+, the conjugate acid of NH_3.

Plan: Although neither F^- nor NH_4^+ appears in the tables, we can find the tabulated values for ionization constants for HF and NH_3, and use the relationship between K_a and K_b to calculate the ionization constants for each of the conjugates.

Solve:

(a) K_a for the weak acid, HF, is given in Table 16.2 and Appendix D as $K_a = 6.8 \times 10^{-4}$. We can use Equation 16.40 to calculate K_b for the conjugate base, F^-:

$$K_b = \frac{K_w}{K_a} = \frac{1.0 \times 10^{-14}}{6.8 \times 10^{-4}} = 1.5 \times 10^{-11}$$

(b) K_b for NH_3 is listed in Table 16.4 and in Appendix D as $K_b = 1.8 \times 10^{-5}$. Using Equation 16.40, we can calculate K_a for the conjugate acid, NH_4^+:

$$K_a = \frac{K_w}{K_b} = \frac{1.0 \times 10^{-14}}{1.8 \times 10^{-5}} = 5.6 \times 10^{-10}$$

■ PRACTICE EXERCISE

(a) Which of the following anions has the largest base-dissociation constant: NO_2^-, PO_4^{3-}, or N_3^-? **(b)** The base quinoline has the following structure:

Its conjugate acid is listed in handbooks as having a pK_a of 4.90. What is the base-dissociation constant for quinoline?
Answers: **(a)** PO_4^{3-} ($K_b = 2.4 \times 10^{-2}$), **(b)** 7.9×10^{-10}

16.9 ACID–BASE PROPERTIES OF SALT SOLUTIONS

Even before you began this chapter, you were undoubtedly aware of many substances that are acidic, such as HNO_3, HCl, and H_2SO_4, and others that are basic, such as NaOH and NH_3. However, our recent discussions have indicated that ions can also exhibit acidic or basic properties. For example, we calculated K_a for NH_4^+ and K_b for F^- in Sample Exercise 16.17. Such behavior implies that salt solutions can be acidic or basic. Before proceeding with further discussions of acids and bases, let's examine the way dissolved salts can affect pH.

Because nearly all salts are strong electrolytes, we can assume that when salts dissolve in water, they are completely dissociated. Consequently, the acid–base properties of salt solutions are due to the behavior of their constituent cations and anions. Many ions are able to react with water to generate $H^+(aq)$ or $OH^-(aq)$. This type of reaction is often called **hydrolysis**. The pH of an aqueous salt solution can be predicted qualitatively by considering the ions of which the salt is composed.

An Anion's Ability to React with Water

In general, an anion, X^-, in solution can be considered the conjugate base of an acid. For example, Cl^- is the conjugate base of HCl, and CH_3COO^- is the conjugate base of CH_3COOH. Whether an anion reacts with water to produce hydroxide depends upon the strength of the acid to which it is conjugate. To identify the acid and assess its strength, we can simply add a proton to the anion's formula:

$$X^- \text{ plus a proton } (H^+) \text{ gives HX}$$

If the acid determined in this way is one of the strong acids listed at the beginning of Section 16.5, then the anion in question will have a negligible tendency to abstract protons from water. ∞ (Section 16.2) Consequently, the anion X^- will not affect the pH of the solution. The presence of Cl^- in an aqueous solution, for example, does not result in the production of any OH^- and does not affect the pH. Thus, Cl^- is always a spectator in acid–base chemistry.

Conversely, if HX is *not* one of the seven strong acids, then it is a weak acid. In this case the conjugate base X^- is a weak base. This anion will therefore react to a small extent with water to produce the weak acid and hydroxide ions:

$$X^-(aq) + H_2O(l) \rightleftharpoons HX(aq) + OH^-(aq) \qquad [16.42]$$

The OH^- ion generated in this way increases the pH of the solution, making it basic. Acetate ion (CH_3COO^-), for example, being the conjugate base of a weak acid, reacts with water to produce acetic acid and hydroxide ions, thereby increasing the pH of the solution.*

$$CH_3COO^-(aq) + H_2O(l) \rightleftharpoons CH_3COOH(aq) + OH^-(aq) \qquad [16.43]$$

 GIVE IT SOME THOUGHT

What effect will each of the following ions have on the pH of a solution: NO_3^- and CO_3^{2-}?

Anions that still have ionizable protons, such as HSO_3^-, are amphiprotic. ∞ (Section 16.2) They can act as either acids or bases. Their behavior toward water will be determined by the relative magnitudes of K_a and K_b for the ion, as shown in Sample Exercise 16.19. If $K_a > K_b$, the ion will cause the solution to be acidic. If $K_b > K_a$, the solution will be basic.

A Cation's Ability to React with Water

Polyatomic cations whose formulas contain one or more protons can be considered the conjugate acids of weak bases. NH_4^+, for example, is the conjugate acid of the weak base NH_3. Thus, NH_4^+ is a weak acid and will donate a proton to water, producing hydronium ions and thereby lowering the pH:

$$NH_4^+(aq) + H_2O(l) \rightleftharpoons NH_3(aq) + H_3O^+(aq) \qquad [16.44]$$

These rules apply to what are called normal salts. These salts contain no ionizable protons on the anion. The pH of an acid salt (such as $NaHCO_3$ or NaH_2PO_4) is affected by the hydrolysis of the anion and by its acid dissociation, as shown in Sample Exercise 16.19.

Most metal ions can also react with water to decrease the pH of an aqueous solution. The mechanism by which metal ions produce acidic solutions is described in Section 16.11. However, ions of alkali metals and of the heavier alkaline earth metals do not react with water and therefore do not affect pH. Note that these exceptions are the cations found in the strong bases. (Section 16.5)

GIVE IT SOME THOUGHT

Which of the following cations has no effect on the pH of a solution: K^+, Fe^{2+}, or Al^{3+}?

Combined Effect of Cation and Anion in Solution

If an aqueous salt solution contains an anion that does not react with water and a cation that does not react with water, we expect the pH to be neutral. If the solution contains an anion that reacts with water to produce hydroxide and a cation that does not react with water, we expect the pH to be basic. If the solution contains a cation that reacts with water to produce hydronium and an anion that does not react with water, we expect the pH to be acidic. Finally, a solution may contain an anion and a cation *both* capable of reacting with water. In this case both hydroxide and hydronium will be produced. Whether the solution is basic, neutral, or acidic will depend upon the relative abilities of the ions to react with water.

To summarize:

1. An anion that is the conjugate base of a strong acid, for example, Br^-, will not affect the pH of a solution. (It will be a spectator ion in acid–base chemistry.)

2. An anion that is the conjugate base of a weak acid, for example, CN^-, will cause an increase in pH.

3. A cation that is the conjugate acid of a weak base, for example, $CH_3NH_3^+$, will cause a decrease in pH.

4. The cations of group 1A and heavier members of group 2A (Ca^{2+}, Sr^{2+}, and Ba^{2+}) will not affect pH. These are the cations of the strong Arrhenius bases. (They will be spectator ions in acid–base chemistry.)

5. Other metal ions will cause a decrease in pH.

6. When a solution contains both the conjugate base of a weak acid and the conjugate acid of a weak base, the ion with the larger equilibrium constant, K_a or K_b, will have the greater influence on the pH.

Figure 16.11 ▼ demonstrates the influence of several salts on pH.

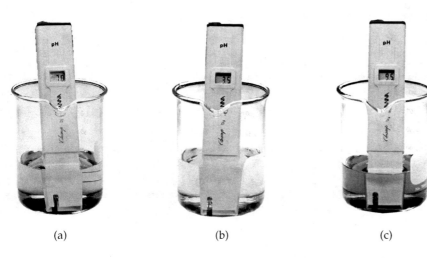

(a)   (b)   (c)

◀ Figure 16.11 **Salt solutions can be neutral, acidic, or basic.** These three solutions contain the acid–base indicator bromthymol blue. (a) The NaCl solution is neutral (pH = 7.0); (b) the NH_4Cl solution is acidic (pH = 3.5); (c) the NaClO solution is basic (pH = 9.5).

■■ SAMPLE EXERCISE 16.18 | Determining Whether Salt Solutions Are Acidic, Basic, or Neutral

Determine whether aqueous solutions of each of the following salts will be acidic, basic, or neutral: (a) $Ba(CH_3COO)_2$, (b) NH_4Cl, (c) CH_3NH_3Br, (d) KNO_3, (e) $Al(ClO_4)_3$.

SOLUTION

Analyze: We are given the chemical formulas of five ionic compounds (salts) and asked whether their aqueous solutions will be acidic, basic, or neutral.

Plan: We can determine whether a solution of a salt is acidic, basic, or neutral by identifying the ions in solution and by assessing how each ion will affect the pH.

Solve:

(a) This solution contains barium ions and acetate ions. The cation, Ba^{2+}, is an ion of one of the heavy alkaline earth metals and will therefore not affect the pH (summary point 4). The anion, CH_3COO^-, is the conjugate base of the weak acid CH_3COOH and will hydrolyze to produce OH^- ions, thereby making the solution basic (summary point 2).

(b) This solution contains NH_4^+ and Cl^- ions. NH_4^+ is the conjugate acid of a weak base (NH_3) and is therefore acidic (summary point 3). Cl^- is the conjugate base of a strong acid (HCl) and therefore has no influence on the pH of the solution (summary point 1). Because the solution contains an ion that is acidic (NH_4^+) and one that has no influence on pH (Cl^-), the solution of NH_4Cl will be acidic.

(c) This solution contains $CH_3NH_3^+$ and Br^- ions. $CH_3NH_3^+$ is the conjugate acid of a weak base (CH_3NH_2, an amine) and is therefore acidic (summary point 3). Br^- is the conjugate base of a strong acid (HBr) and is therefore pH-neutral (summary point 1). Because the solution contains one ion that is acidic and one that is neutral, the solution of CH_3NH_3Br will be acidic.

(d) This solution contains the K^+ ion, which is a cation of group 1A, and the NO_3^- ion, which is the conjugate base of the strong acid HNO_3. Neither of the ions will react with water to any appreciable extent (summary points 1 and 4), making the solution neutral.

(e) This solution contains Al^{3+} and ClO_4^- ions. Cations, such as Al^{3+}, that are not in groups 1A or 2A are acidic (summary point 5). The ClO_4^- ion is the conjugate base of a strong acid ($HClO_4$) and therefore does not affect pH (summary point 1). Thus, the solution of $Al(ClO_4)_3$ will be acidic.

■■ **PRACTICE EXERCISE**

In each of the following, indicate which salt in each of the following pairs will form the more acidic (or less basic) 0.010 M solution: (a) $NaNO_3$, or $Fe(NO_3)_3$; (b) KBr, or KBrO; (c) CH_3NH_3Cl, or $BaCl_2$, (d) NH_4NO_2, or NH_4NO_3.
Answers: (a) $Fe(NO_3)_3$, (b) KBr, (c) CH_3NH_3Cl, (d) NH_4NO_3

■■ SAMPLE EXERCISE 16.19 | Predicting Whether the Solution of an Amphiprotic Anion Is Acidic or Basic

Predict whether the salt Na_2HPO_4 will form an acidic solution or a basic solution on dissolving in water.

SOLUTION

Analyze: We are asked to predict whether a solution of Na_2HPO_4 will be acidic or basic. This substance is an ionic compound composed of Na^+ and HPO_4^{2-} ions.

Plan: We need to evaluate each ion, predicting whether each is acidic or basic. Because Na^+ is a cation of group 1A, we know that it has no influence on pH. It is merely a spectator ion in acid–base chemistry. Thus, our analysis of whether the solution is acidic or basic must focus on the behavior of the HPO_4^{2-} ion. We need to consider the fact that HPO_4^{2-} can act as either an acid or a base.

$$HPO_4^{2-}(aq) \rightleftharpoons H^+(aq) + PO_4^{3-}(aq) \qquad [16.45]$$

$$HPO_4^{2-}(aq) + H_2O \rightleftharpoons H_2PO_4^-(aq) + OH^-(aq) \qquad [16.46]$$

The reaction with the larger equilibrium constant will determine whether the solution is acidic or basic.

Solve: The value of K_a for Equation 16.45, as shown in Table 16.3, is 4.2×10^{-13}. We must calculate the value of K_b for Equation 16.46 from the value of K_a for its conjugate acid, $H_2PO_4^-$. We make use of the relationship shown in Equation 16.40.

$$K_a \times K_b = K_w$$

We want to know K_b for the base HPO_4^{2-}, knowing the value of K_a for the conjugate acid $H_2PO_4^-$:

$$K_b(HPO_4^{2-}) \times K_a(H_2PO_4^-) = K_w = 1.0 \times 10^{-14}$$

Because K_a for $H_2PO_4^-$ is 6.2×10^{-8} (Table 16.3), we calculate K_b for HPO_4^{2-} to be 1.6×10^{-7}. This is more than 10^5 times larger than K_a for HPO_4^{2-}; thus, the reaction shown in Equation 16.46 predominates over that in Equation 16.45, and the solution will be basic.

■ PRACTICE EXERCISE

Predict whether the dipotassium salt of citric acid ($K_2HC_6H_5O_7$) will form an acidic or basic solution in water (see Table 16.3 for data).
Answer: acidic

16.10 ACID–BASE BEHAVIOR AND CHEMICAL STRUCTURE

When a substance is dissolved in water, it may behave as an acid, behave as a base, or exhibit no acid–base properties. How does the chemical structure of a substance determine which of these behaviors is exhibited by the substance? For example, why do some substances that contain OH groups behave as bases, releasing OH^- ions into solution, whereas others behave as acids, ionizing to release H^+ ions? Why are some acids stronger than others? In this section we will discuss briefly the effects of chemical structure on acid–base behavior.

Factors That Affect Acid Strength

A molecule containing H will transfer a proton only if the H—X bond is polarized in the following way:

$$\overset{\longrightarrow}{H—X}$$

In ionic hydrides, such as NaH, the reverse is true; the H atom possesses a negative charge and behaves as a proton acceptor. Essentially nonpolar H—X bonds, such as the H—C bond in CH_4, produce neither acidic nor basic aqueous solutions.

A second factor that helps determine whether a molecule containing an H—X bond will donate a proton is the strength of the bond. Very strong bonds are less easily dissociated than weaker ones. This factor is important, for example, in the case of the hydrogen halides. The H—F bond is the most polar H—X bond. You therefore might expect that HF would be a very strong acid if the first factor were all that mattered. However, HF has the highest bond strength among the hydrogen halides, as seen in Table 8.4. As a result, HF is a weak acid, whereas all the other hydrogen halides are strong acids in water.

A third factor that affects the ease with which a hydrogen atom ionizes from HX is the stability of the conjugate base, X^-. In general, the greater the stability of the conjugate base, the stronger is the acid. The strength of an acid is often a combination of all three factors: (1) the polarity of the H—X bond, (2) the strength of the H—X bond, and (3) the stability of the conjugate base, X^-.

Binary Acids

In general, the H—X bond strength is the most important factor determining acid strength among the binary acids (those containing hydrogen and just one other element) in which X is in the same *group* in the periodic table. The strength of an H—X bond tends to decrease as the element X increases in size. As a result, the bond strength decreases and the acidity increases down a group. Thus, HCl is a stronger acid than HF, and H_2S is a stronger acid than H_2O.

	GROUP			
	4A	**5A**	**6A**	**7A**
Period 2	CH_4 No acid or base properties	NH_3 Weak base	H_2O ---	HF Weak acid
Period 3	SiH_4 No acid or base properties	PH_3 Weak base	H_2S Weak acid	HCl Strong acid

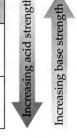

Increasing acid strength →

← Increasing base strength

▲ Figure 16.12 **Trends in acid–base properties of binary hydrides.** The acidity of the binary compounds of hydrogen and nonmetals increases moving left to right across a period and moving top to bottom down a group.

Bond strengths change less moving across a row in the periodic table than they do down a group. As a result, bond polarity is the major factor determining acidity for binary acids in the same *row*. Thus, acidity increases as the electronegativity of the element X increases, as it generally does moving from left to right in a row. For example, the acidity of the second-row elements varies in the following order: $CH_4 < NH_3 \ll H_2O < HF$. Because the C—H bond is essentially nonpolar, CH_4 shows no tendency to form H^+ and CH_3^- ions. Although the N—H bond is polar, NH_3 has a nonbonding pair of electrons on the nitrogen atom that dominates its chemistry, so NH_3 acts as a base rather than as an acid. The periodic trends in the acid strengths of binary compounds of hydrogen and the nonmetals of periods 2 and 3 are summarized in Figure 16.12▲.

GIVE IT SOME THOUGHT

What is the major factor determining the increase in acidity of binary acids going down a column of the periodic table? What is the major factor going across a period?

Oxyacids

Many common acids, such as sulfuric acid, contain one or more O—H bonds:

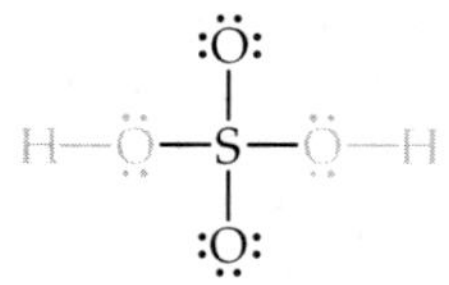

$$H-\ddot{O}-\overset{\overset{\displaystyle :\ddot{O}:}{|}}{\underset{\underset{\displaystyle :\ddot{O}:}{|}}{S}}-\ddot{O}-H$$

Acids in which OH groups and possibly additional oxygen atoms are bound to a central atom are called **oxyacids**. The OH group is also present in bases. What factors determine whether an OH group will behave as a base or as an acid?

Let's consider an OH group bound to some atom Y, which might in turn have other groups attached to it:

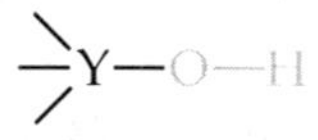

$$\diagdown Y-O-H$$

At one extreme, Y might be a metal, such as Na, K, or Mg. Because of their low electronegativities, the pair of electrons shared between Y and O is completely transferred to oxygen, and an ionic compound containing OH^- is formed. Such compounds are therefore sources of OH^- ions and behave as bases.

Shift of electron density

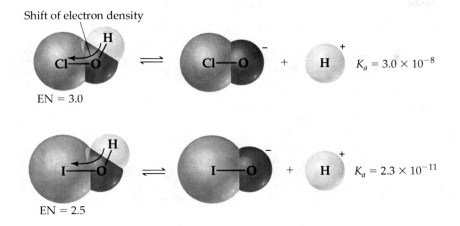

EN = 3.0

EN = 2.5

◀ **Figure 16.13 The acidity of oxyacids increases with increasing electronegativity of the central atom.** As the electronegativity of the atom attached to an OH group increases, the ease with which the hydrogen ion is released increases. The drift of electron density toward the electronegative atom further polarizes the O—H bond, which favors ionization. In addition, the electronegative atom will help stabilize the conjugate base, which also leads to a stronger acid. Because Cl is more electronegative than I, HClO is a stronger acid than HIO.

When Y is a nonmetal, the bond to O is covalent and the substance does not readily lose OH^-. Instead, these compounds are either acidic or neutral. *Generally, as the electronegativity of Y increases, so will the acidity of the substance.* This happens for two reasons: First, as electron density is drawn toward Y, the O—H bond becomes weaker and more polar, thereby favoring loss of H^+ (Figure 16.13 ▲). Second, because the conjugate base is usually an anion, its stability generally increases as the electronegativity of Y increases.

Many oxyacids contain additional oxygen atoms bonded to the central atom Y. The additional electronegative oxygen atoms pull electron density from the O—H bond, further increasing its polarity. Increasing the number of oxygen atoms also helps stabilize the conjugate base by increasing its ability to "spread out" its negative charge. Thus, *the strength of an acid will increase as additional electronegative atoms bond to the central atom Y.*

We can summarize these ideas as two simple rules that relate the acid strength of oxyacids to the electronegativity of Y and to the number of groups attached to Y.

1. For oxyacids that have the same number of OH groups and the same number of O atoms, acid strength increases with increasing electronegativity of the central atom Y. For example, the strength of the hypohalous acids, which have the structure H—O—Y, increases as the electronegativity of Y increases (Table 16.6 ▶).

2. For oxyacids that have the same central atom Y, acid strength increases as the number of oxygen atoms attached to Y increases. For example, the strength of the oxyacids of chlorine steadily increases from hypochlorous acid (HClO) to perchloric acid ($HClO_4$):

TABLE 16.6 ■ Electronegativity Values (EN) of Y and Acid-Dissociation Constants		
Acid	EN of Y	K_a
HClO	3.0	3.0×10^{-8}
HBrO	2.8	2.5×10^{-9}
HIO	2.5	2.3×10^{-11}

Hypochlorous	Chlorous	Chloric	Perchloric
H—Ö—Cl̤:	H—Ö—C̤l—Ö:	H—Ö—C̤l—Ö: with :Ö: above	H—Ö—Cl—Ö: with :Ö: above and :Ö: below
$K_a = 3.0 \times 10^{-8}$	$K_a = 1.1 \times 10^{-2}$	Strong acid	Strong acid

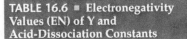

Increasing acid strength

Because the oxidation number of the central atom increases as the number of attached O atoms increases, this correlation can be stated in an equivalent way: In a series of oxyacids, the acidity increases as the oxidation number of the central atom increases.

■■ **SAMPLE EXERCISE 16.20** | **Predicting Relative Acidities from Composition and Structure**

Arrange the compounds in each of the following series in order of increasing acid strength: **(a)** AsH_3, HI, NaH, H_2O; **(b)** H_2SO_4, H_2SeO_3, H_2SeO_4.

SOLUTION

Analyze: We are asked to arrange two sets of compounds in order from weakest acid to strongest acid. In (a), the substances are binary compounds containing H, whereas in (b) the substances are oxyacids.

Plan: For the binary compounds in part (a), we will consider the electronegativities of As, I, Na, and O relative to H. A higher electronegativity will cause the H to have a higher partial positive charge, causing the compound to be more acidic. For the oxyacids in part (b), we will consider both the relative electronegativities of the central atom (S and Se) and the number of oxygen atoms bonded to the central atom.

Solve:

(a) Because Na is on the left side of the periodic table, we know that it has a very low electronegativity. As a result, the hydrogen in NaH carries a negative charge. Thus NaH should be the least acidic (most basic) compound on the list. Because arsenic is less electronegative than oxygen, we might expect that AsH_3 would be a weak base toward water. We would make the same prediction by an extension of the trends shown in Figure 16.12. Further, we expect that the binary hydrogen compounds of the halogens, as the most electronegative element in each period, will be acidic relative to water. In fact, HI is one of the strong acids in water. Thus the order of increasing acidity is $NaH < AsH_3 < H_2O < HI$.

(b) The acids H_2SO_4 and H_2SeO_4 have the same number of O atoms and OH groups. In such cases, the acid strength increases with increasing electronegativity of the central atom. Because S is more electronegative than Se, we predict that H_2SO_4 is more acidic than H_2SeO_4. Next, we can compare H_2SeO_4 and H_2SeO_3. For acids with the same central atom, the acidity increases as the number of oxygen atoms bonded to the central atom increases. Thus, H_2SeO_4 should be a stronger acid than H_2SeO_3. Thus, we predict the order of increasing acidity to be $H_2SeO_3 < H_2SeO_4 < H_2SO_4$.

■■ **PRACTICE EXERCISE**

In each of the following pairs choose the compound that leads to the more acidic (or less basic) solution: **(a)** HBr, HF; **(b)** PH_3, H_2S; **(c)** HNO_2, HNO_3; **(d)** H_2SO_3, H_2SeO_3.
Answers: **(a)** HBr, **(b)** H_2S, **(c)** HNO_3, **(d)** H_2SO_3

Carboxylic Acids

Another large group of acids is illustrated by acetic acid:

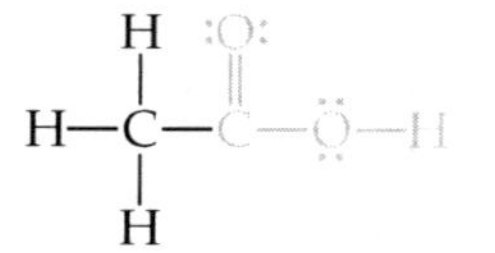

The portion of the structure shown in blue is called the *carboxyl group*, which is often written as COOH. Thus, the chemical formula of acetic acid is written as CH_3COOH, where only the hydrogen atom in the carboxyl group can be ionized. Acids that contain a carboxyl group are called **carboxylic acids**, and they form the largest category of organic acids. Formic acid and benzoic acid, whose structures are drawn below, are further examples of this large and important category of acids.

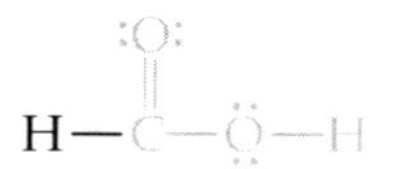

Formic acid 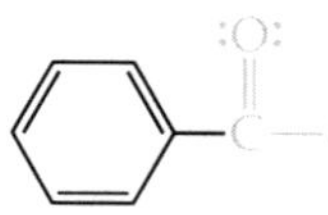   Benzoic acid

Acetic acid (CH_3COOH) is a weak acid ($K_a = 1.8 \times 10^{-5}$). Two factors contribute to the acidic behavior of carboxylic acids. First, the additional oxygen atom attached to the carbon of the carboxyl group draws electron density from the O—H bond, increasing its polarity and helping to stabilize the conjugate base.

Chemistry and Life   THE AMPHIPROTIC BEHAVIOR OF AMINO ACIDS

A mino acids are the building blocks of proteins. The general structure of amino acids is shown here, where different amino acids have different R groups attached to the central carbon atom:

Amine group (basic)   Carboxyl group (acidic)

For example, in *glycine*, which is the simplest amino acid, R is a hydrogen atom, whereas in *alanine*, R is a CH$_3$ group.

Glycine   Alanine

Amino acids contain a carboxyl group and can therefore serve as acids. They also contain an NH$_2$ group, characteristic of amines (Section 16.7), and thus they can also act as bases. Amino acids, therefore, are amphiprotic. For glycine, we might expect that the acid and the base reactions with water would be as follows:

Acid: $H_2N—CH_2—COOH(aq) + H_2O(l) \rightleftharpoons$
$$H_2N—CH_2—COO^-(aq) + H_3O^+(aq) \qquad [16.47]$$

Base: $H_2N—CH_2—COOH(aq) + H_2O(l) \rightleftharpoons$
$$^+H_3N—CH_2—COOH(aq) + OH^+(aq) \qquad [16.48]$$

The pH of a solution of glycine in water is about 6.0, indicating that it is a slightly stronger acid than a base.

The acid–base chemistry of amino acids is somewhat more complicated than shown in Equations 16.47 and 16.48, however. Because the COOH can act as an acid and the NH$_2$ group can act as a base, amino acids undergo a "self-contained" Brønsted–Lowry acid–base reaction in which the proton of the carboxyl group is transferred to the basic nitrogen atom:

$$\qquad [16.49]$$

proton transfer

Neutral molecule   Zwitterion

Although the form of the amino acid on the right side of Equation 16.49 is electrically neutral overall, it has a positively charged end and a negatively charged end. A molecule of this type is called a *zwitterion* (German for "hybrid ion").

Do amino acids exhibit any properties indicating that they behave as zwitterions? If so, they should behave similar to ionic substances. (Section 8.2) Crystalline amino acids (Figure 16.14▼) have relatively high melting points, usually above 200 °C, which is characteristic of ionic solids. Amino acids are far more soluble in water than in nonpolar solvents. In addition, the dipole moments of amino acids are large, consistent with a large separation of charge in the molecule. Thus, the ability of amino acids to act simultaneously as acids and bases has important effects on their properties.
Related Exercise: 16.119

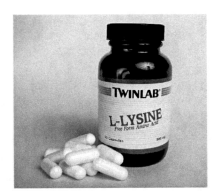

▲ Figure 16.14 **Lysine.** One of the amino acids found in proteins, lysine is available as a dietary supplement. The L on the label refers to a specific arrangement of atoms that is found in naturally occurring amino acids. Molecules with the L arrangement are mirror images of molecules with the D arrangement, much like our left hand is a mirror image of our right hand.

Second, the conjugate base of a carboxylic acid (a *carboxylate anion*) can exhibit resonance (Section 8.6), which contributes further to the stability of the anion by spreading the negative charge over several atoms:

resonance

GIVE IT SOME THOUGHT

What group of atoms is present in all carboxylic acids?

16.11 LEWIS ACIDS AND BASES

For a substance to be a proton acceptor (a Brønsted–Lowry base), it must have an unshared pair of electrons for binding the proton. NH_3, for example, acts as a proton acceptor. Using Lewis structures, we can write the reaction between H^+ and NH_3 as follows:

$$H^+ + :\overset{\overset{\displaystyle H}{|}}{\underset{\underset{\displaystyle H}{|}}{N}}-H \longrightarrow \left[H-\overset{\overset{\displaystyle H}{|}}{\underset{\underset{\displaystyle H}{|}}{N}}-H \right]^+$$

G. N. Lewis was the first to notice this aspect of acid–base reactions. He proposed a definition of acid and base that emphasizes the shared electron pair: A **Lewis acid** is an electron-pair acceptor, and a **Lewis base** is an electron-pair donor.

Every base that we have discussed thus far—whether it be OH^-, H_2O, an amine, or an anion—is an electron-pair donor. Everything that is a base in the Brønsted–Lowry sense (a proton acceptor) is also a base in the Lewis sense (an electron-pair donor). In the Lewis theory, however, a base can donate its electron pair to something other than H^+. The Lewis definition therefore greatly increases the number of species that can be considered acids; H^+ is a Lewis acid, but not the only one. For example, consider the reaction between NH_3 and BF_3. This reaction occurs because BF_3 has a vacant orbital in its valence shell. ∞ (Section 8.7) It therefore acts as an electron-pair acceptor (a Lewis acid) toward NH_3, which donates the electron pair. The curved arrow shows the donation of a pair of electrons from N to B to form a covalent bond:

$$H-\overset{\overset{\displaystyle H}{|}}{\underset{\underset{\displaystyle H}{|}}{N}}\!:\,+\,\overset{\overset{\displaystyle F}{|}}{\underset{\underset{\displaystyle F}{|}}{B}}-F \longrightarrow H-\overset{\overset{\displaystyle H}{|}}{\underset{\underset{\displaystyle H}{|}}{N}}-\overset{\overset{\displaystyle F}{|}}{\underset{\underset{\displaystyle F}{|}}{B}}-F$$

Lewis   Lewis
base   acid

GIVE IT SOME THOUGHT

What feature must any molecule or ion have to act as a Lewis base?

Our emphasis throughout this chapter has been on water as the solvent and on the proton as the source of acidic properties. In such cases we find the Brønsted–Lowry definition of acids and bases to be the most useful. In fact, when we speak of a substance as being acidic or basic, we are usually thinking of aqueous solutions and using these terms in the Arrhenius or Brønsted–Lowry sense. The advantage of the Lewis theory is that it allows us to treat a wider variety of reactions, including those that do not involve proton transfer, as acid–base reactions. To avoid confusion, a substance such as BF_3 is rarely called an acid unless it is clear from the context that we are using the term in the sense of the Lewis definition. Instead, substances that function as electron-pair acceptors are referred to explicitly as "Lewis acids."

Lewis acids include molecules that, like BF_3, have an incomplete octet of electrons. In addition, many simple cations can function as Lewis acids. For example, Fe^{3+} interacts strongly with cyanide ions to form the ferricyanide ion, $Fe(CN)_6^{3-}$.

$$Fe^{3+} + 6[:C\equiv N\!:]^- \longrightarrow [Fe(C\equiv N\!:)_6]^{3-}$$

The Fe^{3+} ion has vacant orbitals that accept the electron pairs donated by the cyanide ions; we will learn more in Chapter 24 about just which orbitals are used by the Fe^{3+} ion. The metal ion is highly charged, too, which contributes to the interaction with CN^- ions.

Some compounds with multiple bonds can behave as Lewis acids. For example, the reaction of carbon dioxide with water to form carbonic acid (H_2CO_3) can be pictured as an attack by a water molecule on CO_2, in which the water acts as an electron-pair donor and the CO_2 as an electron-pair acceptor, as shown in the margin. The electron pair of one of the carbon–oxygen double bonds is moved onto the oxygen, leaving a vacant orbital on the carbon that can act as an electron-pair acceptor. We have shown the shift of these electrons with arrows. After forming the initial acid–base product, a proton moves from one oxygen to another, thereby forming carbonic acid. A similar kind of Lewis acid–base reaction takes place when any oxide of a nonmetal dissolves in water to form an acidic solution.

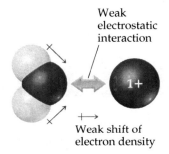

Hydrolysis of Metal Ions

As we have already seen, most metal ions behave as acids in aqueous solution. (Section 16.9) For example, an aqueous solution of $Fe(NO_3)_3$ is quite acidic. An aqueous solution of $ZnCl_2$ is also acidic, though to a lesser extent. The Lewis concept helps explain the interactions between metal ions and water molecules that give rise to this acidic behavior.

Because metal ions are positively charged, they attract the unshared electron pairs of water molecules. It is primarily this interaction, referred to as *hydration*, that causes salts to dissolve in water. (Section 13.1) The process of hydration can be thought of as a Lewis acid–base interaction in which the metal ion acts as a Lewis acid and the water molecules as Lewis bases. When a water molecule interacts with the positively charged metal ion, electron density is drawn from the oxygen, as illustrated in Figure 16.15▶. This flow of electron density causes the O—H bond to become more polarized; as a result, water molecules bound to the metal ion are more acidic than those in the bulk solvent.

The hydrated Fe^{3+} ion, $Fe(H_2O)_6{}^{3-}$, which we usually represent simply as $Fe^{3+}(aq)$, acts as a source of protons:

$$Fe(H_2O)_6{}^{3+}(aq) \rightleftharpoons Fe(H_2O)_5(OH)^{2+}(aq) + H^+(aq) \qquad [16.50]$$

The acid-dissociation constant for this hydrolysis reaction has the value $K_a = 2 \times 10^{-3}$, so $Fe^{3+}(aq)$ is a fairly strong acid. Acid-dissociation constants for hydrolysis reactions generally increase with increasing charge and decreasing radius of the ion (Figure 16.15). Thus, the Cu^{2+} ion, which has a smaller charge and a larger radius than Fe^{3+}, forms less acidic solutions than Fe^{3+}: The K_a for $Cu^{2+}(aq)$ is 1×10^{-8}. The acid hydrolysis of a number of salts of metal ions is demonstrated in Figure 16.16▼. Note that the Na^+ ion, which is large and has only a 1+ charge (and which we have previously identified as the cation of a strong base), exhibits no acid hydrolysis and yields a neutral solution.

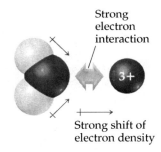

Weak
electrostatic
interaction

Weak shift of
electron density

Strong
electron
interaction

Strong shift of
electron density

▲ Figure 16.15 **The acidity of a hydrated cation depends on cation charge and size.** The interaction between a water molecule and a cation is much stronger when the cation is a smaller ion of higher charge. The pull of electron density toward the cation weakens the polar O—H bond of the water molecule and allows the transfer of a H^+ ion to a nearby water molecule. As a result, hydrated cations tend to be acidic, with their acidities increasing with increasing charge and decreasing size.

Salt:	$NaNO_3$	$Ca(NO_3)_2$	$Zn(NO_3)_2$	$Al(NO_3)_3$
Indicator:	Bromthymol blue	Bromthymol blue	Methyl red	Methyl orange
Estimated pH:	7.0	6.9	5.5	3.5

◀ Figure 16.16 **Effect of cations on the pH of a solution.** The pH values of 1.0 M solutions of a series of nitrate salts are estimated using acid–base indicators.

Which of the following cations will be most acidic and why: Ca^{2+}, Fe^{2+}, Fe^{3+}?

▨ SAMPLE INTEGRATIVE EXERCISE | Putting Concepts Together

Phosphorous acid (H_3PO_3) has the following Lewis structure.

$$\text{H}$$
$$|$$
$$:\!\ddot{\text{O}}\!-\!\text{P}\!-\!\ddot{\text{O}}\!-\!\text{H}$$
$$|$$
$$:\!\underset{\cdot\cdot}{\text{O}}\!-\!\text{H}$$

(a) Explain why H_3PO_3 is diprotic and not triprotic. **(b)** A 25.0-mL sample of a solution of H_3PO_3 is titrated with 0.102 M NaOH. It requires 23.3 mL of NaOH to neutralize both acidic protons. What is the molarity of the H_3PO_3 solution? **(c)** The original solution from part (b) has a pH of 1.59. Calculate the percent ionization and K_{a1} for H_3PO_3, assuming that $K_{a1} \gg K_{a2}$. **(d)** How does the osmotic pressure of a 0.050 M solution of HCl compare qualitatively with that of a 0.050 M solution of H_3PO_3? Explain.

SOLUTION

We will use what we have learned about molecular structure and its impact on acidic behavior to answer part (a). We will then use stoichiometry and the relationship between pH and $[H^+]$ to answer parts (b) and (c). Finally, we will consider acid strength in order to compare the colligative properties of the two solutions in part (d).

(a) Acids have polar H—X bonds. From Figure 8.6 we see that the electronegativity of H is 2.1 and that of P is also 2.1. Because the two elements have the same electronegativity, the H—P bond is nonpolar. ⮞⮞ (Section 8.4) Thus, this H cannot be acidic. The other two H atoms, however, are bonded to O, which has an electronegativity of 3.5. The H—O bonds are therefore polar, with H having a partial positive charge. These two H atoms are consequently acidic.

(b) The chemical equation for the neutralization reaction is

$$H_3PO_3(aq) + 2\,NaOH(aq) \longrightarrow Na_2HPO_3(aq) + 2\,H_2O(l)$$

From the definition of molarity, $M = \text{mol/L}$, we see that moles $= M \times L$. ⮞⮞ (Section 4.5) Thus, the number of moles of NaOH added to the solution is $(0.0233\,\text{L})(0.102\,\text{mol/L}) = 2.38 \times 10^{-3}$ mol NaOH. The balanced equation indicates that 2 mol of NaOH is consumed for each mole of H_3PO_3. Thus, the number of moles of H_3PO_3 in the sample is

$$(2.38 \times 10^{-3}\,\text{mol NaOH})\left(\frac{1\,\text{mol } H_3PO_3}{2\,\text{mol NaOH}}\right) = 1.19 \times 10^{-3}\,\text{mol } H_3PO_3$$

The concentration of the H_3PO_3 solution, therefore, equals $(1.19 \times 10^{-3}\,\text{mol})/(0.0250\,\text{L}) = 0.0476\,M$.

(c) From the pH of the solution, 1.59, we can calculate $[H^+]$ at equilibrium.

$$[H^+] = \text{antilog}(-1.59) = 10^{-1.59} = 0.026\,M \text{ (two significant figures)}$$

Because $K_{a1} \gg K_{a2}$, the vast majority of the ions in solution are from the first ionization step of the acid.

$$H_3PO_3(aq) \rightleftharpoons H^+(aq) + H_2PO_3^-(aq)$$

Because one $H_2PO_3^-$ ion forms for each H^+ ion formed, the equilibrium concentrations of H^+ and $H_2PO_3^-$ are equal: $[H^+] = [H_2PO_3^-] = 0.026\,M$. The equilibrium concentration of H_3PO_3 equals the initial concentration minus the amount that ionizes to form H^+ and $H_2PO_3^-$: $[H_3PO_3] = 0.0476\,M - 0.026\,M = 0.022\,M$ (two significant figures). These results can be tabulated as follows:

	$H_3PO_3(aq)$	$\rightleftharpoons$	$H^+(aq)$	$+$	$H_2PO_3^-(aq)$
Initial	0.0476 M		0		0
Change	−0.026 M		+0.026 M		+0.026 M
Equilibrium	0.022 M		0.026 M		0.026 M

The percent ionization is

$$\text{Percent ionization} = \frac{[H^+]_{\text{equilibrium}}}{[H_3PO_3]_{\text{initial}}} \times 100\% = \frac{0.026\ M}{0.0476\ M} \times 100\% = 55\%$$

The first acid-dissociation constant is

$$K_{a1} = \frac{[H^+][H_2PO_3^-]}{[H_3PO_3]} = \frac{(0.026)(0.026)}{0.022} = 0.031$$

(d) Osmotic pressure is a colligative property and depends on the total concentration of particles in solution. (Section 13.5) Because HCl is a strong acid, a 0.050 M solution will contain 0.050 M $H^+(aq)$ and 0.050 M $Cl^-(aq)$, or a total of 0.100 mol/L of particles. Because H_3PO_3 is a weak acid, it ionizes to a lesser extent than HCl, and, hence, there are fewer particles in the H_3PO_3 solution. As a result, the H_3PO_3 solution will have the lower osmotic pressure.

CHAPTER REVIEW

SUMMARY AND KEY TERMS

Section 16.1 Acids and bases were first recognized by the properties of their aqueous solutions. For example, acids turn litmus red, whereas bases turn litmus blue. Arrhenius recognized that the properties of acidic solutions are due to $H^+(aq)$ ions and those of basic solutions are due to $OH^-(aq)$ ions.

Section 16.2 The Brønsted–Lowry concept of acids and bases is more general than the Arrhenius concept and emphasizes the transfer of a proton (H^+) from an acid to a base. The H^+ ion, which is merely a proton with no surrounding valence electrons, is strongly bound to water. For this reason, the **hydronium ion**, $H_3O^+(aq)$, is often used to represent the predominant form of H^+ in water instead of the simpler $H^+(aq)$.

A **Brønsted–Lowry acid** is a substance that donates a proton to another substance; a **Brønsted–Lowry base** is a substance that accepts a proton from another substance. Water is an **amphiprotic** substance, one that can function as either a Brønsted–Lowry acid or base, depending on the substance with which it reacts.

The **conjugate base** of a Brønsted–Lowry acid is the species that remains when a proton is removed from the acid. The **conjugate acid** of a Brønsted–Lowry base is the species formed by adding a proton to the base. Together, an acid and its conjugate base (or a base and its conjugate acid) are called a **conjugate acid–base pair**.

The acid–base strengths of conjugate acid–base pairs are related: The stronger an acid, the weaker is its conjugate base; the weaker an acid, the stronger is its conjugate base. In every acid–base reaction, the position of the equilibrium favors the transfer of the proton from the stronger acid to the stronger base.

Section 16.3 Water ionizes to a slight degree, forming $H^+(aq)$ and $OH^-(aq)$. The extent of this **autoionization** is expressed by the **ion-product constant** for water:

$K_w = [H^+][OH^-] = 1.0 \times 10^{-14}$ (25 °C). This relationship describes both pure water and aqueous solutions. The K_w expression indicates that the product of $[H^+]$ and $[OH^-]$ is a constant. Thus, as $[H^+]$ increases, $[OH^-]$ decreases. Acidic solutions are those that contain more $H^+(aq)$ than $OH^-(aq)$: basic solutions contain more $OH^-(aq)$ than $H^+(aq)$.

Section 16.4 The concentration of $H^+(aq)$ can be expressed in terms of **pH**: $pH = -\log[H^+]$. At 25 °C the pH of a neutral solution is 7.00, whereas the pH of an acidic solution is below 7.00, and the pH of a basic solution is above 7.00. The pX notation is also used to represent the negative log of other small quantities, as in pOH and pK_w. The pH of a solution can be measured using a pH meter, or it can be estimated using acid–base indicators.

Section 16.5 Strong acids are strong electrolytes, ionizing completely in aqueous solution. The common strong acids are HCl, HBr, HI, HNO_3, $HClO_3$, $HClO_4$, and H_2SO_4. The conjugate bases of strong acids have negligible basicity.

Common strong bases are the ionic hydroxides of alkali metals and the heavy alkaline earth metals. The cations of these metals have negligible acidity.

Section 16.6 Weak acids are weak electrolytes; only some of the molecules exist in solution in ionized form. The extent of ionization is expressed by the **acid-dissociation constant**, K_a, which is the equilibrium constant for the reaction $HA(aq) \rightleftharpoons H^+(aq) + A^-(aq)$, which can also be written $HA(aq) + H_2O(l) \rightleftharpoons H_3O^+(aq) + A^-(aq)$. The larger the value of K_a, the stronger is the acid. For solutions of the same concentration, a stronger acid also has a larger **percent ionization**. The concentration of a weak acid and its K_a value can be used to calculate the pH of a solution.

Polyprotic acids, such as H_2SO_3, have more than one ionizable proton. These acids have acid-dissociation constants that decrease in magnitude in the order

$K_{a1} > K_{a2} > K_{a3}$. Because nearly all the $H^+(aq)$ in a polyprotic acid solution comes from the first dissociation step, the pH can usually be estimated satisfactorily by considering only K_{a1}.

Sections 16.7 and 16.8 Weak bases include NH_3, **amines**, and the anions of weak acids. The extent to which a weak base reacts with water to generate the corresponding conjugate acid and OH^- is measured by the **base-dissociation constant**, K_b. This is the equilibrium constant for the reaction $B(aq) + H_2O(l) \rightleftharpoons HB^+(aq) + OH^-(aq)$, where B is the base.

The relationship between the strength of an acid and the strength of its conjugate base is expressed quantitatively by the equation $K_a \times K_b = K_w$, where K_a and K_b are dissociation constants for conjugate acid–base pairs.

Section 16.9 The acid–base properties of salts can be ascribed to the behavior of their respective cations and anions. The reaction of ions with water, with a resultant change in pH, is called **hydrolysis**. The cations of the alkali metals and the alkaline earth metals and the anions of strong acids do not undergo hydrolysis. They are always spectator ions in acid–base chemistry.

Section 16.10 The tendency of a substance to show acidic or basic characteristics in water can be correlated with its chemical structure. Acid character requires the presence of a highly polar H—X bond. Acidity is also favored when the H—X bond is weak and when the X^- ion is very stable.

For **oxyacids** with the same number of OH groups and the same number of O atoms, acid strength increases with increasing electronegativity of the central atom. For oxyacids with the same central atom, acid strength increases as the number of oxygen atoms attached to the central atom increases. The structures of **carboxylic acids**, which are organic acids containing the COOH group, also help us to understand their acidity.

Section 16.11 The Lewis concept of acids and bases emphasizes the shared electron pair rather than the proton. A **Lewis acid** is an electron-pair acceptor, and a **Lewis base** is an electron-pair donor. The Lewis concept is more general than the Brønsted–Lowry concept because it can apply to cases in which the acid is some substance other than H^+. The Lewis concept helps to explain why many hydrated metal cations form acidic aqueous solutions. The acidity of these cations generally increases as their charge increases and as the size of the metal ion decreases.

KEY SKILLS

- Understand the nature of the hydrated proton, represented as either $H^+(aq)$ or $H_3O^+(aq)$.
- Define and identify Arrhenius acids and bases.
- Define and identify Brønsted–Lowry acids and bases, and identify conjugate acid–base pairs.
- Relate the strength of an acid to the strength of its conjugate base.
- Understand how the equilibrium position of a proton transfer reaction relates the strengths of the acids and bases involved.
- Describe the autoionization of water and understand how $[H_3O^+]$ and $[OH^-]$ are related.
- Calculate the pH of a solution given $[H_3O^+]$ or $[OH^-]$.
- Calculate the pH of a strong acid or strong base given its concentration.
- Calculate K_a or K_b for a weak acid or weak base given its concentration and the pH of the solution.
- Calculate the pH of a weak acid or weak base or its percent ionization given its concentration and K_a or K_b.
- Calculate K_b for a weak base given K_a of its conjugate acid, and similarly calculate K_a from K_b.
- Predict whether an aqueous solution of a salt will be acidic, basic, or neutral.
- Predict the relative strength of a series of acids from their molecular structures.
- Define and identify Lewis acids and bases.

KEY EQUATIONS

- $K_w = [H_3O^+][OH^-] = [H^+][OH^-] = 1.0 \times 10^{-14}$ [16.16]   The ion product of water at 25 °C
- $pH = -\log[H^+]$ [16.17]   Definition of pH
- $pOH = -\log[OH^-]$ [16.18]   Definition of pOH

- pH + pOH = 14.00   [16.20]

    Relationship between pH and pOH

- $K_a = \dfrac{[H_3O^+][A^-]}{[HA]}$ or $K_a = \dfrac{[H^+][A^-]}{[HA]}$ [16.25]

    The acid dissociation constant for a weak acid, HA

- Percent ionization $= \dfrac{[H^+]_{equilibrium}}{[HA]_{initial}} \times 100\%$ [16.27]

    Percent ionization of a weak acid

- $K_b = \dfrac{[BH^+][OH^-]}{[B]}$ [16.34]

    The base dissociation constant for a weak base, B

- $K_a \times K_b = K_w$ [16.40]

    The relationship between the acid and base dissociation constants of a conjugate acid–base pair

VISUALIZING CONCEPTS

16.1 **(a)** Identify the Brønsted–Lowry acid and the Brønsted–
CQ Lowry base in the following reaction:

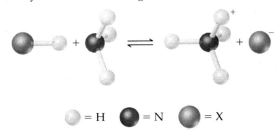

 = H   = N   = X

(b) Identify the Lewis acid and the Lewis base in the reaction. [Sections 16.2 and 16.11]

16.2 The following diagrams represent aqueous solutions of
CQ two monoprotic acids, HA (A = X or Y). The water molecules have been omitted for clarity. **(a)** Which is the stronger acid, HX or HY? **(b)** Which is the stronger base, X⁻ or Y⁻? **(c)** If you mix equal concentrations of HX and NaY, will the equilibrium

$$HX(aq) + Y^-(aq) \rightleftharpoons HY(aq) + X^-(aq)$$

lie mostly to the right ($K_c > 1$) or to the left ($K_c < 1$)? [Section 16.2]

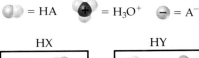 = HA   = H₃O⁺   = A⁻

HX   HY

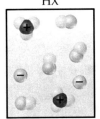

16.3 The following diagrams represent aqueous solutions of
CQ three acids, HX, HY, and HZ. The water molecules have been omitted for clarity, and the hydrated proton is represented as a simple sphere rather than as a hydronium ion. **(a)** Which of the acids is a strong acid? Explain.

(b) Which acid would have the smallest acid-dissociation constant, K_a? **(c)** Which solution would have the highest pH? [Sections 16.5 and 16.6]

HX   HY   HZ

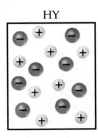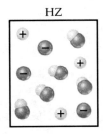

16.4 In which of the following cases is the approximation that
CQ the equilibrium concentration of H⁺(aq) is small relative to the initial concentration of HA likely to be most valid: **(a)** initial [HA] = 0.100 M and $K_a = 1.0 \times 10^{-6}$, **(b)** initial [HA] = 0.100 M and $K_a = 1.0 \times 10^{-4}$, **(c)** initial [HA] = 0.100 M and $K_a = 1.0 \times 10^{-3}$? [Section 16.6]

16.5 **(a)** Which of these three lines represents the effect of
CQ concentration on the percent ionization of a weak acid? **(b)** Explain in qualitative terms why the curve you choose has the shape it does. [Section 16.6]

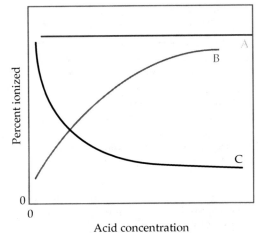

16.6 Refer to the diagrams accompanying Exercise 16.3.
CQ **(a)** Rank the anions, X^-, Y^-, and Z^-, in order of increasing basicity. **(b)** Which of the ions would have the largest base-dissociation constant, K_b? [Sections 16.2 and 16.8]

16.7 (a) Draw the Lewis structure for the following molecule
CQ and explain why it is able to act as a base. **(b)** To what class of organic compounds does this substance belong? (See the color key in Exercise 16.1.) [Section 16.7]

16.8 The following diagram represents an aqueous solution
CQ formed by dissolving a sodium salt of a weak acid in water. The diagram shows only the Na^+ ions, the X^- ions, and the HX molecules. What ion is missing from the diagram? If the drawing is completed by drawing all the ions, how many of the missing ions should be shown? [Section 16.9]

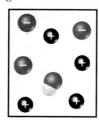

16.9 (a) What kinds of acids are represented by the following
CQ molecular models? **(b)** Indicate how the acidity of each molecule is affected by increasing the electronegativity of the atom X, and explain the origin of the effect. [Section 16.10]

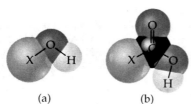

(a)   (b)

16.10 In this model of acetylsalicylic acid (aspirin), identify
CQ the carboxyl group in the molecule. [Section 16.10]

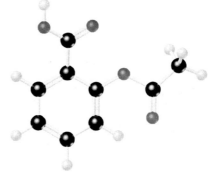

16.11 Rank the following acids in order of increasing acidity:
CQ CH_3COOH, $CH_2ClCOOH$, $CHCl_2COOH$, CCl_3COOH, CF_3COOH. [Section 16.10]

16.12 (a) The following diagram represents the reaction of
CQ PCl_4^+ with Cl^-. Draw the Lewis structures for the reactants and products, and identify the Lewis acid and the Lewis base in the reaction.

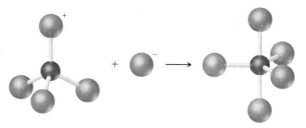

(b) The following reaction represents the acidity of a hydrated cation. How does the equilibrium constant for the reaction change as the charge of the cation increases? [Section 16.11]

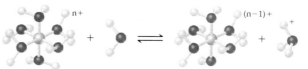

EXERCISES

Arrhenius and Brønsted–Lowry Acids and Bases

16.13 Although HCl and H_2SO_4 have very different properties
CQ as pure substances, their aqueous solutions possess many common properties. List some general properties of these solutions, and explain their common behavior in terms of the species present.

16.14 Although pure NaOH and NH_3 have very different
CQ properties, their aqueous solutions possess many common properties. List some general properties of these solutions, and explain their common behavior in terms of the species present.

16.15 (a) What is the difference between the Arrhenius and the
CQ Brønsted–Lowry definitions of an acid? **(b)** $NH_3(g)$ and HCl(g) react to form the ionic solid $NH_4Cl(s)$ (Figure 16.3). Which substance is the Brønsted–Lowry acid in this reaction? Which is the Brønsted–Lowry base?

16.16 (a) What is the difference between the Arrhenius and the
CQ Brønsted–Lowry definitions of a base? **(b)** When ammonia is dissolved in water, it behaves both as an Arrhenius base and as a Brønsted–Lowry base. Explain.

16.17 (a) Give the conjugate base of the following Brønsted–Lowry acids: **(i)** HIO_3, **(ii)** NH_4^+. **(b)** Give the conjugate acid of the following Brønsted–Lowry bases: **(i)** O^{2-}, **(ii)** $H_2PO_4^-$.

16.18 (a) Give the conjugate base of the following Brønsted–Lowry acids: **(i)** C_6H_5COOH. **(ii)** HPO_4^{2-}. **(b)** Give the conjugate acid of the following Brønsted–Lowry bases: **(i)** CO_3^{2-}, **(ii)** $C_2H_5NH_2$.

16.19 Designate the Brønsted–Lowry acid and the Brønsted–Lowry base on the left side of each of the following equations, and also designate the conjugate acid and conjugate base on the right side:

(a) $NH_4^+(aq) + CN^-(aq) \rightleftharpoons HCN(aq) + NH_3(aq)$

(b) $(CH_3)_3N(aq) + H_2O(l) \rightleftharpoons$
$(CH_3)_3NH^+(aq) + OH^-(aq)$

(c) $HCOOH(aq) + PO_4^{3-}(aq) \rightleftharpoons$
$HCOO^-(aq) + HPO_4^{2-}(aq)$

16.20 Designate the Brønsted–Lowry acid and the Brønsted–Lowry base on the left side of each equation, and also designate the conjugate acid and conjugate base on the right side.

(a) $HBrO(aq) + H_2O(l) \rightleftharpoons H_3O^+(aq) + BrO^-(aq)$

(b) $HSO_4^-(aq) + HCO_3^-(aq) \rightleftharpoons$
$SO_4^{2-}(aq) + H_2CO_3(aq)$

(c) $HSO_3^-(aq) + H_3O^+(aq) \rightleftharpoons H_2SO_3(aq) + H_2O(l)$

16.21 (a) The hydrogen oxalate ion ($HC_2O_4^-$) is amphiprotic.
CQ Write a balanced chemical equation showing how it acts as an acid toward water and another equation showing how it acts as a base toward water. (b) What is the conjugate acid of $HC_2O_4^-$? What is its conjugate base?

16.22 (a) Write an equation for the reaction in which
CQ $H_2C_6H_7O_5^-(aq)$ acts as a base in $H_2O(l)$. (b) Write an equation for the reaction in which $H_2C_6H_7O_5^-(aq)$ acts as an acid in $H_2O(l)$. (c) What is the conjugate acid of $H_2C_6H_7O_5^-$? What is its conjugate base?

16.23 Label each of the following as being a strong base, a weak base, or a species with negligible basicity. In each case write the formula of its conjugate acid, and indicate whether the conjugate acid is a strong acid, a weak acid, or a species with negligible acidity: (a) CH_3COO^-, (b) HCO_3^-, (c) O^{2-}, (d) Cl^-, (e) NH_3.

16.24 Label each of the following as being a strong acid, a weak acid, or a species with negligible acidity. In each case write the formula of its conjugate base, and indicate whether the conjugate base is a strong base, a weak base, or a species with negligible basicity: (a) HNO_2, (b) H_2SO_4, (c) HPO_4^{2-}, (d) CH_4, (e) $CH_3NH_3^+$ (an ion related to NH_4^+).

16.25 (a) Which of the following is the stronger Brønsted–
CQ Lowry acid, HBrO or HBr? (b) Which is the stronger Brønsted–Lowry base, F^- or Cl^-? Briefly explain your choices.

16.26 (a) Which of the following is the stronger Brønsted–
CQ Lowry acid, HNO_3 or HNO_2? (b) Which is the stronger Brønsted–Lowry base, NH_3 or H_2O? Briefly explain your choices.

16.27 Predict the products of the following acid–base reactions, and predict whether the equilibrium lies to the left or to the right of the equation:

(a) $O^{2-}(aq) + H_2O(l) \rightleftharpoons$

(b) $CH_3COOH(aq) + HS^-(aq) \rightleftharpoons$

(c) $NO_2^-(aq) + H_2O(l) \rightleftharpoons$

16.28 Predict the products of the following acid–base reactions, and predict whether the equilibrium lies to the left or to the right of the equation:

(a) $NH_4^+(aq) + OH^-(aq) \rightleftharpoons$

(b) $CH_3COO^-(aq) + H_3O^+(aq) \rightleftharpoons$

(c) $HCO_3^-(aq) + F^-(aq) \rightleftharpoons$

Autoionization of Water

16.29 (a) What does the term *autoionization* mean? (b) Explain
CQ why pure water is a poor conductor of electricity. (c) You are told that an aqueous solution is acidic. What does this statement mean?

16.30 (a) Write a chemical equation that illustrates the au-
CQ toionization of water. (b) Write the expression for the ion-product constant for water, K_w. Why is $[H_2O]$ absent from this expression? (c) A solution is described as basic. What does this statement mean?

16.31 Calculate $[H^+]$ for each of the following solutions, and indicate whether the solution is acidic, basic, or neutral: (a) $[OH^-] = 0.00045\ M$; (b) $[OH^-] = 8.8 \times 10^{-9}\ M$; (c) a solution in which $[OH^-]$ is 100 times greater than $[H^+]$.

16.32 Calculate $[OH^-]$ for each of the following solutions, and indicate whether the solution is acidic, basic, or neutral: (a) $[H^+] = 0.0045\ M$; (b) $[H^+] = 1.5 \times 10^{-9}\ M$; (c) a solution in which $[H^+]$ is 10 times greater than $[OH^-]$.

16.33 At the freezing point of water ($0\ °C$), $K_w = 1.2 \times 10^{-15}$. Calculate $[H^+]$ and $[OH^-]$ for a neutral solution at this temperature.

16.34 Deuterium oxide (D_2O, where D is deuterium, the hydrogen-2 isotope) has an ion-product constant, K_w, of 8.9×10^{-16} at $20\ °C$. Calculate $[D^+]$ and $[OD^-]$ for pure (neutral) D_2O at this temperature.

The pH Scale

16.35 By what factor does $[H^+]$ change for a pH change of (a) 2.00 units, (b) 0.50 units?

16.36 Consider two solutions, solution A and solution B. $[H^+]$ in solution A is 500 times greater than that in solution B. What is the difference in the pH values of the two solutions?

16.37 (a) If NaOH is added to water, how does $[H^+]$ change? How does pH change? (b) Use the pH values in Figure 16.5 to estimate the pH of a solution with $[H^+] = 0.0006\ M$. Is the solution acidic or basic? (c) If the pH of a solution is 5.2, first estimate and then calculate the molar concentrations of $H^+(aq)$ and $OH^-(aq)$ in the solution.

16.38 **(a)** If HNO_3 is added to water, how does $[OH^-]$ change? How does pH change? **(b)** Use the pH values in Figure 16.5 to estimate the pH of a solution with $[OH^-] = 0.014\ M$. Is the solution acidic or basic? **(c)** If pH = 6.6, first estimate and then calculate the molar concentrations of $H^+(aq)$ and $OH^-(aq)$ in the solution.

16.39 Complete the following table by calculating the missing entries and indicating whether the solution is acidic or basic.

$[H^+]$	$OH^-(aq)$	pH	pOH	Acidic or basic?
$7.5 \times 10^{-3}\ M$				
	$3.6 \times 10^{-10}\ M$			
		8.25		
			5.70	

16.40 Complete the following table by calculating the missing entries. In each case indicate whether the solution is acidic or basic.

pH	pOH	$[H^+]$	$[OH^-]$	Acidic or basic?
11.25				
	6.02			
		$4.4 \times 10^{-4}\ M$		
			$8.5 \times 10^{-3}\ M$	

16.41 The average pH of normal arterial blood is 7.40. At normal body temperature (37 °C), $K_w = 2.4 \times 10^{-14}$. Calculate $[H^+]$, $[OH^-]$, and pOH for blood at this temperature.

16.42 Carbon dioxide in the atmosphere dissolves in raindrops to produce carbonic acid (H_2CO_3), causing the pH of clean, unpolluted rain to range from about 5.2 to 5.6. What are the ranges of $[H^+]$ and $[OH^-]$ in the raindrops?

Strong Acids and Bases

16.43 **(a)** What is a strong acid? **(b)** A solution is labeled $0.500\ M$ HCl. What is $[H^+]$ for the solution? **(c)** Which of the following are strong acids: HF, HCl, HBr, HI?

16.44 **(a)** What is a strong base? **(b)** A solution is labeled $0.035\ M\ Sr(OH)_2$. What is $[OH^-]$ for the solution? **(c)** Is the following statement true or false? Because $Mg(OH)_2$ is not very soluble, it cannot be a strong base. Explain.

16.45 Calculate the pH of each of the following strong acid solutions: **(a)** $8.5 \times 10^{-3}\ M$ HBr, **(b)** 1.52 g of HNO_3 in 575 mL of solution, **(c)** 5.00 mL of $0.250\ M\ HClO_4$ diluted to 50.0 mL, **(d)** a solution formed by mixing 10.0 mL of $0.100\ M$ HBr with 20.0 mL of $0.200\ M$ HCl.

16.46 Calculate the pH of each of the following strong acid solutions: **(a)** $0.00135\ M\ HNO_3$, **(b)** 0.425 g of $HClO_4$ in 2.00 L of solution, **(c)** 5.00 mL of $1.00\ M$ HCl diluted to 0.500 L, **(d)** a mixture formed by adding 50.0 mL of $0.020\ M$ HCl to 150 mL of $0.010\ M$ HI.

16.47 Calculate $[OH^-]$ and pH for **(a)** $1.5 \times 10^{-3}\ M\ Sr(OH)_2$, **(b)** 2.250 g of LiOH in 250.0 mL of solution, **(c)** 1.00 mL of $0.175\ M$ NaOH diluted to 2.00 L, **(d)** a solution formed by adding 5.00 mL of $0.105\ M$ KOH to 15.0 mL of $9.5 \times 10^{-2}\ M\ Ca(OH)_2$.

16.48 Calculate $[OH^-]$ and pH for each of the following strong base solutions: **(a)** $0.082\ M$ KOH, **(b)** 1.065 g of KOH in 500.0 mL of solution, **(c)** 10.0 mL of $0.0105\ M\ Ca(OH)_2$ diluted to 500.0 mL, **(d)** a solution formed by mixing 10.0 mL of $0.015\ M\ Ba(OH)_2$ with 40.0 mL of $7.5 \times 10^{-3}\ M$ NaOH.

16.49 Calculate the concentration of an aqueous solution of NaOH that has a pH of 11.50.

16.50 Calculate the concentration of an aqueous solution of $Ca(OH)_2$ that has a pH of 12.05.

Weak Acids

16.51 Write the chemical equation and the K_a expression for the ionization of each of the following acids in aqueous solution. First show the reaction with $H^+(aq)$ as a product and then with the hydronium ion: **(a)** $HBrO_2$, **(b)** C_2H_5COOH.

16.52 Write the chemical equation and the K_a expression for the acid dissociation of each of the following acids in aqueous solution. First show the reaction with $H^+(aq)$ as a product and then with the hydronium ion: **(a)** C_6H_5COOH, **(b)** HCO_3^-.

16.53 Lactic acid ($CH_3CH(OH)COOH$) has one acidic hydrogen. A $0.10\ M$ solution of lactic acid has a pH of 2.44. Calculate K_a.

16.54 Phenylacetic acid ($C_6H_5CH_2COOH$) is one of the substances that accumulates in the blood of people with phenylketonuria, an inherited disorder that can cause mental retardation or even death. A $0.085\ M$ solution of $C_6H_5CH_2COOH$ has a pH of 2.68. Calculate the K_a value for this acid.

16.55 A 0.100 M solution of chloroacetic acid ($ClCH_2COOH$) is 11.0% ionized. Using this information, calculate [$ClCH_2COO^-$], [H^+], [$ClCH_2COOH$)], and K_a for chloroacetic acid.

16.56 A 0.100 M solution of bromoacetic acid ($BrCH_2COOH$) is 13.2% ionized. Calculate [H^+], [$BrCH_2COO^-$], and [$BrCH_2COOH$].

16.57 A particular sample of vinegar has a pH of 2.90. If acetic acid is the only acid that vinegar contains ($K_a = 1.8 \times 10^{-5}$), calculate the concentration of acetic acid in the vinegar.

16.58 How many moles of HF ($K_a = 6.8 \times 10^{-4}$) must be present in 0.200 L to form a solution with a pH of 3.25?

16.59 The acid-dissociation constant for benzoic acid (C_6H_5COOH) is 6.3×10^{-5}. Calculate the equilibrium concentrations of H_3O^+, $C_6H_5COO^-$, and C_6H_5COOH in the solution if the initial concentration of C_6H_5COOH is 0.050 M.

16.60 The acid-dissociation constant for hypochlorous acid (HClO) is 3.0×10^{-8}. Calculate the concentrations of H_3O^+, ClO^-, and HClO at equilibrium if the initial concentration of HClO is 0.0090 M.

16.61 Calculate the pH of each of the following solutions (K_a and K_b values are given in Appendix D): **(a)** 0.095 M propionic acid (C_2H_5COOH), **(b)** 0.100 M hydrogen chromate ion ($HCrO_4^-$), **(c)** 0.120 M pyridine (C_5H_5N).

16.62 Determine the pH of each of the following solutions (K_a and K_b values are given in Appendix D): **(a)** 0.095 M hypochlorous acid, **(b)** 0.0085 M phenol, **(c)** 0.095 M hydroxylamine.

16.63 Saccharin, a sugar substitute, is a weak acid with pK_a = 2.32 at 25 °C. It ionizes in aqueous solution as follows:

$$HNC_7H_4SO_3(aq) \rightleftharpoons H^+(aq) + NC_7H_4SO_3^-(aq)$$

What is the pH of a 0.10 M solution of this substance?

16.64 The active ingredient in aspirin is acetylsalicylic acid ($HC_9H_7O_4$), a monoprotic acid with $K_a = 3.3 \times 10^{-4}$ at 25 °C. What is the pH of a solution obtained by dissolving two extra-strength aspirin tablets, containing 500 mg of acetylsalicylic acid each, in 250 mL of water?

16.65 Calculate the percent ionization of hydrazoic acid (HN_3) in solutions of each of the following concentrations (K_a is given in Appendix D): **(a)** 0.400 M, **(b)** 0.100 M, **(c)** 0.0400 M.

16.66 Calculate the percent ionization of propionic acid (C_2H_5COOH) in solutions of each of the following concentrations (K_a is given in Appendix D): **(a)** 0.250 M, **(b)** 0.0800 M, **(c)** 0.0200 M.

[16.67] Show that for a weak acid, the percent ionization should vary as the inverse square root of the acid concentration.

[16.68] For solutions of a weak acid, a graph of pH versus the log of the initial acid concentration should be a straight line. What is the magnitude of the slope of that line?

[16.69] Citric acid, which is present in citrus fruits, is a triprotic acid (Table 16.3). Calculate the pH and the citrate ion ($C_6H_5O_7^{3-}$) concentration for a 0.050 M solution of citric acid. Explain any approximations or assumptions that you make in your calculations.

[16.70] Tartaric acid is found in many fruits, including grapes, and is partially responsible for the dry texture of certain wines. Calculate the pH and the tartarate ion ($C_4H_4O_6^{2-}$) concentration for a 0.250 M solution of tartaric acid, for which the acid-dissociation constants are listed in Table 16.3. Explain any approximations or assumptions that you make in your calculation.

Weak Bases

16.71 What is the essential structural feature of all Brønsted–
CQ Lowry bases?

16.72 What are two kinds of molecules or ions that commonly function as weak bases?

16.73 Write the chemical equation and the K_b expression for the ionization of each of the following bases in aqueous solution: **(a)** dimethylamine, $(CH_3)_2NH$; **(b)** carbonate ion, CO_3^{2-}; **(c)** formate ion, CHO_2^-.

16.74 Write the chemical equation and the K_b expression for the reaction of each of the following bases with water: **(a)** propylamine, $C_3H_7NH_2$; **(b)** monohydrogen phosphate ion, HPO_4^{2-}; **(c)** benzoate ion, $C_6H_5CO_2^-$.

16.75 Calculate the molar concentration of OH^- ions in a 0.075 M solution of ethylamine ($C_2H_5NH_2$; $K_b = 6.4 \times 10^{-4}$). Calculate the pH of this solution.

16.76 Calculate the molar concentration of OH^- ions in a 0.550 M solution of hypobromite ion (BrO^-; $K_b = 4.0 \times 10^{-6}$). What is the pH of this solution?

16.77 Ephedrine, a central nervous system stimulant, is used in nasal sprays as a decongestant. This compound is a weak organic base:

$$C_{10}H_{15}ON(aq) + H_2O(l) \rightleftharpoons C_{10}H_{15}ONH^+(aq) + OH^-(aq)$$

A 0.035 M solution of ephedrine has a pH of 11.33. **(a)** What are the equilibrium concentrations of $C_{10}H_{15}ON$, $C_{10}H_{15}ONH^+$, and OH^-? **(b)** Calculate K_b for ephedrine.

16.78 Codeine ($C_{18}H_{21}NO_3$) is a weak organic base. A $5.0 \times 10^{-3} M$ solution of codeine has a pH of 9.95. Calculate the value of K_b for this substance. What is the pK_b for this base?

The K_a–K_b Relationship; Acid–Base Properties of Salts

16.79 Although the acid-dissociation constant for phenol
CQ   (C_6H_5OH) is listed in Appendix D, the base-dissociation constant for the phenolate ion ($C_6H_5O^-$) is not. **(a)** Explain why it is not necessary to list both K_a for phenol and K_b for the phenolate ion. **(b)** Calculate K_b for the phenolate ion. **(c)** Is the phenolate ion a weaker or stronger base than ammonia?

16.80 We can calculate K_b for the carbonate ion if we know the
CQ K_a values of carbonic acid (H_2CO_3). **(a)** Is K_{a1} or K_{a2} of carbonic acid used to calculate K_b for the carbonate ion? Explain. **(b)** Calculate K_b for the carbonate ion. **(c)** Is the carbonate ion a weaker or stronger base than ammonia?

16.81 **(a)** Given that K_a for acetic acid is 1.8×10^{-5} and that for hypochlorous acid is 3.0×10^{-8}, which is the stronger acid? **(b)** Which is the stronger base, the acetate ion or the hypochlorite ion? **(c)** Calculate K_b values for CH_3COO^- and ClO^-.

16.82 **(a)** Given that K_b for ammonia is 1.8×10^{-5} and that for hydroxylamine is 1.1×10^{-8}, which is the stronger base? **(b)** Which is the stronger acid, the ammonium ion or the hydroxylammonium ion? **(c)** Calculate K_a values for NH_4^+ and H_3NOH^+.

16.83 Using data from Appendix D, calculate $[OH^-]$ and pH for each of the following solutions: **(a)** 0.10 M NaCN, **(b)** 0.080 M Na_2CO_3, **(c)** a mixture that is 0.10 M in $NaNO_2$ and 0.20 M in $Ca(NO_2)_2$.

16.84 Using data from Appendix D, calculate $[OH^-]$ and pH for each of the following solutions: **(a)** 0.105 M NaF, **(b)** 0.035 M Na_2S, **(c)** a mixture that is 0.045 M in CH_3COONa and 0.055 M in $(CH_3COO)_2Ba$.

16.85 Predict whether aqueous solutions of the following compounds are acidic, basic, or neutral: **(a)** NH_4Br, **(b)** $FeCl_3$, **(c)** Na_2CO_3, **(d)** $KClO_4$, **(e)** $NaHC_2O_4$.

16.86 Predict whether aqueous solutions of the following substances are acidic, basic, or neutral: **(a)** $CrBr_3$, **(b)** LiI, **(c)** K_3PO_4, **(d)** $[CH_3NH_3]Cl$, **(e)** $KHSO_4$.

16.87 An unknown salt is either NaF, NaCl, or NaOCl. When
CQ   0.050 mol of the salt is dissolved in water to form 0.500 L of solution, the pH of the solution is 8.08. What is the identity of the salt?

16.88 An unknown salt is either KBr, NH_4Cl, KCN, or K_2CO_3.
CQ   If a 0.100 M solution of the salt is neutral, what is the identity of the salt?

16.89 Sorbic acid (C_5H_7COOH) is a weak monoprotic acid with $K_a = 1.7 \times 10^{-5}$. Its salt (potassium sorbate) is added to cheese to inhibit the formation of mold. What is the pH of a solution containing 11.25 g of potassium sorbate in 1.75 L of solution?

16.90 Trisodium phosphate (Na_3PO_4) is available in hardware stores as TSP and is used as a cleaning agent. The label on a box of TSP warns that the substance is very basic (caustic or alkaline). What is the pH of a solution containing 35.0 g of TSP in a liter of solution?

Acid–Base Character and Chemical Structure

16.91 How does the acid strength of an oxyacid depend on
CQ   **(a)** the electronegativity of the central atom; **(b)** the number of nonprotonated oxygen atoms in the molecule?

16.92 **(a)** How does the strength of an acid vary with the polar-
CQ   ity and strength of the H—X bond? **(b)** How does the acidity of the binary acid of an element vary as a function of the electronegativity of the element? How does this relate to the position of the element in the periodic table?

16.93 Explain the following observations: **(a)** HNO_3 is a
CQ   stronger acid than HNO_2; **(b)** H_2S is a stronger acid than H_2O; **(c)** H_2SO_4 is a stronger acid than HSO_4^-; **(d)** H_2SO_4 is a stronger acid than H_2SeO_4; **(e)** CCl_3COOH is a stronger acid than CH_3COOH.

16.94 Explain the following observations: **(a)** HCl is a stronger
CQ   acid than H_2S; **(b)** H_3PO_4 is a stronger acid than H_3AsO_4; **(c)** $HBrO_3$ is a stronger acid than $HBrO_2$; **(d)** $H_2C_2O_4$ is a stronger acid than $HC_2O_4^-$; **(e)** benzoic acid (C_6H_5COOH) is a stronger acid than phenol (C_6H_5OH).

16.95 Based on their compositions and structures and on
CQ   conjugate acid–base relationships, select the stronger base in each of the following pairs: **(a)** BrO^- or ClO^-, **(b)** BrO^- or BrO_2^-, **(c)** HPO_4^{2-} or $H_2PO_4^-$.

16.96 Based on their compositions and structures and on con-
CQ   jugate acid–base relationships, select the stronger base in each of the following pairs: **(a)** NO_3^- or NO_2^-, **(b)** PO_4^{3-} or AsO_4^{3-}, **(c)** HCO_3^- or CO_3^{2-}.

16.97 Indicate whether each of the following statements is
CQ   true or false. For each statement that is false, correct the statement to make it true. **(a)** In general, the acidity of binary acids increases from left to right in a given row of the periodic table. **(b)** In a series of acids that have the same central atom, acid strength increases with the number of hydrogen atoms bonded to the central atom. **(c)** Hydrotelluric acid (H_2Te) is a stronger acid than H_2S because Te is more electronegative than S.

16.98 Indicate whether each of the following statements is
CQ true or false. For each statement that is false, correct
the statement to make it true. **(a)** Acid strength in a
series of H—X molecules increases with increasing
size of X. **(b)** For acids of the same general structure
but differing electronegativities of the central atoms,
acid strength decreases with increasing electronegativity of the central atom. **(c)** The strongest acid
known is HF because fluorine is the most electronegative element.

Lewis Acids and Bases

16.99 If a substance is an Arrhenius base, is it necessarily a
CQ Brønsted–Lowry base? Is it necessarily a Lewis base?
Explain.

16.100 If a substance is a Lewis acid, is it necessarily a
CQ Brønsted–Lowry acid? Is it necessarily an Arrhenius
acid? Explain.

16.101 Identify the Lewis acid and Lewis base among the
reactants in each of the following reactions:
(a) $Fe(ClO_4)_3(s) + 6 H_2O(l) \rightleftharpoons$
$Fe(H_2O)_6^{3+}(aq) + 3 ClO_4^-(aq)$
(b) $CN^-(aq) + H_2O(l) \rightleftharpoons HCN(aq) + OH^-(aq)$
(c) $(CH_3)_3N(g) + BF_3(g) \rightleftharpoons (CH_3)_3NBF_3(s)$
(d) $HIO(lq) + NH_2^-(lq) \rightleftharpoons NH_3(lq) + IO^-(lq)$
(*lq* denotes liquid ammonia as solvent)

16.102 Identify the Lewis acid and Lewis base in each of the following reactions:
(a) $HNO_2(aq) + OH^-(aq) \rightleftharpoons NO_2^-(aq) + H_2O(l)$
(b) $FeBr_3(s) + Br^-(aq) \rightleftharpoons FeBr_4^-(aq)$
(c) $Zn^{2+}(aq) + 4 NH_3(aq) \rightleftharpoons Zn(NH_3)_4^{2+}(aq)$
(d) $SO_2(g) + H_2O(l) \rightleftharpoons H_2SO_3(aq)$

16.103 Predict which member of each pair produces the more
CQ acidic aqueous solution: **(a)** K^+ or Cu^{2+}, **(b)** Fe^{2+} or
Fe^{3+}, **(c)** Al^{3+} or Ga^{3+}. Explain.

16.104 Which member of each pair produces the more acidic
CQ aqueous solution: **(a)** $ZnBr_2$ or $CdCl_2$, **(b)** $CuCl$ or
$Cu(NO_3)_2$, **(c)** $Ca(NO_3)_2$ or $NiBr_2$? Explain.

ADDITIONAL EXERCISES

16.105 In your own words, define or explain **(a)** K_w, **(b)** K_a,
CQ **(c)** pOH, **(d)** pK_b.

16.106 Indicate whether each of the following statements is correct or incorrect. For those that are incorrect, explain
why they are wrong.
(a) Every Brønsted–Lowry acid is also a Lewis acid.
(b) Every Lewis acid is also a Brønsted–Lowry acid.
(c) Conjugate acids of weak bases produce more acidic
solutions than conjugate acids of strong bases.
(d) K^+ ion is acidic in water because it causes hydrat-
ing water molecules to become more acidic.
(e) The percent ionization of a weak acid in water increases as the concentration of acid decreases.

16.107 Predict whether the equilibrium lies to the right or to the
left in the following reactions:
(a) $NH_4^+(aq) + PO_4^{3-}(aq) \rightleftharpoons$
$NH_3(aq) + HPO_4^{2-}(aq)$ (The ammonium ion is a
stronger acid than the hydrogen phosphate ion.)
(b) $CH_3COOH(aq) + CN^-(aq) \rightleftharpoons$
$CH_3COO^-(aq) + HCN(aq)$ (The cyanide ion is a
stronger base than the acetate ion.)

16.108 The odor of fish is due primarily to amines, especially
methylamine (CH_3NH_2). Fish is often served with a
wedge of lemon, which contains citric acid. The amine
and the acid react forming a product with no odor, thereby making the less-than-fresh fish more appetizing.
Using data from Appendix D, calculate the equilibrium
constant for the reaction of citric acid with methylamine, if only the first proton of the citric acid (K_{a1}) is
important in the neutralization reaction.

16.109 Hemoglobin plays a part in a series of equilibria involving
protonation-deprotonation and oxygenation-deoxygena-
tion. The overall reaction is approximately as follows:

$$HbH^+(aq) + O_2(aq) \rightleftharpoons HbO_2(aq) + H^+(aq)$$

where Hb stands for hemoglobin, and HbO_2 for oxyhe-
moglobin. **(a)** The concentration of O_2 is higher in the
lungs and lower in the tissues. What effect does high
$[O_2]$ have on the position of this equilibrium? **(b)** The
normal pH of blood is 7.4. Is the blood acidic, basic, or
neutral? **(c)** If the blood pH is lowered by the presence
of large amounts of acidic metabolism products, a condition known as acidosis results. What effect does lowering blood pH have on the ability of hemoglobin to
transport O_2?

[16.110] Calculate the pH of a solution made by adding 2.50 g of
lithium oxide (Li_2O) to enough water to make 1.500 L
of solution.

16.111 Which of the following solutions has the higher pH?
(a) a 0.1 M solution of a strong acid or a 0.1 M solution of
a weak acid, **(b)** a 0.1 M solution of an acid with
$K_a = 2 \times 10^{-3}$ or one with $K_a = 8 \times 10^{-6}$, **(c)** a 0.1 M
solution of a base with $pK_b = 4.5$ or one with $pK_b = 6.5$.

[16.112] What is the pH of a solution that is 2.5×10^{-9} M in NaOH? Does your answer make sense?

16.113 Caproic acid ($C_5H_{11}COOH$) is found in small amounts in coconut and palm oils and is used in making artificial flavors. A saturated solution of the acid contains 11 g/L and has a pH of 2.94. Calculate K_a for the acid.

[16.114] A hypothetical acid H_2X is both a strong acid and a diprotic acid. (a) Calculate the pH of a 0.050 M solution of H_2X, assuming that only one proton ionizes per acid molecule. (b) Calculate the pH of the solution from part (a), now assuming that both protons of each acid molecule completely ionize. (c) In an experiment it is observed that the pH of a 0.050 M solution of H_2X is 1.27. Comment on the relative acid strengths of H_2X and HX^-. (d) Would a solution of the salt NaHX be acidic, basic, or neutral? Explain.

16.115 Butyric acid is responsible for the foul smell of rancid butter. The pK_a of butyric acid is 4.84. (a) Calculate the pK_b for the butyrate ion. (b) Calculate the pH of a 0.050 M solution of butyric acid. (c) Calculate the pH of a 0.050 M solution of sodium butyrate.

16.116 Arrange the following 0.10 M solutions in order of increasing acidity (decreasing pH): (i) NH_4NO_3, (ii) $NaNO_3$, (iii) CH_3COONH_4, (iv) NaF, (v) CH_3COONa.

[16.117] What are the concentrations of H^+, $H_2PO_4^-$, HPO_4^{2-}, and PO_4^{3-} in a 0.0250 M solution of H_3PO_4?

[16.118] Many moderately large organic molecules containing basic nitrogen atoms are not very soluble in water as neutral molecules, but they are frequently much more soluble as their acid salts. Assuming that pH in the stomach is 2.5, indicate whether each of the following compounds would be present in the stomach as the neutral base or in the protonated form: nicotine, $K_b = 7 \times 10^{-7}$; caffeine, $K_b = 4 \times 10^{-14}$; strychnine, $K_b = 1 \times 10^{-6}$; quinine, $K_b = 1.1 \times 10^{-6}$.

[16.119] The amino acid glycine (H_2N-CH_2-COOH) can participate in the following equilibria in water:

$$H_2N-CH_2-COOH + H_2O \rightleftharpoons$$
$$H_2N-CH_2-COO^- + H_3O^+ \quad K_a = 4.3 \times 10^{-3}$$

$$H_2N-CH_2-COOH + H_2O \rightleftharpoons$$
$${}^+H_3N-CH_2-COOH + OH^- \quad K_b = 6.0 \times 10^{-5}$$

(a) Use the values of K_a and K_b to estimate the equilibrium constant for the intramolecular proton transfer to form a zwitterion:

$$H_2N-CH_2-COOH \rightleftharpoons {}^+H_3N-CH_2-COO^-$$

What assumptions did you need to make? (b) What is the pH of a 0.050 M aqueous solution of glycine? (c) What would be the predominant form of glycine in a solution with pH 13? With pH 1?

16.120 The structural formula for acetic acid is shown in Table 16.2. Replacing hydrogen atoms on the carbon with chlorine atoms causes an increase in acidity, as follows:

Acid	Formula	K_a (25 °C)
Acetic	CH_3COOH	1.8×10^{-5}
Chloroacetic	$CH_2ClCOOH$	1.4×10^{-3}
Dichloroacetic	$CHCl_2COOH$	3.3×10^{-2}
Trichloroacetic	CCl_3COOH	2×10^{-1}

Using Lewis structures as the basis of your discussion, explain the observed trend in acidities in the series. Calculate the pH of a 0.010 M solution of each acid.

INTEGRATIVE EXERCISES

16.121 Calculate the number of $H^+(aq)$ ions in 1.0 mL of pure water at 25 °C.

16.122 How many milliliters of concentrated hydrochloric acid solution (36.0% HCl by mass, density = 1.18 g/mL) are required to produce 10.0 L of a solution that has a pH of 2.05?

16.123 The volume of an adult's stomach ranges from about 50 mL when empty to 1 L when full. If the stomach volume is 400 mL and its contents have a pH of 2, how many moles of H^+ does the stomach contain? Assuming that all the H^+ comes from HCl, how many grams of sodium hydrogen carbonate will totally neutralize the stomach acid?

16.124 Atmospheric CO_2 levels have risen by nearly 20% over the past 40 years from 315 ppm to 380 ppm. (a) Given that the average pH of clean, unpolluted rain today is 5.4, determine the pH of unpolluted rain 40 years ago. Assume that carbonic acid (H_2CO_3) formed by the reaction of CO_2 and water is the only factor influencing pH.

$$CO_2(g) + H_2O(l) \rightleftharpoons H_2CO_3(aq)$$

(b) What volume of CO_2 at 25 °C and 1.0 atm is dissolved in a 20.0-L bucket of today's rainwater?

[16.125] In many reactions the addition of $AlCl_3$ produces the same effect as the addition of H^+. (a) Draw a Lewis structure for $AlCl_3$ in which no atoms carry formal charges, and determine its structure using the VSEPR method. (b) What characteristic is notable about the structure in part (a) that helps us understand the acidic character of $AlCl_3$? (c) Predict the result of the reaction between $AlCl_3$ and NH_3 in a solvent that does not participate as a reactant. (d) Which acid–base theory is most suitable for discussing the similarities between $AlCl_3$ and H^+?

[16.126] What is the boiling point of a 0.10 M solution of $NaHSO_4$ if the solution has a density of 1.002 g/mL?

[16.127] Cocaine is a weak organic base whose molecular formula is $C_{17}H_{21}NO_4$. An aqueous solution of cocaine was found to have a pH of 8.53 and an osmotic pressure of 52.7 torr at 15 °C. Calculate K_b for cocaine.

[16.128] The iodate ion is reduced by sulfite according to the following reaction:

$$IO_3^-(aq) + 3\,SO_3^{2-}(aq) \longrightarrow I^-(aq) + 3\,SO_4^{2-}(aq)$$

The rate of this reaction is found to be first order in IO_3^-, first order in SO_3^{2-}, and first order in H^+. **(a)** Write the rate law for the reaction. **(b)** By what factor will the rate of the reaction change if the pH is lowered from 5.00 to 3.50? Does the reaction proceed faster or slower at the lower pH? **(c)** By using the concepts discussed in Section 14.6, explain how the reaction can be pH-dependent even though H^+ does not appear in the overall reaction.

[16.129] **(a)** Using dissociation constants from Appendix D, determine the value for the equilibrium constant for each of the following reactions. (Remember that when reactions are added, the corresponding equilibrium constants are multiplied.)

(i) $HCO_3^-(aq) + OH^-(aq) \rightleftharpoons CO_3^{2-}(aq) + H_2O(l)$

(ii) $NH_4^+(aq) + CO_3^{2-}(aq) \rightleftharpoons NH_3(aq) + HCO_3^-(aq)$

(b) We usually use single arrows for reactions when the forward reaction is appreciable (K much greater than 1) or when products escape from the system, so that equilibrium is never established. If we follow this convention, which of these equilibria might be written with a single arrow?

[16.130] Lactic acid, $CH_3CH(OH)COOH$, received its name because it is present in sour milk as a product of bacterial action. It is also responsible for the soreness in muscles after vigorous exercise. **(a)** The pK_a of lactic acid is 3.85. Compare this with the value for propionic acid (CH_3CH_2COOH, $pK_a = 4.89$), and explain the difference. **(b)** Calculate the lactate ion concentration in a 0.050 M solution of lactic acid. **(c)** When a solution of sodium lactate, $CH_3CH(OH)COONa$, is mixed with an aqueous copper(II) solution, it is possible to obtain a solid salt of copper(II) lactate as a blue-green hydrate, $(CH_3CH(OH)COO)_2Cu \cdot xH_2O$. Elemental analysis of the solid tells us that the solid is 22.9% Cu and 26.0% C by mass. What is the value for x in the formula for the hydrate? **(d)** The acid-dissociation constant for the $Cu^{2+}(aq)$ ion is 1.0×10^{-8}. Based on this value and the acid-dissociation constant of lactic acid, predict whether a solution of copper(II) lactate will be acidic, basic, or neutral. Explain your answer.

17 ADDITIONAL ASPECTS OF AQUEOUS EQUILIBRIA

CANARY SPRING, which is part of Mammoth Hot Springs in Yellowstone National Park.

718

WATER IS THE MOST COMMON AND MOST IMPORTANT SOLVENT ON EARTH. In a sense, it is the solvent of life. It is difficult to imagine how living matter in all its complexity could exist with any liquid other than water as the solvent. Water occupies its position of importance because of its abundance

and its exceptional ability to dissolve a wide variety of substances. For example, the chapter-opening photograph shows a hot spring; this water contains a high concentration of ions (especially Mg^{2+}, Ca^{2+}, Fe^{2+}, CO_3^{2-}, and SO_4^{2-}). The ions are dissolved as the hot water, initially underground, passes through various rocks on its way to the surface and dissolves minerals in the rocks. When the solution reaches the surface and cools, the minerals deposit and make the terracelike formations seen in the photograph.

The various aqueous solutions encountered in nature typically contain many solutes. For example, the aqueous solutions in hot springs and oceans, as well as those in biological fluids, contain a variety of dissolved ions and molecules. Consequently, many equilibria can occur simultaneously in these solutions.

719

In this chapter we take a step toward understanding such complex solutions by looking first at further applications of acid–base equilibria. The idea is to consider not only solutions in which there is a single solute but also those containing a mixture of solutes. We then broaden our discussion to include two additional types of aqueous equilibria: those involving slightly soluble salts and those involving the formation of metal complexes in solution. For the most part, the discussions and calculations in this chapter are an extension of those in Chapters 15 and 16.

17.1 THE COMMON-ION EFFECT

In Chapter 16 we examined the equilibrium concentrations of ions in solutions containing a weak acid or a weak base. We now consider solutions that contain a weak acid, such as acetic acid (CH_3COOH), and a soluble salt of that acid, such as sodium acetate (CH_3COONa). Notice that these solutions contain two substances that share a *common ion* CH_3COO^-. It is instructive to view these solutions from the perspective of Le Châtelier's principle. ⟳ (Section 15.7) Sodium acetate is a soluble ionic compound and is therefore a strong electrolyte. ⟳ (Section 4.1) Consequently, it dissociates completely in aqueous solution to form Na^+ and CH_3COO^- ions:

$$CH_3COONa(aq) \longrightarrow Na^+(aq) + CH_3COO^-(aq)$$

In contrast, CH_3COOH is a weak electrolyte that ionizes as follows:

$$CH_3COOH(aq) \rightleftharpoons H^+(aq) + CH_3COO^-(aq) \qquad [17.1]$$

The CH_3COO^- from CH_3COONa causes this equilibrium to shift to the left, thereby decreasing the equilibrium concentration of $H^+(aq)$.

$$CH_3COOH(aq) \rightleftharpoons H^+(aq) + CH_3COO^-(aq)$$

Addition of CH_3COO^- shifts equilibrium, reducing $[H^+]$

In other words, the presence of the added acetate ion causes the acetic acid to ionize less than it normally would.

Whenever a weak electrolyte and a strong electrolyte contain a common ion, the weak electrolyte ionizes less than it would if it were alone in solution. We call this observation the **common-ion effect**. Sample Exercises 17.1 and 17.2 illustrate how equilibrium concentrations may be calculated when a solution contains a mixture of a weak electrolyte and a strong electrolyte that have a common ion. The procedures are similar to those encountered for weak acids and weak bases in Chapter 16.

■■ **SAMPLE EXERCISE 17.1** | Calculating the pH When a Common Ion Is Involved

What is the pH of a solution made by adding 0.30 mol of acetic acid and 0.30 mol of sodium acetate to enough water to make 1.0 L of solution?

SOLUTION

Analyze: We are asked to determine the pH of a solution of a weak electrolyte (CH_3COOH) and a strong electrolyte (CH_3COONa) that share a common ion, CH_3COO^-.

Plan: In any problem in which we must determine the pH of a solution containing a mixture of solutes, it is helpful to proceed by a series of logical steps:

1. Consider which solutes are strong electrolytes and which are weak electrolytes, and identify the major species in solution.
2. Identify the important equilibrium that is the source of H^+ and therefore determines pH.
3. Tabulate the concentrations of ions involved in the equilibrium.
4. Use the equilibrium-constant expression to calculate $[H^+]$ and then pH.

Solve: First, because CH_3COOH is a weak electrolyte and CH_3COONa is a strong electrolyte, the major species in the solution are CH_3COOH (a weak acid), Na^+ (which is neither acidic nor basic and is therefore a spectator in the acid–base chemistry), and CH_3COO^- (which is the conjugate base of CH_3COOH).

Second, $[H^+]$ and, therefore, the pH are controlled by the dissociation equilibrium of CH_3COOH:

$$CH_3COOH(aq) \rightleftharpoons H^+(aq) + CH_3COO^-(aq)$$

(We have written the equilibrium using $H^+(aq)$ rather than $H_3O^+(aq)$ but both representations of the hydrated hydrogen ion are equally valid.)

Third, we tabulate the initial and equilibrium concentrations as we did in solving other equilibrium problems in Chapters 15 and 16:

	$CH_3COOH(aq) \rightleftharpoons$	$H^+(aq)$	$+ CH_3COO^-(aq)$
Initial	0.30 M	0	0.30 M
Change	$-x$ M	$+x$ M	$+x$ M
Equilibrium	$(0.30 - x)$ M	x M	$(0.30 + x)$ M

The equilibrium concentration of CH_3COO^- (the common ion) is the initial concentration that is due to CH_3COONa (0.30 M) plus the change in concentration (x) that is due to the ionization of CH_3COOH.

Now we can use the equilibrium-constant expression:

$$K_a = 1.8 \times 10^{-5} = \frac{[H^+][CH_3COO^-]}{[CH_3COOH]}$$

(The dissociation constant for CH_3COOH at 25 °C is from Appendix D; addition of CH_3COONa does not change the value of this constant.) Substituting the equilibrium-constant concentrations from our table into the equilibrium expression gives

$$K_a = 1.8 \times 10^{-5} = \frac{x(0.30 + x)}{0.30 - x}$$

Because K_a is small, we assume that x is small compared to the original concentrations of CH_3COOH and CH_3COO^- (0.30 M each). Thus, we can ignore the very small x relative to 0.30 M, giving

$$K_a = 1.8 \times 10^{-5} = \frac{x(0.30)}{0.30}$$

$$x = 1.8 \times 10^{-5} M = [H^+]$$

The resulting value of x is indeed small relative to 0.30, justifying the approximation made in simplifying the problem.

Finally, we calculate the pH from the equilibrium concentration of $H^+(aq)$:

$$pH = -\log(1.8 \times 10^{-5}) = 4.74$$

Comment: In Section 16.6 we calculated that a 0.30 M solution of CH_3COOH has a pH of 2.64, corresponding to $[H^+] = 2.3 \times 10^{-3} M$. Thus, the addition of CH_3COONa has substantially decreased $[H^+]$, as we would expect from Le Châtelier's principle.

■ PRACTICE EXERCISE

Calculate the pH of a solution containing 0.085 M nitrous acid (HNO_2; $K_a = 4.5 \times 10^{-4}$) and 0.10 M potassium nitrite (KNO_2).
Answer: 3.42

▇ **SAMPLE EXERCISE 17.2** | **Calculating Ion Concentrations When a Common Ion Is Involved**

Calculate the fluoride ion concentration and pH of a solution that is 0.20 M in HF and 0.10 M in HCl.

SOLUTION

Analyze: We are asked to determine the concentration of F^- and the pH in a solution containing the weak acid HF and the strong acid HCl. In this case the common ion is H^+.

Plan: We can again use the four steps outlined in Sample Exercise 17.1.

Solve: Because HF is a weak acid and HCl is a strong acid, the major species in solution are HF, H^+, and Cl^-. The Cl^-, which is the conjugate base of a strong acid, is merely a spectator ion in any acid–base chemistry. The problem asks for $[F^-]$, which is formed by ionization of HF. Thus, the important equilibrium is

$$HF(aq) \rightleftharpoons H^-(aq) + F^-(aq)$$

The common ion in this problem is the hydrogen (or hydronium) ion. Now we can tabulate the initial and equilibrium concentrations of each species involved in this equilibrium:

	$HF(aq)$	$\rightleftharpoons$ $H^+(aq)$	$+$ $F^-(aq)$
Initial	0.20 M	0.10 M	0
Change	$-x\ M$	$+x\ M$	$+x\ M$
Equilibrium	$(0.20 - x)\ M$	$(0.10 + x)\ M$	$x\ M$

The equilibrium constant for the ionization of HF, from Appendix D, is 6.8×10^{-4}. Substituting the equilibrium-constant concentrations into the equilibrium expression gives

$$K_a = 6.8 \times 10^{-4} = \frac{[H^+][F^-]}{[HF]} = \frac{(0.10 + x)(x)}{0.20 - x}$$

If we assume that x is small relative to 0.10 or 0.20 M, this expression simplifies to

$$\frac{(0.10)(x)}{0.20} = 6.8 \times 10^{-4}$$

$$x = \frac{0.20}{0.10}(6.8 \times 10^{-4}) = 1.4 \times 10^{-3}\ M = [F^-]$$

This F^- concentration is substantially smaller than it would be in a 0.20 M solution of HF with no added HCl. The common ion, H^+, suppresses the ionization of HF. The concentration of $H^+(aq)$ is

$$[H^+] = (0.10 + x)\ M \simeq 0.10\ M$$

Thus,

$$pH = 1.00$$

Comment: Notice that for all practical purposes, $[H^+]$ is due entirely to the HCl; the HF makes a negligible contribution by comparison.

▇ **PRACTICE EXERCISE**

Calculate the formate ion concentration and pH of a solution that is 0.050 M in formic acid (HCOOH; $K_a = 1.8 \times 10^{-4}$) and 0.10 M in HNO_3.

Answer: $[HCOO^-] = 9.0 \times 10^{-5}$; pH = 1.00

Sample Exercises 17.1 and 17.2 both involve weak acids. The ionization of a weak base is also decreased by the addition of a common ion. For example, the addition of NH_4^+ (as from the strong electrolyte NH_4Cl) causes the base-dissociation equilibrium of NH_3 to shift to the left, decreasing the equilibrium concentration of OH^- and lowering the pH:

$$NH_3(aq) + H_2O(l) \rightleftharpoons NH_4^+(aq) + OH^-(aq) \qquad [17.2]$$

Addition of NH_4^+ shifts equilibrium, reducing $[OH^-]$

A mixture of 0.10 mol of NH_4Cl and 0.12 mol of NH_3 is added to enough water to make 1.0 L of solution. **(a)** What are the initial concentrations of the major species in the solution? **(b)** Which of the ions in this solution is a spectator ion in any acid–base chemistry occurring in the solution? **(c)** What equilibrium reaction determines $[OH^-]$ and therefore the pH of the solution?

17.2 BUFFERED SOLUTIONS

Solutions such as those discussed in Section 17.1, which contain a weak conjugate acid–base pair, can resist drastic changes in pH upon the addition of small amounts of strong acid or strong base. These solutions are called **buffered solutions** (or merely **buffers**). Human blood, for example, is a complex aqueous mixture with a pH buffered at about 7.4 (see the "Chemistry and Life" box near the end of this section). Much of the chemical behavior of seawater is determined by its pH, buffered at about 8.1 to 8.3 near the surface. Buffered solutions find many important applications in the laboratory and in medicine (Figure 17.1▶).

Composition and Action of Buffered Solutions

A buffer resists changes in pH because it contains both an acid to neutralize OH^- ions and a base to neutralize H^+ ions. The acid and base that make up the buffer, however, must not consume each other through a neutralization reaction. These requirements are fulfilled by a weak acid–base conjugate pair such as CH_3COOH–CH_3COO^- or NH_4^+–NH_3. Thus, buffers are often prepared by mixing a weak acid or a weak base with a salt of that acid or base. The CH_3COOH–CH_3COO^- buffer can be prepared, for example, by adding CH_3COONa to a solution of CH_3COOH. The NH_4^+–NH_3 buffer can be prepared by adding NH_4Cl to a solution of NH_3. By choosing appropriate components and adjusting their relative concentrations, we can buffer a solution at virtually any pH.

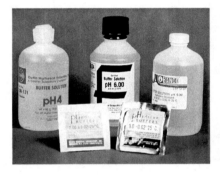

▲ Figure 17.1 **Buffer solutions.** Prepackaged buffer solutions and ingredients for making up buffer solutions of predetermined pH can be purchased.

Which of the following conjugate acid–base pairs will *not* function as a buffer: C_2H_5COOH and $C_2H_5COO^-$; HCO_3^- and CO_3^{2-}; HNO_3 and NO_3^-? Explain.

To understand better how a buffer works, let's consider a buffer composed of a weak acid (HX) and one of its salts (MX, where M^+ could be Na^+, K^+, or another cation). The acid-dissociation equilibrium in this buffered solution involves both the acid and its conjugate base:

$$HX(aq) \rightleftharpoons H^+(aq) + X^-(aq) \qquad [17.3]$$

The corresponding acid-dissociation-constant expression is

$$K_a = \frac{[H^+][X^-]}{[HX]} \qquad [17.4]$$

Solving this expression for $[H^+]$, we have

$$[H^+] = K_a \frac{[HX]}{[X^-]} \qquad [17.5]$$

We see from this expression that $[H^+]$, and thus the pH, is determined by two factors: the value of K_a for the weak-acid component of the buffer and the ratio of the concentrations of the conjugate acid–base pair, $[HX]/[X^-]$.

▶ Figure 17.2 **Buffer action.** When a small portion of OH⁻ is added to a buffer consisting of a mixture of the weak acid HF and its conjugate base (left), the OH⁻ reacts with the HF, decreasing [HF] and increasing [F⁻] in the buffer. Conversely, when a small portion of H⁺ is added to the buffer (right), the H⁺ reacts with the F⁻, decreasing [F⁻] and increasing [HF] in the buffer. Because pH depends on the ratio of F⁻ to HF, the resulting pH change is small.

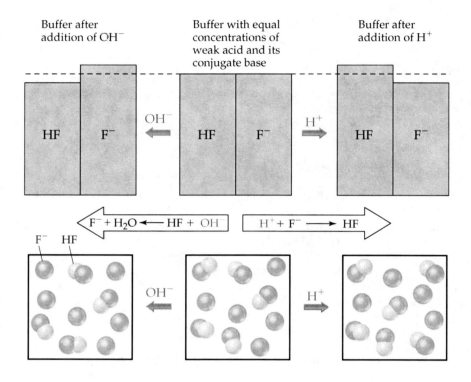

If OH⁻ ions are added to the buffered solution, they react with the acid component of the buffer to produce water and X⁻:

$$\underset{\text{added base}}{\text{OH}^-(aq)} + \underset{\text{weak acid in buffer}}{\text{HX}(aq)} \longrightarrow \text{H}_2\text{O}(l) + \text{X}^-(aq) \qquad [17.6]$$

This reaction causes [HX] to decrease and [X⁻] to increase. As long as the amounts of HX and X⁻ in the buffer are large compared to the amount of OH⁻ added, however, the ratio [HX]/[X⁻] does not change much, and thus the change in pH is small. A specific example of such a buffer, the HF/F⁻ buffer, is shown in Figure 17.2▲.

If H⁺ ions are added, they react with the base component of the buffer:

$$\underset{\text{added base}}{\text{H}^+(aq)} + \underset{\text{weak acid in buffer}}{\text{X}^-(aq)} \longrightarrow \text{HX}(aq) \qquad [17.7]$$

This reaction can also be represented using H₃O⁺:

$$\text{H}_3\text{O}^+(aq) + \text{X}^-(aq) \longrightarrow \text{HX}(aq) + \text{H}_2\text{O}(l)$$

Using either equation, we see that the reaction causes [X⁻] to decrease and [HX] to increase. As long as the change in the ratio [HX]/[X⁻] is small, the change in pH will be small.

Figure 17.2 shows a buffer consisting of equal concentrations of hydrofluoric acid and fluoride ion (center). The addition of OH⁻ (left) reduces [HF] and increases [F⁻]. The addition of H⁺ (right) reduces [F⁻] and increases [HF].

 GIVE IT SOME THOUGHT

(a) What happens when NaOH is added to a buffer composed of CH₃COOH and CH₃COO⁻? **(b)** What happens when HCl is added to this buffer?

Calculating the pH of a Buffer

Because conjugate acid–base pairs share a common ion, we can use the same procedures to calculate the pH of a buffer that we used to treat the common-ion effect (see Sample Exercise 17.1). However, we can sometimes take an alternate approach that is based on an equation derived from Equation 17.5.

Taking the negative log of both sides of Equation 17.5, we have

$$-\log[H^+] = -\log\left(K_a\frac{[HX]}{[X^-]}\right) = -\log K_a - \log\frac{[HX]}{[X^-]}$$

Because $-\log[H^+] = pH$ and $-\log K_a = pK_a$, we have

$$pH = pK_a - \log\frac{[HX]}{[X^-]} = pK_a + \log\frac{[X^-]}{[HX]} \qquad [17.8]$$

In general,

$$pH = pK_a + \log\frac{[base]}{[acid]} \qquad [17.9]$$

where [acid] and [base] refer to the equilibrium concentrations of *the conjugate acid–base pair*. Note that when [base] = [acid], $pH = pK_a$.

Equation 17.9 is known as the **Henderson–Hasselbalch equation.** Biologists, biochemists, and others who work frequently with buffers often use this equation to calculate the pH of buffers. In doing equilibrium calculations, we have seen that we can normally neglect the amounts of the acid and base of the buffer that ionize. Therefore, we can usually use the starting concentrations of the acid and base components of the buffer directly in Equation 17.9.

▄▄ SAMPLE EXERCISE 17.3 | Calculating the pH of a Buffer

What is the pH of a buffer that is 0.12 M in lactic acid [$CH_3CH(OH)COOH$, or $HC_3H_5O_3$] and 0.10 M in sodium lactate [$CH_3CH(OH)COONa$ or $NaC_3H_5O_3$]? For lactic acid, $K_a = 1.4 \times 10^{-4}$.

SOLUTION

Analyze: We are asked to calculate the pH of a buffer containing lactic acid $HC_3H_5O_3$ and its conjugate base, the lactate ion $(C_3H_5O_3^-)$.

Plan: We will first determine the pH using the method described in Section 17.1. Because $HC_3H_5O_3$ is a weak electrolyte and $NaC_3H_5O_3$ is a strong electrolyte, the major species in solution are $HC_3H_5O_3$, Na^+, and $C_3H_5O_3^-$. The Na^+ ion is a spectator ion. The $HC_3H_5O_3$–$C_3H_5O_3^-$ conjugate acid–base pair determines $[H^+]$ and thus pH; $[H^+]$ can be determined using the acid-dissociation equilibrium of lactic acid.

Solve: The initial and equilibrium concentrations of the species involved in this equilibrium are

	$HC_3H_5O_3(aq)$ $\rightleftharpoons$	$H^+(aq)$ +	$C_3H_5O_3^-(aq)$
Initial	0.12 M	0	0.10 M
Change	$-x\ M$	$+x\ M$	$+x\ M$
Equilibrium	$(0.12 - x)\ M$	$x\ M$	$(0.10 + x)\ M$

The equilibrium concentrations are governed by the equilibrium expression:

$$K_a = 1.4 \times 10^{-4} = \frac{[H^+][C_3H_5O_3]}{[HC_3H_5O_3]} = \frac{x(0.10 + x)}{(0.12 - x)}$$

Because K_a is small and a common ion is present, we expect x to be small relative to either 0.12 or 0.10 M. Thus, our equation can be simplified to give

$$K_a = 1.4 \times 10^{-4} = \frac{x(0.10)}{0.12}$$

Solving for x gives a value that justifies our approximation:

$$[H^+] = x = \left(\frac{0.12}{0.10}\right)(1.4 \times 10^{-4}) = 1.7 \times 10^{-4}\ M$$

$$pH = -\log(1.7 \times 10^{-4}) = 3.77$$

Alternatively, we could have used the Henderson–Hasselbalch equation to calculate pH directly:

$$pH = pK_a + \log\left(\frac{[base]}{[acid]}\right) = 3.85 + \log\left(\frac{0.10}{0.12}\right)$$

$$= 3.85 + (-0.08) = 3.77$$

▄▄ PRACTICE EXERCISE

Calculate the pH of a buffer composed of 0.12 M benzoic acid and 0.20 M sodium benzoate. (Refer to Appendix D.)
Answer: 4.42

■ SAMPLE EXERCISE 17.4 | Preparing a Buffer

How many moles of NH_4Cl must be added to 2.0 L of 0.10 M NH_3 to form a buffer whose pH is 9.00? (Assume that the addition of NH_4Cl does not change the volume of the solution.)

SOLUTION

Analyze: Here we are asked to determine the amount of NH_4^+ ion required to prepare a buffer of a specific pH.

Plan: The major species in the solution will be NH_4^+, Cl^-, and NH_3. Of these, the Cl^- ion is a spectator (it is the conjugate base of a strong acid). Thus, the NH_4^+–NH_3 conjugate acid–base pair will determine the pH of the buffer solution. The equilibrium relationship between NH_4^+ and NH_3 is given by the base-dissociation constant for NH_3:

$$NH_3(aq) + H_2O(l) \rightleftharpoons NH_4^+(aq) + OH^-(aq) \qquad K_b = \frac{[NH_4^+][OH^-]}{[NH_3]} = 1.8 \times 10^{-5}$$

The key to this exercise is to use this K_b expression to calculate $[NH_4^+]$.

Solve: We obtain $[OH^-]$ from the given pH:

$$pOH = 14.00 - pH = 14.00 - 9.00 = 5.00$$

and so

$$[OH^-] = 1.0 \times 10^{-5} \, M$$

Because K_b is small and the common ion NH_4^+ is present, the equilibrium concentration of NH_3 will essentially equal its initial concentration:

$$[NH_3] = 0.10 \, M$$

We now use the expression for K_b to calculate $[NH_4^+]$:

$$[NH_4^+] = K_b \frac{[NH_3]}{[OH^-]} = (1.8 \times 10^{-5}) \frac{(0.10 \, M)}{(1.0 \times 10^{-5} \, M)} = 0.18 \, M$$

Thus, for the solution to have pH = 9.00, $[NH_4^+]$ must equal 0.18 M. The number of moles of NH_4Cl needed to produce this concentration is given by the product of the volume of the solution and its molarity:

$$(2.0 \, L)(0.18 \, mol \, NH_4Cl/L) = 0.36 \, mol \, NH_4Cl$$

Comment: Because NH_4^+ and NH_3 are a conjugate acid–base pair, we could use the Henderson–Hasselbalch equation (Equation 17.9) to solve this problem. To do so requires first using Equation 16.41 to calculate pK_a for NH_4^+ from the value of pK_b for NH_3. We suggest you try this approach to convince yourself that you can use the Henderson–Hasselbalch equation for buffers for which you are given K_b for the conjugate base rather than K_a for the conjugate acid.

■ PRACTICE EXERCISE

Calculate the concentration of sodium benzoate that must be present in a 0.20 M solution of benzoic acid (C_6H_5COOH) to produce a pH of 4.00.
Answer: 0.13 M

Buffer Capacity and pH Range

Two important characteristics of a buffer are its capacity and its effective pH range. **Buffer capacity** is the amount of acid or base the buffer can neutralize before the pH begins to change to an appreciable degree. The buffer capacity depends on the amount of acid and base from which the buffer is made. The pH of the buffer depends on the K_a for the acid and on the relative concentrations of the acid and base that comprise the buffer. According to Equation 17.5, for example, $[H^+]$ for a 1-L solution that is 1 M in CH_3COOH and 1 M in CH_3COONa will be the same as for a 1-L solution that is 0.1 M in CH_3COOH and 0.1 M in CH_3COONa. The first solution has a greater buffering capacity, however, because it contains more CH_3COOH and CH_3COO^-. The greater the amounts of the conjugate acid–base pair, the more resistant is the ratio of their concentrations, and hence the pH, is to change.

The **pH range** of any buffer is the pH range over which the buffer acts effectively. Buffers most effectively resist a change in pH in *either* direction when the concentrations of weak acid and conjugate base are about the same. From Equation 17.9 we see that when the concentrations of weak acid and conjugate base are equal, pH = pK_a. This relationship gives the optimal pH of any buffer. Thus, we usually try to select a buffer whose acid form has a pK_a close to the desired pH. In practice, we find that if the concentration of one component of the buffer is more than 10 times the concentration of the other component, the buffering action is poor. Because log 10 = 1, *buffers usually have a usable range within ±1 pH unit of* pK_a (that is, a range of pH = pK_a ± 1).

GIVE IT SOME THOUGHT

What is the optimal pH buffered by a solution containing CH_3COOH and CH_3COONa? (K_a for CH_3COOH is 1.8×10^{-5}.)

Addition of Strong Acids or Bases to Buffers

Let's now consider in a more quantitative way the response of a buffered solution to the addition of a strong acid or base. In solving these problems, it is important to understand that reactions between strong acids and weak bases proceed essentially to completion, as do those between strong bases and weak acids. Thus, as long as we do not exceed the buffering capacity of the buffer, we can assume that the strong acid or strong base is completely consumed by reaction with the buffer.

Consider a buffer that contains a weak acid HX and its conjugate base X^-. When a strong acid is added to this buffer, the added H^+ is consumed by X^- to produce HX; thus, [HX] increases and [X^-] decreases. (See Equation 17.7.) When a strong base is added to the buffer, the added OH^- is consumed by HX to produce X^-; in this case [HX] decreases and [X^-] increases. (See Equation 17.6.) These two situations are summarized in Figure 17.2.

To calculate how the pH of the buffer responds to the addition of a strong acid or a strong base, we follow the strategy outlined in Figure 17.3 ▼:

1. Consider the acid–base neutralization reaction, and determine its effect on [HX] and [X^-]. This step of the procedure is a *stoichiometry calculation*.
2. Use K_a and the new concentrations of [HX] and [X^-] from step 1 to calculate [H^+]. This second step of the procedure is a standard *equilibrium calculation* and is most easily done using the Henderson–Hasselbalch equation.

The complete procedure is illustrated in Sample Exercise 17.5.

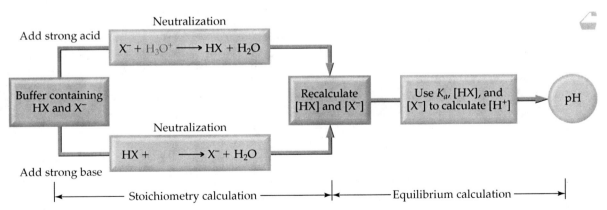

▲ Figure 17.3 **Calculation of the pH of a buffer after the addition of acid or base.** First consider how the neutralization reaction between the added strong acid or strong base and the buffer affects the composition of the buffer (stoichiometry calculation). Then calculate the pH of the remaining buffer (equilibrium calculation). As long as the amount of added acid or base does not exceed the buffer capacity, the Henderson–Hasselbalch equation, Equation 17.9, can be used for the equilibrium calculation.

▪▪ SAMPLE EXERCISE 17.5 | Calculating pH Changes in Buffers

A buffer is made by adding 0.300 mol CH_3COOH and 0.300 mol CH_3COONa to enough water to make 1.00 L of solution. The pH of the buffer is 4.74 (Sample Exercise 17.1). **(a)** Calculate the pH of this solution after 0.020 mol of NaOH is added. **(b)** For comparison, calculate the pH that would result if 0.020 mol of NaOH were added to 1.00 L of pure water (neglect any volume changes).

SOLUTION

Analyze: We are asked to determine the pH of a buffer after addition of a small amount of strong base and to compare the pH change to the pH that would result if we were to add the same amount of strong base to pure water.

Plan: (a) Solving this problem involves the two steps outlined in Figure 17.3. Thus, we must first do a stoichiometry calculation to determine how the added OH^- reacts with the buffer and affects its composition. Then we can use the resultant composition of the buffer and either the Henderson–Hasselbalch equation or the equilibrium-constant expression for the buffer to determine the pH.

Solve: *Stoichiometry Calculation:* The OH^- provided by NaOH reacts with CH_3COOH, the weak acid component of the buffer. Prior to this neutralization reaction, there are 0.300 mol each of CH_3COOH and CH_3COO^-. Neutralizing the 0.020 mol OH^- requires 0.020 mol of CH_3COOH. Consequently, the amount of CH_3COOH *decreases* by 0.020 mol, and the amount of the product of the neutralization, CH_3COO^-, *increases* by 0.020 mol. We can create a table to see how the composition of the buffer changes as a result of its reaction with OH^-:

$$CH_3COOH(aq) + OH^-(aq) \longrightarrow H_2O(l) + CH_3COO^-(aq)$$

	CH_3COOH	OH^-		CH_3COO^-
Buffer before addition	0.300 mol	0	—	0.300 mol
Addition	—	0.020 mol		—
Buffer after addition	0.280 mol	0	—	0.320 mol

Equilibrium Calculation: We now turn our attention to the equilibrium that will determine the pH of the buffer, namely the ionization of acetic acid.

$$CH_3COOH(aq) \rightleftharpoons H^+(aq) + CH_3COO^-(aq)$$

Using the quantities of CH_3COOH and CH_3COO^- remaining in the buffer, we can determine the pH using the Henderson–Hasselbalch equation.

$$pH = 4.74 + \log \frac{0.320 \text{ mol}/1.00 \text{ L}}{0.280 \text{ mol}/1.00 \text{ L}} = 4.80$$

Comment Notice that we could have used mole amounts in place of concentrations in the Henderson–Hasselbalch equation and gotten the same result. The volumes of the acid and base are equal and cancel.

If 0.020 mol of H^+ was added to the buffer, we would proceed in a similar way to calculate the resulting pH of the buffer. In this case the pH decreases by 0.06 units, giving pH = 4.68, as shown in the figure in the margin.

(b) To determine the pH of a solution made by adding 0.020 mol of NaOH to 1.00 L of pure water, we can first determine pOH using Equation 16.18 and subtracting from 14.

$$pH = 14 - (-\log 0.020) = 12.30$$

Note that although the small amount of NaOH changes the pH of water significantly, the pH of the buffer changes very little.

▪▪ PRACTICE EXERCISE

Determine **(a)** the pH of the original buffer described in Sample Exercise 17.5 after the addition of 0.020 mol HCl and **(b)** the pH of the solution that would result from the addition of 0.020 mol HCl to 1.00 L of pure water.
Answers: **(a)** 4.68, **(b)** 1.70

0.280 M
CH_3COOH
0.320 M
CH_3COONa

pH = 4.80

add 0.020 mol OH^-

Buffer

0.300 M
CH_3COOH
0.300 M
CH_3COONa

pH = 4.74

add 0.020 mol H^+

0.320 M
CH_3COOH
0.280 M
CH_3COONa

pH = 4.68

Chemistry and Life   BLOOD AS A BUFFERED SOLUTION

Many of the chemical reactions that occur in living systems are extremely sensitive to pH. Many of the enzymes that catalyze important biochemical reactions, for example, are effective only within a narrow pH range. For this reason the human body maintains a remarkably intricate system of buffers, both within tissue cells and in the fluids that transport cells. Blood, the fluid that transports oxygen to all parts of the body (Figure 17.4 ▶), is one of the most prominent examples of the importance of buffers in living beings.

Human blood is slightly basic with a normal pH of 7.35 to 7.45. Any deviation from this normal pH range can have extremely disruptive effects on the stability of cell membranes, the structures of proteins, and the activities of enzymes. Death may result if the blood pH falls below 6.8 or rises above 7.8. When the pH falls below 7.35, the condition is called *acidosis*; when it rises above 7.45, the condition is called *alkalosis*. Acidosis is the more common tendency because ordinary metabolism generates several acids within the body.

The major buffer system that is used to control the pH of blood is the *carbonic acid–bicarbonate buffer system*. Carbonic acid (H_2CO_3) and bicarbonate ion (HCO_3^-) are a conjugate acid–base pair. In addition, carbonic acid can decompose into carbon dioxide gas and water. The important equilibria in this buffer system are

$$H^+(aq) + HCO_3^-(aq) \rightleftharpoons H_2CO_3(aq) \rightleftharpoons H_2O(l) + CO_2(g)$$
[17.10]

Several aspects of these equilibria are notable. First, although carbonic acid is a diprotic acid, the carbonate ion (CO_3^{2-}) is unimportant in this system. Second, one of the components of this equilibrium, CO_2, is a gas, which provides a mechanism for the body to adjust the equilibria. Removal of CO_2 via exhalation shifts the equilibria to the right, consuming H^+ ions. Third, the buffer system in blood operates at a pH of 7.4, which is fairly far removed from the pK_{a1} value of H_2CO_3 (6.1 at physiological temperatures). For the buffer to have a pH of 7.4, the ratio [base]/[acid] must have a value of about 20. In normal blood plasma the concentrations of HCO_3^- and H_2CO_3 are about 0.024 M and 0.0012 M, respectively. Consequently, the buffer has a high capacity to neutralize additional acid, but only a low capacity to neutralize additional base.

The principal organs that regulate the pH of the carbonic acid–bicarbonate buffer system are the lungs and kidneys. Some of the receptors in the brain are sensitive to the concentrations of H^+ and CO_2 in bodily fluids. When the concentration of CO_2 rises, the equilibria in Equation 17.10 shift to the left, which leads to the formation of more H^+. The receptors trigger a reflex to breathe faster and deeper, increasing the rate of elimination of CO_2 from the lungs and shifting the equilibria back to the right. The kidneys absorb or release H^+ and HCO_3^-; much of the excess acid leaves the body in urine, which normally has a pH of 5.0 to 7.0.

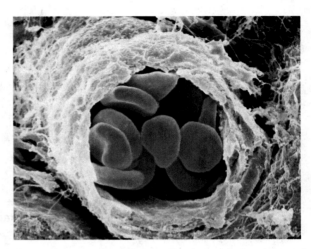

▲ Figure 17.4 **Red blood cells.** A scanning electromicrograph of a group of red blood cells traveling through a small branch of an artery. Blood is a buffered solution whose pH is maintained between 7.35 and 7.45.

The regulation of the pH of blood plasma relates directly to the effective transport of O_2 to bodily tissues. The protein hemoglobin, which is found in red blood cells, carries oxygen. Hemoglobin (Hb) reversibly binds both H^+ and O_2. These two substances compete for the Hb, which can be represented approximately by the following equilibrium:

$$HbH^+ + O_2 \rightleftharpoons HbO_2 + H^+$$
[17.11]

Oxygen enters the blood through the lungs, where it passes into the red blood cells and binds to Hb. When the blood reaches tissue in which the concentration of O_2 is low, the equilibrium in Equation 17.11 shifts to the left and O_2 is released. An increase in H^+ ion concentration (decrease in blood pH) also shifts this equilibrium to the left, as does increasing temperature.

During periods of strenuous exertion, three factors work together to ensure the delivery of O_2 to active tissues: (1) As O_2 is consumed, the equilibrium in Equation 17.11 shifts to the left according to Le Châtelier's principle. (2) Exertion raises the temperature of the body, also shifting the equilibrium to the left. (3) Large amounts of CO_2 are produced by metabolism, which shifts the equilibrium in Equation 17.10 to the left, thus decreasing the pH. Other acids, such as lactic acid, are also produced during strenuous exertion as tissues become starved for oxygen. The decrease in pH shifts the hemoglobin equilibrium to the left, delivering more O_2. In addition, the decrease in pH stimulates an increase in the rate of breathing, which furnishes more O_2 and eliminates CO_2. Without this elaborate arrangement, the O_2 in tissues would be rapidly depleted, making further activity impossible.
Related Exercises: 17.29 and 17.90

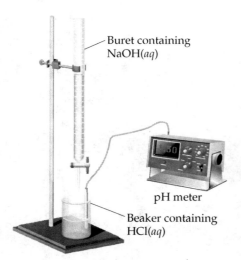

▲ Figure 17.5 **Measuring pH during a titration.** A typical setup for using a pH meter to measure data for a titration curve. In this case a standard solution of NaOH (the titrant) is added by buret to a solution of HCl. The HCl solution is stirred during the titration to ensure uniform composition.

17.3 ACID–BASE TITRATIONS

In Section 4.6 we briefly described *titrations*. In an acid–base titration, a solution containing a known concentration of base is slowly added to an acid (or the acid is added to the base). Acid–base indicators can be used to signal the *equivalence point* of a titration (the point at which stoichiometrically equivalent quantities of acid and base have been brought together). Alternatively, a pH meter can be used to monitor the progress of the reaction producing a **pH titration curve**, a graph of the pH as a function of the volume of the added titrant. The shape of the titration curve makes it possible to determine the equivalence point in the titration. The titration curve can also be used to select suitable indicators and to determine the K_a of the weak acid or the K_b of the weak base being titrated.

A typical apparatus for measuring pH during a titration is illustrated in Figure 17.5 ◄. The titrant is added to the solution from a buret, and the pH is continually monitored using a pH meter. To understand why titration curves have certain characteristic shapes, we will examine the curves for three kinds of titrations: (1) strong acid–strong base, (2) weak acid–strong base, and (3) polyprotic acid–strong base. We will also briefly consider how these curves relate to those involving weak bases.

GIVE IT SOME THOUGHT

For the setup shown in Figure 17.5, will pH increase or decrease as titrant is added?

Strong Acid–Strong Base Titrations

The titration curve produced when a strong base is added to a strong acid has the general shape shown in Figure 17.6 ►. This curve depicts the pH change that occurs as 0.100 M NaOH is added to 50.0 mL of 0.100 M HCl. The pH can be calculated at various stages of the titration. To help understand these calculations, we can divide the curve into four regions:

1. *The initial pH (initial acid):* The pH of the solution before the addition of any base is determined by the initial concentration of the strong acid. For a solution of 0.100 M HCl, $[H^+] = 0.100$ M, and hence pH $= -\log(0.100) = 1.000$. Thus, the initial pH is low.

2. *Between the initial pH and the equivalence point (remaining acid):* As NaOH is added, the pH increases slowly at first and then rapidly in the vicinity of the equivalence point. The pH of the solution before the equivalence point is determined by the concentration of acid that has not yet been neutralized. This calculation is illustrated in Sample Exercise 17.6(a).

3. *The equivalence point:* At the equivalence point an equal number of moles of the NaOH and HCl have reacted, leaving only a solution of their salt, NaCl. The pH of the solution is 7.00 because the cation of a strong base (in this case Na$^+$) and the anion of a strong acid (in this case Cl$^-$) do not hydrolyze and therefore have no appreciable effect on pH. (Section 16.9)

4. *After the equivalence point (excess base):* The pH of the solution after the equivalence point is determined by the concentration of the excess NaOH in the solution. This calculation is illustrated in Sample Exercise 17.6(b).

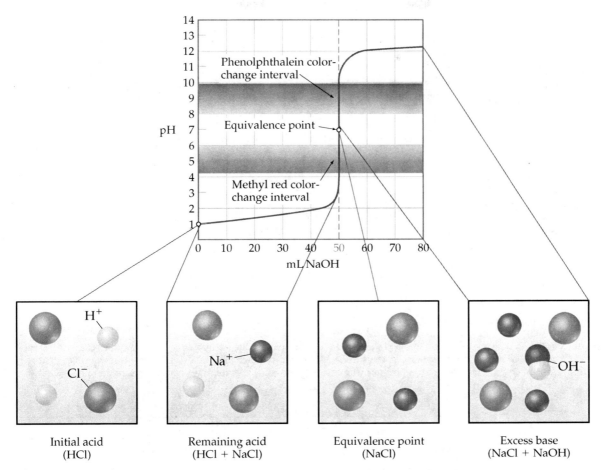

Initial acid
(HCl)

Remaining acid
(HCl + NaCl)

Equivalence point
(NaCl)

Excess base
(NaCl + NaOH)

▲ Figure 17.6 **Adding a strong base to a strong acid.** The pH curve for titration of 50.0 mL of a 0.100 M solution of a strong acid with a 0.100 M solution of a strong base. In this case the acid is HCl and the base is NaOH. The pH starts out at a low value characteristic of the acid and then increases as base is added, rising rapidly at the equivalence point. Both phenolphthalein and methyl red change color at the equivalence point. (For clarity, water molecules have been omitted from the molecular art.)

■■■ **SAMPLE EXERCISE 17.6** | Calculating pH for a Strong Acid–Strong Base Titration

Calculate the pH when the following quantities of 0.100 M NaOH solution have been added to 50.0 mL of 0.100 M HCl solution: **(a)** 49.0 mL, **(b)** 51.0 mL.

SOLUTION

Analyze: We are asked to calculate the pH at two points in the titration of a strong acid with a strong base. The first point is just before the equivalence point, so we expect the pH to be determined by the small amount of strong acid that has not yet been neutralized. The second point is just after the equivalence point, so we expect this pH to be determined by the small amount of excess strong base.

Plan: (a) As the NaOH solution is added to the HCl solution, $H^+(aq)$ reacts with $OH^-(aq)$ to form H_2O. Both Na^+ and Cl^- are spectator ions, having negligible effect on the pH. To determine the pH of the solution, we must first determine how many moles of H^+ were originally present and how many moles of OH^- were added. We can then calculate how many moles of each ion remain after the neutralization reaction. To calculate $[H^+]$, and hence pH, we must also remember that the volume of the solution increases as we add titrant, thus diluting the concentration of all solutes present.

Solve: The number of moles of H^+ in the original HCl solution is given by the product of the volume of the solution (50.0 mL = 0.0500 L) and its molarity (0.100 M):

$$(0.0500 \text{ L soln})\left(\frac{0.100 \text{ mol } H^+}{1 \text{ L soln}}\right) = 5.00 \times 10^{-3} \text{ mol } H^+$$

Likewise, the number of moles of OH^- in 49.0 mL of 0.100 M NaOH is

$$(0.0490 \text{ L soln})\left(\frac{0.100 \text{ mol } OH^-}{1 \text{ L soln}}\right) = 4.90 \times 10^{-3} \text{ mol } OH^-$$

Because we have not yet reached the equivalence point, there are more moles of H^+ present than OH^-. Each mole of OH^- will react with one mole of H^+. Using the convention introduced in Sample Exercise 17.5,

	$H^+(aq)$	+	$OH^-(aq)$	$\longrightarrow$	$H_2O(l)$
Before addition	5.00×10^{-3} mol		0		—
Addition			4.90×10^{-3} mol		
After addition	0.10×10^{-3} mol		0		—

During the course of the titration, the volume of the reaction mixture increases as the NaOH solution is added to the HCl solution. Thus, at this point in the titration, the total volume of the solutions is

$$50.0 \text{ mL} + 49.0 \text{ mL} = 99.0 \text{ mL} = 0.0990 \text{ L}$$

(We assume that the total volume is the sum of the volumes of the acid and base solutions.) Thus, the concentration of $H^+(aq)$ is

$$[H^+] = \frac{\text{moles } H^+(aq)}{\text{liters soln}} = \frac{0.10 \times 10^{-3} \text{ mol}}{0.09900 \text{ L}} = 1.0 \times 10^{-3} \, M$$

The corresponding pH equals

$$-\log(1.0 \times 10^{-3}) = 3.00$$

Plan: (b) We proceed in the same way as we did in part (a), except we are now past the equivalence point and have more OH^- in the solution than H^+. As before, the initial number of moles of each reactant is determined from their volumes and concentrations. The reactant present in smaller stoichiometric amount (the limiting reactant) is consumed completely, leaving an excess of hydroxide ion.

Solve:

	$H^+(aq)$	+	$OH^-(aq)$	$\longrightarrow$	$H_2O(l)$
Before addition	5.00×10^{-3} mol		0		—
Addition			5.10×10^{-3} mol		
After addition	0		0.10×10^{-3} mol		—

In this case the total volume of the solution is

$$50.0 \text{ mL} + 51.0 \text{ mL} = 101.0 \text{ mL} = 0.1010 \text{ L}$$

Hence, the concentration of $OH^-(aq)$ in the solution is

$$[OH^-] = \frac{\text{moles } OH^-(aq)}{\text{liters soln}} = \frac{0.10 \times 10^{-3} \text{ mol}}{0.1010 \text{ L}} = 1.0 \times 10^{-3} \, M$$

Thus, the pOH of the solution equals

$$pOH = -\log(1.0 \times 10^{-3}) = 3.00$$

and the pH equals

$$pH = 14.00 - pOH = 14.00 - 3.00 = 11.00$$

■ **PRACTICE EXERCISE**

Calculate the pH when the following quantities of 0.100 M HNO_3 have been added to 25.0 mL of 0.100 M KOH solution:
(a) 24.9 mL, **(b)** 25.1 mL.
Answers: **(a)** 10.30, **(b)** 3.70

Optimally, an indicator would change color at the equivalence point in a titration. In practice, however, that is unnecessary. The pH changes very rapidly near the equivalence point, and in this region merely a drop of titrant can change the pH by several units. Thus, an indicator beginning and ending its color change anywhere on this rapid-rise portion of the titration curve will give a sufficiently accurate measure of the volume of titrant needed to reach the equivalence point. The point in a titration where the indicator changes color is called the *end point* to distinguish it from the actual equivalence point that it closely approximates.

(a)   (b)

◄ Figure 17.7 **Methyl red indicator.**
Change in appearance of a solution
containing methyl red indicator in the
pH range 4.2 to 6.3. The characteristic
acidic color is shown in (a), and the
characteristic basic color in (b).

In Figure 17.6 we see that the pH changes very rapidly from about 4 to about 10 near the equivalence point. Consequently, an indicator for this strong acid–strong base titration can change color anywhere in this range. Most strong acid–strong base titrations are carried out using phenolphthalein as an indicator (Figure 4.20) because it dramatically changes color in this range. From Figure 16.7, we see that phenolphthalein changes color from pH 8.3 to 10.0. Several other indicators would also be satisfactory, including methyl red, which changes color from pH 4.2 to 6.0 (Figure 17.7 ▲).

Titration of a solution of a strong base with a solution of a strong acid would yield an analogous curve of pH versus added acid. In this case, however, the pH would be high at the outset of the titration and low at its completion, as shown in Figure 17.8 ▶.

GIVE IT SOME THOUGHT

What is the pH at the equivalence point when 0.10 M HNO_3 is added to a solution containing 0.30 g of KOH?

Weak Acid–Strong Base Titrations

The curve for the titration of a weak acid by a strong base is very similar in shape to that for the titration of a strong acid by a strong base. Consider, for example, the titration curve for the titration of 50.0 mL of 0.100 M acetic acid (CH_3COOH) with 0.100 M NaOH shown in Figure 17.9 ▼. We can calculate the pH at points along this curve, using principles we have discussed earlier. As in the case of the titration of a strong acid by a strong base, we can divide the curve into four regions:

1. *The initial pH (initial acid):* We use K_a of the acid to calculate this pH, as shown in Section 16.6. The calculated pH of 0.100 M CH_3COOH is 2.89.

2. *Between the initial pH and the equivalence point (buffer mixture):* Prior to reaching the equivalence point, the acid is being neutralized, and its conjugate base is being formed:

$$CH_3COOH(aq) + OH^-(aq) \longrightarrow CH_3COO^-(aq) + H_2O(l) \qquad [17.12]$$

Thus, the solution contains a mixture of CH_3COOH and CH_3COO^-.

The approach we take in calculating the pH in this region of the titration curve involves two main steps. First, we consider the neutralization reaction between CH_3COOH and OH^- to determine the concentrations of

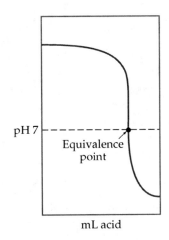

pH 7 ┈┈┈┈┈┈┈┈

Equivalence point

mL acid

▲ Figure 17.8 **Adding a strong acid to a strong base.** The shape of a pH curve for titration of a strong base with a strong acid. The pH starts out at a high value characteristic of the base and then decreases as acid is added, dropping rapidly at the equivalence point.

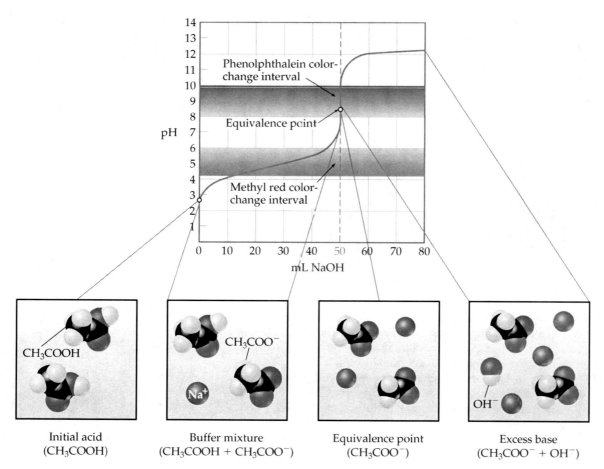

▲ Figure 17.9 **Adding a strong base to a weak acid.** The curve shows the variation in pH as 0.100 *M* NaOH solution is added to 50.0 mL of 0.100 *M* acetic acid solution. Phenolphthalein changes color at the equivalence point, but methyl red does not. (For clarity, water molecules have been omitted from the molecular art.)

▼ Figure 17.10 **Procedure for calculating the pH when a weak acid is partially neutralized by a strong base.** First consider the effect of the neutralization reaction (stoichiometry calculation). Then determine the pH of the resultant buffer mixture (equilibrium calculation). An analogous procedure can be used for the addition of strong acid to a weak base.

CH_3COOH and CH_3COO^- in the solution. Next, we calculate the pH of this buffer pair using procedures developed in Sections 17.1 and 17.2. The general procedure is diagrammed in Figure 17.10▼ and illustrated in Sample Exercise 17.7.

3. *The equivalence point:* The equivalence point is reached after adding 50.0 mL of 0.100 *M* NaOH to the 50.0 mL of 0.100 *M* CH_3COOH. At this point the 5.00×10^{-3} mol of NaOH completely reacts with the 5.00×10^{-3} mol of CH_3COOH to form 5.00×10^{-3} mol of their salt, CH_3COONa. The Na^+ ion of this salt has no significant effect on the pH. The CH_3COO^- ion, however, is a weak base, and the pH at the equivalence point is therefore greater than 7. Indeed, the pH at the equivalence point is always above 7 in a weak acid–strong base titration because the anion of the salt formed is a weak base. The procedure for calculating the pH of the solution of a weak base is described in Section 16.7 and is shown in Sample Exercise 17.8.

4. *After the equivalence point (excess base):* In this region of the titration curve, $[OH^-]$ from the reaction of CH_3COO^- with water is negligible compared to $[OH^-]$ from the excess NaOH. Thus, the pH is determined by the concentration of OH^- from the excess NaOH. The method for calculating pH

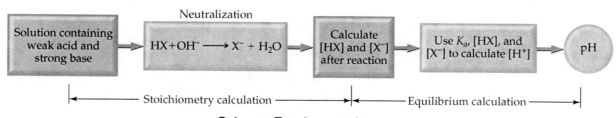

in this region is therefore like that for the strong acid–strong base titration illustrated in Sample Exercise 17.6(b). Thus, the addition of 51.0 mL of 0.100 M NaOH to 50.0 mL of either 0.100 M HCl or 0.100 M CH₃COOH yields the same pH, 11.00. Notice in Figures 17.6 and 17.9 that the titration curves for the titrations of both the strong acid and the weak acid are the same after the equivalence point.

■ SAMPLE EXERCISE 17.7 | Calculating pH for a Weak Acid–Strong Base Titration

Calculate the pH of the solution formed when 45.0 mL of 0.100 M NaOH is added to 50.0 mL of 0.100 M CH₃COOH ($K_a = 1.8 \times 10^{-5}$).

SOLUTION

Analyze: We are asked to calculate the pH before the equivalence point of the titration of a weak acid with a strong base.

Plan: We first must determine the number of moles of CH₃COOH and CH₃COO⁻ that are present after the neutralization reaction. We then calculate pH using K_a together with [CH₃COOH] and [CH₃COO⁻].

Solve: *Stoichiometry Calculation:* The product of the volume and concentration of each solution gives the number of moles of each reactant present before the neutralization:

$$(0.0500 \text{ L soln})\left(\frac{0.100 \text{ mol CH}_3\text{COOH}}{1 \text{ L soln}}\right) = 5.00 \times 10^{-3} \text{ mol CH}_3\text{COOH}$$

$$(0.0450 \text{ L soln})\left(\frac{0.100 \text{ mol NaOH}}{1 \text{ L soln}}\right) = 4.50 \times 10^{-3} \text{ mol NaOH}$$

The 4.50×10^{-3} mol of NaOH consumes 4.50×10^{-3} mol of CH₃COOH:

	CH₃COOH(aq) +	OH⁻(aq) ⟶	CH₃COO⁻(aq) +	H₂O(l)
Before addition	5.00×10^{-3} mol	0	0	—
Addition		4.50×10^{-3} mol		
After addition	0.50×10^{-3} mol	0	4.50×10^{-3} mol	—

The total volume of the solution is

45.0 mL + 50.0 mL = 95.0 mL = 0.0950 L

The resulting molarities of CH₃COOH and CH₃COO⁻ after the reaction are therefore

$$[\text{CH}_3\text{COOH}] = \frac{0.50 \times 10^{-3} \text{ mol}}{0.0950 \text{ L}} = 0.0053 \ M$$

$$[\text{CH}_3\text{COO}^-] = \frac{4.50 \times 10^{-3} \text{ mol}}{0.0950 \text{ L}} = 0.0474 \ M$$

Equilibrium Calculation: The equilibrium between CH₃COOH and CH₃COO⁻ must obey the equilibrium-constant expression for CH₃COOH

$$K_a = \frac{[\text{H}^+][\text{CH}_3\text{COO}^-]}{[\text{CH}_3\text{COOH}]} = 1.8 \times 10^{-5}$$

Solving for [H⁺] gives

$$[\text{H}^+] = K_a \times \frac{[\text{CH}_3\text{COOH}]}{[\text{CH}_3\text{COO}^-]} = (1.8 \times 10^{-5}) \times \left(\frac{0.0053}{0.0474}\right) = 2.0 \times 10^{-6} \ M$$

$$\text{pH} = -\log(2.0 \times 10^{-6}) = 5.70$$

Comment: We could have solved for pH equally well using the Henderson–Hasselbalch equation.

■ PRACTICE EXERCISE

(a) Calculate the pH in the solution formed by adding 10.0 mL of 0.050 M NaOH to 40.0 mL of 0.0250 M benzoic acid (C₆H₅COOH, $K_a = 6.3 \times 10^{-5}$). **(b)** Calculate the pH in the solution formed by adding 10.0 mL of 0.100 M HCl to 20.0 mL of 0.100 M NH₃.
Answers: **(a)** 4.20, **(b)** 9.26

■ SAMPLE EXERCISE 17.8 | Calculating the pH at the Equivalence Point

Calculate the pH at the equivalence point in the titration of 50.0 mL of 0.100 M CH₃COOH with 0.100 M NaOH.

SOLUTION

Analyze: We are asked to determine the pH at the equivalence point of the titration of a weak acid with a strong base. Because the neutralization of a weak acid produces its anion, which is a weak base, we expect the pH at the equivalence point to be greater than 7.

Plan: The initial number of moles of acetic acid will equal the number of moles of acetate ion at the equivalence point. We use the volume of the solution at the equivalence point to calculate the concentration of acetate ion. Because the acetate ion is a weak base, we can calculate the pH using K_b and $[CH_3COO^-]$.

Solve: The number of moles of acetic acid in the initial solution is obtained from the volume and molarity of the solution:

$$\text{Moles} = M \times L = (0.100 \text{ mol/L})(0.0500 \text{ L}) = 5.00 \times 10^{-3} \text{ mol } CH_3COOH$$

Hence 5.00×10^{-3} mol of CH_3COO^- is formed. It will take 50.0 mL of NaOH to reach the equivalence point (Figure 17.9). The volume of this salt solution at the equivalence point is the sum of the volumes of the acid and base, 50.0 mL + 50.0 mL = 100.0 mL = 0.1000 L. Thus, the concentration of CH_3COO^- is

$$[CH_3COO^-] = \frac{5.00 \times 10^{-3} \text{ mol}}{0.1000 \text{ L}} = 0.0500 \text{ } M$$

The CH_3COO^- ion is a weak base.

$$CH_3COO^-(aq) + H_2O(l) \rightleftharpoons CH_3COOH(aq) + OH^-(aq)$$

The K_b for CH_3COO^- can be calculated from the K_a value of its conjugate acid, $K_b = K_w/K_a = (1.0 \times 10^{-14})/(1.8 \times 10^{-5}) = 5.6 \times 10^{-10}$. Using the K_b expression, we have

$$K_b = \frac{[CH_3COOH][OH^-]}{[CH_3COO^-]} = \frac{(x)(x)}{0.0500 - x} = 5.6 \times 10^{-10}$$

Making the approximation that $0.0500 - x \simeq 0.0500$, and then solving for x, we have $x = [OH^-] = 5.3 \times 10^{-6}$ M, which gives pOH = 5.28 and pH = 8.72.

Check: The pH is above 7, as expected for the salt of a weak acid and strong base.

■ **PRACTICE EXERCISE**

Calculate the pH at the equivalence point when **(a)** 40.0 mL of 0.025 M benzoic acid (C_6H_5COOH, $K_a = 6.3 \times 10^{-5}$) is titrated with 0.050 M NaOH; **(b)** 40.0 mL of 0.100 M NH_3 is titrated with 0.100 M HCl.
Answers: **(a)** 8.21, **(b)** 5.28

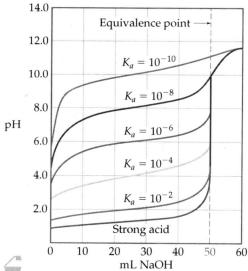

▲ Figure 17.11 **Effect of K_a on titration curves.** This set of curves shows the influence of acid strength (K_a) on the shape of the curve for titration with NaOH. Each curve represents titration of 50.0 mL of 0.10 M acid with 0.10 M NaOH. The weaker the acid, the higher the initial pH and the smaller the pH change at the equivalence point.

The pH titration curves for weak acid–strong base titrations differ from those for strong acid–strong base titrations in three noteworthy ways:

1. The solution of the weak acid has a higher initial pH than a solution of a strong acid of the same concentration.

2. The pH change at the rapid-rise portion of the curve near the equivalence point is smaller for the weak acid than it is for the strong acid.

3. The pH at the equivalence point is above 7.00 for the weak acid–strong base titration.

To illustrate these differences further, consider the family of titration curves shown in Figure 17.11 ◀. Notice that the initial pH increases as the acid becomes weaker (that is, as K_a becomes smaller), and that the pH change near the equivalence point becomes less marked. Notice also that the pH at the equivalence point steadily increases as K_a decreases. It is virtually impossible to determine the equivalence point when pK_a is 10 or higher because the pH change is too small and gradual.

Because the pH change near the equivalence point becomes smaller as K_a decreases, the choice of indicator for a weak acid–strong base titration is more critical than it is for a strong acid–strong base titration. When 0.100 M CH_3COOH ($K_a = 1.8 \times 10^{-5}$) is titrated with 0.100 M NaOH, for example, as shown in Figure 17.9, the pH increases rapidly only over the pH range of about 7 to 10. Phenolphthalein is therefore an ideal indicator because it changes color from pH 8.3 to 10.0, close to the pH at the equivalence point. Methyl red is a poor choice, however, because its color change occurs from 4.2 to 6.0, which begins well before the equivalence point is reached.

Titration of a weak base (such as 0.100 M NH_3) with a strong acid solution (such as 0.100 M HCl) leads to the titration curve shown in Figure 17.12▶. In this particular example the equivalence point occurs at pH 5.28. Thus, methyl red would be an ideal indicator, but phenolphthalein would be a poor choice.

GIVE IT SOME THOUGHT

Why is the choice of indicator more crucial for a weak acid–strong base titration than for a strong acid–strong base titration?

Titrations of Polyprotic Acids

When weak acids contain more than one ionizable H atom, as in phosphorous acid (H_3PO_3), reaction with OH^- occurs in a series of steps. Neutralization of H_3PO_3 proceeds in two stages. (Chapter 16 Sample Integrative Exercise)

$$H_3PO_3(aq) + OH^-(aq) \longrightarrow H_2PO_3^-(aq) + H_2O(l) \quad [17.13]$$

$$H_2PO_3^-(aq) + OH^-(aq) \longrightarrow HPO_3^{2-}(aq) + H_2O(l) \quad [17.14]$$

When the neutralization steps of a polyprotic acid or polybasic base are sufficiently separated, the substance exhibits a titration curve with multiple equivalence points. Figure 17.13▶ shows the two distinct equivalence points in the titration curve for the H_3PO_3–$H_2PO_3^-$–HPO_3^{2-} system.

GIVE IT SOME THOUGHT

Sketch the titration curve for the titration of Na_2CO_3 with HCl.

17.4 SOLUBILITY EQUILIBRIA

The equilibria that we have considered thus far in this chapter have involved acids and bases. Furthermore, they have been homogeneous; that is, all the species have been in the same phase. Through the rest of this chapter we will consider the equilibria involved in the dissolution or precipitation of ionic compounds. These reactions are heterogeneous.

The dissolving and precipitating of compounds are phenomena that occur both within us and around us. Tooth enamel dissolves in acidic solutions, for example, causing tooth decay. The precipitation of certain salts in our kidneys produces kidney stones. The waters of Earth contain salts dissolved as water passes over and through the ground. Precipitation of $CaCO_3$ from groundwater is responsible for the formation of stalactites and stalagmites within limestone caves (Figure 4.1).

In our earlier discussion of precipitation reactions, we considered some general rules for predicting the solubility of common salts in water. (Section 4.2) These rules give us a qualitative sense of whether a compound will have a low or high solubility in water. By considering solubility equilibria, in contrast, we can make quantitative predictions about the amount of a given compound that will dissolve. We can also use these equilibria to analyze the factors that affect solubility.

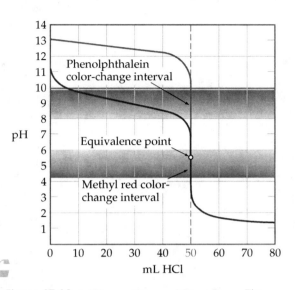

▲ Figure 17.12 **Adding a strong acid to a base.** The blue curve shows pH versus volume of added HCl in the titration of 50.0 mL of 0.10 M ammonia (weak base) with 0.10 M HCl. The red curve shows pH versus added acid for the titration of 0.10 M NaOH (strong base). Both phenolphthalein and methyl red change color at the equivalence point in the titration of the strong base. Phenolphthalein changes color before the equivalence point in the titration of the weak base.

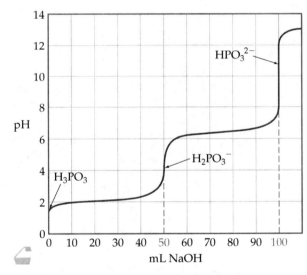

▲ Figure 17.13 **Diprotic acid.** Titration curve for the reaction of 50.0 mL of 0.10 M H_3PO_3 with 0.10 M NaOH.

The Solubility-Product Constant, K_{sp}

Recall that a *saturated solution* is one in which the solution is in contact with undissolved solute. (Section 13.2) Consider, for example, a saturated aqueous solution of $BaSO_4$ that is in contact with solid $BaSO_4$. Because the solid is an ionic compound, it is a strong electrolyte and yields $Ba^{2+}(aq)$ and $SO_4^{2-}(aq)$ ions upon dissolving. The following equilibrium is readily established between the undissolved solid and hydrated ions in solution:

$$BaSO_4(s) \rightleftharpoons Ba^{2+}(aq) + SO_4^{2-}(aq) \qquad [17.15]$$

As with any other equilibrium, the extent to which this dissolution reaction occurs is expressed by the magnitude of its equilibrium constant. Because this equilibrium equation describes the dissolution of a solid, the equilibrium constant indicates how soluble the solid is in water and is referred to as the **solubility-product constant** (or simply the **solubility product**). It is denoted K_{sp}, where sp stands for solubility product.

The equilibrium-constant expression for the equilibrium between a solid and an aqueous solution of its component ions is written according to the rules that apply to any equilibrium-constant expression. Remember, however, that solids do not appear in the equilibrium-constant expressions for heterogeneous equilibria. (Section 15.4) Thus, the solubility-product expression for $BaSO_4$, which is based on Equation 17.15, is

$$K_{sp} = [Ba^{2+}][SO_4^{2-}] \qquad [17.16]$$

In general, *the solubility product of a compound equals the product of the concentration of the ions involved in the equilibrium, each raised to the power of its coefficient in the equilibrium equation.* The coefficient for each ion in the equilibrium equation also equals its subscript in the compound's chemical formula.

The values of K_{sp} at 25 °C for many ionic solids are tabulated in Appendix D. The value of K_{sp} for $BaSO_4$ is 1.1×10^{-10}, a very small number, indicating that only a very small amount of the solid will dissolve in water.

▪ SAMPLE EXERCISE 17.9 | Writing Solubility-Product (K_{sp}) Expressions

Write the expression for the solubility-product constant for CaF_2, and look up the corresponding K_{sp} value in Appendix D.

SOLUTION

Analyze: We are asked to write an equilibrium-constant expression for the process by which CaF_2 dissolves in water.

Plan: We apply the same rules for writing any equilibrium-constant expression, excluding the solid reactant from the expression. We assume that the compound dissociates completely into its component ions.

$$CaF_2(s) \rightleftharpoons Ca^{2+}(aq) + 2 F^-(aq)$$

Solve: Following the italicized rule stated previously, the expression for K_{sp} is

$$K_{sp} = [Ca^{2+}][F^-]^2$$

In Appendix D we see that this K_{sp} has a value of 3.9×10^{-11}.

▪ PRACTICE EXERCISE

Give the solubility-product-constant expressions and the values of the solubility-product constants (from Appendix D) for the following compounds: **(a)** barium carbonate, **(b)** silver sulfate.

Answers: **(a)** $K_{sp} = [Ba^{2+}][CO_3^{2-}] = 5.0 \times 10^{-9}$; **(b)** $K_{sp} = [Ag^+]^2[SO_4^{2-}] = 1.5 \times 10^{-5}$

Solubility and K_{sp}

It is important to distinguish carefully between solubility and the solubility-product constant. The solubility of a substance is the quantity that dissolves to form a saturated solution. (Section 13.2) Solubility is often expressed as grams of solute per liter of solution (g/L). *Molar solubility* is the number of moles of the solute that dissolve in forming a liter of saturated solution of the solute (mol/L). The solubility-product constant (K_{sp}) is the equilibrium constant for the equilibrium between an ionic solid and its saturated solution and is a unitless number. Thus, the magnitude of K_{sp} is a measure of how much of the solid dissolves to form a saturated solution.

▲ Figure 17.14 **Relationships between solubility and K_{sp}.** The solubility of any compound in grams per liter can be converted to molar solubility. The molar solubility can be used to determine the concentrations of ions in solution. The concentration of ions can be used to calculate K_{sp}. The steps can be reversed, and solubility calculated from K_{sp}.

◢ GIVE IT SOME THOUGHT

Without doing a calculation, predict which of the following compounds will have the greatest molar solubility in water: AgCl ($K_{sp} = 1.8 \times 10^{-10}$), AgBr ($K_{sp} = 5.0 \times 10^{-13}$), or AgI ($K_{sp} = 8.3 \times 10^{-17}$).

The solubility of a substance can change considerably as the concentrations of other solutes change. The solubility of $Mg(OH)_2$, for example, depends highly on pH. The solubility is also affected by the concentrations of other ions in solution, especially Mg^{2+}. In contrast, the solubility-product constant, K_{sp}, has only one value for a given solute at any specific temperature.*

In principle, it is possible to use the K_{sp} value of a salt to calculate solubility under a variety of conditions. In practice, great care must be taken in doing so for the reasons indicated in "A Closer Look: Limitations of Solubility Products" at the end of this section. Agreement between measured solubility and that calculated from K_{sp} is usually best for salts whose ions have low charges (1+ and 1−) and do not hydrolyze. Figure 17.14▲ summarizes the relationships among various expressions of solubility and K_{sp}.

■■■ SAMPLE EXERCISE 17.10 | Calculating K_{sp} from Solubility

Solid silver chromate is added to pure water at 25 °C. Some of the solid remains undissolved at the bottom of the flask. The mixture is stirred for several days to ensure that equilibrium is achieved between the undissolved $Ag_2CrO_4(s)$ and the solution. Analysis of the equilibrated solution shows that its silver ion concentration is $1.3 \times 10^{-4}\,M$. Assuming that Ag_2CrO_4 dissociates completely in water and that there are no other important equilibria involving the Ag^+ or CrO_4^{2-} ions in the solution, calculate K_{sp} for this compound.

SOLUTION

Analyze: We are given the equilibrium concentration of Ag^+ in a saturated solution of Ag_2CrO_4. From this information, we are asked to determine the value of the solubility-product constant, K_{sp}, for Ag_2CrO_4.

Plan: The equilibrium equation and the expression for K_{sp} are

$$Ag_2CrO_4(s) \rightleftharpoons 2\,Ag^+(aq) + CrO_4^{2-}(aq) \qquad K_{sp} = [Ag^+]^2[CrO_4^{2-}]$$

To calculate K_{sp}, we need the equilibrium concentrations of Ag^+ and CrO_4^{2-}. We know that at equilibrium $[Ag^+] = 1.3 \times 10^{-4}\,M$. All the Ag^+ and CrO_4^{2-} ions in the solution come from the Ag_2CrO_4 that dissolves. Thus, we can use $[Ag^+]$ to calculate $[CrO_4^{2-}]$.

Solve: From the chemical formula of silver chromate, we know that there must be 2 Ag^+ ions in solution for each CrO_4^{2-} ion in solution. Consequently, the concentration of CrO_4^{2-} is half the concentration of Ag^+:

$$[CrO_4^{2-}] = \left(\frac{1.3 \times 10^{-4}\,\text{mol Ag}^+}{L}\right)\left(\frac{1\,\text{mol CrO}_4^{2-}}{2\,\text{mol Ag}^+}\right) = 6.5 \times 10^{-5}\,M$$

We can now calculate the value of K_{sp}.

$$K_{sp} = [Ag^+]^2[CrO_4^{2-}] = (1.3 \times 10^{-4})^2(6.5 \times 10^{-5}) = 1.1 \times 10^{-12}$$

Check: We obtain a small value, as expected for a slightly soluble salt. Furthermore, the calculated value agrees well with the one given in Appendix D, 1.2×10^{-12}.

This is strictly true only for very dilute solutions. The values of equilibrium constants are somewhat altered when the total concentration of ionic substances in water is increased. However, we will ignore these effects, which are taken into consideration only for work that requires exceptional accuracy.

A saturated solution of $Mg(OH)_2$ in contact with undissolved solid is prepared at 25 °C. The pH of the solution is found to be 10.17. Assuming that $Mg(OH)_2$ dissociates completely in water and that there are no other simultaneous equilibria involving the Mg^{2+} or OH^- ions in the solution, calculate K_{sp} for this compound.
Answer: 1.6×10^{-12}

■ **SAMPLE EXERCISE 17.11** | Calculating Solubility from K_{sp}

The K_{sp} for CaF_2 is 3.9×10^{-11} at 25 °C. Assuming that CaF_2 dissociates completely upon dissolving and that there are no other important equilibria affecting its solubility, calculate the solubility of CaF_2 in grams per liter.

SOLUTION

Analyze: We are given K_{sp} for CaF_2 and are asked to determine solubility. Recall that the *solubility* of a substance is the quantity that can dissolve in solvent, whereas the *solubility-product constant*, K_{sp}, is an equilibrium constant.

Plan: We can approach this problem by using our standard techniques for solving equilibrium problems. We write the chemical equation for the dissolution process and set up a table of the initial and equilibrium concentrations. We then use the equilibrium-constant expression. In this case we know K_{sp}, and so we solve for the concentrations of the ions in solution.

Solve: Assume initially that none of the salt has dissolved, and then allow x moles/liter of CaF_2 to dissociate completely when equilibrium is achieved.

	$CaF_2(s)$	$\rightleftharpoons$	Ca^{2+}	+	$2 F^-(aq)$
Initial	—		0		0
Change	—		$+x\,M$		$+2x\,M$
Equilibrium	—		$x\,M$		$2x\,M$

The stoichiometry of the equilibrium dictates that $2x$ moles/liter of F^- are produced for each x moles/liter of CaF_2 that dissolve. We now use the expression for K_{sp} and substitute the equilibrium concentrations to solve for the value of x:

$$K_{sp} = [Ca^{2+}][F^-]^2 = (x)(2x)^2 = 4x^3 = 3.9 \times 10^{-11}$$

$$x = \sqrt[3]{\frac{3.9 \times 10^{-11}}{4}} = 2.1 \times 10^{-4}\,M$$

(Remember that $\sqrt[3]{y} = y^{1/3}$; to calculate the cube root of a number, you can use the y^x function on your calculator, with $x = \frac{1}{3}$.) Thus, the molar solubility of CaF_2 is 2.1×10^{-4} mol/L. The mass of CaF_2 that dissolves in water to form a liter of solution is

$$\left(\frac{2.1 \times 10^{-4}\text{ mol }CaF_2}{1\text{ L soln}}\right)\left(\frac{78.1\text{ g }CaF_2}{1\text{ mol }CaF_2}\right) = 1.6 \times 10^{-2}\text{ g }CaF_2/\text{L soln}$$

Check: We expect a small number for the solubility of a slightly soluble salt. If we reverse the calculation, we should be able to recalculate the solubility product: $K_{sp} = (2.1 \times 10^{-4})(4.2 \times 10^{-4})^2 = 3.7 \times 10^{-11}$, close to the starting value for K_{sp}, 3.9×10^{-11}.

Comment: Because F^- is the anion of a weak acid, you might expect that the hydrolysis of the ion would affect the solubility of CaF_2. The basicity of F^- is so small ($K_b = 1.5 \times 10^{-11}$), however, that the hydrolysis occurs to only a slight extent and does not significantly influence the solubility. The reported solubility is 0.017 g/L at 25 °C, in good agreement with our calculation.

The K_{sp} for LaF_3 is 2×10^{-19}. What is the solubility of LaF_3 in water in moles per liter?
Answer: 9×10^{-6} mol/L

The concentrations of ions calculated from K_{sp} sometimes deviate appreciably from those found experimentally. In part, these deviations are due to electrostatic interactions between ions in solution, which can lead to ion pairs. (See Section 13.5, "A Closer Look: Colligative Properties of Electrolyte Solutions.") These interactions increase in magnitude both as the concentrations of the ions increase and as their charges increase. The solubility calculated from K_{sp} tends to be low unless it is corrected to account for these interactions between ions. Chemists have developed procedures for correcting for these "ionic-strength" or "ionic-activity" effects, and these procedures are examined in more advanced chemistry courses. As an example of the effect of these interionic interactions, consider $CaCO_3$ (calcite), whose solubility product, $K_{sp} = 4.5 \times 10^{-9}$, gives a calculated solubility of 6.7×10^{-5} mol/L. Making corrections for the interionic interactions in the solution yields a higher solubility, 7.3×10^{-5} mol/L. The reported solubility, however, is twice as high $(1.4 \times 10^{-4}$ mol/L), so there must be one or more additional factors involved.

Another common source of error in calculating ion concentrations from K_{sp} is ignoring other equilibria that occur simultaneously in the solution. It is possible, for example, that acid–base equilibria take place simultaneously with solubility equilibria. In particular, both basic anions and cations with high charge-to-size ratios undergo hydrolysis reactions that can measurably increase the solubilities of their salts. For example, $CaCO_3$ contains the basic carbonate ion $(K_b = 1.8 \times 10^{-4})$, which hydrolyzes in water: $CO_3^{2-}(aq) + H_2O(l) \rightleftharpoons HCO_3^-(aq) + OH^-(aq)$. If we consider both the effect of the interionic interactions in the solution and the effect of the simultaneous solubility and hydrolysis equilibria, we calculate a solubility of 1.4×10^{-4} mol/L, in agreement with the measured value.

Finally, we generally assume that ionic compounds dissociate completely into their component ions when they dissolve. This assumption is not always valid. When MgF_2 dissolves, for example, it yields not only Mg^{2+} and F^- ions but also MgF^+ ions in solution. Thus, we see that calculating solubility using K_{sp} can be more complicated than it first appears and it requires considerable knowledge of the equilibria occurring in solution.

17.5 FACTORS THAT AFFECT SOLUBILITY

The solubility of a substance is affected by temperature as well as by the presence of other solutes. The presence of an acid, for example, can have a major influence on the solubility of a substance. In Section 17.4 we considered the dissolving of ionic compounds in pure water. In this section we examine three factors that affect the solubility of ionic compounds: (1) the presence of common ions, (2) the pH of the solution, and (3) the presence of complexing agents. We will also examine the phenomenon of *amphoterism*, which is related to the effects of both pH and complexing agents.

Common-Ion Effect

The presence of either $Ca^{2+}(aq)$ or $F^-(aq)$ in a solution reduces the solubility of CaF_2, shifting the solubility equilibrium of CaF_2 to the left.

$$CaF_2(s) \rightleftharpoons Ca^{2+}(aq) + 2\,F^-(aq)$$

Addition of Ca^{2+} or F^- shifts equilibrium, reducing solubility

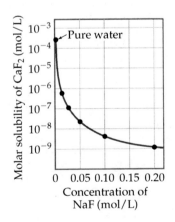

▲ Figure 17.15 **Common-ion effect.** The way in which NaF concentration affects the solubility of CaF_2 demonstrates the common-ion effect. Notice that the CaF_2 solubility is on a logarithmic scale.

This reduction in solubility is another application of the common-ion effect.   (Section 17.1) In general, *the solubility of a slightly soluble salt is decreased by the presence of a second solute that furnishes a common ion.* Figure 17.15 ▶ shows how the solubility of CaF_2 decreases as NaF is added to the solution. Sample Exercise 17.12 shows how the K_{sp} can be used to calculate the solubility of a slightly soluble salt in the presence of a common ion.

■■■ SAMPLE EXERCISE 17.12 | **Calculating the Effect of a Common Ion on Solubility**

Calculate the molar solubility of CaF_2 at 25 °C in a solution that is **(a)** 0.010 M in $Ca(NO_3)_2$, **(b)** 0.010 M in NaF.

SOLUTION

Analyze: We are asked to determine the solubility of CaF_2 in the presence of two strong electrolytes, each of which contains an ion common to CaF_2. In (a) the common ion is Ca^{2+}, and NO_3^- is a spectator ion. In (b) the common ion is F^-, and Na^+ is a spectator ion.

Plan: Because the slightly soluble compound is CaF_2, we need to use the K_{sp} for this compound, which is available in Appendix D:

$$K_{sp} = [Ca^{2+}][F^-]^2 = 3.9 \times 10^{-11}$$

The value of K_{sp} is unchanged by the presence of additional solutes. Because of the common-ion effect, however, the solubility of the salt will decrease in the presence of common ions. We can again use our standard equilibrium techniques of starting with the equation for CaF_2 dissolution, setting up a table of initial and equilibrium concentrations, and using the K_{sp} expression to determine the concentration of the ion that comes only from CaF_2.

Solve: (a) In this instance the initial concentration of Ca^{2+} is 0.010 M because of the dissolved $Ca(NO_3)_2$:

	$CaF_2(s)$	$\rightleftharpoons$	$Ca^{2+}(aq)$	+	$2 F^-(aq)$
Initial	—		0.010 M		0
Change	—		+x M		+2x M
Equilibrium	—		(0.010 + x) M		2x M

Substituting into the solubility-product expression gives

$$K_{sp} = 3.9 \times 10^{-11} = [Ca^{2+}][F^-]^2 = (0.010 + x)(2x)^2$$

This would be a messy problem to solve exactly, but fortunately it is possible to simplify matters greatly. Even without the common-ion effect, the solubility of CaF_2 is very small (2.1×10^{-4} M). Thus, we assume that the 0.010 M concentration of Ca^{2+} from $Ca(NO_3)_2$ is very much greater than the small additional concentration resulting from the solubility of CaF_2; that is, x is small compared to 0.010 M, and 0.010 + x ≈ 0.010. We then have

$$3.9 \times 10^{-11} = (0.010)(2x)^2$$
$$x^2 = \frac{3.9 \times 10^{-11}}{4(0.010)} = 9.8 \times 10^{-10}$$
$$x = \sqrt{9.8 \times 10^{-10}} = 3.1 \times 10^{-5} M$$

The very small value for x validates the simplifying assumption we have made. Our calculation indicates that 3.1×10^{-5} mol of solid CaF_2 dissolves per liter of the 0.010 M $Ca(NO_3)_2$ solution.

(b) In this case the common ion is F^-, and at equilibrium we have

$$[Ca^{2+}] = x \quad \text{and} \quad [F^-] = 0.010 + 2x$$

Assuming that 2x is small compared to 0.010 M (that is, 0.010 + 2x ≈ 0.010), we have

$$3.9 \times 10^{-11} = x(0.010)^2$$
$$x = \frac{3.9 \times 10^{-11}}{(0.010)^2} = 3.9 \times 10^{-7} M$$

Thus, 3.9×10^{-7} mol of solid CaF_2 should dissolve per liter of 0.010 M NaF solution.

Comment: The molar solubility of CaF_2 in pure water is 2.1×10^{-4} M (Sample Exercise 17.11). By comparison, our calculations above show that the solubility of CaF_2 in the presence of 0.010 M Ca^{2+} is 3.1×10^{-5} M, and in the presence of 0.010 M F^- ion it is 3.9×10^{-7} M. Thus, the addition of either Ca^{2+} or F^- to a solution of CaF_2 decreases the solubility. However, the effect of F^- on the solubility is more pronounced than that of Ca^{2+} because $[F^-]$ appears to the second power in the K_{sp} expression for CaF_2, whereas Ca^{2+} appears to the first power.

■■■ PRACTICE EXERCISE

The value for K_{sp} for manganese(II) hydroxide, $Mn(OH)_2$, is 1.6×10^{-13}. Calculate the molar solubility of $Mn(OH)_2$ in a solution that contains 0.020 M NaOH.
Answer: 4.0×10^{-10} M

Solubility and pH

The pH of a solution will affect the solubility of any substance whose anion is basic. Consider $Mg(OH)_2$, for example, for which the solubility equilibrium is

$$Mg(OH)_2(s) \rightleftharpoons Mg^{2+}(aq) + 2 OH^-(aq) \quad K_{sp} = 1.8 \times 10^{-11} \quad [17.17]$$

Science Fundamentals

A saturated solution of $Mg(OH)_2$ has a calculated pH of 10.52 and contains $[Mg^{2+}] = 1.7 \times 10^{-4} M$. Now suppose that solid $Mg(OH)_2$ is equilibrated with a solution buffered at a more acidic pH of 9.0. The pOH, therefore, is 5.0, so $[OH^-] = 1.0 \times 10^{-5}$. Inserting this value for $[OH^-]$ into the solubility-product expression, we have

$$K_{sp} = [Mg^{2+}][OH^-]^2 = 1.8 \times 10^{-11}$$

$$[Mg^{2+}](1.0 \times 10^{-5})^2 = 1.8 \times 10^{-11}$$

$$[Mg^{2+}] = \frac{1.8 \times 10^{-11}}{(1.0 \times 10^{-5})^2} = 0.18 \, M$$

Thus, $Mg(OH)_2$ dissolves in the solution until $[Mg^{2+}] = 0.18 \, M$. It is apparent that $Mg(OH)_2$ is quite soluble in this solution. If the concentration of OH^- were reduced even further by making the solution more acidic, the Mg^{2+} concentration would have to increase to maintain the equilibrium condition. Thus, a sample of $Mg(OH)_2$ will dissolve completely if sufficient acid is added (Figure 17.16 ▼).

▼ Figure 17.16 **Dissolution of a precipitate in acid.** A white precipitate of $Mg(OH)_2(s)$ in contact with its saturated solution is in the test tube on the left. The dropper poised above the solution surface contains hydrochloric acid. (The anions accompanying the acid have been omitted to simplify the art.)

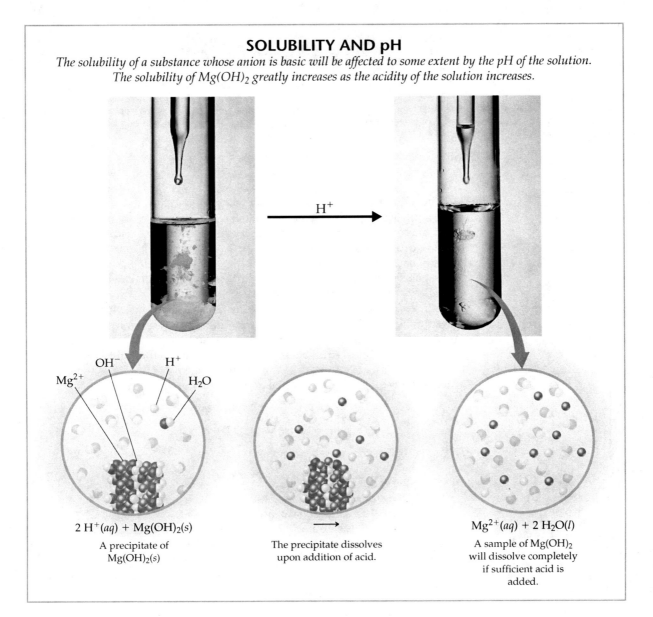

SOLUBILITY AND pH

The solubility of a substance whose anion is basic will be affected to some extent by the pH of the solution. The solubility of $Mg(OH)_2$ greatly increases as the acidity of the solution increases.

H^+

OH^- H^+

Mg^{2+} H_2O

$2 \, H^+(aq) + Mg(OH)_2(s)$

A precipitate of $Mg(OH)_2(s)$

$\longrightarrow$

The precipitate dissolves upon addition of acid.

$Mg^{2+}(aq) + 2 \, H_2O(l)$

A sample of $Mg(OH)_2$ will dissolve completely if sufficient acid is added.

Chemistry and Life SINKHOLES

A principal cause of sinkholes is the dissolution of limestone, which is calcium carbonate, by groundwater. Although $CaCO_3$ has a relatively small solubility-product constant, it is quite soluble in the presence of acid.

$$CaCO_3(s) \rightleftharpoons Ca^{2+}(aq) + CO_3^{2-}(aq)$$
$$K_{sp} = 4.5 \times 10^{-9}$$

Rainwater is naturally acidic, with a pH range of 5 to 6, and can become more acidic when it comes into contact with decaying plant matter. Because carbonate ion is the conjugate base of the weak acid, hydrogen carbonate ion (HCO_3^-), it readily combines with hydrogen ion.

$$CO_3^{2-}(aq) + H^+(aq) \longrightarrow HCO_3^-(aq)$$

The consumption of carbonate ion shifts the dissolution equilibrium to the right, thus increasing the solubility of $CaCO_3$. This can have profound consequences in areas where the terrain consists of porous calcium carbonate bedrock covered by a relatively thin layer of clay and/or topsoil. As acidic water percolates through and gradually dissolves the limestone, it creates underground voids. A sinkhole results when the overlying ground can no longer be supported by the remaining bedrock and collapses into the underground cavity [Figure 17.17▶].

The sudden formation of large sinkholes can pose a serious threat to life and property. The existence of deep sinkholes also increases the risk of contamination of the aquifer.

▲ Figure 17.17 **Sinkhole formation.** An underground void develops as limestone, $CaCO_3(s)$, dissolves. Collapse of the overlying ground into an underground cavity causes sinkhole formation. The large sinkhole shown here occured in Orlando, Florida and destroyed several buildings and part of a highway.

The solubility of almost any ionic compound is affected if the solution is made sufficiently acidic or basic. The effects are very noticeable, however, only when one or both ions involved are at least moderately acidic or basic. The metal hydroxides, such as $Mg(OH)_2$, are examples of compounds containing a strongly basic ion, the hydroxide ion.

In general, *if a compound contains a basic anion (that is, the anion of a weak acid), its solubility will increase as the solution becomes more acidic.* As we have seen, the solubility of $Mg(OH)_2$ greatly increases as the acidity of the solution increases. The solubility of CaF_2 increases as the solution becomes more acidic, too, because the F^- ion is a weak base; it is the conjugate base of the weak acid HF. As a result, the solubility equilibrium of CaF_2 is shifted to the right as the concentration of F^- ions is reduced by protonation to form HF. Thus, the solution process can be understood in terms of two consecutive reactions:

$$CaF_2(s) \rightleftharpoons Ca^{2+}(aq) + 2\,F^-(aq) \qquad [17.18]$$

$$F^-(aq) + H^+(aq) \rightleftharpoons HF(aq) \qquad [17.19]$$

The equation for the overall process is

$$CaF_2(s) + 2\,H^+(aq) \rightleftharpoons Ca^{2+}(aq) + 2\,HF(aq) \qquad [17.20]$$

Figure 17.18 ◀ shows how the solubility of CaF_2 changes with pH.

Other salts that contain basic anions, such as CO_3^{2-}, PO_4^{3-}, CN^-, or S^{2-}, behave similarly. These examples illustrate a general rule: *The solubility of slightly soluble salts containing basic anions increases as $[H^+]$ increases (as pH is lowered).* The more basic the anion, the more the solubility is influenced by pH. Salts with anions of negligible basicity (the anions of strong acids) are unaffected by pH changes.

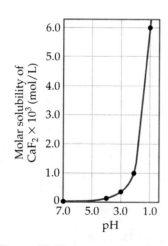

▲ Figure 17.18 **The effect of pH on the solubility of CaF₂.** The solubility increases as the solution becomes more acidic (lower pH). Notice that the vertical scale has been multiplied by 10^3.

SAMPLE EXERCISE 17.13 | Predicting the Effect of Acid on Solubility

Which of the following substances will be more soluble in acidic solution than in basic solution: **(a)** $Ni(OH)_2(s)$, **(b)** $CaCO_3(s)$, **(c)** $BaF_2(s)$, **(d)** $AgCl(s)$?

SOLUTION

Analyze: The problem lists four sparingly soluble salts, and we are asked to determine which will be more soluble at low pH than at high pH.

Plan: Ionic compounds that dissociate to produce a basic anion will be more soluble in acid solution.

Solve:

(a) $Ni(OH)_2(s)$ will be more soluble in acidic solution because of the basicity of OH^-; the H^+ ion reacts with the OH^- ion, forming water.

$$Ni(OH)_2(s) \rightleftharpoons Ni^{2+}(aq) + 2\,OH^-(aq)$$

$$\underline{2\,OH^-(aq) + 2\,H^+(aq) \rightleftharpoons 2\,H_2O(l)}$$

$$\text{Overall:}\quad Ni(OH)_2(s) + 2\,H^+(aq) \rightleftharpoons Ni^{2+}(aq) + 2\,H_2O(l)$$

(b) Similarly, $CaCO_3(s)$ dissolves in acid solutions because CO_3^{2-} is a basic anion.

$$CaCO_3(s) \rightleftharpoons Ca^{2+}(aq) + CO_3^{2-}(aq)$$

$$CO_3^{2-}(aq) + 2\,H^+(aq) \rightleftharpoons H_2CO_3(aq)$$

$$\underline{H_2CO_3(aq) \rightleftharpoons CO_2(g) + H_2O(l)}$$

$$\text{Overall:}\quad CaCO_3(s) + 2\,H^+(aq) \rightleftharpoons Ca^{2+}(aq) + CO_2(g) + H_2O(l)$$

The reaction between CO_3^{2-} and H^+ occurs in a stepwise fashion, first forming HCO_3^-. H_2CO_3 forms in appreciable amounts only when the concentration of H^+ is sufficiently high.

(c) The solubility of BaF_2 is also enhanced by lowering the pH, because F^- is a basic anion.

$$BaF_2(s) \rightleftharpoons Ba^{2+}(aq) + 2\,F^-(aq)$$

$$\underline{2\,F^-(aq) + 2\,H^+(aq) \rightleftharpoons 2\,HF(aq)}$$

$$\text{Overall:}\quad BaF_2(s) + 2\,H^+(aq) \rightleftharpoons Ba^{2+}(aq) + 2\,HF(aq)$$

(d) The solubility of $AgCl$ is unaffected by changes in pH because Cl^- is the anion of a strong acid and therefore has negligible basicity.

PRACTICE EXERCISE

Write the net ionic equation for the reaction of the following copper(II) compounds with acid: **(a)** CuS, **(b)** $Cu(N_3)_2$.
Answers: **(a)** $CuS(s) + H^+(aq) \rightleftharpoons Cu^{2+}(aq) + HS^-(aq)$
(b) $Cu(N_3)_2(s) + 2\,H^+(aq) \rightleftharpoons Cu^{2+}(aq) + 2\,HN_3(aq)$

Formation of Complex Ions

A characteristic property of metal ions is their ability to act as Lewis acids, or electron-pair acceptors, toward water molecules, which act as Lewis bases, or electron-pair donors. (Section 16.11) Lewis bases other than water can also interact with metal ions, particularly with transition-metal ions. Such interactions can dramatically affect the solubility of a metal salt. $AgCl$, for example, which has $K_{sp} = 1.8 \times 10^{-10}$, will dissolve in the presence of aqueous ammonia because Ag^+ interacts with the Lewis base NH_3, as shown in Figure 17.19▼. This process can be viewed as the sum of two reactions, the dissolution of $AgCl$ and the Lewis acid–base interaction between Ag^+ and NH_3.

$$AgCl(s) \rightleftharpoons Ag^+(aq) + Cl^-(aq) \qquad [17.21]$$

$$\underline{Ag^+(aq) + 2\,NH_3(aq) \rightleftharpoons Ag(NH_3)_2{}^+(aq)} \qquad [17.22]$$

$$\text{Overall:}\quad AgCl(s) + 2\,NH_3(aq) \rightleftharpoons Ag(NH_3)_2{}^+(aq) + Cl^-(aq) \qquad [17.23]$$

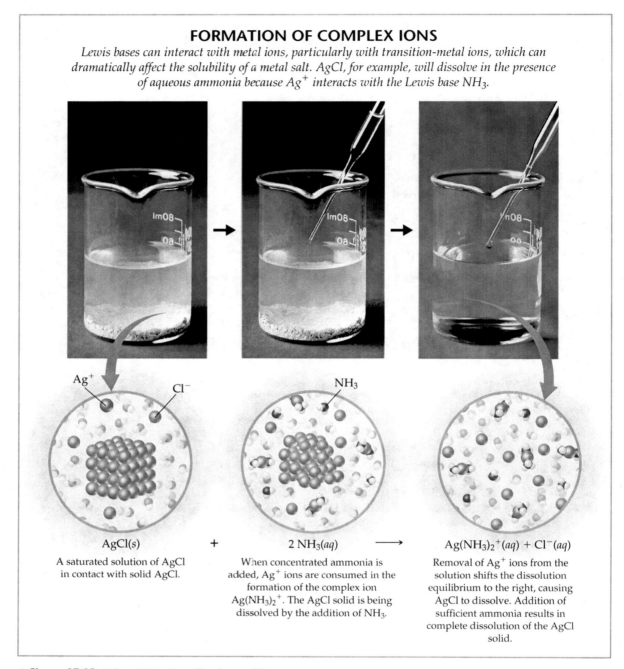

FORMATION OF COMPLEX IONS

Lewis bases can interact with metal ions, particularly with transition-metal ions, which can dramatically affect the solubility of a metal salt. AgCl, for example, will dissolve in the presence of aqueous ammonia because Ag$^+$ interacts with the Lewis base NH$_3$.

$$AgCl(s) \quad + \quad 2\,NH_3(aq) \quad \longrightarrow \quad Ag(NH_3)_2{}^+(aq) + Cl^-(aq)$$

| A saturated solution of AgCl in contact with solid AgCl. | When concentrated ammonia is added, Ag$^+$ ions are consumed in the formation of the complex ion Ag(NH$_3$)$_2$$^+$. The AgCl solid is being dissolved by the addition of NH$_3$. | Removal of Ag$^+$ ions from the solution shifts the dissolution equilibrium to the right, causing AgCl to dissolve. Addition of sufficient ammonia results in complete dissolution of the AgCl solid. |

▲ Figure 17.19 **Using NH$_3$(*aq*) to dissolve AgCl(*s*).**

The presence of NH$_3$ drives the reaction, the dissolution of AgCl, to the right as Ag$^+$(*aq*) is consumed to form Ag(NH$_3$)$_2$$^+$.

For a Lewis base such as NH$_3$ to increase the solubility of a metal salt, it must be able to interact more strongly with the metal ion than water does. The NH$_3$ must displace solvating H$_2$O molecules (Sections 13.1 and 16.11) in order to form Ag(NH$_3$)$_2$$^+$:

$$Ag^+(aq) + 2\,NH_3(aq) \rightleftharpoons Ag(NH_3)_2{}^+(aq) \qquad [17.24]$$

Chemistry and Life   TOOTH DECAY AND FLUORIDATION

Tooth enamel consists mainly of a mineral called hydroxyapatite, $Ca_{10}(PO_4)_6(OH)_2$. It is the hardest substance in the body. Tooth cavities are caused when acids dissolve tooth enamel.

$$Ca_{10}(PO_4)_6(OH)_2(s) + 8\,H^+(aq) \longrightarrow$$
$$10\,Ca^{2+}(aq) + 6\,HPO_4^{2-}(aq) + 2\,H_2O(l)$$

The resultant Ca^{2+} and HPO_4^{2-} ions diffuse out of the tooth enamel and are washed away by saliva. The acids that attack the hydroxyapatite are formed by the action of specific bacteria on sugars and other carbohydrates present in the plaque adhering to the teeth.

Fluoride ion, present in drinking water, toothpaste, and other sources, can react with hydroxyapatite to form fluoroapatite, $Ca_{10}(PO_4)_6F_2$. This mineral, in which F^- has replaced OH$^-$, is much more resistant to attack by acids because the fluoride ion is a much weaker Brønsted–Lowry base than the hydroxide ion.

Because the fluoride ion is so effective in preventing cavities, it is added to the public water supply in many places to give a concentration of 1 mg/L (1 ppm). The compound added may be NaF or Na_2SiF_6. Na_2SiF_6 reacts with water to release fluoride ions by the following reaction:

$$SiF_6^{2-}(aq) + 2\,H_2O(l) \longrightarrow 6\,F^-(aq) + 4\,H^+(aq) + SiO_2(s)$$

About 80% of all toothpastes now sold in the United States contain fluoride compounds, usually at the level of 0.1% fluoride by mass. The most common compounds in toothpastes are sodium fluoride (NaF), sodium monofluorophosphate (Na_2PO_3F), and stannous fluoride (SnF_2).

Related Exercise: 17.110

An assembly of a metal ion and the Lewis bases bonded to it, such as $Ag(NH_3)_2^+$, is called a **complex ion**. The stability of a complex ion in aqueous solution can be judged by the size of the equilibrium constant for its formation from the hydrated metal ion. For example, the equilibrium constant for formation of $Ag(NH_3)_2^+$ (Equation 17.24) is 1.7×10^7:

$$K_f = \frac{[Ag(NH_3)_2^+]}{[Ag^+][NH_3]^2} = 1.7 \times 10^7 \qquad [17.25]$$

The equilibrium constant for this kind of reaction is called a **formation constant**, K_f. The formation constants for several complex ions are listed in Table 17.1 ▼.

TABLE 17.1 ■ Formation Constants for Some Metal Complex Ions in Water at 25 °C

Complex Ion	K_f	Equilibrium Equation
$Ag(NH_3)_2^+$	1.7×10^7	$Ag^+(aq) + 2\,NH_3(aq) \rightleftharpoons Ag(NH_3)_2^+(aq)$
$Ag(CN)_2^-$	1×10^{21}	$Ag^+(aq) + 2\,CN^-(aq) \rightleftharpoons Ag(CN)_2^-(aq)$
$Ag(S_2O_3)_2^{3-}$	2.9×10^{13}	$Ag^+(aq) + 2\,S_2O_3^{2-}(aq) \rightleftharpoons Ag(S_2O_3)_2^{3-}(aq)$
$CdBr_4^{2-}$	5×10^3	$Cd^{2+}(aq) + 4\,Br^-(aq) \rightleftharpoons CdBr_4^{2-}(aq)$
$Cr(OH)_4^-$	8×10^{29}	$Cr^{3+}(aq) + 4\,OH^-(aq) \rightleftharpoons Cr(OH)_4^-(aq)$
$Co(SCN)_4^{2-}$	1×10^3	$Co^{2+}(aq) + 4\,SCN^-(aq) \rightleftharpoons Co(SCN)_4^{2-}(aq)$
$Cu(NH_3)_4^{2+}$	5×10^{12}	$Cu^{2+}(aq) + 4\,NH_3(aq) \rightleftharpoons Cu(NH_3)_4^{2+}(aq)$
$Cu(CN)_4^{2-}$	1×10^{25}	$Cu^{2+}(aq) + 4\,CN^-(aq) \rightleftharpoons Cu(CN)_4^{2-}(aq)$
$Ni(NH_3)_6^{2+}$	1.2×10^9	$Ni^{2+}(aq) + 6\,NH_3(aq) \rightleftharpoons Ni(NH_3)_6^{2+}(aq)$
$Fe(CN)_6^{4-}$	1×10^{35}	$Fe^{2+}(aq) + 6\,CN^-(aq) \rightleftharpoons Fe(CN)_6^{4-}(aq)$
$Fe(CN)_6^{3-}$	1×10^{42}	$Fe^{3+}(aq) + 6\,CN^-(aq) \rightleftharpoons Fe(CN)_6^{3-}(aq)$

■ **SAMPLE EXERCISE 17.14** | **Evaluating an Equilibrium Involving a Complex Ion**

Calculate the concentration of Ag^+ present in solution at equilibrium when concentrated ammonia is added to a $0.010\ M$ solution of $AgNO_3$ to give an equilibrium concentration of $[NH_3] = 0.20\ M$. Neglect the small volume change that occurs when NH_3 is added.

SOLUTION

Analyze: When $NH_3(aq)$ is added to $Ag^+(aq)$, a reaction occurs forming $Ag(NH_3)_2^+$ as shown in Equation 17.22. We are asked to determine what concentration of $Ag^+(aq)$ will remain uncombined when the NH_3 concentration is brought to $0.20\ M$ in a solution originally $0.010\ M$ in $AgNO_3$.

Plan: We first assume that the $AgNO_3$ is completely dissociated, giving $0.10\ M\ Ag^+$. Because K_f for the formation of $Ag(NH_3)_2^+$ is quite large, we assume that essentially all the Ag^+ is then converted to $Ag(NH_3)_2^+$ and approach the problem as though we are concerned with the *dissociation* of $Ag(NH_3)_2^+$ rather than its *formation*. To facilitate this approach, we will need to reverse the equation to represent the formation of Ag^+ and NH_3 from $Ag(NH_3)_2^+$ and also make the corresponding change to the equilibrium constant.

$$Ag(NH_3)_2^+(aq) \rightleftharpoons Ag^+(aq) + 2\,NH_3(aq)$$

$$\frac{1}{K_f} = \frac{1}{1.7 \times 10^7} = 5.9 \times 10^{-8}$$

Solve: If $[Ag^-]$ is $0.010\ M$ initially, then $[Ag(NH_3)_2^+]$ will be $0.010\ M$ following addition of the NH_3. We now construct a table to solve this equilibrium problem. Note that the NH_3 concentration given in the problem is an *equilibrium* concentration rather than an initial concentration.

	$Ag(NH_3)_2^+(aq)$ $\rightleftharpoons$	$Ag^+(aq)$ +	$2\,NH_3(aq)$
Initial	$0.010\ M$	$0\ M$	
Change	$-x\ M$	$+x\ M$	
Equilibrium	$0.010 - x\ M$	$x\ M$	$0.20\ M$

Because the concentration of Ag^+ is very small, we can ignore x in comparison with 0.010. Thus, $0.010 - x \simeq 0.010\ M$. Substituting these values into the equilibrium-constant expression for the dissociation of $Ag(NH_3)_2^+$, we obtain

$$\frac{[Ag^+][NH_3]^2}{[Ag(NH_3)_2^+]} = \frac{(x)(0.20)^2}{0.010} = 5.9 \times 10^{-8}$$

Solving for x, we obtain $x = 1.5 \times 10^{-8}\ M = [Ag^+]$. Thus, formation of the $Ag(NH_3)_2^+$ complex drastically reduces the concentration of free Ag^+ ion in solution.

■ **PRACTICE EXERCISE**

Calculate $[Cr^{3+}]$ in equilibrium with $Cr(OH)_4^-$ when 0.010 mol of $Cr(NO_3)_3$ is dissolved in a liter of solution buffered at pH 10.0.
Answer: $1 \times 10^{-16}\ M$

The general rule is that the solubility of metal salts increases in the presence of suitable Lewis bases, such as NH_3, CN^-, or OH^-, if the metal forms a complex with the base. The ability of metal ions to form complexes is an extremely important aspect of their chemistry. In Chapter 24 we will take a much closer look at complex ions. In that chapter and others we will see applications of complex ions to areas such as biochemistry, metallurgy, and photography.

Amphoterism

Some metal oxides and hydroxides that are relatively insoluble in neutral water dissolve in strongly acidic and strongly basic solutions. These substances are soluble in strong acids and bases because they themselves are capable of behaving as either an acid or base; they are **amphoteric oxides and hydroxides**.

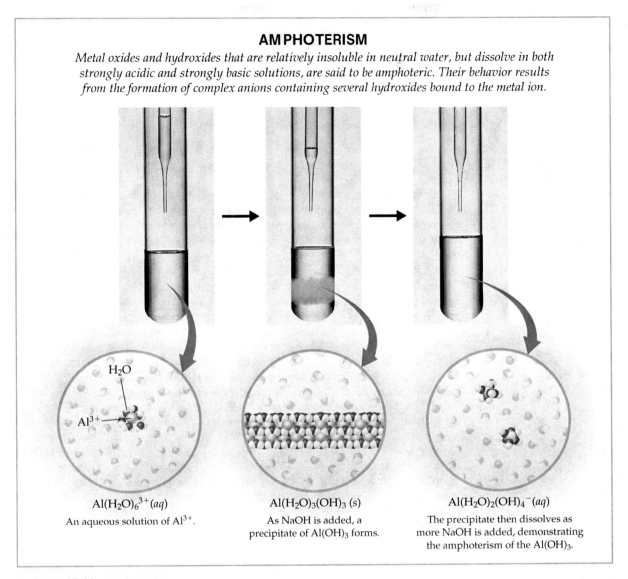

AMPHOTERISM

Metal oxides and hydroxides that are relatively insoluble in neutral water, but dissolve in both strongly acidic and strongly basic solutions, are said to be amphoteric. Their behavior results from the formation of complex anions containing several hydroxides bound to the metal ion.

$Al(H_2O)_6^{3+}(aq)$

An aqueous solution of Al^{3+}.

$Al(H_2O)_3(OH)_3 (s)$

As NaOH is added, a precipitate of $Al(OH)_3$ forms.

$Al(H_2O)_2(OH)_4^{-}(aq)$

The precipitate then dissolves as more NaOH is added, demonstrating the amphoterism of the $Al(OH)_3$.

▲ Figure 17.20 **Amphoterism.**

Amphoteric oxides and hydroxides include those of Al^{3+}, Cr^{3+}, Zn^{2+}, and Sn^{2+}. Notice that the term *amphoteric* is applied to the behavior of insoluble oxides and hydroxides that can be made to dissolve in either acidic or basic solutions. The similar term *amphiprotic*, which we encountered in Section 16.2, relates more generally to any molecule or ion that can either gain or lose a proton.

Amphoteric species dissolve in acidic solutions because they contain basic anions. What makes amphoteric oxides and hydroxides special, though, is that they also dissolve in strongly basic solutions (Figure 17.20 ▲). This behavior results from the formation of complex anions containing several (typically four) hydroxides bound to the metal ion.

$$Al(OH)_3(s) + OH^-(aq) \rightleftharpoons Al(OH)_4^-(aq) \qquad [17.26]$$

Amphoterism is often explained by the behavior of the water molecules that surround the metal ion and that are bonded to it by Lewis acid–base interactions. (Section 16.11) For example, $Al^{3+}(aq)$ is more accurately represented as $Al(H_2O)_6^{3+}(aq)$ because six water molecules are bonded to the Al^{3+} in aqueous solution. Recall from Section 16.11 that this hydrated ion is a weak acid.

As a strong base is added, $Al(H_2O)_6^{3+}$ loses protons in a stepwise fashion, eventually forming neutral and water-insoluble $Al(H_2O)_3(OH)_3$. This substance then dissolves upon removal of an additional proton to form the anion $Al(H_2O)_2(OH)_4^-$. The reactions that occur are as follows:

$$Al(H_2O)_6^{3+}(aq) + OH^-(aq) \rightleftharpoons Al(H_2O)_5(OH)^{2+}(aq) + H_2O(l)$$

$$Al(H_2O)_5(OH)^{2+}(aq) + OH^-(aq) \rightleftharpoons Al(H_2O)_4(OH)_2^+(aq) + H_2O(l)$$

$$Al(H_2O)_4(OH)_2^+(aq) + OH^-(aq) \rightleftharpoons Al(H_2O)_3(OH)_3(s) + H_2O(l)$$

$$Al(H_2O)_3(OH)_3(s) + OH^-(aq) \rightleftharpoons Al(H_2O)_2(OH)_4^-(aq) + H_2O(l)$$

Removing additional protons is possible, but each successive reaction occurs less readily than the one before. As the charge on the ion becomes more negative, it becomes increasingly difficult to remove a positively charged proton. Addition of an acid reverses these reactions. The proton adds in a stepwise fashion to convert the OH^- groups to H_2O, eventually re-forming $Al(H_2O)_6^{3+}$. The common practice is to simplify the equations for these reactions by excluding the bound H_2O molecules. Thus, we usually write Al^{3+} instead of $Al(H_2O)_6^{3+}$, $Al(OH)_3$ instead of $Al(H_2O)_3(OH)_3$, $Al(OH)_4^-$ instead of $Al(H_2O)_2(OH)_4^-$, and so forth.

The extent to which an insoluble metal hydroxide reacts with either acid or base varies with the particular metal ion involved. Many metal hydroxides—such as $Ca(OH)_2$, $Fe(OH)_2$, and $Fe(OH)_3$—are capable of dissolving in acidic solution but do not react with excess base. These hydroxides are not amphoteric.

The purification of aluminum ore in the manufacture of aluminum metal provides an interesting application of the property of amphoterism. As we have seen, $Al(OH)_3$ is amphoteric, whereas $Fe(OH)_3$ is not. Aluminum occurs in large quantities as the ore *bauxite*, which is essentially Al_2O_3 with additional water molecules. The ore is contaminated with Fe_2O_3 as an impurity. When bauxite is added to a strongly basic solution, the Al_2O_3 dissolves because the aluminum forms complex ions, such as $Al(OH)_4^-$. The Fe_2O_3 impurity, however, is not amphoteric and remains as a solid. The solution is filtered, getting rid of the iron impurity. Aluminum hydroxide is then precipitated by addition of acid. The purified hydroxide receives further treatment and eventually yields aluminum metal. (Section 23.3)

 GIVE IT SOME THOUGHT

What kind of behavior characterizes an amphoteric oxide or an amphoteric hydroxide?

17.6 PRECIPITATION AND SEPARATION OF IONS

Equilibrium can be achieved starting with the substances on either side of a chemical equation. The equilibrium among $BaSO_4(s)$, $Ba^{2+}(aq)$, and $SO_4^{2-}(aq)$ (Equation 17.15) can be achieved starting with solid $BaSO_4$. It can also be reached starting with solutions of salts containing Ba^{2+} and SO_4^{2-}, say $BaCl_2$ and Na_2SO_4. When these two solutions are mixed, $BaSO_4$ will precipitate if the product of the initial ion concentrations, $Q = [Ba^{2+}][SO_4^{2-}]$, is greater than K_{sp}.

The use of the reaction quotient, Q, to determine the direction in which a reaction must proceed to reach equilibrium was discussed earlier. (Section 15.6) The possible relationships between Q and K_{sp} are summarized as follows:

- If $Q > K_{sp}$, precipitation occurs until $Q = K_{sp}$.

- If $Q = K_{sp}$, equilibrium exists (saturated solution).

- If $Q < K_{sp}$, solid dissolves until $Q = K_{sp}$.

■ SAMPLE EXERCISE 17.15 | Predicting Whether a Precipitate Will Form

Will a precipitate form when 0.10 L of $8.0 \times 10^{-3}\,M$ $Pb(NO_3)_2$ is added to 0.40 L of $5.0 \times 10^{-3}\,M$ Na_2SO_4?

SOLUTION

Analyze: The problem asks us to determine whether a precipitate will form when two salt solutions are combined.

Plan: We should determine the concentrations of all ions immediately upon mixing of the solutions and compare the value of the reaction quotient, Q, to the solubility-product constant, K_{sp}, for any potentially insoluble product. The possible metathesis products are $PbSO_4$ and $NaNO_3$. Sodium salts are quite soluble; $PbSO_4$ has a K_{sp} of 6.3×10^{-7} (Appendix D), however, and will precipitate if the Pb^{2+} and SO_4^{2-} ion concentrations are high enough for Q to exceed K_{sp} for the salt.

Solve: When the two solutions are mixed, the total volume becomes $0.10\,L + 0.40\,L = 0.50\,L$. The number of moles of Pb^{2+} in 0.10 L of $8.0 \times 10^{-3}\,M$ $Pb(NO_3)_2$ is

$$(0.10\,L)\left(8.0 \times 10^{-3}\,\frac{mol}{L}\right) = 8.0 \times 10^{-4}\,mol$$

The concentration of Pb^{2+} in the 0.50-L mixture is therefore

$$[Pb^{2+}] = \frac{8.0 \times 10^{-4}\,mol}{0.50\,L} = 1.6 \times 10^{-3}\,M$$

The number of moles of SO_4^{2-} in 0.40 L of $5.0 \times 10^{-3}\,M$ Na_2SO_4 is

$$(0.40\,L)\left(5.0 \times 10^{-3}\,\frac{mol}{L}\right) = 2.0 \times 10^{-3}\,mol$$

Therefore, $[SO_4^{2-}]$ in the 0.50-L mixture is

$$[SO_4^{2-}] = \frac{2.0 \times 10^{-3}\,mol}{0.50\,L} = 4.0 \times 10^{-3}\,M$$

We then have

$$Q = [Pb^{2+}][SO_4^{2-}] = (1.6 \times 10^{-3})(4.0 \times 10^{-3}) = 6.4 \times 10^{-6}$$

Because $Q > K_{sp}$, $PbSO_4$ will precipitate.

■ PRACTICE EXERCISE

Will a precipitate form when 0.050 L of $2.0 \times 10^{-2}\,M$ NaF is mixed with 0.010 L of $1.0 \times 10^{-2}\,M$ $Ca(NO_3)_2$?
Answer: Yes, CaF_2 precipitates because $Q = 4.6 \times 10^{-8}$ is larger than $K_{sp} = 3.9 \times 10^{-11}$

Selective Precipitation of Ions

Ions can be separated from each other based on the solubilities of their salts. Consider a solution containing both Ag^+ and Cu^{2+}. If HCl is added to the solution, AgCl ($K_{sp} = 1.8 \times 10^{-10}$) precipitates, while Cu^{2+} remains in solution because $CuCl_2$ is soluble. Separation of ions in an aqueous solution by using a reagent that forms a precipitate with one or a few of the ions is called *selective precipitation*.

■ SAMPLE EXERCISE 17.16 | Calculating Ion Concentrations for Precipitation

A solution contains $1.0 \times 10^{-2}\,M$ Ag^+ and $2.0 \times 10^{-2}\,M$ Pb^{2+}. When Cl^- is added to the solution, both AgCl ($K_{sp} = 1.8 \times 10^{-10}$) and $PbCl_2$ ($K_{sp} = 1.7 \times 10^{-5}$) precipitate from the solution. What concentration of Cl^- is necessary to begin the precipitation of each salt? Which salt precipitates first?

SOLUTION

Analyze: We are asked to determine the concentration of Cl^- necessary to begin the precipitation from a solution containing Ag^+ and Pb^{2+} ions, and to predict which metal chloride will begin to precipitate first.

Plan: We are given K_{sp} values for the two possible precipitates. Using these and the metal ion concentrations, we can calculate what concentration of Cl^- ion would be necessary to begin precipitation of each. The salt requiring the lower Cl^- ion concentration will precipitate first.

Solve: For AgCl we have

$$K_{sp} = [Ag^+][Cl^-] = 1.8 \times 10^{-10}$$

Because $[Ag^+] = 1.0 \times 10^{-2}\,M$, the greatest concentration of Cl^- that can be present without causing precipitation of AgCl can be calculated from the K_{sp} expression:

$$K_{sp} = [1.0 \times 10^{-2}][Cl^-] = 1.8 \times 10^{-10}$$

$$[Cl^-] = \frac{1.8 \times 10^{-10}}{1.0 \times 10^{-2}} = 1.8 \times 10^{-8}\,M$$

Any Cl⁻ in excess of this very small concentration will cause AgCl to precipitate from solution. Proceeding similarly for PbCl₂, we have

$$K_{sp} = [Pb^{2+}][Cl^-]^2 = 1.7 \times 10^{-5}$$

$$[2.0 \times 10^{-2}][Cl^-]^2 = 1.7 \times 10^{-5}$$

$$[Cl^-]^2 = \frac{1.7 \times 10^{-5}}{2.0 \times 10^{-2}} = 8.5 \times 10^{-4}$$

$$[Cl^-] = \sqrt{8.5 \times 10^{-4}} = 2.9 \times 10^{-2}\ M$$

Thus, a concentration of Cl⁻ in excess of $2.9 \times 10^{-2}\ M$ will cause PbCl₂ to precipitate.

Comparing the concentrations of Cl⁻ required to precipitate each salt, we see that as Cl⁻ is added to the solution, AgCl will precipitate first because it requires a much smaller concentration of Cl⁻. Thus, Ag⁺ can be separated from Pb²⁺ by slowly adding Cl⁻ so [Cl⁻] is between $1.8 \times 10^{-8}\ M$ and $2.9 \times 10^{-2}\ M$.

■ PRACTICE EXERCISE

A solution consists of 0.050 M Mg²⁺ and 0.020 M Cu²⁺. Which ion will precipitate first as OH⁻ is added to the solution? What concentration of OH⁻ is necessary to begin the precipitation of each cation? [$K_{sp} = 1.8 \times 10^{-11}$ for Mg(OH)₂, and $K_{sp} = 4.8 \times 10^{-20}$ for Cu(OH)₂.]
Answer: Cu(OH)₂ precipitates first. Cu(OH)₂ begins to precipitate when [OH⁻] exceeds $1.5 \times 10^{-9}\ M$; Mg(OH)₂ begins to precipitate when [OH⁻] exceeds $1.9 \times 10^{-5}\ M$.

Sulfide ion is often used to separate metal ions because the solubilities of sulfide salts span a wide range and depend greatly on the pH of the solution. Cu²⁺ and Zn²⁺, for example, can be separated by bubbling H₂S gas through an acidified solution. Because CuS ($K_{sp} = 6 \times 10^{-37}$) is less soluble than ZnS ($K_{sp} = 2 \times 10^{-25}$), CuS precipitates from an acidified solution (pH = 1) while ZnS does not (Figure 17.21 ▼):

$$Cu^{2+}(aq) + H_2S(aq) \rightleftharpoons CuS(s) + 2\,H^+(aq) \qquad [17.27]$$

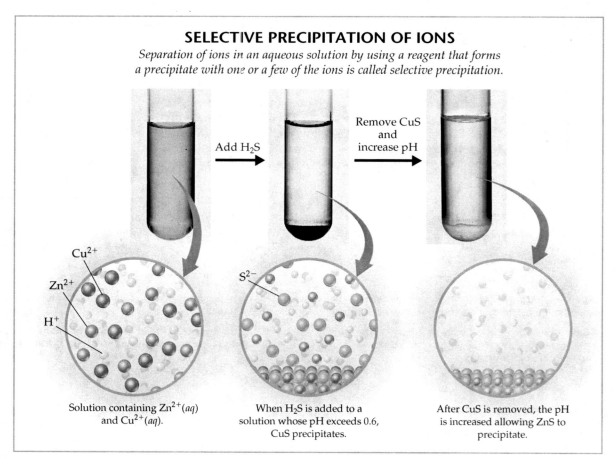

SELECTIVE PRECIPITATION OF IONS

Separation of ions in an aqueous solution by using a reagent that forms a precipitate with one or a few of the ions is called selective precipitation.

Add H₂S

Remove CuS and increase pH

Cu²⁺
Zn²⁺
H⁺
S²⁻

Solution containing Zn²⁺(aq) and Cu²⁺(aq).

When H₂S is added to a solution whose pH exceeds 0.6, CuS precipitates.

After CuS is removed, the pH is increased allowing ZnS to precipitate.

 ▲ Figure 17.21 **Selective precipitation.**

The CuS can be separated from the Zn^{2+} solution by filtration. The CuS can then be dissolved by using a high concentration of H^+, shifting the equilibrium shown in Equation 17.27 to the left.

GIVE IT SOME THOUGHT

What experimental conditions will leave the smallest concentration of Cu^{2+} ions in solution according to Equation 17.27?

17.7   QUALITATIVE ANALYSIS FOR METALLIC ELEMENTS

In this chapter we have seen several examples of equilibria involving metal ions in aqueous solution. In this final section we look briefly at how solubility equilibria and complex-ion formation can be used to detect the presence of particular metal ions in solution. Before the development of modern analytical instrumentation, it was necessary to analyze mixtures of metals in a sample by so-called wet chemical methods. For example, a metallic sample that might contain several metallic elements was dissolved in a concentrated acid solution. This solution was then tested in a systematic way for the presence of various metal ions.

Qualitative analysis determines only the presence or absence of a particular metal ion, whereas **quantitative analysis** determines how much of a given substance is present. Wet methods of qualitative analysis have become less important as a means of analysis. They are frequently used in general chemistry laboratory programs, however, to illustrate equilibria, to teach the properties of common metal ions in solution, and to develop laboratory skills. Typically, such analyses proceed in three stages: (1) The ions are separated into broad groups on the basis of solubility properties. (2) The individual ions within each group are then separated by selectively dissolving members in the group. (3) The ions are then identified by means of specific tests.

A scheme in general use divides the common cations into five groups, as shown in Figure 17.22▶. The order of addition of reagents is important. The most selective separations—those that involve the smallest number of ions—are carried out first. The reactions that are used must proceed so far toward completion that any concentration of cations remaining in the solution is too small to interfere with subsequent tests. Let's take a closer look at each of these five groups of cations, briefly examining the logic used in this qualitative analysis scheme.

1. *Insoluble chlorides:* Of the common metal ions, only Ag^+, Hg_2^{2+}, and Pb^{2+} form insoluble chlorides. When dilute HCl is added to a mixture of cations, therefore, only AgCl, Hg_2Cl_2, and $PbCl_2$ will precipitate, leaving the other cations in solution. The absence of a precipitate indicates that the starting solution contains no Ag^+, Hg_2^{2+}, or Pb^{2+}.

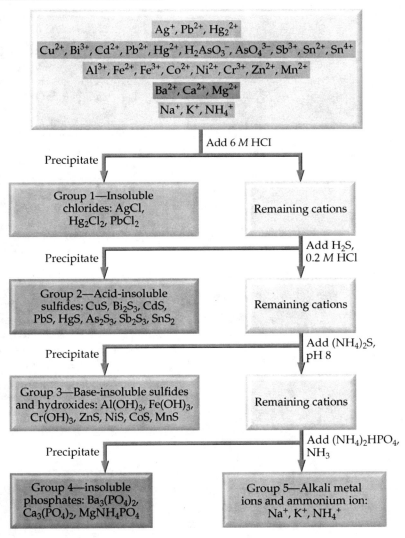

▲ Figure 17.22 **Qualitative analysis.** A flowchart showing the separation of cations into groups as a part of a common scheme for identifying cations.

2. *Acid-insoluble sulfides:* After any insoluble chlorides have been removed, the remaining solution, now acidic, is treated with H_2S. Only the most insoluble metal sulfides—CuS, Bi_2S_3, CdS, PbS, HgS, As_2S_3, Sb_2S_3, and SnS_2—can precipitate. (Note the very small values of K_{sp} for some of these sulfides in Appendix D.) Those metal ions whose sulfides are somewhat more soluble—for example, ZnS or NiS—remain in solution.

3. *Base-insoluble sulfides and hydroxides:* After the solution is filtered to remove any acid-insoluble sulfides, the remaining solution is made slightly basic, and $(NH_4)_2S$ is added. In basic solutions the concentration of S^{2-} is higher than in acidic solutions. Thus, the ion products for many of the more soluble sulfides are made to exceed their K_{sp} values and precipitation occurs. The metal ions precipitated at this stage are Al^{3+}, Cr^{3+}, Fe^{3+}, Zn^{2+}, Ni^{2+}, Co^{2+}, and Mn^{2+}. (Actually, the Al^{3+}, Fe^{3+}, and Cr^{3+} ions do not form insoluble sulfides; instead they are precipitated as insoluble hydroxides at the same time.)

4. *Insoluble phosphates:* At this point the solution contains only metal ions from periodic table groups 1A and 2A. Adding $(NH_4)_2HPO_4$ to a basic solution precipitates the group 2A elements Mg^{2+}, Ca^{2+}, Sr^{2+}, and Ba^{2+} because these metals form insoluble phosphates.

5. *The alkali metal ions and NH_4^+:* The ions that remain after removing the insoluble phosphates form a small group. We can test the original solution for each ion individually. A flame test can be used to determine the presence of K^+, for example, because the flame turns a characteristic violet color if K^+ is present.

GIVE IT SOME THOUGHT

If a precipitate forms upon addition of HCl to an aqueous solution, what conclusions can you draw about the contents of the solution?

Additional separation and testing is necessary to determine which ions are present within each of the groups. Consider, for example, the ions of the insoluble chloride group. The precipitate containing the metal chlorides is boiled in water. The $PbCl_2$ is relatively soluble in hot water, whereas AgCl and Hg_2Cl_2 are not. The hot solution is filtered, and a solution of Na_2CrO_4 is added to the filtrate. If Pb^{2+} is present, a yellow precipitate of $PbCrO_4$ forms. The test for Ag^+ consists of treating the metal chloride precipitate with dilute ammonia. Only Ag^+ forms an ammonia complex. If AgCl is present in the precipitate, it will dissolve in the ammonia solution.

$$AgCl(s) + 2\,NH_3(aq) \rightleftharpoons Ag(NH_3)_2{}^+(aq) + Cl^-(aq) \qquad [17.28]$$

After treatment with ammonia, the solution is filtered and the filtrate made acidic by adding nitric acid. The nitric acid removes ammonia from solution by forming NH_4^+, thus releasing Ag^+, which re-forms the AgCl precipitate.

$$Ag(NH_3)_2{}^+(aq) + Cl^-(aq) + 2\,H^+(aq) \rightleftharpoons AgCl(s) + 2\,NH_4^+(aq) \qquad [17.29]$$

The analyses for individual ions in the acid-insoluble and base-insoluble sulfides are a bit more complex, but the same general principles are involved. The detailed procedures for carrying out such analyses are given in many laboratory manuals.

■ SAMPLE INTEGRATIVE EXERCISE │ Putting Concepts Together

A sample of 1.25 L of HCl gas at 21 °C and 0.950 atm is bubbled through 0.500 L of 0.150 M NH$_3$ solution. Calculate the pH of the resulting solution assuming that all the HCl dissolves and that the volume of the solution remains 0.500 L.

SOLUTION

The number of moles of HCl gas is calculated from the ideal-gas law.

$$n = \frac{PV}{RT} = \frac{(0.950 \text{ atm})(1.25 \text{ L})}{(0.0821 \text{ L-atm/mol-K})(294 \text{ K})} = 0.0492 \text{ mol HCl}$$

The number of moles of NH$_3$ in the solution is given by the product of the volume of the solution and its concentration.

$$\text{Moles NH}_3 = (0.500 \text{ L})(0.150 \text{ mol NH}_3/\text{L}) = 0.0750 \text{ mol NH}_3$$

The acid HCl and base NH$_3$ react, transferring a proton from HCl to NH$_3$, producing NH$_4^+$ and Cl$^-$ ions.

$$\text{HCl}(g) + \text{NH}_3(aq) \longrightarrow \text{NH}_4^+(aq) + \text{Cl}^-(aq)$$

To determine the pH of the solution, we first calculate the amount of each reactant and each product present at the completion of the reaction.

	HCl(g) +	NH$_3$(aq) ⟶	NH$_4^+$(aq) +	Cl$^-$(aq)
Before addition	0.0492 mol	0 mol	0 mol	0 mol
Addition		0.0750 mol		
After addition	0 mol	0.0258 mol	0.0492 mol	0.0492 mol

Thus, the reaction produces a solution containing a mixture of NH$_3$, NH$_4^+$, and Cl$^-$. The NH$_3$ is a weak base ($K_b = 1.8 \times 10^{-5}$), NH$_4^+$ is its conjugate acid, and Cl$^-$ is neither acidic nor basic. Consequently, the pH depends on [NH$_3$] and [NH$_4^+$].

$$[\text{NH}_3] = \frac{0.0258 \text{ mol NH}_3}{0.500 \text{ L soln}} = 0.0516 \text{ } M$$

$$[\text{NH}_4^+] = \frac{0.0492 \text{ mol NH}_4^+}{0.500 \text{ L soln}} = 0.0984 \text{ } M$$

We can calculate the pH using either K_b for NH$_3$ or K_a for NH$_4^+$. Using the K_b expression, we have

	NH$_3$(aq) +	H$_2$O(l) ⇌	NH$_4^+$(aq) +	OH$^-$(aq)
Initial	0.0516 M	—	0.0984 M	0
Change	$-x$ M	—	$+x$ M	$+x$ M
Equilibrium	$(0.0516 - x)$ M	—	$(0.0984 + x)$ M	x M

$$K_b = \frac{[\text{NH}_4^+][\text{OH}^-]}{[\text{NH}_3]} = \frac{(0.0984 + x)(x)}{(0.0516 - x)} \simeq \frac{(0.0984)x}{0.0516} = 1.8 \times 10^{-5}$$

$$x = [\text{OH}^-] = \frac{(0.0516)(1.8 \times 10^{-5})}{0.0984} = 9.4 \times 10^{-6} \text{ } M$$

Hence, pOH = $-\log(9.4 \times 10^{-6})$ = 5.03 and pH = 14.00 − pOH = 14.00 − 5.03 = 8.97.

CHAPTER REVIEW

SUMMARY AND KEY TERMS

Section 17.1 In this chapter we have considered several types of important equilibria that occur in aqueous solution. Our primary emphasis has been on acid–base equilibria in solutions containing two or more solutes and on solubility equilibria. The dissociation of a weak acid or weak base is repressed by the presence of a strong electrolyte that provides an ion common to the equilibrium. This phenomenon is called the **common-ion effect**.

Section 17.2 A particularly important type of acid–base mixture is that of a weak conjugate acid–base pair. Such mixtures function as **buffered solutions (buffers)**. Addition of small amounts of a strong acid or a strong base to a buffered solution causes only small changes in pH because the buffer reacts with the added acid or base. (Strong acid–strong base, strong acid–weak base, and weak acid–strong base reactions proceed essentially to completion.) Buffered solutions are usually prepared from a weak acid and a salt of that acid or from a weak base and a salt of that base. Two important characteristics of a buffered solution are its **buffer capacity** and its pH. The pH can be calculated using K_a or K_b. The relationship between pH, pK_a, and the concentrations of an acid and its conjugate base can be expressed by the **Henderson–Hasselbalch equation**: $pH = pK_a + \log \dfrac{[\text{base}]}{[\text{acid}]}$.

Section 17.3 The plot of the pH of an acid (or base) as a function of the volume of added base (or acid) is called a **pH titration curve**. Titration curves aid in selecting a proper pH indicator for an acid–base titration. The titration curve of a strong acid–strong base titration exhibits a large change in pH in the immediate vicinity of the equivalence point; at the equivalence point for this titration, pH = 7. For strong acid–weak base or weak acid–strong base titrations, the pH change in the vicinity of the equivalence point is not as large. Furthermore, the pH at the equivalence point is not 7 in either of these cases. Rather, it is the pH of the salt solution that results from the neutralization reaction. It is possible to calculate the pH at any point of the titration curve by first considering the effects of the reaction between the acid and base on solution concentrations and then examining equilibria involving remaining solute species.

Section 17.4 The equilibrium between a solid compound and its ions in solution provides an example of heterogeneous equilibrium. The **solubility-product constant** (or simply the **solubility product**), K_{sp}, is an equilibrium constant that expresses quantitatively the extent to which the compound dissolves. The K_{sp} can be used to calculate the solubility of an ionic compound, and the solubility can be used to calculate K_{sp}.

Section 17.5 Several experimental factors, including temperature, affect the solubilities of ionic compounds in water. The solubility of a slightly soluble ionic compound is decreased by the presence of a second solute that furnishes a common ion (the common-ion effect). The solubility of compounds containing basic anions increases as the solution is made more acidic (as pH decreases). Salts with anions of negligible basicity (the anions of strong acids) are unaffected by pH changes.

The solubility of metal salts is also affected by the presence of certain Lewis bases that react with metal ions to form stable **complex ions**. Complex-ion formation in aqueous solution involves the displacement by Lewis bases (such as NH_3 and CN^-) of water molecules attached to the metal ion. The extent to which such complex formation occurs is expressed quantitatively by the **formation constant** for the complex ion. **Amphoteric oxides and hydroxides** are those that are only slightly soluble in water but dissolve on addition of either acid or base. Acid–base reactions involving the OH^- or H_2O groups bound to the metal ions give rise to the amphoterism.

Section 17.6 Comparison of the ion product, Q, with the value of K_{sp} can be used to judge whether a precipitate will form when solutions are mixed or whether a slightly soluble salt will dissolve under various conditions. Precipitates form when $Q > K_{sp}$. Ions can be separated from each other based on the solubilities of their salts.

Section 17.7 Metallic elements vary a great deal in the solubilities of their salts, in their acid–base behavior, and in their tendencies to form complex ions. These differences can be used to separate and detect the presence of metal ions in mixtures. **Qualitative analysis** determines the presence or absence of species in a sample, whereas **quantitative analysis** determines how much of each species is present. The qualitative analysis of metal ions in solution can be carried out by separating the ions into groups on the basis of precipitation reactions and then analyzing each group for individual metal ions.

KEY SKILLS

- Describe the common-ion effect.
- Explain how a buffer functions.
- Calculate the pH of a buffer solution.
- Calculate the pH of a buffer after the addition of small amounts of a strong acid or a strong base.
- Calculate the pH at any point in an acid–base titration of a strong acid and strong base.
- Calculate the pH at any point in a titration of a weak acid with a strong base or a weak base with a strong acid.
- Understand the differences between the titration curves for a strong acid–strong base titration and those when either the acid or base is weak.
- Calculate K_{sp} from molar solubility and molar solubility from K_{sp}.
- Calculate molar solubility in the presence of a common ion.
- Predict the effect of pH on solubility.
- Predict whether a precipitate will form when solutions are mixed by comparing Q and K_{sp}.
- Calculate the ion concentrations required to begin precipitation.
- Explain the effect of complex-ion formation on solubility.

KEY EQUATIONS

- $pH = pK_a + \log \dfrac{[\text{base}]}{[\text{acid}]}$ [17.9]   The Henderson–Hasselbalch equation, used to calculate the pH of a buffer from the concentrations of a conjugate acid–base pair

VISUALIZING CONCEPTS

17.1 The following boxes represent aqueous solutions containing a weak acid, HX, and its conjugate base, X^-. Water molecules and cations are not shown. Which solution has the highest pH? Explain. [Section 17.1]

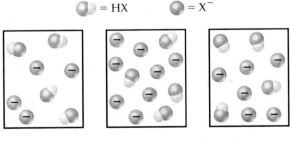

17.2 The beaker on the right contains 0.1 M acetic acid solution with methyl orange as an indicator. The beaker on the left contains a mixture of 0.1 M acetic acid and 0.1 M sodium acetate with methyl orange. **(a)** Using Figure 16.7, estimate the pH of each solution, and explain the difference. **(b)** Which solution is better able to maintain its pH when small amounts of NaOH are added? Explain. [Sections 17.1 and 17.2]

17.3 A buffer contains a weak acid, HX, and its conjugate base.
CQ The weak acid has a pK_a of 4.5, and the buffer solution has a pH of 4.3. Without doing a calculation, predict whether [HX] = [X$^-$], [HX] > [X$^-$], or [HX] < [X$^-$]. Explain. [Section 17.2]

17.4 The drawing on the left represents a buffer composed of
CQ equal concentrations of a weak acid, HX, and its conjugate base, X$^-$. The heights of the columns are proportional to the concentrations of the components of the buffer. **(a)** Which of the three drawings, (1), (2), or (3), represents the buffer after the addition of a strong acid? **(b)** Which of the three represents the buffer after the addition of a strong base? **(c)** Which of the three represents a situation that cannot arise from the addition of either an acid or a base? [Section 17.2]

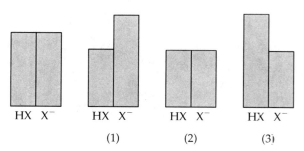

HX X$^-$ HX X$^-$ HX X$^-$ HX X$^-$
(1)   (2)   (3)

17.5 The following drawings represent solutions at various
CQ stages of the titration of a weak acid, HA, with NaOH. (The Na$^+$ ions and water molecules have been omitted for clarity.) To which of the following regions of the titration curve does each drawing correspond: **(a)** before addition of NaOH, **(b)** after addition of NaOH but before equivalence point, **(c)** at equivalence point, **(d)** after equivalence point? [Section 17.3]

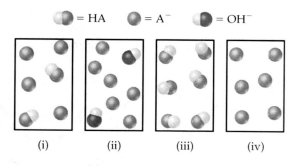

= HA   = A$^-$ = OH$^-$

(i)   (ii)   (iii)   (iv)

17.6 Match the following descriptions of titration curves
CQ with the diagrams: **(a)** strong acid added to strong base, **(b)** strong base added to weak acid, **(c)** strong base added to strong acid, **(d)** strong base added to polyprotic acid. [Section 17.3]

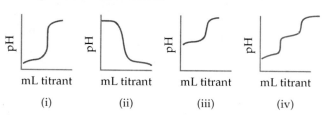

mL titrant   mL titrant   mL titrant   mL titrant
(i)   (ii)   (iii)   (iv)

17.7 Equal volumes of two acids are titrated with 0.10 M
CQ NaOH resulting in the two titration curves shown in the following figure. **(a)** Which curve corresponds to the more concentrated acid solution? **(b)** Which corresponds to the acid with the largest K_a? Explain. [Section 17.3]

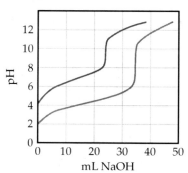

mL NaOH

17.8 The following drawings represent saturated solutions of
CQ three ionic compounds of silver—AgX, AgY, and AgZ. (Na$^+$ cations, which might also be present for charge balance, are not shown.) Which compound has the smallest K_{sp}? [Section 17.4]

= Ag$^+$ = X$^-$, Y$^-$, or Z$^-$

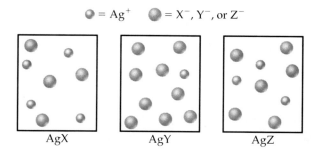

AgX   AgY   AgZ

17.9 The figures below represent the ions in a saturated
CQ aqueous solution of the slightly soluble ionic compound MX: MX(s) $\rightleftharpoons$ M^{2+}(aq) + X^{2-}(aq). (Only the M^{2+} and X^{2-} ions are shown.) **(a)** Which figure represents a solution prepared by dissolving MX in water? **(b)** Which figure represents a solution prepared by dissolving MX in a solution containing Na$_2$X? **(c)** If X^{2-} is a basic anion, which figure represents a saturated solution with the lowest pH? **(d)** If you were to calculate the K_{sp} for MX, would you get the same value in each of the three scenarios? Why or why not? [Sections 17.4 and 17.5]

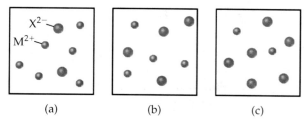

X^{2-} M^{2+}

(a)   (b)   (c)

17.10 The following graphs represent the behavior of BaCO$_3$
CQ under different circumstances. In each case the vertical axis indicates the solubility of the BaCO$_3$ and the

horizontal axis represents the concentration of some other reagent. **(a)** Which graph represents what happens to the solubility of $BaCO_3$ as HNO_3 is added? **(b)** Which graph represents what happens to the $BaCO_3$ solubility as Na_2CO_3 is added? **(c)** Which represents what happens to the $BaCO_3$ solubility as $NaNO_3$ is added? [Section 17.5]

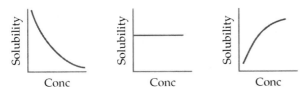

17.11 What is the name given to the kind of behavior demonstrated by a metal hydroxide in this graph? [Section 17.5]

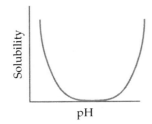

17.12 Three cations, Ni^{2+}, Cu^{2+}, and Ag^+, are separated using two different precipitating agents. Based on Figure 17.22, what two precipitating agents could be used? Using these agents, indicate which of the cations is A, which is B, and which is C. [Section 17.7]

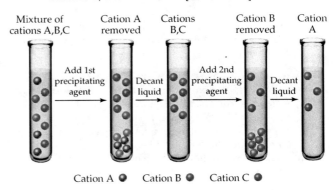

Cation A ●   Cation B ●   Cation C ●

EXERCISES

Common-Ion Effect

17.13 **(a)** What is the common-ion effect? **(b)** Give an example of a salt that can decrease the ionization of HNO_2 in solution.

17.14 **(a)** Consider the equilibrium $B(aq) + H_2O(l) \rightleftharpoons HB^+(aq) + OH^-(aq)$. Using Le Châtelier's principle, explain the effect of the presence of a salt of HB^+ on the ionization of B. **(b)** Give an example of a salt that can decrease the ionization of NH_3 in solution.

17.15 Use information from Appendix D to calculate the pH of **(a)** a solution that is 0.060 M in potassium propionate (C_2H_5COOK or $KC_3H_5O_2$) and 0.085 M in propionic acid (C_2H_5COOH or $HC_3H_5O_2$); **(b)** a solution that is 0.075 M in trimethylamine, $(CH_3)_3N$, and 0.10 M in trimethylammonium chloride, $(CH_3)_3NHCl$; **(c)** a solution that is made by mixing 50.0 mL of 0.15 M acetic acid and 50.0 mL of 0.20 M sodium acetate.

17.16 Use information from Appendix D to calculate the pH of **(a)** a solution that is 0.150 M in sodium formate (HCOONa) and 0.200 M in formic acid (HCOOH); **(b)** a solution that is 0.210 M in pyridine (C_5H_5N) and 0.350 M in pyridinium chloride (C_5H_5NHCl); **(c)** a solution that is made by combining 125 mL of 0.050 M hydrofluoric acid with 50.0 mL of 0.10 M sodium fluoride.

17.17 **(a)** Calculate the percent ionization of 0.0075 M butanoic acid ($K_a = 1.5 \times 10^{-5}$). **(b)** Calculate the percent ionization of 0.0075 M butanoic acid in a solution containing 0.085 M sodium butanoate.

17.18 **(a)** Calculate the percent ionization of 0.085 M lactic acid ($K_a = 1.4 \times 10^{-4}$). **(b)** Calculate the percent ionization of 0.095 M lactic acid in a solution containing 0.0075 M sodium lactate.

Buffers

17.19 Explain why a mixture of CH_3COOH and CH_3COONa can act as a buffer while a mixture of HCl and NaCl cannot.

17.20 Explain why a mixture formed by mixing 100 mL of 0.100 M CH_3COOH and 50 mL of 0.100 M NaOH will act as a buffer.

17.21 **(a)** Calculate the pH of a buffer that is 0.12 M in lactic acid and 0.11 M in sodium lactate. **(b)** Calculate the pH of a buffer formed by mixing 85 mL of 0.13 M lactic acid with 95 mL of 0.15 M sodium lactate.

17.22 **(a)** Calculate the pH of a buffer that is 0.105 M in $NaHCO_3$ and 0.125 M in Na_2CO_3. **(b)** Calculate the pH of a solution formed by mixing 65 mL of 0.20 M $NaHCO_3$ with 75 mL of 0.15 M Na_2CO_3.

17.23 A buffer is prepared by adding 20.0 g of acetic acid (CH$_3$COOH) and 20.0 g of sodium acetate (CH$_3$COONa) to enough water to form 2.00 L of solution. **(a)** Determine the pH of the buffer. **(b)** Write the complete ionic equation for the reaction that occurs when a few drops of hydrochloric acid are added to the buffer. **(c)** Write the complete ionic equation for the reaction that occurs when a few drops of sodium hydroxide solution are added to the buffer.

17.24 A buffer is prepared by adding 7.00 g of ammonia (NH$_3$) and 20.0 g of ammonium chloride (NH$_4$Cl) to enough water to form 2.50 L of solution. **(a)** What is the pH of this buffer? **(b)** Write the complete ionic equation for the reaction that occurs when a few drops of nitric acid are added to the buffer. **(c)** Write the complete ionic equation for the reaction that occurs when a few drops of potassium hydroxide solution are added to the buffer.

17.25 How many moles of sodium hypobromite (NaBrO) should be added to 1.00 L of 0.050 M hypobromous acid (HBrO) to form a buffer solution of pH 9.15? Assume that no volume change occurs when the NaBrO is added.

17.26 How many grams of sodium lactate [CH$_3$CH(OH)COONa or NaC$_3$H$_5$O$_3$] should be added to 1.00 L of 0.150 M lactic acid [CH$_3$CH(OH)COOH or HC$_3$H$_5$O$_3$] to form a buffer solution with pH 4.00? Assume that no volume change occurs when the sodium lactate is added.

17.27 A buffer solution contains 0.10 mol of acetic acid and 0.13 mol of sodium acetate in 1.00 L. **(a)** What is the pH of this buffer? **(b)** What is the pH of the buffer after the addition of 0.02 mol of KOH? **(c)** What is the pH of the buffer after the addition of 0.02 mol of HNO$_3$?

17.28 A buffer solution contains 0.10 mol of propionic acid (C$_2$H$_5$COOH) and 0.13 mol of sodium propionate (C$_2$H$_5$COONa) in 1.50 L. **(a)** What is the pH of this buffer? **(b)** What is the pH of the buffer after the addition of 0.01 mol of NaOH? **(c)** What is the pH of the buffer after the addition of 0.01 mol of HI?

17.29 **(a)** What is the ratio of HCO$_3$$^-$ to H$_2$CO$_3$ in blood of pH 7.4? **(b)** What is the ratio of HCO$_3$$^-$ to H$_2$CO$_3$ in an exhausted marathon runner whose blood pH is 7.1?

17.30 A buffer, consisting of H$_2$PO$_4$$^-$ and HPO$_4$$^{2-}$, helps control the pH of physiological fluids. Many carbonated soft drinks also use this buffer system. What is the pH of a soft drink in which the major buffer ingredients are 6.5 g of NaH$_2$PO$_4$ and 8.0 g of Na$_2$HPO$_4$ per 355 mL of solution?

17.31 You have to prepare a pH 3.50 buffer, and you have the following 0.10 M solutions available: HCOOH, CH$_3$COOH, H$_3$PO$_4$, HCOONa, CH$_3$COONa, and NaH$_2$PO$_4$. Which solutions would you use? How many milliliters of each solution would you use to make approximately a liter of the buffer?

17.32 You have to prepare a pH 4.80 buffer, and you have the following 0.10 M solutions available: formic acid, sodium formate, propionic acid, sodium propionate, phosphoric acid, and sodium dihydrogen phosphate. Which solutions would you use? How many milliliters of each solution would you use to make approximately a liter of the buffer?

Acid–Base Titrations

17.33 The accompanying graph shows the titration curves for
CQ two monoprotic acids. **(a)** Which curve is that of a strong acid? **(b)** What is the approximate pH at the equivalence point of each titration? **(c)** How do the original concentrations of the two acids compare if 40.0 mL of each is titrated to the equivalence point with 0.100 M base?

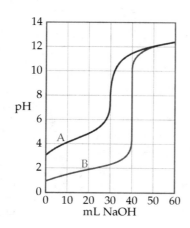

17.34 How does titration of a strong, monoprotic acid with a
CQ strong base differ from titration of a weak, monoprotic acid with a strong base with respect to the following: **(a)** quantity of base required to reach the equivalence point, **(b)** pH at the beginning of the titration, **(c)** pH at the equivalence point, **(d)** pH after addition of a slight excess of base, **(e)** choice of indicator for determining the equivalence point?

17.35 Predict whether the equivalence point of each of the following titrations is below, above, or at pH 7: **(a)** NaHCO$_3$ titrated with NaOH, **(b)** NH$_3$ titrated with HCl, **(c)** KOH titrated with HBr.

17.36 Predict whether the equivalence point of each of the following titrations is below, above, or at pH 7: **(a)** formic acid titrated with NaOH, **(b)** calcium hydroxide titrated with perchloric acid, **(c)** pyridine titrated with nitric acid.

17.37 Two monoprotic acids, both 0.100 M in concentration,
CQ are titrated with 0.100 M NaOH. The pH at the equivalence point for HX is 8.8, and that for HY is 7.9. **(a)** Which is the weaker acid? **(b)** Which indicators in Figure 16.7 could be used to titrate each of these acids?

17.38 Assume that 30.0 mL of a 0.10 M solution of a weak base
CQ   B that accepts one proton is titrated with a 0.10 M solution of the monoprotic strong acid HX. **(a)** How many moles of HX have been added at the equivalence point? **(b)** What is the predominant form of B at the equivalence point? **(c)** What factor determines the pH at the equivalence point? **(d)** Which indicator, phenolphthalein or methyl red, is likely to be the better choice for this titration?

17.39 How many milliliters of 0.0850 M NaOH are required to titrate each of the following solutions to the equivalence point: **(a)** 40.0 mL of 0.0900 M HNO_3, **(b)** 35.0 mL of 0.0850 M CH_3COOH, **(c)** 50.0 mL of a solution that contains 1.85 g of HCl per liter?

17.40 How many milliliters of 0.105 M HCl are needed to titrate each of the following solutions to the equivalence point: **(a)** 45.0 mL of 0.0950 M NaOH, **(b)** 22.5 mL of 0.118 M NH_3, **(c)** 125.0 mL of a solution that contains 1.35 g of NaOH per liter?

17.41 A 20.0-mL sample of 0.200 M HBr solution is titrated with 0.200 M NaOH solution. Calculate the pH of the solution after the following volumes of base have been added: **(a)** 15.0 mL, **(b)** 19.9 mL, **(c)** 20.0 mL, **(d)** 20.1 mL, **(e)** 35.0 mL.

17.42 A 30.0-mL sample of 0.150 M KOH is titrated with 0.125 M $HClO_4$ solution. Calculate the pH after the following volumes of acid have been added: **(a)** 30.0 mL, **(b)** 35.0 mL, **(c)** 36.0 mL, **(d)** 37.0 mL, **(e)** 40.0 mL.

17.43 A 35.0-mL sample of 0.150 M acetic acid (CH_3COOH) is titrated with 0.150 M NaOH solution. Calculate the pH after the following volumes of base have been added: **(a)** 0 mL, **(b)** 17.5 mL, **(c)** 34.5 mL, **(d)** 35.0 mL, **(e)** 35.5 mL, **(f)** 50.0 mL.

17.44 Consider the titration of 30.0 mL of 0.030 M NH_3 with 0.025 M HCl. Calculate the pH after the following volumes of titrant have been added: **(a)** 0 mL, **(b)** 10.0 mL, **(c)** 20.0 mL, **(d)** 35.0 mL, **(e)** 36.0 mL, **(f)** 37.0 mL.

17.45 Calculate the pH at the equivalence point for titrating 0.200 M solutions of each of the following bases with 0.200 M HBr: **(a)** sodium hydroxide (NaOH), **(b)** hydroxylamine (NH_2OH), **(c)** aniline ($C_6H_5NH_2$).

17.46 Calculate the pH at the equivalence point in titrating 0.100 M solutions of each of the following with 0.080 M NaOH: **(a)** hydrobromic acid (HBr), **(b)** lactic acid [$CH_3CH(OH)COOH$], **(c)** sodium hydrogen chromate ($NaHCrO_4$).

Solubility Equilibria and Factors Affecting Solubility

17.47 **(a)** Why is the concentration of undissolved solid not
CQ   explicitly included in the expression for the solubility-product constant? **(b)** Write the expression for the solubility-product constant for each of the following strong electrolytes: AgI, $SrSO_4$, $Fe(OH)_2$, and Hg_2Br_2.

17.48 **(a)** Explain the difference between solubility and
CQ   solubility-product constant. **(b)** Write the expression for the solubility-product constant for each of the following ionic compounds: $MnCO_3$, $Hg(OH)_2$, and $Cu_3(PO_4)_2$.

17.49 **(a)** If the molar solubility of CaF_2 at 35 °C is 1.24 × 10^{-3} mol/L, what is K_{sp} at this temperature? **(b)** It is found that 1.1 × 10^{-2} g of SrF_2 dissolves per 100 mL of aqueous solution at 25 °C. Calculate the solubility product for SrF_2. **(c)** The K_{sp} of $Ba(IO_3)_2$ at 25 °C is 6.0 × 10^{-10}. What is the molar solubility of $Ba(IO_3)_2$?

17.50 **(a)** The molar solubility of $PbBr_2$ at 25 °C is 1.0 × 10^{-2} mol/L. Calculate K_{sp}. **(b)** If 0.0490 g of $AgIO_3$ dissolves per liter of solution, calculate the solubility-product constant. **(c)** Using the appropriate K_{sp} value from Appendix D, calculate the solubility of $Cu(OH)_2$ in grams per liter of solution.

17.51 A 1.00-L solution saturated at 25 °C with calcium oxalate (CaC_2O_4) contains 0.0061 g of CaC_2O_4. Calculate the solubility-product constant for this salt at 25 °C.

17.52 A 1.00-L solution saturated at 25 °C with lead(II) iodide contains 0.54 g of PbI_2. Calculate the solubility-product constant for this salt at 25 °C.

17.53 Using Appendix D, calculate the molar solubility of AgBr in **(a)** pure water, **(b)** 3.0 × 10^{-2} M $AgNO_3$ solution, **(c)** 0.10 M NaBr solution.

17.54 Calculate the solubility of LaF_3 in grams per liter in **(a)** pure water, **(b)** 0.010 M KF solution, **(c)** 0.050 M $LaCl_3$ solution.

17.55 Calculate the solubility of $Mn(OH)_2$ in grams per liter when buffered at pH **(a)** 7.0, **(b)** 9.5, **(c)** 11.8.

17.56 Calculate the molar solubility of $Fe(OH)_2$ when buffered at pH **(a)** 8.0, **(b)** 10.0, **(c)** 12.0.

17.57 Which of the following salts will be substantially more
CQ   soluble in acidic solution than in pure water: **(a)** $ZnCO_3$, **(b)** ZnS, **(c)** BiI_3, **(d)** AgCN, **(e)** $Ba_3(PO_4)_2$?

17.58 For each of the following slightly soluble salts, write the
CQ   net ionic equation, if any, for reaction with acid: **(a)** MnS, **(b)** PbF_2, **(c)** $AuCl_3$, **(d)** $Hg_2C_2O_4$, **(e)** CuBr.

17.59 From the value of K_f listed in Table 17.1, calculate the concentration of Cu^{2+} in 1.0 L of a solution that contains a total of 1 × 10^{-3} mol of copper(II) ion and that is 0.10 M in NH_3.

17.60 To what final concentration of NH_3 must a solution be adjusted to just dissolve 0.020 mol of NiC_2O_4 ($K_{sp} = 4 \times 10^{-10}$) in 1.0 L of solution? (*Hint:* You can neglect the hydrolysis of $C_2O_4^{2-}$ because the solution will be quite basic.)

17.61 By using the values of K_{sp} for AgI and K_f for $Ag(CN)_2^-$, calculate the equilibrium constant for the reaction

$$AgI(s) + 2\,CN^-(aq) \rightleftharpoons Ag(CN)_2^-(aq) + I^-(aq)$$

17.62 Using the value of K_{sp} for Ag_2S, K_{a1} and K_{a2} for H_2S, and $K_f = 1.1 \times 10^5$ for $AgCl_2^-$, calculate the equilibrium constant for the following reaction:

$$Ag_2S(s) + 4\,Cl^-(aq) + 2\,H^+(aq) \rightleftharpoons 2\,AgCl_2^-(aq) + H_2S(aq)$$

Precipitation; Qualitative Analysis

17.63 (a) Will $Ca(OH)_2$ precipitate from solution if the pH of a 0.050 M solution of $CaCl_2$ is adjusted to 8.0? (b) Will Ag_2SO_4 precipitate when 100 mL of 0.050 M $AgNO_3$ is mixed with 10 mL of 5.0×10^{-2} M Na_2SO_4 solution?

17.64 (a) Will $Co(OH)_2$ precipitate from solution if the pH of a 0.020 M solution of $Co(NO_3)_2$ is adjusted to 8.5? (b) Will $AgIO_3$ precipitate when 20 mL of 0.010 M $AgNO_3$ is mixed with 10 mL of 0.015 M $NaIO_3$? (K_{sp} of $AgIO_3$ is 3.1×10^{-8}.)

17.65 Calculate the minimum pH needed to precipitate $Mn(OH)_2$ so completely that the concentration of Mn^{2+} is less than 1 μg per liter [1 part per billion (ppb)].

17.66 Suppose that a 10-mL sample of a solution is to be tested for Cl^- ion by addition of 1 drop (0.2 mL) of 0.10 M $AgNO_3$. What is the minimum number of grams of Cl^- that must be present for $AgCl(s)$ to form?

17.67 A solution contains 2.0×10^{-4} M Ag^+ and 1.5×10^{-3} M Pb^{2+}. If NaI is added, will AgI ($K_{sp} = 8.3 \times 10^{-17}$) or PbI_2 ($K_{sp} = 7.9 \times 10^{-9}$) precipitate first? Specify the concentration of I^- needed to begin precipitation.

17.68 A solution of Na_2SO_4 is added dropwise to a solution that is 0.010 M in Ba^{2+} and 0.010 M in Sr^{2+}. (a) What concentration of SO_4^{2-} is necessary to begin precipitation? (Neglect volume changes. $BaSO_4$: $K_{sp} = 1.1 \times 10^{-10}$; $SrSO_4$: $K_{sp} = 3.2 \times 10^{-7}$.) (b) Which cation precipitates first? (c) What is the concentration of SO_4^{2-} when the second cation begins to precipitate?

17.69 A solution containing an unknown number of metal
CQ ions is treated with dilute HCl; no precipitate forms. The pH is adjusted to about 1, and H_2S is bubbled through. Again, no precipitate forms. The pH of the solution is then adjusted to about 8. Again, H_2S is bubbled through. This time a precipitate forms. The filtrate from this solution is treated with $(NH_4)_2HPO_4$. No precipitate forms.

Which metal ions discussed in Section 17.7 are possibly present? Which are definitely absent within the limits of these tests?

17.70 An unknown solid is entirely soluble in water. On addi-
CQ tion of dilute HCl, a precipitate forms. After the precipitate is filtered off, the pH is adjusted to about 1 and H_2S is bubbled in; a precipitate again forms. After filtering off this precipitate, the pH is adjusted to 8 and H_2S is again added; no precipitate forms. No precipitate forms upon addition of $(NH_4)_2HPO_4$. The remaining solution shows a yellow color in a flame test. Based on these observations, which of the following compounds might be present, which are definitely present, and which are definitely absent: CdS, $Pb(NO_3)_2$, HgO, $ZnSO_4$, $Cd(NO_3)_2$, and Na_2SO_4?

17.71 In the course of various qualitative analysis procedures,
CQ the following mixtures are encountered: (a) Zn^{2+} and Cd^{2+}, (b) $Cr(OH)_3$ and $Fe(OH)_3$, (c) Mg^{2+} and K^+, (d) Ag^+ and Mn^{2+}. Suggest how each mixture might be separated.

17.72 Suggest how the cations in each of the following solution
CQ mixtures can be separated: (a) Na^+ and Cd^{2+}, (b) Cu^{2+} and Mg^{2+}, (c) Pb^{2+} and Al^{3+}, (d) Ag^+ and Hg^{2+}.

17.73 (a) Precipitation of the group 4 cations (Figure 17.22) requires a basic medium. Why is this so? (b) What is the most significant difference between the sulfides precipitated in group 2 and those precipitated in group 3? (c) Suggest a procedure that would serve to redissolve the group 3 cations following their precipitation.

17.74 A student who is in a great hurry to finish his laboratory
CQ work decides that his qualitative analysis unknown contains a metal ion from the insoluble phosphate group, group 4 (Figure 17.22). He therefore tests his sample directly with $(NH_4)_2HPO_4$, skipping earlier tests for the metal ions in groups 1, 2, and 3. He observes a precipitate and concludes that a metal ion from group 4 is indeed present. Why is this possibly an erroneous conclusion?

ADDITIONAL EXERCISES

17.75 Derive an equation similar to the Henderson–Hasselbalch equation relating the pOH of a buffer to the pK_b of its base component.

17.76 Benzenesulfonic acid is a monoprotic acid with $pK_a = 2.25$. Calculate the pH of a buffer composed of $0.150\ M$ benzenesulfonic acid and $0.125\ M$ sodium benzensulfonate.

17.77 Furoic acid ($HC_5H_3O_3$) has a K_a value of 6.76×10^{-4} at 25 °C. Calculate the pH at 25 °C of **(a)** a solution formed by adding 25.0 g of furoic acid and 30.0 g of sodium furoate ($NaC_5H_3O_3$) to enough water to form 0.250 L of solution; **(b)** a solution formed by mixing 30.0 mL of $0.250\ M\ HC_5H_3O_3$ and 20.0 mL of $0.22\ M\ NaC_5H_3O_3$ and diluting the total volume to 125 mL; **(c)** a solution prepared by adding 50.0 mL of $1.65\ M$ NaOH solution to 0.500 L of $0.0850\ M\ HC_5H_3O_3$.

17.78 The acid–base indicator bromcresol green is a weak acid. The yellow acid and blue base forms of the indicator are present in equal concentrations in a solution when the pH is 4.68. What is the pK_a for bromcresol green?

17.79 Equal quantities of $0.010\ M$ solutions of an acid HA and a base B are mixed. The pH of the resulting solution is 9.2. **(a)** Write the equilibrium equation and equilibrium-constant expression for the reaction between HA and B. **(b)** If K_a for HA is 8.0×10^{-5}, what is the value of the equilibrium constant for the reaction between HA and B? **(c)** What is the value of K_b for B?

17.80 Two buffers are prepared by adding an equal number of moles of formic acid (HCOOH) and sodium formate (HCOONa) to enough water to make 1.00 L of solution. Buffer A is prepared using 1.00 mol each of formic acid and sodium formate. Buffer B is prepared by using 0.010 mol of each. **(a)** Calculate the pH of each buffer, and explain why they are equal. **(b)** Which buffer will have the greater buffer capacity? Explain. **(c)** Calculate the change in pH for each buffer upon the addition of 1.0 mL of $1.00\ M$ HCl. **(d)** Calculate the change in pH for each buffer upon the addition of 10 mL of $1.00\ M$ HCl. **(e)** Discuss your answers for parts (c) and (d) in light of your response to part (b).

17.81 A biochemist needs 750 mL of an acetic acid–sodium acetate buffer with pH 4.50. Solid sodium acetate (CH_3COONa) and glacial acetic acid (CH_3COOH) are available. Glacial acetic acid is 99% CH_3COOH by mass and has a density of 1.05 g/mL. If the buffer is to be $0.15\ M$ in CH_3COOH, how many grams of CH_3COONa and how many milliliters of glacial acetic acid must be used?

17.82 A sample of 0.2140 g of an unknown monoprotic acid was dissolved in 25.0 mL of water and titrated with $0.0950\ M$ NaOH. The acid required 27.4 mL of base to reach the equivalence point. **(a)** What is the molar mass of the acid? **(b)** After 15.0 mL of base had been added in the titration, the pH was found to be 6.50. What is the K_a for the unknown acid?

17.83 Show that the pH at the halfway point of a titration of a weak acid with a strong base (where the volume of added base is half of that needed to reach the equivalence point) is equal to pK_a for the acid.

17.84 Potassium hydrogen phthalate, often abbreviated KHP, can be obtained in high purity and is used to determine the concentrations of solutions of strong bases. Strong bases react with the hydrogen phthalate ion as follows:

$$HP^-(aq) + OH^-(aq) \longrightarrow H_2O(l) + P^{2-}(aq)$$

The molar mass of KHP is 204.2 g/mol and K_a for the HP^- ion is 3.1×10^{-6}. **(a)** If a titration experiment begins with 0.4885 g of KHP and has a final volume of about 100 mL, which indicator from Figure 16.7 would be most appropriate? **(b)** If the titration required 38.55 mL of NaOH solution to reach the end point, what is the concentration of the NaOH solution?

17.85 If 40.00 mL of $0.100\ M\ Na_2CO_3$ is titrated with $0.100\ M$ HCl, calculate **(a)** the pH at the start of the titration; **(b)** the volume of HCl required to reach the first equivalence point and the predominant species present at this point; **(c)** the volume of HCl required to reach the second equivalence point and the predominant species present at this point; **(d)** the pH at the second equivalence point.

17.86 A hypothetical weak acid, HA, was combined with NaOH in the following proportions: 0.20 mol of HA, 0.080 mol of NaOH. The mixture was diluted to a total volume of 1.0 L, and the pH measured. **(a)** If pH = 4.80, what is the pK_a of the acid? **(b)** How many additional moles of NaOH should be added to the solution to increase the pH to 5.00?

[17.87] What is the pH of a solution made by mixing 0.30 mol NaOH, 0.25 mol Na_2HPO_4, and 0.20 mol H_3PO_4 with water and diluting to 1.00 L?

[17.88] Suppose you want to do a physiological experiment that calls for a pH 6.5 buffer. You find that the organism with which you are working is not sensitive to the weak acid H_2X ($K_{a1} = 2 \times 10^{-2}$; $K_{a2} = 5.0 \times 10^{-7}$) or its sodium salts. You have available a $1.0\ M$ solution of this acid and a $1.0\ M$ solution of NaOH. How much of the NaOH solution should be added to 1.0 L of the acid to give a buffer at pH 6.50? (Ignore any volume change.)

[17.89] How many microliters of $1.000\ M$ NaOH solution must be added to 25.00 mL of a $0.1000\ M$ solution of lactic acid [$CH_3CH(OH)COOH$ or $HC_3H_5O_3$] to produce a buffer with pH = 3.75?

17.90 A person suffering from anxiety begins breathing rapid-
CQ ly and as a result suffers alkalosis, an increase in blood
pH. **(a)** Using Equation 17.10, explain how rapid breathing can cause the pH of blood to increase. **(b)** One cure
for this problem is breathing in a paper bag. Why does
this procedure lower blood pH?

17.91 For each pair of compounds, use K_{sp} values to determine
which has the greater molar solubility: **(a)** CdS or CuS,
(b) $PbCO_3$ or $BaCrO_4$, **(c)** $Ni(OH)_2$ or $NiCO_3$, **(d)** AgI or
Ag_2SO_4.

17.92 Describe the solubility of $CaCO_3$ in each of the following solutions compared to its solubility in water: **(a)** in
0.10 M NaCl solution; **(b)** in 0.10 M $Ca(NO_3)_2$ solution;
(c) 0.10 M Na_2CO_3; **(d)** 0.10 M HCl solution. (Answer
same, less soluble, or more soluble.)

17.93 Tooth enamel is composed of hydroxyapatite, whose simplest formula is $Ca_5(PO_4)_3OH$, and whose corresponding
$K_{sp} = 6.8 \times 10^{-27}$. As discussed in the "Chemistry and
Life" box in Section 17.5, fluoride in fluorinated water or
in toothpaste reacts with hydroxyapatite to form fluoroapatite, $Ca_5(PO_4)_3F$, whose $K_{sp} = 1.0 \times 10^{-60}$. **(a)** Write
the expression for the solubility-constant for hydroxyapatite and for fluoroapatite. **(b)** Calculate the molar
solubility of each of these compounds.

17.94 Calculate the solubility of $Mg(OH)_2$ in 0.50 M NH_4Cl.

[17.95] Seawater contains 0.13% magnesium by mass, and has a
density of 1.025 g/mL. What fraction of the magnesium
can be removed by adding a stoichiometric quantity of
CaO (that is, one mole of CaO for each mole of Mg^{2+})?

17.96 The solubility-product constant for barium permanganate, $Ba(MnO_4)_2$, is 2.5×10^{-10}. Assume that solid
$Ba(MnO_4)_2$ is in equilibrium with a solution of $KMnO_4$.
What concentration of $KMnO_4$ is required to establish
a concentration of $2.0 \times 10^{-8} M$ for the Ba^{2+} ion in
solution?

17.97 Calculate the ratio of $[Ca^{2+}]$ to $[Fe^{2+}]$ in a lake in which
CQ the water is in equilibrium with deposits of both $CaCO_3$
and $FeCO_3$. Assume that the water is slightly basic and
that the hydrolysis of the carbonate ion can therefore be
ignored.

[17.98] The solubility products of $PbSO_4$ and $SrSO_4$ are
CQ 6.3×10^{-7} and 3.2×10^{-7}, respectively. What are the
values of $[SO_4^{2-}]$, $[Pb^{2+}]$, and $[Sr^{2+}]$ in a solution at
equilibrium with both substances?

[17.99] What pH buffer solution is needed to give a Mg^{2+} concentration of $3.0 \times 10^{-2} M$ in equilibrium with solid
magnesium oxalate?

[17.100] The value of K_{sp} for $Mg_3(AsO_4)_2$ is 2.1×10^{-20}.
CQ The AsO_4^{3-} ion is derived from the weak acid H_3AsO_4
($pK_{a1} = 2.22$; $pK_{a2} = 6.98$; $pK_{a3} = 11.50$). When asked
to calculate the molar solubility of $Mg_3(AsO_4)_2$ in water,
a student used the K_{sp} expression and assumed that
$[Mg^{2+}] = 1.5[AsO_4^{3-}]$. Why was this a mistake?

[17.101] The solubility product for $Zn(OH)_2$ is 3.0×10^{-16}.
The formation constant for the hydroxo complex,
$Zn(OH)_4^{2-}$, is 4.6×10^{17}. What concentration of OH^- is
required to dissolve 0.015 mol of $Zn(OH)_2$ in a liter of
solution?

INTEGRATIVE EXERCISES

17.102 **(a)** Write the net ionic equation for the reaction that occurs when a solution of hydrochloric acid (HCl) is mixed
with a solution of sodium formate ($NaCHO_2$).
(b) Calculate the equilibrium constant for this reaction.
(c) Calculate the equilibrium concentrations of Na^+, Cl^-,
H^+, CHO_2^-, and $HCHO_2$ when 50.0 mL of 0.15 M HCl is
mixed with 50.0 mL of 0.15 M $NaCHO_2$.

17.103 **(a)** A 0.1044-g sample of an unknown monoprotic acid
requires 22.10 mL of 0.0500 M NaOH to reach the end
point. What is the molecular weight of the unknown?
(b) As the acid is titrated, the pH of the solution after the
addition of 11.05 mL of the base is 4.89. What is the K_a
for the acid? **(c)** Using Appendix D, suggest the identity
of the acid. Do both the molecular weight and K_a value
agree with your choice?

17.104 A sample of 7.5 L of NH_3 gas at 22 °C and 735 torr is bubbled into a 0.50-L solution of 0.40 M HCl. Assuming that
all the NH_3 dissolves and that the volume of the solution
remains 0.50 L, calculate the pH of the resulting solution.

17.105 Aspirin has the structural formula

At body temperature (37 °C), K_a for aspirin equals
3×10^{-5}. If two aspirin tablets, each having a mass of
325 mg, are dissolved in a full stomach whose volume is
1 L and whose pH is 2, what percent of the aspirin is in
the form of neutral molecules?

17.106 What is the pH at 25 °C of water saturated with CO_2 at a
partial pressure of 1.10 atm? The Henry's law constant
for CO_2 at 25 °C is 3.1×10^{-2} mol/L-atm. The CO_2 is an
acidic oxide, reacting with H_2O to form H_2CO_3.

17.107 Excess $Ca(OH)_2$ is shaken with water to produce a saturated solution. The solution is filtered, and a 50.00-mL sample titrated with HCl requires 11.23 mL of 0.0983 M HCl to reach the end point. Calculate K_{sp} for $Ca(OH)_2$. Compare your result with that in Appendix D. Do you think the solution was kept at 25 °C?

17.108 The osmotic pressure of a saturated solution of strontium sulfate at 25 °C is 21 torr. What is the solubility product of this salt at 25 °C?

17.109 A concentration of 10–100 parts per billion (by mass) of Ag^+ is an effective disinfectant in swimming pools. However, if the concentration exceeds this range, the Ag^+ can cause adverse health effects. One way to main-

tain an appropriate concentration of Ag^+ is to add a slightly soluble salt to the pool. Using K_{sp} values from Appendix D, calculate the equilibrium concentration of Ag^+ in parts per billion that would exist in equilibrium with **(a)** AgCl, **(b)** AgBr, **(c)** AgI.

[17.110] Fluoridation of drinking water is employed in many places to aid in the prevention of tooth decay. Typically the F^- ion concentration is adjusted to about 1 ppb. Some water supplies are also "hard"; that is, they contain certain cations such as Ca^{2+} that interfere with the action of soap. Consider a case where the concentration of Ca^{2+} is 8 ppb. Could a precipitate of CaF_2 form under these conditions? (Make any necessary approximations.)

CHAPTER

23

Organic Chemistry

▲ Flamingos owe their color to organic chemicals in their diet. Without these compounds, the feathers eventually turn white.

CONTENTS

From the very beginning of chemical studies in the mid-1700s, people noticed that substances obtained from plants and animals were different from those obtained from minerals. Not only did they have lower melting points, they also tended to decompose when heated and were generally more difficult to work with and purify. To express this difference, the term *organic chemistry* was used to mean the study of compounds from living organisms, while *inorganic chemistry* was used for the study of compounds from nonliving sources.

Today we know that there are no fundamental differences between organic and inorganic compounds—the same principles apply to both. The only common characteristic of compounds from living sources is that all contain the element *carbon*. Thus, **organic chemistry** is now defined as the study of carbon compounds.

Why is carbon special, and why do chemists still treat organic chemistry as a separate branch of science? The answers to these questions involve the ability of carbon atoms to bond together, forming long chains and rings. Of all the elements, only carbon is able to form such an immense array of compounds, from methane, with one carbon atom, to deoxyribonucleic acid (DNA), with tens of billions of carbon atoms. More than 30 million organic compounds have been made, and thousands of new ones are made every day in laboratories throughout the world.

23.1 | THE NATURE OF ORGANIC MOLECULES

Let's review what we've seen in earlier chapters about organic molecules:

• Carbon is *tetravalent* (Section 7.5). It has four outer-shell electrons $(1s^2 2s^2 2p^2)$ and forms four bonds. In methane, for instance, carbon is bonded to four hydrogen atoms.

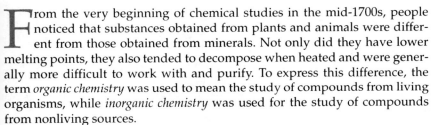

Methane, CH_4

937

- Organic molecules have *covalent bonds* (Section 7.1). In ethane, for instance, all bonds result from the sharing of two electrons, either between C and C or between C and H.

$$\begin{array}{c} \text{H H} \\ \text{H:\ddot{C}:\ddot{C}:H} \\ \text{H H} \end{array} = \begin{array}{c} \text{H H} \\ | \;\; | \\ \text{H}-\text{C}-\text{C}-\text{H} \\ | \;\; | \\ \text{H H} \end{array} \qquad \text{Ethane, C}_2\text{H}_6 \text{ or CH}_3\text{CH}_3$$

- Organic molecules have *polar covalent bonds* when carbon bonds to an element on the right or left side of the periodic table (Section 7.4). In chloromethane, the electronegative chlorine atom attracts electrons more strongly than carbon does, polarizing the C–Cl bond so that carbon has a partial positive charge, $\delta+$. In methyllithium, the lithium attracts electrons less strongly than carbon does, polarizing the carbon–lithium bond so that carbon has a partial negative charge, $\delta-$. Electrostatic potential maps thus show the carbon of chloromethane as blue, or electron-poor, while the methyllithium carbon appears red, or electron-rich.

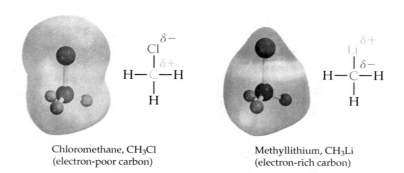

Chloromethane, CH$_3$Cl
(electron-poor carbon)

Methyllithium, CH$_3$Li
(electron-rich carbon)

- Carbon can form *multiple covalent bonds* by sharing more than two electrons with a neighboring atom (Section 7.5). In ethylene, the two carbon atoms share four electrons in a double bond. In acetylene, the two carbons share six electrons in a triple bond.

$$\begin{array}{c} \text{H} \quad\quad \text{H} \\ \text{:C::C:} \\ \text{H} \quad\quad \text{H} \end{array} = \begin{array}{c} \text{H} \quad\quad \text{H} \\ \diagdown \quad\quad \diagup \\ \text{C}=\text{C} \\ \diagup \quad\quad \diagdown \\ \text{H} \quad\quad \text{H} \end{array} \qquad \text{Ethylene, C}_2\text{H}_4$$

$$\text{H:C:::C:H} = \text{H}-\text{C}\equiv\text{C}-\text{H} \qquad \text{Acetylene, C}_2\text{H}_2$$

- Organic molecules have specific three-dimensional shapes, which can be predicted by the VSEPR model (Section 7.9). When carbon is bonded to four atoms, as in methane, the bonds are oriented toward the four corners of a tetrahedron with carbon in the center and with H–C–H angles near 109.5°.

$$\begin{array}{c} \text{H} \\ | \\ \text{H}\text{-}\text{-}\text{-}\overset{\text{C}}{}\text{H} \\ \text{H} \end{array}$$

109.5°

When carbon bonds to three atoms, as in ethylene, the bonds are at angles of approximately 120° to one another. When carbon bonds to two atoms, as in acetylene, the bonds are at angles of 180°.

Ethylene (120° angles)

Acetylene (180° angles)

- Carbon uses *hybrid atomic orbitals* for bonding (Sections 7.11 and 7.12). A carbon that bonds to four atoms uses sp^3 orbitals, formed by the combination of an atomic *s* orbital with three atomic *p* orbitals. These sp^3 orbitals point toward the corners of a regular tetrahedron, accounting for the observed geometry of carbon.

  Doubly bonded carbons are sp^2-hybridized. Carbon has three sp^2 hybrid orbitals, which lie in a plane and point toward the corners of an equilateral triangle, and one unhybridized *p* orbital, which is oriented at a 90° angle to the plane of the sp^2 hybrids. When two sp^2-hybridized carbon atoms approach each other with sp^2 orbitals aligned head-on for sigma bonding, the unhybridized *p* orbitals on each carbon overlap to form a pi bond, resulting in a net carbon–carbon double bond.

  Triply bonded carbons are sp-hybridized. Carbon has two sp hybrid orbitals, which are oriented 180° away from each other, and two unhybridized *p* orbitals, which are oriented 90° from the sp hybrids and 90° from each other. When two sp-hybridized carbon atoms approach each other with sp orbitals aligned head-on for sigma bonding, the *p* orbitals on each carbon overlap to form two pi bonds, resulting in a net carbon–carbon triple bond.

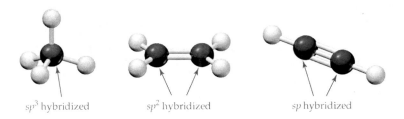

sp^3 hybridized sp^2 hybridized sp hybridized

Covalent bonding gives organic compounds properties that are quite different from those of ionic compounds. Intermolecular forces between individual organic molecules are relatively weak, and organic compounds therefore have lower melting and boiling points than do ionic compounds. In fact, many simple organic compounds are liquid at room temperature. In addition, most organic compounds are insoluble in water and don't conduct electricity. Only a few small polar organic molecules such as glucose, acetic acid, and ethyl alcohol dissolve in water.

23.2 | ALKANES AND THEIR ISOMERS

Why are there so many organic compounds? The answer is that a relatively small number of atoms can bond together in a great many ways. Take molecules that contain only carbon and hydrogen (**hydrocarbons**) and have only single bonds. Such compounds belong to the family of organic molecules called **alkanes**.

▲ The paraffin wax coating that makes these apples so shiny is a mixture of alkanes.

If you imagine ways that one carbon and four hydrogens can combine, only methane, CH_4, is possible. If you imagine ways that two carbons and six hydrogens can combine, only ethane, C_2H_6, is possible; and if you imagine the combination of three carbons with eight hydrogens, only propane, C_3H_8, is possible.

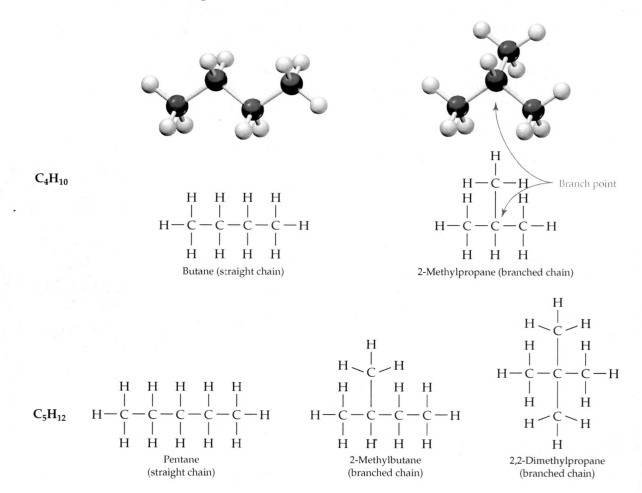

Methane, CH_4 Ethane, C_2H_6 Propane, C_3H_8

When larger numbers of carbons and hydrogens combine, though, more than one structure can result. There are two ways in which molecules with the formula C_4H_{10} can be formed: Either the four carbons can be in a row, or they can be in a branched arrangement. Similarly, there are three ways in which molecules with the formula C_5H_{12} can result, and even more ways for larger alkanes. Compounds with all their carbons connected in a row are called **straight-chain alkanes,** and those with a branching connection of carbons are called **branched-chain alkanes.**

C_4H_{10}

Butane (straight chain)

2-Methylpropane (branched chain)

Branch point

C_5H_{12}

Pentane
(straight chain)

2-Methylbutane
(branched chain)

2,2-Dimethylpropane
(branched chain)

Compounds like the two different C_4H_{10} molecules and the three different C_5H_{12} molecules, which have the same molecular formula but different chemical structures, are called *isomers* (Section 20.8). The number of possible alkane isomers grows rapidly as the number of carbon atoms increases, from five isomers for C_6H_{14} to more than 6×10^{13} isomers for $C_{40}H_{82}$!

As noted in Section 20.8, different isomers are different chemical compounds. They have different structures, different chemical properties, and different physical properties, such as melting point and boiling point. For example, ethyl alcohol (ethanol, or grain alcohol) and dimethyl ether both have the formula C_2H_6O, yet ethyl alcohol is a liquid with a boiling point of 78.5 °C, whereas dimethyl ether is a gas with a boiling point of −23 °C.

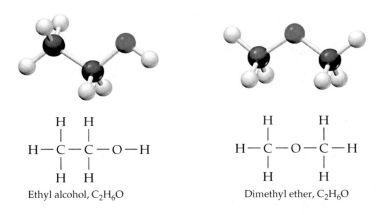

Ethyl alcohol, C_2H_6O Dimethyl ether, C_2H_6O

▶ **PROBLEM 23.1** Draw the straight-chain isomer with the formula C_7H_{16}.

▶ **PROBLEM 23.2** Draw the five alkane isomers with the formula C_6H_{14}.

23.3 | DRAWING ORGANIC STRUCTURES

It's both awkward and time-consuming to draw all the bonds and all the atoms in an organic molecule, even for a relatively small compound like C_4H_{10}. Thus, a short-hand way of drawing **condensed structures** is often used. In condensed structures, carbon–hydrogen and most carbon–carbon single bonds aren't shown; rather, they're "understood." If a carbon atom has three hydrogens bonded to it, we write CH_3; if the carbon has two hydrogens bonded to it, we write CH_2; and so on. For example, the four-carbon, straight-chain alkane (called butane) and its branched-chain isomer (called 2-methylpropane, or isobutane) can be written in the following way:

$$ \text{H}-\overset{\overset{\displaystyle \text{H}}{|}}{\underset{\underset{\displaystyle \text{H}}{|}}{\text{C}}}-\overset{\overset{\displaystyle \text{H}}{|}}{\underset{\underset{\displaystyle \text{H}}{|}}{\text{C}}}-\overset{\overset{\displaystyle \text{H}}{|}}{\underset{\underset{\displaystyle \text{H}}{|}}{\text{C}}}-\overset{\overset{\displaystyle \text{H}}{|}}{\underset{\underset{\displaystyle \text{H}}{|}}{\text{C}}}-\text{H} \quad = \quad CH_3CH_2CH_2CH_3 \quad \text{Butane} $$

$$ \text{H}-\overset{\overset{\displaystyle \text{H}}{|}}{\underset{\underset{\displaystyle \text{H}}{|}}{\text{C}}}-\overset{\overset{\displaystyle \text{C}}{|}}{\underset{\underset{\displaystyle \text{H}}{|}}{\text{C}}}-\overset{\overset{\displaystyle \text{H}}{|}}{\underset{\underset{\displaystyle \text{H}}{|}}{\text{C}}}-\text{H} \quad = \quad CH_3CHCH_3 \quad \begin{matrix} \text{2- Methylpropane} \\ \text{(Isobutane)} \end{matrix} $$

Note that the horizontal bonds between carbons aren't shown—the CH_3 and CH_2 units are simply placed next to each other—but the vertical bond in 2-methylpropane is shown for clarity.

☞ WORKED KEY CONCEPT EXAMPLE 23.1

INTERPRETING A MOLECULAR MODEL

Give the formula of the following compound, and convert the model into a condensed structure:

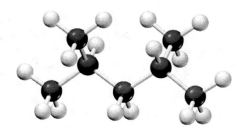

STRATEGY AND SOLUTION

The compound has 7 carbons and 16 hydrogens: C_7H_{16}. Its condensed structure is

$$\underset{\begin{array}{c}\\ CH_3CHCH_2CHCH_3\end{array}}{\overset{\begin{array}{cc}CH_3 & CH_3 \\ | & | \end{array}}{}}$$

▸ **PROBLEM 23.3**   Draw the three isomers of C_5H_{12} as condensed structures.

☞ KEY CONCEPT PROBLEM 23.4   Give the formula of the following molecular model, and convert the model into a condensed structure.

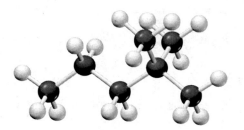

23.4 | THE SHAPES OF ORGANIC MOLECULES

The condensed structure of an organic molecule indicates the connections among atoms but implies nothing about three-dimensional shape. Thus, a molecule can be arbitrarily drawn in many different ways. The branched-chain alkane called 2-methylbutane, for instance, might be represented by any of the following structures. All have four carbons connected in a row, with a $-CH_3$ branch on the second carbon from the end.

$$\underset{CH_3CHCH_2CH_3}{\overset{\overset{CH_3}{|}}{}} \qquad \underset{CH_3CH_2CHCH_3}{\overset{\overset{CH_3}{|}}{}} \qquad CH_3CH_2CH(CH_3)_2$$

$$\underset{\overset{|}{CH_3}}{CH_3CHCH_2CH_3} \qquad \underset{\overset{|}{CH_3}}{CH_3CH_2CHCH_3}$$

Some representations of 2-methylbutane

In fact, 2-methylbutane has no one single shape because rotation occurs around carbon–carbon single bonds. The two parts of a molecule joined by a carbon–carbon single bond are free to spin around the bond, giving rise to an infinite number of possible three-dimensional structures. Thus, a large sample of 2-methylbutane contains a great many molecules that are constantly changing their shape. At any given instant, though, most of the molecules have an extended, zigzag shape, which is slightly more stable than other possibilities. The same is true for other alkanes.

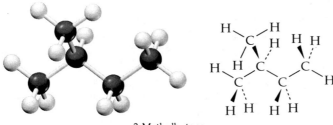

2-Methylbutane

WORKED EXAMPLE 23.2

IDENTIFYING ISOMERIC COMPOUNDS

The following condensed structures have the same formula, C_8H_{18}. Which of them represent the same molecule?

(a)
$$
\begin{array}{cc}
CH_3 & CH_3 \\
| & | \\
\end{array}
$$
$CH_3CHCH_2CHCH_2CH_3$

(b)
$$
\begin{array}{cc}
CH_3 & CH_3 \\
| & | \\
\end{array}
$$
$CH_3CH_2CHCH_2CHCH_3$

(c)
$$
\begin{array}{cc}
CH_3 & CH_3 \\
| & | \\
\end{array}
$$
$CH_3CHCH_2CH_2CHCH_3$

STRATEGY

Pay attention to the order of connection between atoms. Don't get confused by the apparent differences caused by writing a structure right-to-left versus left-to-right.

SOLUTION

Structure (a) has a straight chain of six carbons with $-CH_3$ branches on the second and fourth carbons from the end. Structure (b) also has a straight chain of six carbons with $-CH_3$ branches on the second and fourth carbons from the end and is therefore identical to (a). The only difference between (a) and (b) is that one is written "forward" and one is written "backward." Structure (c) has a straight chain of six carbons with $-CH_3$ branches on the second and *fifth* carbons from the end, so it is an isomer of (a) and (b).

▸ **PROBLEM 23.5** Which of the following structures are identical?

(a)
$$
\begin{array}{cc}
CH_3 & CH_3 \\
| & | \\
\end{array}
$$
$CH_3CH_2CCH_2CHCH_3$
$$
\begin{array}{c}
| \\
CH_3 \\
\end{array}
$$

(b)
$$
\begin{array}{cc}
CH_3 & CH_3 \\
| & | \\
\end{array}
$$
$CH_3CHCH_2CH_2CHCH_2CH_3$

(c)
$$
\begin{array}{c}
CH_2CH_3 \\
| \\
\end{array}
$$
$CH_3CCH_2CHCH_3$
$$
\begin{array}{cc}
| & | \\
CH_3 & CH_3 \\
\end{array}
$$

⊙ **KEY CONCEPT PROBLEM 23.6** Are the following two structures identical, isomers, or unrelated?

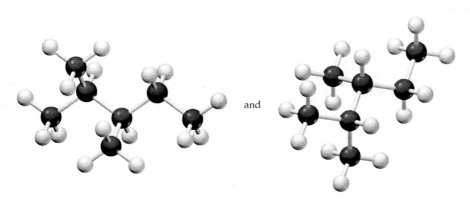

and

23.5 | NAMING ALKANES

In earlier times, when relatively few pure organic chemicals were known, new compounds were named at the whim of their discoverer. Thus, urea is a crystalline substance first isolated from urine, and the barbiturates are a group of tranquilizing agents said to be named by their discoverer in honor of his friend Barbara. As more and more compounds became known, however, the need for a systematic method of naming organic compounds became apparent.

The system of naming generally used is that devised by the International Union of Pure and Applied Chemistry, abbreviated IUPAC. In the IUPAC system, a chemical name has three parts: prefix, parent, and suffix. The parent name tells how many carbon atoms are present in the longest continuous chain; the suffix identifies what family the molecule belongs to; and the prefix (if needed) specifies the location of various substituent groups attached to the parent chain:

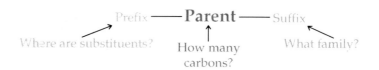

Prefix ——**Parent**—— Suffix

Where are substituents?   How many carbons?   What family?

Straight-chain alkanes are named by counting the number of carbon atoms in the chain and adding the suffix -*ane*. With the exception of the first four compounds—methane, ethane, propane, and butane—whose names have historical origins, the alkanes are named from Greek numbers according to the number of carbons present. Thus, *pent*ane is the five-carbon alkane, *hex*ane is the six-carbon alkane, and so on, as shown in Table 23.1.

TABLE 23.1 Names of Straight-Chain Alkanes

Number of Carbons	Structure	Name	Number of Carbons	Structure	Name
1	CH_4	*Methane*	6	$CH_3CH_2CH_2CH_2CH_2CH_3$	*Hexane*
2	CH_3CH_3	*Ethane*	7	$CH_3CH_2CH_2CH_2CH_2CH_2CH_3$	*Heptane*
3	$CH_3CH_2CH_3$	*Propane*	8	$CH_3CH_2CH_2CH_2CH_2CH_2CH_2CH_3$	*Octane*
4	$CH_3CH_2CH_2CH_3$	*Butane*	9	$CH_3CH_2CH_2CH_2CH_2CH_2CH_2CH_2CH_3$	*Nonane*
5	$CH_3CH_2CH_2CH_2CH_3$	*Pentane*	10	$CH_3CH_2CH_2CH_2CH_2CH_2CH_2CH_2CH_2CH_3$	*Decane*

Branched-chain alkanes are named by following four steps:

Step 1. Name the main chain. Find the longest continuous chain of carbons in the molecule, and use the name of that chain as the parent name. The longest chain may not always be obvious from the manner of writing; you may have to "turn corners" to find it:

$$CH_3 - CH_2$$
$$CH_3 - CH - CH_2 - CH_2 - CH_3$$

Named as hexane, not as a pentane, because the longest chain has six carbons.

If you prefer, you can redraw the structure so that the longest chain is on one line:

$$CH_3 - CH_2$$
$$CH_3 - CH - CH_2 - CH_2 - CH_3$$

same as

$$CH_3$$
$$CH_3 - CH_2 - CH - CH_2 - CH_2 - CH_3$$

Science Fundamentals

Step 2. Number the carbon atoms in the main chain. Beginning at the end nearer the first branch point, number each carbon atom in the parent chain:

$$CH_3 - CH_2 - \underset{3}{\overset{\overset{\displaystyle CH_3}{|}}{CH}} - CH_2 - CH_2 - CH_3$$

$$\begin{array}{cccccc} 1 & 2 & 3 & 4 & 5 & 6 \\ [\,6 & 5 & 4 & 3 & 2 & 1\,] \end{array}$$

Wrong numbering

The first (and only) branch occurs at the third carbon, C3, if we start numbering from the left, but would occur at C4 if we started from the right by mistake.

Step 3. Identify and number the branching substituent. Assign a number to each branching substituent group on the parent chain according to its point of attachment.

$$CH_3 - CH_2 - \underset{3}{\overset{\overset{\displaystyle CH_3}{|}}{CH}} - CH_2 - CH_2 - CH_3$$

$$\begin{array}{cccccc} 1 & 2 & 3 & 4 & 5 & 6 \end{array}$$

The main chain is a hexane. There is a $-CH_3$ substituent group connected to C3 of the chain.

If there are two substituent groups on the same carbon, assign the same number to both. There must always be as many numbers in the name as there are substituents.

$$CH_3 - CH_2 - \underset{\underset{\displaystyle CH_3}{|}}{\overset{\overset{\displaystyle CH_2 - CH_3}{|}}{C}} - CH_2 - CH_2 - CH_3$$

$$\begin{array}{cccccc} 1 & 2 & 3 & 4 & 5 & 6 \end{array}$$

The main chain is hexane. There are two substituents, a $-CH_3$ and a $-CH_2CH_3$, both connected to C3 of the chain.

The $-CH_3$ and $-CH_2CH_3$ substituents that branch off the main chain in this compound are called **alkyl groups.** You can think of an alkyl group as the part of an alkane that remains when a hydrogen is removed. For example, removal of a hydrogen from methane, CH_4, gives the *methyl group,* $-CH_3$, and removal of a hydrogen from ethane, CH_3CH_3, gives the *ethyl group,* $-CH_2CH_3$. Alkyl groups are named by replacing the *-ane* ending of the parent alkane with an *-yl* ending.

$$H - \underset{\underset{\displaystyle H}{|}}{\overset{\overset{\displaystyle H}{|}}{C}} - H \xrightarrow[\text{one H}]{\text{Remove}} H - \underset{\underset{\displaystyle H}{|}}{\overset{\overset{\displaystyle H}{|}}{C}} \ddagger \qquad H - \underset{\underset{\displaystyle H}{|}}{\overset{\overset{\displaystyle H}{|}}{C}} - \underset{\underset{\displaystyle H}{|}}{\overset{\overset{\displaystyle H}{|}}{C}} - H \xrightarrow[\text{one H}]{\text{Remove}} H - \underset{\underset{\displaystyle H}{|}}{\overset{\overset{\displaystyle H}{|}}{C}} - \underset{\underset{\displaystyle H}{|}}{\overset{\overset{\displaystyle H}{|}}{C}} \ddagger$$

Methane   A methyl group   Ethane   An ethyl group

Step 4. Write the name as a single word. Use hyphens to separate the different prefixes, and use commas to separate numbers when there are more than one. If two or more different substituent groups are present, list them in alphabetical order. If two or more identical substituents are present, use one of the prefixes *di-, tri-, tetra-,* and so forth, but don't use these numerical prefixes for alphabetizing purposes. That is, a prefix like "dimethyl" is listed alphabetically under "m" rather than under "d". Look at the following examples to see how names are written:

$$CH_3 - CH_2 - \underset{3}{\overset{\overset{\displaystyle CH_3}{|}}{CH}} - CH_2 - CH_2 - CH_3$$

$$\begin{array}{cccccc} 1 & 2 & 3 & 4 & 5 & 6 \end{array}$$

3-Methylhexane—a six-carbon main chain with a 3-methyl substituent

$$CH_3 - CH_2 - \underset{3}{\overset{\overset{\displaystyle CH_2 - CH_3}{|}}{C}} - CH_2 - CH_2 - CH_3$$

$$\begin{array}{cccccc} 1 & 2 & 3 & 4 & 5 & 6 \end{array}$$

$$CH_3$$

3-Ethyl-3-methylhexane—a six-carbon main chain with 3-ethyl and 3-methyl substituents

$$\begin{array}{cc} 1 & 2 \\ CH_3 - CH_2 \end{array}$$

$$CH_3 - \underset{3}{\overset{\overset{\displaystyle |}{}}{C}} - CH_2 - CH_2 - CH_3$$

$$\begin{array}{cccc} 3 & 4 & 5 & 6 \end{array}$$

$$CH_3$$

3,3-Dimethylhexane—a six-carbon main chain with two 3-methyl substituents

Science Fundamentals

817

More about Alkyl Groups

It doesn't matter which hydrogen is removed from CH_4 to form a methyl group or which hydrogen is removed from CH_3CH_3 to form an ethyl group because all the hydrogen atoms in both molecules are equivalent. The eight hydrogens in $CH_3CH_2CH_3$, however, are not all equivalent. Propane has two sorts of hydrogens— six on the end carbons and two on the middle carbon. Depending on which sort of hydrogen is removed, two different propyl groups result. Removing one of the six hydrogens attached to an end carbon yields a straight-chain group called *propyl*, and removing one of the two hydrogens attached to the middle carbon yields a branched-chain group called *isopropyl*.

Similarly, there are four different butyl groups. Two (butyl and *sec*-butyl) are derived from straight-chain butane, and two (isobutyl and *tert*-butyl) are derived from branched-chain isobutane. The prefixes *sec*- (for *secondary*) and *tert*- (for *tertiary*) refer to the number of other carbon atoms attached to the branching carbon. There are two other carbons attached to the branch point in a *sec*-butyl group and three other carbons attached to the branch point in a *tert*-butyl group.

C_3
| $CH_3CH_2CH_3$ | $CH_3CH_2CH_2{-}$ | and CH_3CHCH_3 |
| Propane | Propyl | Isopropyl |

C_4
| $CH_3CH_2CH_2CH_3$ | $CH_3CH_2CH_2CH_2{-}$ | and $CH_3CH_2CHCH_3$ |
| Butane | Butyl | *sec*-Butyl |

CH_3	CH_3	CH_3
CH_3CHCH_3	$CH_3CHCH_2{-}$	and $CH_3C{-}$
		CH_3
Isobutane	Isobutyl	*tert*-Butyl

Keep in mind that alkyl groups themselves are not stable compounds and that the "removal" of a hydrogen from an alkane is just a useful way of looking at things, not a chemical reaction. Alkyl groups are simply parts of molecules that help us to name compounds.

WORKED EXAMPLE 23.3

NAMING AN ORGANIC COMPOUND

What is the IUPAC name of the following alkane?

$$\begin{array}{cc} CH_2CH_3 & CH_3 \\ | & | \\ CH_3CHCH_2CH_2CH_2CHCH_3 \end{array}$$

STRATEGY

Follow the steps outlined in the text. First, identify and number the longest continuous chain. Then identify the substituents and write the name.

SOLUTION

The molecule has a chain of eight carbons (octane) with two methyl substituents. Numbering from the end nearer the first methyl substituent indicates that the methyls are at C2 and C6, giving the name 2,6-dimethyloctane. The numbers are separated by a comma and are set off from the rest of the name by a hyphen.

$$\begin{array}{cc} \overset{7}{C}H_2\overset{8}{C}H_3 & CH_3 \\ | & | \\ CH_3CHCH_2CH_2CH_2CHCH_3 \\ 654321 \end{array}$$ 2,6-Dimethyloctane

WORKED EXAMPLE 23.4

CONVERTING A NAME INTO A CHEMICAL STRUCTURE

Draw the structure of 3-isopropyl-2-methylhexane.

STRATEGY AND SOLUTION

First, look at the parent name (hexane) and draw its carbon structure:

C—C—C—C—C—C Hexane

Next, find the substituents (3-isopropyl and 2-methyl) and place them on the proper carbons:

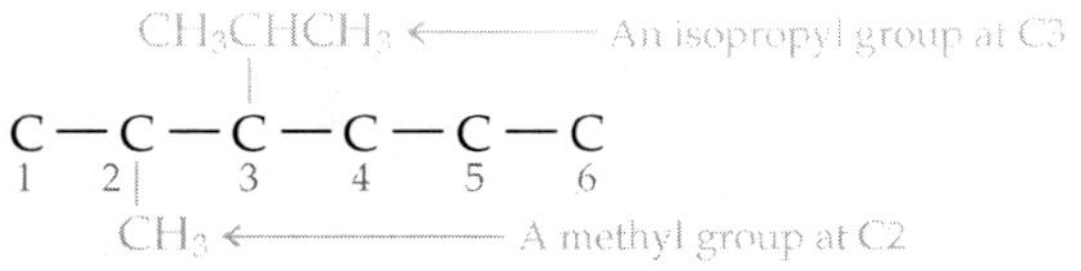

CH₃CHCH₃ ←———— An isopropyl group at C3

C—C—C—C—C—C
1 2| 3 4 5 6
    CH₃ ←———————— A methyl group at C2

Finally, add hydrogens to complete the structure:

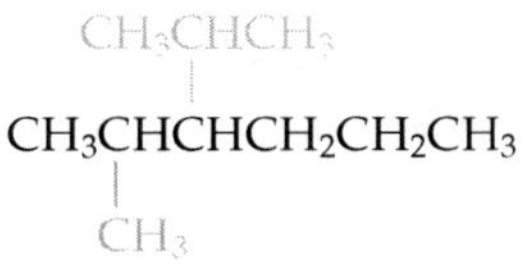

CH₃CHCH₃
|
CH₃CHCHCH₂CH₂CH₃   3-Isopropyl-2-methylhexane
|
CH₃

▸ **PROBLEM 23.7**   What are the IUPAC names of the following alkanes?

(a) The three isomers of C₅H₁₂

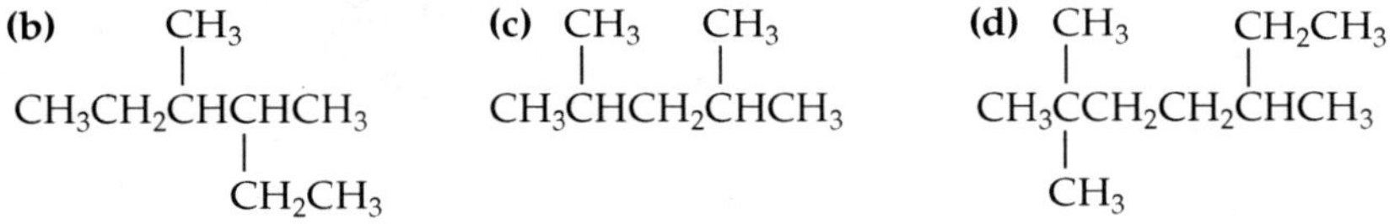

(b)
CH₃
|
CH₃CH₂CHCHCH₃
|
CH₂CH₃

(c) CH₃   CH₃
| |
CH₃CHCH₂CHCH₃

(d) CH₃   CH₂CH₃
| |
CH₃CCH₂CH₂CHCH₃
|
CH₃

▸ **PROBLEM 23.8**   Draw condensed structures corresponding to the following IUPAC names:

(a) 3,4-Dimethylnonane   **(b)** 3-Ethyl-4,4-dimethylheptane
(c) 2,2-Dimethyl-4-propyloctane   **(d)** 2,2,4-Trimethylpentane

KEY CONCEPT PROBLEM 23.9   What is the IUPAC name of the following alkane?

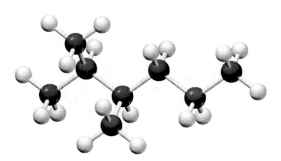

23.6 | CYCLOALKANES

The compounds we've been dealing with thus far have all been open-chain, or *acyclic*, alkanes. **Cycloalkanes,** which contain rings of carbon atoms, are also well known and are widespread throughout nature. Compounds of all ring sizes from 3 through 30 carbons and beyond have been prepared. The four simplest cycloalkanes having three carbons (cyclopropane), four carbons (cyclobutane), five carbons (cyclopentane), and six carbons (cyclohexane) are shown:

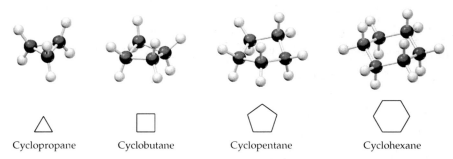

Cyclopropane   Cyclobutane   Cyclopentane   Cyclohexane

Even condensed structures are awkward for cyclic molecules, so a streamlined way of drawing structures is often used in which cycloalkanes are represented by polygons. A triangle represents cyclopropane, a square represents cyclobutane, and so on. Carbon and hydrogen atoms aren't shown explicitly in these structures. A carbon atom is simply understood to be at every junction of lines, and the proper number of hydrogen atoms needed to give each carbon four bonds is supplied mentally. Methylcyclohexane, for instance, looks like this:

This three-way intersection is a CH group.

This intersection is a CH$_2$ group.

Methylcyclohexane

As you might suspect, the C–C bonds in cyclopropane and cyclobutane are considerably distorted from the ideal 109.5° tetrahedral value. Cyclopropane, for example, has the shape of an equilateral triangle, with C–C–C angles of 60°. As a result, the bonds in three- and four-membered rings are weaker than normal, and the molecules are more reactive than other alkanes. Cyclopentane, cyclohexane, and larger cycloalkanes, however, pucker into shapes that allow bond angles to be near their normal tetrahedral value, as shown in the computer-generated models at the top of this page.

Substituted cycloalkanes are named using the cycloalkane as the parent name and identifying the positions on the ring where substituents are attached. Start numbering at the group that has alphabetical priority, and proceed around the ring in the direction that gives the second substituent the lower possible number. For example,

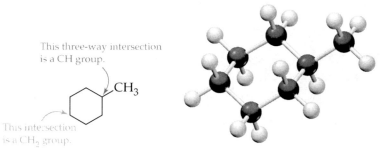

1-Ethyl-3-methylcyclohexane

Not 1-methyl-3-ethylcyclohexane
or 1-ethyl-5-methylcyclohexane
or 1-methyl-5-ethylcyclohexane

WORKED EXAMPLE 23.5

NAMING A CYCLOALKANE

What is the IUPAC name of the following cycloalkane?

continued on next page

STRATEGY

First, identify the parent cycloalkane (cyclopentane) and the two substituents (a methyl group and an isopropyl group). Then, number the ring beginning at the group having alphabetical priority (isopropyl rather than methyl) and proceed in a direction that gives the second group the lower possible number.

SOLUTION

1-Isopropyl-3-methylcyclopentane

▶ **PROBLEM 23.10** Give IUPAC names for the following cycloalkanes:

(a)

(b)

(c)

▶ **PROBLEM 23.11** Draw structures corresponding to the following IUPAC names. Use polygons for the rings.

  (a) 1,1-Dimethylcyclobutane   **(b)** 1-*tert*-Butyl-2-methylcyclopentane

  (c) 1,3,5-Trimethylcycloheptane

23.7 | REACTIONS OF ALKANES

Alkanes have relatively low chemical reactivity and are inert to acids, bases, and most other common laboratory reagents. They do, however, react with oxygen and with halogens under appropriate conditions. The chemical reaction of alkanes with oxygen occurs during combustion in an engine or furnace when the alkane is burned as fuel. Carbon dioxide and water are formed as products, and a large amount of heat is released. For example, methane, the main component of natural gas, reacts with oxygen to release 890 kJ per mole of methane burned:

$$CH_4(g) + 2\,O_2(g) \longrightarrow CO_2(g) + 2\,H_2O(l) \qquad \Delta H° = -890 \text{ kJ}$$

Propane (the LP gas used in campers and rural homes), gasoline (a mixture of C_5–C_{11} alkanes), kerosene (a mixture of C_{11}–C_{14} alkanes), and other alkanes burn similarly.

◀ Methane gas is burned off from this oil well.

    The reaction of alkanes with Cl_2 or Br_2 occurs when a mixture of the two reactants is irradiated with ultraviolet light, denoted by *hv*. Depending on the relative amounts of the two reactants and on the time allowed for the reaction, a sequential substitution of the alkane hydrogen atoms by halogen occurs, leading to a mixture of halogenated products. Methane, for example, reacts with chlorine to yield a mixture of chloromethane (CH_3Cl), dichloromethane (methylene chloride; CH_2Cl_2), trichloromethane (chloroform; $CHCl_3$), and tetrachloromethane (carbon tetrachloride; CCl_4):

$$CH_4 + Cl_2 \xrightarrow{h\nu} CH_3Cl + HCl$$
$$\xrightarrow{Cl_2} CH_2Cl_2 + HCl$$
$$\xrightarrow{Cl_2} CHCl_3 + HCl$$
$$\xrightarrow{Cl_2} CCl_4 + HCl$$

▸ **PROBLEM 23.12** Draw all the monochloro substitution products ($C_5H_{11}Cl$) you would expect to obtain from reaction of 2-methylbutane with Cl_2.

23.8 | FAMILIES OF ORGANIC MOLECULES: FUNCTIONAL GROUPS

Chemists have learned through experience that organic compounds can be classified into families according to their structural features and that the chemical behavior of the members in a given family is often predictable. The structural features that make it possible to class compounds together are called *functional groups*. A **functional group** is an atom or group of atoms within a molecule that has a characteristic chemical behavior and that undergoes the same kinds of reactions in every molecule where it occurs. Look at the carbon–carbon double-bond functional group, for instance. Ethylene (C_2H_4), the simplest compound with a double bond, undergoes reactions that are remarkably similar to those of menthene ($C_{10}H_{18}$), a much larger and more complex molecule. Both, for example, react with Br_2 to give products in which a Br atom has added to each of the double-bond carbons (Figure 23.1).

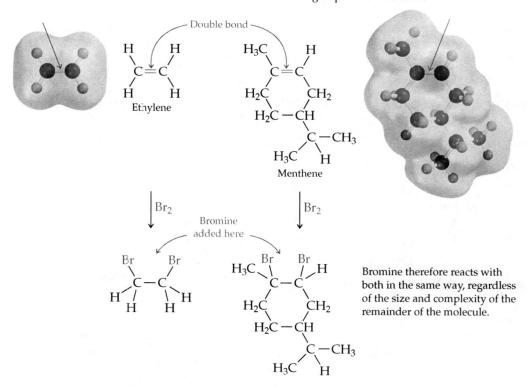

Electrostatic potential maps show similar polarity patterns for the carbon–carbon double bond functional group in both molecules.

Bromine therefore reacts with both in the same way, regardless of the size and complexity of the remainder of the molecule.

FIGURE 23.1
The reactions of ethylene and menthene with bromine.

The example shown in Figure 23.1 is typical: The chemistry of an organic molecule, regardless of its size and complexity, is largely determined by the functional groups it contains. Table 23.2 lists some of the most common functional groups and gives examples of their occurrence. Some functional groups, such as alkenes,

TABLE 23.2 Some Important Families of Organic Molecules

Family Name	Functional Group Structure	Simple Example	Name	Name Ending
Alkane	(contains only C—H and C—C single bonds)	CH_3CH_3	Ethane	*-ane*
Alkene		$H_2C=CH_2$	Ethene (Ethylene)	*-ene*
Alkyne	—C≡C—	H—C≡C—H	Ethyne (Acetylene)	*-yne*
Arene (aromatic)			Benzene	None
Alcohol	—C—O—H	CH_3OH	Methanol	*-ol*
Ether	—C—O—C—	CH_3OCH_3	Dimethyl ether	*ether*
Amine	—C—N—	CH_3NH_2	Methylamine	*-amine*
Aldehyde	—C—C—H (with O double bond)	CH_3CH (with O double bond)	Ethanal (Acetaldehyde)	*-al*
Ketone	—C—C—C— (with O double bond)	CH_3CCH_3 (with O double bond)	Propanone (Acetone)	*-one*
Carboxylic acid	—C—C—O—H (with O double bond)	CH_3COH (with O double bond)	Ethanoic acid (Acetic acid)	*-oic acid*
Ester	—C—C—O—C— (with O double bond)	CH_3COCH_3 (with O double bond)	Methyl ethanoate (Methyl acetate)	*-oate*
Amide	—C—C—N— (with O double bond)	CH_3CNH_2 (with O double bond)	Ethanamide (Acetamide)	*-amide*

The bonds whose connections aren't specified are assumed to be attached to carbon or hydrogen atoms in the rest of the molecule.

alkynes, and aromatic rings, have only carbon–carbon double or triple bonds; others contain single bonds to oxygen, nitrogen, or halogen atoms; and still others have carbon–oxygen double bonds.

▶ PROBLEM 23.13 Locate and identify the functional groups in the following molecules:

(a) Lactic acid, from sour milk

(b) Styrene, used to make polystyrene

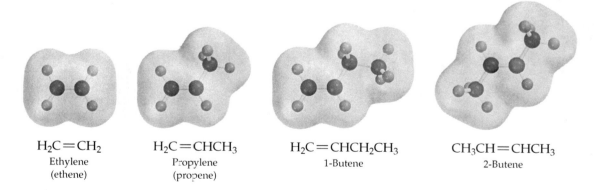

▶ PROBLEM 23.14 Propose structures for molecules that fit the following descriptions:
(a) C_2H_4O, containing an aldehyde functional group
(b) $C_3H_6O_2$, containing a carboxylic acid functional group

23.9 | ALKENES AND ALKYNES

In contrast to alkanes, which have only single bonds, alkenes and alkynes have multiple bonds. **Alkenes** are hydrocarbons that contain a carbon–carbon double bond, and **alkynes** are hydrocarbons that contain a carbon–carbon triple bond. Both groups of compounds are **unsaturated**, meaning that they have fewer hydrogens per carbon than the related alkanes, which have the maximum possible number of hydrogens and are thus **saturated**. Ethylene ($H_2C=CH_2$), for example, is unsaturated and has the formula C_2H_4, whereas ethane (CH_3CH_3) is saturated and has the formula C_2H_6.

Alkenes are named by counting the longest chain of carbons that contains the double bond and adding the suffix *-ene*. Thus, ethylene, the simplest alkene, is followed by propene, butene, pentene, hexene, and so on. Note that ethylene should properly be called *ethene*, but the name ethylene has been used for so long that it is universally accepted. Similarly, the name *propylene* is often used for propene.

$H_2C=CH_2$
Ethylene
(ethene)

$H_2C=CHCH_3$
Propylene
(propene)

$H_2C=CHCH_2CH_3$
1-Butene

$CH_3CH=CHCH_3$
2-Butene

Isomers are possible for butene and higher alkenes, depending on the position of the double bond in the chain, which must be specified by a numerical prefix. Numbering starts from the chain end nearer the double bond, and only the first of the double-bond carbons is cited. If a substituent is present on the chain, its identity is noted and its position of attachment is given. If the double bond is equidistant from both ends of the chain, numbering starts from the end nearer the substituent.

$$CH_3CH = CHCH_2CHCH_3$$
$$\overset{1 \quad 2 \quad 3 \quad 4 \quad 5 \quad 6}{}$$

5-Methyl-2-hexene

(numbered to give double
bond the lower number)

$$CH_3CH_2CH = CHCHCH_3$$
$$\overset{6 \quad 5 \quad 4 \quad 3 \quad 2 \quad 1}{}$$

2-Methyl-3-hexene

(numbered to give substituent
the lower number when the double
bond is equidistant from both ends)

In addition to the alkene isomers that exist because of double-bond *position*, alkene isomers can also exist because of double-bond *geometry*. For instance, there are two geometrical isomers, or **cis–trans isomers,** of 2-butene, which differ in their geometry about the double bond. The cis isomer has its two –CH_3 groups on the same side of the double bond, and the trans isomer has its two –CH_3 groups on opposite sides. Like other kinds of isomers we've discussed, the individual cis and trans isomers of an alkene are different substances with different physical properties and different (although often similar) chemical behavior. *cis*-2-Butene boils at 4 °C, for example, but *trans*-2-butene boils at 0.9 °C.

cis-2-Butene
(methyl groups on
the same side)

(Top view)

(Side view)

trans-2-Butene
(methyl groups on
opposite sides)

(Top view)

(Side view)

Cis–trans isomerism in alkenes arises because the electronic structure of the carbon–carbon double bond makes bond rotation energetically unfavorable at normal temperatures. Were it to occur, rotation would break the pi part of the double bond by disrupting the sideways overlap of two parallel *p* orbitals (Figure 23.2). In fact, an energy input of 240 kJ/mol is needed to cause bond rotation.

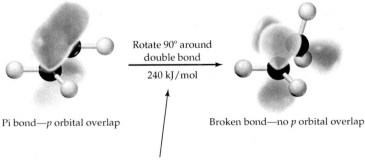

Rotate 90° around
double bond

240 kJ/mol

Pi bond—*p* orbital overlap

Broken bond—no *p* orbital overlap

A large amount of energy is required because
p orbital overlap is destroyed. Cis–trans alkene
isomers are stable and do not interchange
because of this barrier to rotation.

FIGURE 23.2

Rotation around a carbon–carbon double bond.

Alkynes are similar in many respects to alkenes and are named using the suffix *-yne*. The simplest alkyne, HC≡CH, is often called by its alternative name *acetylene* rather than by its systematic name *ethyne*.

HC≡CH   CH₃C≡CH $\overset{1}{C}H_3\overset{2}{C}≡\overset{3}{C}\overset{4}{C}H_3$ $\overset{4}{C}H_3\overset{3}{C}H_2\overset{2}{C}≡\overset{1}{C}H$

Ethyne   Propyne   2-Butyne   1-Butyne
(Acetylene)

As with alkenes, isomers are possible for butyne and higher alkynes, depending on the position of the triple bond in the chain. Unlike the alkenes, however, no cis–trans isomers are possible for alkynes because of their linear geometry.

WORKED EXAMPLE 23.6

CONVERTING A NAME INTO A STRUCTURE

Draw the structure of *cis*-3-heptene.

STRATEGY

The name 3-heptene indicates that the molecule has seven carbons (*hept-*) and has a double bond between carbons 3 and 4. The prefix *cis-* indicates that the two alkyl groups attached to the double-bond carbons lie on the same side of the double bond.

SOLUTION

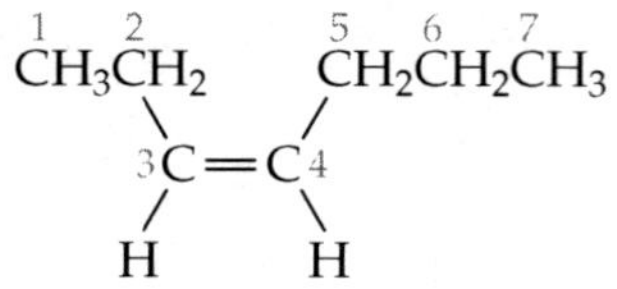

$\overset{1}{C}H_3\overset{2}{C}H_2$ $\overset{5}{C}H_2\overset{6}{C}H_2\overset{7}{C}H_3$

$_3C=C_4$

H   H   *cis*-3-Heptene

▶ **PROBLEM 23.15** Give IUPAC names for the following alkenes and alkynes:

(a)
      CH₃
      |
CH₃CHCH=CH₂

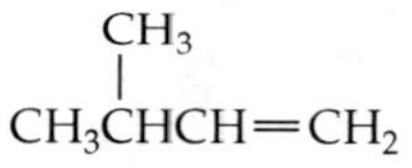

(b) CH₃CH₂CH₂
           |
   CH₃C=CHCH₂CH₃

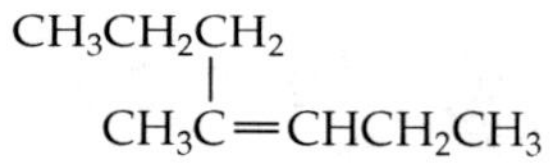

(c)
      CH₂CH₃
      |
HC≡CCHCH₂CH₂CH₃

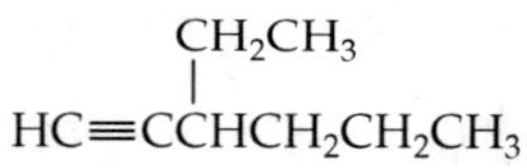

▶ **PROBLEM 23.16** Draw structures corresponding to the following IUPAC names:
(a) 2,2-Dimethyl-3-hexene
(b) 4-Isopropyl-2-heptyne
(c) *trans*-3-Heptene

23.10 | REACTIONS OF ALKENES AND ALKYNES

The most important transformations of alkenes and alkynes are **addition reactions.** That is, a reagent we might write in a general way as X–Y adds to the multiple bond of the unsaturated reactant to yield a saturated product. Alkenes and alkynes react similarly, but we'll look only at alkenes because they're more common.

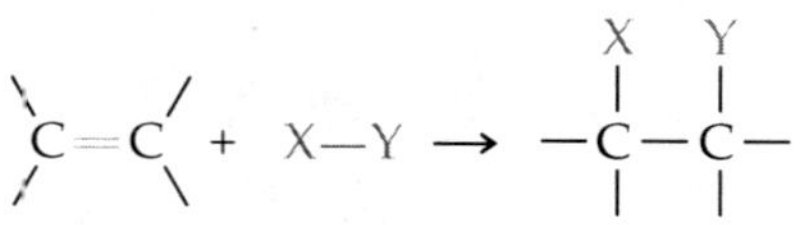

                   X Y

                   | |

\C=C/ + X—Y → —C—C—   **An addition reaction**
/   \ | |

Addition of Hydrogen Alkenes react with hydrogen gas in the presence of a platinum or palladium catalyst to yield the corresponding alkane product. For example,

CH₃CH₂CH=CH₂ + H₂ $\xrightarrow[\text{catalyst}]{\text{Pd}}$ CH₃CH₂CH₂CH₃

1-Butene   Butane

This addition of hydrogen to an alkene, often called **hydrogenation,** is used commercially to convert unsaturated vegetable oils to the saturated fats used in margarine and cooking fats.

$$
\overset{O}{\underset{\parallel}{+OCCH_2CH_2CH_2CH_2CH_2CH}} = CHCH_2CH_2CH_2CH_2CH_2CH_3
$$
Partial structure of a vegetable oil

H_2, Pd catalyst

$$
\overset{O}{\underset{\parallel}{+OCCH_2CH_2CH_2CH_2CH_2CH}} \overset{H}{\underset{|}{-}} \overset{H}{\underset{|}{-}} CHCH_2CH_2CH_2CH_2CH_2CH_3
$$
Partial structure of a saturated cooking fat

Addition of Cl$_2$ and Br$_2$ Alkenes react with the halogens Cl$_2$ and Br$_2$ to give dihaloalkane addition products, a process called **halogenation.** For example,

$$
H_2C=CH_2 + Cl_2 \longrightarrow H-\overset{\overset{\displaystyle Cl}{|}}{C}-\overset{\overset{\displaystyle Cl}{|}}{C}-H
$$
Ethene
(Ethylene)

1,2-Dichloroethane

Approximately 13 million tons of 1,2-dichloroethane are manufactured each year in the United States by the reaction of ethylene with chlorine. The process is the first step in making PVC [poly(vinyl chloride)] plastics.

Addition of Water Alkenes don't react with pure water, but in the presence of a strong acid catalyst such as sulfuric acid, a **hydration** reaction takes place to yield an *alcohol.* An –H from water adds to one carbon, and an –OH adds to the other. For example, approximately 110 million gallons of ethanol are produced each year in the United States by the acid-catalyzed addition of water to ethylene:

$$
H_2C=CH_2 + H_2O \xrightarrow[\text{catalyst}]{H_2SO_4} H-\overset{\overset{\displaystyle H}{|}}{C}-\overset{\overset{\displaystyle OH}{|}}{C}-H
$$
Ethene
(Ethylene)

Ethanol
(an alcohol)

▶ **PROBLEM 23.17** Show the products of the reaction of 2-butene with the following:
(a) H$_2$, Pd catalyst　　　(b) Br$_2$　　　(c) H$_2$O, H$_2$SO$_4$ catalyst

▶ **PROBLEM 23.18** The reaction of 2-pentene with H$_2$O in the presence of H$_2$SO$_4$ yields a mixture of two alcohol products. Draw their structures.

KEY CONCEPT PROBLEM 23.19 Draw the structure of the alcohol you would expect to obtain by acid-catalyzed reaction of the following cyclic alkene with H$_2$O:

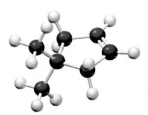

23.11 | AROMATIC COMPOUNDS AND THEIR REACTIONS

In the early days of organic chemistry, the word *aromatic* was used to describe certain fragrant substances found in fruits, trees, and other natural sources. Chemists soon realized, however, that substances grouped as aromatic behaved in a chemically different manner from most other organic compounds. Today, the term **aromatic** refers to the class of compounds that contain a six-membered ring with three double bonds. Benzene is the simplest aromatic compound, but aspirin, the steroid sex hormone estradiol, and many other important compounds also contain aromatic rings.

Benzene | Aspirin | Estradiol

Benzene is a flat, symmetrical molecule that is often represented as a six-membered ring with three double bonds. The problem with this representation, however, is that it gives the wrong impression about benzene's chemical reactivity. Because benzene appears to have three double bonds, we might expect it to react with H_2, Br_2, and H_2O to give the same kinds of addition products that alkenes do. In fact, though, benzene and other aromatic compounds are much less reactive than alkenes and don't normally undergo addition reactions.

Benzene's relative lack of reactivity is a consequence of its electronic structure. As shown by the orbital picture in Figure 23.3b, each of the six carbons in benzene is sp^2-hybridized and has a p orbital perpendicular to the ring. When these p orbitals overlap to form pi bonds, there are two possibilities, shown in Figure 23.3c.

▲ Benzaldehyde, a close structural relative of benzene, is an aromatic compound responsible for the odor of cherries.

(a) An electrostatic potential map.

(b) An orbital picture.

(c) Two equivalent resonance structures, which differ only in the positions of the double bonds.

FIGURE 23.3
Some representations of benzene.

Remember...

Different **resonance forms** of a substance differ only in the placement of bonding and nonbonding electrons. The connections between atoms and the relative positions of the atoms remain the same.

(Section 7.7)

Neither of the two equivalent structures in Figure 23.3c is correct by itself. Rather, each represents one resonance form of the true benzene structure, which is a resonance hybrid of the two forms. (For a review of resonance, you might want to reread Section 7.7.) Benzene is stable because its six pi-bond electrons are spread equally around the entire ring. The six electrons aren't confined to specific double bonds in the normal way, so benzene doesn't react to give addition products in the normal way.

Substituted aromatic compounds are named using the suffix -*benzene*. Thus, C_6H_5Br is bromobenzene, $C_6H_5CH_3$ is methylbenzene (also called *toluene*), $C_6H_5NO_2$

is nitrobenzene, and so on. Disubstituted aromatic compounds are named using one of the prefixes *ortho-*, *meta-*, or *para-*. An *ortho-* or *o*-disubstituted benzene has its two substituents in a 1,2 relationship on the ring; a *meta-* or *m*-disubstituted benzene has its two substituents in a 1,3 relationship; and a *para-* or *p*-disubstituted benzene has its substituents in a 1,4 relationship. When the benzene ring itself is a substituent, the name *phenyl* (pronounced **fen**-nil) is used.

ortho-Dimethylbenzene   *meta*-Dibromobenzene   *para*-Dinitrobenzene   A phenyl group

Unlike alkenes, which undergo addition reactions, aromatic compounds usually undergo **substitution reactions.** That is, a group Y substitutes for one of the hydrogen atoms on the aromatic ring without changing the ring itself. It doesn't matter which of the six ring hydrogens in benzene is replaced, because all six are equivalent.

$$\text{Ph-H} + \text{X-Y} \longrightarrow \text{Ph-Y} + \text{H-X} \qquad \textbf{A substitution reaction}$$

Nitration Substitution of a nitro group ($-NO_2$) for a ring hydrogen occurs when benzene reacts with nitric acid in the presence of sulfuric acid as catalyst. Nitration of aromatic rings is a key step in the synthesis of explosives such as TNT (trinitrotoluene) and many important pharmaceutical agents. Nitrobenzene itself is a starting material for preparing many of the brightly colored dyes used in clothing.

Benzene $+ HNO_3 \xrightarrow{H_2SO_4}$ Nitrobenzene $+ H_2O$ Trinitrotoluene (TNT)

▲ The dyes used to add the bright colors to clothing are made by a process that begins with an aromatic nitration reaction.

Halogenation Substitution of a bromine or chlorine for a ring hydrogen occurs when benzene reacts with Br_2 or Cl_2 in the presence of $FeBr_3$ or $FeCl_3$ as catalyst. The chlorination of an aromatic ring is a step used in the synthesis of numerous pharmaceutical agents, such as the antianxiety agent diazepam, marketed as Valium.

Benzene $+ Cl_2 \xrightarrow{FeCl_3}$ Chlorobenzene $+ HCl$ Diazepam (Valium)

▶ **PROBLEM 23.20** Draw structures corresponding to the following names:
(a) *o*-Dibromobenzene   **(b)** *p*-Chloronitrobenzene
(c) *m*-Diethylbenzene

▶ **PROBLEM 23.21** Write the products from reaction of the following reagents with *p*-dimethylbenzene (also called *p*-xylene):

(a) Br_2, $FeBr_3$ **(b)** HNO_3, H_2SO_4

▶ **PROBLEM 23.22** Reaction of $Br_2/FeBr_3$ with toluene (methylbenzene) can lead to a mixture of *three* substitution products. Show the structure of each.

23.12 | ALCOHOLS, ETHERS, AND AMINES

Alcohols

Alcohols can be viewed either as derivatives of water, in which one of the hydrogens is replaced by an organic substituent, or as derivatives of alkanes, in which one of the hydrogens is replaced by a hydroxyl group (–OH).

Water

A hydrocarbon

An alcohol

for example: CH_3CH_2OH

Ethanol

Like water, alcohols form hydrogen bonds (Section 10.2), which affect many of their chemical and physical properties. Alcohols are generally higher-boiling than alkanes of similar size, and simple alcohols are often soluble in water because of their ability to form hydrogen bonds to the solvent (Figure 23.4).

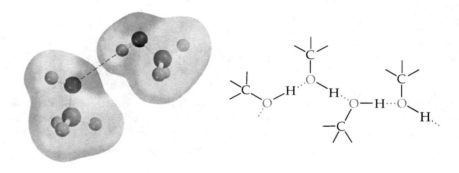

FIGURE 23.4
Alcohols, like water, form intermolecular hydrogen bonds. As a result, alcohols are relatively high boiling and are often soluble in water.

Alcohols are named by identifying the point of attachment of the –OH group to the hydrocarbon chain and using the suffix *-ol* to replace the terminal *-e* in the alkane name. Numbering of the chain begins at the end nearer the –OH group. For example,

$$CH_3CH_2CH_2OH$$
$$3 \quad 2 \quad 1$$

1-Propanol

$$CH_3CHCH_3$$
$$1 \quad 2 \quad 3$$
OH

2-Propanol

$$CH_3CCH_3$$
$$1 \quad 2 \quad 3$$
OH
$$CH_3$$

2-Methyl-2-propanol

OH

Cyclohexanol

Alcohols are among the most important and commonly encountered of all organic chemicals. Methanol (CH_3OH), the simplest member of the family, was once known as *wood alcohol* because it was prepared by heating wood in the absence of air.

Approximately 1.3 billion gallons of methanol are manufactured each year in the United States by catalytic reduction of carbon monoxide with hydrogen gas:

$$CO + 2H_2 \xrightarrow[\text{ZnO/Cr}_2\text{O}_3 \text{ catalyst}]{400\ °C} CH_3OH$$

Although toxic to humans, causing blindness in low doses (15 mL) and death in larger amounts (100–200 mL), methanol is an important industrial starting material for preparing formaldehyde (CH_2O), acetic acid (CH_3CO_2H), and other chemicals.

Ethanol (CH_3CH_2OH) is one of the oldest known pure organic chemicals. Its production by fermentation of grains and sugars goes back at least 8000 years in the Middle East and perhaps as many as 9000 years in China. Sometimes called *grain alcohol*, ethanol is the "alcohol" present in all wines (10–13%), beers (3–5%), and distilled liquors (35–90%). Fermentation is carried out by adding yeast to an aqueous sugar solution and allowing enzymes in the yeast to break down carbohydrates into ethanol and CO_2:

$$C_6H_{12}O_6 \xrightarrow{\text{Yeast}} 2CO_2 + 2CH_3CH_2OH$$

Glucose · · · · · · · · · · · · · · · · Ethanol

2-Propanol [$(CH_3)_2CHOH$], commonly called isopropyl alcohol or *rubbing alcohol*, is used primarily as a solvent. It is prepared industrially by addition of water to propene:

$$CH_3CH{=}CH_2 + H_2O \xrightarrow[\text{catalyst}]{\text{Acid}} \overset{\displaystyle OH}{\underset{}{CH_3CHCH_3}}$$

Propene · · · · · · · · · · · · · 2-Propanol
(Propylene)

Still other important alcohols include 1,2-ethanediol (ethylene glycol), 1,2,3-propanetriol (glycerol), and the aromatic compound phenol. Ethylene glycol is the principal constituent of automobile antifreeze, glycerol is used as a moisturizing agent in many foods and cosmetics, and phenol is used for preparing nylon, epoxy adhesives, and heat-setting resins.

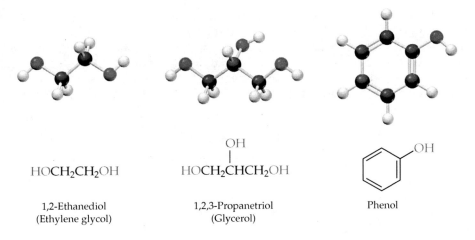

$HOCH_2CH_2OH$ · · · · · · · · · · $\overset{\displaystyle OH}{\underset{}{HOCH_2CHCH_2OH}}$ · · · · · · · · · · OH

1,2-Ethanediol · · · · · · · · · · · · · · 1,2,3-Propanetriol · · · · · · · · · · · · · · Phenol
(Ethylene glycol) · · · · · · · · · · · · · · (Glycerol)

Ethers

Ethers can be viewed as derivatives of water in which both hydrogens are replaced by organic substituents. They are fairly inert chemically and so are often used as reaction solvents. Diethyl ether, the most common member of the ether family, was used for many years as a surgical anesthetic agent but has now been replaced by safer nonflammable alternatives (see the Chapter 9 Interlude on Inhaled Anesthetics).

$CH_3CH_2OCH_2CH_3$
Diethyl ether

Amines

Amines are organic derivatives of ammonia in the same way that alcohols and ethers are organic derivatives of water. That is, one or more of the ammonia hydrogens is replaced in amines by an organic substituent. As the following examples indicate, the suffix -*amine* is used in naming these compounds:

Ammonia   Methylamine   Dimethylamine   Trimethylamine   Benzeneamine
(Aniline)

Like ammonia, amines are bases because they can use the lone pair of electrons on nitrogen to accept H^+ from an acid and give ammonium salts (Section 14.12). Because they're ionic, ammonium salts are much more soluble in water than are neutral amines. Thus, a water-insoluble amine such as triethylamine dissolves readily in water when converted to its ammonium salt by reaction with HCl.

▲ The characteristic aroma of ripe fish is due to methylamine, CH_3NH_2.

$$CH_3CH_2-\overset{..}{N}-CH_2CH_3 + HCl(aq) \longrightarrow CH_3CH_2-\overset{\overset{H}{|}}{\underset{|}{N^+}}-CH_2CH_3 \quad Cl^-(aq)$$
$$\underset{CH_2CH_3}{|} \qquad\qquad\qquad\qquad \underset{CH_2CH_3}{|}$$

Triethylamine
(water-insoluble)

Triethylammonium chloride
(water-soluble)

This increase in water solubility on conversion of an amine to its protonated salt has enormous practical consequences in drug delivery. Many important amine-containing drugs, such as morphine (a painkiller) and tetracycline (an antibiotic), are insoluble in aqueous body fluids and are thus difficult to deliver to the appropriate site within the body. Converting these drugs to their ammonium salts, however, increases their water solubility to the point where delivery through the bloodstream becomes possible.

▶ **PROBLEM 23.23** Write the structures of the ammonium salts produced by reaction of the following amines with HCl:

(a) $NHCH_3$ (b)

$CH_3CH_2CH_2NH_2$

23.13 | ALDEHYDES AND KETONES

Look back at the functional groups listed in Table 23.2 and you'll see that many of them have a carbon–oxygen double bond (C=O), called a **carbonyl group** (pronounced car-bo-**neel**). Carbonyl-containing compounds are everywhere. Carbohydrates, fats, proteins, and nucleic acids all contain carbonyl groups; most pharmaceutical agents contain carbonyl groups; and many of the synthetic polymers used for clothing and other applications contain carbonyl groups.

As shown by the electrostatic potential maps in Figure 23.5, the C=O bond in carbonyl compounds is polar because the electronegative oxygen atom attracts electrons from the carbon atom. Nevertheless, some carbonyl compounds are more polar than others because of what else is bonded to the carbonyl carbon atom.

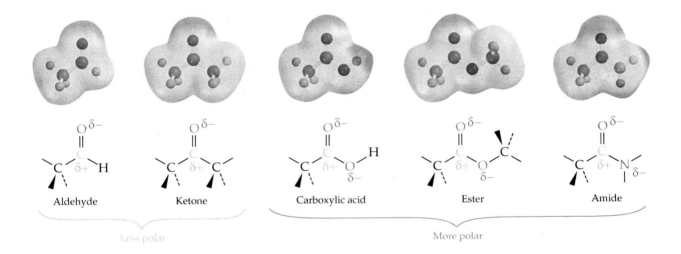

FIGURE 23.5
Carbonyl compounds can be classified into two categories. Aldehydes and ketones are less polar, while carboxylic acids, esters, and amides are more polar.

It's useful to classify carbonyl compounds into two categories based on the nature of the groups bonded to the C=O and on the chemical consequences that result. In one category are *aldehydes* and *ketones*. In the other are *carboxylic acids, esters, and amides*. In aldehydes and ketones, the carbonyl carbon is bonded to atoms (H and C) that are not strongly electronegative and thus contribute no additional polarity to the molecule. In carboxylic acids, esters, and amides, however, the carbonyl carbon *is* bonded to an atom (O or N) that is strongly electronegative, giving these compounds even greater polarity and greater chemical reactivity (Figure 23.5).

Aldehydes, which have a hydrogen atom bonded to the carbonyl group, and **ketones,** which have two carbon atoms bonded to the carbonyl group, are used throughout chemistry and biology. For example, an aqueous solution of formaldehyde (properly named *methanal*) is used under the name *formalin* as a biological sterilant and preservative. Formaldehyde is also used in the chemical industry as a starting material for the manufacture of the plastics Bakelite and melamine, as a component of the adhesives used to bind plywood, and as a part of the foam insulation used in houses. Note that formaldehyde differs from other aldehydes in having two hydrogens attached to the carbonyl group rather than one. Acetone (properly named *propanone*) is perhaps the most widely used of all organic solvents. You might have seen cans of acetone sold in paint stores for general-purpose cleanup work. When naming these groups of compounds, use the suffix *-al* for aldehydes and use the suffix *-one* for ketones.

$$\underset{\text{Formaldehyde}}{\underset{\text{(Methanal)}}{HCH}} \quad \underset{\text{Acetaldehyde}}{\underset{\text{(Ethanal)}}{CH_3CH}} \quad \underset{\text{Acetone}}{\underset{\text{(Propanone)}}{CH_3CCH_3}} \quad \underset{\text{2-Butanone}}{CH_3CCH_2CH_3} \quad \underset{\text{Cyclohexanone}}{}$$

Aldehyde and ketone functional groups are also present in many biologically important compounds. Glucose and most other sugars contain aldehyde groups, for instance. Testosterone and many other steroid hormones contain ketone groups.

Glucose—a pentahydroxyhexanal

Testosterone—a steroid hormone

The industrial preparation of simple aldehydes and ketones usually involves an oxidation reaction of the related alcohol. Thus, formaldehyde is prepared by oxidation of methanol, and acetone is prepared by oxidation of 2-propanol.

Methanol $\xrightarrow{\text{Air, 300 °C}}$ Formaldehyde

2-Propanol $\xrightarrow{\text{Air, 300 °C}}$ Acetone

23.14 | CARBOXYLIC ACIDS, ESTERS, AND AMIDES

Carboxylic acids, esters, and amides have their carbonyl groups bonded to a strongly electronegative atom (O or N). All three families undergo carbonyl-group substitution reactions, in which a group we can represent as –Y substitutes for the –OH, –OC, or –N group of the carbonyl reactant.

A carboxylic acid   An ester   An amide

A carbonyl-group substitution reaction

Carboxylic Acids

Carboxylic acids, which contain the $-\overset{\overset{\text{O}}{\|}}{\text{C}}-\text{OH}$ functional group, occur widely throughout the plant and animal kingdoms. Acetic acid (ethanoic acid), for instance, is the principal organic constituent of vinegar, and butanoic acid is responsible for the odor of rancid butter. In addition, long-chain carboxylic acids such as stearic acid are constituents of all animal fats and vegetable oils. Although many carboxylic acids have common names—*acetic* acid instead of *ethanoic* acid, for instance—systematic names are derived by replacing the final *-e* of the corresponding alkane with *-oic acid*.

$$\overset{\overset{\text{O}}{\|}}{\text{CH}_3\text{COH}}$$

Acetic acid
(Ethanoic acid)

$$\overset{\overset{\text{O}}{\|}}{\text{CH}_3\text{CH}_2\text{CH}_2\text{COH}}$$

Butanoic acid

Benzoic acid

$$\overset{\overset{\text{O}}{\|}}{\text{CH}_3\text{CH}_2\text{CH}_2\text{CH}_2\text{CH}_2\text{CH}_2\text{CH}_2\text{CH}_2\text{CH}_2\text{CH}_2\text{CH}_2\text{CH}_2\text{CH}_2\text{CH}_2\text{CH}_2\text{CH}_2\text{COH}}$$

Stearic acid
(Octadecanoic acid)

As their name implies, carboxylic acids are *acidic*—they dissociate slightly in aqueous solution to give H_3O^+ and a **carboxylate anion.** Carboxylic acids are much weaker than inorganic acids like HCl or H_2SO_4, however. The K_a of acetic acid, for example, is 1.75×10^{-5} ($pK_a = 4.76$), meaning that only about 1% of acetic acid molecules dissociate in a 1.0 M aqueous solution. Note in the following electrostatic potential map of acetic acid that the acidic –OH hydrogen is positively polarized (blue).

$$\overset{\overset{\text{O}}{\|}}{\text{CH}_3\text{COH}} + \text{H}_2\text{O} \rightleftharpoons \overset{\overset{\text{O}}{\|}}{\text{CH}_3\text{CO}^-} + \text{H}_3\text{O}^+$$

Acetic acid   Acetate ion

One of the most important chemical transformations of carboxylic acids is their acid-catalyzed reaction with an alcohol to yield an ester. Acetic acid, for example, reacts with ethanol in the presence of H_2SO_4 to yield ethyl acetate, a widely used solvent. The reaction is a typical carbonyl-group substitution, with $-OCH_2CH_3$ from the alcohol replacing –OH from the acid.

$$\text{CH}_3-\overset{\overset{\text{O}}{\|}}{\text{C}}\boxed{-\text{OH} + \text{H}}-\text{OCH}_2\text{CH}_3 \xrightarrow[\text{catalyst}]{\text{H}^+} \text{CH}_3-\overset{\overset{\text{O}}{\|}}{\text{C}}-\text{OCH}_2\text{CH}_3 + \text{H}_2\text{O}$$

Acetic acid   Ethanol   Ethyl acetate

Esters

Esters, which contain the $-\overset{\overset{\text{O}}{\|}}{\text{C}}-\text{O}-\text{C}$ functional group, have many uses in medicine, industry, and living systems. In medicine, a number of important pharmaceutical agents, including aspirin and the local anesthetic benzocaine, are esters. In industry, polyesters such as Dacron and Mylar are used to make synthetic fibers and films. In nature, many simple esters are responsible for the fragrant odors of fruits and flowers. As examples, pentyl acetate is found in bananas and octyl acetate is found in oranges.

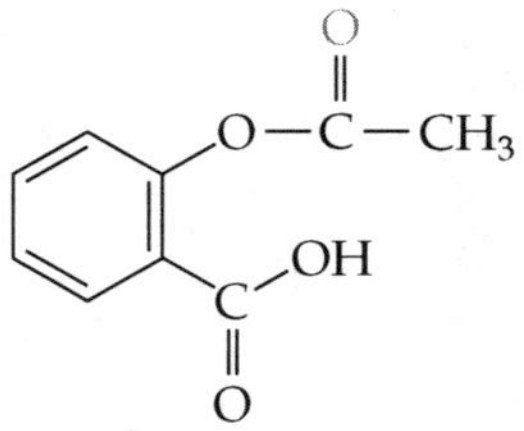

Aspirin

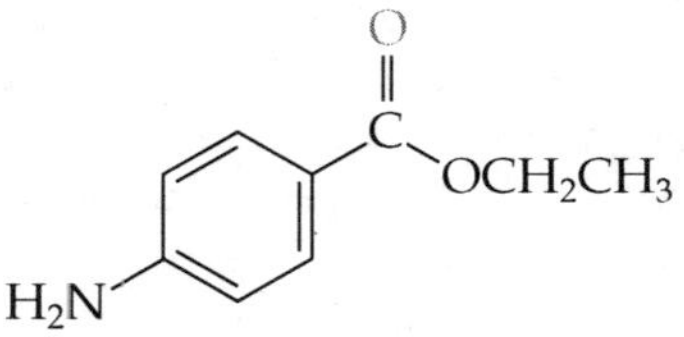

Benzocaine

$$CH_3\overset{O}{\overset{\|}{C}}OCH_2CH_2CH_2CH_2CH_3$$

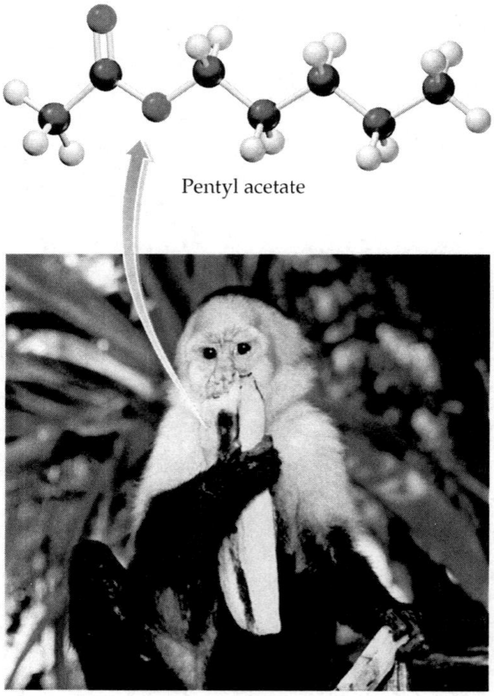
Pentyl acetate

▶ The odor of these bananas is due to pentyl acetate, a simple ester.

The most important reaction of esters is their conversion by a carbonyl-group substitution reaction into carboxylic acids. Both in the laboratory and in the body, esters undergo a reaction with water—a *hydrolysis*—that splits the ester molecule into a carboxylic acid and an alcohol. The net effect is a substitution of –OC by –OH. Although the reaction is slow in pure water, it is catalyzed by both acid and base. Base-catalyzed ester hydrolysis is often called *saponification,* from the Latin word *sapo* meaning "soap." Soap, in fact, is a mixture of sodium salts of long-chain carboxylic acids and is produced by hydrolysis with aqueous NaOH of the naturally occurring esters in animal fat.

$$\underset{\text{Ethyl acetate}}{CH_3-\overset{O}{\overset{\|}{C}}-OCH_2CH_3} + H-O-H \xrightarrow[\text{catalyst}]{H^+ \text{ or } OH^-} \underset{\text{Acetic acid}}{CH_3-\overset{O}{\overset{\|}{C}}-OH} + \underset{\text{Ethanol}}{H-OCH_2CH_3}$$

Because esters are derived from carboxylic acids and alcohols, they are named by first identifying the alcohol-related part and then the acid-related part, using the *-ate* ending. Ethyl acetate, for example, is the ester derived from ethanol and acetic acid.

Amides

Amides are compounds with the $-\overset{O}{\overset{\|}{C}}-N$ functional group. Without amides, there would be no life. As we'll see in the next chapter, the amide bond between nitrogen and a carbonyl-group carbon is the fundamental link used by organisms for forming proteins. In addition, some synthetic polymers such as nylon contain amide groups, and important pharmaceutical agents such as acetaminophen, the aspirin substitute found in Tylenol and Excedrin, are amides.

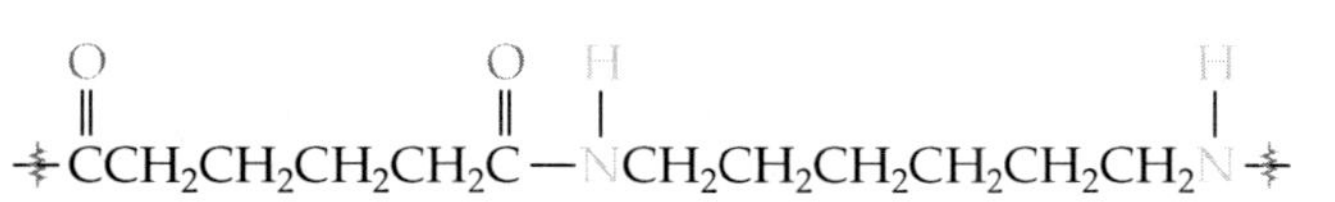

Repeating unit of nylon 66 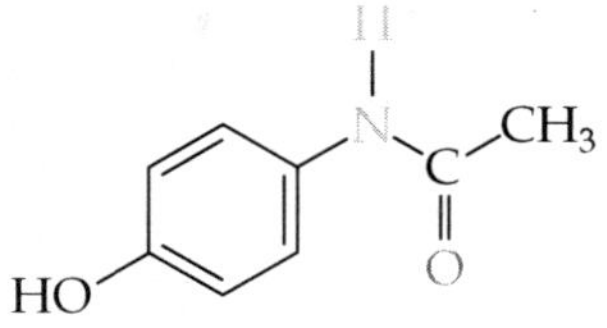   Acetaminophen

Unlike amines, which also contain nitrogen (Section 23.12), amides are neutral rather than basic. Amides do not act as proton acceptors and do not form ammonium salts when treated with acid. The neighboring carbonyl group causes the unshared pair of electrons on nitrogen to be held tightly, thus preventing the electrons from bonding to H^+.

Although better methods are normally used, amides can sometimes be prepared by the reaction of a carboxylic acid with ammonia or an amine, just as esters are prepared by the reaction of a carboxylic acid with an alcohol. In both cases, water is a by-product, and the –OH part of the carboxylic acid is replaced. Amides are named by first citing the N-alkyl group on the amine part (N because the group is attached to nitrogen) and then identifying the carboxylic acid part using the -amide ending.

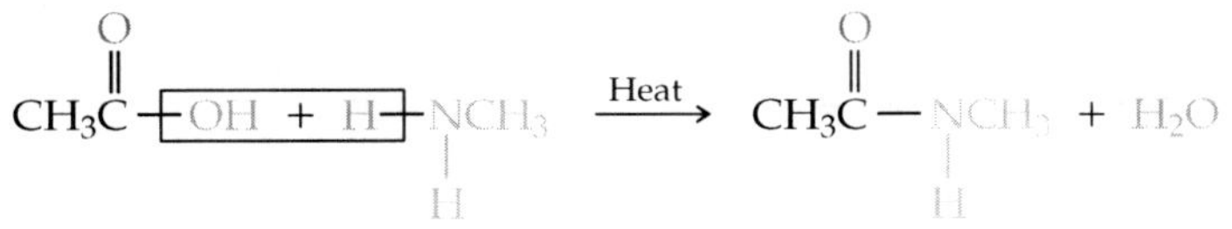

Acetic acid   Methylamine   N-Methylacetamide
                                      (an amide)

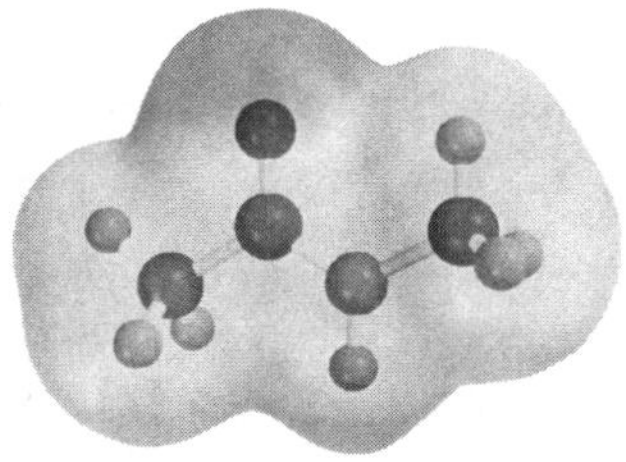

Amides undergo an acid- or base-catalyzed hydrolysis reaction with water in the same way that esters do. Just as an ester yields a carboxylic acid and an alcohol, an amide yields a carboxylic acid and an amine (or ammonia). The net effect is a substitution of –N by –OH. This hydrolysis of amides is the key process that occurs in the stomach during digestion of proteins.

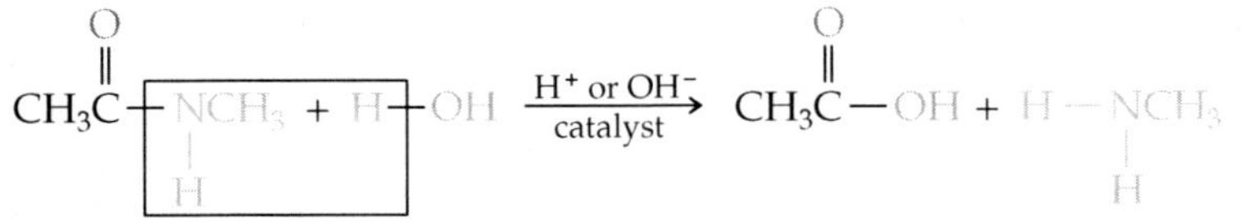

N-Methylacetamide   Acetic acid   Methylamine

WORKED EXAMPLE 23.7
NAMING ORGANIC COMPOUNDS

Give the systematic names of the following compounds:

(a)

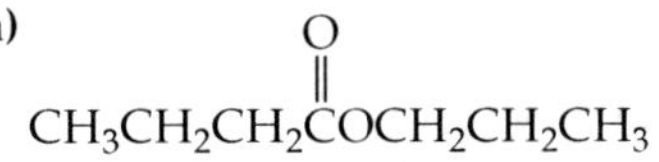

$$CH_3CH_2CH_2COCH_2CH_2CH_3$$

(b)

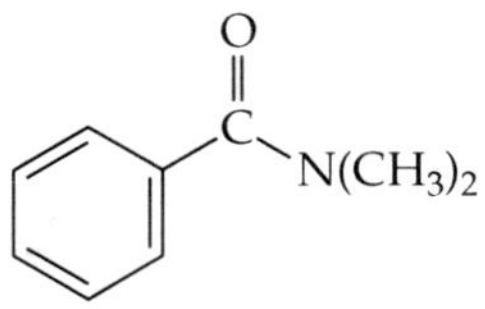

STRATEGY

First identify the alcohol-derived or amine-derived part, and then assign the name.

continued on next page

SOLUTION

(a) This ester is derived from propyl alcohol and butanoic acid. Its name is propyl butanoate.

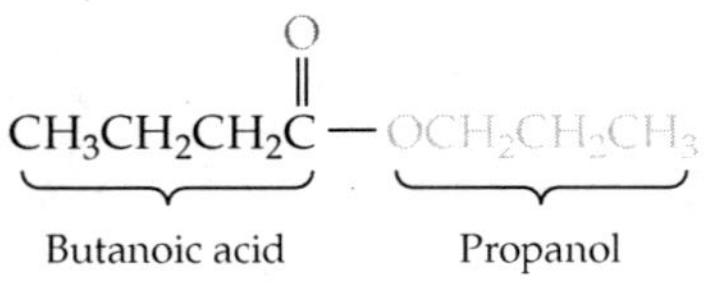

$$CH_3CH_2CH_2\overset{\displaystyle O}{\overset{\displaystyle \|}{C}} - OCH_2CH_2CH_3 \quad \text{Propyl butanoate}$$

Butanoic acid Propanol

(b) This amide is derived from dimethylamine and benzoic acid. Its name is *N,N*-dimethylbenzamide.

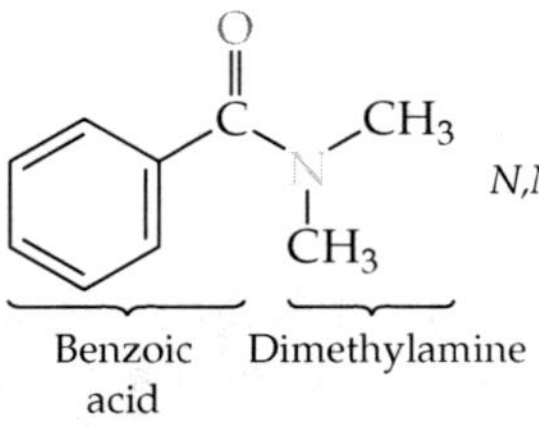

N,N-Dimethylbenzamide

Benzoic Dimethylamine
acid

WORKED EXAMPLE 23.8

PREDICTING THE PRODUCTS OF ORGANIC REACTIONS

Write the products of the following reactions:

(a)
$$\underset{\text{CH}_3\overset{\displaystyle |}{\underset{\displaystyle}{\text{CHCH}_2}}\overset{\displaystyle O}{\overset{\displaystyle \|}{\text{C}}}\text{OH}}{} + \text{HOCHCH}_3 \longrightarrow ?$$

(b)
$$\underset{\text{CH}_3\text{CH}_2\overset{\displaystyle |}{\underset{\displaystyle}{\text{CHCH}_2}}\overset{\displaystyle O}{\overset{\displaystyle \|}{\text{C}}}\text{NH}_2}{} + \text{H}_2\text{O} \longrightarrow ?$$

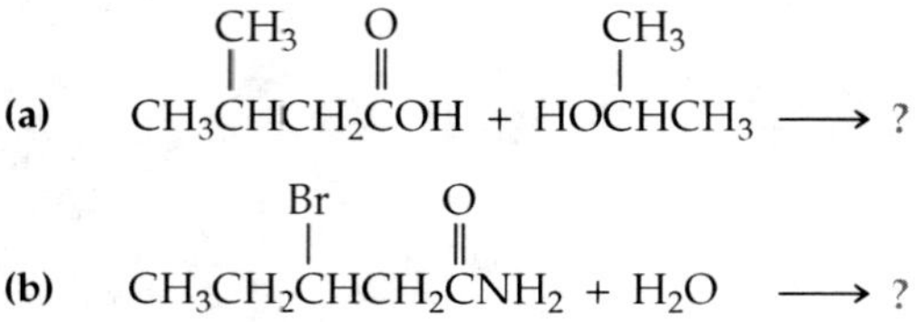

STRATEGY

The reaction of a carboxylic acid with an alcohol yields an ester plus water, and the reaction of an amide with water yields a carboxylic acid and an amine (or ammonia). Write the reagents to show how H_2O is removed, and then connect the remaining fragments to complete the substitution reaction.

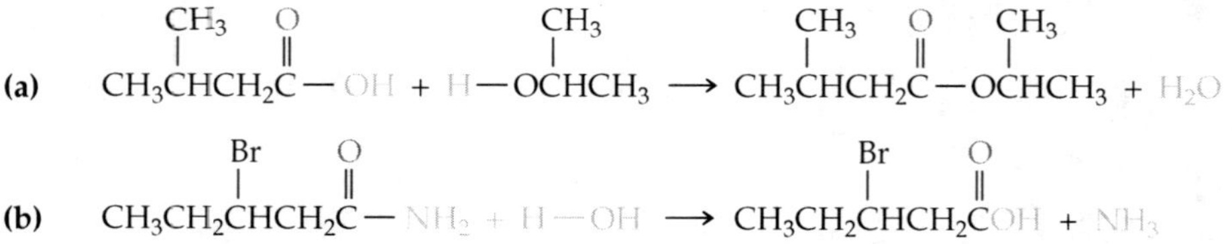

(a)
$$CH_3CHCH_2C - OH + H - OCHCH_3 \rightarrow CH_3CHCH_2C - OCHCH_3 + H_2O$$

(b)
$$CH_3CH_2CHCH_2C - NH_2 + H - OH \rightarrow CH_3CH_2CHCH_2COH + NH_3$$

▶ **PROBLEM 23.24** Draw structures corresponding to the following names:
(a) 4-Methylpentanoic acid **(b)** Isopropyl benzoate
(c) *N*-Ethylpropanamide

▶ **PROBLEM 23.25** Write the products of the following reactions:

(a)

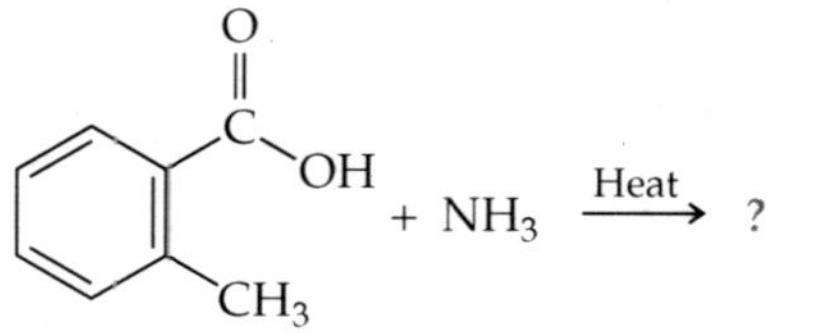

$+ \text{NH}_3 \xrightarrow{\text{Heat}} ?$

(b)
$$\underset{\text{CH}_3\overset{\displaystyle |}{\underset{\displaystyle}{\text{CHCH}_2}}\overset{\displaystyle O}{\overset{\displaystyle \|}{\text{C}}}\text{OH}}{} + \text{CH}_3\text{CH}_2\overset{\displaystyle CH_3}{\overset{\displaystyle |}{\text{CHOH}}} \xrightarrow[\text{catalyst}]{\text{H}^+} ?$$

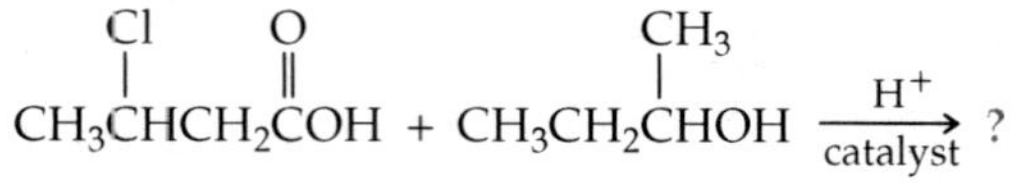

KEY CONCEPT PROBLEM 23.26 Draw the structure of the ester you would obtain by acid-catalyzed reaction of the following carboxylic acid with 2-propanol:

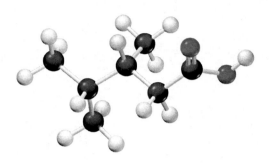

23.15 | SYNTHETIC POLYMERS

Polymers are large molecules formed by the repetitive bonding together of many smaller molecules, called **monomers.** As we'll see in the next chapter, biological polymers occur throughout nature. Cellulose and starch are polymers built from small sugar monomers, proteins are polymers built from amino acid monomers, and nucleic acids are polymers built from nucleotide monomers. The basic idea is the same, but synthetic polymers are much less complex than biopolymers because the starting monomer units are usually smaller and simpler.

Many simple alkenes called **vinyl monomers** undergo polymer-forming (*polymerization*) reactions. Ethylene yields polyethylene, propylene (propene) yields polypropylene, styrene yields polystyrene, and so forth. The polymer molecules that result may have anywhere from a few hundred to many thousands of monomer units incorporated into a long chain. Some commercially important polymers are listed in Table 23.3.

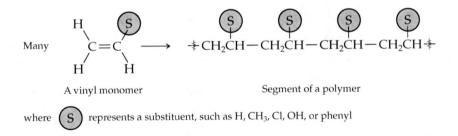

A vinyl monomer   Segment of a polymer

where (S) represents a substituent, such as H, CH_3, Cl, OH, or phenyl

TABLE 23.3 Some Alkene Polymers and Their Uses

Monomer Name	Structure	Polymer Name	Uses
Ethylene	$H_2C=CH_2$	Polyethylene	Packaging, bottles
Propylene	$H_2C=CH-CH_3$	Polypropylene	Bottles, rope, pails medical tubing
Vinyl chloride	$H_2C=CH-Cl$	Poly(vinyl chloride)	Insulation, plastic pipe
Styrene	$H_2C=CH-\langle\bigcirc\rangle$	Polystyrene	Foams and molded plastics
Acrylonitrile	$H_2C=CH-C\equiv N$	Orlon, Acrilan	Fibers, outdoor carpeting

The fundamental process in alkene polymerization is a double-bond addition reaction similar to those discussed in Section 23.10. A species called an *initiator,* In·, first adds to the double bond of an alkene, yielding a reactive intermediate that in turn adds to a second alkene molecule to produce another reactive intermediate, and so on.

▲ These classic examples of suburban yard art are made of polypropylene, an alkene polymer.

A different kind of polymerization process occurs when molecules with two functional groups react. We've seen, for example, that a carboxylic acid reacts with an amine to yield an amide (Section 23.14). If a molecule with two carboxylic acid groups reacts with a molecule having two amino groups, an initial reaction joins the two molecules together, and further reactions then link more and more molecules together until a giant polyamide chain results. Nylon 66, one of the most important such polymers, is prepared by heating adipic acid (hexanedioic acid) with 1,6-hexanediamine at 280 °C.

$$H_2NCH_2CH_2CH_2CH_2CH_2CH_2NH_2 + HOCCH_2CH_2CH_2CH_2COH$$

1,6-Hexanediamine

Hexanedioic acid (Adipic acid)

280 °C

$$\left[NHCH_2CH_2CH_2CH_2CH_2CH_2NH-CCH_2CH_2CH_2CH_2C \right]_n + n\,H_2O$$

A segment of nylon 66

Amide bond

Nylons have many uses, both in engineering applications and in fibers. High impact strength and resistance to abrasion make nylon an excellent material for bearings and gears. High tensile strength makes it suitable as fibers for a range of applications from clothing to mountaineering ropes to carpets.

Just as diacids and diamines react to give *polyamides*, diacids and dialcohols react to give *polyesters*. The most industrially important polyester, made from reaction of terephthalic acid (1,4-benzenedicarboxylic acid) with ethylene glycol (1,2-ethanediol),

▶ Climbing ropes are made of Perlon, one of the many varieties of nylon.

is used under the trade name Dacron to make clothing fiber and under the name Mylar to make plastic film and recording tape.

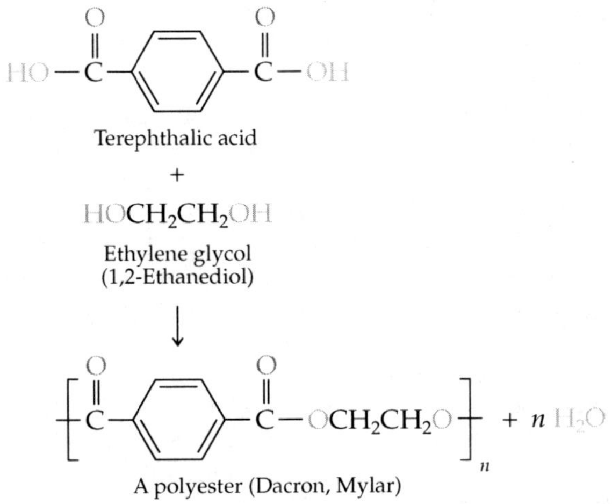

Terephthalic acid

+

$HOCH_2CH_2OH$

Ethylene glycol
(1,2-Ethanediol)

A polyester (Dacron, Mylar)

▶ **PROBLEM 23.27** Identify the monomer units used to make the following polymers:

(a)

$$\left[\begin{array}{c} CO_2CH_3 \quad\quad CO_2CH_3 \\ | \quad\quad\quad\quad | \\ CH—CH_2—CH—CH_2 \end{array} \right]_n$$

(b)

$$\left[OCH_2CH_2CH_2O—\overset{O}{\overset{||}{C}}CH_2CH_2\overset{O}{\overset{||}{C}}—O \right]_n$$

Natural or Synthetic?

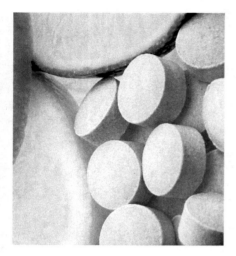

▲ Whether from the laboratory or from food, the vitamin C is the same.

Prior to the development of the chemical industry in the late nineteenth and early twentieth centuries, only substances from natural sources were available for treating our diseases, dying our clothes, cleansing and perfuming our bodies, and so forth. Extracts of the opium poppy, for instance, have been used since the seventeenth century for the relief of pain. The prized purple dye called *Tyrian purple,* obtained from a Middle Eastern mollusk, has been known since antiquity. Oils distilled from bergamot, sweet bay, rose, and lavender have been employed for centuries in making perfume.

Many of these so-called *natural products* were first used without any knowledge of their chemical composition. As organic chemistry developed, though, chemists learned how to work out the structures of the compounds in natural products. The disease-curing properties of limes and other citrus fruits, for example, were known for centuries but the chemical structure of vitamin C, the active ingredient, was not determined until 1933. Today there is a revival of interest in folk remedies, and a large effort is being made to identify medicinally important chemical compounds found in plants.

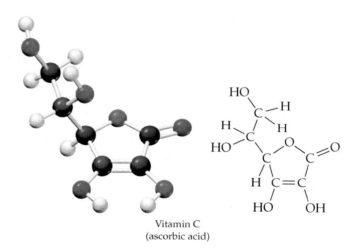

Vitamin C
(ascorbic acid)

Once a structure is known, organic chemists try to synthesize the compound in the laboratory. If the starting materials are inexpensive and the synthesis process is simple enough, it may become more economical to manufacture a compound than to isolate it from a plant or bacterium. In the case of vitamin C, a complete synthesis was achieved in 1933, and it is now much cheaper to synthesize it from glucose than to extract it from citrus or other natural sources. Worldwide, more than 80 million pounds are synthesized each year.

But is the "synthetic" vitamin C as good as the "natural" one? Some people still demand vitamins only from natural sources, assuming that natural is somehow better. Although eating an orange is probably better than taking a tablet, the difference lies in the many other substances present in the orange. The vitamin C itself is exactly the same, just as the NaCl produced by reacting sodium and chlorine in the laboratory is exactly the same as the NaCl found in the ocean. Natural and synthetic compounds are identical in all ways; neither is better than the other.

▸ **PROBLEM 23.28** Identify the functional groups present in vitamin C.

SUMMARY

Organic chemistry is the study of carbon compounds. The more than 30 million known organic compounds can be organized into families according to the functional groups they contain. A **functional group** is an atom or group of atoms within a molecule that has characteristic chemical behavior and undergoes the same kinds of reactions in every molecule it's a part of.

The simplest compounds are the **alkanes,** which contain only carbon and hydrogen **(hydrocarbons)** and have only single bonds. **Straight-chain alkanes** have all their carbons connected in a row, **branched-chain alkanes** have a branched connection of atoms in their chain, and **cycloalkanes** have a ring of carbon atoms. Isomerism is possible in alkanes having four or more carbons. Straight-chain alkanes are named in the IUPAC system by adding the family ending *-ane* to the Greek number that tells how many carbon atoms are present. Branched-chain alkanes are named by identifying the longest continuous chain of carbon atoms and then telling what **alkyl groups** are present as branches off the main chain. Alkanes are chemically rather inert, although they undergo combustion with oxygen and undergo a **substitution reaction** with chlorine.

Alkenes are hydrocarbons that contain a carbon–carbon double bond, and **alkynes** are hydrocarbons that contain a carbon–carbon triple bond. **Cis–trans isomers** are possible for substituted alkenes because of the lack of rotation about the carbon–carbon double bond. The cis isomer has two substituents on the same side of the double bond, and the trans isomer has two substituents on opposite sides. The most important transformations of alkenes and alkynes are **addition reactions,** in which a substance adds to the multiple bond to yield a saturated product.

Aromatic compounds are often represented as having a six-membered ring with three double bonds. These compounds usually undergo **substitution reactions,** in which a group substitutes for one of the hydrogen atoms on the aromatic ring. **Alcohols** and **ethers** can be thought of as derivatives of water in which one or both of the hydrogens are replaced by an organic substituent. Similarly, **amines** are derivatives of ammonia in which one or more of the ammonia hydrogens are replaced by an organic substituent. Amines are bases and can be protonated by acids to yield ammonium salts.

Compounds that contain a **carbonyl group,** C=O, can be classified into two categories. In **aldehydes** and **ketones,** the carbonyl-group carbon is bonded to atoms (H and C) that don't attract electrons strongly. In **carboxylic acids, esters,** and **amides,** the carbonyl-group carbon is bonded to an electronegative atom (O or N) that *does* attract electrons strongly. As a result, these three families of compounds undergo **carbonyl-group substitution reactions,** in which a group –Y substitutes for the –OH, –OC, or –N group of the carbonyl reactant.

Polymers are large molecules formed when many smaller **monomers** bond together. Alkene polymers such as polyethylene result from the polymerization of simple alkenes. Nylons and polyesters result from the sequential reaction of two difunctional molecules.

KEY WORDS

addition reaction *954*	aromatic *956*	ester *963*	organic chemistry *937*
alcohol *958*	branched-chain	ether *960*	polymer *967*
aldehyde *961*	alkane *940*	functional group *950*	saturated *952*
alkane *939*	carbonyl group *961*	halogenation *955*	straight-chain
alkene *952*	carboxylate anion *963*	hydration *955*	alkane *940*
alkyl group *945*	carboxylic acid *963*	hydrocarbon *939*	substitution
alkyne *952*	cis–trans isomers *953*	hydrogenation *955*	reaction *957*
amide *964*	condensed structure *941*	ketone *961*	unsaturated *952*
amine *960*	cycloalkane *947*	monomer *967*	vinyl monomer *967*

⬤ KEY CONCEPT PROBLEMS

Problems 23.1–23.28 appear within the chapter.

23.29 Convert the following model into a condensed structure, and draw the structures of two isomeric compounds.

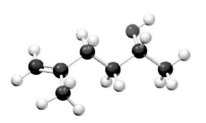

23.30 Convert each of the following models into a condensed formula:

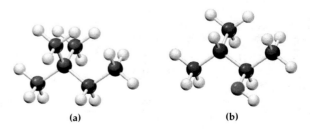

(a)   (b)

23.31 Convert each of the following models into a chemical structure:

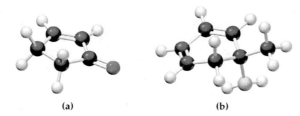

(a)   (b)

23.32 Identify the functional groups in each of the following compounds:

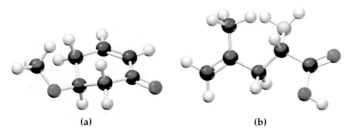

(a)   (b)

23.33 Give systematic names for the following compounds:

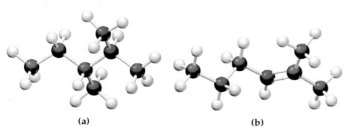

(a)   (b)

23.34 The following structure represents a segment of an alkene polymer. Identify the monomer from which the polymer was made.

23.35 Identify the carboxylic acid and alcohol from which the following ester was made:

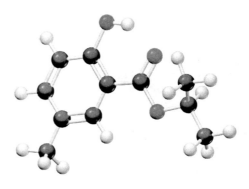

23.36 Draw two isomers of the following compound:

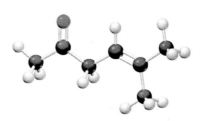

23.37 Draw three resonance forms for naphthalene, showing the positions of the double bonds.

SECTION PROBLEMS

Functional Groups and Isomers (Sections 23.2, 23.8)

23.38 What are functional groups, and why are they important?

23.39 Describe the structure of the functional group in each of the following families:
   (a) Alkene   (b) Alcohol
   (c) Ester   (d) Amine

23.40 Propose structures for molecules that meet the following descriptions:
   (a) A ketone with the formula $C_5H_{10}O$
   (b) An ester with the formula $C_6H_{12}O_2$
   (c) A compound with formula $C_2H_5NO_2$ that is both an amine and a carboxylic acid

23.41 Write structures for each of the following molecular formulas. You may have to use rings and/or multiple bonds in some instances.
   (a) C_2H_7N (b) C_4H_8 (c) C_2H_4O (d) CH_2O_2

23.42 There are three isomers with the formula C_3H_8O. Draw their structures.

23.43 Write as many isomers as you can that fit the following descriptions:
   (a) Alcohols with formula $C_4H_{10}O$
   (b) Amines with formula C_3H_9N
   (c) Ketones with formula $C_5H_{10}O$
   (d) Aldehydes with formula $C_5H_{10}O$

23.44 Identify the functional groups in the following molecules:

(a)

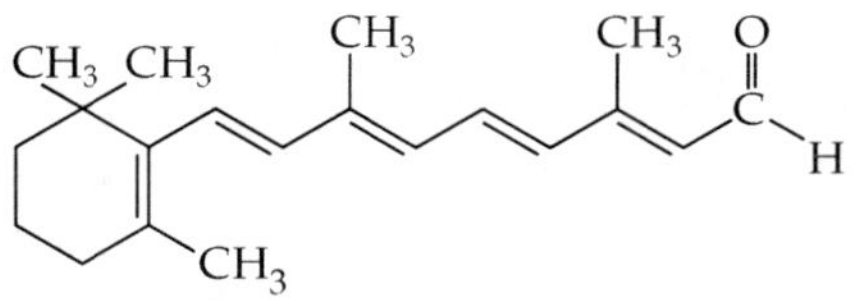

Retinal (Vitamin A)

(b)

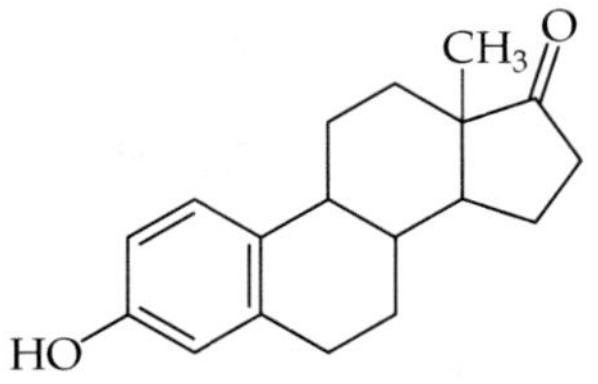

Estrone, a female sex hormone

23.45 Identify the functional groups in cocaine.

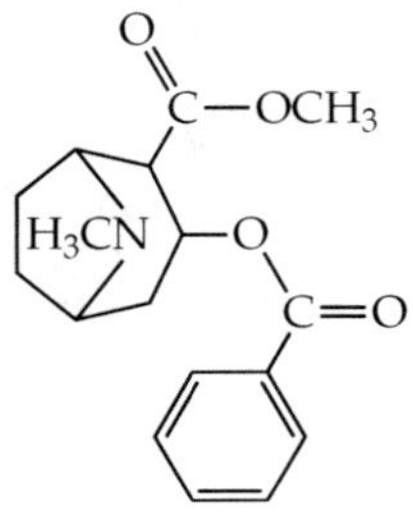

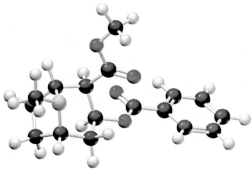

Cocaine

Alkanes (Sections 23.2–23.6)

23.46 What is the difference between a straight-chain alkane and a branched-chain alkane?

23.47 What is the difference between an alkane and an alkyl group?

23.48 What kind of hybrid orbitals does carbon use in forming alkanes?

23.49 Why are alkanes said to be saturated?

23.50 If someone reported the preparation of a compound with the formula C_3H_9, most chemists would be skeptical. Why?

23.51 What is wrong with each of the following structures?

(a) $CH_3 \!=\! CHCH_2CH_2OH$

(b) 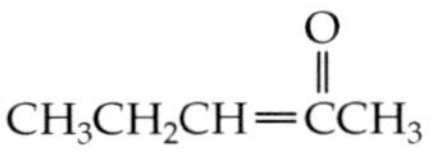 $CH_3CH_2CH \!=\! \overset{\overset{\displaystyle O}{\|}}{C}CH_3$

(c) $CH_3CH_2C \!\equiv\! CH_2CH_3$

23.52 What are the IUPAC names of the following alkanes?

(a) 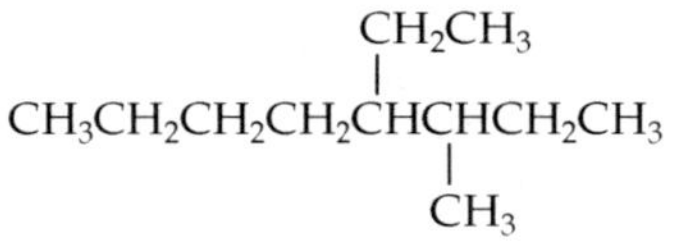 $CH_3CH_2CH_2CH_2\underset{\underset{\displaystyle CH_3}{|}}{\overset{\overset{\displaystyle CH_2CH_3}{|}}{C}H}CHCH_2CH_3$

(b) $CH_3CH_2CH_2\overset{\overset{\displaystyle CH_3CHCH_3}{|}}{C}HCH_2\underset{\underset{\displaystyle CH_3}{|}}{C}HCH_3$

(c) $CH_3\overset{\overset{\displaystyle CH_3}{|}}{\underset{\underset{\displaystyle CH_3}{|}}{C}}CH_2CH_2CH_2\overset{\overset{\displaystyle CH_3}{|}}{C}HCH_3$

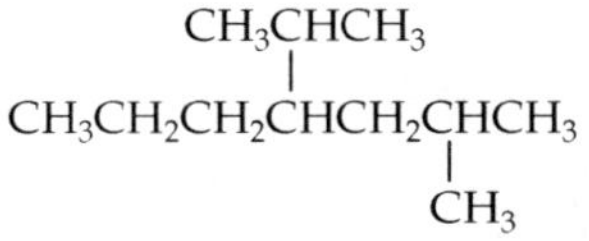

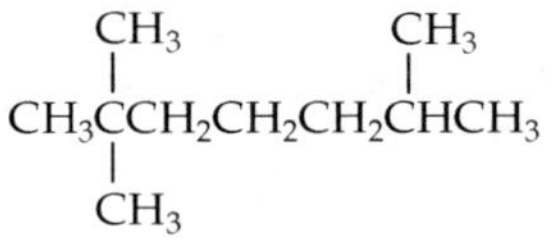

(d) 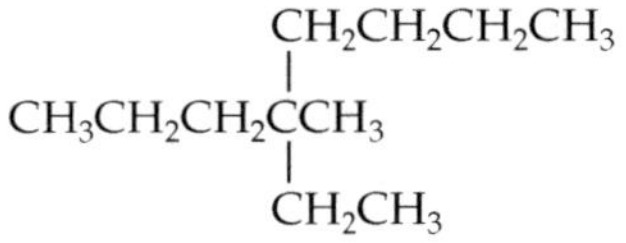 $CH_3CH_2CH_2\underset{\underset{\displaystyle CH_2CH_3}{|}}{\overset{\overset{\displaystyle CH_2CH_2CH_2CH_3}{|}}{C}}CH_3$

23.53 The following compound, known commonly as isooctane, is used as a reference substance for determining the octane rating of gasoline. What is the IUPAC name of isooctane?

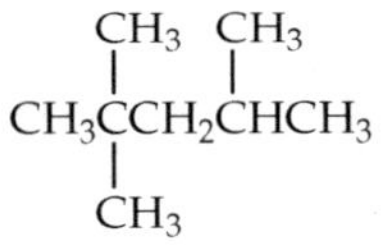

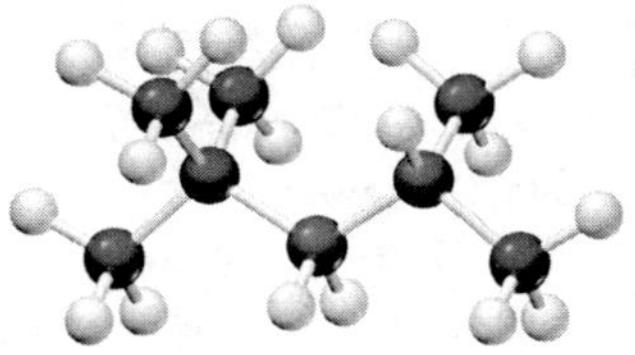

$CH_3\overset{\overset{\displaystyle CH_3}{|}}{\underset{\underset{\displaystyle CH_3}{|}}{C}}CH_2\overset{\overset{\displaystyle CH_3}{|}}{C}HCH_3$

Isooctane

23.54 Write condensed structures for each of the following compounds:

(a) 3-Ethylhexane

(b) 2,2,3-Trimethylpentane

(c) 3-Ethyl-3,4-dimethylheptane

(d) 5-Isopropyl-2-methyloctane

23.55 Draw structures corresponding to the following IUPAC names:

(a) Cyclooctane

(b) 1,1-Dimethylcyclopentane

(c) 1,2,3,4-Tetramethylcyclobutane

(d) 4-Ethyl-1,1-dimethylcyclohexane

23.56 Give IUPAC names for each of the following cycloalkanes:

(a)

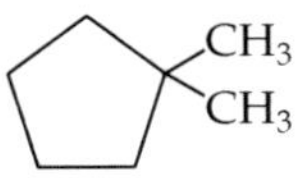

(b)

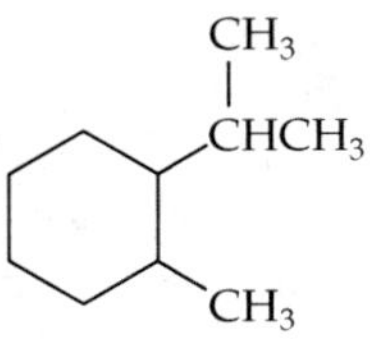

(c)

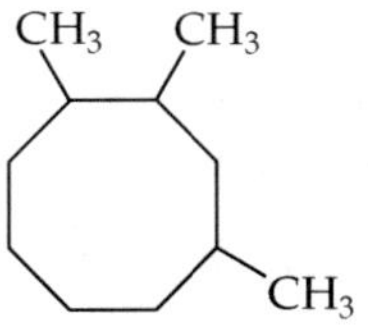

23.57 The following names are incorrect. What is wrong with each, and what are the correct names?

(a)
$$CH_3CCH_2CH_2CH_3$$
with CH_3 above and CH_2CH_3 below the second carbon
4-Ethyl-4-methylpentane

(b)
$$CH_3CHCH_2CHCH_2CH_3$$
with CH_2CH_3 above the second carbon and CH_3 below the fourth carbon
5-Ethyl-3-methylhexane

(c)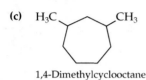

1,4-Dimethylcyclooctane

23.58 Give IUPAC names for each of the five isomers with the formula C_6H_{14}.

23.59 Draw structures and give IUPAC names for the nine isomers of C_7H_{16}.

23.60 Write the formulas of all monochlorinated substitution products that might result from a substitution reaction of the following substances with Cl_2:

(a) Hexane

(b) 3-Methylpentane

(c) Methylcyclohexane

23.61 Which of the following reactions is likely to have a higher yield? Explain.

(a)
$$CH_3CCH_3 + Cl_2 \xrightarrow{h\nu} CH_3CCH_2Cl$$
(each central carbon bears a CH_3 group above and below)

(b)
$$CH_3CHCH_2CH_3 + Cl_2 \xrightarrow{h\nu} CH_3CHCH_2CH_2Cl$$
(each carbon bears a CH_3 group above)

Alkenes, Alkynes, and Aromatic Compounds (Sections 23.9–23.11)

23.62 What kind of hybrid orbitals does carbon use in forming the following?

(a) Double bonds (b) Triple bonds

(c) Aromatic rings

23.63 Why are alkenes, alkynes, and aromatic compounds said to be unsaturated?

23.64 Not all compounds that smell nice are called "aromatic," and not all compounds called "aromatic" smell nice. Explain.

23.65 What is meant by the term *addition reaction*?

23.66 Write structural formulas for compounds that meet the following descriptions:

(a) An alkene with five carbons

(b) An alkyne with four carbons

(c) A substituted aromatic compound with eight carbons

23.67 How many dienes (compounds with two double bonds) are there with the formula C_5H_8? Draw structures of as many as you can.

23.68 Give IUPAC names for the following compounds:

(a) $CH_3CHCH=CHCH_3$ (with CH_3 above the second carbon)

(b) $CH_3CH_2CHCH_3$ (with $CH=CH_2$ above the third carbon)

(c) (benzene ring with two Cl substituents on adjacent carbons)

(d) $CH_3CH=CCH_3$ (with CH_3 above the third carbon)

(e) $CH_3CH_2C\equiv CCH_2CH_2CHCH_3$ (with CH_3 above the seventh carbon)

23.69 Draw structures corresponding to the following IUPAC names:

(a) *cis*-2-Hexene

(b) 2-Methyl-3-hexene

(c) 2-Methyl-1,3-butadiene

23.70 Ignoring cis–trans isomers, there are five alkenes with the formula C_5H_{10}. Draw structures for as many as you can, and give their IUPAC names. Which can exist as cis–trans isomers?

23.71 There are three alkynes with the formula C_5H_8. Draw and name them.

23.72 Which of the following compounds are capable of cis–trans isomerism?

(a) 1-Hexene

(b) 2-Hexene

(c) 3-Hexene

23.73 Which of the following compounds are capable of cis–trans isomerism?

(a) $CH_3CHCH=CHCH_3$ (with CH_3 above the second carbon)

(b) $CH_3CH_2CHCH_3$ (with $CH=CH_2$ above the third carbon)

(c) $CH_3CH=CHCHCH_2CH_3$ (with Cl above the fourth carbon)

23.74 Draw structures of the following compounds, indicating the cis or trans geometry of the double bond if necessary:

(a) *cis*-3-Heptene

(b) *cis*-4-Methyl-2-pentene

(c) *trans*-2,5-Dimethyl-3-hexene

23.75 The following names are incorrect by IUPAC rules. Draw the structures represented and give the correct names.

(a) 2-Methyl-4-hexene

(b) 5,5-Dimethyl-3-hexyne

(c) 2-Butyl-1-propene

(d) 1,5-Diethylbenzene

23.76 Why is cis–trans isomerism possible for alkenes but not for alkanes or alkynes?

23.77 Why do you suppose small-ring cycloalkenes such as cyclohexene don't exist as cis–trans isomers?

23.78 Write equations for the reaction of 2,3-dimethyl-2-butene with each of the following reagents:

(a) H_2 and Pd catalyst

(b) Br_2

(c) H_2O and H_2SO_4 catalyst

23.79 Write equations for the reaction of 2-methyl-2-butene with the reagents given in Problem 23.78.

23.80 Write equations for the reaction of *p*-dichlorobenzene with the following reagents:

(a) Br_2 and $FeBr_3$ catalyst

(b) HNO_3 and H_2SO_4 catalyst

(c) Cl_2 and $FeCl_3$ catalyst

23.81 Benzene and other aromatic compounds don't normally react with hydrogen in the presence of a palladium catalyst. If very high pressures (200 atm) and high temperatures are used, however, benzene will add three molecules of H_2 to give an addition product. What is a likely structure for the product?

Alcohols, Amines, and Carbonyl Compounds (Sections 23.12–23.14)

23.82 Draw structures corresponding to the following names:

(a) 2,4-Dimethyl-2-pentanol

(b) 2,2-Dimethylcyclohexanol

(c) 5,5-Diethyl-1-heptanol

(d) 3-Ethyl-3-hexanol

23.83 Draw structures corresponding to the following names:

(a) Propylamine

(b) Diethylamine

(c) *N*-Methylpropylamine

23.84 Assume that you have samples of quinine (an amine) and menthol (an alcohol). What simple chemical test could you do to distinguish between them?

23.85 Assume that you're given samples of pentanoic acid and methyl butanoate, both of which have the formula $C_5H_{10}O_2$. Describe how you can tell them apart.

23.86 What is the structural difference between an aldehyde and a ketone?

23.87 How do aldehydes and ketones differ from carboxylic acids, esters, and amides?

23.88 How are industrially important ketones and aldehydes usually prepared?

23.89 What general kind of reaction do carboxylic acids, esters, and amides undergo?

23.90 Identify the kinds of carbonyl groups in the following molecules (aldehyde, amide, ester, or ketone):

(a) [structure: cyclohexanone]

(b) $CH_3CH_2CH_2CHO$

(c) $CH_3\overset{\underset{\displaystyle CH_3}{|}}{C}HCH_2COCH_3$

(d) [structure: cyclopentane-CONH₂]

(e) $CH_3\overset{\underset{\displaystyle CH_3}{|}}{C}HCH_2COOCH_3$

23.91 Draw and name compounds that meet the following descriptions:

(a) Three different amides with the formula $C_5H_{11}NO$

(b) Three different esters with the formula $C_6H_{12}O_2$

23.92 Write the equation for the dissociation of benzoic acid in water. If the K_a of benzoic acid is 6.5×10^{-5}, what is its percent dissociation in a 1.0 M solution?

23.93 Assume that you have a sample of acetic acid ($pK_a = 4.75$) dissolved in water.

(a) Draw the structure of the major species present in the water solution.

(b) Now assume that aqueous HCl is added to the acetic acid solution until pH 2 is reached. Draw the structure of the major species present.

(c) Finally, assume that aqueous NaOH is added to the acetic acid solution until pH 12 is reached. Draw the structure of the major species present.

23.94 Give the IUPAC names of the following compounds:

(a) $CH_3\overset{\underset{\displaystyle CH_3}{|}}{C}HCH_2CH_2\overset{\overset{\displaystyle O}{\|}}{C}OCH_3$

(b) $CH_3\overset{\underset{\displaystyle CH_3}{|}}{C}CH_2CH_2\overset{\overset{\displaystyle O}{\|}}{C}OH$

(c) $CH_3CH_2CH_2\overset{\underset{\displaystyle CH_3}{|}}{C}H\overset{\overset{\displaystyle O}{\|}}{C}NH_2$

23.95 Give the IUPAC names of the following compounds:

(a) $CH_3\overset{\underset{\displaystyle CH_2CH_3}{|}}{C}HCH_2CH_2\overset{\overset{\displaystyle O}{\|}}{C}N\overset{\underset{\displaystyle CH_3}{|}}{}CH_3$

(b) $CH_3\overset{\underset{\displaystyle CH_3}{|}}{C}H\overset{\overset{\displaystyle O}{\|}}{C}OCH\overset{\underset{\displaystyle CH_3}{|}}{}CH_3$

(c)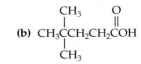

23.96 Draw structures corresponding to the following IUPAC names:

(a) Methyl pentanoate

(b) Isopropyl 2-methylbutanoate

(c) Cyclohexyl acetate

23.97 Draw structures corresponding to the following IUPAC names:

(a) 3-Methylpentanamide

(b) *N*-Phenylacetamide

(c) *N*-Ethyl-*N*-methylbenzamide

23.98 Write equations showing how you could prepare each of the esters in Problem 23.96 from the appropriate alcohols and carboxylic acids.

23.99 Write equations showing how you could prepare each of the amides in Problem 23.97 from the appropriate amines and carboxylic acids.

23.100 Novocaine, a local anesthetic, has the following structure. Identify the functional groups present in novocaine, and show the structures of the alcohol and carboxylic acid you would use to prepare it.

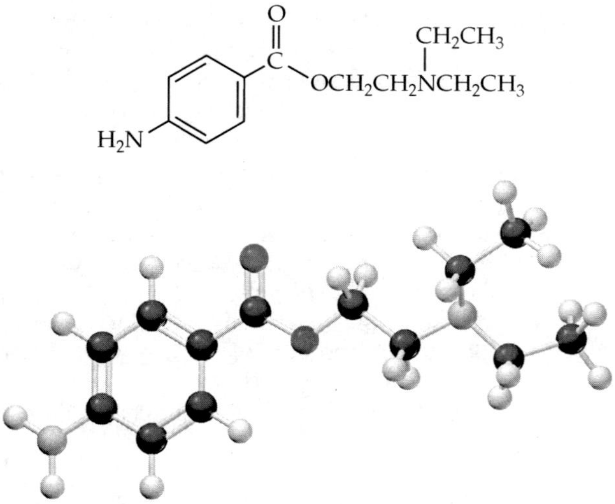

Novocaine

23.101 Ordinary soap is a mixture of the sodium or potassium salts of long-chain carboxylic acids that arise from saponification of animal fat. Draw the structures of soap molecules produced in the following reaction:

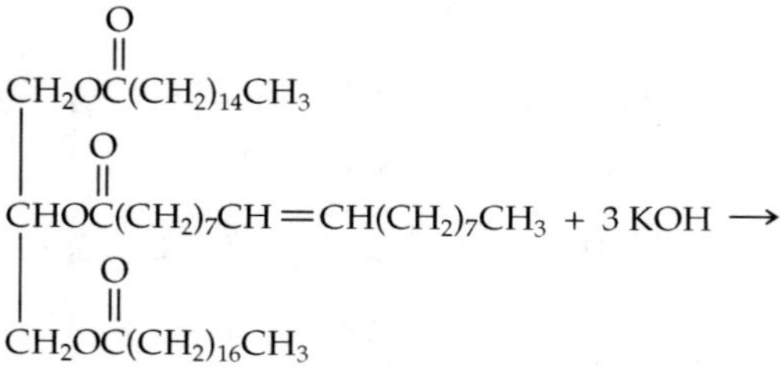

$$CH_2OC(CH_2)_{14}CH_3$$
$$| \quad O$$
$$\quad ||$$
$$CHOC(CH_2)_7CH=CH(CH_2)_7CH_3 + 3\ KOH \longrightarrow$$
$$| \quad O$$
$$\quad ||$$
$$CH_2OC(CH_2)_{16}CH_3$$

A fat

Polymers (Section 23.15)

23.102 What is the difference between a monomer and a polymer?

23.103 What is the difference between a polymer like polyethylene and a polymer like nylon?

23.104 Show the structure of poly(vinyl chloride) by drawing several repeating units. Vinyl chloride is $H_2C=CHCl$.

23.105 Show the structures of the polymers you would obtain from the following monomers:
(a) $F_2C=CF_2$ gives Teflon
(b) $H_2C=CHCO_2CH_3$ gives Lucite

23.106 Show the monomer units you would use to prepare the following alkene polymers:

(a) 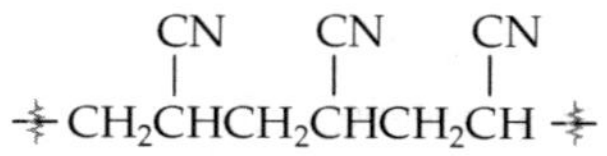 $\begin{array}{ccc} CN & CN & CN \\ | & | & | \\ \end{array}$
   $\dagger CH_2CHCH_2CHCH_2CH \dagger$

(b) 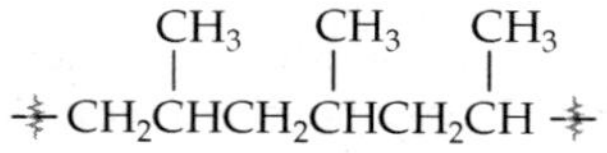 $\begin{array}{ccc} CH_3 & CH_3 & CH_3 \\ | & | & | \\ \end{array}$
   $\dagger CH_2CHCH_2CHCH_2CH \dagger$

(c) 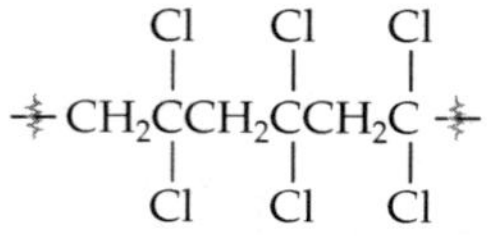 $\begin{array}{ccc} Cl & Cl & Cl \\ | & | & | \\ \end{array}$
   $\dagger CH_2CCH_2CCH_2C \dagger$
   $\begin{array}{ccc} | & | & | \\ Cl & Cl & Cl \\ \end{array}$

23.107 What monomer unit is used to prepare poly(methyl cyanoacrylate), also known as "superglue"?

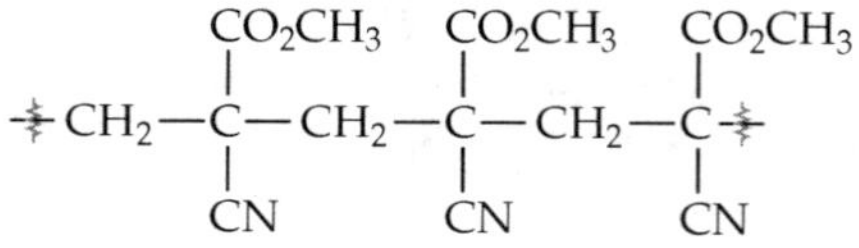

$$\begin{array}{ccc} CO_2CH_3 & CO_2CH_3 & CO_2CH_3 \\ | & | & | \\ \end{array}$$
$$\dagger CH_2-C-CH_2-C-CH_2-C\dagger$$
$$\begin{array}{ccc} | & | & | \\ CN & CN & CN \\ \end{array}$$

Poly(methyl cyanoacrylate)

23.108 Kevlar, a nylon polymer prepared by the reaction of 1,4-benzenedicarboxylic acid (terephthalic acid) with *p*-diaminobenzene, is so strong that it's used to make bulletproof vests. Draw the structure of a segment of Kevlar.

23.109 Draw the structure of a segment of the polyester that results from the reaction of ethylene glycol ($HOCH_2CH_2OH$) with butanedioic acid ($HO_2CCH_2CH_2CO_2H$).

CHAPTER PROBLEMS

23.110 Draw structural formulas for the following compounds:
(a) 2-Methylheptane
(b) 4-Ethyl-2-methylhexane
(c) 4-Ethyl-3,4-dimethyloctane
(d) 2,4,4-Trimethylheptane
(e) 1,1-Dimethylcyclopentane
(f) 4-Isopropyl-3-methylheptane

23.111 Give IUPAC names for the following alkanes:

(a) 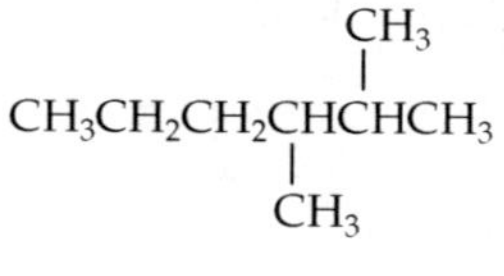 $\begin{array}{c} CH_3 \\ | \\ \end{array}$
   $CH_3CH_2CH_2CHCHCH_3$
   $\begin{array}{c} | \\ CH_3 \\ \end{array}$

(b) $\begin{array}{c} CH_3 \\ | \\ \end{array}$
   $CH_3CH_2CH_2CHCHCH_3$
   $\begin{array}{c} | \\ CH_2CH_2CH_2CH_3 \\ \end{array}$

(c) $\begin{array}{cc} CH_3 & CH_2CH_3 \\ | & | \\ \end{array}$
   $CH_3CHCH_2CCH_3$
   $\begin{array}{c} | \\ CH_2CH_3 \\ \end{array}$

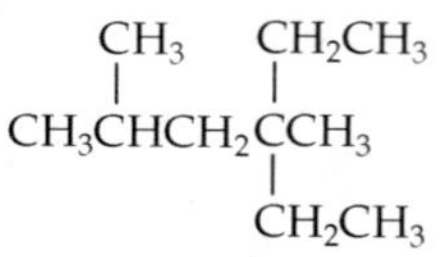

(d) 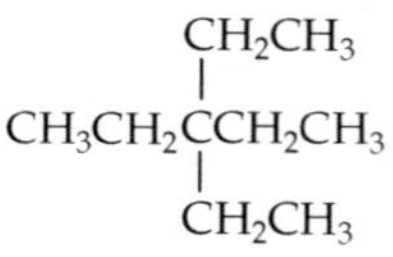 $\begin{array}{c} CH_2CH_3 \\ | \\ \end{array}$
   $CH_3CH_2CCH_2CH_3$
   $\begin{array}{c} | \\ CH_2CH_3 \\ \end{array}$

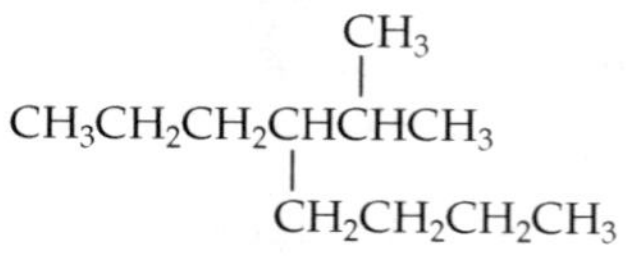

23.112 Assume that you have two unlabeled bottles, one with cyclohexane and one with cyclohexene. How could you tell them apart by doing chemical reactions?

23.113 Assume you have two unlabeled bottles, one with cyclohexene and one with benzene. How could you tell them apart by doing chemical reactions?

23.114 Write the products of the following reactions:

(a) $CH_3CH_2CH=CHCHCH_3$ overset with CH_3 group, $\xrightarrow[\text{Pd catalyst}]{H_2}$

(b) Br—⟨benzene ring⟩—Br $\xrightarrow[\text{H}_2\text{SO}_4]{\text{HNO}_3}$

(c)   ⟨cyclohexene ring with two CH_3 groups⟩ $\xrightarrow[\text{H}_2\text{SO}_4]{\text{H}_2\text{O}}$

23.115 Show the structure of the nylon polymer that results from heating 6-aminohexanoic acid.

$$H_2NCH_2CH_2CH_2CH_2CH_2\overset{\overset{\displaystyle O}{\|}}{C}OH \xrightarrow{\text{Heat}}$$
6-Aminohexanoic acid

MULTI-CONCEPT PROBLEMS

23.116 Fumaric acid is an organic substance widely used as a food additive. Its elemental composition is 41.4% C, 3.5% H, and 55.1% O. A solution made by dissolving 0.1500 g of fumaric acid in water and diluting to a volume of 100.0 mL gave rise to an osmotic pressure of 240.3 mm Hg at 298 K. On titration of a sample weighing 0.573 g, 94.1 mL of 0.105 M NaOH was required to reach an equivalence point. Fumaric acid reacts with 1 mol of HCl to give an addition product and with 1 mol of H_2 to give a reduction product.

(a) What is the empirical formula of fumaric acid?

(b) What is the molecular mass of fumaric acid?

(c) Draw three possible structures for fumaric acid.

(d) If fumaric acid contains a trans double bond, which of your structures is correct?

23.117 When 0.0552 g of an unknown liquid containing only C, H, and O was subjected to combustion analysis, 0.1213 g of CO_2 and 0.0661 g of H_2O were formed.

(a) Calculate a formula for the unknown, and write a balanced equation for the combustion reaction.

(b) Is the formula you calculated an empirical formula or a molecular formula? Explain.

(c) Draw three possible structures for the compound, and identify the functional groups in each.

(d) Reaction of the compound with CrO_3 yields acetone. Which of the three structures you drew in part (c) is most likely to be correct?

(e) Combustion of 5.000 g of the compound releases 166.9 kJ of heat. Look up $\Delta H°_f$ values for $CO_2(g)$ and $H_2O(l)$ in Appendix B, and calculate $\Delta H°_f$ for the compound.

23.118 Reaction of methyl propanoate ($CH_3CH_2CO_2CH_3$) with ammonia gives methanol plus a second product with the formula C_3H_7NO.

(a) Propose a structure, and give a name for the second product.

(b) Draw two resonance structures for the product.

(c) Predict the geometry around the three carbon atoms and the nitrogen atom in the product according to VSEPR theory.

(d) Experimentally, the nitrogen atom in the product is found to be trigonal planar, with bond angles near 120°. How does this result compare with your prediction? Sketch a p-orbital picture of the product, and account for the experimental geometry.

CHAPTER

24

Biochemistry

▲ You are what you eat.

If the ultimate goal of chemistry is to understand the world around us on a molecular level, then a knowledge of **biochemistry**—the chemistry of living organisms—is a crucial part of that goal. In this chapter, we'll take a brief look at biochemical energy to see where it comes from and how it is used by organisms. Then, we'll look at the main classes of biomolecules: proteins, carbohydrates, lipids, and nucleic acids.

24.1 | BIOCHEMICAL ENERGY

All living organisms do mechanical work. Microorganisms engulf food, plants bend toward the sun, animals move about. Organisms also do chemical work in synthesizing the biomolecules needed for energy storage, growth, and repair. Even individual cells do work when they move molecules and ions across cell membranes.

In animals, it is the energy extracted from food and released in the exquisitely interconnected reactions of *metabolism* that allows work to be done. Animals are powered by the cellular oxidation of biomolecules containing mainly carbon, hydrogen, and oxygen. The end products of this biological oxidation are carbon dioxide, water, and energy, just as they are when an organic fuel such as methane is burned with oxygen in a furnace.

$$C, H, O \text{ (food molecules)} + O_2 \longrightarrow CO_2 + H_2O + \text{Energy}$$

The energy used by the vast majority of living organisms comes ultimately from the sun through photosynthesis in plants, which converts sunlight to potential energy stored mainly in carbohydrates. Plant-eating animals use some of this energy for living and store the rest of it, primarily in fats. Other animals, including humans, then eat plants and smaller animals and make use of the chemical energy these organisms have stored.

The sum of the many organic reactions that take place in cells is called **metabolism.** These reactions usually occur in long sequences, which may be either linear or cyclic. In a linear sequence, the product of one reaction serves as the starting material for the next. In a cyclic sequence, a series

CONTENTS

▲ The energy used by almost all living organisms ultimately comes from the sun. Plants use solar energy for the photosynthesis of glucose from CO_2, and animals then eat the plants.

979

of reactions regenerates the first reactant and produces various products along the way.

$$A \longrightarrow B \longrightarrow C \longrightarrow D \longrightarrow \ldots$$

A linear sequence

A cyclic sequence

where E and F are products

Those reaction sequences that break molecules apart are known collectively as **catabolism,** while those that put building blocks back together to assemble larger molecules are known as **anabolism.** Catabolic reactions generally release energy that is used to power living organisms, while anabolic reactions generally absorb energy. The overall picture of catabolism and energy production can be roughly divided into the four stages shown in Figure 24.1.

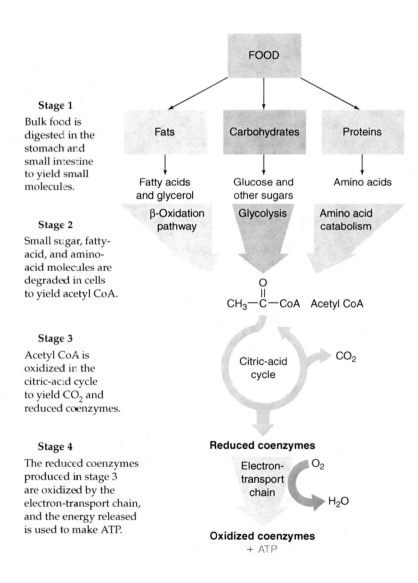

Stage 1
Bulk food is digested in the stomach and small intestine to yield small molecules.

Stage 2
Small sugar, fatty-acid, and amino-acid molecules are degraded in cells to yield acetyl CoA.

Stage 3
Acetyl CoA is oxidized in the citric-acid cycle to yield CO_2 and reduced coenzymes.

Stage 4
The reduced coenzymes produced in stage 3 are oxidized by the electron-transport chain, and the energy released is used to make ATP.

FIGURE 24.1
An overview of catabolic pathways in the four stages of food degradation and the production of biochemical energy.

The first stage of catabolism, *digestion*, takes place in the stomach and small intestine when bulk food is broken down into small molecules such as simple sugars, long-chain carboxylic acids called *fatty acids*, and amino acids. In stage 2, these small molecules are further degraded in cells to yield two-carbon acetyl groups ($CH_3\overset{|}{C}=O$) attached to a large carrier molecule called *coenzyme A*. The resultant compound, *acetyl coenzyme A* (*acetyl CoA*), is an intermediate in the breakdown of all the main classes of food molecules.

Acetyl groups are oxidized in the third stage of catabolism, the *citric acid cycle*, to yield carbon dioxide and water. This stage releases a great deal of energy that is used in stage 4, the *electron-transport chain*, to make molecules of adenosine triphosphate (ATP). ATP, the final product of food catabolism, plays a pivotal role in the production of biological energy. As the crucial molecule for driving many metabolic reactions, ATP has been called the "energy currency of the living cell." Catabolic reactions "pay off" in ATP by synthesizing it from adenosine diphosphate (ADP) plus hydrogen phosphate ion, HPO_4^{2-}. Anabolic reactions "spend" ATP by transferring a phosphate group to other molecules, thereby regenerating ADP. The entire process of energy production revolves around the ATP $\rightleftharpoons$ ADP interconversion.

Adenosine diphosphate (ADP)   Adenosine triphosphate (ATP)

Because the primary metabolic function of ATP is to drive reactions, biochemists often refer to it as a "high-energy molecule" or an "energy storehouse." These words don't mean that ATP is somehow different from other compounds; they mean only that ATP releases a large amount of energy when it reacts with other compounds to break its P–O–P (*phosphoric anhydride*) bonds and transfer a phosphate group.

What does the body do with ATP? Recall from Sections 8.14 and 16.7 that a chemical reaction is favorable, or spontaneous, if the free-energy change (ΔG) for the process is negative. Conversely, a reaction is unfavorable if the free-energy change is positive. The change in free energy depends on two factors: the release or absorption of heat (ΔH) and the increase or decrease in entropy (ΔS), as given by the equation $\Delta G = \Delta H - T\Delta S$.

Reactions in living organisms are no different from reactions in laboratory flasks: Both follow the same laws, and both have the same kinds of energy requirements. For any biochemical reaction to occur spontaneously, ΔG must be negative. For example, oxidation of 1 mol of glucose, the principal source of energy for animals, has $\Delta G° = -2870$ kJ.

Glucose ($C_6H_{12}O_6$)

Reactions in which the free-energy change is positive can also occur, but such reactions can't be spontaneous. An example is the conversion of glucose to glucose 6-phosphate, an important step in the breakdown of dietary carbohydrates.

$$\underset{\text{Glucose}}{\text{HOCH}_2\text{CHCHCHCHCH}} \xrightarrow[-\text{H}_2\text{O}]{\text{HPO}_4^{2-}} \underset{\text{Glucose 6-phosphate}}{\text{OPOCH}_2\text{CHCHCHCHCH}} \quad \Delta G° = +13.8 \text{ kJ}$$

What usually happens for an energetically unfavorable reaction to occur is that it is "coupled" to an energetically favorable reaction so that the overall free-energy change for the two reactions together is favorable. To see what this means, imagine that the conversion of reactant **A** to product **C** in reaction 1 does not occur to any appreciable extent because it is energetically unfavorable, with $\Delta G > 0$.

$$(1) \quad \mathbf{A} + b \rightleftharpoons \mathbf{C} + d \qquad \Delta G > 0$$

Imagine also that byproduct d in reaction (1) can react with substance e to yield f and g in a second, strongly favorable reaction with $\Delta G \ll 0$.

$$(2) \quad d + e \rightleftharpoons f + g \qquad \Delta G \ll 0$$

Taking the two reactions together, they share, or are coupled through, the common intermediate d. When even a small amount of d is formed in reaction 1, it is completely consumed in reaction 2, forcing reaction 1 to continually replenish it until all of reactant **A** is gone. That is, the two reactions added together have a favorable $\Delta G < 0$, and we say that the favorable reaction 2 "drives" the unfavorable reaction 1. Thus, the transformation of **A** to **C** becomes possible.

$$(1) \quad \mathbf{A} + b \rightleftharpoons \mathbf{C} = d \qquad \Delta G > 0$$
$$(2) \quad d + e \rightleftharpoons f + g \qquad \Delta G \ll 0$$

Net: $\mathbf{A} + b + e \rightleftharpoons \mathbf{C} + f + g \qquad \Delta G < 0$

An example of coupled reactions occurs in the formation of glucose 6-phosphate from glucose. Glucose does not react directly with HOPO_3^{2-} because the process is energetically unfavorable, with $\Delta G° = +13.8$ kJ. Glucose does, however, undergo an energetically favorable reaction with ATP to yield glucose 6-phosphate plus ADP, with $\Delta G° = -30.5$ kJ. Coupling the two reactions together makes the overall process favorable by about 16.7 kJ/mol. That is, ATP drives the phosphorylation reaction of glucose.

Glucose + HOPO_3^{2-} ⟶ Glucose 6-phosphate + H_2O $\Delta G° = +13.8$ kJ/mol

ATP + H_2O ⟶ ADP + HOPO_3^{2-} + H^+ $\Delta G° = -30.5$ kJ/mol

Net: Glucose + ATP ⟶ Glucose 6-phosphate + ADP + H^+ $\Delta G° = -16.7$ kJ/mol

It's this ability to drive otherwise unfavorable reactions that makes ATP so useful. In fact, most of the thousands of reactions going on in your body every minute are somehow coupled to ATP. It's no exaggeration to say that the transfer of a phosphate group from ATP is the single most important chemical reaction in making life possible.

▶ **PROBLEM 24.1** One of the steps in fat metabolism is the reaction of glycerol [$\text{HOCH}_2-\text{CH(OH)}-\text{CH}_2\text{OH}$] with ATP to yield glycerol-1-phosphate. Draw the structure of glycerol-1-phosphate.

24.2 | AMINO ACIDS AND PEPTIDES

Taken from the Greek *proteios,* meaning "primary," the name *protein* aptly describes a group of biological molecules that are of primary importance to all living organisms. Approximately 50% of the body's dry weight is protein, and almost all the reactions that occur in the body are catalyzed by proteins. In fact, a human body contains over *100,000* different kinds of proteins.

Proteins have many different biological functions. Some, such as the keratin in skin, hair, and fingernails, serve a structural purpose. Others, such as the insulin that controls glucose metabolism, act as hormones—chemical messengers that coordinate the activities of different cells in an organism. And still other proteins, such as DNA polymerase, are **enzymes,** the biological catalysts that carry out body chemistry. As discussed previously in the Chapter 12 Interlude, enzymes are highly specific in their action and often catalyze only a single reaction of a single chemical substrate.

Chemically, **proteins** are biological polymers made up of many amino acid molecules linked together to form a long chain. As their name implies, amino acids contain two functional groups, a basic amino group ($-NH_2$) and an acidic $-CO_2H$ group. Alanine is one of the simplest examples.

▲ Bird feathers are made largely of the protein *keratin.*

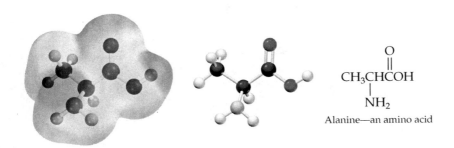

$$CH_3CHCOH$$

Alanine—an amino acid

Two or more amino acids can link together by forming amide bonds (Section 23.14), usually called **peptide bonds.** A *dipeptide* results when two amino acids link together by formation of a peptide bond between the $-NH_2$ group of one and the $-CO_2H$ group of the other. Similarly, a *tripeptide* results when three amino acids link together with two peptide bonds, and so on. Short chains of up to 100 amino acids are usually called **polypeptides,** while the term *protein* is reserved for longer chains.

Remember...

An **amide** is a compound with the $-C-N-$ functional group and can be prepared by reaction of a carboxylic acid ($-CO_2H$) with an amine ($-NH_2$).
(Section 23.14)

α Amino acids—The groups symbolized by R and R′ represent different amino acid side chains.

A peptide bond

Twenty different amino acids are commonly found in proteins, as shown in Figure 24.2. Each amino acid is referred to by a three-letter shorthand code, such as Ala (alanine), Gly (glycine), Pro (proline), and so on. All 20 are called **alpha- (α-) amino acids** because the amino group in each is connected to the carbon atom *alpha to* (next to) the carboxylic acid group. Nineteen of the 20 have an $-NH_2$ amino group, and one (proline) has an $-NH-$ amino group as part of a ring.

The 20 amino acids differ only in the nature of the group attached to the α carbon. Called the *side chain,* this group can be symbolized in a general way by the letter R. (In a broader context, the symbol R is used throughout organic chemistry to refer to an organic fragment of unspecified structure.) Our bodies can synthesize only 11 of

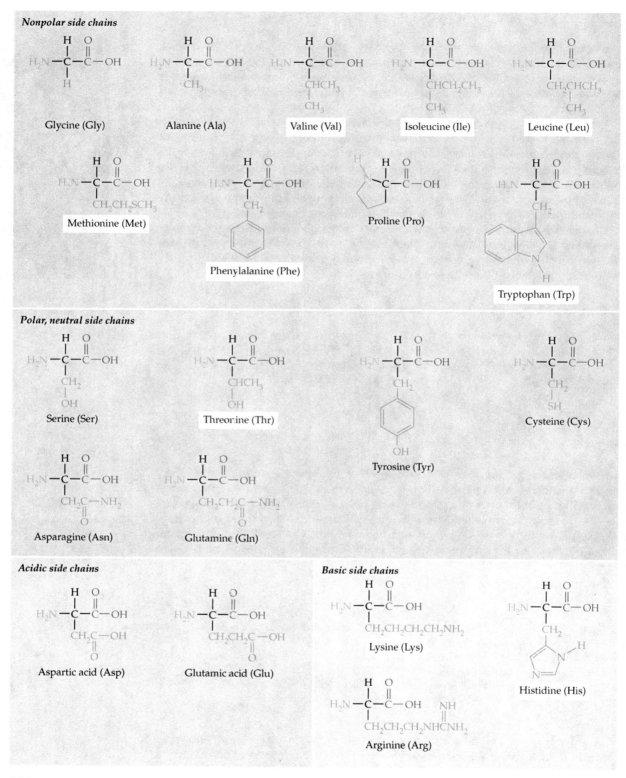

FIGURE 24.2

Structures of the 20 α-amino acids found in proteins. Fifteen of the 20 have neutral side chains, two have acidic side chains, and three have basic side chains. The names of the 9 essential amino acids are highlighted.

the 20 amino acids. The remaining 9, highlighted in Figure 24.2, are called *essential amino acids* because they must be obtained from the diet.

 α carbon

R—CH—COH

Side chain — NH₂

Generalized structure of an α-amino acid

The 20 common amino acids are classified as *neutral*, *basic*, or *acidic*, depending on the structure of their side chains. Fifteen of the 20 have neutral side chains. Two (aspartic acid and glutamic acid) have an additional carboxylic acid group in their side chains and are classified as acidic amino acids. Three (lysine, arginine, and histidine) have an additional amine function in their side chains and are classified as basic amino acids. The 15 neutral amino acids can be further divided into those with nonpolar side chains and those with polar functional groups such as amide or hydroxyl groups. Nonpolar side chains are often described as *hydrophobic* (water fearing) because they are not attracted to water, while polar side chains are described as *hydrophilic* (water loving) because they *are* attracted to water.

▲ Corn is particularly low in lysine, one of the essential amino acids.

⊂▷ WORKED KEY CONCEPT EXAMPLE 24.1

INTERPRETING AN ELECTROSTATIC POTENTIAL MAP

Identify the following amino acid, and tell from the electrostatic potential map whether its side chain is acidic, basic, neutral nonpolar, or neutral polar.

STRATEGY

Identify the amino acid by looking at Figure 24.2, and predict its polarity by looking for electron-rich (red) or electron-poor (blue) regions in the side chain.

SOLUTION

The amino acid is leucine. It is nonpolar because it contains a hydrocarbon side chain that has neither electron-rich nor electron-poor groups.

▶ PROBLEM 24.2 Which common amino acids contain an aromatic (benzene-like) ring? Which contain sulfur? Which are alcohols? Which have alkyl-group side chains?

▶ PROBLEM 24.3 Draw alanine using wedges and dashes to show the tetrahedral geometry of its α carbon.

KEY CONCEPT PROBLEM 24.4 Identify the following amino acid, and tell from the electrostatic potential map whether its side chain is acidic, basic, neutral non-polar, or neutral polar.

24.3 | AMINO ACIDS AND MOLECULAR HANDEDNESS

We saw in Section 20.9 that certain molecules lack a plane of symmetry and are there-fore *chiral*. When held up to a mirror, a chiral molecule is not identical to its reflected image. Instead, the molecule and its mirror image have a right-hand/left-hand rela-tionship. Compare alanine and propane, for example (Figure 24.3). An alanine mole-cule is chiral; it has no symmetry plane and can exist in two forms—a "right-handed" form called D-alanine (from *dextro*, Latin for "right") and a "left-handed" form called L-alanine (from *levo*, Latin for "left"). Propane, however, is achiral. It has a symmetry plane cutting through the three carbons and thus exists in only a single form.

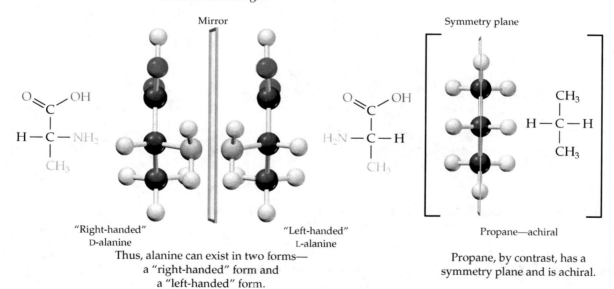

Alanine has no symmetry plane; the two "halves" of the molecule are not mirror images.

"Right-handed" D-alanine

"Left-handed" L-alanine

Thus, alanine can exist in two forms— a "right-handed" form and a "left-handed" form.

Propane—achiral

Propane, by contrast, has a symmetry plane and is achiral.

FIGURE 24.3
The structure of alanine (2-aminopropanoic acid).

Why are some organic molecules chiral while others are not? The answer has to do with the three-dimensional structure of organic molecules. We've seen that carbon forms four bonds that are oriented toward the four corners of a regular tetrahedron. Whenever a carbon atom is bonded to four *different* atoms or groups of atoms, chirality results. If a carbon is bonded to two or more of the same groups, however, no chirality is possible. In alanine, for example, carbon 2 is bonded to four different groups: a $-CO_2H$ group, an $-H$ atom, an $-NH_2$ group, and a $-CH_3$ group. Thus, alanine is chiral. In propane, however, each of the carbons is bonded to at least two groups—the $-H$ atoms—that are identical. Thus, propane is achiral.

Groups attached to C2		*Groups attached to C2*	
1. $-CO_2H$		1. $-CH_3$	Identical
2. $-H$	Different	2. $-CH_3$	
3. $-NH_2$		3. $-H$	Identical
4. $-CH_3$		4. $-H$	

Alanine—chiral   Propane—achiral

As mentioned in Section 20.9, the two mirror-image forms of a chiral molecule are called *enantiomers*. The mirror-image relationship of the enantiomers of a molecule with four different groups on a chiral carbon atom is shown in Figure 24.4.

Of the 20 common amino acids, 19 are chiral because they have four different groups bonded to their α carbons, $-H$, $-NH_2$, $-CO_2H$, and $-R$ (the side chain). Only glycine, $H_2NCH_2CO_2H$, is achiral. Even though the naturally occurring chiral α-amino acids can exist as pairs of enantiomers, only L-amino acids are found in proteins. When drawn with the $-CO_2H$ group at the top and the side-chain R group at the bottom, an L-amino acid has its $-NH_2$ group coming out of the plane of the paper on the left side of the structure:

An L-amino acid

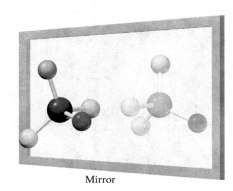

Mirror

FIGURE 24.4
A molecule with a carbon atom that is bonded to four different groups is chiral and is not identical to its mirror image. It thus exists in two enantiomeric forms.

WORKED EXAMPLE 24.2

IDENTIFYING CHIRAL MOLECULES

Lactic acid can be isolated from sour milk. Is lactic acid chiral?

$$CH_3 \underset{3}{-} \underset{2}{CH} \underset{1}{-} COH$$

with OH on C2 and O double-bonded to C1.   Lactic acid

STRATEGY

To find out if lactic acid is chiral, list the groups attached to each carbon, and see if any carbon is attached to four different groups.

SOLUTION

Groups on Carbon 1	Groups on Carbon 2	Groups on Carbon 3
1. $-OH$	1. $-CO_2H$	1. $-CH(OH)CO_2H$
2. $=O$	2. $-OH$	2. $-H$
3. $-CH(OH)CH_3$	3. $-H$	3. $-H$
	4. $-CH_3$	4. $-H$

Of the three carbons, carbon 2 has four different groups, so lactic acid is chiral.

▸ **PROBLEM 24.5** Which of the following objects are chiral?

  (a) A glove   **(b)** A baseball   **(c)** A screw   **(d)** A nail

▸ **PROBLEM 24.6** 2-Aminopropane is an achiral molecule, but 2-aminobutane is chiral. Explain.

▸ **PROBLEM 24.7** Which of the following molecules are chiral?

  (a) 3-Chloropentane

  (b) 2-Chloropentane

$$\text{(c)} \ \ CH_3CHCH_2CHCH_2CH_3 \ \ \overset{\overset{\displaystyle CH_3 \quad CH_3}{|\quad\quad|}}{}$$

▸ **PROBLEM 24.8** Two of the 20 common amino acids have two chiral carbon atoms in their structures. Identify them.

⟐ **KEY CONCEPT PROBLEM 24.9** Two of the following three molecules are identical, and one is the enantiomer of the other two. Which one is the enantiomer?

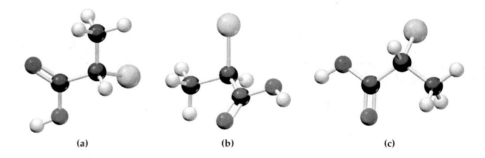

      (a)   (b)   (c)

24.4 | PROTEINS

Proteins are amino acid polymers in which the individual amino acids, often called *residues*, are linked together by peptide (amide) bonds. The repeating chain of amide linkages to which the side chains are attached is called the *backbone*.

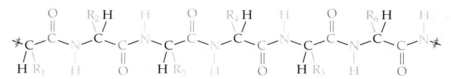

A segment of a protein backbone. The side-chain R groups
of the individual amino acids are substituents on the backbone.

    Because amino acids can be assembled in any order, depending on which –CO$_2$H group joins with which –NH$_2$ group, the number of possible isomeric peptides increases rapidly as the number of amino acid residues increases. There are six ways in which three different amino acids can be joined, more than 40,000 ways in which the eight amino acids present in the blood pressure-regulating hormone angiotensin II can be joined (Figure 24.5), and a staggering number of ways in which the *1800* amino acids in myosin, the major component of muscle filaments, can be arranged.

    No matter how long the chain, all noncyclic proteins have an **N-terminal amino acid** with a free –NH$_2$ group on one end and a **C-terminal amino acid** with a free –CO$_2$H group on the other end. By convention, a protein is written with the N-terminal residue on the left and the C-terminal residue on the right, and its name is indicated with the three-letter abbreviations listed in Figure 24.2. Thus, angiotensin II (Figure 24.5) is abbreviated Asp-Arg-Val-Tyr-Ile-His-Pro-Phe.

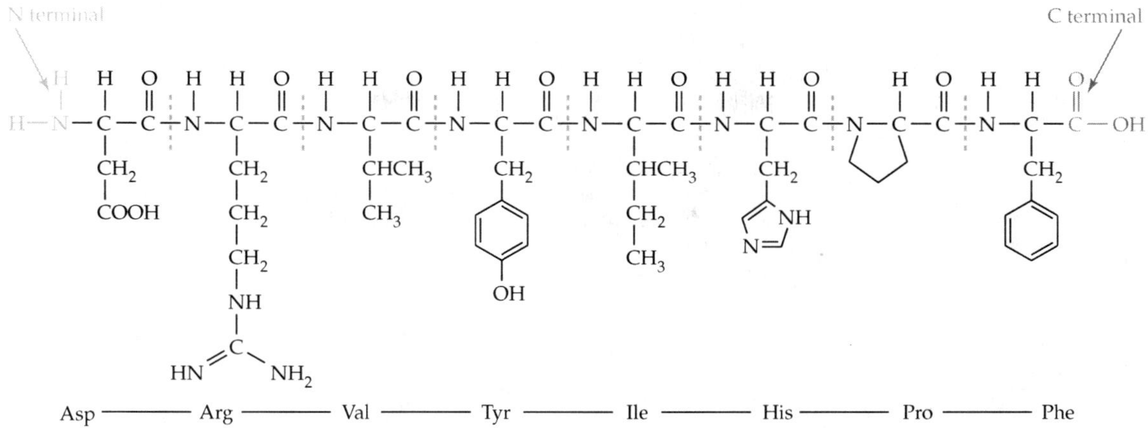

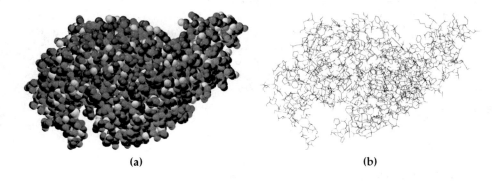

Asp ——— Arg ——— Val ——— Tyr ——— Ile ——— His ——— Pro ——— Phe

FIGURE 24.5

The structure of angiotensin II, an octapeptide in blood plasma that regulates blood pressure.

Proteins are classified according to their three-dimensional shape as either *fibrous* or *globular*. Fibrous proteins, such as collagen and the keratins, consist of polypeptide chains arranged side by side in long filaments. Because these proteins are tough and insoluble in water, they are used in nature for structural materials like skin, tendons, hair, ligaments, and muscle. Globular proteins, by contrast, are usually coiled into compact, nearly spherical shapes, as in the digestive enzyme pepsin (Figure 24.6). Most of the 2000 or so known enzymes present inside cells are globular proteins.

(a)   (b)

FIGURE 24.6

Computer-generated models of the enzyme pepsin, a typical globular protein, in both **(a)** space-filling and **(b)** wire-frame formats.

Another way to classify proteins is according to biological function. As indicated in Table 24.1, proteins have a remarkable diversity of roles.

TABLE 24.1 Some Biological Functions of Proteins

Type	Function	Example
Enzymes	Catalyze biological processes	Pepsin
Hormones	Regulate body processes	Insulin
Storage proteins	Store nutrients	Ferritin
Transport proteins	Transport oxygen and other substances through the body	Hemoglobin
Structural proteins	Form an organism's structure	Collagen
Protective proteins	Help fight infection	Antibodies
Contractile proteins	Form muscles	Actin, myosin
Toxic proteins	Serve as a defense for the plant or animal	Snake venoms

WORKED EXAMPLE 24.3

DRAWING A DIPEPTIDE STRUCTURE

Draw the structure of the dipeptide Ala-Ser.

STRATEGY

First, look up the names and structures of the two amino acids, Ala (alanine) and Ser (serine). Since alanine is N-terminal and serine is C-terminal, Ala-Ser must have an amide bond between the alanine $-CO_2H$ and the serine $-NH_2$.

SOLUTION

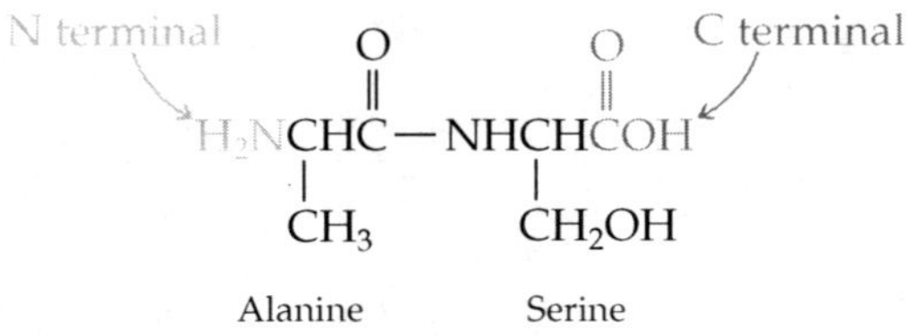

N terminal
O
‖
$H_2NCHC-NHCHCOH$
|
CH_3
|
CH_2OH
C terminal

Alanine   Serine

Ala-Ser

▶ **PROBLEM 24.10**   Use the three-letter shorthand notations to name the two isomeric dipeptides that can be made from valine and cysteine. Draw both structures.

▶ **PROBLEM 24.11**   Name the six tripeptides that contain valine, tyrosine, and glycine.

24.5 | LEVELS OF PROTEIN STRUCTURE

With molecular masses of up to one-half million amu, many proteins are so large that the word *structure* takes on a broader meaning with these immense molecules than it does with simpler organic molecules. In fact, chemists usually speak about four levels of structure when describing proteins. The **primary structure** of a protein specifies the sequence in which the various amino acids are linked together. **Secondary structure** refers to how segments of the protein chain are oriented into a regular pattern. **Tertiary structure** refers to how the entire protein chain is coiled and folded into a specific three-dimensional shape, and **quaternary structure** refers to how several protein chains can aggregate to form a larger unit.

Primary Structure

Primary structure is the most fundamental of the four structural levels because it is the protein's amino acid sequence that determines its overall shape and function. So crucial is primary structure to function that the change of only one amino acid out of several hundred can drastically alter biological properties. The disease sickle-cell anemia, for example, is caused by a genetic defect in blood hemoglobin whereby valine is substituted for glutamic acid at only one position in a chain of 146 amino acids.

Secondary Protein Structure

When looking at the primary structure of a protein like angiotensin II in Figure 24.5, you might get the idea that the molecule is long and threadlike. In fact, though, most proteins fold in such a way that segments of the protein chain orient into regular patterns, called *secondary structures*. There are two common kinds of patterns: the *alpha-helix* and the *beta-pleated sheet*.

Keratin, a fibrous protein found in wool, hair, fingernails, and feathers, wraps into a helical coil, much like the cord on a telephone (Figure 24.7). Called an **alpha- (α-) helix,** this secondary structure is stabilized by the formation of hydrogen bonds (Section 10.2) between the N–H group of one amino acid and the C=O group of another amino acid four residues away. Each turn of the helix contains 3.6 amino acid residues, with a distance between turns of 0.54 nm.

Remember...

A **hydrogen bond** is a strong dipole–dipole attraction between a hydrogen atom bonded to a very electronegative atom (O, N, or F) and an unshared electron pair on another electronegative atom.

(Section 10.2)

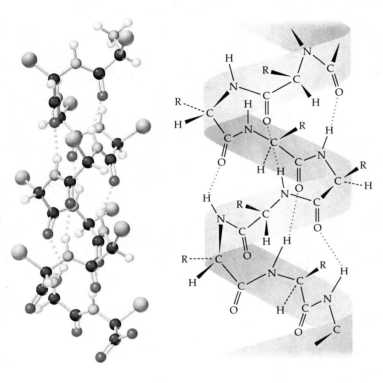

The amino acid backbone winds in a spiral, much like that of a telephone cord.

▲ Sheep's wool is made largely of keratin, a fibrous protein with an α-helical secondary structure.

FIGURE 24.7
The α-helical secondary structure of keratin.

Fibroin, the fibrous protein found in silk, has a secondary structure called a **beta- (β-) pleated sheet,** in which a polypeptide chain doubles back on itself after a hairpin bend. The two sections of the chain on either side of the bend line up in a parallel arrangement held together by hydrogen bonds (Figure 24.8). Although not as common as the α-helix, small pleated-sheet regions are often found in proteins.

◄ Silk is made of fibroin, a fibrous protein with a pleated-sheet secondary structure.

FIGURE 24.8
The β-pleated-sheet secondary
structure of silk fibroin.

The amino acid side chains, shown in green, alternate
above and below the rough plane of the sheet.

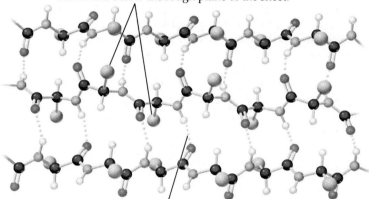

Dotted lines indicate hydrogen bonds between chains.

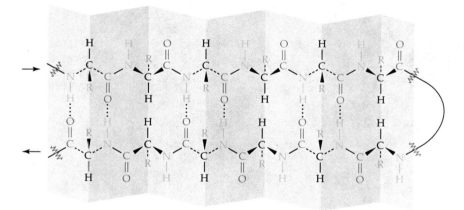

Tertiary Protein Structure

Secondary protein structures result primarily from hydrogen bonding between
amide linkages along the protein backbone, but higher levels of structure result primarily from interactions of amino acid side-chains in the protein. Myoglobin, for
example, is a globular protein found in the skeletal muscles of sea mammals, where
it stores oxygen needed to sustain the animals during long dives. With a single chain
of 153 amino acid residues, myoglobin consists of eight straight segments, each of
which adopts an α-helical secondary structure. These helical sections then fold up
further to form a compact, nearly spherical, tertiary structure (Figure 24.9).

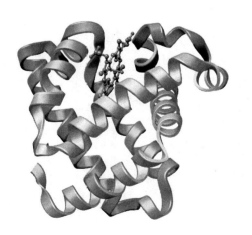

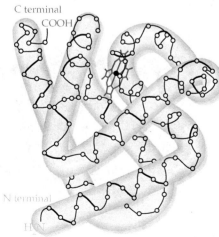

FIGURE 24.9
Secondary and tertiary structure of
myoglobin, a globular protein found
in the muscles of sea mammals.

The most important force stabilizing a protein's tertiary structure results from the hydrophobic interactions of hydrocarbon side chains on amino acids. Those amino acids with neutral, nonpolar side chains have a strong tendency to congregate on the hydrocarbonlike interior of a protein molecule, away from the aqueous medium. Those amino acids with polar side chains, by contrast, are usually found on the exterior of the protein where they can be solvated by water. Also important for stabilizing a protein's tertiary structure are *disulfide bridges* (covalent S–S bonds formed between nearby cysteine residues), *salt bridges* (ionic attractions between positively and negatively charged sites on the protein), and hydrogen bonds between nearby amino acids.

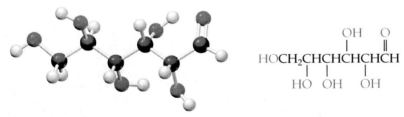

Two cysteine residues   A disulfide bridge

24.6 | CARBOHYDRATES

Carbohydrates occur in every living organism. The starch in food and the cellulose in grass are nearly pure carbohydrate. Modified carbohydrates form part of the coating around all living cells, and other carbohydrates are found in the DNA that carries genetic information from one generation to the next.

The word *carbohydrate* was used originally to describe glucose, which has the formula $C_6H_{12}O_6$ and was once thought to be a "hydrate of carbon," $C_6(H_2O)_6$. This view was soon abandoned, but the word persisted and is now used to refer to a large class of polyhydroxylated aldehydes and ketones. Glucose, for example, is a six-carbon aldehyde with five hydroxyl groups.

$$\underset{\underset{HO}{|}\quad\underset{OH}{|}\quad\underset{OH}{|}}{HOCH_2CHCHCHCHCH} \overset{OH\quad O}{\overset{|\quad\;||}{}}$$

Glucose—a pentahydroxy aldehyde

Carbohydrates are classified as either *simple* or *complex*. Simple sugars, or **monosaccharides,** are carbohydrates such as glucose and fructose that can't be broken down into smaller molecules by hydrolysis with aqueous acid. Complex carbohydrates, or **polysaccharides,** are compounds such as cellulose and starch that are made of many simple sugars linked together. On hydrolysis, polysaccharides are cleaved to yield many molecules of simple sugars.

Monosaccharides are further classified as either aldoses or ketoses. An *aldose* contains an aldehyde carbonyl group; a *ketose* contains a ketone carbonyl group (Section 23.13). The *-ose* suffix indicates a sugar, and the number of carbon atoms in the sugar is specified by using one of the prefixes *tri-*, *tetr-*, *pent-*, or *hex-*. Thus, glucose is an aldohexose (a six-carbon aldehyde sugar), fructose is a ketohexose (a six-carbon ketone sugar), and ribose is an aldopentose (a five-carbon aldehyde sugar). Most commonly occurring sugars are either aldopentoses or aldohexoses.

Fructose—a ketohexose   Ribose—an aldopentose

Remember...

An **aldehyde** has a carbonyl functional group bonded to a hydrogen, and a **ketone** has a carbonyl functional group bonded to two carbon atoms.

(Section 23.13)

Aldehyde   Ketone

▶ **PROBLEM 24.12**   Classify each of the following monosaccharides:

$$\text{(a) } \underset{\underset{\overset{|}{OH}}{}}{HOCH_2\overset{\overset{OH}{|}}{C}H\overset{\overset{HO}{|}}{C}H\overset{\overset{O}{\parallel}}{C}HCH}$$

$$\text{(b) } HOCH_2\overset{\overset{O}{\parallel}}{C}CH_2OH$$

$$\text{(c) } HOCH_2\overset{\overset{OH}{|}}{C}H\underset{\underset{\overset{|}{OH}}{}}{C}H\overset{\overset{O}{\parallel}}{C}H$$

24.7 | HANDEDNESS OF CARBOHYDRATES

We saw in Section 24.3 that compounds are chiral if they have a carbon atom bonded to four different atoms or groups of atoms. Such compounds lack a plane of symmetry and can exist as a pair of enantiomers in either a "right-handed" D form or a "left-handed" L form. For instance, the simple triose glyceraldehyde is chiral because it has four different groups bonded to C2: –CHO, –H, –OH, and –CH₂OH. Of the two enantiomers, only D-glyceraldehyde occurs naturally.

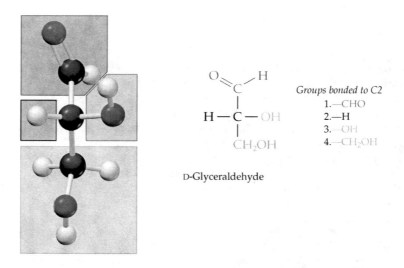

Groups bonded to C2
1.—CHO
2.—H
3.—OH
4.—CH₂OH

D-Glyceraldehyde

Glyceraldehyde has only one chiral carbon atom and can exist as two enantiomers, but larger sugars have two, three, four, or even more chiral carbons. In general, a compound with n chiral carbon atoms has a maximum of 2^n possible isomeric forms. Glucose, for example, has four chiral carbon atoms, so a total of $2^4 = 16$ isomers are possible, differing in the spatial arrangements of the substituents around the chiral carbon atoms.

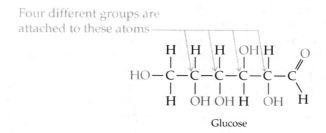

Four different groups are attached to these atoms

Glucose

▶ **PROBLEM 24.13**   Draw tetrahedral representations of the two glyceraldehyde enantiomers using wedged, dashed, and normal lines to show three-dimensionality.

▶ **PROBLEM 24.14**   Ribose has three chiral carbon atoms. What is the maximum number of isomers?

KEY CONCEPT PROBLEM 24.15 Classify the following monosaccharide, and identify each chiral carbon in its structure.

24.8 | CYCLIC STRUCTURES OF MONOSACCHARIDES

Glucose and other monosaccharides are often shown for convenience as having open-chain structures. They actually exist, however, primarily as cyclic molecules in which an –OH group near the bottom of the chain adds to the carbonyl group near the top of the chain to form a ring. In glucose itself, ring formation occurs between the –OH group on C5 and the C=O group at C1 (Figure 24.10).

FIGURE 24.10
The cyclic α and β forms of D-glucose that result from ring formation between the –OH group at C5 and the C=O group at C1.

Note that two cyclic forms of glucose can result from ring formation, depending on whether the newly formed –OH group at C1 is on the bottom or top side of the ring. The ordinary crystalline glucose you might take from a bottle is entirely the cyclic α form, in which the C1 –OH group is on the bottom side of the ring. At equilibrium in water solution, however, all three forms are present in the proportion 0.02% open-chain form, 36% α form, and 64% β form.

24.9 | SOME COMMON DISACCHARIDES AND POLYSACCHARIDES

Lactose

Lactose, or *milk sugar*, is the major carbohydrate present in mammalian milk. Human milk, for example, is about 7% lactose. Structurally, lactose is a disaccharide whose hydrolysis with aqueous acid yields one molecule of glucose and one molecule of another monosaccharide called galactose. The two sugars are bonded together by what is called a *1→4 link*, with a bridging oxygen atom between C1 of β-galactose and C4 of β-glucose.

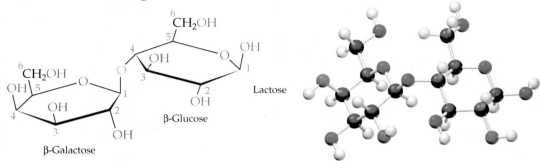

Lactose

β-Galactose   β-Glucose

Sucrose

Sucrose, or plain table sugar, is probably the most common pure organic chemical in the world. Although sucrose is found in many plants, sugar beets (20% by mass) and sugar cane (15% by mass) are the most common sources. Hydrolysis of sucrose yields one molecule of glucose and one molecule of fructose. The 1 : 1 mixture of glucose and fructose that results, often called *invert sugar*, is commonly used as a food additive.

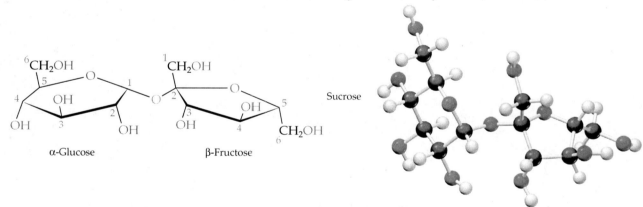

Sucrose

α-Glucose   β-Fructose

Cellulose and Starch

Cellulose, the fibrous substance that forms the structural material in grasses, leaves, and stems, consists of several thousand β-glucose molecules joined together by 1→4 links to form an immense polysaccharide.

Cellulose

β-Glucose units

Starch, like cellulose, is also a polymer of glucose. Unlike cellulose, though, starch is edible. Indeed, the starch in such vegetables as beans, rice, and potatoes is an essential part of the human diet. Structurally, starch differs from cellulose in that it contains α- rather than β-glucose units. Starch is also more structurally complex than cellulose and is of two types: *amylose* and *amylopectin*. Amylose, which accounts for about 20% of starch, consists of several hundred to 1000 α-glucose units joined together in a long chain by 1→4 links (Figure 24.11a). Amylopectin, which accounts for about 80% of starch, is much larger than amylose (up to 100,000 glucose units per molecule) and has branches approximately every 25 units along its chain. A glucose molecule at a branch point uses two of its hydroxyl groups (those at C4 and C6) to form links to two other sugars (Figure 24.11b).

α-Glucose units

CH₂OH   CH₂OH   A 1→4 *link*   CH₂OH

(a) Amylose consists of linear chains of α-glucose units joined by 1→4 links.

A 1→6 *link*

α-Glucose units   CH₂OH

(b) Amylopectin has branch points about every 25 sugars in the chain. A glucose unit at a branch point uses two of its hydroxyls to form 1→4 and 1→6 links to two other sugars.

FIGURE 24.11
Glucose polymers in starch.

Starch molecules are digested in the stomach by enzymes called α-glycosidases, which break down the polysaccharide chain and release individual glucose molecules. As is usually the case with enzyme-catalyzed reactions, α-glycosidases are highly specific in their action. They hydrolyze only the links between α units while leaving the links between β units untouched. Thus, starch is easily digested but cellulose is not.

Glycogen

Glycogen, sometimes called *animal starch*, serves the same food storage role in animals that starch serves in plants. After we eat starch and the body breaks it down into simple glucose units, some of the glucose is used immediately as fuel and some is stored in the body as glycogen for later use. Structurally, glycogen is similar to amylopectin in being a long polymer of α-glucose units with branch points in its chain. Glycogen has many more branches than amylopectin, however, and is much larger—up to 1 million glucose units per glycogen molecule.

▲ Glycogen provides the stored energy that lets these marathoners finish the race.

24.10 | LIPIDS

Lipids are less well known to most people than are proteins or carbohydrates, yet they are just as essential to life. Lipids have many important biological roles, serving as sources of fuel, as protective coatings around many plants and insects, and as major components of the membranes that surround every living cell.

Chemically, a **lipid** is a naturally occurring organic molecule that dissolves in a nonpolar organic solvent when a sample of plant or animal tissue is crushed or ground. Because they're defined by solubility, a physical property, rather than by chemical structure, it's not surprising that there are a great many different kinds of lipids (Figure 24.12). Note that all the lipids in Figure 24.12 contain large hydrocarbon portions, which accounts for their solubility behavior.

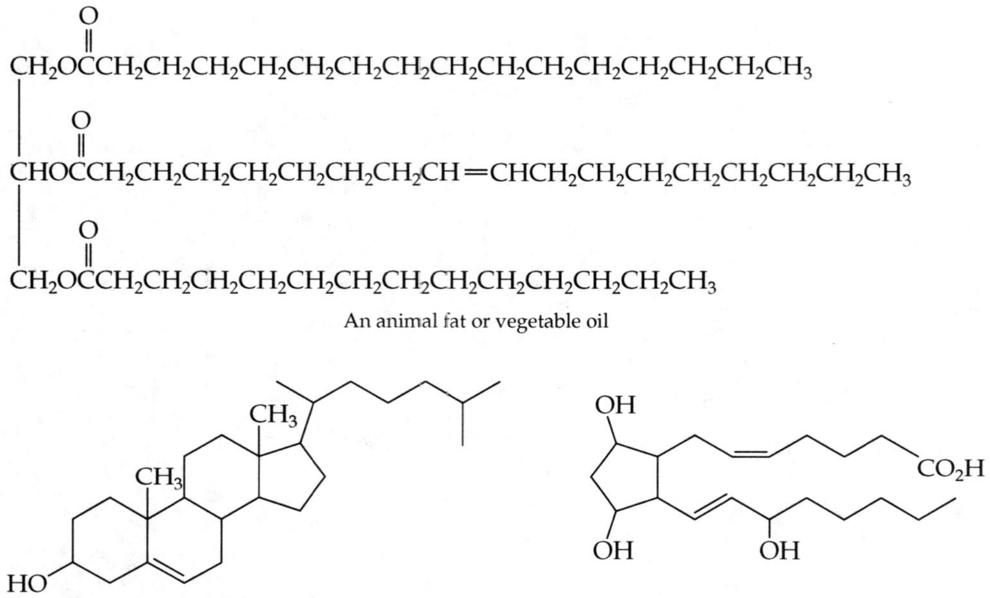

An animal fat or vegetable oil

Cholesterol—a steroid

$PGF_{2\alpha}$—a prostaglandin

FIGURE 24.12
Structures of some representative lipids isolated from plant and animal tissue by extraction with nonpolar organic solvents. All have large hydrocarbon portions.

Fats and Oils

Animal fats and vegetable oils are the most abundant lipids in nature. Although they appear physically different—animal fats like butter and lard are usually solid, whereas vegetable oils like corn and peanut oil are liquid—their structures are similar. All fats and oils are **triacylglycerols,** or *triglycerides,* esters of glycerol (1,2,3-propanetriol) with three long-chain carboxylic acids called **fatty acids.** The fatty acids are usually unbranched and have an even number of carbon atoms in the range 12–22.

As shown by the triacylglycerol structure in Figure 24.12, the three fatty acids of a given molecule need not be the same. Furthermore, the fat or oil from a given source is a complex mixture of many different triacylglycerols. Table 24.2 shows the structures of some commonly occurring fatty acids, and Table 24.3 lists the composition of several fats and oils. Note that vegetable oils are largely unsaturated, but animal fats contain a high percentage of saturated fatty acids.

TABLE 24.2 Structures of Some Common Fatty Acids

Name	No. of Carbons	No. of Double Bonds	Structure	Melting Point (°C)
Saturated				
Myristic	14	0	$CH_3(CH_2)_{12}CO_2H$	54
Palmitic	16	0	$CH_3(CH_2)_{14}CO_2H$	63
Stearic	18	0	$CH_3(CH_2)_{16}CO_2H$	69
Unsaturated				
Oleic	18	1	$CH_3(CH_2)_7CH=CH(CH_2)_7CO_2H$	13
Linoleic	18	2	$CH_3(CH_2)_4CH=CHCH_2CH=CH(CH_2)_7CO_2H$	−5
Linolenic	18	3	$CH_3CH_2CH=CHCH_2CH=CHCH_2CH=CH(CH_2)_7CO_2H$	−11

TABLE 24.3 Approximate Composition of Some Common Fats and Oils

Source	Saturated Fatty Acids (%)			Unsaturated Fatty Acids (%)	
	C_{14} Myristic	C_{16} Palmitic	C_{18} Stearic	C_{18} Oleic	C_{18} Linoleic
Animal Fat					
Butter	10	25	10	25	5
Human fat	3	25	8	46	10
Whale blubber	8	12	3	35	10
Vegetable Oil					
Corn	1	10	4	35	45
Olive	1	5	5	80	7
Peanut	—	7	5	60	20

About 40 different fatty acids occur naturally. Palmitic acid (C_{16}) and stearic acid (C_{18}) are the most abundant saturated acids; oleic and linoleic acids (both C_{18}) are the most abundant unsaturated ones. Oleic acid is monounsaturated because it has only one double bond, but linoleic and linolenic acids are *polyunsaturated fatty acids* because they have more than one carbon–carbon double bond. Although the reasons are not yet clear, it appears that a diet rich in saturated fats leads to a higher level of blood cholesterol and consequent higher risk of heart attack than a diet rich in saturated fats.

The data in Table 24.3 show that unsaturated fatty acids generally have lower melting points than their saturated counterparts, a trend that's also true for triacylglycerols. Since vegetable oils have a higher proportion of unsaturated fatty acids than do animal fats, they have lower melting points and appear as liquids rather than solids. This behavior arises because the carbon–carbon double bonds in unsaturated vegetable oils introduce bends and kinks into the hydrocarbon chains, making it difficult for the chains to nestle closely together in crystals.

The carbon–carbon double bonds in vegetable oils can be hydrogenated to yield saturated fats in the same way that any alkene can react with hydrogen to yield an alkane (Section 23.10). By carefully controlling the extent of hydrogenation, the final product can have any desired consistency. Margarine, for example, is prepared so that only about two-thirds of the double bonds present in the starting vegetable oil are hydrogenated.

Remember...
Hydrogenation of an alkene adds H_2 to the unsaturated C=C bond and yields the saturated product.
(Section 23.10)

One problem with this hydrogenation of vegetable oils that has recently come to light is that the catalyst used for the reaction also causes 10–15% of the double bonds remaining in the product to isomerize from cis to trans stereochemistry. Dietary intake of these trans fats has been found to increase cholesterol levels in blood, leading to an increased risk of heart disease. The conversion of linoleic acid into elaidic acid is an example.

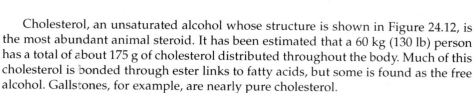

Linoleic acid

Elaidic acid

▶ **PROBLEM 24.16** Show the structure of glyceryl trioleate, a fat molecule whose components are glycerol and three oleic acid units.

Steroids

A **steroid** is a lipid whose structure is based on the tetracyclic (four-ring) system shown in the following examples. Three of the rings are six-membered, while the fourth is five-membered. Steroids have many diverse roles throughout both the plant and animal kingdoms. Some steroids, such as digitoxigenin, isolated from the purple foxglove *Digitalis purpurea*, are used in medicine as heart stimulants. Others, such as hydrocortisone, are hormones, and still others have a variety of different physiological functions.

▲ The purple foxglove, a common backyard plant, contains the steroidal heart stimulant digitoxigenin.

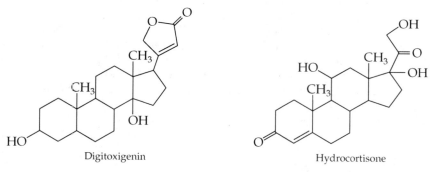

Digitoxigenin   Hydrocortisone

Cholesterol, an unsaturated alcohol whose structure is shown in Figure 24.12, is the most abundant animal steroid. It has been estimated that a 60 kg (130 lb) person has a total of about 175 g of cholesterol distributed throughout the body. Much of this cholesterol is bonded through ester links to fatty acids, but some is found as the free alcohol. Gallstones, for example, are nearly pure cholesterol.

Cholesterol serves two important functions in the body. First, it is a minor component of cell membranes, where it helps to keep the membranes fluid. Second, it serves as the body's starting material for the synthesis of all other steroids, including the sex hormones. Although news reports sometimes make cholesterol sound dangerous, there would be no life without it. The human body obtains its cholesterol both by synthesis in the liver and by ingestion of food. Even on a strict no-cholesterol diet, an adult is able to synthesize approximately 800 mg per day.

24.11 | NUCLEIC ACIDS

How does a seed "know" what kind of plant to become? How does a fertilized ovum know how to grow into a human being? How does a cell know what part of the body it's in so that it can carry out the right reactions? The answers to such questions involve the biological molecules called **nucleic acids. Deoxyribonucleic acid (DNA)** and **ribonucleic acid (RNA)** are the chemical carriers of an organism's genetic information. Coded in an organism's DNA is all the information that determines the nature of the organism and all the directions that are needed for producing the many thousands of different proteins required by the organism.

Just as proteins are polymers made of amino acid units, nucleic acids are polymers made up of **nucleotide** units linked together to form a long chain. Each nucleotide is composed of a **nucleoside** plus phosphoric acid, H_3PO_4, and each nucleoside is composed of an aldopentose sugar plus an amine base.

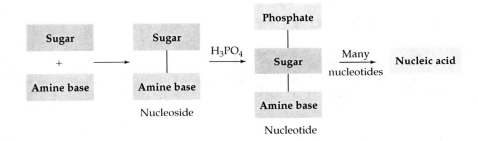

Nucleoside   Nucleotide

The sugar component in RNA is ribose, and the sugar in DNA is 2-deoxyribose (2-deoxy means that oxygen is missing from C2 of ribose).

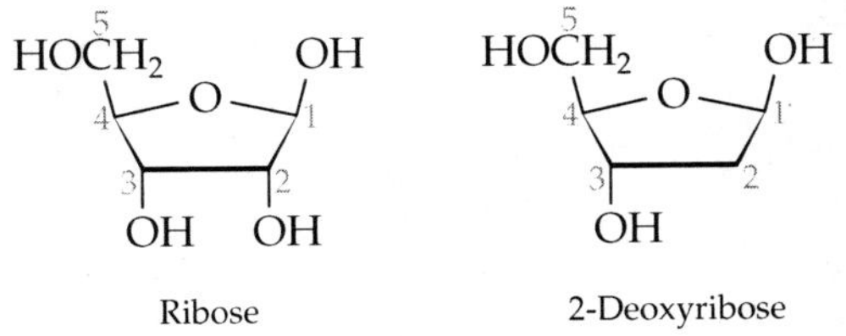

Ribose   2-Deoxyribose

Four different cyclic amine bases occur in DNA: adenine, guanine, cytosine, and thymine. Adenine, guanine, and cytosine also occur in RNA, but thymine is replaced in RNA by a related base called uracil.

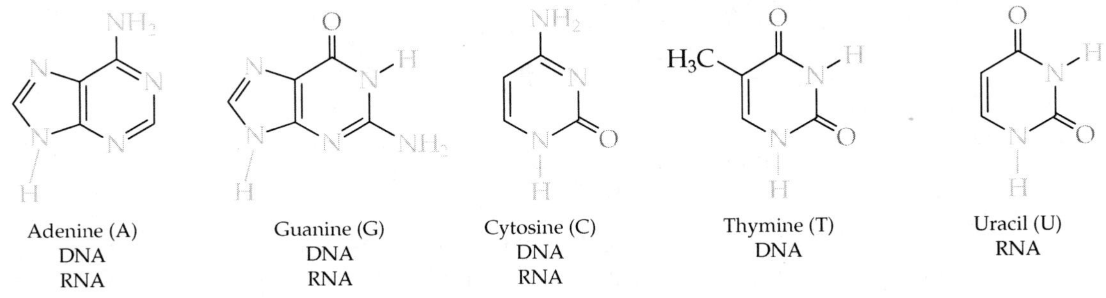

Adenine (A)	Guanine (G)	Cytosine (C)	Thymine (T)	Uracil (U)
DNA	DNA	DNA	DNA	RNA
RNA	RNA	RNA		

In both DNA and RNA, the cyclic amine base is bonded to C1' of the sugar, and the phosphoric acid is bonded to the C5' sugar position. Thus, nucleosides and nucleotides have the general structures shown in Figure 24.13. (In discussions of RNA and DNA, numbers with a prime superscript refer to positions on the sugar component of a nucleotide; numbers without a prime refer to positions on the cyclic amine base.)

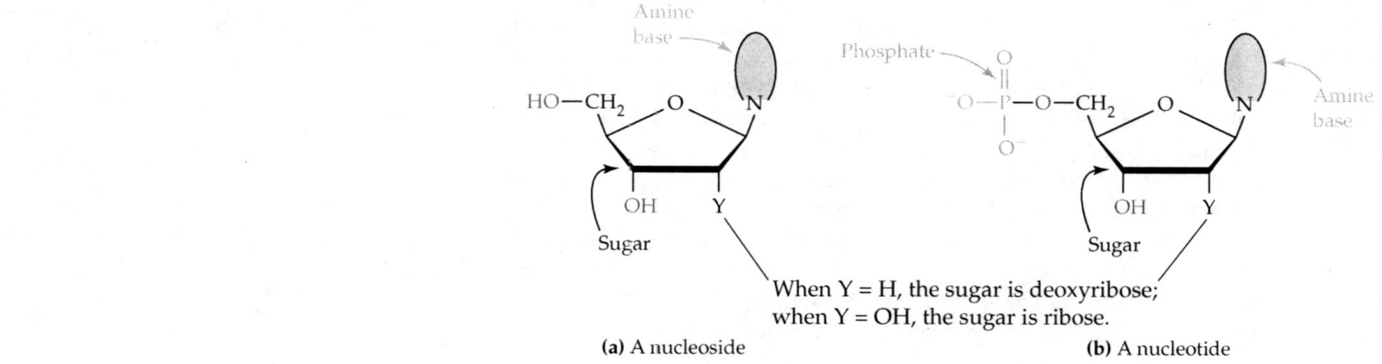

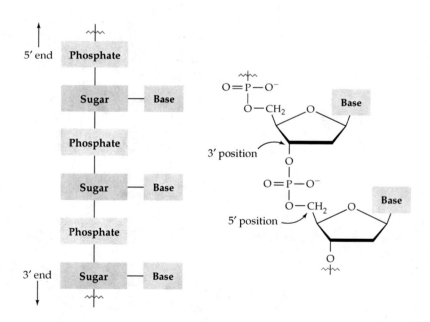

When Y = H, the sugar is deoxyribose;
when Y = OH, the sugar is ribose.

(a) A nucleoside   **(b)** A nucleotide

FIGURE 24.13
General structures of **(a)** a nucleoside and **(b)** a nucleotide.

Nucleotides join together in nucleic acids by forming a phosphate ester bond between the phosphate group at the 5' end of one nucleotide and the hydroxyl group on the sugar component at the 3' end of another nucleotide (Figure 24.14).

FIGURE 24.14
Generalized structure of a nucleic acid.

Just as the structure of a protein depends on its sequence of individual amino acids, the structure of a nucleic acid depends on its sequence of individual nucleotides. To carry the analogy further, just as a protein has a polyamide backbone with different side chains attached to it, a nucleic acid has an alternating sugar–phosphate backbone with different amine base side chains attached.

Different side chains

A protein $\left(\!\!\begin{array}{c} \\ \end{array}\!\!\right.$ NH—CH—C—NH—CH—C—NH—CH—C $\left.\!\!\begin{array}{c} \\ \end{array}\!\!\right)$

Amide bond

Different bases

A nucleic acid $\left(\!\!\begin{array}{c} \\ \end{array}\!\!\right.$ Phosphate—Sugar — Phosphate—Sugar — Phosphate—Sugar $\left.\!\!\begin{array}{c} \\ \end{array}\!\!\right)$

Phosphate ester bonds

The sequence of nucleotides is described by starting at the 5′ phosphate end and identifying the bases in order. Abbreviations are used for each nucleotide: A for adenosine, G for guanosine, C for cytidine, T for thymidine, and U for uracil. Thus, a typical DNA sequence might be written as -T-A-G-G-C-T-.

WORKED EXAMPLE 24.4

DRAWING THE STRUCTURE OF A DINUCLEOTIDE

Draw the full structure of the DNA dinucleotide C-T.

SOLUTION

Deoxycytidine (C)

Deoxythymidine (T)

▸ **PROBLEM 24.17** Draw the full structure of the DNA dinucleotide A-G.

▸ **PROBLEM 24.18** Draw the full structure of the RNA dinucleotide U-A.

KEY CONCEPT PROBLEM 24.19 Identify the following bases, and tell whether each is found in DNA, RNA, or both.

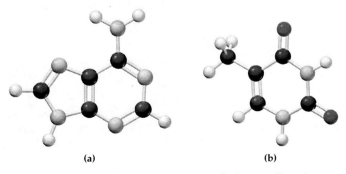

(a)   (b)

Science Fundamentals

24.12 | BASE PAIRING IN DNA: THE WATSON–CRICK MODEL

Molecules of DNA isolated from different tissues of the same species have the same proportions of nucleotides, but molecules from different species can have quite different proportions. For example, human DNA contains about 30% each of A and T and about 20% each of G and C, but the bacterium *Clostridium perfringens* contains about 37% each of A and T and only 13% each of G and C. Note that in both cases, the bases occur in pairs. Adenine and thymine are usually present in equal amounts, as are guanine and cytosine. Why should this be?

According to the **Watson–Crick model,** DNA consists of two polynucleotide strands coiled around each other in a *double helix* like the handrails on a spiral staircase. The sugar–phosphate backbone is on the outside of the helix, and the amine bases are on the inside, so that a base on one strand points directly in toward a base on the second strand. The two strands run in opposite directions and are held together by hydrogen bonds between pairs of bases. Adenine and thymine form two strong hydrogen bonds to each other, but not to G or C; G and C form three strong hydrogen bonds to each other, but not to A or T (Figure 24.15).

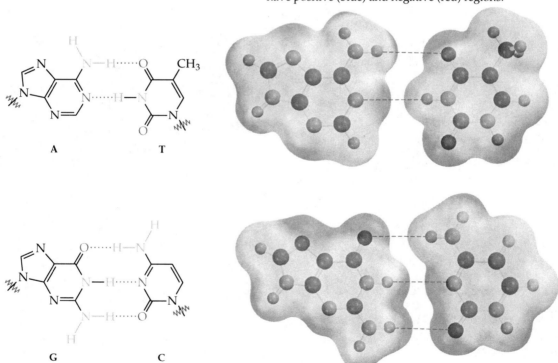

Electrostatic potential maps show that the faces of the bases are relatively neutral (green), while the edges have positive (blue) and negative (red) regions.

Pairing A with T and G with C brings together oppositely charged regions.

FIGURE 24.15
Hydrogen bonding between base pairs in the DNA double helix.

The two strands of the DNA double helix aren't identical; rather, they're complementary. Whenever a G base occurs in one strand, a C base occurs opposite it in the other strand. When an A base occurs in one strand, a T base occurs in the other strand. This complementary pairing of bases explains why A and T are always found in equal amounts, as are G and C. Figure 24.16 illustrates this base pairing, showing how the two complementary strands coil into the double helix. X-ray measurements show that the DNA double helix is 2.0 nm wide, that there are exactly 10 base pairs in each full turn, and that each turn is 3.4 nm high.

WORKED EXAMPLE 24.5

DNA COMPLEMENTARITY

What sequence of bases on one strand of DNA is complementary to the sequence G-C-A-T-T-A-T on another strand?

STRATEGY

Since A and G form complementary pairs with T and C, respectively, go through the given sequence replacing A with T, G with C, T with A, and C with G.

SOLUTION

Original:	G-C-A-T-T-A-T
Complement:	C-G-T-A-A-T-A

▶ **PROBLEM 24.20** What sequence of bases on one strand of DNA is complementary to the following sequence on another strand?

G-G-C-C-C-G-T-A-A-T

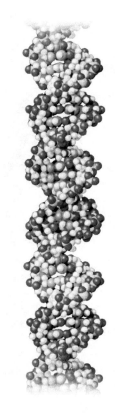

24.13 | NUCLEIC ACIDS AND HEREDITY

Most DNA of higher organisms, both plant and animal, is found in the nucleus of cells in the form of threadlike strands that are coated with proteins and wound into complex assemblies called **chromosomes.** Each chromosome is made up of several thousand **genes,** where a gene is a segment of a DNA chain that contains the instructions necessary to make a specific protein. By decoding the right genes at the right time, an organism uses genetic information to synthesize the thousands of proteins needed for living. Thus, the function of DNA is to act as a storage medium for an organism's genetic information. The function of RNA is to read, decode, and use the information received from DNA to make proteins.

Three main processes take place in the transfer and use of genetic information. **Replication** is the means by which identical copies of DNA are made, forming additional molecules and preserving genetic information for passing on to offspring. **Transcription** is the means by which information in the DNA is transferred to and decoded by RNA. **Translation** is the means by which RNA uses the information to build proteins.

Replication

DNA replication is an enzyme-catalyzed process that begins with a partial unwinding of the double helix. As the DNA strands separate and bases are exposed, new nucleotides line up on each strand in a complementary manner, A to T and C to G, and two new strands begin to grow. Each new strand is complementary to its old template strand, and two new, identical DNA double helixes are produced (Figure 24.17).

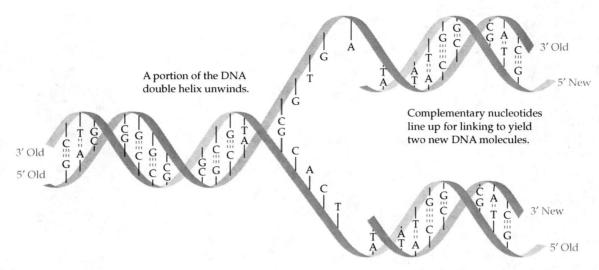

A portion of the DNA double helix unwinds.

Complementary nucleotides line up for linking to yield two new DNA molecules.

Each of the new DNA molecules contains one of the original strands and one new strand.

FIGURE 24.17
DNA replication.

The magnitude of the replication process is extraordinary. The nucleus of a human cell contains 46 chromosomes (23 pairs), each of which consists of one large DNA molecule. Each chromosome, in turn, is made up of several thousand genes, and the sum of all genes in a human cell (the *genome*) is approximately 3 billion base pairs. This immense base sequence is faithfully copied during replication, with an error occurring only about once each 10–100 billion bases.

Transcription

The genetic instructions contained in DNA are transcribed into RNA when a small portion of the DNA double helix unwinds and one of the two DNA strands acts as a template for complementary *ribonucleotides* to line up, a process similar to that of DNA replication (Figure 24.18). The only difference is that uracil (U) rather than thymine lines up opposite adenine. Once completed, the RNA molecule separates from the DNA template, and the DNA rewinds to its stable double-helix conformation.

A small portion of the DNA double helix unwinds.

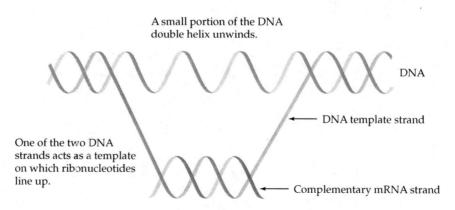

DNA

DNA template strand

One of the two DNA strands acts as a template on which ribonucleotides line up.

Complementary mRNA strand

FIGURE 24.18
Transcription of DNA to synthesize RNA.

The RNA produced is complementary to the DNA strand from which it is transcribed.

Translation

Protein biosynthesis is directed by a special kind of RNA called *messenger RNA*, or *mRNA*, and takes place on knobby protuberances within a cell called *ribosomes*. The specific ribonucleotide sequence in mRNA acts like a long coded sentence to specify the order in which different amino acid residues are to be joined. Each of the estimated 100,000 proteins in the human body is synthesized from a different mRNA that has been transcribed from a specific gene segment on DNA.

Each "word" along the mRNA chain consists of a series of three ribonucleotides that is specific for a given amino acid. For example, the series cytosine-uracil-guanine (C-U-G) on mRNA is a three-letter word directing that the amino acid leucine be incorporated into the growing protein. The words are read by another kind of RNA called *transfer RNA*, or *tRNA*. Each of the 60 or so different tRNAs contains a complementary base sequence that allows it to recognize a three-letter word on mRNA and act as a carrier to bring a specific amino acid into place for transfer to the growing peptide chain (Figure 24.19). When synthesis of the protein is completed, a "stop" word signals the end, and the protein is released from the ribosome.

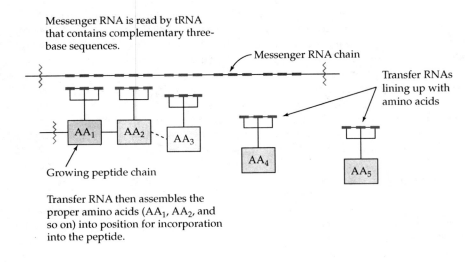

Messenger RNA is read by tRNA that contains complementary three-base sequences.

Messenger RNA chain

Transfer RNAs lining up with amino acids

Growing peptide chain

Transfer RNA then assembles the proper amino acids (AA$_1$, AA$_2$, and so on) into position for incorporation into the peptide.

FIGURE 24.19
Protein biosynthesis.

RNA COMPLEMENTARITY TO DNA

What RNA base sequence is complementary to the following DNA base sequence?

G-C-C-T-A-A-G-T-G

STRATEGY

Go through the DNA sequence replacing A with U, G with C, T with A, and C with G.

SOLUTION

Original DNA:	G-C-C-T-A-A-G-T-G
Complementary RNA:	C-G-G-A-U-U-C-A-C

▸ **PROBLEM 24.21** Show how uracil can form strong hydrogen bonds to adenine.

▸ **PROBLEM 24.22** What RNA sequence is complementary to the following DNA sequence?

C-G-T-G-A-T-T-A-C-A

▸ **PROBLEM 24.23** From what DNA sequence was the following RNA sequence transcribed?

U-G-C-A-U-C-G-A-G-U

DNA Fingerprinting

▲ Historians have wondered for many years whether Thomas Jefferson fathered a child by Sally Hemings. DNA fingerprinting evidence obtained in 1998 is not conclusive but strongly suggests that he did.

Being a criminal is a lot harder now than it was in the good old days, and part of the reason is the development of *DNA fingerprinting*. DNA fingerprinting arose from the discovery in 1984 that human genes contain short, repeating sequences of noncoding DNA, called *short tandem repeat* (STR) loci. The base sequences in these STR loci are slightly different for every individual (except identical twins), so a pattern unique to each person can be obtained by determining the sequences.

Perhaps the most common and well-publicized use of DNA fingerprinting is that carried out by crime laboratories to link suspects to biological evidence—blood, hair follicles, skin, semen, or even items of clothing—found at a crime scene. Many thousands of court cases have now been decided based on DNA evidence.

Forensic laboratories in the United States have agreed on 13 core STR loci that are most accurate for identification of an individual. Based on these 13 loci, a Combined DNA Index System (CODIS) has been established to serve as a registry of convicted offenders. If the profile of sequences from a known individual and the profile from DNA obtained at a crime scene match, the probability is approximately 82 billion to 1 that the DNA is from the same individual. In paternity cases, where the DNA of father and offspring are related but not fully identical, the identity of the father can be established with a probability of 100,000 to 1.

Even after several generations have passed, paternity can still be implied by DNA analysis of the Y chromosome of direct male-line descendants. The most well-known such case is that of Thomas Jefferson, who is thought to have fathered a child by his slave Sally Hemings. Although Jefferson himself has no male-line descendants, DNA analysis of the male-line descendants of Jefferson's paternal uncle showed the same Y chromosome as a male-line descendant of Eston Hemings, youngest son of Sally Hemings. Thus, a mixing of the two genomes is clear.

Among its many other applications, DNA fingerprinting is widely used for the diagnosis of genetic disorders. Cystic fibrosis, hemophilia, Huntington's disease, Tay–Sachs disease, and sickle-cell anemia are among the many diseases that can be detected, enabling early treatment of an affected child. In addition, the U.S. Department of Defense now requires blood and saliva samples from all military personnel. The samples are stored, and DNA is extracted should the need for identification of a casualty arise.

▸ PROBLEM 24.24   What characteristic of human DNA makes fingerprinting possible?

SUMMARY

Fats, carbohydrates, and proteins are **metabolized** in the body to yield acetyl CoA, which is further degraded in the citric acid cycle to yield two molecules of CO_2 plus a large amount of energy. The energy output of the various steps in the citric acid cycle is coupled to the electron-transport chain, a series of enzyme-catalyzed reactions whose ultimate purpose is to synthesize **adenosine triphosphate (ATP).**

Proteins are large biomolecules consisting of **α-amino acids** linked together by amide, or peptide, bonds. Twenty amino acids are commonly found in proteins, and all except glycine have a handedness. In general, any carbon atom bonded to four different groups has a handedness and is said to be chiral. Proteins can be classified either by shape or biological function. Fibrous proteins are tough, threadlike, and water insoluble; globular proteins are compact, water soluble, and mobile within cells. Some proteins are enzymes, some are hormones, and some are structural or transport agents.

A protein's **primary structure** is its amino acid sequence. Its **secondary structure** is the orientation of segments of the protein chain into a regular pattern, such as an **α-helix** or a **β-pleated sheet.** Its **tertiary structure** is the three-dimensional shape into which the entire protein molecule is coiled. **Enzymes** are large proteins that function as biological catalysts.

Carbohydrates are polyhydroxy aldehydes and ketones. Simple carbohydrates such as glucose can't be hydrolyzed to smaller molecules; complex carbohydrates such as starch and cellulose contain many simple sugars linked together. **Monosaccharides** such as glucose exist as a mixture of an open-chain form and two cyclic forms called the α form and the β form. Disaccharides such as sucrose contain two simple sugars joined by a linking oxygen atom.

Lipids are the naturally occurring organic molecules that dissolve in a nonpolar solvent. There are a great many different kinds of lipids. Animal fats and vegetable oils are **triacylglycerols**—esters of glycerol with three long-chain **fatty acids.** The fatty acids are unbranched, have an even number of carbon atoms, and may be either saturated or unsaturated.

Deoxyribonucleic acid (DNA) and **ribonucleic acid (RNA)** are the chemical carriers of an organism's genetic information. Nucleic acids are made up of many individual building blocks, called **nucleotides,** linked together to form a long chain. Each nucleotide consists of a cyclic amine base linked to C1 of a sugar, with the sugar in turn linked to phosphoric acid. The sugar component in RNA is ribose; the sugar in DNA is 2-deoxyribose. The bases in DNA are adenine (A), guanine (G), cytosine (C), and thymine (T); the bases in RNA are adenine, guanine, cytosine, and uracil (U). Molecules of DNA consist of two complementary polynucleotide strands held together by hydrogen bonds between bases on the two strands and coiled into a double helix. Adenine and thymine form hydrogen bonds only to each other, as do cytosine and guanine.

Three processes take place in the transfer of genetic information. **Replication** is the process by which identical copies of DNA are made and genetic information is preserved. **Transcription** is the process by which messenger RNA is produced. **Translation** is the process by which mRNA directs protein synthesis.

KEY WORDS

alpha- (α-) amino acid   *983*
alpha- (α-) helix   *991*
anabolism   *980*
beta- (β-) pleated sheet   *991*
biochemistry   *979*
C-terminal amino acid   *988*
carbohydrate   *993*
catabolism   *980*
chromosome   *1005*
deoxyribonucleic acid (DNA)   *1001*
enzyme   *983*
fatty acid   *998*

gene   *1005*
lipid   *998*
metabolism   *979*
monosaccharide   *993*
N-terminal amino acid   *988*
nucleic acid   *1001*
nucleoside   *1001*
nucleotide   *1001*
peptide bond   *983*
polypeptide   *983*
polysaccharide   *993*
primary structure   *990*

protein   *983*
quaternary structure   *990*
replication   *1005*
ribonucleic acid (RNA)   *1001*
secondary structure   *990*
steroid   *1000*
tertiary structure   *990*
transcription   *1005*
translation   *1005*
triacylglycerol   *998*
Watson–Crick model   *1004*

KEY CONCEPT PROBLEMS

Problems 24.1–24.24 appear within the chapter.

24.25 Identify the following amino acids, and tell whether each is acidic, basic, or neutral.

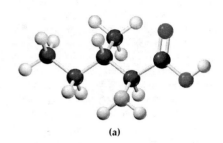

(a)

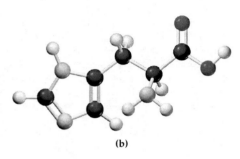

(b)

24.26 Identify the following amino acids:

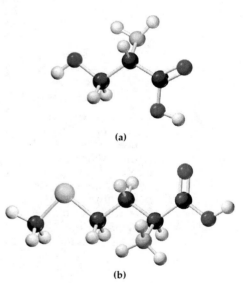

(a)

(b)

24.27 Does the following model represent a D-amino acid or an L-amino acid? Identify it.

24.28 Is the following model of glucose in the α form or the β form?

24.29 The following model represents D-ribose in its open-chain form. Is ribose an aldose or a ketose? How many chiral carbon atoms does ribose have?

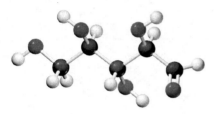

24.30 Identify the following dipeptide:

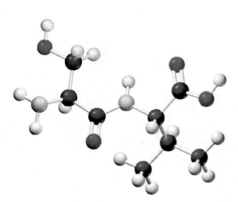

24.31 Identify the following amine bases found in nucleic acids:

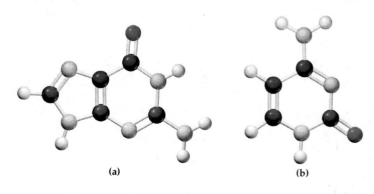

(a)   (b)

SECTION PROBLEMS

Amino Acids, Peptides, and Proteins (Sections 24.2–24.5)

24.32 What does the prefix "α" mean when referring to α-amino acids?

24.33 Why are the naturally occurring amino acids called L-amino acids?

24.34 What amino acids do the following abbreviations stand for?

(a) Ser (b) Thr (c) Pro

(d) Phe (e) Cys

24.35 Name and draw the structures of amino acids that fit the following descriptions:

(a) Contains an isopropyl group

(b) Contains an alcohol group

(c) Contains a thiol (–SH) group

(d) Contains an aromatic ring

24.36 Much of the chemistry of amino acids is the familiar chemistry of carboxylic acid and amine functional groups. What products would you expect to obtain from the following reactions of glycine?

$$\text{(a) } H_2NCH_2\overset{\overset{\displaystyle O}{\|}}{C}OH \ + \ CH_3OH \ \xrightarrow[\text{catalyst}]{H_2SO_4}$$

$$\text{(b) } H_2NCH_2\overset{\overset{\displaystyle O}{\|}}{C}OH \ + \ HCl \ \longrightarrow$$

24.37 *Aspartame*, marketed under the trade name Nutra-Sweet for use as a nonnutritive sweetener, is the methyl ester of a simple dipeptide. Identify the two amino acids present in aspartame, and show all the products of digestion, assuming that both amide and ester bonds are hydrolyzed in the stomach.

$$H_2N-CH-\overset{\overset{\displaystyle O}{\|}}{C}-NH-CH-\overset{\overset{\displaystyle O}{\|}}{C}-OCH_3$$

with CH_2 / $COOH$ on the first residue and CH_2 / phenyl ring on the second. Aspartame

24.38 Identify the amino acids present in the following hexapeptide:

$$H_2N-\underset{\underset{\displaystyle CH(CH_3)_2}{|}}{CH}-\overset{\overset{\displaystyle O}{\|}}{C}-NH-\underset{\underset{\displaystyle CH_2OH}{|}}{CH}-\overset{\overset{\displaystyle O}{\|}}{C}-NH-\underset{\underset{\displaystyle CH_2}{|}}{CH}-\overset{\overset{\displaystyle O}{\|}}{C}-NH-\underset{\underset{\displaystyle CH_2CH_2SCH_3}{|}}{CH}-\overset{\overset{\displaystyle O}{\|}}{C}-NH-\underset{\underset{\displaystyle CHOH}{|}}{CH}-\overset{\overset{\displaystyle O}{\|}}{C}-NH-\underset{\underset{\displaystyle CH_3}{|}}{CH}-\overset{\overset{\displaystyle O}{\|}}{C}-OH$$

with phenyl ring on the third residue and CH_3 below $CHOH$ on the fifth residue.

24.39 Look at the structure of angiotensin II in Figure 24.5, and identify both the N-terminal and C-terminal amino acids.

24.40 What is meant by the following terms as they apply to proteins?

(a) Primary structure

(b) Secondary structure

(c) Tertiary structure

24.41 What is the difference between fibrous and globular proteins?

24.42 What kinds of intramolecular interactions are important in stabilizing a protein's tertiary structure?

24.43 What kind of bonding stabilizes helical and β-pleated-sheet secondary protein structures?

24.44 Why is cysteine such an important amino acid for defining the tertiary structure of proteins?

24.45 Which of the following amino acids are most likely to be found on the outside of a globular protein, and which on the inside? Explain.

(a) Valine

(b) Leucine

(c) Aspartic acid

(d) Asparagine

24.46 Use the three-letter abbreviations to name all tripeptides containing methionine, isoleucine, and lysine.

24.47 How many tetrapeptides containing alanine, serine, leucine, and glutamic acid do you think there are? Use the three-letter abbreviations to name three.

24.48 Write structural formulas for the two dipeptides containing phenylalanine and glutamic acid.

24.49 Write the structural formula of Asp-Met-Pro-Gly.

Molecular Handedness (Section 24.3)

24.50 Which of the following objects are chiral?

(a) A shoe

(b) A bed

(c) A lightbulb

(d) A flowerpot

24.51 Give two examples of chiral objects and two examples of achiral objects.

24.52 Which of the following compounds are chiral?

(a) 2,4-Dimethylheptane

(b) 5-Ethyl-3,3-dimethylheptane

24.53 Draw chiral molecules that meet the following descriptions:

(a) A chloroalkane, $C_5H_{11}Cl$ (b) An alcohol, $C_6H_{14}O$

(c) An alkene, C_6H_{12} (d) An alkane, C_8H_{18}

24.54 There are eight alcohols with the formula $C_5H_{12}O$. Draw them, and tell which are chiral.

24.55 Propose structures for compounds that meet the following descriptions:

(a) A chiral alcohol with four carbons

(b) A chiral aldehyde

(c) A compound with two chiral centers

Carbohydrates (Sections 24.6–24.9)

24.56 What is the structural difference between an aldose and a ketose?

24.57 Classify each of the following carbohydrates by indicating the nature of its carbonyl group and the number of carbon atoms present. For example, glucose is an aldohexose.

(a)
$$\overset{\displaystyle OH}{HOCH_2CH}\overset{\displaystyle O}{CHCHCHCH}$$
$$\underset{\displaystyle OH\quad OH}{}$$

(b)
$$\overset{\displaystyle OH}{HOCH_2CHCHCHCHCH}\overset{\displaystyle O}{}$$
$$\underset{\displaystyle OH\ HO\ OH}{}$$

(c)
$$\overset{\displaystyle OH}{HOCH_2CHCHCHCCH_2OH}\overset{\displaystyle O}{}$$
$$\underset{\displaystyle HO\ OH}{}$$

24.58 Starch and cellulose are both polymers of glucose. What is the main structural difference between them, and what different roles do they serve in nature?

24.59 Starch and glycogen are both α-linked polymers of glucose. What is the structural difference between them, and what different roles do they serve in nature?

24.60 Write the open-chain structure of a ketotetrose.

24.61 Write the open-chain structure of a four-carbon deoxy sugar.

24.62 D-Mannose, an aldohexose found in orange peels, has the following structure in open-chain form. Coil mannose around, and draw it in cyclic α and β forms.

$$HOCH_2-\overset{\displaystyle OH}{CH}-\overset{\displaystyle OH}{CH}-CH-\overset{\displaystyle OH}{CH}-\overset{\displaystyle O}{CH}$$
$$\underset{\displaystyle OH\quad OH}{}$$

D-Mannose

24.63 Draw D-galactose in its cyclic α and β forms.

$$HOCH_2-\overset{\displaystyle OH}{CH}-\overset{\displaystyle OH}{CH}-CH-\overset{\displaystyle OH}{CH}-\overset{\displaystyle O}{CH}$$
$$\underset{\displaystyle OH\qquad OH}{}$$

D-Galactose

24.64 Show two D-mannose molecules (Problem 24.62) attached by an α-1→4 link.

24.65 Show two D-galactose molecules (Problem 24.63) attached by a β-1→4 link.

Lipids (Section 24.10)

24.66 What is a fatty acid?

24.67 What does it mean to say that fats and oils are triacylglycerols?

24.68 Draw the structure of glycerol myristate, a fat made from glycerol and three myristic acid molecules (see Table 24.3).

24.69 Spermaceti, a fragrant substance isolated from sperm whales, was a common ingredient in cosmetics until its use was banned in 1976 to protect the whales from extinction. Chemically, spermaceti is cetyl palmitate, the ester of palmitic acid (see Table 24.3) with cetyl alcohol (the straight-chain C_{16} alcohol). Show the structure of spermaceti.

24.70 There are two isomeric fat molecules whose components are glycerol, one palmitic acid, and two stearic acids (see Table 24.3). Draw the structures of both, and explain how they differ.

24.71 One of the two molecules you drew in Problem 24.70 is chiral. Which molecule is chiral, and why?

24.72 Draw the structures of all products you would obtain by reaction of the following lipid with aqueous KOH. What are the names of the products?

$$CH_2-O-\overset{\displaystyle O}{\overset{\|}{C}}(CH_2)_{16}CH_3$$
$$|$$
$$CH-O-\overset{\displaystyle O}{\overset{\|}{C}}(CH_2)_7CH=CH(CH_2)_7CH_3$$
$$|$$
$$CH_2-O-\overset{\displaystyle O}{\overset{\|}{C}}(CH_2)_7CH=CHCH_2CH=CHCH_2CH=CHCH_2CH_3$$

24.73 Draw the structure of the product you would obtain on hydrogenation of the lipid in Problem 24.72. What is its name? Would the product have a higher or lower melting point than the original lipid? Why?

24.74 What products would you obtain by treating oleic acid with the following reagents?

(a) Br_2 (b) H_2, Pd catalyst   (c) CH_3OH, HCl catalyst

24.75 Look up the structure of linoleic acid in Table 24.3, and draw all potential products of its reaction with 2 mol of HCl.

Nucleic Acids (Sections 24.11–24.13)

24.76 What is a nucleotide, and what three kinds of components does it contain?

24.77 What are the names of the sugars in DNA and RNA, and how do they differ?

24.78 Where in the cell is most DNA found?

24.79 What is meant by the following terms as they apply to nucleic acids?
    (a) Base pairing   **(b)** Replication
    (c) Translation   **(d)** Transcription

24.80 What is the difference between a gene and a chromosome?

24.81 What genetic information does a single gene contain?

24.82 Show by drawing structures how the phosphate and sugar components of a nucleic acid are joined.

24.83 Show by drawing structures how the sugar and amine base components of a nucleic acid are joined.

24.84 Draw the complete structure of deoxycytidine 5'-phosphate, one of the four deoxyribonucleotides.

24.85 Draw the complete structure of guanosine 5'-phosphate, one of the four ribonucleotides.

24.86 If the sequence T-A-C-C-G-A appeared on one strand of DNA, what sequence would appear opposite it on the other strand?

24.87 What sequence would appear on the mRNA molecule transcribed from the DNA in Problem 24.86?

24.88 Human insulin is composed of two polypeptide chains. One chain contains 21 amino acids, and the other contains 30 amino acids. How many nucleotides are present in the DNA to code for each chain?

24.89 The DNA from sea urchins contains about 32% A and about 18% G. What percentages of T and C would you expect in sea urchin DNA? Explain.

CHAPTER PROBLEMS

24.90 One of the constituents of the carnauba wax used in floor and furniture polish is an ester of a C_{32} straight-chain alcohol with a C_{20} straight-chain carboxylic acid. Draw the structure of this ester.

24.91 Cytochrome c is an important enzyme found in the cells of all aerobic organisms. Elemental analysis of cytochrome c shows that it contains 0.43% iron. What is the minimum molecular mass of this enzyme?

24.92 The catabolism of glucose to yield carbon dioxide and water has $\Delta G° = -2870$ kJ/mol. What is the value of $\Delta G°$ for the photosynthesis of glucose from carbon dioxide and water in green plants?

24.93 The *endorphins* are a group of naturally occurring neuroproteins that act in a manner similar to morphine to control pain. Research has shown that the biologically active part of the endorphin molecule is a simple pentapeptide called an *enkephalin*, with the structure Tyr-Gly-Gly-Phe-Met. Draw the complete structure of this enkephalin.

24.94 Write full structures for the following peptides, and indicate the positions of the amide bonds:
    (a) Val-Phe-Cys   **(b)** Glu-Pro-Ile-Leu

24.95 The α-helical segments of myoglobin and other proteins stop when a proline residue is encountered in the chain. Why is proline never encountered in a protein α-helix?

24.96 Jojoba wax, used in candles and cosmetics, is partially composed of the ester of stearic acid and a straight-chain C_{22} alcohol. Draw the structure of this ester.

24.97 Write representative structures for the following:
    (a) A fat   **(b)** A vegetable oil   **(c)** A steroid

24.98 What DNA sequence is complementary to the following sequence?

$$\text{A-G-T-T-C-A-T-C-G}$$

24.99 Protonation of the side chain in arginine occurs on the double-bonded nitrogen atom. Draw three resonance structures of the protonated product.

MULTI-CONCEPT PROBLEMS

24.100 The relative degree of unsaturation in a fat or oil is expressed as an *iodine number*. Olive oil, for instance, is highly unsaturated and has an iodine number of 172, while butter is much less unsaturated and has an iodine number of 37. Defined as the number of grams of I_2 absorbed per 100 grams of fat, the iodine number is based on the fact that the carbon–carbon double bonds in fats and oils undergo an addition reaction with I_2. The larger the number of double bonds, the larger the amount of I_2 that reacts.

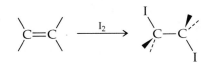

To determine an iodine number, a known amount of fat is treated with a known amount of I_2. When the reaction is complete (about 1 h), the amount of excess I_2 remaining is determined by titration with $Na_2S_2O_3$ according to the equation

$$2\,Na_2S_2O_3(aq) + I_2(aq) \longrightarrow Na_2S_4O_6(aq) + 2\,NaI(aq)$$

Knowing both the amount of I_2 originally added and the amount remaining after reaction, the iodine number can be calculated.

Assume that 0.500 g of human milk fat is allowed to react with 25.0 mL of 0.200 M I_2 solution and that 81.99 mL of 0.100 M $Na_2S_2O_3$ is required for complete reaction with the excess I_2.

(a) What amount (in grams) of I_2 was added initially?

(b) How many grams of I_2 reacted with the milk fat, and how many grams were in excess?

(c) What is the iodine number of human milk fat?

(d) Assuming a molecular mass of 800 amu, how many double bonds does an average molecule of milk fat contain?

24.101 The protonated form of a neutral amino acid such as alanine is a diprotic acid, H_2A^+, with two acid dissociation constants, one for the $-NH_3^+$ group and one for the $-CO_2H$ group.

$$pK_a = 9.69 \qquad pK_a = 2.34$$

$$\underset{\underset{\text{Alanine}}{\underset{\text{(protonated)}}{}}}{H_3\overset{+}{N}-\underset{\underset{CH_3}{|}}{CH}-\overset{\overset{O}{\|}}{C}-OH}$$

(a) Which group is more acidic, the $-NH_3^+$ or the $-CO_2H$?

(b) What percentage of each form—protonated (H_2A^+), neutral (HA), and deprotonated (A^-)—is present in aqueous solution at pH = 4.00?

(c) What percentage of each form—protonated (H_2A^+), neutral (HA), and deprotonated (A^-)—is present in aqueous solution at pH = 8.50?

(d) At what pH is the neutral form present in maximum amount?